LIBRARY OF CONGRESS

# A LIST OF
# GEOGRAPHICAL ATLASES
## IN THE LIBRARY OF CONGRESS

WITH BIBLIOGRAPHICAL NOTES

COMPILED UNDER THE DIRECTION OF
PHILIP LEE PHILLIPS, F. R. G. S.
CHIEF, DIVISION OF MAPS AND CHARTS

Volume I
ATLASES

WASHINGTON
GOVERNMENT PRINTING OFFICE
1909

*THIS REPRINT IS STRICTLY
LIMITED TO 100 COPIES*

MAURIZIO MARTINO PUBLISHER
746 MANSFIELD CITY ROAD
STORRS- MANSFIELD, CT 06268

# PREFATORY NOTE

That atlases have not received the consideration in bibliography due to their importance in literature and as contributions to knowledge is shown by the paucity of works on the subject. No exhaustive study of them has been attempted, and the available sources consist merely of a few monographs and some scattered information to be found only after much research in many out of the way places.

The present work is not a bibliography, but a list of the geographical atlases in the Library of Congress. It attempts, however, a fullness of description and an analysis unusual in a mere catalogue.

The arrangement starts with general atlases of special subjects, followed by general atlases of the world arranged chronologically. Following, come America, Europe, Asia, Africa, and Oceanica, arranged in the same manner. Included in the collection are the atlases of cities, those to accompany voyages of circumnavigation, historical works, scientific explorations, and reproductions in atlases to accompany boundary disputes between nations.

Accessions received after the work had gone to press are noted in the index and author list only. These are designated by a star at the end of the title and will be fully described in a future volume of accessions. The collection, with these various additions, numbers somewhat over thirty-four hundred, in addition to seventy lettered titles.

The maps relating to America, plans of cities throughout the world, and material of some specific interest not usually found in atlases are brought to the attention of the student in bibliographical notes and contents. Numerous inserted maps, so frequently hidden away in these atlases, are fully described. An author list of abridged titles, referring to the main entries of the collection, precedes the general index. This list gives the full and correct name of the author, when found, also his birth and death. The latter is most important, as from it an approximate date may be given to the many atlases which are published without a date. To prevent repetition, full names and dates of birth and death are eliminated in the body of the work and given only in the author list.

For easy reference the letters "t," "n," "c" have been placed before the title numbers in the index, referring to the subjects described in titles, notes, and contents. The index contains over forty thousand references. Under "Publishers" is found an alphabetical list of all the atlas publishers referred to in the body of the work.

That a bibliography of atlases is much needed is evident from the general ignorance of their contents. The Library of Congress, like other libraries, has in its collection of maps many detached ones, and it may be said that the collections of most libraries are made up of such maps. The voluminous catalogue of maps of the British Museum is composed to a great extent of such "separates," entered without bibliographical information. The maps in the older atlases have all the marks of separate publications and can be taken from their original place of publication without showing their origin on their face. Any considerable collector of American maps must have in his possession many by Capt. John Smith, Popple, Mitchell, Green, Fry and Jefferson, and others, which are taken from atlases. A good collection of unimpaired atlases or even a perfect atlas will thus be difficult to find. The present list will be of some assistance in identifying and locating some of these detached maps.

Owing to the nature of the material its compilation has involved considerable anxiety. Atlases rarely contain tables of contents, and it is frequently difficult to determine whether the maps described were originally published in the work or inserted by some former owner who was anxious to safeguard the "separates" in his collection. While this practice has saved from destruction many rare maps it brings cares to the bibliographer. The old atlases rarely have any date of publication and the recent ones often lack one. Every effort has been made, either from internal evidence or contemporaneous reviews—as in the case of Wolfgang's Atlas minor, 1681, title 502—to supply this defect. The geographical information is frequently given as a reason for a supplied date. The objection to this is readily seen when frequently half a century elapsed before new geographical facts were known and published, so that the old maps were republished over and over again in later atlases.

Justin Winsor, in the Narrative and Critical History of America, volume 4, page 369, in an article entitled "The general atlases and charts of the sixteenth and seventeenth centuries," says: "The general atlases at this time becoming familiar to Europe were unfortunately made up on a thrifty principle, little conducive to keeping the public mind abreast of current discovery—so far as America, at least, was concerned—and very perplexing now to anyone studying the course of the cartographical development of American geography. Dates were sedulously erased with a deceitful purpose (which is not yet gone into disuse) from plates thus made to do service for many years, and united with other dated maps, to convey an impression of a like period of production."

Some of the separate maps relating to America in these atlases have been described more in detail in the List of Maps of America in the Library of Congress.

In the notes attached to the entries of the earliest editions of Ptolemy, Ortelius, Mercator, Blaeu, and some others, are given in tabulated form not only all the editions possessed by the Library, but also other editions known to have been published. The early Italian, Dutch, French, German, and English schools are well represented.

As it is impossible to possess the old manuscript maps preserved in the libraries and museums of Europe, the works of Santarem, Jomard, Fischer, Müller, Nordenskiöld, and others, containing reproductions of these maps, have been carefully analyzed, as have also the atlases to accompany the various disputed boundary questions between nations, which are rich in such reproductions.

As no library has published a complete description of its atlas collection, it is impossible to state authoritatively how the collection in the Library of Congress compares in size and importance with others.

Of the forty editions of Ptolemy listed by Eames the Library has all except the Latin editions of 1478, 1482, and 1514. The earliest of these, except the manuscript reprint of the twelfth century—the metrical translation into Italian by Berlinghieri, published in Florence about 1478—is the first atlas entirely engraved on copper. The 1508 edition is remarkable for containing, in an atlas, a map showing a part of America. This is the famous Ruysch map of the world.

Of the folio edition of Ortelius twenty-four copies are described. There are three impressions of the second edition, one more than heretofore known to the bibliographer. The 1597 edition contains a manuscript dedication and notes by Ortelius. His "Additamentum" of 1590 has a map entitled "Maris Pacifici," the first in which America is separated by name into North and South.

The earliest of the eleven folio Mercator atlases in the Library is the one dated 1607. In this edition the general map of America by Hondius is the first map of America separated and named North and South.

One of the most valuable atlases to the American student is that entitled Dell' Arcano del Mare, 1647–1648, by Sir Robert Dudley, styled Duke of Northumberland, and minutely described in this work. This is the first marine atlas in which the maps were drawn on the Mercator projection. On account of its rarity and the difficulty of finding a copy it has been little consulted, notwithstanding that the maps were mainly drawn from manuscript charts, now mostly lost, of early navigators.

Wytfliet's Descriptionis Ptolemaicæ avgmentvm, 1597, is the earliest distinctively American atlas. It is as important to the history of the early cartography of the new world as Ptolemy's maps are to the study of the old.

The earliest maps of the United States, separately dated from 1792 to 1793, are found in Jedidiah Morse's The American Geography, published in London in 1794. This work can not strictly be regarded as an atlas, but is valuable owing to these maps. An especially noteworthy one is the Filson map of Kentucky, usually wanting in Stockdale's London edition, 1794, of Filson's History of Kentucky.

The manuscript atlases of Rochambeau and Hills are invaluable to the study of American history at the period of the Revolutionary war, as are also the published atlases of Jefferys, Faden, Le Rouge, Atlantic Neptune, and Kitchin. The early roads of the United States are described by Christopher Colles in a scarce work entitled A Survey of the Roads of the United States, 1789; and in Moore and Jones's Travellers' Directory, 1802 and the revised edition of 1804.

The state and county atlases of the United States are probably the most consulted in the collection, especially by the various departments of the National Government.

One of the most interesting items in the European division is a collection of maps known as Saxton's Atlas, 1574-1579, which contains the earliest surveys of England and Wales. A complete set of these maps is very scarce, especially with the frontispiece by Augustine Ryther, representing Queen Elizabeth enthroned as patroness of geography and astronomy.

The following works have been among those most consulted:

RAEMDONCK, JEAN VAN.
   Gérard Mercator, sa vie et ses œuvres. 8°. St. Nicolas, E. Dalschaert-Praet, 1869.
TIELE, PIETER ANTON.
   Nederlandsche bibliographie van land- en volkenkunde. 4°. Amsterdam, F. Muller & co., 1884.
HESSELS, JAN HENDRIK.
   Ecclesiae londino-batavae archivvm. 4°. Cantabrigiae, typis Academiae svmptibvs ecclesiae londino-batavae, 1887. v. 1. Abrahami Ortelii . . . epistvlae.
EAMES, WILBERFORCE.
   A list of editions of Ptolemy's geography. 1475-1730. 8°. New York, 1886.
WOLTERSDORF, ERNST GABRIEL.
   Repertorium der land- und seekarten, so wie der vorzüglichsten grundrisse und topographischen ansichten der merkwürdigsten städte. 8°. Wien, in der Camesinaschen buchhandlung, 1813.
NEW YORK PUBLIC LIBRARY.
   General atlases of geography (ancient and modern) in the New York Public Library. [Bulletin of the New York Public Library. v. 4, no. 2, Feb., 1900, pp. 63-68.]
BAUDET, PIERRE JOSEPH HENRI.
   Leven en werken van Willem Jansz. Blaeu. 8°. Utrecht, C. van der Post, jr., 1871.

NORDENSKIÖLD, ADOLF ERICK.
   Periplus. An essay on the early history of charts and sailing directions. fol. Stockholm [P. A. Norstedt & söner], 1897.
   —— Facsimile atlas to the early history of cartography with reproductions of the most important maps printed in the XV and XVI centuries. fol. Stockholm [P. A. Norstedt & söner], 1889.

WAUVERMANS, HENRI EMMANUEL.
   Histoire de l'école cartographique Belge et Anversoise du XVI° siècle. 2 v. 8°. Bruxelles, Institut national de géographie, 1895.

P. LEE PHILLIPS
*Chief, Division of Maps and Charts*

HERBERT PUTNAM
   *Librarian of Congress*
      *Washington, August, 1909*

# CONTENTS.

Numbers refer to titles.

## VOLUME I.

**WORLD.**
SPECIAL.

| | |
|---|---|
| Ancient | 1–54 |
| Cities | 55–67 |
| Colonial | 68 |
| Commercial | 69–78 |
| Ecclesiastical | 79–91 |
| Ethnographical | 92–93 |
| Games | 94 |
| Harbors | 95 |
| Historical | 96–159 |
| Hydrographical | 160–161 |
| Islands | 162–169 |
| Itineraries | 170–171 |
| Light-houses | 95 |
| Maritime | 172–175 |
| Meteorology | 175a |
| Military | 176–177a |
| Missionary | 178–183 |
| Oceans | 184–206 |
| Orography | 207–208 |
| Outline | 209–210 |
| Physical | 211–234 |
| Postal | 235 |
| Railroads | 236–244 |
| Relief | 245–246 |
| Reproductions | 247–264 |
| School | 265–343 |
| Scientific | 344 |
| Stamps | 345 |
| Statistical | 346 |
| Volcanoes | 347 |
| Wars | 348–349 |

GENERAL.

| | |
|---|---|
| 12th century–1908 | 350–1133 |

**AMERICA.**
SPECIAL.

| | |
|---|---|
| Historical | 1134 |
| Reproductions | 1135–1139 |

GENERAL.

| | |
|---|---|
| 1597–1879 | 1140–1184 |

IX

## CONTENTS.

**NORTH AMERICA.**
SPECIAL.
Cities.................................................. 1185
Cities and forts ................................... 1186
Forestry............................................... 1187
Forts................................................... 1186
Historical............................................ 1188-1190
Reproductions .................................... 1191-1194
GENERAL.
1604-1879 ........................................... 1195-1233

**CANADA.**
SPECIAL.
Physical............................................... 1234
Reproductions .................................... 1235
GENERAL.
1806-1906 ........................................... 1236-1249
PROVINCES.
Nova Scotia........................................ 1250-1252
Ontario............................................... 1253
Quebec............................................... 1255

**LABRADOR** .......................................... 1254

**NEWFOUNDLAND** ............................... 1256

**UNITED STATES.**
SPECIAL.
Agricultural ....................................... 1257
Bankers and brokers .......................... 1258
Boundary .......................................... 1259-1264
Canals................................................ 1265-1266
Cities.................................................. 1267
Coal................................................... 1268
Coast.................................................. 1269
Commercial....................................... 1270-1276
Diplomatic ........................................ 1277
Forestry............................................. 1278
Geological......................................... 1279-1283
Hieroglyphic ..................................... 1284
Historical.......................................... 1285-1296
Lakes ................................................ 1297
Political............................................. 1298-1299
Railroads........................................... 1300-1306
Reproductions ................................... 1307
Rivers................................................ 1308-1325
Roads................................................ 1325a-1328
Statistical.......................................... 1329-1334
Wars.................................................. 1335-1358
Weather............................................. 1359-1360
GENERAL.
1794-1908 ......................................... 1361-1448
STATES.
Alabama ........................................... 1449-1451
Alaska .............................................. 1452
Arkansas .......................................... 1453-1456

CONTENTS. XI

**UNITED STATES**—Continued.
STATES—Continued.
California ..................................................... 1457–1470
Colorado ...................................................... 1471–1475
Connecticut ................................................... 1476–1491
Delaware ...................................................... 1492–1494
District of Columbia .......................................... 1495–1506
Georgia ....................................................... 1507–1509
Illinois ...................................................... 1510–1597
Indiana ....................................................... 1598–1638
Iowa .......................................................... 1639–1709
Kansas ........................................................ 1710–1745
Kentucky ...................................................... 1746–1770
Louisiana ..................................................... 1771a
Maine ......................................................... 1772–1777
Maryland ...................................................... 1778–1798
Massachusetts ................................................. 1799–1959
Michigan ...................................................... 1960–2005
Minnesota ..................................................... 2006–2058a
Missouri ...................................................... 2059–2106
Nebraska ...................................................... 2107–2130
Nevada ........................................................ 2131–2134
New Hampshire ................................................. 2135–2140
New Jersey .................................................... 2141–2200
New York ...................................................... 2201–2337
North Dakota .................................................. 2338–2345
Ohio .......................................................... 2346–2436
Oklahoma ...................................................... 2436a
Oregon ........................................................ 2437–2438
Pennsylvania .................................................. 2439–2561
Rhode Island .................................................. 2562–2569
South Carolina ................................................ 2570
South Dakota .................................................. 2571–2584
Tennessee ..................................................... 2585–2589
Utah .......................................................... 2590–2591
Vermont ....................................................... 2592–2604
Virginia ...................................................... 2605–2621
Washington .................................................... 2622–2626a
West Virginia ................................................. 2627–2631
Wisconsin ..................................................... 2632–2679

**MEXICO.**
SPECIAL.
Boundary ...................................................... 2680–2681
GENERAL.
1812–1887 ..................................................... 2682–2688
STATES.
San Luis Potosi ............................................... 2689
Tehuantepec ................................................... 2690

**CENTRAL AMERICA.**
Costa Rica .................................................... 2691
Panama ........................................................ 2692–2693

## WEST INDIES.
### GENERAL.
1675–1856............................................ 2694–2711
### ISLANDS.
Cuba.............................................. 2712–2714
Dutch West Indies............................. 2715
Haiti.............................................. 2716–2717
Martinique...................................... 2718

## SOUTH AMERICA.
### SPECIAL.
Reproductions................................. 2719–2724
Rivers............................................ 2725
### GENERAL.
1805–1839........................................... 2726–2729
### REPUBLICS.
Argentina....................................... 2730–2737
Bolivia........................................... 2738
Brazil............................................ 2739–2752
British Guiana.................................. 2753–2756
Chile............................................. 2756a–2758a
Colombia........................................ 2759–2762
Ecuador......................................... 2763
French Guiana.................................. 2764
Paraguay........................................ 2765–2766
Peru............................................. 2767–2772
Uruguay......................................... 2773–2774
Venezuela....................................... 2775–2779

## EUROPE.
### SPECIAL.
Cities............................................ 2779a–2782
Colonies......................................... 2782a
Commercial..................................... 2783
Ecclesiastical................................... 2784–2785
Ethnographical................................. 2786
Historical....................................... 2786a–2796
Railroads........................................ 2797–2798
Reproductions.................................. 2798a–2799
Rivers............................................ 2800
School........................................... 2801
Statistical...................................... 2808
Travels.......................................... 2809–2811
Wars............................................. 2812–2827
### GENERAL.
1594–1905........................................... 2828–2857
### STATES.
Austria-Hungary............................... 2858–2877
British Isles.................................... 2878–2944
Denmark........................................ 2945–2947
France........................................... 2948–3017
Germany........................................ 3018–3048
Greece........................................... 3049–3052
Italy............................................. 3053–3071
Netherlands.................................... 3072–3090

CONTENTS. XIII

**EUROPE**—Continued.
  STATES—Continued.
    Norway .................................................. 3091-3092
    Portugal ................................................. 3093-3095
    Roumania ................................................ 3096-3097
    Russia .................................................. 3098-3126
    Spain ................................................... 3127-3140
    Sweden .................................................. 3141-3144
    Switzerland ............................................. 3145-3157
    Turkey .................................................. 3158-3161

**ASIA.**
  GENERAL.
    1690-1907 ............................................... 3162-3181
  STATES.
    China ................................................... 3182-3196
    India ................................................... 3197-3204
    Indo-China .............................................. 3205-3206
    Japan ................................................... 3207-3211
    Korea ................................................... 3212
    Malay Archipelago ....................................... 3213-3220
    Palestine ............................................... 3221-3222
    Philippine Islands ...................................... 3223-3226
    Siberia ................................................. 3227-3228

**AFRICA.**
  GENERAL.
    1700-1903 ............................................... 3229-3238
  STATES.
    Egypt ................................................... 3239
    Tunis ................................................... 3240

**OCEANICA.**
  GENERAL.
    1769-1900 ............................................... 3241-3248
  ISLANDS.
    Australia.
      SPECIAL.
        Explorations ....................................... 3249-3251
        Historical ......................................... 3252
      GENERAL.
        1886 ............................................... 3253
      PROVINCES.
        New South Wales .................................... 3254-3255
        Queensland ......................................... 3256
        South Australia .................................... 3257
    Caroline islands ........................................ 3258
    Hawaiian islands ........................................ 3259-3263
    New Guinea island ....................................... 3264
    New Zealand ............................................. 3265

VOLUME I.       Pages.
Atlases ...................................................... 1-1208

VOLUME II.
Author List .................................................. 1209-1313
Index ........................................................ 1315-1659

# WORLD

## ANCIENT

**Anville, J. B. B. d'**
Géographie ancienne abrégée . . . Nouv. éd., rev. par l'auteur. 2 p. l., iv, 141 pp., 9 maps. fol. Paris, Merlin, 1769. 1

A complete body of ancient geography. 1 p. l., 13 maps. fol. London, R. Sayer & J. Bennet, 1775. 2

A complete body of ancient geography . . . The whole materially improved, by inserting the modern names of places under the ancient. 1 p. l., 13 maps. fol. London, R. Laurie & J. Whittle, 1806. 3

Atlas and geography of the antients, with twelve maps in atlas folio; being the geography of the greeks and romans in the æras of Alexander the great and Augustus . . . Now first translated into english, under the patronage of the officers of the british army, by the editor of the Military chronicle. iv, 8, [v]—110, [2] pp., 12 maps. fol. London, T. Chaplin, for J. Davis, 1815. 4

**Bohn, H. G.**
The standard library atlas of classical geography completed to the present state of knowledge. With a general index giving the latitude & longitude of every place named in the maps. v, 24 pp., 22 maps. 4°. London, H. G. Bohn, 1861. 5

**Brué, A. H.**
Atlas classique de géographie, physique, politique, ancienne & moderne, composé de 36 feuilles, rédigé conformément aux progrès de la science, pour servir à l'intelligence de l'histoire, de la géographie & des voyages. Ouvrage approuvé & recommandé par le conseil général de l'instruction publique . . . 2. éd. 4 p. l., 36 maps. fol. Paris, chez l'auteur, 1830-[1832] 6

Note.—Maps dated as late as 1832.
The following maps relate to America:
no. 10. Mappe monde . . . 2. éd. 1830 . . .
" 11. Mappe monde en deux hémisphères . . . 2. éd. . . . 1830 . . .
" 29. Carte générale de l'Océanie . . . 1827 . . .
" 33. Carte générale de l'Amérique Septentrionale . . . 1828 . . .

**Brué, A. H.—Continued.**
  no. 34. Carte générale des États-Unis, du haut et bas Canada... 1832...
  " 35. Carte des Îles Antilles, des États-Unis, l'Amérique-Centrale et de la mer du Mexique. 2. éd. ... 1832.
  " 36. Carte générale de l'Amérique Méridionale ... 1826.

**Butler, S.**
  An atlas of antient geography ...    3 p. l., 3–34 pp., 21 maps. 8°. Philadelphia, Carey & Lea, 1832.    7

  An atlas of antient geography ...    3 p. l., 3–34 pp., 21 maps. 8°. Philadelphia, Carey, Lea & Blanchard, 1838.    8

  An atlas of antient geography ...    3 p. l., 3–34 pp., 21 maps. 8°. Philadelphia, Lea & Blanchard, 1839.    9

  Atlas of antient geography ...    3 p. l., 3–34 pp., 21 maps. 8°. Philadelphia, Lea & Blanchard, 1841.    10

  An atlas of antient geography ...    3 p. l., 3–34 pp., 21 maps. 8°. Philadelphia, Lea & Blanchard, 1844.    11

**Dunning, A. G.**
  An ancient, classical and scriptural geography; with a map of the countries mentioned in the ancient classics and sacred scriptures.   37 pp., 1 map.   fol.   New York, A. S. Barnes & co. 1850.    12

**Findlay, A. G.**
  A classical atlas, to illustrate ancient geography; comprised in twenty-five maps, showing the various divisions of the world as known to the ancients; composed from the most authentic sources. With an index of the ancient and modern names. By Alexander G. Findlay.   xvi, 44 pp., 26 maps.   4°.   London, W. Tegg & co. 1853.    13

**Finley, A.**
  Atlas classica; or select maps of ancient geography, both sacred and profane. [By Anthony Finley]   2 p. l., 1 l., 9 maps, 1 chart.   fol.   Philadelphia, A. Finley, 1829.    14

  [*With his* A new general atlas ... fol. Philadelphia, A. Finley, 1829]

**Götz, A.**
  Brevis introdvctio ad geographiam antiqvam in jvventvtis vsvm avctore Andrea Goetzio ...   48, [16] pp., 10 col. maps. 8°. Norimbergae, B. J. C. Weigel, 1729.    15

  NOTE.—Maps are ornamented with illustrations relating to ancient history and mythology.

**Horn, G.**
Accuratissima orbis antiqui delineatio. Sive geographia vetus, sacra & profana. Exhibens, quicquid imperiorum, regnorum, principatuum, rerum publicarum, ab initio rerum, ad præsentem usque mundi statum fuit. Præmissa est introductio ad geographiam antiquam. Qua orbis vetus, gentium migrationes, populorum origines & quicquid historias illustrare potest, breviter refertur . . . [19] 1., 52 maps, 1 pl. fol. Amstelodami, J. Janssonium, 1654. 16

NOTE.—Like the "Accuratissima orbis delineatio . . . Hagæ, 1740", with the following exceptions: It does not contain maps: Africae antiquae, Asia antiqua, Macedonia, Epirus, Thessaliæ, Achaiæ, Peloponnesus and Europa antiqua. Maps 9–11 and 49 differ slightly from 7–9 and 55.
"Introductio ad geographiam antiquam", by Georg Horn, pp. [3–34]
A collection of maps by various geographers, including: Stella, Adrichem, Keer, Hareius, du Val, Ortelius, Cluver, Briet and Lhuyd.
no. 3 has an inset of the world showing America.
" 6. "Situs Terræ Promissionis . . . per Chr. Adrichom" is a reduced copy of a map in Adrichem's "Theatrvm Terræ Sanctæ et biblicarvm historiarvm. Colon, 1590." Maps 7–12, to which map 6 serves as an index, are based upon the special maps by Adrichem in the same work.
" 43. "Britannia" has 14 border illustrations representing the kings of the Anglo-Saxon heptarchy.
" 49–52 are reproductions of parts of the ancient roman map known as "Peutinger's Table."

Accuratissima orbis delineatio; sive geographia vetus, sacra et profana. Exhibens, quicquid imperiorum, regnorum, principatuum, rerum publicarum, ab initio rerum, ad præsentem usque mundi statum fuit. Præmissa est introductio ad geographiam antiquam: qua orbis vetus, gentium migrationes, populorum origines & quicquid historias illustrare potest, breviter refertur . . . 1 p. l., 30 pp., 55 maps, diagr. fol. Hagæ, P. Hondt, 1740. 17

NOTE.—Like the "Accuratissima orbis antiqui delineatio . . . Amstelodami, 1654," with the following exceptions: It does not contain maps: Judæa, Hispania vetus and Italiae antiquae. Maps nos. 7–9 and 55 differ slightly from nos. 9–11 and 49.
"Introductio ad geographiam antiquam," pp. 1–30.
A collection of maps by various geographers, including: Ortelius, du Val, Laurenberg and Blancard.
no. [2] has an inset of the world showing America.
" [5–9] are based upon the special maps by Adrichem in his "Theatrvm Terræ Sanctæ et biblicarvm historiarvm. Colon, 1590."
" [49] "Britannia" has 14 border illustrations representing the kings of the Anglo-Saxon heptarchy.
" [55] is a reproduction of parts of the ancient roman map known as "Peutinger's table."

**Hughes, W.**
An atlas of classical geography. Constructed by William Hughes, and edited by George Long. With a sketch of ancient geography, and other additions by the american editor . . . 76 pp., 26 maps on 44 l. fol. Philadelphia, Blanchard & Lea, 1856. 18

An atlas of classical geography. Constructed by William Hughes, and edited by George Long . . . With a sketch of classical geography and other additions, by the american editor . . . 76 pp., 26 maps on 44 l. 4°. New York, Sheldon & co. [1856] 19

**Ivison, Blakeman, Taylor & co.**
Standard classic atlas for schools and colleges, with an alphabetical index giving the latitudes and longitudes of 20,000 places. 1 p. l., 30 pp., 21 maps. 4°. New York and Chicago, Ivison, Blakeman, Taylor & co. [1885] 20

**Johnston, A. K.**
A school atlas of classical geography; comprising, in twenty plates, maps and plans of all the important countries and localities referred to by classical authors . . . 2 p. l., 24 pp., 19 maps. fol. Edinburgh and London, W. Blackwood & sons, 1853. 21

**Joly, J. R.**
Atlas de l'Ancienne géographie universelle comparée à la moderne, précédé d'une table générale, en forme de dictionnaire, de tous les noms anciens des royaumes, provinces, villes, fleuves, rivières, lacs, montagnes, etc., qui se trouvent dans l'Ancienne géographie universelle . . . 2 p. l., 78 pp., 1 l., 18 maps. 4°. Paris, A. A. Lottin; A. Bertrand, an ix (1801) 22

**Kampen, A. van.**
Orbis terrarum antiquus in scholarum usum descriptus . . . 1 p. l., 16 tab. on 8 l. obl. 8°. Gothae, I. Perthes, 1884. 23

**Keller, C.**
Christophori Cellarii. Geographia antiqua in compendium redacta novis praefationibus nunc exornata a Francisco Tirolio et Joanne Baptista Ghisio communi sumptu atque labore amplioribus tabulis aucta et accuratioribus catalogis locupletata. 2 p. l., x pp., 1 l., 24, ii, v–x, 40 pp., front. 35 maps, 2 pl. obl. fol. Romae, 1774. 24

Geographia antiqua; being a complete set of maps of antient geography, beautifully engraved from Cellarius. On thirty-three copper plates. Designed for the use of schools, and of gentlemen

who make the antient writers their delight or study. New ed.
4 p. l., 33 fold. maps. 4°. London, for F. & C. Rivington [etc.]
1799. 25
NOTE.—Maps engraved by R. W. Seale and W. H. Toms.

**Kiepert, J. S. H.**
Atlas antiquus. Zwölf karten zur alten geschichte. [12$^{te}$ berichtigte aufl.] 1 p. l., [2], 27 pp., 12 maps. fol. Berlin, D. Reimer [1898?] 26

Formae orbis antiqui . . . pt. 1. cover title, 6 maps. fol. Berlin, D. Reimer, 1894. 27

CONTENTS.
pt. 1, no. IX. Asia provincia.
" XII. Insulae maris. Aegael.
" XV. Graecia septentrionalis.
" XVII. Illyricum et Thracia.
" XXVI. Insulae Britannicae.
" XXVII. Hispania.

Historisch-geographischer atlas der alten welt, zum schulgebrauche bearbeitet und mit erläuternden bemerkungen begleitet von H. Kiepert. 13. verb. aufl. 2 p. l., 30 pp., 16 maps. obl. 8°. Weimar, geographisches institut, 1860. 28

**Knapton, J. & P.**
Geographia classica: the geography of the ancients so far described as it is contained in the greek and latin classicks . . . 8th ed. vi pp., 29 maps. obl. 8°. London, J. & P. Knapton, 1747. 29

**Köhler, J. D.**
[Descriptio orbis antiqui in XLIV tabulis exhibita a Joh. Davide Koelero . . .] 44 maps. fol. [Norimbergæ, Christophori Weigelii, 1720?] 30

NOTE.—Title page wanting.
Maps by various cartographers, including Gale, Ligorio, Coronelli, Reland, and Coccejo.
Same atlas published by Homann heirs.

Descriptio orbis antiqvi in XLIV tabulis exhibita a Io. Davide Koelero hist. et polit. p. p. Altdorfino studio atque opera Homannianorum heredum, nunc C. Fembo. 2 p. l., 44 maps. fol. Norimbergae [1720?] 31

NOTE.—The title-page and many of the maps of these two editions are ornamented by illustrations of the coins of the countries represented.
Same as atlas published by Christoph Weigel ca. 1720.

**Lenormant, F.,** *i. e.*, **C. F.**
Atlas d'histoire ancienne de l'Orient. Antérieurement aux guerres médiques . . . 8 p. l., 24 maps. sm. fol. Paris, A. Lévy [1868] 31a

NOTE.—"Les dessins des cartes ont été faits par m. Hermann Schroeder." To accompany his, Manuel d'histoire de l'Orient. 3 v. 1868.

CONTENTS.

no. 1. L'Europe et l'Asie pendant la période quaternaire.
" 2. Âge de la prépondérance des Chamites et des Touraniens, avant les migrations aryennes.
" 3. Ethnographie de la Genèse.
" 4. La Palestine partagée entre les douze tribus.
" 5. États successifs de la Palestine.
" 6. L'Égypte d'après les monuments hiérogliphiques et les géographes grecs et latins.
" 7. Géographie des monuments égyptiens. L'empire pharaonique au temps de Thoutmès III.
" 8. L'Égypte au temps des pasteurs et la XVII° dynastie.—Les 20 royaumes institués en Égypte par Assarahaddon.—La Basse-Égypte au temps de l'expédition de Piaakhi.—La Basse Égypte au temps de la dodécarchie.
" 9. Confédération libyo-pélasgique contre Ramsès III.—Confédération asiatique contre Ramsès II.
" 10. L'Assyrie, la Babylonie, la Chaldée, une portion de la Médie et de l'Arménie, d'après les monuments assyriens et les géographes classiques.
" 11. Géographie des monuments assyriens. L'empire ninivite.
" 12. Ruines d'Our [en Chaldée]—Ruines de Ninive.—Ruines de Babylone.—La cité royale de Babylone restituée d'après m. Oppert.
" 13. Les deux empires chaldéen et médique au temps de Nabuchodorossor.
" 14. Migrations et séjours primitifs des Aryas orientaux.
" 15. L'empire de Cyrus avant la prise de Babylone.
" 16. Les vingt-trois provinces de l'empire perse au commencement du règne de Darius.
" 17. L'empire perse divisé par Darius et vingt satrapies.
" 18. L'Asie au temps de Nabonahid et Astyage.
" 19. L'Asie au temps de Darius, fils d'Hystaspe.
" 20. Établissements et commerce des phéniciens.
" 21. Établissements des Carthagnois [!] sur la côte occidentale d'Afrique et voyage de Hannon.—Le Phénicie et ses cités.
" 22. Plan de Tyr.—Ruines de Thèbes.—Ruines de Carthage.—Jérusalem au temps des rois.
" 23. L'Arabie antérieurement au V° siècle avant l'ère chrétienne.
" 24. L'Inde antique.

**Lord, J. K.**
Atlas of the geography and history of the ancient world; edited and arranged from latest sources. 2 p. l., 28 l., 29–43 pp. incl. 20 maps. fol. Boston, B. H. Sanborn & co. [1902] 32

**Mayo, R.**
[Atlas to accompany Mayo's ancient geography & history]
1 l., 8 maps, 1 tab. fol. [Philadelphia, J. Watson, 1813] 33

NOTE.—Title-page wanting.

**Menke, T.**
Orbis antiqui descriptio. In usum scholarum edidit Th. Menke.
Editio secunda. 1 p. l., [8] pp., 17 maps. 8°. Gothae, I.
Perthes, 1854. 34

**Mitchell, S. A.**
Mitchell's ancient atlas. Containing maps illustrating classical and sacred geography. 1 p. l., 7 maps. fol. Philadelphia, T. Cowperthwait & co. [1844] 35

Mitchell's ancient atlas, classical and sacred, containing maps illustrating the geography of the ancient world, as described by the writers of antiquity; also, the political divisions, cities, towns, places distinguished by remarkable events . . . 12 pp., 7 maps. fol. Philadelphia, E. H. Butler & co. 1859. 36

**Möller, J. H.**
Orbis terrarum antiquus. Schul-atlas der alten welt nach d'Anville, Mannert, Uckert, Reichard, Kruse, Wilhelm u. a. 23. aufl. 1 p. l., 14 pp., 15 maps. obl. 8°. Gotha, J. Perthes [1851] 37

**Moll, H.**
Geographia antiqua latinorum & graecorum, tabulis XXXII novis & accuratis expressa . . . Thirty-two new and accurate maps of the geography of the ancients as contained in the greek and latin classicks . . . 1 p. l., [12] l., 31 maps. sm 4°. London. H. Moll, 1721. 38

NOTE.—Title and explanation in latin and english.
Map no. 24 wanting.

**Ortelius, A.**
Parergon theatri. Lectori s. Descriptione orbis terrarum abfoluta, en candide lector tres hæ fequentes tabulæ . . . 26 col. maps. 39

[*In his* Theatrvm orbis terrarvm. fol. Antverpiæ, apud Ægid. Coppenium Diesth, 1570. Copy 3]
NOTE.—Maps dated 1579–90.
Title on recto of map no. 23.

Parergon theatri. [Mss: " in quo veteris geographię aliquot tabulæ]: Lector s. Descriptione orbis terrarum abfoluta, en can-

**Ortelius, A.—Continued.**

dide lector tres hæ fequentes tabulæ, quas in gratiā veteris tam facræ quàm profanæ hiftoriæ ftudioforum à me delineatas feorfum publicare decreueram; nihil enim ad noftrum in hoc Theatro, quo tantùm hodiernum regionum fitum exhibere propofueram, inftitutum facere videbantur, victus tamen amicorum precibus, eas in huius noftri operis calcem, tamquam Parergon reieci. 20 l. incl. 10 maps. 40

[*In his* Theatrvm orbis terrarvm. fol. Antverpiæ, apud C. Plantinum, 1579]
NOTE.—Title on recto of map 91.

Parergon, in quo veteris geographiæ aliquot tabulæ. Descriptione orbis terrarum abfoluta, en candide lector hæ fequentes tabulæ, quas in gratiam veteris tam facræ quàm profanæ hiftoriæ ftudioforum à me delineatas, feorfum publicare decreueram ... 26 l. incl. 12 col. maps. 41

[*In his* Theatrvm orbis terrarvm. fol. Antverpiæ, apud C. Plantinum, 1584]
NOTE.—Title on recto of l. no. 101.

Parergon dv théâtre. Combien que ces cartes fuiuantes ne femblent feruir aucunement à noftre intention; qui eftoit tant feulement de mettre en noftre Théâtre la fituation des lieux & prouinces comme elle eft à prefent: toutefoys par les prières de quelques mes amis, & pour complaire aux amateurs de l'ancienne hiftoire, tant faincte, que prophane, ie les ay voulu icy adioufter, & mettre à part, à la fin de ceft œuure, comme parergon. 24 l. incl. 12 col. maps. 42

[*In his* Théâtre de l'vnivers, contenant les cartes de tovt le monde fol. Anvers, C. Plantin, 1587]
NOTE.—Title on recto of map 101.

Parergon, sive veteris geographiæ aliqvot tabvlæ. Descriptione orbis terrarum abfoluta, en, candide lector, hæ fequentes tabulæ: quas in gratiam prifcæ tam facræ quàm profanæ hiftoriæ ftudioforum à me delineatas, feorfum publicare decreueram. 56 l. incl. 26 maps. 43

[*In his* Theatrvm orbis terrarvm. fol. Antverpiæ, in officina Plantiniana, 1592]

Parergon, sive veteris geograpiæ [!] aliqvot tabvlæ. Lector s. Ad noftram orbis terrarum defcriptionem habe fequentes tabulas: quas in gratiam prifcæ tam facræ quàm profanæ hiftoriæ ftudioforum à me delineatas, feorfum publicare decreueram. 68 l. incl. 32 maps. 44

[*In his* Treatrvm orbis terrarvm. fol. Antverpiæ, 1595]

Parergon, sive veteris geographiæ aliqvot tabvlæ. Lector s.
Ad noftram orbis terrarum defcriptionem habe sequentes tabulas:
quas in gratiam prifcæ tam facræ quàm profane hiftoriæ ftudioforum à me delineatas, feorfum publicare decreueram. 74 l. incl.
35 maps. 45
[*In his* Theatrvm orbis terrarvm. fol. Antverpiæ, apud Ioannem Moretum, 1601]

Parergon, sive veteris geograpiæ [!] aliqvot tabvlæ. Lector s.
Ad noftram orbis terrarum defcriptionem habe fequentes tabulas:
quas in gratiam prifcæ tam facræ quàm profanæ hiftoriæ ftudiosorum à me delineatas, seorfum publicare decreueram. 82 l.
incl. 35 maps, 3 pl. 46
[*In his* Theatrvm orbis terrarvm. Editio vltima. fol. Antverpiæ, apud Ioannem Bapt. Vrintivm, 1603]

Parergon, cioe fvor d' opera, et givnta, overo alcvne tavole dell' antica geografia. Al lettore salvte. Prendi infieme con la defcrittion noftra del circuito della terra, le tauole feguenti diffegnate per me in gratia de gli ftudiofi della prifca hiftoria, sacra, & profana.
84 l. incl. 35 maps, 3 pl. 47
[*In his* Theatro del mondo di Abrahamo Ortelio. fol. Anversa, libraria Plantiniana, 1612]

Parergon, sive veteris geograpiæ [!] aliqvot tabvlæ. Lector s.
Ad noftram orbis terrarum defcriptionem habe fequentes tabulas:
quas in gratiam prifcæ tam facræ quàm profanæ hiftoriæ ftudiosorum à me delineatas, seorfum publicare decreueram. 82 l.
incl. 35 col. maps, 3 pl. 48
[*In his* Treatrvm orbis terrarvm. fol. Antverpiæ, apvd Ioannem Bapt. Vrintivm. 1609]

NOTE.—L. C. has also a separate copy of this Parergon, with which is bound the "Nomenclator Ptolemaicvs" 1609.

Abrahami Ortelii theatri orbis terrarvm parergon; sive veteris geographiæ tabvlæ, commentarijs geographicis et hiftoricis illuftratæ. Editio novissima tabulis aliquot aucta, et variè emendata atq$_3$ innouata cvra et stvdio Balthasaris Moreti. 1 p. l., 101 l. incl. 41 maps, 4 pl., 32, [3] pp. fol. Antverpiæ, ex officina Plantiniana, 1624. 49

NOTE.—Collation: 4 l. (*i. e.* 2 l. unsig., sig. *3, 1 l. unsig.)—maps i–xi, sheet xij (4 pp. of text), map xiii, sheet xiiii (4 pp. of text), map xv, sheet xvi (4 pp. of text), maps xvii–xix, sheet xx (4 pp. of text).—pl. xxj, xxij, maps xxiij–xl, sheet xlj (4 pp. of text), maps xlij–xlviij, pl. xlix.—Sig. A–C in sixes.

**Ortelius, A.—Continued.**
L. [1] recto: eng. title, verso: arms of the king of Spain.—l. [2] recto: Dedication Philippo IV, Hispaniarvm et Indiarvm regi catholico ... verso: blank.—sig. *3, recto-verso: Balthasar Moretvs benevolo lectori S. P.—l. [4] recto: Index tabvlarvm hvivs parergi sive veteris geographiae theatri.—verso: A Iove principivm inqvit vetvstas.—Itaqve a sacris avspicandvm hvnc nostrvm laborem dvximvs.—Maps and text as above described.—Pl. xxj, xxij: De institvtione et ordine imperii Germanici tabvla I.—II.—Pl. xlix: Scenographia totivs fabricæ S. Lavrentii in Escvriaco. Sig. [A] recto: title, Nomenclator Ptolemaievs, omnia locorvm vocabvla qvæ in Ptolemæi geographia occvrrvnt complectens: Ad fidem Græci codicis purgatus, & in ordinem non minùs vtilem quàm elegantem digeſtus.—verso: Abrahamvs Ortelivs candido lectori.—sig. A 2 recto—C 2 verso: Ptolemaeo geographorvm ... —sig. C 3 recto—C 4 verso: Nobilis et ervditi viri Hvmfredi Lhvyd de Mona drvidvm insvla et armamentario romano epistola (dated 1568)—sig. [C 5] recto: Approbatio.—Svmma privilegii.—Ad libri compactorem.—verso: Antverpiae ex officina Plantiniana Balthasar Moreti. M.DC.XXIV.—sig. [C 6] recto: Vignette: Plantin's printer mark.—verso: blank.

According to Hessel (*Cf.* Epistolae Ortelianae) the following maps were added by Moretus: vj ... Lvmen historiarvm per Orientem ... Concinn. Fran. Hareio Antverpiæ.—vij. Lvmen historiarvm per Occidentem ex conatibus Fran. Haræi Antuerpiæ.—xliij-xlvj. Tabvla itineraria ex illvstri Pevtingerorvm ... Marco Velsero ... Ioannes Moretvs typographvs Antverp. S. P. D ...

**Perthes, J.**
Justus Perthes' atlas antiquus. Taschen-atlas der alten welt von dr. Alb. van Kampen. 24 karten in kupfersticht mit namenverzeichnis und einem abrisse der alten geschichte. 6. aufl. 32, [1], 6–60 pp., 24 maps. 16°. Gotha, J. Perthes, 1898. 50

**Reichard, C. G.**
Orbis terrarum antiquus ... quondam in usum iuventutis descriptus. Denuo delineavit et commentario illustravit Albertus Forbiger. 6th ed. 1 p. l., 10, 20 pp., 20 maps. obl. fol. Norimbergae, J. L. Lotzbeck [1861] 51
NOTE.—First edition 1830.
The following maps relate to cities:
no. 10. Roma sub imperatoribus.
" 17. Hierosolyma. Inset to map entitled: Palaestina.

**Smith, *Sir* W. and Grove, *Sir* G.**
Dr. William Smith's ancient atlas. An atlas of ancient geography, biblical & classical, to illustrate the dictionary of the bible and the classical dictionaries. The biblical maps from recent surveys and the classical maps drawn by dr. Charles Müller. 3 p. l., 26, [186] pp. incl. 43 maps. fol. London, J. Murray, 1874. 52

**Vidal de La Blache, P.**
Atlas classique Vidal-Lablache... 2 p. l., 131, 27, [1] pp.
incl. 100 col. maps. sm. fol. Paris, A. Colin, 1907. 53

NOTE.—At head of title: Histoire et géographie.

**Wilkinson, R.**
Atlas classica, being a collection of maps of the countries mentioned by the ancient authors, both sacred and profane. With their various subdivisions at different periods. 1 p. l., 46 maps, 7 charts. fol. London, R. Wilkinson [1797] 54

## BIBLICAL.

See Ecclesiastical; also Missionary.

### CITIES.

**Aa, P. van der.**
Représentation, où l'on voit un grand nombre des isles, côtes, rivières et ports de mer, comme aussi les habillemens & meurs des peuples, les cérémonies, les pompes & les magnificençes, item les animaux, arbres & plantes dans les quatre parties de l'univers. Les eftampes aiant été deffinées fur les lieux, & gravées exactement en tailledouce par les célébres, Luyken, Mulder, Georée, Stoopendaal & par d'autres maîtres renomméz. 2 p. l., 2 maps, 89 pl. fol. à Leide, P. vander Aa [1730?] 55

NOTE.—Plates without change from La galerie agréable du monde... Leide [1729?]
Views, with both french and dutch titles, principally of Asia and Africa, with a plan and view of Paris and the following relating to America:
no. [ 3] Nouvelle mappe-monde...
" [54] Animaux des Indes Occidentales...
" [73] Tyrannie des espagnols dans les Indes Occidentales...
" [79] Sucreries du Brésil...
" [83] Cérémonies de Virginie. [Shows capt. John Smith and Pocahontas]
" [84] Prêtres mendians et sacrifians aux divinitez des méxiquains.
" [85] Poissons, etc. des Indes Occidentales... —Monstres des Indes Occidentales...

**Andrews, J.**
A collection of plans of the most capital cities of every empire kingdom republic and electorate in Europe and some remarkable cities in the other three parts of the world. With a description of their most remarkable buildings, trade, situation, extent, &c., &c.

**Andrews, J.—Continued.**
Selected from the best authorities from actual surveys.  4 p. l., 140 pp., 42 maps.  8°. [London, 1792?]  56

NOTE.—Reviewed in The Monthly review London, for may, 1792. p. 99.
The following maps relate to America:
no. 40. A plan of the city of Quebec. 1771.
" [41] A plan of the city of Lima.
" [42] A plan of the city of Carthagena.

Plans of the principal cities in the world . . .  cover title, [2] l., 42 maps. obl. 4°.  London, J. Stockdale [1792?]  57

NOTE.—The edition without text or date.
Published also under title, A collection of plans of the most capital cities of every empire kingdom republic and electorate in Europe and some remarkable cities in the other three parts of the world, etc.
Reviewed in The Monthly review London for may, 1792. p. 99.
The following maps relate to America:
no. 40. A plan of the city of Quebec. 1771.
" [41] A plan of the city of Lima.
" [42] A plan of the city of Carthagena.

**Avity, P. d'.**
Neŭwe archontologia cosmica [das ift befchreibung aller kaÿfer thumber, kónigreichen und republicken der gantzen welt . . . alles . . . verfaffet durch Johann Ludwig Gottfried [pseud. of J. P. Abelin] . . . und verlegt von Matthæo Merian]  1 p. l., [31] maps, [61] pl. obl. fol.  Franckfurt am Maÿn, M. Merian [1646?]  58

NOTE.—These plates, with the exception of the engraved title, accompany the text of the 1646 ed. which also includes additional plates.

CONTENTS.

no. [1] Nova totius terrarum orbis geographica ac hydrographica tabula . . .
" [2] Nova Italiæ delineatio.
" [3] Roma.
" [4] Caftell: St. Angeli . . .—St. Bartolomei inful . . .—Zwei marmorfteinerne pferdt auff dem berg Quirinalis . . .—Arcus Septimii Seuri . . .
" [5] Campo Vacchina.
" [6] Nova totius Germaniæ descriptio . . .
" [7] Mores et ritvs veterum . . .
" [8] Gallia le royavme de France . . .
" [9] Parys.
" [10] Reims en Champagne.
" [11] Cales.—Calais.—Duynkerke.
" [12] Diepe.—St. Malo.
" [13] La Rochelle.
" [14] Silvanectum . . .—Lemovicvm . . .

no. [15] Lyon.
" [16] Massilia...
" [17] Vtrivsqve Bvrgvndiæ...
" [18] Hispania.
" [19] ... Sevillia.
" [20] Burgos.
" [21] Portvgallia et Algarbia...
" [22] Olisippo. Lisabona.
" [23] Neapolis.
" [24] Sicilia regnvm.
" [25] Messina.
" [26] Mediolanvm.
" [27] Caſtell zu Meÿlandt.
" [28] Angræ vrbis terceræ que insularum quas azores vocant maxima...
" [29] Goa.
" [30] America noviter delineata.
" [31] Magnæ Britanniæ et Hiberniæ tabvlæ...
" [32] London.
" [33] Edynbvrgum.
" [34] Hvngaria regnvm.
" [35] Bvda...
" [36] Topographia regiæ liberæq civitatis Posoniensis...
" [37] Cracovia...
" [38] Polonia regnum, et Silesia...
" [39] ... Statt Elbing... 1626...
" [40] Riga.
" [41] Revalia...—Nerva...
" [42] Dania regnvm.
" [43] ... Coppenhagen.
" [44] Bergen.
" [45] Tabula exantiffima regnorū Sueciæ et Norvegiæ...
" [46] Stockholm.
" [47] Tabula Russiæ...
" [48] Moscva.
" [49] Lotharingia dvcatvs...
" [50] Nanceivm...
" [51] Sabavdia dvcatvs...
" [52] Pedemontana regio cum Genvensivm territorio et Montisferrati...
" [53] Charboniere.—Chambery.
" [54] Tvrino.
" [55] Florentia.
" [56] Pisa.
" [57] Sena.
" [58] Mantva dvcatvs.
" [59] Belgii. Sive Germania...
" [60] Antverpia.
" [61] Amsterdam...
" [62] Campia...
" [63] Dordracvm.—Briela.
" [64] Enckhuysen.

Avity, P. d'—Continued.
no. [65] Groninga.
" [66] Haerlema.
" [67] Leyda.
" [68] Neomagvm.
" [69] Zvtphania.
" [70] Rotterdam.
" [71] Die eÿdtgnofchafft pünten vnd wallis Helvetia ...
" [72] Nova et accvrata dvcatvs Venetiani, Mediolani, Genvæ, Mantvæq, et finitimorvm principatvum delineatio.
" [73] Plates A—F.
" [74] Candia.—Corphv.
" [75] Genva.
" [76] Lvca.
" [77] Geneve ...
" [78] Tvrcicvm imperivm ...
" [79] ... Constantinopolis ...
" [80] Ierusalem.
" [81] Nova defcriptio Africæ.
" [82] Algier.
" [83] Tvnes.
" [84] Persia sive Sophorvm regnvm.
" [85] Tartaria sive magnichami imperiorum.
" [86] China ...
" [87] Xvntien alias Qvinzay.
" [88] India orientalis ...
" [89] Æthiopia svperior vel interior ...
" [90] Æthiopia inferior ...
" [91] Fezzæ et Marocchi ...
" [92] Valletta citta nova di Malta.
Additional plates contained in 1646 ed.:
no. 45. Stato della Chiesa, con la Tofcana ...
bet. pp. 2–3. Capitolivm.
"  " 6–7. Civilitatis Avenionis omnimq viarvm et ædificiorvm eivs perfecta delineatio. 1635.
"  " 120–121. Troye.—Chaalons en Champaigne.
"  " 200–201. Regno di Napoli.
"  " 392–393. Mantova.
"  " 482–483. Venetia.
"  " 484–485. Piazza de S. Marco di Venetia.
"  "  "  " ... Piazza di S. Marco in Venetia.
"  " 512–513. Ragusa.—Negroponte.

**Braun, G.**
Civitates orbis terrarvm. 6 v. in 3. fol. [Coloniæ Agrippinæ, sumptibus auctorum 1612–1618] 59

NOTE.—Entered in Brunet and Græsse as follows: Bruin (George) Civitates orbis terrarum in æs incisæ et excusæ, et descriptione topographica, morali et politica illustratæ. 6 v. in 3. Coloniæ, 1572–1618.
Other editions as follows: french ed., " Le grand théâtre des différentes cités du monde." Bruxelles, 1572; german ed., " Beschreibung und contrafactur der vornehmsten städte der welt." Cölln., 1574.

Titles vary as follows: v. 1, Civitates orbis terrarum. (Colophon dated 1612) ;—v. 2, De præcipvis, totivs vniversi vrbibys . . . ("Præfaetio" dated 1575) ; v. 3, Vrbivm præcipvarvm totivs mvndi. ("Præfatio" dated 1616) ; v. 4, Vrbivm præcipvarvm totivs mvndi. (Colophon dated 1617) ; v. 5, Vrbivm præcipvarm mvndi theatrvm . . . [n. d.]; v. 6, Theatri præcipvarvm totivs mvndi vrbivm . . . Anno 1618.
Imperfect:—v. 3, no. 37, v. 5, nos. 60 and 65, v. 6, nos. 35 and 52, wanting.

"Privilegivm Caesareæ maiestatis" which occurs in each volume generally on the reverse of the title-page, refers to Francis Hogenberg as the author's collaborator.

Descriptive text is on verso of plates.

Title-pages and plans are highly colored. Figures in the costumes of the period, arms of the country represented, and minor accessories, add interest and value to the entire work.

Plans of some important cities as follow: v. 1, no. [1] Londinvm.— v. 1, no. [46] Roma.—v. 2, no. [49] Vrbis Romae.—v. 3, no. [3] Chester [showing old Roman wall and forts] v. 4 no. [55] Roma.—v. 4, nos. [58–59] Jerusalem.—v. 5, no. [27] Antverpia.—v. 6, no. [24] Vienna. The following plans relate to America :
v. 1, no. [58] Mexico, regia celebris Hispaniæ Novae civitas.—Cusco, regni Peru in Novo orbe caput.
v. 1, no. [3] contains a view of Sevilla on which the dwelling place of Columbus "La casa de Colon" is marked.

"Hogenberg s'était associé avec Georges Braun ou Bruin, de Cologne, et Simon Novellanus pour publier ensemble un vaste recueil de vues et de plans, accompagnés de descriptions des principales villes du monde. Ce recueil avait été entrepris par eux sur les instances d'Ortelius qui le regardait comme le complément indispensable de son *Theatrum orbis terrarum*. Ils lui donnèrent l'aspect de celui-ci et le titre *Civitates orbis terrarum*. Le premier privilège qu'ils obtinrent de l'empereur Maximilien est daté de Vienne, le 28 août 1572 . . ."

"L'entreprise était vaste, et les deux associés durent recourir à quelques collaborateurs, qu'ils trouvèrent surtout dans les Pays-Bas . . . Georges Hoefnaghel et Corneille Chaymox, d'Anvers; Remade Limbourg, de Liège, etc."

. . . Le tome III . . . est entièrement gravé par Hogenberg et renferme toute une suite de plans de villes des Pays-Bas . . . En comparant tous ces plans avec ceux de Jacques de Deventer . . . on voit qu'ils ont été manifestement copiés sur ces derniers."—*cf.* C. Ruelens' "Jacques de Deventer" in "Atlas des villes de la Belgique au XVI° siècle. Bruxelles, Institut national de géographie" [1903] liv. 7.

## Du Pinet, A.

Plantz, povrtraitz et descriptions de plvsievrs villes et forteresses, tant de l'Evrope, Afie, & Afrique, que des Indes, & terres neuues: leurs fondations, antiquitez, & manières de viure: auec plufieurs cartes générales & particulières, feruans à la cosmographie, iointes à leurs declarations: deux tables fort amples, l'vne des chapitres, & l'autres des matières contenuës en ce préfent liure. Le tout mis par ordre, région par région . . . 4 p. l., xxxvii, 308,

## Du Pinet, A.—Continued.

[21] pp., [1] l. incl. 10 maps, 20 fold. pl., 14 pl. in text. fol. A'Lyon, par. I. D'Ogerolles, 1564. 60

> NOTE.—This work treats critically of cosmography and gives a list of atlases and maps. The map of the world by Gemma Frisius is remarkable for the correctness with which South America is delineated. In his "Dictionnaire historique et critique," Bayle gives an account of Du Pinet and his writings and quotes from Le Laboureur and Du Verdier.
> pp. xiii–xxiiii are misplaced.
> The following plates relate to America:
> pp. 292–293. "Plant & pourtraict de l'illuftre cité de Cufco, ville capitale du royaume de Péru.—Il Cvscho citta principale della provincia del Pérv."
> p. 297. "Povrtrait et description de la grande cité de Temiftitan, ou, Tenuctutlan, ou felon aucuns Mefsico, ou, Mexico, ville capitale de la Nueua Espaigne."

## Homann heirs.

Städt-atlas, oder: schauplatz berühmter städte, veftungen, profpeckte, gegenden, grundriffe, belagerungen, etc: welche beÿ denen Homännifchen erben ... zu finden find. 1 p. l., [192] l. incl. [108] col. maps, 5 pl. fol. Nürnberg, 1762. 61

> NOTE.—In addition to maps of the principal cities of Europe, this atlas contains the following: no. [3] Batavia.—no. [35] Carte topographique des pays et côtes maritimes qui forment le détroit de Gibraltar.—no. [67] Topographica repræsentatio Barbarici portvs et vrbis mvnitæ Oran ... —no. [69] Verschiedene prospecte der vornemsten städten in Persien ...
> On the lower half of the title page, is the "Register." Maps variously dated and by the following cartographers: C. B. Bestehorn, I. Baumeister, F. W. Zollman, Perizot, F. B. Werner.
> The following maps relate to America:
> no. [38] Vorstellvng einiger gegenden und plaetze in Nord-America ... —
>     Plan du port et ville de Louisbourg, dans l'Ile Royale ...
> " [39] Plan de la ville de Québec ...
> " [40] Plan of the town of Halifax ...
> " [46] Neu und verbesserter plan der st. u. hafens Havana.
> " [47] Neu und verbesserter plan des hafens von Carthagena ...
> " [73] Portus Pulchri in isthmo Panamensi ...
> " [74] Scenographia portusi Pulchri ..

## Luffman, J.

Select plans of the principal cities, harbours, forts &c. in the world ... 2 v. 8°. London, J. Luffman, 1801–[1802] [Copy no. 1] 62

> NOTE.—Collation: v. 1, 1 p. l., 80 col. maps; v. 2, 1 p. l., 79 col. maps.
> Map no. 27, v. 2, City of Boulogne, wanting.
> The following maps relate to America:
> v. 1, no. 3. Port Royal in Jamaica. 1799.
> " 2, " 10. Brazil. 1801.

v. 2, no. 37. Porto Bello. 1801.
" " " 43. San Domingo. 1801.
" " " 46. Charleston harbour. 1801.
" " " 54. St. Augustine. 1802.
" " " 59. Havanna. 1802.
" " " 62. The isthmus of Panama. 1802.
" " " 65. Carthagena. 1802.
" " " 67. Behring's strait. 1802.
" " " 70. Philadelphia. 1802.
" " " 72. Boston. 1802.
" " " 75. The island of St. Domingo. 1802.
" " " 78. New York. 1802.

Same. 2 v. 8°. London, J. Luffman, 1801–[1803] [Copy no. 2] 63

NOTE.—Collation: v. 1, 1 p. l., 79 col. maps; v. 2, 1 p. l., 87 col. maps. v. 1, no. 11, " Strait and bay of Gibraltar," wanting.
Inserted map " Brussels," from Luffman's Geographical & topographical atlas [1815]–1816, in place of map no. 30, copy no. 1, " The department of Morbihan."
Inserted map [Elba] from same, replaces no. 58, copy no. 1, which is a different map of Elba.
Map no. 63, " Vienna," imprint july 21, 1800. Same map in copy no. 1, oct$^r$. 1, 1800.
Maps of " Mouth of Vistula " and " Dantzic " while not numbered, correspond to nos. 62 and 75 in copy no. 1, v. 2.—Maps no. 64, " Valenciennes," no. 65, " Carthagena " and no. 72, " Boston " are not in this edition.
nos. 8–10, 12–15, 17 are duplicated.
Map. no. [2] " The river Elbe " . . . publish'd july 4, 1803," differs from that in copy no. 1, "publish'd jan$^y$. 1, 1801."
Maps of " Salem and Marblehead " and " The Mediterranean sea," inserted. Same in Luffman's atlas [1815]–1816.
The following inserted maps are from the atlas:
Granville, in place of no. 41. Smyrna.
Leipzig, " " " " 44. Olivenza.
St. Marlo, " " " " 62. The isthmus of Panama.
L'Orient, " " " " 67. Behring's strait.
Chambray, " " " " 68. Fort Monterey.
Crimea, " " " " 69. Geneva.
Map of " The island of St. Domingo," not numbered, corresponds to no. 75 in copy no. 1.

**Meisner, D.**

Thesavrvs philo-politicvs. Hoc est: emblemata sive moralia politica, figvris æneis incisa, et ad instar albi amicorvm exhibita, versibvs qvoqve latinis ac rhytmis germanicis confcripta . . . 9 pts. in 1 v.; [142] pp., 468 pl. obl. 16°. Franckfurt, E. Kieser, 1625–1627. 64

NOTE.—Complete latin ed. 1625–26 (in 8 pts.) The ninth part mentioned above is pt. 1 of v. 2 of the german ed. 1627, bound at the beginning of the present copy.

**Meisner, D.—Continued.**
Titles vary: pts. 2-6. Thesavri philo-politici ... Hoc est; emblemata sive moralia politica imaginibvs artificiosis in æs incisis illvstrata, descripta ac continuata studio atq; inventione. Danielis Meisneri ... Francofurti, 1625. pts. 7-8. Thesavri philo-politici .... Francofvrti, 1626.—Title of german ed. pt. 1, v. 2, reads: Thesavri philopolitici; oder, Politifches schatz-käftleins zweyten buchs, erfter theil. Franckfurt am Mayn, 1627.

"Das werk erschien zuerst 1623 ... sodann mit 800 kupfern 1642 zu Nürnberg unter dem titel: Sciagraphia curiosa, sive libelius novus politicus emblematicus civitatum" *cf.* Lipperheide'schen, kostüm bibliothek. Katalog. Berlin, 1896-1901. v. 1, no. 549. Another ed., 1678, is mentioned, "Bulletin du bibliophile," 1842. 5°. serie, p. 408.

Views of cities having in the foreground allegorical pictures with figures in costume of the 17th century.

Verses in latin and german above and beneath the plates.

pt. 7, no. [10] contains a view of "Cufco in Weft Indien."

**Romanus, A.**
Parvvm theatrvm vrbivm sive vrbivm præcipvarvm totivs orbis brevis et methodica descriptio. 4 p. l., 366 pp., 12 l. incl. 63 plans, 1 pl. 12°. Francoforti, ex. officina typographica N. Bassæi, 1595.
65

NOTE.—Pages 359-365 contain descriptions of cities in Nova Francia, Florida, Nova Hispania, Nova Galicia, Civola regnum, Ivcatan, Fvndvra, Cvba, Borichen, S. Dominici insvla, Iamaica insvla, Nicaragva, Gvattimala regio, Castilia d'Oro, Cartagena, Granata Nova, Andalvzzia Nova, Brasilia, Perv regnvm, Popaian regio.

**Schenk, P.**
Petri Schenkii Hecatompolis, sive totius orbis terrarum oppida nobiliora centum; exquisite collecta atque eleganter depicta ... 2 p. l., 100 pl., port. obl. 4°. [Amstelædami, P. Schenk] 1702. 66

NOTE.—Engraved title and portrait of Wilhelm, elector of Brandenburg, to whom the work is dedicated.

"Blad-wyser" signed: Lud. Smids, M. D.

The view of New Amsterdam is mentioned by Asher as the only separate view of New Amsterdam that he has seen. He calls it a copy of Allard's engraving and says: "Like all the other engravings of Schenk, this one was executed between 1690 and 1700 and most likely published in one of the various collections of views [of] different cities, published by him." *cf.* Asher, G. M. A list of the maps and charts of the New-Netherland. Amsterdam, 1855. p. 21-22.

"Mr. Asher saw the plate but did not know this work. [Hecatompolis] Of this work there exists a very rare edition publ. by C. Allard, 1700 [also] same work but with title: Af beeldinge van een hondert der voornaamste en sterkste steeden in Europa. Amsterdam, Jan Roman. 1752. With printed table and index, without the portrait of the elector, the plates numbered 1-100." *cf.* Muller, Frederick. Catalogue. Amsterdam, 1872. Portraits. p. 115, no. 7793-94.

pl. 1-65, Europa; 66-77, Asia; 78-90, Afrika; 91-100, Amerika.
The following views relate to America:
no. 91. Acapulco. [Mexico]
" 92. Nieu Amsterdam.
" 93. Fernambuco. [Brazil]
" 94. S. Francisco de Campesche. [Mexico]
" 95. Havana.
" 96. Kartagena. [Colombia]
" 97. Nombre de Dios. [Mexico]
" 98. Panama.
" 99. Iuan de Porto Riko.
" 100. S. Salvador. [Brazil]

Afbeeldinge van eenhondert der voornaamste en sterkste steeden in Europa. 2 p. l., 100 pl. obl. 4°. Amsterdam, J. Roman, 1752. 67

NOTE.—Issued 1702 under title: Petri Schenkii Hecatompolis, sive totius orbis terrarum oppida nobiliora centum.
This edition does not contain the portrait of the elector of Brandenburg.
The views are numbered 1–100 and are unchanged.
For descriptive note see his: Hecatompolis.

## COLONIAL.

Mager, H.
Atlas colonial . . . Avec notices historiques et géographiques . . . 2 p. l., [432] pp. incl. 18 col. maps. fol. Paris, C. Bayle [1885] 68

NOTE.—Half-title: Atlas colonial.
Preface dated 1885.
Various paging.
Imperfect: map no. [6] Les possessions françaises de l'Inde, wanting.

## COMMERCIAL.

Bartholomew, J. G.
Atlas of commercial geography, illustrating the general facts of physical, political, economic and statistical geography, on which international commerce depends. . . . With introductory notes by Hugh Robert Mill . . . vii, [1] pp., 25 col. maps on 27 l. fol. Cambridge, university press, 1889. 69
[Pitt press series]

Atlas of the world's commerce; a new series of maps with descriptive text and diagrams showing products, imports, exports, commercial conditions and economic statistics of the countries of the world. Compiled from the latest official returns at the Edin-

**Bartholomew, J. G.—Continued.**
burgh geographical institute . . .     2 p. l., iv, lvi (*i. e.* lx), 176,
42 pp. incl. maps, tab., diagr. fol. London, G. Newnes, limited
[1907]     70

NOTE.—Published in 22 pts., 1906–1907.

**Commercial intelligence.** *London.* [*Weekly*]
An atlas of the world's chief industries. Prepared under the direction of "Commercial intelligence." 2 p. l., 48 pp. incl. 12 col. maps. fol. London, G. Philip & son, 1905.     71

**Freytag, G.**
G. Freytag's export-atlas für welthandel and industrie. Statistische darstellung der ein- und ausfuhr aller wichtigen handelsartikel nach ihrem werte . . . 28 tafeln und karten, eine karte der verkehrswege für den weltexport mit der verbreitung der verkehrssprachen. 2 pts. in 1 v.    5 p. l., 24 (*i. e.* 29) l. incl. 20 col. maps (1 fold. map) obl. 4°. Wien, G. Freytag & Berndt [1903]     72

NOTE.—At head of title: Herausgegben mit unterstützung des k. k. österr. handelsmuseums in Wien.
Maps contain statistical tables for 1894–98.
The following maps relate to America:
no. 17. Vereinigte Staaten von Amerika.
" 18. Central-Amerika und West-Indien.
" 19. Mittleres Süd-Amerika.

**Johnston, W. & A. K.**
Atlas of commercial geography containing 48 maps, with explanatory letterpress by H. de B. Gibbins.    2 p. l., ii, 23 pp., 1 l., 48 maps. 12°. Edinburgh and London, W. & A. K. Johnston [1892]     73

**Lehmann, R.** *and* **Scobel, A.**
Atlas für höhere lehranstalten mit besonderer berücksichtigung der handelsgeographie. 74 haupt-und 66 nebenkarten auf 80 kartenseiten. 2 p. l., 58 maps on 80 l., 2 pl. fol. Bielefeld und Leipzig, Velhagen & Klasing, 1903.     74

**Levasseur, E.**
Atlas de géographie économique . . .     1p. l., 21 fold. maps. 12°. Paris, C. Delagrave [1904]     75

NOTE.—At head of title: Programmes du 31 mai 1902, second cycle—seconde.

**McCulloch, J. R.**
[A dictionary, practical, theoretical, and historical, of commerce and commercial navigation . . . Atlas] 7 maps. 8°. [London, Longmans, 1859] 76

NOTE.—Without title-page. To accompany text.
The following maps relate to America:
no. 1. The world on Mercator's projection.
" 6. British possessions in North America, with part of the United States . . . Insets: Plans of Montreal and Quebec.—Map of Newfoundland.
" 7. Central America & the West Indies . . . Insets: Harbours of Port Royal & Kingston, Jamaica.—Harbour & city of Havana . . .

**Philip, G. & son,** *ltd.*,
Philips' commercial atlas of the world; a series of sixty-one maps, illustrating every aspect of geographical science . . . Each map is accompanied by a complete index in which the latitude & longitude of every place is given. 2 p. l., [84] l., 60 (*i. e.* 62) maps. fol. London, Liverpool, G. Philip & son, ltd. 1908. 76a

**Savage, R. F.**
An atlas of commercial geography . . . xii, 6 pp., 36 l. incl. 34 maps. fol. Edinburgh and London, W. & A. K. Johnston, 1905. 77

**Scobel, A.**
Handels-atlas zur verkehrs- und wirtschaftsgeographie. Für handelshochschulen, kaufmännische, gewerbliche und landwirtschaftliche lehranstalten, sowie für kaufleute und nationalökonomen . . . 3 p. l., 40 l. incl. 39 maps. fol. Bielefeld und Leipzig, Velhagen & Klasing, 1902. 78

## ECCLESIASTICAL.

**American tract society.**
Bible atlas and gazetteer; containing six new and accurate maps, and a list of all geographical names, with references to their scripture places and to the proper maps; also a variety of most useful tables. 32 pp., 6 maps. 4°. New York, american tract society [1862] 79

**Brion de la Tour, L.**
Atlas ecclésiastique comprenant tous les évêchés des quatre parties du monde, sous leurs métropoles respectives, soit archevêchez ou patriarchats, y compris même les siéges des églises

**Brion de la Tour, L.—Continued.**

schismatiques répandues hors de l'Europe, et dont on a une connoissance assûrée, avec quelques rectifications. Ouvrage nouveau adapté à la géographie de l'abbé Nicolle de la Croix & ca; et servant de supplément à l'atlas général dressé pour l'étude de la géographie . . . 1 p. l., 41 maps. fol. Paris, Desnos; DeLalin, 1766. 80

> NOTE.—Engraved title. Maps dated 1763–1766.
> The following maps relate to America:
> no. [1] Mappe-monde drefsé . . . en 1741, par mrs. Tchirikcow et de l'Isle . . . par le ch$^r$. de Beaurain . . . 1763.
> " 40. L'Amérique . . . 1764.
> " 41. Chili, Paraguay, Brésil, Amazones, et Pérou . . . 1766.
> " 42. Guayane, Terre Ferme, Isles Antilles, et Nlle. Espagne . . . 1766.
> " 43. Nouveau Mexique, Louisiane, Canada, et Nlle. Angleterre . . . 1766.

**Denis, L.**

Empire des Solipses, divisé en cinq affistances et subdivifé par provinces. 1764. 3 p. l., 41 maps, 1 pl. obl. 48°. Paris, Denis, 1764. 81

> NOTE.—" C'est un atlas du gouvernement des jésuites; il est fort curieux, mais devenu très-incomplet."
> The following maps relate to America:
> p. 78. Amérique Septentr$^{le}$.
> " 104. Partie sep$^{le}$. de la province du Mexique.
> " 108. la. pr. du Mexique. Partie mérid$^{le}$.
> " 110. Nouv Royaume.
> " 114. Prov de Quito.
> " 118. la province du Pérou.
> " 122. la provin. de Parag. [!]
> " 126. Province du Brésil.
> " 130. I. Phillippines [!]

**Heussi, K.** *and* **Mulert, H.**

Atlas zur kirchengeschichte. 66 karten auf 12 blättern . . . 18 pp., [1] l., 12 maps. 4°. Tübingen, J. C. B. Mohr, 1905. 82

> CONTENTS.
>
> no. 1. Zur geschichte der alten kirche.
> " 2. Einzelkarten zur geschichte der alten kirche.
> " 3. Zur kirchengeschichte von Asien bis zum xiv. jahrhundert.
> " 4. Zur kirchengeschichte Osteuropas.
> " 5. Zur abendländischen kirchengeschichte vom v. bis zum ix. jahrhundert.
> " 6. Romanische länder im mittelalter.
> " 7. Germanische länder im mittelalter, 1.
> " 8. Germanische länder im mittelalter, 2.

no. 9. Zur geschichte des papsttums.
" 10. Zur geschichte der deutschen reformation und gegenreformation.
" 11. Zur neueren westeuropäischen kirchengeschichte.
" 12. Zur verbreitung der religionen und konfessionen um 1900.

## Holman, A. J. & co.

New biblical atlas with index. 1 p. l., viii pp., 11 maps, 1 pl. 8°. Philadelphia, A. J. Holman & co. 1898. 83

## Hurlbut, J. L.

Manual of biblical geography. A text-book on bible history, especially prepared for the use of students and teachers of the bible, and for sunday school instruction, containing maps, plans, review charts, colored diagrams, and illustrated with accurate views of the principal cities and localities known to bible history. With an introduction by rev. J. H. Vincent. 158 pp. incl. 52 maps, 6 pl. fol. Chicago, Rand, McNally & co. [1884] 84

## Jenks, W.

The explanatory bible atlas and scripture gazetteer . . . with . . . a colored missionary map of the world; a dictionary of the national history of the bible, with engravings; and tables of time, weights, measures and coins, tabular views, etc. 1 p. l., [5]–157 pp., front., incl. 17 maps. 2 pl. sm. fol. Boston, C. Hickling, 1847.
84a

The explanatory bible atlas and scripture gazetteer; geographical, topographical and historical; containing maps of all the countries and places mentioned in the old and new testaments . . . 4th ed. 157 pp. incl. 17 maps, 3 pl. fol. Boston, C. Hickling, 1849. 85

## McClure, E.

Historical church atlas . . . illustrating the history of eastern and western christendom until the reformation, and that of the anglican communion until the present day. 132 pp. (incl. 43 maps) 18 col. maps. fol. London, society for promoting christian knowledge, 1897. 86

NOTE.—Published under the direction of the tract committee.

## Mathews & Leigh.

The scripture atlas; or, a series of maps, to illustrate the old and new testament: drawn from the best authorities ancient and modern, by eminent artists. 5 p. l., 25 l., incl. 19 col. maps, 1 pl. fol. London, for Mathews & Leigh, 1812. 87

NOTE.—Engraved title.
Contains " Plan of the city of Jerusalem " 1812.

**Riess, R. von**

Bibel-atlas in zehn karten nebst geographischem index. 2. aufl. viii, 32 pp., 10 maps. fol. Freiburg im Breisgau, Herder, 1887. 88

**Starkweather, G. A.**

Starkweather's sunday school geography, a work on sacred geography, designed for bible students generally, and particularly adapted to sunday schools and bible classes . . . 3 p. l., 26 pp., 7 col. maps. 8°. New York, U. D. Ward; Chicago, Sumner & Fuller, 1872. 89

**Werner, O.**

Katholischer kirchen-atlas. Vierzehn colorirte karten mit begleitendem text. 2 p. l., 96 pp., 14 maps. 4°. Freiburg im Breisgau, Herder, 1888. 90

NOTE.—The following maps relate to America:
no. 1. Übersichtskarte der kirchlichen eintheilung der erde.
" 13. Mexico und Central America.
" 14. Süd-America.

**Wheeler, J. T.**

An analysis and summary of the historical geography of the old and new testaments. Illustrated by coloured maps, and view and plan of Jerusalem. 2 p. l., 34 pp., front, 6 maps. 4°. London, A. Hall, Virtue & co. 1853. 91

## ETHNOGRAPHICAL.

**Prichard, J. C.**

[Six ethnographical maps, with a sheet of letterpress . . . In illustration of his works: "The natural history of man", and "Researches into the physical history of mankind"] 3 pp., 6 fold. maps. fol. [London, H. Baillère, 1843] 92

NOTE.—Title taken from label mounted on cover.
The following maps relate to America:
no. [4] Ethnographical map of North America.
" [5]  "  "  " South America.
" [6]  "  "  " Polynesia.

[Six ethnographical maps, illustrative of "The natural history of man" and "Researches into the physical history of mankind" . . . 2d ed.] 3 pp., 6 fold. maps. fol. [London, New York, H. Baillière, 1851] 93

NOTE.—No title page; title supplied from label mounted on cover of a copy of the 2d [i. e. 3d] edition, 1861, in the Surgeon-general's library. Each map has title: "Ethnographical map . . . illustrative of dr.

Prichard's Natural history of man." And his "Researches into the physical history of mankind." 2d ed. 1851.
The following maps relate to America:
no. [4] Ethnographical map of North America.
no. [5] " " " South America.
no. [6] " " " Polynesia.

## GAMES.

### Gaultier, A. E. C.

A complete course of geography by means of instructive games invented by the abbé Gaultier. 4th ed. 50 pp., 6 col. maps, 1 pl. fol. London, W. & C. Spilsbury, 1800. 94

NOTE.—Maps dated 1792-1802.
The following maps relate to America:
no. [1] A plain map of America. 1797.
" [5] A plain map for the geographical game of Asia, Africa, America . . . 1792.

## HARBORS AND LIGHTHOUSES.

### Coulier, P. J.

Atlas général des phares et fanaux à l'usage des navigateurs, . . . publié sous les auspices de s. a. r. mgr. le prince de Joinville . . . 23 pts. in 1 v. fol. Paris, l'auteur; H. Bossange, 1850. 95

NOTE.—Published in 23 separate parts, Paris, l'auteur; Saint-Pétersbourg, J. Issakoff, 1844-1848. Issued in one volume with general title-page 1850.
Frontispiece, engraved portrait of the author.
The following parts relate to America:
no. 20. Amérique équatoriale . . . 1$^{re}$ section. 1846.
" 21. Amérique équatoriale et continentale. 1846.
" 22. Brésil. 1846.
" 23. Mer des Indes. 1$^{re}$ division. 1845.

CONTENTS.

no. 1. Russie, Mer Blanche. 12 pp., 12 maps. 1846.
" 2. Norvège. 12 pp., 22 maps. 1847.
" 3. Suède. 12 pp., 22 maps. 1847.
" 4. Russie, mer Baltique. 12 pp., 22 maps. 1846.
" 5. Prusse. 12 pp., 12 maps. 1846.
" 6. Danemarck. 12 pp., 17 maps. 1847.
" 7. Hanovre. 12 pp., 12 maps. 1848.
" 8. Pays-Bas. 12 pp., 22 maps. 1848.
" 9. Espagne, côtes n., mer de Biscaye. 12 pp., 12 maps. 1845.
" 10. Portugal. 15 pp., 12 maps. 1845.
" 11. Espagne, mer Méditerranée. 12 pp., 7 maps. 1846.
" 12. Sardaigne. 12 pp., 22 maps. 1846.
" 13. Deux-Siciles, 1$^{re}$ section. 12 pp., 22 maps. 1847.
" 14. " " 2$^{re}$ section. 12 pp., 22 maps. 1847.

**Coulier, P. J.**—Continued.
- no. 15. Autriche, mer Adriatique. 11 pp., 22 maps. 1845.
- " 16. Grèce et îles Ioniennes. 11 pp., 22 maps. 1845.
- " 17. Turquie. 8 pp., 22 maps. 1844.
- " 18. Russie, Mer Noire. 12 pp., 12 maps. 1847.
- " 19. Afrique. 12 pp., 27 maps. 1845.
- " 20. Amérique équatoriale ... 1$^{re}$ section. 12 pp., 17 maps. 1846.
- " 21. Amérique équatoriale et continentale. 12 pp., 17 maps. 1846.
- " 22. Brésil. 1846.
- " 23. Mer des Indes. 1$^{re}$ division. 1845.

## HISTORICAL.

**Aa, P. van der.**

Atlas nouveau et curieux des plus célèbres itinéraires, ou recueil de nouvelles cartes géographiques des voiages modernes de long-cours, qui ont été faits tant par mer que par terre dans toutes les parties du monde, & principalement dans l' Afie, l'Afrique, & l'Amérique, par les portugais, efpagnols, hollandois, françois, anglois, & autres nations; tant fous les ordres exprès des souverains, que par des compagnies de négocians, comme auffi par des particuliérs curieux & fcavans, depuis l'an 1246 jusqu' à l'an 1696. La pluspart de ces cartes aiant été dreffées fur les lieux par les voiageurs mêmes, & les autres confrontées & rectifiées sur les nouvelles observations des plus habiles géographes. Sur lefquelles cartes eft exactement marqué la véritable fituation des lieux, & la jufte étenduë des limites de chaque païs, avec les routes & chemins qu'ont tenu les voiageurs. Ouvrage très-utile pour la comodité de ceux qui veulent lire avec fruit les relations des voiages ... 2v. in 1. obl. fol. à Leide, P. van der Aa [1728]    96

NOTE.—Collation: v. 1; 8 pp., 1 l., 74 maps; v. 2: 1 p. l., 1 l., 65 maps.
The maps in "Naaukeurige versameling der gedenkwaardigste zee en landreysen na Oost en West-Indiën ... Leyden, 1707," were issued separately in this form with added french titles and ornamental engraved borders.

The following maps relate to America:
- v. 1. no. [1] Mappe-monde ...
- " " " [2] F. Draakx schip-vaart door de straat en Zuyd Zee ...
- " " " [3] Zee-togten door Thomas Candys na de West Indien ...
- " " " [4] Dry-jaarige scheep-togt der Nederlanders onder Olivier van Noort door de Straat Magellaan ...
- " " " [5] Indien onder den heer Lopo Vaz de Sampayo ... tot aan Nieuw-Spanje in America en kuften van Peru en Chili bevaaren.
- " " " [6] d'Oostindize voyagien door Johan Davis ...
- " " " [17] Jan Huygen van Linschotens reys-weg door zee, na Oostindien en verder eylanden.
- " " " [73] De manilles of Philippines eylanden benevens de Moluccos, Macassar, Tymor en andere, door P. W. Verhoeven aangedaan.
- v. 2. no. [11] Andries Battels scheeptogt na Brasille ...

v. 2. no. [12] A. Knivets zeldzame reystogt door de Straat Magellaan ...
" " " [13] Scheepstogt na d'Africa anze kusten van Congo en Angola ...
" " " [14] Nouvelle carte de l'Amérique ...
" " " [15] Amerika, of de nieuwe weereld ...
" " " [16] America, of nieuw-ontdekte weereld, tot de beschryving van Joseph d'Acosta afgebakend.
" " " [17] De voor eylanden van America ...
" " " [18] L'Amérique Septentrionale ...
" " " [19] 'T noorder deel van Amerika ...
" " " [20] De Graaf van Cumberlands verfcheyde reyfen na de kusten van Africa na Porto Rico en andere gewesten van America.
" " " [21] Scheeps-togt door Ferdinand Magellaan ...
" " " [22] Iukatan en vaste kusten van Nieuw Spanje ...
" " " [23] Land togten door Ferdinand Cortes aan de Golf van Nieuw Spanje ...
" " " [24] Nieuw Spaanje ...
" " " [25] De land-togt door Ferdinand Cortes gedaan uyt Mexico, na Las Ybueras.
" " " [26] De landschappen Tabasco en Iucatan ...
" " " [27] 'T landschap Guatimala door Pedro d'Alvarado in een land-togt uyt Mexico bevolkt. 1523.
" " " [28] Reys togt door Gil Gonzales Davila van't eyland St. Dominica gedaan na de Honduras en Nicaragua.
" " " [29] Nicaragua en de kusten der Zuyd-Zee, noorwaard van Panama, door Gil Gonzales Davila ontdeckt.
" " " [30] Scheeps togt van Iamaica gedaan na Panuco en rio de las Palmas ...
" " " [31] Zee en land-togten der franszen gedaan na, en in't Americaans gewest van Florida, aller eerst door Ioh. Pontius ontdekt.
" " " [32] 'T Amerikaans gewest van Florida door Ferdinand de Soto ...
" " " [33] De vaste kust van Chicora tussen Florida en Virginie door Lucas Vasquez d'Ayllon ...
" " " [34] d'Engelze volkplanting in Virginie door Iohan Smith ...
" " " [35] 't Noorder gedeelte van Virginie, door Bartholomeus Gosnol en Martin Pringe ...
" " " [36] Nieuw Engeland in twee scheep togten door kapitein Johan Smith ...
" " " [37] Jonathan Dickenson ramspoedige reystogt van Jamaika na Pensylvani nagespoord.
" " " [38] Land en volk-ontdekking in 't noorder gedeelte van America, door P. Marquette en Joliet; gedaan in 't jaar 1673.
" " " [39] De voorgenome scheeps-togt van Sebastiaan Gaboto, om door de Straat Magellaan ...
" " " [40] L'Amérique Méridionale ...
" " " [41] 'T Zuider America ...
" " " [42] H. Benzös scheep-togt uit Italie over Spanje na de Westindize eylanden en kusten van't Zuider America.
" " " [43] Terra Firma oft vaste land van Darien, Veragua, Cartagena en Nieuw Andalusie, etc.

**Aa, P. van der**—Continued.

v. 2. no. [44] 'T vaste land van Darien ten zuyden Cuba en Hispaniola gelegen.
" " " [45] Scheeps-togt door Robrigue de Bastides en P. Alvares Polomina uyt de haven van St. Domingo op Hispaniola, gedaan na St. Martha.
" " " [46] 'T landschap Cumana tussen golfo de Venezuela en Rio de Paria gelegen.
" " " [47] De vaste kust van Cheribichi door Alonzo d'Ojeda van't eyland Cubagua besogt.
" " " [48] Zee en land togt door Fr. Pizarrus en D. Almagrus van Panama gedaan na Peru.
" " " [49] De kusten van Chili en Peru, onder den hr. Oliver van Noort, bezogt in't jaar 1598.
" " " [50] De schipvaard, by Jacob Mahu, door de Straat Magellaan; na de Moluccos ondernomen; a an de Zuyd Zee mislukt.
" " " [51] De Straat van Magellaen sedert desfelfs eerfte ondekker, F. Magellaen. A°. 1520 . . .
" " " [52] P. Carders zee en land reyse na Brasil, Rio de la Plata en de Zuyd Zee.
" " " [53] Jan Stadens scheepstogten over Portugaal en Spanje, na Rio de Janeiro en elders in Brasil gedaan 1547.
" " " [54] Brasiliaanze scheepvaard, door Johan Lerius gedaan uit Vrankryk, in't iaar 1556.
" " " [55] De reyse over zee na Rio de la Plata, door Laurens Bikker en Cornelis van Heemskerk, ongelukkig volbragt.
" " " [56] d'Engelze volkplanting in't Amerikaans gewest Gujana en Rio de las Amazones, door de scheeps-togt van Charles Leig, begonnen.
" " " [57] Scheepstogt door Robert Harcourt gedaan na Gujana.
" " " [58] Het goudryk gewest Guiana tot de drywerfze scheepstogten van den ridder Walter Ralegh afgebakend.
" " " [59] De Bermudes of Summer eylanden . . .
" " " [60] Hispaniola . . .
" " " [61] Cuba en Iamaica . . .
" " " [62] M. Frobichers acheeps togt, gedaan om de noord, ter ontdekking van een straat na Cataya en China.
" " " [63] D. Blefkenius scheeps-togt gedaan na Ysland en kusten van Groenland.
" " " [64] De scheeps-togt agter Noorwegen en Tartary en om, na Cataya en China door Willem Barents . . .
" " " [65] De scheeps-togt benoorden om na Waygats; door Jan Huygen van Linschoten . . .

**Atlas** contenant des cartes géographiques et chronologiques propres à faciliter l'étude de l'histoire ancienne et moderne. [Manuscript] 1 pl., 30 col. maps, 1 diagr., 14 tab.  obl. fol. [1840?]  97

NOTE.—A collection of manuscript maps and tables by an unknown author, similar to those in Las Cases, E. A. D. Atlas historique, généalogique, chronologique et géographique.
no. 45. "Généalogie . . . de la maison de Lorraine," contains date 1840.
nos. 2, 32, relate to America.

## CONTENTS.

no. [1] Problêmes de géographie.
" [2] Mappe-monde dont le pôle est au centre.
" [3] Carte de l'histoire sainte.
" [4] Carte de l'histoire ancienne.
" [5] Empire d'Alexandre.
" [6] L'ancienne Grèce . . .
" [7] Carte de l'histoire romaine.
" [8] Tableau de l'empire romain.
" [9] Histoire du Bas Empire.
" [10] Tableau de la transmigration des Barbares . . .
" [11] Histoire du Bas Empire, depuis 400 jusqu'en 534.
" [12] Histoire du Bas Empire, depuis 534 jusqu'en 750.
" [13] Histoire du Bas Empire, depuis 750 jusqu'en 888.
" [14] Histoire du B. Empire, depuis 888 jusqu'en 1000.
" [15] Histoire du Bas-Empire, depuis 1000 jusqu'en 1204.
" [16] Histoire du Bas-Empire, depuis 1261 jusqu'en 1453.
" [17] Histoire de l'empire turc, depuis 1453 jusqu'en 1680.
" [18] Histoire de l'empire turc, depuis 1680 jusqu'en 1789.
" [19] Des duchês primitifs d'Allemagne . . .
" [20] Formation graduelle du territoire français . . .
" [21] Traités célèbres de notre histoire.
" [22] Empire français . . .
" [23] L'Europe politique en 1826 . . .
" [24] [Europe]
" [25] Batailles célèbres de l'histoire d'Espagne et de Portugal.
" [26] Carte du tems de Charles Quint.
" [27] Carte de l'histoire d'Angleterre.
" [28] Carte de l'histoire de Rufsie.
" [29] Carte de l'histoire de Pologne.
" [30] Carte de l'histoire de Suède.
" [31] Amérique, historique, physique, politique actuelle.
" [32] Tableau général de l'histoire universelle ancienne . . . 2 sheets.
" [33] Géographie de l'histoire . . . 8 sheets.
" [34] Chronologie de l'histoire sainte. 8 sheets.
" [35] Formation graduelle de l'empire romain.
" [36] Esquisse généalogique des maisons impériales . . . d'Allemagne . . .
" [37] Histoire de France . . .
" [38] Carte généalogique générale de France . . .
" [39] Details généalogiques des Capétiens des Valois &c.
" [40] Second tableau de la généalogie detaillée des branches Capétiennes . . .
" [41] Famille de Bigorre . . .
" [42] Histoire de Danemarck.—Histoire de Russie.—Histoire de Suède.
" [43] Tableau généalogique de l'ancienne maison d'Autriche.
" [44] Généalogie historique en detaillée de la maison de Lorraine.
" [45] Généalogie de la maison de Hohenzolern. 2 sheets.

**Arrowsmith, A.,** *jr.*
Orbis terrarum veteribus noti descriptio. A comparative atlas of ancient and modern geography, from original authorities, and upon a new plan, for the use of Eton school ... 3 p. l., 27 (*i. e.* 53) maps. fol. London, author, 1828. 98

NOTE.—Another edition published in 1830, also an index in 1828, entitled: Index to the Eton comparative atlas of ancient and modern geography. The following map relates to America:
no. 27. Western hemisphere.

**Baquol, J.** *and* **Schnitzler, J. H.**
Atlas historique et pittoresque ou histoire universelle disposée en tableaux synoptiques embrassant à la fois les faits politiques, religieux, littéraires et artistiques, et illustrée de cartes et de planches. Ouvrage fondé par J. Baquol, continué sur le même plan depuis l'an 1000 et augmenté d'instructions, de répertoires, etc., par m. J. H. Schnitzler ... 3 v. fol. Strasbourg, E. Simon, 1860. 99

NOTE.—Each vol. has an engraved title.
pl. no. 46, v. 3, shows plans of Paris in 1200, 1820, 1860.

CONTENTS.

v. 1. Histoire ancienne (Antiquité) Paged continuously. xx pp., 5 maps, 16 pl., 41 tab.
Maps: no. 1. Carte comparative du monde connu des anciens ... Insets: Le monde d'après Homère ... —Le monde d'après Hérodote.
" 1 bis. Les pays helléniques (Grèce, Asie-Mineure, Gran-le-Grèce & Sicile) ... par m. J.-H. Schnitzler. Inset: Athènes et ses alentours.
" 2. Carte de l'empire d'Alexandre.
" 3. Carte de l'empire romain dans sa plus grande étendue au 2$^{me}$ siècle de notre ère ... 1857.
" 4. L'empire romain d'occident et d'orient et 'e monde barbare de l'Europe ... au IV siècle de J. C.
v. 2. Histoire moderne. 1$^e$ section, le moyen-âge. Pa_ d continuously. 4 p. l., 5–7 maps, 17–32 pl., 42–105 tab.
Maps: no. 5. L'empire de Charlemagne et celui des Arabes ... ommencement du IX$^{me}$ siècle de J. C. ... 1857.
" 6. L'Europe et l'Orient au temps de la 3$^{me}$ grande croisade (fin du XII$^e$ siècle) ... 1858.—États latins d'Orient (Royaume de Jérusalem, princ.$^{té}$ d'Antioche et comté d'Edesse) avant 1144.
" 7. L'Asie au temps de la plus grande étendue de la domination des Mongols sous le règne de Koubilaï-Khan (1260–1294) ... 1858.
v. 3. Histoire moderne. II$^e$ sectio..., les temps mo..ternes proprement dits. Paged continuously. 4 p. l., 33 pp., 8–16 maps, 33–52 pl., 106–163 tab.
Maps: no. 8. L'Europe orientale dans la seconde moitié du XV$^e$ siècle ... 1859.

Maps: no. 9. L'Europe centrale à la fin du XVe siècle (ou à la naissance de Charles-Quint) . . . 1859.
" 10. L'Amérique avant 1776 . . . par. m. J. H. Schnitzler. 1859.
" 11. L'empire français vers 1812, avec les états qui en étaient vassaux . . . 1860.
" 12. L'Océanie, avec la partie adjacente de l'Asie . . . 1860.
" 13. L'Amérique actuelle . . . par m. J.-H. Schnitzler . . . 1860.
" 14. L'Afrique suivant les connaissances géographiques actuelles. 1860.
" 15. L'Asie actuelle et l'empire russe. 1860.
" 16. L'Europe centrale à la fin de 1860 avec indication de tous les chemins de fer.

Atlas historique et pittoresque, ou histoire universelle disposée en tableaux synoptiques embrassant à la fois les faits politiques, religieux, littéraires et artistiques, et illustrée de cartes et de planches. Ouvrage fondé par J. Baquol, continué sur le même plan depuis l'an 1000 et augmenté d'introductions, de répertoires, etc. par J. H. Schnitzler . . .   3 v. fol. Strasbourg, E. Simon, 1861–64.   100

NOTE.—Each vol. has an engraved title.
Plate no. 46, v. 3, shows plans of Paris in 1200, 1820, and 1860.
For continuation of this work, see Schnitzler J.-H., La période décennale de 1850 à 1860.

CONTENTS.

v. 1. Histoire ancienne. Antiquité. 1 p. l., xx pp. 5 maps, 16 pl., 41 tab.
Maps: no. 1. Carte comparative du monde connu des anciens. Insets: Le monde d'après [Homère . . . —Le monde d'après Hérodote.
  1 bis. [Les pays helléniques (Grèce, Asie-Mineure, Grande-Grèce, & Sicile)   1857.—Inset: Athènes et ses alentours.
" 2. Carte de l'empire d'Alexandre.
" 3. Carte de l'empire romain . . . au 2$^{me}$ siècle de notre ère . . . 1857.
" 4. L'empire romain d'occident et d'orient et le monde barbare d'Europe . . . au IV siècle de J.-C.
v. 2. Histoire moderne. 1$^{re}$ section, le moyen-âge. Paged continuously. 5 p. l., 5–7 maps, XVII–XXXII pl., 42–105 tab.
Maps: no. 5. L'empire de Charlemagne et celui des Arabes . . . au commencement du IX$^{me}$. siècle de J.-C. 1857.
" 6. L'Europe et l'Orient au temps de la 3$^{me}$ grande croisade (fin du XII siècle) 1858.—États latins d'Orient (royaume de Jérusalem princ$^{te}$ d'Antioche et comté d'Edesse) avant 1144.
" 7. L'Asie au temps de la plus grande étendue de la domination des Mongols sous le règne de Koubilaï-Khan (1260–1294) 1858.
v. 3. Histoire moderne. II$^{e}$ section, les temps modernes proprement dits. Paged continuously, although the tab., pl. & maps have not been bound in consecutive order. 5 p. l., 32 pp., 8–16 maps, 33–52 pl., 106–163 tab.

**Baquol, J.** *and* **Schnitzler, J. H.**—Continued.

Maps: no. 8. L'Europe orientale dans la seconde moitié du XV° siècle. 1859.
" " 9. L'Europe centrale à la fin du XV° siècle. 1859.
" " 10. L'Amérique avant 1776 . . . par m. J. H. Schnitzler. 1859.
" " 11. L'empire français vers 1812 avec les états qui en étaient ou vassaux ou alliés. 1860.
" " 12. L'Océanie, avec la partie adjacente de l'Asie, selon nos connaissances actuelles de sa géographie. 1860.
" " 13. L'Amérique actuelle . . . par m. J. H. Schnitzler. 1860.
" " 14. L'Afrique suivant les connaissances géographiques actuelles. 1860.
" " 15. L'Asie actuelle et l'empire russe. 1860.
" " 16. L'Europe centrale à la fin de 1860 avec indication de tous les chemins de fer.

**Bouillet, M. N.**

Atlas universel d'histoire et de géographie. . . . 3. éd.  2 p. l., ii, 1101 pp., 88 maps, 12 col. pl. 8°. Paris, Hachette & cie. 1877.   101

NOTE.—First edition published posthumously in 1865, edited by Ph. Bouillet.

CONTENTS.

1. Chronologie [avec la collaboration de m. Caillet]
2. Généalogie [ "     "     "     "  " Garnier]
3. Géographie [ "     "     "     "  " Desjardins]

**Bretschneider, C. A.**

Historisch-geographischer wand-atlas nach Karl von Spruner. 2 pts., cover title, 10 maps. fol. Gotha, J. Perthes, 1856   102

CONTENTS.

pt. 1, no. 1. Europa um 350 nach Christo.
" 2. Europa im anfange des sechsten jahrhunderts.
" 3. Europa zur zeit Carls des Grossen.
" 4. Europa in der zweiten hälfte des zehnten jahrhunderts.
" 5. Europa zur zeit der kreuzzüge.
" 2. " 6. Europa zur zeit des vierzehnten jahrhunderts.
" 7. Europa zur zeit der reformation.
" 8. Europa zur zeit des 30 jährigen krieges und bis 1700.
" 9. Europa im achtzehnten jahrhundert von 1700 bis 1789.
" 10. Europa im zeitalter Napoleons, 1789 bis 1815.

**Cacciatore, L.**

Nuovo atlante istorico . . . 4. ed. . . .   3 v. obl 8°. Firenze, tipografia all' insegna di Dante, 1832–33.   103

NOTE.—Collation: v. 1, viii, [6], 11–368, 15 pp., 8 maps, 3 plans, 21 pl.; v. 2, 384, 19 pp., 9 maps, 42 pl.; v. 3, 481, 19 pp., 1 l., 13 maps, 47 pl.

"Cenni biografici del cavaliere Leonardo Cacciatore", pp. 367–68. L. C. has also the third edition of this atlas, dated 1831–33, with slightly different imprint. The work, left unfinished by the author, was completed and published after his death.

The following maps relate to America:
v. 3, no. 109. America Settentrionale di Arrowsmit [!]
" 119. America Meridionals di Arrowsmit.

## Colbeck, C.
The public schools historical atlas . . . 2d ed. 35 pp., 69 (i. e. 101) maps. 8°. London, Longmans, Green & co. 1885. 104

NOTE.—Concludes with "Europe in 1815."
The following maps relate to America:
no. 76. The world (1770)
" 77. The North American colonies.
" 78. North America before the war.
" 79. North America after the war.

## Droysen, G.
Professor G. Droysens allgemeiner historischer handatlas in sechsundneunzig karten mit erläuterndem text. Ausgeführt von der geographischen anstalt von Velhagen & Klasing in Leipzig unter leitung von dr. Richard Andree. 2 p. l., 92 pp., 75 maps. fol. Bielefeld und Leipzig, Velhagen & Klasing, 1886. 105

## Gage, W. L.
A modern historical atlas, for the use of colleges, schools, and general readers. 4 pp., 15 maps. 8°. New York, D. Appleton & co. 1869. 106

## Gardiner, S. R.
A school atlas of english history . . . A companion atlas to ' The students history of England ' . . . New ed. 23 pp., 72 maps. 8°. London and New York, Longmans, Green, & co. 1895. 107

NOTE.—The following maps relate to America:
no. 46. Eastern & Central America 1755.—Eastern & Central America 1763.
" 47. The world (1772)
" 48. United States of America 1783.
" 65. The world. 1892 . . .

## Gover, E.
Atlas of universal historical geography, a series of upwards of thirty maps and plans embracing the three divisions of sacred and classical-mediæval-and modern geography. The whole forming a complete geographical chronology, from the period of the Noachic deluge to that of the general peace 1815. 3 p. l., 28 maps, 26 pp. 4°. London, E. Gover, 1854. 108

NOTE.—The following maps relate to America:
no. 27. North America, showing the progress of discovery, and colonization.
" 28. America (South) showing the progress of discovery, foundation of the early spanish & portuguese settlem[ts].

**Hildebrand, E.** *and* **Selander, N.**

Atlas till allmänna och svenska historien för skolornas bruk ... 1 p. l., [6] l, 29 col. maps. obl. 4°. Stockholm, P. A. Norstedt & söners [1883]    109

    Note.—Preface to pts. 2-4, dated 1883.

**Houzé, A. P.**

Atlas universel historique et géographique composé de cent une cartes, donnant les différentes divisions et modifications territoriales des diverses nations aux principales époques de leur histoire, avec une notice sur tous les faits importants, et l'indication des lieux où ils se sont passés; destiné à faciliter la lecture et l'intelligence de tous les ouvrages historiques, et rédigé d'après les meilleures sources ... 3 p. l., 101 maps on 103 l. fol. Paris. P. Duménil, 1848.    110

    Note.—The following maps relate to America:
    no. [98] Amérique Septentrionale, en 1846.
    " [99] Amérique Méridionale, en 1846.

Atlas universel historique et géographique composé de cent une cartes donnant les différentes divisions et modifications territoriales des diverses nations aux principales époques de leur histoire ... 3 p. l., 101 maps. fol. Paris, librairie universelle [1849]    111

    Note.—The following maps relate to America:
    no. [98] Amérique Septentrionale, en 1846.
    " [99] Amérique Méridionale, en 1849.

**Hughes, W.**

A popular atlas of comparative geography: comprehending a chronological series of maps of Europe and other lands, at successive periods from the fifth to the later half of the nineteenth century: based upon the Historisch-geographischer hand-atlas of dr. Spruner; and continued with historical memoirs to the maps. 3 p. l., 48 pp., 28 maps on 22 sheets. fol. London, G. Philip & son, 1876.    112

    Note.—Cover title: Philips' historical atlas.

**Hunt, F. W.**

J. H. Colton's historical atlas. A practical class-book of the history of the world. Comprising, in a series of inductive lessons, the origin and progress of nations, their history, chronology, and ethnology, combined with their ancient and modern geography. ... 52 pp., 12 pl. fol. New York, Ivison, Phinney & co. 1860.    113

**Johnston, W. & A. K.**
    Johnston's historical atlas. 2 v. 4°. Edinburgh & London, W. & A. K. Johnston, 1880.      114
        NOTE.—Collation: v. 1, 21 pp., 31 maps; v. 2, 2 p. l., 148 pp.
        The following maps relate to America:
           v. 1, no. 21. World showing discoveries from XV to XVII cent.
           " 26. North America illustrating the conquest of Canada and the war of independence 1757–1783.
           " 31. World showing british possessions and dependencies.

**Jones, C. H.** *and* **Hamilton, T. F.**
    Historical atlas of the world illustrated. Giving histories and maps of all the countries in their geographical statistical and commercial aspects together with a complete history of the original surveys of the United States. 88 pp. incl. 56 maps, 18 pl. fol. Chicago, Higgins, bro. & co. 1876.      115

**Kiepert, J. S. H.** *and* **Wolf, C.**
    Historischer schul-atlas zur alten, mittleren und neueren geschichte in sechsunddreissig karten. [7$^{te}$ berichtigte aufl.] 1 p. l., 36 maps. obl. 8°. Berlin, D. Reimer [1897]      116

**Labberton, R. H.**
    An historical atlas containing a chronological series of one hundred maps, at successive periods, from the dawn of history to the present day. xvi pp., 40 maps. obl. 8°. Philadelphia, Claxton, Remsen & Haffelfinger, 1872.      117

    An historical atlas containing a chronological series of one hundred and four maps, at successive periods, from the dawn of history to the present day. 6th ed. xvi pp., 44 col. maps. obl. 16°. Philadelphia, Claxton, Remsen & Haffelfinger, 1880.      118
        NOTE.—Copyrighted 1879.
        The following maps relate to America:
        no. 30. The discoveries of the spaniards and portuguese.
        " 41. Theatre of war in the U. S. 1861–1865.

    An historical atlas. A chronological series of one hundred and twelve maps at successive periods from the dawn of history to the present day. 7th & enl. ed. vii, [1] pp., 51 maps. 4°. New York, T. Mac Coun, 1884.      119

    An historical atlas: comprising 141 maps: to which is added, besides an explanatory text on the period delineated in each map, a carefully selected bibliography of the english books and magazine articles bearing on that period. xv, 58 pp., 58 maps. 4°. New York, T. Mac Coun, 1885.      120

**Labberton, R. H.**—Continued.
New historical atlas and general history. xvi, 213 pp., 72 maps. 4°. New York, T. Mac Coun, 1886.
[Mac Coun's historical series]     121

Historical atlas 3800 B. C. to 1900 A. D. ... 16th ed. 2 p. l., 73 pl. on 37 l. 8°. New York, Boston [etc.] Silver, Burdett & co. 1901.     122

**Lapie, P.** *and* **Lapie, A. É.**
Atlas universel de géographie ancienne et moderne, d'un abrégé de géographie physique et historique. 4 p. l., 100 pp., 51 maps. fol. Paris, Eymery, Fruger & cie. 1829–[1842]     123
    NOTE.—Date on title page 1829; maps dated from 1828–1833.

Atlas universel de géographie ancienne et moderne, précédé d'un abrégé de géographie physique et historique ... 2 p. l., 98 pp., 49 maps, 1 pl. fol. Paris, P. C. Lehuby, 1841–[1842]     123a
    NOTE.—Date on the title-page 1841; date on each map 1842.
    The following maps relate to America:
    no. 17. Mappe-monde en deux hémisphères. 1842.
    " 42. Carte de l'Amérique Septentrionale. 1842.
    " 43. Carte des États-Unis d'Amérique, du Canada, du Nouveau Brunswick et d'une partie de la Nouvelle Bretagne. 1842.
    " 44. Carte des États-Unis du Mexique. Inset: Carte du Guatémala. 1842.
    " 45. Carte des Antilles, du golfe du Mexique et d'une partie des états voisins. 1842.
    " 46. Carte générale de l'Amérique Méridionale. 1842.
    " 47. Carte de Colombie ... 1842.
    " 48. Carte du Brésil. 1842.
    " 49. Carte du Pérou et du Haut Pérou.
    " 50. Carte de la Plata, du Chili et de la Patagonie.

**Las Cases, E.**
Atlas historique, généalogique, chronologique et géographique de A. Le Sage (comte de Las Cases) 1 p. l., [64] l. incl. 16 maps. fol. Paris, C. A. Teste [1803]     124
    NOTE.—First edition.
    Maps have marginal text.
    The following maps relate to America:
    no. [8] L'empire russe ...
    " [14] [L'Asie Philippine is.]
    " [16] [L'Amérique Septentrionale et Méridionale]

[Atlas historique, généalogique, chronologique et géographique de A. Le Sage [pseud.]     [66] l. front., incl. 20 maps. fol. [Paris, P. Didot 1807]     125
    NOTE.—Without title-page.

Engraved frontispiece: Les fastes Napoléens. De 1796, à 1806. Quérard states that this frontispiece disappeared in the editions after the restoration—1814.
Maps have marginal text.
The following maps relate to America:
no. [6] [L'Asie]
" [8] [L'Amérique Septentrionale et Méridionale]
" [16] [L'Empire russe . . .

Atlante storico geografico genealogico e cronologico del sig. A. Le Sage [pseud.] . . . 1 p. l., 71 l. incl. 18 maps. fol. Napoli, stamperia reale, 1826. 126

NOTE.—Engraved title.
The following maps relate to America:
no. 1. Mappamondo storico. 1823.
" 14. L'America colle sue divisioni geografiche e politiche. 1824.

Atlante storico, geografico, genealogico, cronologico e letterario di m. A. Le Sage [pseud.] 1. Veneta ed. 3 v. fol. Venezia, G. Tasso, 1826[–40] 127

NOTE.—Issued in parts 1826–40.
Translated into italian by Giambatista Albrizzi.
Titles vary: v. 2: "Mappe geografiche storiche concernenti l'epoche più celebri e le maggiori nazioni del mondo"; v. 3: "Atlante storico letterario, biografico, archeologico . . . Venezia, 1840."
v. 1 & 3 contain the text and tables, v. 2 the maps.
The following maps relate to America.
no. 20. L'America storica, fisica e politica nel 1825.
" 21a. America Settentrionale. 1832.
" 21b. Stati-Uniti dell' America Settentrionale. 1832.
" 22a. Antico impero Messicano.
" 22b. Confederazione Messicana. 1835.
" 22c. Confederazione Guatimalese. 1834.
" 22d. Arcipelago Colombiano. 1834.
" 23a. La Colombia. 1835.
" 23b. Le due repubbliche cioè la confederazione Peruviana. La confederazione Bolivia. 1835.
" 23c. I quattro novelli stati meridionali Americani. 1835.
" 23d. Impero Brasiliano.
" 24. [Map of the world in hemispheres]

Atlas historique, généalogique, chronologique et géographique de A. Le Sage [pseud.] Édition populaire et d'étude. 81 l. incl. 28 maps. fol. [Paris, Delloye, 1835] 128

NOTE.—The following maps relate to America:
no. [22] Mappemonde historique.
no. [27] Amérique historique, physique et politique actuelle.
no. [28] Carte spéciale, historique et géographique de la république des États-Unis de l'Amérique du Nord.

**Las Cases, E.**—Continued.

Atlas historique, généalogique, chronologique et géographique de A. Lesage (comte de Las Cases) Avec des augmentations et des annotations, par le chevalier Marchal, de Bruxelles ... 7 p. l., front., 72 l. incl. 18 maps, 18 tab. fol. Bruxelles, A. de Mat, 1853. 129

>NOTE.—Frontispiece: "Les fastes Napoléens, de 1796 à 1821", reappears in this edition with slight changes and a view of Napoleon's tomb in St. Helena.
>The following map relates to America:
>no. [18] Amérique historique, physique et politique en 1827.

Le Sage's [pseud.] historical, genealogical, chronological and geographical atlas, exhibiting all the royal families in Europe, their origin, descent, marriages, etc. ... Translated from the last and much improved french edition; to which have been added six maps, composed by madame Coindé, and never before published, making it a complete universal atlas. 2d ed. 2 p. l., 18 maps, 21 tab. fol. London, for H. Berthoud, 1818. 130

>NOTE.—The following maps relate to America:
>no. [17] Geographical map of America. Printed by R. Juigne.
>" [42] Historical map of the world.

**Lavoisne, C. V.**

A complete genealogical, historical, chronological, and geographical atlas; being a general guide to history, both ancient and modern: exhibiting an accurate account of the origin, descent, and marriages of all the royal families ... together with the various possessions ... and remarkable events, to the battle of Waterloo and general peace of 1815. 2d american ed. 288 pp. incl. 32 col. maps. fol. Philadelphia, M. Carey & son, 1820. 131

>NOTE.—The following maps relate to America:
>no. 67. North America ... improved to 1820 by E. Paguenaud.—South America ... for the elucidation of Lavoisne's ... atlas. By J. Aspin, improved to 1820 by E. Paguenaud.
>" 68. United States of America ... by John Melish. 1820.
>" 71. Map of South America intended for the elucidation of Lavoisne's ... atlas. By E. Paguenaud. 1820.

A complete genealogical, historical, chronological, and geographical atlas; being a general guide to ancient and modern history, exhibiting an accurate account of the origin, descent, and marriages of the principal royal families from the earliest authentic records; together with the various possessions, wars, celebrated battles, and remarkable events to the year 1821. According to the plan of Le Sage [pseud. of E. Las Cases] greatly improved. The whole forming a complete system of history and geography. From the last London edition, improved by C. Gros . . . and J. Aspin . . . Enlarged by the addition of several new maps of american history and geography, extended to the beginning of the year 1821. 3d american ed. rev. 5 p. l., 138 l., incl. 28 maps. fol. Philadelphia, M. Carey & sons, 1821. 132

NOTE.—Maps nos. 38, 43, 46, 51 and 71 by E. Paguenaud.
The maps of America show differences in detail in the 3 copies of this atlas in L. C.
The following maps relate to America:
no. 1. Geographical map of the world.
" 67. North America.—South America.
" 68. United States of America . . . by John Melish.
" 71. Map of South America . . . by E. Paguenaud.

**Lelewel, J.**

Atlas do J. Lelewela badań starożytności we względzie geografji, z. 19, tablic złożony. 2 p. l., 19 maps. obl. 4°. w. Wilnie i Warszawie, nakladami i drukiem Józefa Zawadzkiego typografa imperatorskiego Wilenskiego uniwersytetu, 1818. 133

NOTE.—To accompany: J. Lelewela badania starozytnósci we wzgleazie geografji.

**Löwenberg, J.**

Historisch-geographischer atlas zu den allgemeinen geschichtswerken von C. v. Rotteck, Pölitz u. Becker in 40 colorirten karten. 2 p. l., 50 maps. fol. Freiburg im Breisgau, Herder, 1839. 134

**Lyman, A. S.**

Lyman's historical chart. Containing the prominent events of the civil, religious and literary history of the world. From the earliest times to the present day. Revised, enlarged and improved. 5 p. l., 24 col. charts. fol. Cincinnati, O., national publishing co. 1874. 135

**Perthes, J.**

Justus Perthes' geschichts-atlas. Taschen-atlas zur mittleren und neueren geschichte von dr. Alfred Schulz. 24 karten in kupferstich mit einem abrisse der deutschen geschichte und der geschichte der wichtigsten anderen staaten bis auf die neueste zeit. 2 aufl. 68 pp., 24 col. maps. nar. 16°. Gotha, J. Perthes. 1904. 136

NOTE.—The following maps relate to America:
no. 7. Seefahrten und entdeckungen.
" 24. Vereinigte staaten von Nordamerika.

**Playfair, J.**

    A new general atlas, ancient and modern; accurately constructed . . . Elegantly engraved by the most eminent artists in London. 2 p. l., 46 maps. fol. London, for the author, 1814.    137

    NOTE.—Three historical maps of the world not noted in contents.
The following maps relate to America:
no. [11] Western hemisphere.
" [16] North America.
" [17] South America.
" [43] West Indies.

**Putzger, F. W.**

    Historischer schul-atlas zur alten, mittleren und neuen geschichte in 59 haupt- und 57 nebenkarten. Neu bearbeitet von dr. A. Baldamus. 17te aufl. xii pp., 32 maps. 8°. Bielefeld und Leipzig, Velhagen & Klasing, 1891.    138

    Historischer schul-atlas zur alten, mittleren und neuen geschichte . . . Bearb. und hrsg. von Alfred Baldamus und Ernst Schwabe . . . 30. aufl. xvi pp., 40 (*i. e.* 86) col. maps. 4°. Bielefeld und Leipzig, Velhagen & Klasing, 1906.    139

    NOTE.—Outline and detail maps on reverse of numbered maps.

    F. W. Putzger's historical school atlas of ancient, mediaeval and modern history revised and edited by Alfred Baldamus and Ernst Schwabe for the geographical institute of Velhagen and Klasing, Leipzig. American edition with an english rendering of the introductions, lettering and explanatory notes, and german-english glossary and index of names, edited by Ernest G. Lemcke. xxviii, xvi pp., 85 maps on 40 sheets. 4°. New York, Lemcke & Buechner [1903]    140

    NOTE.—The 27th german edition, Bielefeld & Leipzig, 1903, to which is prefixed the english title page, explanation and index.

**Quin, E.**

    An historical atlas; in a series of maps of the world as known at different periods, constructed upon an uniform scale, and coloured according to the political changes of each period . . . New edition with the maps on a greatly enlarged scale . . . the whole drawn and engraved by W. Hughes. 1 p. l., 21 col. maps. obl. fol. London, Seeley, Burnside & Seeley, 1846.    141

    NOTE.—To accompany his: Universal history.
The following maps relate to America:
no. 16 . . . 1498. The discovery of America.
" 17 . . . 1551. At the death of Charles V.
" 18 . . . 1660. At the restoration of the Stuarts.
" 19 . . . 1783. At the independence of the United States.
" 20 . . . 1811. Empire of Napoleon.
" 21 . . . 1846. At the present time.

**Rothert, E.**
* Die acht grossmächte in ihrer räumlichen entwicklung seit 1750.
. . . 2 p. l., 1 fold. l., 21 fold. maps. 4°. Düsseldorf, A. Bagel
[1904] 142

  NOTE.—Each map has explanatory letterpress. "Die gesamtlage 1903" folded leaf at end.
  The following maps relate to America:
  no. 5. Die Vereinigten Staaten bis 1815.
  " 6. Die Vereinigten Staaten. 1860.
  " 7. Die vorherrschaft des nordens in den Vereinigten Staaten 1903.
  " 8. Die reste der durch die europäischen kriege zusammengeschmolzenen kolonien 1815.
  " 9. Vorsichtige erweiterung der kolonien bis 1860.
  " 10. Frankreich 1903 . . . Glückliche kolonisationen.
  " 11. Grofsbritannien aufserhalb Europas.
  " 12. Englands politische und wirtschaftliche entwicklung 1860.
  " 13. Grofsbritanniens jüngste entwicklung. 1903.

**Rousset de Missy, J.**
Nieuwe astronomische geographische en historische atlas, tot klaar verstant en gemakkelyke oefeninge der hemel- en aartryskunde, en der historien, als mede tot begrip der openbaare tydingen, zo in den oorlog als in den vrede. . . . [152] pp., 32 fold. maps. nar. 12°. t'Amsterdam, H. de Leth [1742?] 143

  NOTE.—Engraved title page in french and dutch.

**Schrader, F.**
Atlas de géographie historique par une réunion de professeurs et de savants sous la direction géographique de F. Schrader; contenant en 55 feuilles doubles, 167 cartes en couleurs accompagnées d'un texte historique au dos de 115 cartes figures et plans en noir dans le texte et d'un index alphabétique des noms contenus dans l'atlas. 2 p. l., 32 pp., 55 fold. col. maps. fol. Paris, Hachette & cie. 1896. 144

  NOTE.—Text on reverse of maps.

Atlas de géographie historique par une réunion de professeurs et de savants sous la direction géographique de F. Schrader, contenant 55 cartes doubles en couleurs accompagnées au verso d'un texte historique d'un grand nombre de cartes de détail, figures, diagrammes et d'un index alphabétique d'environ 30,000 noms. Nouv. éd. rev. 2 p. l., 32 pp., 55 fold. col. maps. fol. Paris, Hachette & c[ie], 1907. 145

**Ségur, L. P., comte de.**

Atlas pour l'histoire universelle . . . Partie ancienne, romaine et du Bas-empire. Dirigé, dessiné et gravé par P[ierre] Tardieu. 23 pp., 10 col. maps, 10 pl. obl. 12°. Paris, A. Eymery, 1822. 146

NOTE.—To accompany his: Histoire universelle, ancienne et moderne. Paris, 1821–1822.

CONTENTS.

no. 1. Monde connu des anciens.
" 2. Égypte ancienne.
" 3. Palestine ou Judée.
" 4. Grèce.
" 5. Empire d'Alexandre.
" 6. Empire romain.
" 7. Empire grec.
" 8. Athènes et Sparte.
" 9. Jérusalem et Syracuse.
" 10. Rome et Constantinople.

**Sheahan, J. W.**

The universal historical atlas, genealogical, chronological and geographical . . . being a comprehensive history of the world. 282 pp. incl., 25 maps. fol. New York and Chicago, Warren, Cockcroft & co. 1873. 147

**Spruner von Merz, K.**

Spruner-Menke hand-atlas für die geschichte des mittelalters und der neueren zeit. 3. aufl. . . . neu bearb. von d$^r$. Th. Menke. 90 colorirte karten in kupferstich mit 376 nebenkarten. 3 p. l., 42 pp., 90 fold. maps. fol. Gotha, J. Perthes, 1880. 148

v. Spruner-Sieglin hand-atlas zur geschichte des altertums, des mittelalters und der neuzeit. I. Abteilung: atlas antiquus; atlas zur geschichte des altertums. 34 kolorierte karten in kupferstich . . . Entworfen und bearbeitet von dr. Wilhelm Sieglin. Erscheint in 8 lieferungen. lief. 1–5. fol. Gotha, J. Perthes, 1893– 149

Dr. Karl von Spruner's historisch-geographischer hand-atlas. 3 v. obl. fol. Gotha, J. Perthes, 1846–51. 150

CONTENTS.

1 abt. Atlas antiquus. 1850.
2 " Historisch-geographischer hand-atlas zur gesch'chte der staaten Europa's vom aufang des mittelalters bis auf die neueste zeit. 1846.
3 " Historisch-geographischer hand-atlas zur geschichte Asien's, Africa's, Amerika's und Australiens. 1851.

———— 2. aufl. 3 v. obl. fol. Gotha, J. Perthes, 1854–55. 151
NOTE.—1, 3 abt. 1855; 2 abt. 1854.

Dr. K. von Spruner's historisch-geographischer schul-atlas. 6 p. l., 22 maps. obl. 4°. Gotha, J. Perthes, 1856. 152

**Thalheimer, M. E.**
The eclectic historical atlas: a hand-book for students and general readers. vi pp., 1 l., 25 maps. 8°. Cincinnati, New York, Van Antwerp, Bragg & co. [1874] 153
NOTE.—"The maps comprised in this atlas were first published in Thalheimer's Manuals of ancient, mediaeval, and modern history, Thalheimer's General history, and the Eclectic history of the United States."—Introd. Maps by Russell Hinman, A. von Steinwehr and H. H. Vail.

The eclectic historical atlas: a hand-book for students and general readers. vi pp., 1 l., 19 maps, 1 pl. 8°. Cincinnati, New York, Wilson, Hinkle & co. [1874] 154

The eclectic historical atlas and charts: a hand-book for students and general readers. vi pp., 1 l., 26 maps, 5 tab. 8°. Cincinnati, New York, Van Antwerp, Bragg & co. [1885] 155

**Tyson, J. W.**
An atlas of ancient and modern history; presenting in a chronological series, the rise, progress, revolutions, decline and fall of the principal states and empires of the world; comprising details of the most important events . . . 1 p. l., 5 fold. tab. fol. Philadelphia, S. A. Mitchell, 1845. 156

**Wedell, R. von.**
Historisch-geographischer hand-atlas in sechs und dreissig karten nebst erläuterndem text . . . Mit einem vorwort von dr. F. A. Pischon. 2. aufl. 1 p. l., 36 maps. fol. Glogau, C. Flemming [1843] 157
NOTE.—Accompanied by "Erläuternder text".

**Wolff, C.**
Carl Wolff's historischer atlas. Neunzehn karten zur mittleren und neueren geschichte. Mit erläuterndem texte. iv, 7 pp., 19 maps. fol. Berlin, D. Reimer, 1877. 158

**Worcester, J. E.**
An historical atlas . . . New ed. 1 p. l., 10 tab. fol. Boston, Hillard, Gray, Little, & Wilkins, 1827. 159
NOTE.—Chart of France, wanting.

**Worcester, J. E.**—Continued.

CONTENTS.

Chart of general history.
" " sacred "
" " ancient chronology.
" " sovereigns of Europe.
" " modern chronology.
Historical chart of England.
" " " France.
Chart of american history.
" " biography.
" " mythology.

## HYDROGRAPHICAL.

**Sydow, E. von.**

E. von Sydow's hydrographischer atlas. 27 flussnetze über alle theile der erde . . .  8 pp., 28 maps. fol. Gotha, J. Perthes, 1847. 160

E. von Sydow's hydrotopischer atlas . . .  2 p. l., 28 maps. obl. 8°. Gotha, J. Perthes, 1856. 161

## ISLANDS.

**Bordone, B.**

Libro di Benedetto Bordone. Nel quale fi ragiona de tutte l'ifole del mondo con li lor nomi antichi & moderni, hiftorie, fauole, & modi del loro uiuere, & in qual parte del mare ftanno, & in qual parallelo & clima giacciono. Con il breve di papa Leone . . .  10 p. l., lxxiii numb. l. incl. 111 maps, 1 diagr. fol. [*Colophon:* Vinegia, N. d'Ariftotile, detto Zoppino] 1528. 162

NOTE.—First edition, evidently completed in manuscript in 1521 and first published in 1528.

Signatures:—AA in four, BB in two, CC in four, A–C in sixes, D–E in fours, F–H in sixes, I–K in fours, L in six, M in two, N–O in fours, P in five.

Title in red and black within ornamental wood-cut border.

Privilege and dedication verso of AA.

Fol. X [Plan of the city of "Temistitan", or Mexico before its destruction by Cortez]

The following maps relate to America:

no. [3] [Map of the world showing] "modo nouo", "terra del laboratore."
" [11] Pte del modo nouo [showing] "Terra de lauozatoze", "brafil."
" [12] [Plan of] la gran citta di Temiftitan.
" [13-15] Iamaique, Spagnola . . .
" [16] Cuba.
" [17] Dominica, Buchima, S. Martino, Santa ✠, S. Maria Antica, S. Maria rotonda, Moferato.
" [18] Guadalupe.
" [19] Martinina [*i. e.*, Martinique]
" [24] [Map showing] "Brafil"

Isolario di Benedetto Bordone. Nel qual fi ragiona di tutte l'ifole del mondo con li lor nomi antichi & moderni, hiftorie, fauole, & modi del loro viuere, & in qual parte del mare ftanno, & in qual parallelo & clima giaciono. Con la gionta del Monte del Oro nouamente ritrouato con il breve del papa . . . 10 p. l., lxxiiii numb. l. incl. 111 maps. 1 diagr. fol. [*Colophon:* Vinegia, N. d'Ariftotile, detto Zoppino] 1534. 163

NOTE.—Signatures:—AA in four, BB-DD in twos, A-D in sixes, E in four, F in two, G-M in sixes, N in eight.
Third ed., like the edition of 1528, with one additional leaf containing the "Copia delle lettere del prefetto della India " . . .
The following maps relate to America :
no. [3] [Map of the world showing] " mõdo nouo," " terra del laboratore."
" [11] Pte del mõdo nouo [showing] "Terra de lauoratore ", "brafil."
" [12] [Plan of] la gran citta di Temiftitan.
" [13-15] Iamaiqua, Spagnola . . .
" [16] Cuba.
" [17] Dominica, Buchima, S. Martino, Santa ✠, S. Maria Antica, S. Maria rotonda, Moferato.
" [18] Guadalupe.
" [19] Martinina [*i. e.* Martinique]
" [24] [Map showing] "Brafil."

Isolario di Benedetto Bordone. Nel qual fi ragiona di tutte l'ifole del mondo, con li lor nomi antichi & moderni, hiftorie, fauole, & modi del loro viuere, & in qual parte del mare ftanno, & in qual parallelo & clima giaciono. Ricoreto, & di nuouo riftampato. Con la gionta del Monte del Oro nouamente ritrouato con il breve del papa . . . 10 p. l., lxxiiii numb. l. incl. 111 maps, 1 diagr. fol. [*Colophon:* Vinegia ad inftantia, & fpefe del nobile huomo F. Torefano] 1547. 164

NOTE.—Like the edition of 1534, with corrections in the text.
Printer's mark on title-page.
The following maps relate to America :
no. [3] [Map of the world showing] " mõdo nouo," " terra del laboratore."
" [11] Pte del mõdo nouo [showing] "Terra de lauoratore," "brafil."
" [12] [Plan of] la gran citta di Temiftitan.
" [13-15] Iamaiqua, Spagnola . . .
" [16] Cuba.
" [17] Dominica, Buchima, S. Martino, Santa ✠, S. Maria Antica, S. Maria rotonda, Moferato.
" [18] Guadalupe.
" [19] Martinina [*i. e.* Martinique]
" [24] [Map showing] "Brafil."

Isolario di Benedetto Bordone. Nel qval si ragiona di tvtte le isole del mondo, con li lor nomi antichi & moderni, hiftorie, fauole, & modi del loro viuere, & in qual parallelo & clima giaciono. Ricorretto et di nvovo ristampato con la gionta del Monte del Oro nouamente ritrouato. 10 p. l., lxxiiii numb. l. incl. 111

**Bordone, B.—Continued.**

maps, 1 diagr. fol. In Venetia. [*Colophon:* Venetia. F. di Leno] [1562?]    165

> NOTE.—Signatures:—AA in four, BB in six, A-D in sixes, E in four, F in two, G-M in sixes, N in eight.
> Maps and text like the edition of 1547. Title-page is not the same; privilege and dedication on verso of sig. AA omitted.
> This edition is probably the one referred to in Jöcher as published in 1562. Notwithstanding, Harrisse places it, upon the authority of Rich, as 1537. It is noticeable in this edition that the two "privileges" dated 1521 and 1526 are not given, while they are in the editions of 1528, 1534 and 1547. If this edition were published in 1537 the inference is the "privilege" should not be omitted. The printer of this edition, Francesco di Leno, flourished about 1562. Brunet mentions an edition without date as being 1857 [!] [1557]
> The following maps relate to America:
> no. [3] [Map of the world showing] "mŏdo nouo," "terra del laboratore."
> " [11] Pte del mŏdo nouo [showing] "Terra de lauoratore," "brafil."
> " [12] [Plan of] la gran citta di Temiftitan.
> " [13-15] Iamaiqua, Spagnola . . .
> " [16] Cuba.
> " [17] Dominica, Bucbima, S. Martino, Santa ■, S. Maria Antica, S. Maria rotonda, Moferato.
> " [18] Guadalupe.
> " [19] Martinina [*i. c.* Martinique]
> " [24] [Map showing] "Brafil."

**Porcacchi, T.**

L'isole piv famose del mondo descritte da Thomaso Porcacchi, da Castiglione Arretino e intagliate da Girolamo Porro Padovano al sereniss. principe et sig.re il s. don Giovanni d'Avstria . . . 11 p. l., 117 pp., 1 l. incl. 30 maps. 4°. Venetia, apprefso S. Galignani & G. Porro, 1572.    166

> NOTE.—First edition.
> Engraved title-page. Engraved maps, in text.
> [Plan of the] "citta di Venetia." p. 1.
> The following maps relate to America:
> p. 81. Spagnvola.
> " 88. Cvba.
> " 101. Mondo Nvovo.
> " 105. [Plan of the] citta Temistitan.
> " 109. Mappa mondo.
> " 114. . . . La carta navigare. [Showing North and South America]

L'isole piv famose del mondo descritte da Thomaso Porcacchi da Castiglione Arretino e intagliate da Girolamo Porro Padovano. Con l'aggiunta di molte isole all' ill.re s. conte Georgio Trivltio . . . 3 pts. in 1 v.; 14 p. l., 201, [1] pp. incl. 47 maps. 4°. Venetia, apprefso S. Galigani & G. Porro, 1576.    167

> NOTE.—Colophon: In Venetia, apprefso Giorgio Angelieri, a instantia di Simon Galignani de Karera, M. D. LXXV.

Engraved title-page. Engraved maps, in text.
Second edition, containing 17 maps not found in the first edition; pp. 154-184 relate to America and contain 2 new maps:
p. 175. Iamaica hora detta di S. Iacopo.
" 182. S. Giovanni detta Borichen.
Besides these two the following maps relate to America:
p. 165. Spagnvola.
" 172. Cvba.
" 161. Mondo Nvovo.
" 157. [Plan of the] citta Temistitan.
" 193. Mappa mondo.
" 198. . . . La carta da navigare. [Showing North and South America]

L'isole piv famose del mondo descritte da Thomaso Porcacchi da Castiglione Arretino e intagliate de Girolamo Porro Padovano. Con l'agiunta di molte isole. All' ill.$^{re}$ s. conte Georgio Trivltio . . . 3 pts. in 1 v.; 12 p. l., 211 pp. incl. 48 maps. 4°. Venetia, appresso gli heredi di S. Galignani, 1604.  168

NOTE.—Engraved title-page. Engraved maps, in text.
To this edition are added "Descrittione dell' Istria," and "Descrittione dell' isola d'Elandia, isola de Gotti," with one additional map:—p. 201. Istria.
In some copies the imprint date is altered (?) to MDCIIIII.
The following maps relate to America:
p. 165. Spagnvola.
" 172. Cvba.
" 161. Mondo Nvova.
" 157. [Plan of the] citta Temistitan.
" 193. Mappa mondo.
" 197. . . . La carta da navigare. [Showing North and South America]
" 175. Iamaica hora detta di S. Iacopo.
" 182. S. Giovanni detta Borichen.

L'isole piv famose del mondo descritte da Thomaso Porcacchi da Castiglione Arretino e intagliate da Girolamo Porro Padovano. Con nova aggionta dedicate all' ill$^{mo}$. et rev$^{mo}$. mons$^r$. Gio. Francesco Moresini . . . 3 pts. in 1 v.; 12 p. l., 211 pp. incl. 48 maps. 4°. Padova, appresso P. & F. Galignani fratelli, 1620.  169

NOTE.—Like the Venetian edition of 1604, except the dedication.
The following maps relate to America:
p. 165. Spagnvola.
" 172. Cvba.
" 161. Mondo Nvova.
" 157. [Plan of the] citta Temistitan.
" 193. Mappa mondo.
" 197. . . . La carta da navigare. [Showing North and South America]
" 175. Iamaica hora detta di S. Iacopa.
" 182. S. Giovanni detta Borichen.

## ITINERARIES.

**Aa, P. van der.**

Atlas nouveau et curieux des plus célèbres itinéraires, ou recueil de nouvelles cartes géographiques des voiages modernes de long-cours, qui ont été faits tant par mer que par terre dans toutes les parties du monde, & principalement dans l'Afie, l'Afrique, & l'Amérique, par les portugais, efpagnols, hollandois, françois, anglois, & autres nations; tant fous les ordres exprès des souverains, que par des compagnies de négocians, comme auffi par des particuliérs curieux et fcavans, depuis l'an 1246 jusqu' a l'an 1696. La pluspart de ces cartes aiant été dreffées fur les lieux par les voiageurs mêmes, & les autres confrontées & rectifiées fur les nouvelles obfervations des plus habiles géographes. Sur lefquelles cartes eft exactement marqué la véritable fituation des lieux, & la jufte étenduë des limites de chaque païs, avec les routes & chemins qu'ont tenu les voiageurs. Ouvrage très-utile pour la comodité de ceux qui veulent lire avec fruit les relations des voiages. 2 v. in 1. obl. fol. à Leide, P. van der Aa [1728] 170

NOTE.—Collation: v. 1, 8 pp., 1 l., 74 maps; v. 2, 1 p. l., 1 l., 65 maps.
The maps in "Naaukeurige versameling der gedenk-waardigste zee en landreysen na Oost en West-Indiën . . . Leyden, 1707," were issued separately in this form with added french titles and ornamental engraved borders.

The following maps relate to America:

v. 1, no. [1] Mappe–monde . . .
" " " [2] F. Draakx schip-vaart door de straat en Zuyd Zee . . .
" " " [3] Zee-togten door Thomas Candys na de West Indien . . .
" " " [4] Dry-jaarige scheep-togt der Nederlanders onder Olivier van Noort door de Straat Magellaan . . .
" " " [5] Indien onder den heer Lopo Vaz de Sampayo . . . tot aan Nieuw-Spanje in America en kuften van Peru en Chili bevaaren.
" " " [6] d'Oostindize voyagien door Johan Davis . . .
" " " [17] Jan Huygen van Linschotens reys-weg door zee, na Oostindien en verder eylanden.
" " " [73] De Manilles of Philippines eylanden benevens de Moluccos, Macassar, Tymor en andere, door P. W. Verhoeven aangedaan.
v. 2, no. [11] Andries Battels scheeptogt na Brasilie . . .
" " " [12] A. Knivets zeldzame reystogt door de Straat Magellaan . . .
" " " [13] Scheepstogt na d'Africa anze kusten van Congo en Angola . . .
" " " [14] Nouvelle carte de l'Amérique . . .
" " " [15] Amerika, of de nieuwe weereld . . .
" " " [16] America, of nieuw-ontdekte weereld, tot de beschryving van Joseph d'Acosta afgebakend.
" " " [17] De voor eylanden van America . . .
" " " [18] L'Amérique Septentrionale . . .
" " " [19] 'T noorder deel van Amerika . . .

v. 2, no. [20] De Graaf van Cumberlands verfcheyde reyfen na de kusten van Africa na Porto Rico en andere gewesten van America.
" " " [21] Scheeps-togt door Ferdinand Magellaan ...
" " " [22] Iukatan en vaste kusten van Nieuw Spanje ...
" " " [23] Land togten door Ferdinand Cortes aan de Golf van Nieuw Spanje ...
" " " [24] Nieuw Spaanje ...
" " " [25] De land-togt door Ferdinand Cortes gedaan ugt Mexico, na Las Ybueras.
" " " [26] De landschappen Tabasco en Iucatan ...
" " " [27] 'T landschap Guatimala door Pedro d'Alvarado in en landtogt uyt Mexico bevolkt, 1523.
" " " [28] Reys togt door Gil Gonzales Davila van't eyland S$^t$. Dominica gedaan na de Honduras en Nicaragua.
" " " [29] Nicaragua en de kusten der Zuyd-Zee, noordwaard van Panama, door Gil Ganzales Davila ontdekt.
" " " [30] Scheeps togt van Jamaica gedaan na Panuco en rio de Las Palmas ...
" " " [31] Zee en land-togten der franszen gedaan na, en in't Americaans gewest van Florida, aller-eerst door Joh. Pontius ontdekt.
" " " [32] 'T Amerikans gewest van Florida door Ferdinand de Soto ...
" " " [33] De vaste kust van Chicora tussen Florida en Virginie door Lucas Vasquez d'Ayllon ...
" " " [34] d'Engelze volkplanting in Virginie door Johan Smith ...
" " " [35] 't Noorder gedeelte van Virginie, door Bartholomeus Gosnol en Martin Pringe ...
" " " [36] Nieuw Engeland in twee scheep togten door Kapitein Johan Smith ...
" " " [37] Jonathan Dickenson ramspoedige reyslogt van Jamaika na Pensylvani nagespoord.
" " " [38] Land en volk-ontdekking in't noorder gedeelte van America, door P. Marquette en Joliet; gedan in't jaar 1673.
" " " [39] De voorgenome scheeps-togt van Sebastiaan Gaboto, om door de Straat Magellaan ...
" " " [40] L'Amérique Méridionale ...
" " " [41] 'T Zuider America ...
" " " [42] H. Benzös scheep-togt uit Italie over Spanje nade Westindize eylanden en kusten van't Zuider America.
" " " [43] Terra Firma oft vaste land van Darien, Veragua, Cartagena en Nieuw Anda'asie, etc.
" " " [44] 'T vaste land van Darien ten zuyden Cuba en Hispaniola gelegen.
" " " [45] Scheeps-togt door Rodrigue de Bastides en P. Alvares Polomina uyt de haven van S$^t$. Domingo op Hispaniola, gedaan na S$^t$. Martha.
" " " [46] 'T landschap Cumana tussen golfo de Venezuela en Rio de Paria gelegen.
" " " [47] De vaste kust van Cheribichi door Alonzo d'Ojeda van't eyland Cubagua besogt.
" " " [48] Zee en land togt door Fr. Pizarrus en D. Almagrus van Panama gedaan na Peru.

## Aa, P.—Continued.

v. 2, no. [49] De kusten van Chili en Peru, onder den H$^r$. Olivier van Noort, bezogt in't jaar 1598.

" " " [50] De schipvaard, by Jacob Mahu, door de Straat Magellaan na Moluccos ondernomen; aan de Zuyd Zee mislukt.

" " " [51] De Straat van Magellaen sedert desfelfs eerft ondekker, F. Magellaen. A° 1520 . . .

" " " [52] P. Carders zee en land reyse na Brasil, Rio de la Plata en de Zuyd Zee.

" " " [53] Jan Stadens scheepstogten over Portugaal en Spanje, na Rio de Janeiro en elders in Brasil gedaan 1547.

" " " [54] Brasiliaanze scheepvaard, door Johan Lerius gedaan uit Vrankryk, in't iaar 1556.

" " " [55] De reyse over zee na Rio de la Plata, door Laurens Bikker en Cornelis van Heemskerk, ongelukkig volbragt.

" " " [56] d'Engelze volkplanting in't Amerikaans gewest Gujana en Rio de las Amazones, door de scheeps-togt van Charles Leig, begonnen.

" " " [57] Scheepstogt door Robert Harcourt gedaan na Gujana.

" " " [58] Het goudryk gewest Guiana tot de drywerfze scheepstogten van den ridder Walter Ralegh afgebakend.

" " " [59] De Bermudes of Summer eylanden . . .

" " " [60] Hispaniola . . .

" " " [61] Cuba en Iamaica . . .

" " " [62] M. Frobichers scheeps togt, gedaan om de noord, ter ontdekking van een straat na Cataya en China.

" " " [63] D. Blefkenius scheeps-togt gedaan na Island en Rusten van Groenland.

" " " [64] De scheeps-togt agter Noorwegen en Tartary en om, na Cataya en China door Willem Barents . . .

" " " [65] De scheeps-togt benoorden om na Waygats; door Jan Huygen van Linschoten . . .

## Du Val, P.

Diverses cartes et tables pour la géographie ancienne pour la chronologie et pour les itinéraires et voyages modernes . . . 3 pts. in 1 v. obl. 8°. Paris, l'auteur [1669?]    171

NOTE.—Date 1669 appears on l. 14, pt. 2.

The following maps relate to America:

pt. 3, no. [4] La France antarctique autrement le Rio Janeiro, tirée des voyages que Villegagnon, et Jean de Leri ont faits au Brésil les années 1557 et 1558.

" [5] La Floride françoise drefsée sur la relation des voiages que Ribaut, Laudonier, et Gourges y ont faits en 1562, 1564 et 1567 . . .

" [7] Carte du voyage de Pirard, aux Iades Orientales les années 1601 et les fuiuantes . . .

CONTENTS.

pt. 1. Cartes géographiqves drefsées pour bien entendre les historiens, pour connoistre l'estendüe des anciennes monarchies; et pour lire auec fruit, les vies, les voyages, les guerres et les conquestes des grands capitaines . . . 3 p. l., 2 l., 28 maps.

pt. 2. La chronologie en plusieurs tables . . .   1 p. l., 14, [21] l.
" 3. Cartes pour les itinéraires et voïages modernes, qui ont esté faits tant par mer que par terre dans toutes les parties du monde, et particulièrement dans le Levant . . .   1 p. l., 26 maps.

## MARITIME.

**Bellin, J. N.**
Atlas maritime ou recueil des cartes réduites dréssées au Dépost des cartes et plans de la marine, pour le service des vaisseaux du roi. Par ordre du ministère . . .   1 p. l., 22 maps. fol. [Paris] 1751.
172

NOTE.—Engraved title-page.  F. Boucher, invenit.  F. A. Aveline, sculpsit. Beneath title: " Quos ego.  Sed motos præstat componere fluctus: Eneid. Virg. lib. I."

CONTENTS.

no. [1] . . . Les parties connuees du globe terrestre. 1784.
"   [2] Carte réduite des mers du nord. 1751.
"   [3] Carte réduite de l'océan occidental. 1742.
"   [4] Carte réduite de l'océan méridional. 1739.
"   [5] Carte réduite de l'océan oriental. 1740.
"   [6] Carte réduite des mers comprises entre l'Asie et l'Amérique. 1742.
"   [7] Nouvelle carte réduite de la Manche. 1749.
"   [8] Carte réduite du golphe de Gascogne. 1750.
"   [9] Carte réduite des costes d'Espagne et de Portugal. 1751.
"   [10] Carte générale de la coste de Guinée. 1750.
"   [11] Carte particulière de la coste d'Or. 1750.
"   [12] Carte réduite du golphe du Mexique. 1749.
"   [13] Carte réduite de l'isle de Saint Domingue. 1750.
"   [14] Carte réduite de la mer Méditerranée. 1737.
"   [15-16] Noms de quelques isles comprises entre le méridien de Gènes et celuy de Candie.
"   [17] Carte réduite de l'Archipel. 1738.
"   [18] Carte des isles de Majorque, Minorque et Yvice. 1740.
"   [19] Nouvelle carte de l'isle de Corse. 1749.
"   [20] Partie orientale de la Nouvelle France. 1745.
"   [21] Partie occidentale de la Nouvelle France. 1745.
"   [22] Carte de la Louisiane. 1750.

**Langhans, P.**
Justus Perthes' deutscher marine-atlas . . . Mit begleitworten von . . . Bruno Meyer.  2. verm. und verb. aufl.  12 pp., 5 col. maps.  4°.  Gotha, J. Perthes, 1898.
173

**Perthes, J.**
Justus Perthes' see-atlas.  Eine ergänzung zu Justus Perthes' taschen-atlas, entworfen und bearbeitet von Hermann Habenicht. 24 kolorierte karten in kupferstich mit 127 hafenplänen. Mit nautischen notizen und tabellen von Erwin Knipping.  5. aufl. 48 pp., 24 maps.  16°.  Gotha, J. Perthes, 1901.
174

**Philip, G.**

Philips' mercantile marine atlas, a series of 30 plates containing over 100 charts & plans, with tables of 8,600 distances between ports, national and house flags, lists of british & United States consulates and complete index of 20,000 ports, &c. Specially designed for merchant shippers, exporters & ocean travellers and for general use. ... 2d ed. viii, 27 pp., 28 maps, 2 pl. fol. London, G. Philip & son, ltd, 1905. 175

## METEOROLOGY.

**Dunwoody, H. H. C.**

Summary of international meteorological observations. Published by authority of the secretary of Agriculture. x l., 53 maps. obl. fol. Washington, weather bureau, 1893.
[United States. Weather bureau. Bulletin A] 175a

## MILITARY.

**Atlas** de géographie militaire. Anciennement atlas de Saint-Cyr. Nouvelle édition entièrement revue et mise au courant. 2 p. l., 42 maps. fol. Paris, Combet & cie. 1902. 176

> NOTE.—The following maps relate to America:
> no. [34] Planisphère.
> " [37] Amérique Septentrionale.
> " [38] Carte militaire des États Unis. (Partie orientale)
> " [39] Carte militaire des Etats Unis. (Partie occidentale)
> " [40] Amérique Méridionale.

**Lavallée, T. S.**

Atlas de géographie militaire adopté par. m. le ministre de la guerre pour l'École impériale militaire de Saint-Cyr. Accompagné de tableaux de statistique militaire ... 3 p. l., 16 pp., 34 col. maps. fol. Paris, Furne & cie. 1859. 177

> NOTE.—First published 1851.

**Sternegg, —**

Schlachten-atlas des neunzehnten jahrhunderts. Zeitraum: 1820 bis zur gegenwart. Pläne der wichtigsten schlachten, gefechte und belagerungen mit begleitendem texte, nebst uebersichts-karten mit compendiösen darstellungen des verlaufes der feldzüge in Europa, Asien, und Amerika. lief. 1–62 (in 37 pts.) fol. Iglau, P. Bäuerle [1907–08] 177a

> NOTE.—In progress.
> The following maps relate to the civil war:
> no. 2. Schlacht am Bull Run am 21. juli 1861. (lief. 3)
> " 3. Gefecht und einnahme von Donelson am 15. februar 1862. (lief. 9)
> " 4. Schlacht bei Shiloh am 6. und 7. april 1862. (lief. 1)

no. 4ł. Schlacht bei Perryville am 8. october 1862. (lief. 10/11)
" 5. Schlacht bei Murfreesborough am 31. december 1862. (lief. 5)
" 6. Der halbinsel-feldzug. April bis august 1862.—A. Übersichtskarte.—B. Schlacht bei Fair-Oaks am 31. mai.—C. Rückzugsgefechte der unions-armee. 28. juni bis 1. juli. (lief. 14/15)
" 7. Der feldzug in Nordvirginien im august 1862.—Zweite schlacht am Bull-Run (Manassas) am 29. und 30. august. (lief. 18/19)
" 8. Schlacht am Antietam. 17. september 1862. (lief. 20/21)
" 9. Schlacht bei Fredericksburg am 13. december 1862. (lief. 24/25)
" 10. Schlacht bie Chancellorsville am 3. mai 1863.—A1. A. B. C. Situation am 27. april.—Gefecht bei Newton am 1. mai.—A2. D. Gefecht bei Dowdalls-tavern am 2. mai.—B1. E Die Kämpfe am 3. mai.—Schlacht bei Chancellorsville.—Erstürmung der Maryesheights und gefecht bei Salem-Church.—B2. F. Gefecht bei Downman am 4. mai. (lief. 34/35)
" 11. Schlacht bei Gettysburg vom 1. bis 3. juli 1863.—A. Die operationen vom 3. bis 28. juni.—B. Die operationen vom 28. juni bis 1. juli.—C. Situation am 1. juli 2 uhr 30 m. nachmittags.—D. Situation am 2. juli 6 uhr 45 m. abends.—E. Situation am 3. juli. (lief. 45/46)
" 12. Die feldzüge gegen Vicksburg im jahre 1862 und 1863.—A. Uebersichtskarte für die gesammten operationen.—B. Die operationen bei Vicksburg im april und mai 1863.—C. Der sturm auf Corinth am 4. october 1862.—D. Schlacht beim Champion-Hill am 16. mai 1863.—E. Gefecht on der Big-black-brücke vom 17. mai 1863.—F. Der fall von Vicksburg am 3. juli 1863. (lief. 49/50)

## MISSIONARY.

**Beach, H. P.**

A geography and atlas of protestant missions; their environment, forces, distribution, methods, problems, results, and prospects at the opening of the twentieth century . . . [Atlas] v. 2. 54, [2] pp., 20 maps on 18 sheets. fol. New York, student volunteer movement for foreign missions, 1903. 178

NOTE.—The following maps relate to America :
no. 1. Distribution of mission stations throughout the world.
" 2. Dominion of Canada.
" 3. United States.
" 4. Mexico, Central America & West Indies.
" 5. South America.

### Church missionary society.

The church missionary atlas containing an account of the various countries in which the church missionary society labours and of its missionary operations. New ed. (8th) xiv, [3]–239, [1] pp., front., 31 maps. 8°. London, church missionary society, 1896. 179

**Fulneck academy.**
   The moravian atlas, embracing statistics of the church of the united brethren in her home and foreign departments, compiled from the most recent and authentic sources, by teachers of Fulneck academy. iv, 36 pp., 12 maps. obl. 12°. [Fulneck] 1853.
   180

   NOTE.—The preface states that this atlas is based on a similar work entitled, "Maps and statistics relating to the missions of the church of the brethren," by Linder, published shortly before, at Herrnhut.
   The following maps relate to America:
   no. 1. Map of the world.
   " 4. United States and Canada.
   " 5. Greenland and Labrador.

**Grundemann, R.**
   Neuer missions-atlas aller evangelischen missionsgebiete mit besonderer berücksichtigung der deutchen missionen. . . . 2. verm. und verb. aufl. vii, [1] pp., 36 maps. 4°. Calw & Stuttgart, verlag der vereinsbuchhandlung, 1903.
   181

   NOTE.—The following maps relate to America:
   no. 1. Religionskarte der erde.
   " 27. Nordamerika.
   " 28. Die missionen in Nordamerika.
   " 29. Westindien.
   " 30. Guyana.
   " 31. Südamerika.

**Morse, S. E., & co.**
   The cerographic missionary atlas.   cover title, 18 maps. 4°. [New York] S. E. Morse & co. [1848]
   182

   NOTE.—Gratuitously and exclusively for the subscribers to the New York observer.
   The following maps relate to America:
   no. 1. [North and South America. Hemisphere]
   " 3. Indian territory.
   " 4. Greenland and Labrador.
   " 18. Hawaiian islands.

**Streit, K.**
   Katholischer missionsatlas. Enthaltend die gesamten missionsgebiete des erdkreises. . . . 38 pp., [1] l., 28 (*i. e.* 29) col. maps on 46 l. fol. Steyl, verlag der missionsdruckerei, 1906.
   183

   NOTE.—Accompanied by pamphlet entitled: Statistische notizen zum katholischen missionsatlas. 28 pp.

## OCEANS.
### Atlantic.

**Germany.** *Deutsche seewarte.*
Atlantischer ozean; ein atlas von 36 karten, die physikalischen verhältnisse und die verkehrs-strassen darstellend ... und als beilage zum segelhandbuch für den Atlantischen ozean, hrsg. von der dircktion. 2 p. l., 11 pp., 36 maps. fol. Hamburg, L. Friedcrichsen & co. 1882. 184

> NOTE.—Contains maps showing depths, temperature, etc., of water, currents, atmospheric pressure, weather, best routes for sailing vessels, and distribution of various kinds of whales.

**Vincendon-Dumoulin, C. A.**
Portulan général contenant les plans des ports, rades, baies, etc. du globe. Océan Atlantique. 2 p. l., 24 maps. 4°. Paris, dépôt général de la marine, 1852. 185

Portulan général contenant les plans des ports et mouillages du globe. Océan Atlantique. Côtes d'Afrique. 1 p. l., 89 maps. 4°. Paris, dépôt-général de la marine, 1852. 186

**Ayrouard, J.**
Recüeil de plusieurs plans des ports et rades et de quelques cartes particulières de la mer Méditerranée, avec les figures des terres remarquables pour les reconnoissances des atterrages dediée á monseigneur le comte de Maurepas ... Levé et dessigné par le s.$^r$ Ayrouard pilote réal des galères du roy, dans le voyages qu'il a fait à la visite des côtes, et dans d'autres occasions, avec les remarques nêcessaries qu'il faut observer pour l'entrée à certains ports, et autres endroits ... 1 p. l., 69 maps, 10 pl. obl. fol. [Paris?] 1732–1746 187

> NOTE.—Engraved title. Maps engraved by Louis Corne, and by H. Coussin at Aix.

**Barendsz, W.**
Description de la mer Méditerranée, auquel font déliniées & defcriptes au vif toutes les costes de la mer Méditerranée ... par Guilliaume [!] Bernard, pilote, 1608. 1 p. l., [118] pp. incl. 9 maps (1 fold. map) fol. Amsterdam, C. Nicolas, 1607. 188

> NOTE.—This french title was pasted over the following dutch title: "Caertboeck vande Midlandtfche zee ... door Willem Barentzoen." Engraved title, with a view of "Genoa." Descriptive text in french; maps in latin and dutch. The majority of maps are dated 1593–95, and bear the name: "Pieter Vanden Keere."
> At the end of the atlas is: "La [!] gvide des ports de la mer Méditerranée: c'est à dire; spéciale déclaration de tovs les havres de la mer Méditerranée" ...

**Barendsz, W.—Continued.**
    Tiele mentions the following editions in his " Nederlandsche bibliographie, Amst. 1884 ":
    " Nieuwe beschryvinghe ende caertboeck vande Midlandtsche zee . . . door W. B. Amst., C. Claesz . . . 1595. (Zeer zeldsame atlas)
    " Description de la mer Méditerrannée . . . Par Guilliaume Bernard, pilote. 1599. Chez Corneille Nicolas, à Amsterdam . . . 1598," affixed to the french edition of Waghenaer of 1600.
    Another edition dated 1607–09.
    The following quotation from Gerritt de Veer's "A true description of three voyages by the North-east towards Cathays and China. Edited by C. T. Beke. London, Hakluyt society, 1853 " (p. lvi) explains the different forms of Barendsz' name: " The name of this able navigator has been written in various ways. The dutch usually have Barendtsz which has been adopted in the notes on Phillip's text in the present volume, it being the usual native contraction of the full name, Barentszoon. In the Amsterdam latin and french versions of De Veer's work the name is translated " filius Bernardi " and " fils de Bernard." Purchas and other early english writers have Barents or Barentson, and sometimes even Bernardson."

**Bellue, P.**
    Atlas, ou Neptune, des cartes de la mer Méditerranée par les cap'nes Smyth, Elson, Beaufort, Zannoni, Visconti, Tofino etc. . . . Cet atlas, faisant suite au nouveau portulan contient: le routier depuis le détroit jusques et compris la mer Noire, les cartes de détails et des plans particuliérs, des mouillages les plus fréquentés. 1 p. l., 20 maps on 17 sheets. fol. Toulon, Bellue, 1830–[1834]
    189

**English, The, pilot.**
    Part III. Describing the sea-coafts, capes, head-lands, bays, roads, harbours, rivers and ports; together with the soundings, sands, rocks and dangers in the whole Mediterranian sea. Likewise the courfes and diftances from one place to another. The setting of the tides and currents. The ebbing and flowing of the sea. The bearing, diftance, and profpects of the land, and how they fhew themfelves at sea. Carefully corrected, with new editions of several ports, harbours, bays and prospects of land, never before made publick. 1 p. l., 86 pp., 16 maps (36 maps in text) fol. London, for W. Mount & T. Page, 1736.    190

    Describing the sea-coafts, capes, head-lands, bays, roads, harbours, rivers and ports; together with the soundings, sands, rocks and dangers in the whole Mediterranean sea; likewise the courfes and diftances from one place to another; the setting of the tides and currents: the ebbing and flowing of the sea: the bearing, diftance and profpects of the land, and how they fhew themselves at sea. Carefully corrected, with new additions of feveral ports, harbours, bays, and profpects of land, never before made public.

1 p. l., 86 pp., 17 maps (38 maps in text) fol. London, for Mount & Page, 1786.    191

**Heather, W.**
The new Mediterranean pilot containing two hundred and twenty-four accurate plans of the principal harbours, bays, roadsteads, and islands in the Mediterranean sea, including those in the gulf of Venice, Archipelago, sea of Mamora, and the Levant, drawn from the french & italian surveys of Michelot, Bremond, & Ayrouard; and from those of . . . John Wilson and Joseph Foss Dessiou. The whole arranged and improved from the journals and observations of several distinguished navigators.  2 p. l., 224 maps. obl. 16°. London, W. Heather, 1802.    192

The new Mediterranean harbour pilot, containing two hundred and twenty-four accurate plans of the principal harbours, bays, roadsteds, gulfs, islands, & ports in the Mediterranean sea, gulf of Venice, Archipelago, sea of Marmora, & the Levant; with the addition of a large plan of Cadiz, the straits of Gibraltar, Bonifacio, &c. Drawn from the latest english, french, spanish, italian, and venetian surveys, and corrected from the journals and observations of several distinguished navigators . . . A new edition improved by J. W. Norie, hydrographer, &c.  2 p. l., 229 maps on 60 sheets. obl. 4°. London, J. W. Norie & co. (successors to the late W. Heather) 1814.    193

**Jacobsz, T.**
Lighting colom of the Midland-sea, containing a defcription of all the knowne coasts, iflands, sands, depthes and roads: beginning from the narroweft of the streat unto Alexandrette in the Levant. 1 p. l., 4 l., 3–104 pp., 19 maps. fol. Amsterdam, C. Loots-Man, 1692.    194

[*With his:* The lightning columne, or, sea-mirrour. fol. Amsterdam, C. Loots-Man, 1689]
NOTE.—This is considered the third part of "The lightning columne, or, sea-mirrour."
Map. no. 1, by Theunis Iacobfz, no. 2 by Anthoni Iacobfz, the others not credited.

**Roux, J.**
Carte de la mer Méditerranée.  12 sheets. fol. Marseille, J. Roux, 1764.    195

NOTE.—Title on first sheet.

Recueil des principaux plans des ports et rades de la mer Méditerranée estraits de ma carte en douze feuilles. 1 p. l., 1 l., 123 pl. obl. 16°. Gènes, Y. Gravier. 1779.

## Pacific.

**Vancouver, G.**

Voyage of discovery to the North Pacific ocean and round the world; in which the coast of north-west America has been carefully examined and accurately surveyed. ... Atlas. 2 p. l., 10 maps, 6 pl. fol. London, for G. G. & J. Robinson & J. Edwards, 1798. 197

> NOTE.—Atlas without title page.
> To accompany Vancouver's Voyage of discovery. London, 1798.
> Published also in french. Another edition bears date 1801.
> The following maps relate to America:
> no. [2-9] A chart shewing part of the coast of n. w. America ...

Voyage de découvertes à l'océan Pacifique du nord, et autour du monde; dans lequel la côte nordouest de l'Amérique a été ... reconnue et ... relevée: ... Atlas. 1 p. l., [2] pp., 10 maps, 6 pl. fol. Paris, imprimerie de la république, an VIII [1799] 198

> NOTE.—Atlas without title page.
> To accompany Vancouver's Voyage de découvertes. Paris, 1799.
> The following maps relate to America:
> no. [2-9] A chart shewing part of the coast of n. w. America ...

**Duperrey, L. I.**

Voyage autour du monde, exécuté par ordre du roi, sur la corvette de sa majesté, la Coquille, pendant les années 1822, 1823, 1824 et 1825 ... Atlas. 2 p. l., 21 pp., 49 maps, 4 pl. fol. Paris, A. Bertrand, 1826-1830. 199

> NOTE.—Atlas to accompany v. 5, "Hydrographie et physique" of his "Voyage autour du monde."
> A collection of maps by various hydrographers, many of whom were officers in the french navy:—m. m. Bérard, de Blois, de Blossville, Givry and Lottin.
> Engraved title by Abel Malo.
> Atlas dated 1827. Map no. 33 bears date 1828.
> pp. 5-21, "Tableaux des positions géographiques des stations principales ... "
> Routes of various french and english navigators are indicated on maps 3 bis, 8, 8 bis and 33.
> The following maps relate to America:
> no. 1. Carte et plan des ilots de Martin-Vaz et de la Trinité levés par m. Bérard ...
> " 2. Carte de la baye de Payta levée par m. Bérard ...—Inset:— Carte de l'entrée de l'anse de Séchura ...
> " 41. Carte d'une partie de la côte du Brésil comprise entre le rio Guaratuba et la laguna de Gurupaba ...—Plan de l'île Santa Catharina ...
> " 41 bis. Plan du port de Valparaiso ...
> " 42. Carte des iles Gallapagos ...—Plan de la baie Albany ...—Plan du mouillage de l'ile Hood ... —Plan de la baie Salango ...— Plan du mouillage de Tacames (Colombie) ...—Plan du banc de la Perle ...

**Krusenstern, A. J. von.**
Атласъ Южнаго моря сочиненный контръ адмираломъ Крузенштерномъ.
—Atlas de l'océan Pacifique . . . Publié par ordre de sa majesté impériale. 8 p. l., 34 maps. fol. St. Pétersbourg, 1827-[1838] 200
> NOTE.—Title, dedication and table of contents in russian and french.
> Russian title dated 1826. Maps corrected to 1835 and 1838.
> For contents of atlas and accompanying text, see "Atlas. Oceanica."
> The following maps relate to America:
> no. 1. Carte générale de l'océan Pacifique. Hémisphère austral . . . 1824.
> " 16. Carte générale de l'océan Pacifique. Hémisphère boréal . . . 1827.
> " 17. Carte de l'archipel des isles Kodiack et du détroit de Chélighoff . . . 1827.
> " 20. Carte de la presqu'ile d'Aliaska et de la baie de Bristol . . . 1827.

**Dumont d'Urville, J. S. C.**
Voyage de la corvette l'Astrolabe exécuté pendant les années 1826-1828-1829, sous le commandement de m. Jules Dumont d'Urville, capitaine de vaisseau. Atlas. 2 p. l., 25 pp., 42 maps, 3 pl. fol. Paris, J. Tastu, 1833. 201
> NOTE.—Engraved title. This atlas is v. [6 a] of a set of 14 v. on the Astrolabe expedition prepared by Dumont d'Urville.
> The maps are by various cartographers including: Lottin, Gressien, Guilbert, and E. Pâris.
> The following map relates to America:
> no. 1. Carte générale de l'océan Pacifique. 1834.

**Laplace, C. P. T.**
Voyage autour du monde exécuté, pendant les années 1830, 1831 et 1832, sur la corvette la Favorite . . . Atlas hydrographique . . . 2 p. l., 11 maps. fol. Paris, imprimerie royale, 1833-1839. 202
> NOTE.—Title of atlas varies: . . . Publié par ordre du roi . . . au dépôt-général de la marine, 1833.
> For contents see Asia subdivision.

**Lütke, F. P.**
Путешествіе вокругъ свѣта, совершенное по повелѣнію императора Николая I, на военномъ шлюпѣ Сенявинѣ, въ 1826, 1827, 1828 и 1829 годахъ, флота капитаномъ Ѳеодоромъ Литке. Атласъ. 6 p. l., 29 maps, 4 pl. fol. Санктпетербургъ, Х. Гинце, 1835. 203
> NOTE.—Atlas accompanying this work has title: Атласъ къ путешествію вокругъ свѣта шлюпа сенявина . . .
> French title as follows: Atlas du voyage autour du monde de la corvette Seniavine fait en 1826, 1827, 1828 et 1829 sous les ordres de Frédéric Lutké . . .
> Maps dated 1827-28.
> Titles and lettering in french and russian.
> The following maps relate to America:
> no. 1. Генеральная карта Берингова моря.—Carte générale de la mer de Behring.
> " 2. Меркаторская карта западнаго берега Берингова пролива.—Carte réduite de la côte occid.lᵉ du détroit de Behring.
> " 10. Планъ губы губы Св. Лаврентія.—Plan de l'embouchure de la baie St. Laurent.

**Lütke, F. P.**—Continued.
" 13. Карта острова Беринга.—Carte de l'île de Behring.—Карта островов Прибылова.—Carte des îles Pribyloff.—План гухты на . . . острова Беринга.—Plan d'une baie . . . de l'île Behring.
" 14. Карта . . . полуострова Аляски.—Carte . . . de la presqu'île Alaska.
" 15. Виды разных пунктов Америки и островов в Беринговом море.—Vues des différens points de l'Amérique.

### Bougainville, H. Y. P. P.

Journal de la navigation autour du globe de la frégate la Thétis et de la corvette l'Espérance pendant les années 1824, 1825 et 1826 publié par ordre du roi sous les auspices du département de la marine . . . Atlas. 2 p. l., 9 maps, on 14 l., 49 pl. fol. Paris, A. Bertrand, 1837. 204

NOTE.—Atlas has same title.

CONTENTS.

no. [1] Carte de la partie de la mer de Chine . . . levée et dressée par m.m. Fabré, La Pierre . . . et Jeanneret . . . publiée par ordre du roi . . . en 1828.
" [2] Carte de la partie septentrionale de l'Atoll Suadiva (Îles Maldives) levée et dressée par m. m. Fabré, La Pierre et Jeanneret . . . 1828.
" [3] Carte d'une partie des îles Kangelang, Longue, Wick et Lombock levée et dressée par m. m. Fabré, La Pierre et Jeanneret . . . 1828.
" [4] Carte d'une partie des Anambas . . . levée et dressée par m. m. Fabré, La Pierre, Penaud, et Jeanneret . . . 1828.
" [5] Plan du port Clermont-Tonnerre situé à la partie nordest des îles Anambas levé en 1825 par m. m. La Pierre et Jeanneret . . . 1828.
" [6] Plan du détroit de Madura depuis la pointe Panka jusqu'à l'embouchure de la rivière de Sourabaya . . . 1825.
" [7] Plan de la baie de Peejow située à la partie orientale de l'île Lombock levé en 1825 par m. m. Fabré et Jeanneret . . . 1828.
" [8] Plan du port Jackson levé . . . par. m. m. La Pierre et Jeanneret . . . 1828.
" [9] Carte générale pour servir au voyage de la frégate Thétis et de la corvette Espérance . . .

### Du Petit Thouars, A. A.

Voyage autour du monde sur la frégate la Vénus pendant les années 1836–1839, publié par ordre du roi sous les auspices du ministre de la marine . . . Atlas. 1 p. l., 17 maps. fol. Paris, Gide, 1840–1855. 205

NOTE.—"Atlas hydrographique" to accompany v. 6–10, "Physique, par U. de Tessan."
Title of atlas varies: . . . Atlas hydrographique. Rédigé par U. de Tessan, ingénieur hydrographe . . . Dépôt-général de la marine, 1845.
Maps dated 1837–1845.

CONTENTS.

no. [1] Carte générale du globe . . .
" 1. [bis] (905) Plan d'atterrage de la baie de Valparaiso . . . 1840.
" 2. (1013) Plan d'atterage du Callao de Lima (Pérou) . . 1844.
" 3. (1045) Plan du port d'Acapulco à la côte sud-ouest du Mexique . . . 1845.

no. 4. (1036) Plan d'atterrage de la baie de la Magdeleine (Basse Californie)
" 5. (1018) Plan de la baie de Monterey (Haute Californie) . . . 1844.
" 6. (1002) Croquis des atterrages de la baie de San Francisco . . . 1843.
" 7. (1030) Plan de la baie d'Avatscha au Kamtschatka . . . 1844.
" 8. (1026) Plan de la rade de Papeiti . . . (archipel de la Société) . . . 1844.
" 9. (1037) Plan de la baie des îles à la Nouvelle-Zélande . . . 1845.
" 10. (1038) Plan de l' ile Charles ou Floriana (archipel des Galapagos) . . .
" 11. (961) Carte d'une partie de l'archipel des Galapagos . . . 1842.
" 12. (962) Carte des îles Marquises . . . 1842.
" 13. (1011) Positions des îles St. Félix et St. Ambroise sur la côte du Chili . . . — Positions des îles Hormigas sur la côte du Callao de Lima (Pérou)
" [14] (1029) Croquis de plan de l'ile de Pâques . . . — Croquis de plan des îles Juan-Fernandez et Mas-a-Fuera . . .
" [15] (1027) Croquis de plan de l'ile de la Guadeloupe . . . — Croquis de plan des roches Alijos . . .
" [16] (1028) Positions des îles Hull, Mangia et Rarotonga . . .

**Germany.** *Deutsche seewarte.*
Stiller ozean; ein atlas von 31 karten, die physikalischen verhältnisse und die verkehrsstrassen darstellend . . . und als beilage zum segelhandbuch für den Stillen ozean; hrsg. von der direktion. 3 p. l., [7]-14 pp., 31 maps. obl. fol. Hamburg, L. Friederichsen & co. 1896. 206

NOTE.—Contains maps showing depths, temperature, etc., of water, currents, atmospheric pressure, weather maps, best routes for sailing vessels, and the distribution of whales.

## OROGRAPHY.
**Sydow, E. von.**
E. von Sydow's orographischer atlas . . . 2 p. l., 24 maps. obl. 8°. Gotha, J. Perthes, 1855. 207

E. von Sydow's oro-hydrographischer atlas . . . 2 p. l., 25 maps. obl. 8°. Gotha, J. Perthes, 1856. 208

## OUTLINE.
**Sydow, E. von.**
E. von Sydow's gradnetz-atlas . . . 10 pp., 16 maps. fol. Gotha, J. Perthes, 1847. 209

**Worcester, J. E.**
Worcester's outline maps, to be filled up by the younger students in geography . . . Corresponding to the new altas, accompanying The elements of geography. cover-title, 11 maps. fol. Boston, Hilliard, Gray, Little & Wilkins [1829?] 210

NOTE.—The following maps relate to America:
no. 1. The world.
" 2. North America.
" 3. United States.
" 4. Eastern & middle states.
" 5. South America.

## PHYSICAL.

**Ansted, D. T.** *and* **Nicolay, C. G.**

An atlas of physical and historical geography, to accompany the Manual of geographical science. Engraved by J. W. Lowry ... cover-title, 6 fold. maps. fol. London, J. W. Parker & son, [1852–59]     211

    Note.—A copy of the "Manual" is in the Library of Congress.

CONTENTS.

no. 1. Reference map [world]
" 2. Meteorological map of the world.
" 3. Relief map of the world.
" 4. Phytographical map shewing the distribution of plants in various parts of the world.
" 5. Zoological map shewing the distribution of animals in various parts of the world.—Ethnographical map.
" 6. Comparative chart of ancient and modern geography and geographical discovery.

**Barral, J. A.**

Atlas du Cosmos, contenant les cartes géographiques, physiques, thermiques . . . applicables à tous les ouvrages de sciences physiques et naturelles et particulièrement aux œuvres d'Alexandre de Humboldt et de François Arago. Dressées par m. Vuillemin. Gravées sur acier par m. Jacobs . . . Edité par L. Guérin. 55 l. incl. 25 maps, 1 pl. fol. Paris, T. Morgand, 1867.     212

    Note.—Lorenz, "Catalogue général de la librairie française," states the atlas was issued in parts from 1861 to 1870: "La publication de cet atlas avait été interrompue après la 4ᵉ livraison; elle a été reprise en 1864 et le nouvel éditeur a divisé les 4 premières livraisons en 8 livraisons, de sorte que la 9ᵉ forme bien la suite à l'ancienne 4ᵉ."—Besides physical maps, this atlas contains the following historical map: no. 25. Principaux itinéraires maritimes et de découvertes géographiques et scientifiques (planisphère terrestre suivant la projection de Mercator), with 3½ pages of text, in which the items are arranged chronologically.

pl. 26 is entitled: Distribution des connaissances humaines du ressort de la philosophie naturelle par m. E. Chevreuil (with one page of text)—Each map is accompanie l by explanatory text, generally printed on the recto of the leaf following the map (the verso remaining blank.)

The following maps relate to America:

no. 3. Projection stéréographique polaire des deux hémisphères terrestres.
    Lignes isothermes.
" 4. Projection stéréographique polaire des deux hémisphères terrestres.
    Lignes isodynamiques.
" 5. Planisphère terrestre suivant la projection de Mercator. Lignes isothermes. Planisphère terrestre suivant la projection de Mercator.
    Lignes isodynamiques.
" 12. Carte physique de l'Amérique du Nord. Lignes isodynamiques, isogoniques, et isocliniques.
" 13. Carte physique de l'Amérique du Nord. Lignes isothermes, isochimènes et isothères.
" 14. Carte physique de l'Amérique du Sud. Lignes isodynamiques, isocliniques et isogoniques.

no. 15. Carte physique de l'Amérique du Sud. Lignes isothermes, isochimènes et isothères.
" 17. Projection stéréographique polaire des deux hémisphères terrestres. Méridiens et parallèles magnétiques.
" 18. Planisphère terrestre suivant la projection de Mercator. Méridiens et parallèles magnétiques.
" 19. Planisphère terrestre suivant la projection de Mercator. Activité volcanique du globe terrestre.
" 20. Planisphère terrestre suivant la projection de Mercator. Géographie botannique. Distribution proportionnelle des plantes.
" 24. Planisphère terrestre suivant la projection de Mercator. Carte des pluies.
" 25. Planisphère terrestre suivant la projection de Mercator. Principaux itinéraires maritimes et de découvertes géographiques et scientifiques.

**Bartholomew, J. G. and Herbertson, A. J.**
Atlas of meteorology; a series of over four hundred maps . . . ed. by Alex$^r$ Buchan . . . Under the patronage of the Royal geographical society, prepared by the Edinburgh geographical institute. 6 p. l., 40 pp., 1 l., xiv pp., front., 34 fold. maps. fol. Westminster, A. Constable & co. 1899. 213

NOTE.—Half-title: Physical atlas. vol. III.
All published to date.

**Berghaus, H. K. W.**
Dr. Heinrich Berghaus' physikalischer schul-atlas . . . 1 p. l., 12 pp., 28 col. maps. obl. 4°. Gotha, J. Perthes, 1850. 214

Physikalischer atlas. Geographisches jahrbuch zur mittheilung aller wichtigern neuen erforschungen. 3 v. in 1. 4°. Gotha, J. Perthes, 1850–1851. 215

Dr. Heinrich Berghaus' physikalischer atlas. Eine, unter der fördernden anregung Alexander's von Humboldt verfasste, sammlung von 93 karten, auf denen die hauptsächlichsten erscheinungen der anorganischen und organischen natur nach ihrer geographischen verbreitung und vertheilung bildlich dargestellt sind. 2. grösstentheils umgearb. und verb. aufl. 8 pts. in 2 v. Gotha, J. Perthes, 1852. 216

NOTE.—Various paging.

CONTENTS.

v. 1. Meteorologie und klimatographie.—Hydrologie und hydrographie.—Geologie.—Tellurischer magnetismus.
v. 2. Pflanzen-geographie. — Thier-geographie. — Anthropographie. — Ethnographie.

Berghaus' physikalischer atlas. Begründet 1836 durch Heinrich Berghaus . . . 75 karten in sieben abteilungen, enthaltend 514 darstellungen über geologie, hydrographie, meteorologie, erdmagnetismus, pflanzenverbreitung, tierverbreitung und völkerkunde.

**Berghaus, H. K. W.**—Continued.
Vollständig neu bearb. und unter mitwirkung von . . . Oscar Drude . . . Georg Gerland . . . Julius Hann . . . William Marshall . . . Georg Neumayer . . . Karl v. Zittel . . . hrsg. von . . . Herm. Berghaus. 3. ausg. [85] pp., 75 (*i. e.* 74) maps. fol. Gotha, J. Perthes, 1892.     217

NOTE.—Various paging.

**Bromme, T.**
Atlas zu Alex. v. Humboldt's Kosmos in zweiundvierzig tafeln mit erläuterndem texte . . . 2 p. l., [1], 136 pp., 39 maps, 3 pl. obl. 4°. Stuttgart, Krais & Hoffmann [1851–1853]     218

NOTE.—Primary title reads: Atlas zur physik der welt in zweiundvierzig tafeln mit erläuterndem texte.
Explanatory text precedes each map.
The following maps relate to America:
no. 4. Die erde . . .
" 5. Der erdkörper in seiner gestaltung . . .
" 7. Die gebirgsketten der erde.
" 9. Geologische erdkarte . . .
" 12. Die vulkanischen erscheinungen der erdoberfläche . . .
" 13. Die elektro-magnetischen strömungen des erdkörpers karte der isogonen, isoklinen und isodynamen.
" 15. Erdkarte zur übersicht der isorachien . . .
" 16. Erdkarte zur übersicht der luft und meeres-strömungen, handelsstrassen im Atlantischen, Grossen und Indischen ocean.
" 17. Die stromsysteme der erde.
" 18. Vergleichende übersicht der grössten seen der erde im verhältniss zum Schwarzen meere.
" 19. Karte der jahres . . . oder der linien gleicher mittlerer jahres-sommer und winter temperatur.
" 20. Karte der isobaren und oscillationen des luftdrucks . . .
" 21. Hyetographische karte der erde.
" 27. Asien . . . (Die Philippinen)
" 29. Nord-Amerika in physikalischer beziehung.—Inset: Die bedeutendsten höhen von Nord-Amerika.
" 30. Süd Amerika . . . —Inset: Querprofil der Andeskette Antioquia's, von der Cordillera de Choco bis zum plateau von Santa-Fé de Bogotá, nach A. von Humboldt's nivell.
" 31. Übersicht der verbreitung der pflanzen in wagrechter richtung . . .
" 32. Geographische verbreitung der vorzüglicheren säugethiere auf der erde.
" 33. Verbreitung und vertheilung der vorzüglichsten vögel und reptilien auf der erde.
" 34. Ethnographische karte der erde, zur übersicht der geographischen verbreitung der menschenrassen.
" 42. Die ozeanischen entdeckungen und die um die kunde des erdballs verdienten forscher und reisenden, vom jahre 840–1850.

**Cartée, C. S.**
A school atlas of physical geography, illustrating, in a series of maps compiled from the celebrated atlases of A. Keith Johnston, and of Milner and Petermann, the elementary facts of geology,

hydrology, meteorology, and natural history, and designed to accompany Cartée's Elements of physical geography.   2 p. l., 13 pl.   8°.
Boston, Hickling, Swan & Brown, 1856. 219

**Delisle, G.** *and* **Buache, P.**
Cartes et tables de la géographie physique ou naturelle. Présentées au roi le 15 mai 1757.   1 p. l., 10 maps, 3 tab.   obl. fol.
Paris, G. Delisle & P. Buache, 1754–[1757] 220

> NOTE.—Engraved title page.
> "Cet ouvrage approuvé et publié sous le priv$^{se}$. de l'acad$^e$. du 4 sept$^{bre}$. 1754 se trouve à Paris. Avec les cartes de Guill. Delisle et de Phil. Buache.—Presentées au roi le 15 mai 1757."
> Maps dated 1737, 1739, 1740–42, 1744, 1746, 1754, 1756.

**Desmarest, N.** *and* **Bory de St. Vincent, J. B. G. M.**
Atlas encyclopédique contenant les cartes et les planches relatives à la géographie physique . . .   2 p. l., 120 pp., 36 maps, 12 pl. 4°.   Paris [H.] Agasse, 1827. 221

> NOTE.—Atlas to accompany "Géographie physique," v. 100—104, of "Encyclopédie méthodique."
> Contains "Analyse des cartes."
> Maps no. 1, 26, 47–48 are hand colored.
> The following maps relate to America:
> no. 1. Distribution primitive du genre humain à la surface du globe . . .
> " 2. Carte des glaces circompolaires boréales.
> " 3. Carte des glaces circompolaires australes.
> " 4–7. Théorie des vents.
> " 8. Carte du courant qui sort par le canal de Bahama, appelé Gulf-stream.
> " 14. Carte des montagnes coupées par des rivières, situées en Virginie et Pensylvanie.

**Fay, T. S.**
Great outline of geography for high schools and families . . . Atlas.   2 p. l., 8 maps, 3 pl.   fol.   New York, G. P. Putnam & son, 1867. 222

> NOTE.—Atlas accompanying this work entitled: Atlas to Fay's Great outline of geography for high schools and families.
> The following maps relate to America:
> no. 1. [Hemispheres]
> " 2. Natural land and water divisions of the world.
> " 3. Principal countries of the world.
> " 4. Chief towns of the world . . .   (Mercator's projection)
> " 5. Part of United States of America.
> " 6. Outline of towns, rivers etc. of the United States . . .

**Gover, E.**
Gover's two shilling physical atlas . . .   With descriptive letterpress, by the editor of the "Atlas of universal historical geography" . . .   24 pp., 8 maps.   8°.   London, E. Gover, 1854.   223

**Hansteen, C.**
Magnetischer atlas gehörig zum magnetismus der erde.   1 p. l., 7 pl.   obl. fol.   Christiania, 1819. 224

**Johnston, A. K.**

 The physical atlas. A series of maps & illustrations exhibiting the geographical distribution of natural phenomena . . . Based on the physikalischer atlas of professor H. Berghaus with the co-operation in their several departments of sir David Brewster, professors J. D. Forbes, Edward Forbes . . .   5 p. l., [94] pp., 40 maps. fol. Edinburgh, London, W. Blackwood & sons, 1849.
  225

 The physical atlas. A series of maps & illustrations of the geographical distribution of natural phenomena embracing I Geology. II Hydrography. III Meteorology. IV Natural history . . . 5 p. l., [94] pp., 40 maps. fol. Edinburgh, London, W. Blackwood & sons, 1849. 226

 NOTE.—Same as above; differs only in title.

 The physical atlas of natural phenomena . . .   2 p. l., 122 pp., front., 24 pl. fol. Philadelphia, Lea & Blanchard, 1850. 227

 A school atlas of physical geography, illustrating . . . the elementary facts of geology, hydrology, meteorology, and natural history. . . 8 pp., 18 (*i.e.*17) col. maps, 1 pl. 8°. Edinburgh and London, W. Blackwood & sons, 1852. 228

 NOTE.—The following maps relate to America:
 no. 2. Chart of the world showing the forms & directions of the ocean currents.
 " 3. Comparative form and extent of the inland seas and lakes of the globe.
 " 4. The river systems of the world.
 " 8. The mountains table lands plains & valleys of N. America.
 " 9. The mountains table lands plains & valleys of South America.
 " 11. The distribution of earthquakes & volcanoes over the globe.
 " 12. Climatological chart.
 " 13. The distribution of constant periodical & variable winds over the globe.
 " 14. The distribution of rain and snow over the globe.
 " 15. The distribution of the most important trees, shrubs, grains, and fruits.
 " 16. The distribution of animals.
 " 17. Ethnographic map of the world.
 " 18. Moral and statistical chart.

 The physical atlas of natural phenomena . . . New enl. ed. 3 p. l., 137 (*i.e.*139) pp. incl. 7 maps. 35 maps. fol. Edinburgh; London, W. Blackwood & sons, 1856. 229

 NOTE.—The following maps relate to America:
 no. 7. The physical features of North & South America . . .
 " 8. Geological map of the United States and British North America.
 " 17. The river systems of America . . .

 The half-crown atlas of physical geography . . .   1 p. l., 24 pp. incl. 31 maps. 8°. Edinburgh & London, W. & A. K. Johnston [1870] 230
[Middle class series]

 NOTE.—To accompany his: Handbook of physical geography.

**Milner, T.,** *and* **Petermann, A. H.**
A descriptive atlas of astronomy, and of physical and political geography. With descriptive letter-press, by the rev. Thomas Milner. . . The maps of physical and political geography constructed or carefully revised and corrected by Augustus Petermann. . . 3 p. 1., 174, 11 pp., 1 l., 55 pp., front, 71 maps. fol. London, W. S. Orr & co. 1850. 231

NOTE.—pp. 64–73 misplaced.
The following maps relate to America:
no. 1–2. Orographical maps of the globe . . .
" 3. Map of the world, showing the distribution of active volcanoes.
" 4–5. Hydrographical map of the world . . .
" 6. Hydrographical map of the world . . .
" 7. Meteorological map of the world . . .
" 8. Map of the world showing the distribution of the winds.
" 9. Hyetographic map . . .
" 10. Botanical map . . .
" 11. Zoological map . . . distribution of mammiferous animals . . .
" 12. Zoological map . . . distribution of birds and reptiles . . .
" 13. Ethnographical map . . .
" 14. Map of the Orinoco.
" 16. Western hemisphere.
" 17. The world . . .
" 37. North America.
" 38. Canada &c.
" 39. United States.
" 40. California, Mexico, Guatemala &c.
" 41. South America.
" 42. Colombia.
" 43. Brazil &c.
" 44. Chile and La Plata.
" 45. Peru and Bolivia.
" 46. West Indies.
" 47. Australia.
" 48. Tasmania . . .
" 49. East India Isles.
" 50. Pacific Ocean.
" 51. New Zealand.

The library atlas of physical and political geography; the physical maps constructed, revised, and corrected by Augustus Petermann. With letter-press descriptive of the physical phenomena of the globe, and of the respective political divisions and countries, copiously illustrated, by the rev. Thomas Milner. 1 p. l., 140, 131 pp., front., 65 maps. fol. London, W. S. Orr & co. 1855. 232

**Nicolet, H.**
Atlas de physique et de météorologie agricoles . . . 10, [6] pp., [3] l., 13 maps, 1 pl. fol. Paris, Bachelier, 1855. 233

**Sydow, E. von.**
Methodischer hand-atlas für das wissenschaftliche studium der erdkunde. 4. aufl. cover-title, 4, 7 pp., 34 col. maps on 31 sheets. fol. Gotha, J. Perthes, 1853. 234

## POSTAL.

**Ruhnstruck, W.**

Atlas der post-geographie in 36 haupt- und 21 nebenkarten. .. 3. ber. und verm aufl. 3 p. l., 36 col. maps. sm. fol. Cassel, G. Dufayel, 1907. 235

## RAILROADS.

**Cram, G. F.**

Cram's bankers' and brokers' railroad atlas . . . 608 pp. incl. 186 col. maps. fol. New York, Chicago, G. F. Cram, 1899. 236

Cram's bankers' and brokers' railroad atlas . . . with a complete alphabetical index . . . 606 pp. incl. 177 col. maps. fol. Chicago, New York, G. F. Cram, c1900. 237

Cram's standard american railway system atlas of the world accompanied by a complete and simple index of the United States showing the true location of all railroads, towns, villages and post offices . . . 451 pp. incl. 153 maps. fol. Chicago, G. F. Cram, 1892. 238

NOTE.—Contains plans of the principal cities of the United States.

Cram's standard american railway system atlas of the world accompanied by a complete and simple index of the United States showing the true location of all railroads, towns, villages and post offices . . . 562 pp. incl. 194 col. maps. fol. New York, Chicago, G. F. Cram, 1897. 239

Cram's standard american railway system atlas of the world accompanied by a complete and simple index of the United States showing the true location of all railroads, towns, villages and post offices . . . 590 pp. incl. 184 col. maps. fol. New York, Chicago, G. F. Cram, 1898. 240

Cram's standard american railway system atlas of the world, accompanied with a complete and simple index of the United States showing the true location of all railroads, towns, villages and post offices . . . 2 p. l., 5–608 pp., incl. 187 col. maps. fol. New York, Chicago, G. F. Cram, 1899. 241

Cram's standard american railway system atlas of the world, showing all the railway systems in colors. Accompanied by a complete and simple index of the United States showing the true location of all railroads, towns, villages and post-offices . . . 654, 27 pp. incl. 159 col. maps. fol. New York, Chicago, G. F. Cram, 1903. 242

Cram's standard american railway system atlas of the world, showing all the railway systems in colors. Accompanied by a complete and simple index of the United States, showing the true location of all railroads, towns, villages and post-offices . . . 632 pp. [15] l. incl. 154 col. maps. fol. New York, Chicago, G. F. Cram, 1904. 243

>   Note.—Map of North America, pp. 498–499, shows the new alaskan boundary. Maps of Canada differ from those in 1903 edition.

Cram's standard american railway system atlas of the world, showing all the railway systems in colors. Accompanied by a complete and simple index of the United States showing the true location of all railroads, towns, villages and post offices . . . 604 (*i. e.* 614), [30] pp. incl. 157 maps. fol. New York, Chicago, G. F. Cram, 1905. 244

### RELIEF.

**Bevan, G. P.**
Royal relief atlas of all parts of the world. 3d ed. 2 p. l., 61 pp. incl. 31 maps. 4°. London, S. Sonnenschein & co. 1885. 245

>   Note.—With physical, political, and statistical descriptions facing each map.

**Philip, G., & son.**
Philips' model atlas . . . 40, 11 pp. incl. 38 col. maps. 8°. London, G. Philip & son [1907] 246

>   Note.—Relief-models are the same scale as the corresponding political maps.

### REPRODUCTIONS.

**Bianco, A.**
Fac-simile dell' atlante di Andrea Bianco prefazione di O. S. Peschel anno 1436. L' originale si conserva nella R. biblioteca Marciana in Venezia. 1 p. l., 8 maps, pl. obl. 4°. Venezia, Ongania, 1879. 247

>   Note.—Imperfect: map no. 8, and preface wanting.
>   Library of Congress has Peschel's prefaces to the german edition of 1869 and the italian translation of 1871, with the atlas dated 1871.

**Crawford, J. L. L.**, *26th earl of*,
Bibliotheca Lindesiana. Collations and notes no. 4. Autotype facsimiles of three mappemondes . . . With an introduction including a short notice on Desceliers' later mappemonde of 1553 by Charles Henry Coote . . . 18 pp.; atlas. fol. [Aberdeen, Aberdeen university press] 1898. 248

>   Note.—Collation:—A., index map and 15 sheets; B., index map and 15 sheets; C., index map and 16 sheets.

CONTENTS.

A. The Harleian (or anonymous) mappemonde, circa 1536 . . .
B. The mappemonde by Desceliers of 1546 . . .
C. The mappemonde by Desceliers of 1550.

**Fischer, T.**
 Raccolta di mappamondo e carte nautiche del XIII al XVI secolo. 15 pts. obl. 4°. fol. [Venezia] F. Ongania, 1871–1881.

249

NOTE.—Size varies: pts. 2, 4–9, 11, 17, obl. 4°; pts. 1, 3, 10, 13–15, fol.; pts. 9, 14 accompanied by text; pt. 9 ed. by Oscar Peschel. pt. 14 ed. by G. Berchet; pts. 12, 16 not yet published.
A series of important facsimiles, from originals in libraries of Milan, Florence and Venice.

CONTENTS.

pt. 1. Fac-simile dell carta nautica araba (Carattere Magrebino) del XIII secolo . . . L'originale si conserva nella R. bibl. Ambrosiana di Milano . . .
" 2. Fac-simile della carta nautica di Pietro visconte di Genova dell' anno 1311 . . . L'originale si conserva nel R. archivio di stato di Firenze . . .
" 3. Fac-simile del planisfero di prète Giovanni da Carignano di Genova del XIV secolo . . . L'originale si conserva nel R. archivio di stato di Firenze . . .
" 4. Fac-simile del portolano di visconte di Genova dell' anno 1318 . . . L' originale si conserva nel museo civico e racc. Correr di Venezia . . .
" 5. Fac-simile del portolano Laurenziano-Gaddiano dell' anno 1351 . . . L'originale si conserva nella R. bibl. Mediceo-Laurenziana di Firenze . . .
" 6. Fac-simile delle carte nautiche di Francesco Pizigani dell' anno 1373 . . . L'originale si conserva nella R. bibl. Ambrosiana di Milano . . .
" 7. Fac-simile del portolano del XIV secolo . . . L'originale si conserva nella R. bibl. Marciana di Venezia . . .
" 8. Fac-simile del portolano di Giacomo Giraldi di Venezia dell' anno 1426 . . . L'originale si conserva nella R. bibl. Marciana di Venezia . . .
" 9. Fac-simile dell' atlante di Andrea Bianco dell' anno 1436; illustrato da Oscar Peschel. L'originale si conserva nella R. bibl. Marciana di Venezia . . .
" 10. Fac-simile del planisfero terrestre di forma ellittica (in lingua latina) dell' anno 1447 . . . L'originale si conserva nella R. bibl. nazionale di Firenze . . .
" 11. Fac-simile della carta nautica di Andrea Bianco dell' anno 1448 . . . L' originale si conserva nella R. bibl. Ambrosiana di Milano . . .
" 12. Portolano membranaceo di anonimo dell' anno 1450 (circa) Dall'originale che si conserva nel Museo comunale di Mantova.
" 13. Fac-simile del planisfero del mondo conosciuto (in lingua catalana) del XV secolo . . . L'originale si conserva nella R. bibl. nazionale di Firenze . . .
" 14. Fac-simile del planisfero di Giovanni Leardo dell' anno 1452 illustrato da G. Berchet. L' originale è di proprietà del comm. de Pilat . . .
" 15. Fac-simile del mappamondo di fra Mauro dell' anno 1457 . . . L' originale si conserva nella R. bibl. Marciana di Venezia . . .
" 16. Carta da navigare per le isole nuovamente trovate in la parte dell' Indie, attribuita a Alberto Cantino dell' anno 1501-03 (3° viaggio di Christoforo Colombo)
" 17. Fac-simile delle carte nautiche di Battista Agnese dell' anno 1554 . . . L' originale si conserva nella R. Bibl. Marciana di Venezia . . .

**Hantzsch, V.** *and* **Schmidt, L.**
Kartographische denkmäler zur entdeckungsgeschichte von Amerika, Asien, Australien und Afrika aus dem besitz der königlichen öffentlichen bibliothek zu Dresden, mit unterstützung der generaldirektion der königlichen sammlungen für kunst und wissenschaft und der könig Johann-Stiftung . . . 1 p. l., [3] pp., 3 maps on 17 l. obl. fol. Leipzig, K. W. Hiersemann, 1903. 250

>   NOTE.—A series of facsimiles illustrating the map-work of three prominent 16th century draughtsmen.
>   Atlas in portfolio with added cover-title.
>   pp. 1–3 contain biographical and cartographical notes.
>
>   CONTENTS.
>
>   no. 1. Karte des Atlantischen ozeans. Pero Fernandez. 1528.
>   " 2. Weltkarte. Nicolas Desliens. 1541.
>   " 3. Karten der aussereuropäischen erdteile. Diogo Homem. 1568.

**Jomard, E. F.**
Les monuments de la géographie; ou, recueil d'anciennes cartes européennes et orientales. Accompagnées de sphères terrestres et célestes, de mappemondes et tables cosmographiques, d'astrolabes et autres instruments d'observation, depuis les temps les plus reculés jusqu'à l'époque d'Ortelius et de Gérard Mercator, publiés en facsimilé de la grandeur des originaux. 2 p. l., 21 maps on 81 l. fol. Paris, Duprat [1842–62] 251

>   NOTE.—Described in a pamphlet entitled: "Introduction à l'atlas des monuments de la géographie par feu m. Jomard . . . publiée par les soins et avec des remarques de m. E. Cortambert. Paris, A. Bertrand, 1879." (Extrait du bulletin de la Société de géographie de Paris)—"M. Jomard voulait consacrer une description développée à chacune des planches qui composent son bel Atlas des monuments de la géographie. La mort ne lui a pas permis de la composer; mais il avait réuni, pour cette description, un grand nombre de matériaux, que m. d'Avezac, d'après le vœu que l'auteur avait exprimé par écrit, se chargea d'utiliser et de compléter; malheureusement la mort vint encore interrompre le travail du savant légataire; on possède du moins l'Introduction qui était destinée à précéder l'ouvrage, et les amis de la géographie nous saurons gré de leur offrir ce dernier fruit des veilles de l'homme éminent qui fut un des fondateurs et longtemps le chef vénéré de la Société de géographie."—E. Cortambert.
>   Reviewed by d'Avezac in the "Annales des voyages." Paris, 1868, v. 1. (pp. 222–236) in an article entitled: "Inventaire et classement raisonné des monuments de la géographie, publiés par m. Jomard de 1842 à 1862."
>
>   CONTENTS.
>
>   no. 1. Globe céleste arabe-koufique en bronze, du xi$^e$ siècle (de la collection géographique de la Bibliothèque royale de Paris)
>   " 2. Globe céleste arabe en bronze, grandeur naturelle, fait à la Mecque au xvi$^e$ siècle (de la collection géographique de la Bibliothèque impériale de Paris)

**Jomard, E. F.**—Continued.

no. 3. Astrolabe koufique rapporté d'Egypte (tiré de la collection de m. Marcel)
" 4. Sujets tirés d'un manuscript florentin du xv$^e$ siècle. Les figures de cette planche sont empruntées à un beau manuscrit du poëme de la Sfera, de Leonardo Dati.
" 5. Carte itinéraire d'un pèlerinage de Londres à Jérusalem (tirée de la Chronique de Matthieu Pâris, xiii$^e$ siècle, conservée au Musée Britannique)
" 6. Carte militaire du moyen-âge, représentant le théâtre de la guerre à l'époque des premières conquêtes de la république de Venise en terre ferme.
" 7. Carte de l'ancien Padouan (tirée de la Bibliothèque Ambrosienne).
Cette carte, signée Hannibal de Madiis, 1449, avait été copiée sur le grand sceau d'argent de la ville de Padoue.
" 8. Carte perspective italienne du xv$^e$ siècle.
Cette carte représente l'état des conquêtes des turcs en Europe, peu de temps avant la prise de Constantinople, en 1453.
" 9. Atlas de Petrus Vessconte, de l'an mcccxviii (Bibliothèque impériale de Vienne)
" 10. Mappemonde des frères Pizzigani, de l'an mccclxvii. L'original de cette carte se conserve dans la Bibliothèque de Parme.
" 11. Carte marine du xiv$^e$ siècle (provenant d'une ancienne famille pisane)
" 12. Carte du globe, par Mohhammed ebn-Aly ebn-Ahmed al-Scharfy de Sfax, an 1009 de l'hégire.
" 13. Dix mappemondes des x$^e$, xiii$^e$, et xiv$^e$ siècles, des bibliothèques de Turin, Leipzig, Copenhague, Londres, Paris, Reims, etc.
" 14. Mappemonde du xiii$^e$ siècle conservée à Hereford.
Cette carte, signée de Richard de Haldingham et de Lafford, paraît avoir été terminée au commencement de l'année 1314.
" 15. Mappemonde de Martin Behaim. (Hémisphère occidental.—Hémisphère oriental)
Cette carte, conforme au fameux globe terrestre exécuté à Nüremberg en 1492, passe pour contemporaine du dessin original de ce monument. Les légendes étendues et nombreuses qui l'accompagnent seront reproduites dans le volume de texte explicatif.
" 16. Mappemonde de Jean de la Cosa, pilote de Christophe Colomb, fin du xv$^e$ siècle.
" 17. Globe terrestre de la première moitié du xvi$^e$ siècle, conservé à Francfort-sur-le-Mein.
" 18. Cartes du xvi$^e$ siècle, figurées sur une cassette de la collection Trivulci, dite Cassettina all' agemina.
" 19. Mappemonde peinte sur parchemin par ordre de Henri II, roi de France.
Cette carte, provenant du roi Henri II, a été reconnue, après examen, plus ancienne que le règne de ce prince, et remonter à François I$^{er}$, des indices certains constatent qu'elle a été exécutée en l'année 1542; en sorte que le titre à lui donner est plutôt celui de mappemonde royale de 1542.
" 20. Mappemonde de Sébastien Cabot, pilote-major de Charles-Quint, de la première moitié du xvi$^e$ siècle.
Cette carte porte la date de 1544; elle contient, dans l'original, des légendes nombreuses et étendues, qui seront fidèlement reproduites dans le volume du texte explicatif.

no. 21. Mappemonde de Gérard Mercator, Duisbourg, 1569. Cette carte, où Gérard Mercator a employé pour la première fois la célèbre projection à latitudes croissantes dont il est l'inventeur, contient, dans l'original, des légendes nombreuses et étendues, qui seront scrupuleusement reproduites dans le volume de texte destiné à compléter cette publication.

## Lelewel, J.

Géographie du moyen âge . . . 5 v. in 4. Atlas. xiv, 30 pp., 2 l., 50 maps. obl. 8º. Bruxelles, v<sup>e</sup> & J. Pilliet, 1852–57. 252

Note.—Atlas accompanying this work dated 1850; Épilogue dated 1857.

Title of atlas: . . . Atlas composé de cinquante planches gravées par l'auteur, contenant 145 figures et cartes générales ou spéciales de 88 géographes arabes et latins de différentes époques, y compris les cartes comparatives, doubles ou triples, accompagnées de 11 cartes explicatives et de deux articles géographiques: 1. Table ou indicateur de longitudes et latitudes des géographes arabes, de l'intervalle de cinq siècles, 830–1330. 2. Portulan général des cartes qui composent l'atlas, spécialement de la carte Catalane 1375–1377 et de la carte 1476 de l'anconitain André Benincasa.

A collection of facsimiles of rare, ancient maps, including the oriental geographies.

The result of "Great research embracing the whole subject of early maritime discoveries." *cf.* Sabin; Bibliotheca Americana.

no. [47] is on the title-page.

Several maps are hand colored.

The following maps relate to America:

no. [36] Tavola di navicare di Nicolo et Antonio Zeni, 1380–1405, per Nicolaum Zeno 1557 . . .
" [37] Grœnland regio ante a 1418 cognita, denuo 1585–1622 reperta. (Carte explicative)
" [41] Terræ recentissime lustratæ, 1500 (America) segmentum mappae mundi Iohannis de la Cosa, naucleri Christophori Columbi 1493 postea navigatoris 1499–1509.—Inset: Cuba. America segmentum extractum e mappa mundi Diegonis Ribero, 1529.
" [43] Orbis, typus universalis 1501–1504, hydrographia, charta marina Portugalensium.
" [45] Bernardi Sylvani eboliensis opera 1511 tabula Ptolemaei universalis reformata, cum additione locorum quæ a recentioribus reperta sunt.
" [46] Hemisphærium globi a Johanne Schoner karlostadio, Bambergæ 1520 fabricati.—Petrus Apianus leisnicensis, Reinerus Gemma Frisius, 1540.—Franciscus monachus ordinis franciscanorum 1526.
" [47] Gerardus Mercator rupelmundanus 1569.
" [48] Abbozzo della mappa di Marco Polo, nella sala del scudo, del palazzo ducale di Venezia, volgato da Placido Zurla.

## Mercator, G.

Drei karten . . . Europa—Britische Inseln—weltkarte. Facsimile-lichtdruck nach den originalen der stadtbibliothek zu Breslau hergestellt von der reichsdruckerei herausgegeben von der Gesellschaft für erdkunde zu Berlin. 3 pts. in 1 v. 3 p. l., [2] l., 3 maps on 41 l. fol. Berlin [etc.] W. H. Kühl, 1891. 253

Note.—Atlas in portfolio.

CONTENTS.

pt. 1. Europa. 1554 . . .
" 2. Britische Inseln. 1564 . . .
" 3. Weltkarte. 1569 . . .

**Marcel, G. A.**
    Choix de cartes et de mappemondes des XIV° et XV° siècles . . .
1 p. l., vi pp., 4 maps on 16 l.   fol.   Paris, E. Leroux, 1896.   254
    NOTE.—"Avertissement" contains explanatory notes on the maps.

CONTENTS.

no. 1. Carte dite pisane. 2 sheets.
"  2. Mappemonde de Dulcert.  1339 (?)  4 sheets.
"  3. Mappemonde de Mecia de Viladestes.  6 sheets.
"  4. Mappemonde de Soleri.  4 sheets.

**Miller, K.**
    Mappaemundi: die ältesten weltkarten.  6 v.  4°.  Stuttgart,
J. Roth, 1895–1898.     255
    NOTE.—Imprint date varies: v. 1, 3, 1895; v. 2, 1897; v. 4–5, 1896; v. 6, 1898.
    v. 2, *i. e.* heft 2, zweiter abdruck.
    Each part, except the second, accompanied by text.

CONTENTS.

v. 1. Die weltkarte des Beatus (776 n. Chr.) Mit abbildungen im text und der karte von St. Sever in den farben des originals.
"  2. Atlas von 16 lichtdruck-tafeln:
"  "  no. 1. Psalter-karte von London.
"  "  "  2. Beatus   "   2. (Paris II)
"  "  "  3.   "   "  3 u. 8. Osma u. Gerona.
"  "  "  4.   "   "  4. Ashburnham.
"  "  "  5. Beatus-karte.  5. Valladolid.
"  "  "  6.   "   "  6. Madrid.
"  "  "  7.   "   "  7. London.
"  "  "  8.   "   "  9. Turin.
"  "  "  9.   "   "  10. (Paris III)
"  "  "  10. Cottoniana. London.
"  "  "  11–12. Hieronymus 1 & 2. London.
"  "  "  13. Heinrich v. Mainz. Cambridge.
"  "  "  14–16. Ranulf Higden. 1 & 2. London.
        5. & 6. London u. Cambridge.
"  3. Die kleineren weltkarten. Mit 74 abbildungen im text und 4 tafeln in farbendruck: 1. Mappamundi ex libro ms. S. Hieronymi . . . — 2. Henrici canon. Moguntini mappamundi Cantabrigiensis (A. D. MCX)—3. Mappamundi ex libro ms. "Psalter" Londinensi . . .— Lamberti mon. Audom. mappamundi Guelferbytana. (A. D. MCXX)
"  4. Die Herefordkarte. Mit 2 uebersichtskarten im text und der Herefordkarte in farbendruck . . .
"  5. Die Ebstorfkarte. Mit dem facsimile der karte in den farben des originals.
"  6. Rekonstruierte karten. Mit 58 clichés (darunter 49 karten) im text und 8 kartenbeilagen:—
"  "  no. 1. Weltkarten des Ravennaten.
"  "  "  2. Mappamundi. Jsidori Hispalensis.
"  "  "  3.   "   "  P. Orosii.
"  "  "  4. Sphaera Jvlii Honorii.
"  "  "  5. Castori tabvlae dictae Pevtingerianae. segmentum primum . . .

v 6. no 6. Pinax Dionysii Periegetis.
" " " 7. Orbis habitabilis ad mentum Pomponii Melae.
" " " 8. a. Orbis habitabilis secundum Eratosthenem.
" " " " b. Tabula climatum secundum Plinii libr. VI, 212–220.
" ‹ " " c. Orbis habitabilis secundum Strabonem.

**Nordenskiöld, N. A. E.,** *friherre.*
Bidrag till Nordens äldsta kartografi. Vid fyrahundraårsfesten till minne af nya verldens upptäckt, utgifna af Svenska sällskapet för antropologi och geografi 1892. 3 p. l., 9 maps. fol. Stockholm, Samson & Wallin [1892] 256

NOTE.—"Tryckt i 100 numrerade exemplar. no. 038."

CONTENTS.

no. 1. Karta öfver norra Europa och Grönland.
" 2. Karta öfver Skandinavien och Grönland.
" 3. Karta öfver Skandinavien och Grönland.
" 4. Karta öfver Germanien och södra Skandinavien.
" 5. Del af en catalansk portulan från 15: e århundradet.
" 6. Nordvestra hörnet af en portulan från början af 16: e ärhundradet.
" 7. Del af en portulan af Bartolomeo Olives. 1584.
" 8. Del af en portulan af Matteo Prunes. 1586.
" 9. Karta öfver Island af biskop Gudbrand Thorlaksen. 1595.

Facsimile atlas to the early history of cartography with reproductions of the most important maps printed in the xv and xvi centuries. Translated from the swedish original by J. A. Ekelöf . . . and C. R. Markham . . . 2 p. l., [6], 141 pp, 51 [60] maps. fol. Stockholm [for P. A. Norstedt & söner] 1889. 257

NOTE.—Engraved title-page. Original has title: Facsimile-atlas till kartografiens äldsta historia innehållande afbildningar af de vigtigaste kartor tryckta före år 1600.
Collection of important reproductions, excluding "manuscript maps" found in atlases of Jomard, Santarem, T. Fischer, and others. *cf.* Preface.
Text, pp. 1–134, contains 76 maps not included in the collation.
The text has 10 parts:—1. The geographical atlas of Ptolemy. pp. 1–9.— 2. Editions of Ptolemy's geography. pp. 9–29.—3. Pseudo-editions of Ptolemy. Ptolemy's errors and merits. pp. 29–34.—4. Ancient, not Ptolemaic maps. pp. 35–52.—5. Extension of Ptolemy's Oikumene towards the north and north-west. pp. 52–61.—6. The first maps of the New World and of the newly discovered parts of Africa and Asia. pp. 62–71.—7. Terrestrial globes from the 15th and the first part of the 16th century. pp. 71–83.—8. Mapprojections. pp. 84–98.—9. The end of the early period of cartography, 1520–1550. pp. 98–116.—10. The transition to, and the beginning of the modern period. Jacopo Gastaldi. Philip Apianus. Abraham Ortelius. Gerard Mercator. pp. 116–134.
The following maps relate to America:—
no. 30. Tabula regionum septentrionalium e codice Ptolemæi seculi xv (c. 1467) in Bibliotheca Zamoiskiensi varsoviæ conservato.
" 32. Ruysch, Universalior cogniti orbis tabula ex recentibus confecta observationibus. Ptolemæus, Romæ, 1508.
" 35. Orbis typvs vniversalis ivxta hydrographorvm traditionem. Ptolemæus, Argentinæ, 1513.

**Nordenskiöld, N. A. E.—Continued.**

no. 37. Mappa mundi ad globum inducendum lustro tertio seculi xvi, in lignum incisa.
" 38b. Tipvs orbis vniversalis ivxta Ptolomei cosmographi traditionem et Americ Vespvcii aliorque lvstrationes a Petro Apiano . . . 1520.
" 39b. Orbis typvs vniversalis . . . Laurentius Frisius, from Ptolemaeus, Argentorati 1522.
" 40. Mappa mundi, Caspar Vopel, 1543.—Mappi mundi, Franciscus Demongenet. 1552.
" 41a–b. Septentrio orbis vniversalis descriptio. Robert Thorne. 1527.— Nova, et integra vniversi orbis descriptio. Orontius Finæus, 1531.
" 42. Typvs cosmographicvs vniversalis. Sim. Grynæus, Novvs orbis, Basileæ 1532.
" 43. [Double cordiform map of Gerardus Mercator] 1538.
" 44a–d. Typvs orbis vniversalis, from Ptolemæus, Basileæ, 1540.—b. Vniversalis cosmographia, from: Joh. Honterus, Rudimenta cosmographica. Tiguri 1546.—c. Charta cosmographica, cvm ventorvm propria natvra et operatione, from: Cosmographia, Petri Apiani, per Gemmam Frisium illustrata. Parisiis 1551.—d. [Globe from the same work] 1551.
" 45a–d. Orbis descriptio, from: Ptolemæus. Venetia, 1561.—b. Universalia novo. & c. Carta marina nova tabvla, from: La geografia di Claudio Ptolemeo. Venetia, 1548.—d. Typo de la carta cosmogpaphica de Gaspar Vopellio Medeburgense, from: Hieronymo Girava, Dos libros de cosmographia, Milan, 1556.
" 46. Typvs orbis terrarvm. from: Abr. Ortelius, Theatrum orbis terrarum. Antverpiæ. 1570.
" 47. Orbis terræ compendiosa descriptio, by Mercator, 1587.
" 48. Hemispheriŷ ab æqvinoctiali linea, ad circvlv̄ poli Arctici. & Hemispheriŷ ab æqvinoctiali linea, ad circvlv̄ poli Ātarctici. from: Cornelius de Judæis, Speculum orbis terræ. Antverpiæ. 1593.
" 49a–c. Vniversalis orbis descriptio, from: Joannes Myritius, Opusculum geographicum rarum. Ingolstadii 1590.—b. L'isole più famose del mondo. Venetia. Descritte da Thomaso Porcacchi. 1572. c. Typvs orbis terrarvm, ad imitationem vniversalis Gerhardi Mercatoris, from: Matthias Quadus, Fasciculus geographicus. Köln, 1608.
" 50. [A true hydrographical description of so much of the world as hath beene hetherto discouered] from: Richard Hakluyt, The principal navigations, London, 1599.
" 51. [Sixteen maps of different parts of America] from: Cornelius Wytfliet, Descriptionis Ptolemaicæ augmentum. Lovarii, 1597.

The following are in the text:

p. 81. Mappemonde of the middle of the 16th century in gores by Antonius Florianus, from Lafreri's atlas.
" 89. Cordiform map of the world by Orontius Finæus. 1566.
" 91. G. Mercator's double cordiform map of the world of 1538.
" 95. G. Mercator's map of the northpolar regions of 1569 . . .
" 97. India quae orientalis dicitur, et insvlæ adiacentes [Philippine islands] 1599.
" 109. Map of the city of Mexico with environs, by Alonzo de Santa Cruz, about 1550.
" 127. Map of South America, by Paulo di Forlani.
" 129. Map of North America, Venice 1566. From Lafreri's atlas.
" 131. Map of the New World. From Petrus Martyr, De orbe novo decades viii, annot Rich. Hakluyti. Paris, 1587.

Periplus; an essay on the early history of charts and sailing-directions translated from the swedish original by Francis A. Bather with numerous reproductions of old charts and maps. x, 208 pp. incl. 100 maps and illus., 97 maps on 120 l. fol. Stockholm [for P. A. Norstedt & söner] 1897. 258

NOTE.—Engraved title-page. Original has title: Periplus. Utkast till sjökortens och sjöböckernas äldsta historia.

A continuation of his Facsimile atlas, and sometimes regarded as the second volume. It differs from the former, in that it does not exclude "manuscript maps."

The explanatory text deals with the following subjects: 1. Greek and roman cartography before Ptolemy.—2. The Periplus of Skylax.—3. Maps and sailing-directions from the 2nd century A. D. down to the Crusades.—4-9. Portolanos.—10. Maps of the coasts and islands of the North sea, the Baltic, and the Arctic ocean during the incunabula period of cartography.—11. Sailing directions for the northern seas, by E. W. Dahlgren.—12. The discovery and charting of the ocean-coast of Africa. 13. Mapping of the south and east coasts of Asia.—14. America.—15. The Pacific.

The text has also 100 maps and illustrations "to elucidate the history of mediæval geography."

The atlas proper, or second part of the Periplus, contains 60 sheets of maps reproduced from originals.

Maps no. 25-26 are colored.

The following maps relate to America:
p. 79. Carta marina nova tabula from Ptolemy, Venetia 1598 and Padua 1621.
" 93. Map of Europe in Mercator's atlas 1595 [Americae pars]
" 99. Nouvelle carte des découvertes faites par des vaisseaux russiens aux côtes inconnues de l'Amérique Septentrionale . . . 1758. After G. P. Muller.
" 146. Map of the world, 1554. Western hemisphere.
" 149. Map of the world by Honter, 1542.
" 163. Universale della parte del mondo nuovamente ritrovata. 1566.
" 165. Map of the world by Gastaldi, 1562.
" 177. The Atlantic ocean and the east coast of America. From Ptolemaeus, Argentorati 1525.
" 183. The Atlantic by Ferando Berteli, about 1565.
" 187. Map of the Pacific by Herrera, 1601.
" 191. Chart " " ocean . . . by George Anson 1748.

The above occur in the text; the following are in the atlas proper.
no. 24. (Battista Agnese) Charta navigatoria seculi xvi, in Bibliotheca Regia Holmiensi conservata. [Four charts (full size) from a portolan-atlas by Battista Agnese, middle of the 16th century]
Portolan atlas by Georgio Calapoda, 1552 [Map of the world]
" 27. Nicolaus de Nicolay, Charta navigatoria maris Atlantici . . . Venetiis, 1560.
" 32. Tabula regionum septentrionalium e codice Christ. Ensenii (Buondelmonte) seculi xv, in Bibliotheca Laurenziana Florentiae conservato [Greenland 15th century]
" 44. [Map of the world] Petrus Apianus, 1530.
" 45. Charta navigatoria auctoris incerti (1502) in Bibliotheca Domini Hamy conservata.
48–49. [Map of the world] Diego Ribero, 1529.
" 50. [Map of the world] Alonzo de Santa Cruz 1542.

**Nordenskiöld, N. A. E.**—Continued.
 no. 51-53. [Map of the world] Pierre Descelliers, 1546. From Jomard.
 " 56. Tertia pars Asiæ. Jacopo Gastaldi, 1561 [Philippine islands]
 " 57. Mar del Zvr Hispanis. Mare Pacificum. Ioannes Ianssonius, 1650.
 " 58. Polus Antarcticus. Ioannes Ianssonius, 1650.
 " 59. Carte générale de toutes les costes du monde et les pays nouvellement découvert [!] . . . Amsterdam . . . 1710.
 " 60. Insulæ Indiæ Orientalis. Jan Huyghen van Linschoten, 1599.

**Paris, France.** Bibliothèque Nationale.
 Choix de documents géographiques . . .   1 p. l., [2] pp., 11 maps, 4 pl. fol. Paris, Maisonneuve & cie. 1883.   259
 NOTE.—Collection made in 1881 by the ministère de l'instruction publique for the "Exposition géographique de Venise."

CONTENTS.

 no. 1-2. Notice des provinces de l'Empire.
 " 3-5. Notice des cités de la Gaule.
 " 6. Mappemonde de Saint-Sever. xi$^e$ siècle.
 " 7-8. Carte pisane xiv$^e$ siècle.
 " 9-20. Atlas catalan de Charles v. 1375.

**Remarkable maps** of the xvth, xvith & xviith centuries reproduced in their original size . . .   6 pts. in 4 portfolios. fol. Amsterdam, F. Muller & co. 1894-1899.   260
 NOTE.—Only 100 copies printed, numbered on the press. The present copy is no. 53. The publishers are considered responsible for the compilation, but the collection is usually cited by the general title.
 Introduction and notes on pts. 1-3 by C. H. Coote; pts. 2-3 (supplement) with notes by J. E. Heeres. Notes on pt. 4 by F. G. Kramp.
 Special titles as follows:
 pt. 1 . . . The Bodel Nyenhuis collection at Leyden . . . 1894.
 " 2-3 . . . The geography of Australia as delineated by the dutch cartographers of the xviith century. Edited by C. H. Coote . . . 1895.
 " 2-3. (Supplement) . . . Huych Allardt's map of India (The part delineating Australia) . . . 1899.
 " 4. . . . Nicolaes Witsen's map of northern Asia from the Bodel Nyenhuis collection (University library, Leyden) . . . 1897.
 " 5-6. . . . Maps of various parts of Europe delineated in the xvth & xvith centuries chiefly from the Isaac Vossius collection . . . 1897.

CONTENTS.

 pt. 1. no. 1-4. Gastaldi's (?) map of the world. Venice, Tramizini, 1554.
 "   "   " 5-6. Globe published at Lyons by Guilielmus Nicolai Belga. 1603.
 "   "   " 7-8. Franciscus Hoeius' map of the world, c$^a$ 1600: republished with later discoveries, by Hugo Allardt. Amsterdam, c$^a$ 1640.
 "   "   " 9. Abraham Goos' globe, publ. by Joh. Janssonius at Amsterdam. 1621.
 "   "   " 10. Ferrando Berteli's map of parts of America, western Europe and Africa. c$^a$ 1560.
 "   "   " 11. Paulo Forlani's map of Africa. Venice, 1562.

v. 1. no. 12. America and the Pacific ocean. Venice, publ. by Rascicotti, engraved by Mazza, cⁿ 1583.
" " " 13. Nova Francia. Italian map. cⁿ 1560.
" " " 14. Dutch East Indies. Venice, cⁿ 1560.
" 2. " 1. Benedict. Arias Montanvs sacrae geographiae tabulam . . . describebat. 1571.
" " " 2. Tabula itineraria octo navium ductore J. C. Van Neck . . . 1600.
" " " 3. Insvlae Molvccae . . . I. C. Visscher excudebat 1617.
" " " 4. Caert van't landt van d'Eendracht uyt de iournalen ende afteykeningen der Stierluyden t'samengestelt . . . 1627 bij Hessel Gerritsz.
" " " 5. [Chart made by Arent Mortensz de Leeuw . . . 1623]
" " " 6. Nova totivs terrarvm orbis greographica ac hydrographica tabvla. Auct: Henr: Hondio, 1630.
" " " 7. Indiæ Orientalis nova descriptio. Amstelodami. I. Ianssonius.
" " " 8. Noua orbis terrarum delineatio . . . P. Eckebrecht . . . 1630.
" " " 9. Orbis terrarum typus de integro multis in locis emendatus . . . Nicolaus Ioannis Visscherius . . . 1639.
" " " 10. India quæ orientalis dicitur, et insvlæ adiacentes. Guiljelmus Blaeu [1640]
" " " 11. Polus antarcticus. Henricus Hondius excudit [1642]
" " " 12. Mar di India. [J. Jansson, 1652]
" " " 13. Mar del Zur. Hispanis mare Pacificum [J. Jansson, 1650]
" " " 14. Oosterdees van Oost Indien door Arnold Colom [1642-1644]
" 3. " 1. [Australasian portion of the gores of Guil. Blaeu's globe. 1647-56?]
" " " 2. Orbis terrarum . . . Auct. Nicolaus Ioã. Visschero [1657]
" " " 3. [Polus antarcticus] . . . 1644.
" " " 4. Indiæ Orientalis nec non insularum adiacentium . . . per N. Visscher.
" " " 5. Nova totius terrarum orbis tabula auctore F. de Wit. 1660.
" " " 6. 't ooster deel van Oost Indien streckende van Ceylon tot Iapan en Hollandia Nova . . . bij H. Doncker [1660]
" " " 7. Terre Avstrale découuerte l'an 1644.
" 2-3 (supplement) [India quae Orientalis dicitur, et insvlae adiacentes . . .] bij Huych Allardt [1652-53]
" 4. no. 1-6. Nieuwe landkaarte van het noorder en ooster deel van Asia en Europa strekkende van Nova Zemla tot China . . . door Nicolaes Witsen. 1687.
" " " [7] Vavassor's map of the world. Venice, between 1530-1550.
" " " [8] Giacomo Gastaldi's universale. Venice, 1546. (Vossius' collection, University library, Leyden)
" " " [9] Paulo Forlani's universale descrittione di tutta la terra conosciuta fin qui. Venice, Fer. Bertelli, 1565. (Vossius' collection, University library, Leyden)
" 5-6. no. 1. England; from Berlinghieri, Romae, 1478.
" " " 2. France; from Berlinghieri, Romae, 1478.
" " " 3. Spain and Portugal; from Berlinghieri, Romae, 1478.
" " " 4. Germany; from Berlinghieri, Romae, 1478.
" " " 5. Rhaetia, Vindelicia, Noricum, Pannonia, Illyria and Dalmatia; from Berlinghieri, Romae, 1478.
" " " 6. Italy; fr. " " "
" " " 7. Sarmatia de Europe . . . from Berlinghieri, Romae, 1478.
" " " 8. Turkey; fr. Berlinghieri, " " " "

**Remarkable maps**—Continued.

v. 5-6. no. 9. Greece; from Berlinghieri, Romae, 1478.
" " " 10. Britannia Insvla . . . 1556.
" " " 11. Novatotivs Galliae descriptio. Orontius F. Delphinas . . . 1546.
" " " 12. Hispaniae descriptio . . . Dominicus Zenoi Venetus restituit, Venetiis, 1560.
" " " 13. Portugal, designed by Fernando Alvarez Secco . . .
" " " 14. Tabvla moderna Poloniae, Vngariae, Boemiae, Germaniae, Russiae, Lithv(ani)ae . . . 1548.
" " " 15. Hollandiae Batavor veteris insvlae et locorvm adiacentivm exacta descriptio M. Tramezini formis . . . 1558. Designed by Jac. van Deventer.
" " " 16. Frisiae antiqvissimae trans Renum provinc. et adiacentivm regionvm nova . . . descriptio. M. Tramezinii formis . . . 1558. Designed by Jac. van Deventer.
" " " 17. Gelriae Cliviae Ivliae nec non aliarvm regionvm adjacentivm nova descriptio. M. Tramezini formis . . . 1558. Designed by Jac. van Deventer.
" " " 18. Brabantiae Belgarvm provinciae recens exactaqve descriptio. M. Tramezini formis . . . 1558. Designed by Jac. van Deventer.
" " " 19. Flandriae recens exactaq(ue) descriptio . . . M. Tramezini formis . . . 1555. Designed by Jac. van Deventer.
" " " 20. Septemtrionalivm regionvm Svetiae Gothiae Norvegiae Daniae . . . descriptio. M. Tramezini formis . . . 1558.
" " " 21. Switzerland. Published by Ant. Salamanca with dedication to Jodocus a Meggen of Lucern. Rome. 1555.
" " " 22. Il golfo de Venetia . . . Venetia, 1567. Pub. by Domenico Zenoi.
" " " 23. Vngariae tanst. (?) descriptio nunc correcta, et aucta Maximil(iano) II . . . dicata per I. Samb(ucus) 1566 . . . 2 sheets.
" " " 24. La discrittione della Transiluania, et parte dell' Vngaria, et il simile delle Romania . . . Opera de N. Giac$^{mo}$ Castaldi Piamo(n)tese cosmographo in Venetia . . . 1566. 3 sheets.
" " " 25. Totius Graeciae descriptio . . . Venetiis, 1564. Fernando Bertelli aereis formis . . .
" " " 26. Noua descriptione de la Moscouia per . . . N. Giacomo Gastaldo Piamontose cosmographo in Venetia . . . 1566 . . .

**Sandler, C.**

Die reformation der kartographie um 1700. Mit 4 tabellarischen und text-beilagen und 6 kartentafeln. Atlas. cover-title, 6 maps on 7 l. fol. München und Berlin, R. Oldenbourg, 1905. 261

CONTENTS.

no. 1. La carte de France . . . 1682.
" 2. Planisphère terrestre . . . J. Cassini. 1694.
" 3. Mappemonde . . . par le s. Sanson. 1691.
" 4. Mappemonde ou, carte générale de la terre . . . par N. de Fer . . . 1705.
" 5. Mappemonde . . . par G. Delisle. 1700.
" 6.  "         "  "  " 1724. 2 sheets.

**Santarem, M. F.**
Essai sur l'histoire de la cosmographie et de la cartographie pendant le moyen-âge, et sur les progrès de la géographie après les grandes découvertes du xv$^e$ siècle ... Atlas. 4 pts. in 1 v. 3 p. l., 3 pp., 4 l., 79 maps. fol. Paris, Maulde & Renou, 1849–1852. 262

  NOTE.—Title of atlas accompanying this work varies:—1. Atlas composé de mappemondes, et de cartes hydrographiques et historiques depuis le xi$^e$ jusqu'au xvii$^e$ siècle pour la plupart inédites et tirées de plusieurs bibliothèques de l'Europe devant servir de preuves à l'ouvrage sur la priorité de la découverte de la côte occidentale d'Afrique au delà du cap Bojador par les portugais et à l'histoire de la géographie du moyen âge, recueillies et gravées sous la direction du viscomte de Santarem ... Publié aux frais du gouvernement portugais. Paris, Fain & Thunot, 1842.—2. Atlas composé de mappemondes, de portulans et de cartes hydrographiques et historiques depuis le vi$^e$ jusqu'au xvii$^e$ siècle ... devant servir de preuves à l'histoire de la cosmographie et de la cartographie pendant le moyen âge et à celle des progrès de la géographie ... Publié sous les auspices du gouvernement portugais. Paris, E. Thunot & c$^e$. 1849.
  Inserted is a copy of the title and table of contents edited by Bernard Quaritch in 1864, reprinted in 1908; the table of contents has the following, which may serve as an explanation of the variation in title above noted: "The Vicomte de Santarem published originally, in 1842, a work entitled, 'Recherches sur la priorité de la découverte de la côte occidentale d'Afrique,' with an atlas consisting of 30 plates. He afterwards made this atlas (which in fact was unfinished at the time) the foundation of the present great work ..." M. de Santarem's original idea was that this atlas should accompany his "Recherches sur la priorité de la découverte de la côte occidentale d'Afrique" and also, his "Essai sur l'histoire de la géographie du moyen âge."
  The first title is followed by an "Avertissement" beginning: Dans le texte de notre ouvrage. After the second title is an "Avertissement" beginning: La présente livraison comprend la suite des monuments de la géographie du moyen âge.
  No list or index was published originally with the atlas. Sheets are numbered according to the "Lenox copy" in which the arrangement follows the natural order of development suggested by the titles of the four divisions. *cf.* Sabin. Maps 41 and 60 are colored. Imperfect; wanting no. 11, Mappemondes ... (Lambertus) ... xii$^{ème}$ siècle.
  Sabin, in his Bibliotheca Americana, describes fully the copy in the Lenox library. Each part has half title:
  Première partie.—Représentations du système des zones habitables et inhabitables dessinées pendant le moyen âge, pour servir de démonstration aux théories des cosmographes de cette période historique. Roses des vents, en douze divisions, telles qu'elles sont figurées dans les manuscrits du moyen âge. Mappemondes et planisphères, représentant la forme de la terre et de ses divisions, dressées depuis le vi$^e$ siècle jusqu'au commencement du xv$^e$ siècle, antérieurement aux grandes découvertes des portugais et des espagnols. A variation of this title follows in smaller type.
  Deuxième partie.—Portulans, cartes historiques et hydrographiques du moyen âge, antérieurement aux découvertes des portugais et des espagnols effectuées au xv$^e$ siècle.
  Troisième partie. Série de mappemondes à partir de celle du célèbre Fra-Mauro, de 1459 jusqu'au xvii$^e$ siècle, destinées à montrer, par leur rappro

**Santarem, M. F.**—Continued.

ment avec les mappemondes antérieures aux grandes découvertes des portugais et des espagnols (données dans la première partie) les progrès que les explorations maritimes de ces deux nations ont fait faire à la science géographique et à la connaissance du globe que nous habitons.

Quatrième partie.—Cartes marines et portulans postérieurs à 1434 époque du passage du cap Bojador par le marin portugais Gil Eannes qui constatent les progrès de l'hydrographie dus aux grandes découvertes des portugais sur toutes les côtes de l'Afrique occidentale et orientale les côtes et péninsules de l'Asie méridionale et orientale et dans les immenses archipels de la mer Indienne et orientale jusqu'au Japon.

CONTENTS.

no. [1] Mappemonde de Cosmas Indico-pleustes du vi$^e$ siècle qui se trouve dans un mss. du ix$^{ème}$.—Planisphère du ix ou du commencement du x siècle trouvé par mr. Miller dans un mss. de Madrid qui a appartenu à la Bibliothèque de la Roda en Aragon.—Planisphère du x siècle qui se trouve dans la Bibliothèque de Florence.—Mappemonde du xii siècle qui se trouve dans un mss. de Salluste de la Bibliothèque Laurentienne à Florence.—Planisphère qu'on voit dans un mss. de Salluste à la Bibliothèque des Médicis à Florence du xiv siècle.—Planisphère qui se trouve dans un mss. du xiii$^e$ siècle à la Bibliothèque des Médicis à Florence.—Mappemonde du xiv siècle dans un mss. de la Bibliothèque Laurentienne à Florence. Globe terrestre qui se trouve à la fin d'un manuscrit de Marco Polo de la Bibliothèque de Stockholm . . .

" [2] Mappemonde du viii. siècle renfermée dans un manuscrit de la Bibliothèque d'Alby.—Mappemonde renfermée dans un manuscrit de Priscien du x$^e$ siècle conservé au Musée Britanique.

" [3] Mappemonde tirée d'un manuscrit du ix$^e$ siècle de la Bibliothèque de Strasbourg.—Mappemonde du x$^e$ au xi$^e$ siècle tirée d'un manuscrit de la Bibliothèque de Saint-Omer.—Mappemonde du xii$^e$ siècle, tirée du manuscrit de Lambertus (Floridus) de la Bibliothèque de l'université de Gand.—Mappemonde du xii$^e$ siècle du manuscrit de Lambertus de la Bibliothèque de Gand, et qui dans le texte porte le titre—"Sp. (h)era triplicata gentium mundi: Gentes Asie, Europe, Africe diverse.—Mappemonde du xiv$^e$ siècle renfermée dans le manuscrit français de la Bibliothèque nationale de Paris, n? 6808, intitulé "Archiloge Sophie."—Mappemonde du xiv$^e$ siècle, renfermée dans le même manuscrit de la Bibliothèque Nationale, no. 6808.

" [4] Mappemonde tirée d'un manuscrit de Macrobe du x$^{ème}$ siècle.—Planisphère qui se trouve dans un manuscrit du x$^e$ siècle.—Mappemonde du xii$^e$ siècle (1119) tirée du manuscrit intitulé "Liber Guidonis" de la Bibliothèque royale de Bruxelles.—Mappemonde du xii$^e$ siècle, qui se trouve dans le "Liber Guidonis," en Belgique.—Planisphère islandais tiré d'un manuscrit du xiii$^e$ siècle et publié dans les Antiquitates Americanae de la Société r. des antiquaires du Nord. (Copenhague.)—Monument tiré du xiv$^e$ siècle, d'un manuscrit de la Bibliothèque royale de Paris, pour servir de démonstration aux théories de quelques cosmographes du moyen-âge.—Monument du xiv$^e$ siècle, tiré d'un manuscrit de la Biblioth. r. de Paris, pour servir d'explication aux théories de quelques cosmographes du moyen âge.—Mappemonde du xiv$^e$ siècle, qui se trouve dans un manuscrit de la Biblioth. r. de Paris.

no. [5] Mappemonde qui se trouve dans un manuscrit latin du x<sup>e</sup> siècle.—Mappemonde du x<sup>e</sup> siècle qui se trouve dans un manuscrit latin de la Bibliothèque n<sup>le</sup> de Paris.—Mappemonde du x<sup>e</sup> siècle qui se trouve dans un man<sup>t</sup> latin de la Bibliothèque n<sup>le</sup> de Paris.—Mappemonde du x<sup>e</sup> siècle, qui se trouve dans le man<sup>t</sup> latin, no. 595.—Mappemonde du xi<sup>e</sup> siècle tirée d'un manuscrit précieux de la Bibl. de la ville de Dijon, renfermant divers traités sur l'astronomie.—Mappemonde du xi<sup>e</sup> siècle, que se trouve dans un man<sup>t</sup> de cette époque à la Bibliothèque n<sup>le</sup> de Paris.—Mappemonde du xii<sup>e</sup> siècle, qui se trouve dans le man<sup>t</sup> latin, no. 87, de la même bibliothèque.—Mappemonde du xiii<sup>e</sup> siècle qui se trouve dans le man<sup>t</sup> latin, no. 7590, de la même bibliothèque.—Mappemonde du xiii<sup>e</sup> siècle, qui se trouve dans le même manuscrit.—Mappemonde du xiii<sup>e</sup> siècle qui se trouve dans un beau manuscrit d'Isidore de Séville, de cette époque.—Mappemonde du xiii<sup>e</sup> siècle qui se trouve dans un manusc. latin no. 6 (Fonds de Navarre) dans la Bibl. nle. de Paris.—Système cosmographique qu'on trouve dans un manuscrit du commencement du xiv<sup>e</sup> siècle.

" [6] Systèmes des zones habitables et inhabitables dessinés au moyen-âge pour servir de démonstration aux théories des cosmographes de cette époque et différentes mappemondes.

" [7] Facsimile d'un planisphère qui se trouve à la Bibliothèque du roi . . . dans un manuscrit du xi<sup>e</sup> siècle de la cosmographie d'Azaph.—Facsimile d'un planisphère qui se trouve au Musée Britanique dans un manuscrit du Polichronicon de Ranulplus Hugeden du xiv<sup>e</sup> siècle.

" [8] Planisphère qu'on présume avoir été dessiné au xi<sup>e</sup> siècle, dans un manuscrit de la Bibliothèque de Leipsik.—Planisphère dessiné dans un manuscrit du xiv<sup>e</sup> siècle à la suite du livre du Guillaume de Tripoli: De statu sarracenorum.—Planisphère d'un manuscrit du xiv<sup>e</sup> siècle de la Bibliothèque I. M. P. de Vienne.

" [9] Mappemonde qu'on a supposé du x<sup>e</sup> siècle mais qui se trouve dans un mss. du xii<sup>e</sup> siècle de la Bibl. r. de Turin.—Mappemonde du xi<sup>e</sup> siècle à la Bibliothèque Cottonienne, au Musée Britanique.—Planisphère de Cecco d'Ascoli (xiii<sup>e</sup> siècle) dans ses commentaires au traité de la sphère.

" [10] Mappemonde du xii<sup>e</sup> siècle, dressée par Henri chanoine de Mayence dédiée à l'empereur d'Allemagne Henri. v.

" [11] Mappemondes et systèmes renfermés dans les manuscrits de Paris et de la Haye de Floridus (Lambertus) auteur du xii<sup>ème</sup> siècle. [5 small maps wanting]

" [12] Mappemonde renfermée dans un manuscrit qui contient un commentaire de l'apocalypse composé par un auteur anonyme probablement natif d'Espagne, rédigé vers l'an 787, (viii<sup>e</sup> siècle) et dédié à Eutherus, evêque d'Osma . . .

" [13] Planisphère du traité intitulé Imago Mundi d'Honoré d'Autun xii<sup>e</sup> siècle.—Planisphère du xii<sup>e</sup> siècle qui se trouve dans un mss. de l' Imago Mundi de Honoré d'Autun.—Planisphère qu'on trouve dans un mss. de l' Image du Monde de Gauthier de Metz du xiii<sup>e</sup> siècle.—Planisphère qu'on trouve dans un mss. de l' Image du Monde de Gauthier de Metz du xiii<sup>e</sup> siècle à la Bibliothèque du Roi.—Planisphère qu'on trouve dans un mss. de l' Image du Monde de Gauthier de Metz du xiii<sup>e</sup> siècle à la Bibliothèque Royale.—Planisphère qui se trouve dans un autre mss. de Gauthier de Metz du xiii<sup>e</sup> siècle.—Planisphère qui se trouve dans le traité de Pierre d'Ailly intitulé Imago Mundi de 1410.

**Santarem, M. F.**—Continued.

" [14] Mappemonde renfermée dans un manuscrit du xiiie siècle, de la Bibliothèque de Leipsig.—Trois planisphères tirés d'un manuscrit du xive siècle de l' Imago Mundi, attribué à mr. Gonneim, conservés dans la Bibliothèque royale de Bruxelles.—Figure représentant le système des terres opposées et le monde de la forme d'une pomme renfermée dans le même manuscrit.—Figure représentant les différentes parties de la terre séparées par les mers, tirée du même manuscrit.—Représentation figurant l'Asie occupant tout le centre du plan et les quatre points cardinaux, tirée du même manuscrit.—Système cosmographique renfermé dans un manuscrit du xive siècle, copié d'un autre plus ancien de l' Imago Mundi d'Honoré d'Autun, conservé à la Bibliothèque royale de Stuttgard.—Mappemonde renfermée dans le même manuscrit de l' Imago Mundi d'Honoré d'Autun, conservé à la Bibliothèque royale de Stuttgard.—Mappemonde tirée d'un manuscrit du xive siècle de la Bibliothèque d'Arras.—Systèmes des zones habitables et inhabitables tirés d'un manuscrit du xve siècle, renfermant le poëme géographique de Goro Dati.

" [15] Mappemonde du xiii siècle qui se trouve au Musée Britanique . . .

" [16] Mappa terræ habitabilis flores historiarum; sive historia ab orbe condito ad ann 1251 per Matlhæum de Parisio. Mss. Cotton du Musée Britannique du xiii ou xiv siècle.

" [17] Mappemonde de Marinus Sanuto du xive siècle, (1321) renfermée dans le manuscrit no. 9404 de l'ouvrage de cet auteur conservé dans le Bibliothèque royale de Bruxelles.

" [18] Mappemonde renfermée dans le Rudimentum Nuvitiorum imprimé en 1475.

" [19] Mappemonde de la fin du xve siècle qui se trouve dans l'ouvrage très rare de la salle du xve siècle.—Planisphère du xive siècle placé en tête d'un manuscrit latin de la Bibliothèque royale de Paris no. 4126.

" [20] Mappemonde du xiiie siècle d'après le ms. royal 14. C. xii. du Musée Britannique.

" [21] Mappemonde des Grandes Chroniques de St. Denis du tems de Charles v. (1364 à 1372) manuscript de la Bibliothèque de Ste. Génevièvre.—Globe de Nicolas d'Oresme dessiné en 1377, à la suite de son traité de la sphère.

" [21 bis] Mappemonde des Grandes Chroniques de St. Denis du tems de Charles V. (1364 à 1372) manuscrit de la Bibliothéque de Ste. Geneviève.

" [22] Mappemonde de Marino Sanuto qui se trouve dans un mss. du xive siècle de la Bibliothèque royale de Paris. . . .

" [23] Mappemonde du commencement du xve siècle du Musée Borgia dressée avant les grandes découvertes.

" [24] Mappemonde du xve siècle renfermée dans une collection de différentes cartes du xive et autres, conservées dans la Bibliothèque Medicea de Florence.

" [25] Mappemonde de Marino Sanuto de 1321.

" [26] Mappemonde du mss. du Pomponius Mela de la Bibliothèque de Reims de 1417.

## Deuxième partie.

no. [27] Carte de l'Empire d'occident, tirée d'un manuscrit de l'an 1119, du Guidonis de la Bibliothèque royale de Bruxelles.—Carte géographique de l'Europe du XII$^e$ siècle renfermée dans le manuscrit de Lambertus de la Bibliothèque de l'Université de Gand.—Carte qui se trouve dans un manuscrit du XII$^e$ siècle du Musée Britannique qui renferme des ouvrages de Saint Jérome.
" [28-30] Portulan de Petrus Vesconte de Gênes dressé en 1318, conservé à Venise dans la Bibliothèque du Musée Correr. 3 sheets.
" [31] Carte de Pizzigani de 1367 à la Bibliothèque de Parme.—Carte Catalane manuscrit de 1375 à la Bibliothèque du roi de Paris.—Carte de l'atlas mss. de la Bibliothèque Pinelli de 1384 à 1400.
" [32-33] Carte Catalane de 1375, donnée en fac-simile, copiée d'après l'original conservé à la Bibliothèque nationale de Paris.
" [34-36] Portulan du XIV et du XV siècles (1384-1434) donné en fac-simile d'après l'original qui a appartenu à la Bibliothèque Pinelli . . . 3 sheets.
" [37] Portulan de la fin du XIV$^e$ siècle, qui se conserve à la Bibliothèque impériale de Paris et qu'on dit avoir appartenu à la Bibliothèque du cardinal de Richelieu.
" [38] Planisphère qui se trouve dans un manuscrit d'un poëme géographique du XV$^e$ siècle.—Mappemonde d'Andrea Bianco dressée en 1436.
" [39] Carte d'Andrea Bianco de 1436.—Planisphère d'Andrea Bianco.—Mappemonde de F. Mauro. (1460)
" [40] Fac-simile des cartes marginales et figures renfermées dans le manuscrit du traité de la sphère de Léonardo Dati de Florence, du commencement du XV$^e$ siècle.
" [41] Carte marine de la fin du XIV$^{me}$ ou XV$^{me}$ siècle conservée aux archives de Lucerne.
" [42] Carte de la Bibliothèque de Weimar de MCCCCXXIV.
" [43-48] Mappemonde dressée en 1459, par Fra Mauro, cosmographe vénetien, par ordre d'Alphonse V, roi de Portugal . . . 6 sheets.

## Troisième partie.

" [49] Mappemonde dressée en 1448, par Johanès Leardus de Venise, conservée à Vicenza dans la bibliothèque Trento, publiée pour la première fois et donnée en fac-simile.
" [50] Mappemonde dressée en 1489 qui se trouve dans un manuscrit du Musée Britannique reproduite pour la première fois.
" [51] Mappemonde de Ruych de 1508, renfermant les dernières découvertes faites jusqu'à cette époque.
" [52] Globe de Jean Schoener de 1520.—Mappemonde d'Apianus de 1520, tirée du Solin de Camers.
" [53] Mappemonde dressée par Francesco Roselli de Florence, en 1532.—Mappemonde de la cosmographie de Sébastien Munster, de 1544.—Mappemonde de Vadianus, 1546.
" [54] Carte de Gabriell de Valsequa; fait à Mallorcha anj MCCCCXXXVÜY.
" [55] Carte de Grazioso Benincasa, dessinée en 1467. (Bibliothèque du roi à Paris, départ. des cartes)
" [56-57] [Carte du même cosmographe ayant pour titre]: Gratiosos Benincasa Anconitanus composuit Venecys, anno domini MCCCCLXXI. 2 sheets.

**Santarem, M. F.**—Continued.

*Quatrième partie.*

no. [58] Geographische vorstellung eines globi, welchen anno 1492. Herr martin [!] Behaim im diametro beij 20 zollen zu Nurnberg exibiret.
" [59] Carte de Freduci d'Ancone, dressée en 1497, et donnée pour la première fois en fac-simile, d'après l'original qui se trouve à la Bibliothèque de Wölfenbuttel.
" [60] Africa do mappamundi de Juan de la Cosa piloto de Christovaõ Colombo en 1493 desenhado em 1500 . . .
" [61] [Mappemonde dressée par Ruych, et publiée en 1508, sous le titre de]: Universalior coguiti orbis tabula ex recentibus confecta observationibus fragmentum depromptum ex edi. geograph Ptolemæi Romae MDVIII.
" [62] Carte d'Afrique du Ptolémée. Publiée à Strasbourg en 1513, d'après les cartes portugaises.
" [63] Afrique d'une mappemonde conservée à la Bibliothèque de Weimar avec le titre: Carta universal en que se contiene todo lo que del mondo sea descubierto hasta a ora: hizola um cosmographo de su magestad, ano MDXXVII.
" [64] Carte de Diego Ribero, 1529, à la Bibliothèque de Weimar.
" [65–70] Portulan, dressé entre les années 1524–1530, par Francisco Rodrigues, pilote portuguais, qui a fait le voyage aux Moluques. 6 sheets.
" [71] Les premières œuvres de Jacques de Vaulx, pilote pour le roy en la marine, 1533.
" [72] [Carte de] Guillaume le Testu [Afrique de 1555]
" [73] Carte de l'atlas de Joan Martines, dessinée à Messine a. 1567.
" [74] Côtes occid$^{les}$ d'Afrique. Extraites de la carte réduite de Guillaume Levasseur de Dieppe. 1601.
" [75] Côtes occid$^{les}$ d'Afrique. Extraites de la carte réduite par Jean Dupont de Dieppe. 1625.
" [76–77] Côtes occid$^{les}$ d'Afrique. Extraites de la carte faitte en Dieppe, par Jean Guérard. 1631. 2 sheets.
" [78] Roses-des-vents en usage au moyen âge, antérieurement aux grandes navigations du xv$^e$ siècle.—Rose des vents en 12 divisions de l'horison, et indiquant leurs effets météorologiques, tirée d'un manuscrit du x$^e$ siècle.—Rose des vents en 12 divisions de l'horison tirée d'un manuscrit du x$^o$ siècle.—Rose des vents en 12 divisions de l'horison tirée d'un manuscrit inédit de la cosmographie d'Asaph, auteur du xi$^e$ siècle.—Rose des vents en 12 divisions tirée d'un manuscrit de Vitruve du xi$^e$ siècle.—Rose des vents en 16 divisions de l'horison, tirée d'un manuscrit du commencem$^t$ du xiv$^e$ siècle renfermant le poème d'Ermengaud de Bésiers.—Rose de vents en 12 divisions de l'horison avec les noms grecs de la rose de Timosthènes et les correspondants adoptés au moyen-âge tiré de l'ouvrage rarissime de Schoner intitulé: Opusculum geographicum.

**Spitzer, F.** *and* **Wiener, C.**

Portulan de Charles-Quint donné à Philippe II. Accompagné d'une notice explicative . . .  37 pp., [1] l., 11 maps, 3 pl. obl. 4°.  Paris, J. Claye, 1875. 263

NOTE.—At head of title: Collection Frédéric Spitzer.
Half-title: Portulan de Charles-Quint donné à Philippe II.

Harrisse, Major and Winsor were inclined to attribute the original to Baptista Agnese. There is a difference of opinion in regard to the date; Spitzer and Wiener assigned 1539, because the atlas shows no recognition of the coast of Chili, which was developed about 1540. Harrisse places it under 1542; Fischer, Wieser and Kretschmer say 1548; and Ruge prefers 1550. *cf.* Winsor's Baptista Agnese and american cartography in the sixteenth century. p. 11. M. Malte Brun in a "Compte rendu" before the Soc. de géogr. de Paris, juin 1876, mentions Santa-Cruz as the author, and places the date about 1536. *cf.* Soc. de géogr. de Paris. Bulletin. 1876. pp. 625–631.

The following maps relate to America:
no. 4. [Un planisphère]
" 13. [L'Amérique Méridionale]
" 14. [Partie de l'Amérique Septentrionale et Méridionale]

**Vivien de Saint-Martin, L.**
Histoire de la géographie et des découvertes géographiques depuis les temps les plus reculés jusqu'à nos jours . . . Atlas. 2 p. l., 4 pp., 13 maps. fol. Paris, Hachette & cie. 1873–1874. 264

NOTE.—Atlas has title: Atlas dressé pour l'Histoire de la géographie . . .
pp. 1–4 contain: Notices analytiques sur l'Atlas de l'Histoire de la géographie.
The following maps relate to America:
no. 2 (VIII) Planisphère selon les connaissances actuelles. 1873.
" [10] Le monde connu en 1491 avant le premier voyage de Colomb.
" [11] Le monde connu en 1550.
" [12] Mappemonde d'Ortelius 1587. Typvs orbis terrarvm.
" [13] Planisphère sur la projection de Mercator.

## SCHOOL.

**Andree, R.**
Dr. Richard Andrees allgemeiner schul-atlas. Mit besonderer berücksichtigung der politischen verhältnisse. Mit einer heimatskarte und zwei geschichtskarten. 44. aufl. ausg. B. 1 p. l., 36 pp. incl. 33 maps. 4°. Bielefeld und Leipzig, Velhagen & Klasing, 1898. 265

**Arrowsmith, A.,** *jr.*
Orbis terrarum veteribus noti descriptio. A comparative atlas of ancient and modern geography, from original authorities, and upon a new plan, for the use of Eton school . . . 3 p. l., 27 (*i. e.* 53) maps. fol. London, author, 1828. 266

NOTE.—Another edition published in 1830, also an index in 1828, entitled: Index to the Eton comparative atlas of ancient and modern geography.
The following map relates to America:
no. 27. Western hemisphere.

**Beekman, A. A.** *and* **Schuiling, R.**
Schoolatlas van de geheele aarde . . . 3. verm. druk. 2 p. l., 50 col. maps. fol. Zutphen, W. J. Thieme & cie. [1903] 267

NOTE.—Contains special maps of the Netherlands.

**Bos, P. R.**
Bos' schoolatlas der geheele aarde. Zestiende, verb. en verm. druk. Herzien door J. F. Niermeyer. 2 p. l., 46 maps. fol. Groningen, J. B. Wolters, 1904. 268

NOTE.—Contains the following plans of cities:
no. 35. Batavia.—Soerabaja.—Weltevreden.
" 42. New-York.—Groei van Chicago.
The following maps relate to America:
no. 40. Noord-Amerika.
" 41. Noord-Amerika.
" 43. De Vereenigde Staten en Mexico.
" 44. Zuid-Amerika.
" 45. Middel-Amerika en West-Indie.

**Browne, C. H.**
Butler's atlas adapted for the grammar and primary grades of school. 47 pp., incl. 16 maps. sq. 8°. [Philadelphia] E. H. Butler & co. ᶜ1883. 269

An atlas adapted for the eighth, seventh, sixth, and fifth grammar grades of New York schools. Arranged according to course of instruction prescribed for 1883 . . . 1 p. l., [10] pp., 17 maps. 8°. [Philadelphia] E. H. Butler & co. ᶜ1883. 270

**Chisholm, G. G.** *and* **Leete, C. H.**
Longmans' new school atlas; edited by Geo. G. Chisholm . . . and C. H. Leete . . . New ed. 1 p. l., iv pp., 32 pp., 42 col. maps on 40 sheets. 4°. New York, Longmans, Green & co. 1901. 271

**Collins, H. G.**
The college atlas, for schools and families; with an alphabetical index of the latitudes and longitudes of 30,000 places . . . Thirty-eighth thousand. 2 p. l., 47, [1] pp., 32 col. maps, 1 pl. 4°. London, H. G. Collins [1855?] 272

NOTE.—The following maps relate to America:
no. 1ᵃ. The western hemisphere.
" 26. North America.
" 27. United States.
" 28. South America.

**Cornell, S. S.**
Cornell's companion atlas to Cornell's high school geography: comprising a complete set of maps, designed for the student to memorize, together with numerous maps for reference, etc . . . 1 p. l., [18] l. incl. 26 maps. 8 pp. fol. New York, D. Appleton & co. 1864. 273

**Cummings, J. A.**
 School atlas to Cummings' ancient & modern geography. 4th ed. cover-title, 8 maps. 8°. Boston, Cummings & Hilliard [1817]   274

> Note.—First edition published in 1813.
> To accompany: An introduction to ancient and modern geography . . . 4th ed. Boston, 1817.
> Maps engraved by T. Wightman.
> The following maps relate to America:
> no. [1] The world . . .
> " [2] North America . . .
> " [3] The United States of America . . .
> " [4] South America . . .

 School atlas to Cummings' ancient & modern geography. 7th ed. cover-title, 8 maps. 4°. Boston, Cummings & Hilliard [1820]   275

> Note.—The following maps relate to America:
> no. [1] The world . . .
> " [2] North America . . .
> " [3] The United States . . .
> " [4] South America . . .

 School atlas to Cummings' ancient and modern geography. 8th ed. cover-title, 8 maps. 8°. Boston, Cummings & Hilliard [1821?]   276

**Debes, E.**
 E. Debes' schul-atlas für die mittleren unterrichtsstufen in verbindung mit hervorragenden schulmännern. Bearbeitet in der geographischen anstalt der verlagshandlung . . . 1 p. l., 60 (*i. e.* 58) col. maps, 2 pl. 4°. Leipzig, H. Wagner & E. Debes [1900]   277

**Diercke, C.** *and* **Gaebler, E.**
 Diercke schul-atlas für höhere lehranstalten. 44. neubearbeitete aufl. vi, 155 pp. incl. 116 col. maps, 3 col. pl. fol. Braunschweig, G. Westermann, 1908.   278

**Drury, L.**
 A geography for schools, upon a plan entirely new, consisting of an analytical arrangement of all the great features of nature, particularly adapted to an atlas of forty luminous and concise maps . . . also gives tabular and comprehensive views of statistical geography . . . also of ancient geography, upon the same plan . . . 42 pp., 40 maps. 4°. Providence, R. I., Miller & Hutchens, 1822.   279

**Dubois, E. M.** *and* **Sieurin, E.**
Cartes d'étude pour servir à l'enseignement de la géographie . . . Asie, Insulinde, Afrique. Classe de cinquième. 9. éd. complètement mise à jour. Avec 8 cartes nouvelles et 7 cartes refaites. 3 p. l., 33 maps. 4°. Paris, Masson & cie. 1905. 280

Cartes d'étude pour servir à l'enseignement de la géographie . . . Géographie générale. Amérique. Australasie. Classe de sixième. 9. éd. complètement mise à jour, avec 6 cartes nouvelles et 7 cartes refaites. 3 p. l., 33 maps. 4°. Paris, Masson & cie. 1905. 281

**Fay, T. S.**
Great outline of geography for high schools and families . . . Atlas. 2 p. l., 8 maps, 3 pl. fol. New York, G. P. Putnam & son, 1867. 282
> Note.—Atlas accompanying has title: Atlas to Fay's Great outline of geography for high schools and families . . . New York [1867]
> The following maps relate to America:
> no. 1. [Hemispheres]
> " 2. Natural land and water divisions of the world.
> " 3. Principal countries of the world.
> " 4. Chief towns of the world . . . (Mercator's projection)
> " 6. Part of United States of America.
> " 8. Outline of towns, rivers, etc., of the United States . . .

**Field, B.**
Atlas designed to accompany the American school geography . . . cover-title, 8 maps. 4°. Boston, W. Hyde & co. ᶜ1832. 283

**Frye, A. E.**
Home and school atlas . . . 4 p. l., 48, 31 pp. incl. 4 col. maps. 21 col. maps. fol. Boston, London, Ginn & co. 1896. 284
> Note.—New England edition.

**Goodrich, S. G.**
Atlas designed to illustrate the Malte-Brun school geography . . . cover-title, 11 maps, 1 pl., 3 tab. 4°. Hartford, H. & F. J. Huntington, 1830. 285
> Note.—The following maps relate to America:
> no. 1. New England states.
> " 2. The middle states, Maryland & Virginia.
> " 3. United States.
> " 4. North America.
> " 5. South America.
> " 6. Atlantic Ocean its islands & coasts.
> " 10. Pacific Ocean its islands & coasts.
> " 11-14. Western hemisphere.—Eastern hemisphere.—Northern hemisphere.—Southern hemisphere.

Atlas designed to illustrate the Malte-Brun school geography . . . cover-title, 15 maps. 4°. New York, F. J. Huntington & co. ᶜ1838. 286

> NOTE.—The following maps relate to America:
> no. 1. The New England states.
> " 2. The middle states.
> " 3-4. The southern states. 2 sheets.
> " 5. The western states.
> " 6. The United States, Texas, & the british provinces of the Canadas . . .
> " 7. N. America and the West Indies.
> " 8. South America.
> " 9. The Atlantic Ocean, its islands & coasts.
> " 14. The Pacific Ocean, its islands & coasts.
> " 15-18. Western hemisphere. — Eastern hemisphere. — Northern hemisphere.—Southern hemisphere.—

**Gregory, H. D.**
An index to Mitchell's new school atlas, containing over 17,000 names . . . 112 pp. 8°. Philadelphia, author, 1871. 287

> NOTE.—See title 302 for "Atlas."

**Grenet,** *l'abbé* —
Atlas portatif à l'usage des collèges, pour servir à l'intelligence des auteurs classiques. Par m. l'abbé Grenet, professeur au collège de Lisieux. Dédié à l'université de Paris. 3 p. l., 44 maps. 4°. [Paris, 1779-82?] 288

> NOTE.—Engraved title. The maps, dated from 1779 to 1782, are by Bonne.
> The following maps relate to America:
> no. [1] Mappemonde en deux hémisphères. 1781.
> " [2] Carte réduite des terres et des mers du globe terrestre. 1782.
> " [3] Carte de la direction des vents généraux et des moussons.
> " [39] Carte générale de l'Amérique Septentrionale. 1781.
> " [40] Les États-Unis de l'Amérique Septentrionale. 1781.
> " [41] Carte des isles de Cuba et de la Jamaïque.
> " [42] Carte des isles de Sᵗ Domingue et de Porto-Rico. 1782.
> " [43] Isles Antilles ou du Vent avec les isles Sous le Vent. 1782.
> " [44] Carte générale de l'Amérique Méridionale. 1781.

**Griffen, J.**
Atlas designed to illustrate "Elements of modern geography"; for the use of schools . . . cover-title, 9 maps, 1 tab. 4°. Glen's Falls [N. Y.] A. Smith, 1833. 289

> NOTE.—The following maps relate to America:
> no. 1. The world.
> " 2. North America.
> " 3. United States of N. America.
> " 4. The middle states and part of the southern & western states.
> " 5. South America.
> " 9. Isothermal chart.

**Hart, J. C.**
A modern atlas of fourteen maps. Drawn and engraved to illustrate Hart's geographical exercises . . . 5th ed. rev. and corr. 1 p. l., 14 fold. maps. fol. New York, R. Lockwood; Philadelphia, J. Grigg & A. Finley, 1828.  290

CONTENTS.

no. 1. The world on Mercator's projection.
" 2. Map of North America.
" 3. Map of the United States.
" 4. Map of the state of New York.
" 5. The West Indies.
" 6. Map of South America.
" 7. Europe.
" 8. Great Britain and Ireland.
" 9. Map of Germany.
" 10. The Mediterranean sea with the countries on its borders.
" 11. Map of Asia.
" 12. The Pacific ocean.
" 13. Map of Africa.
" 14. Map of the interior of Africa.

A modern atlas, of fourteen maps. Drawn and engraved to illustrate Hart's geographical exercises . . . 7th ed. rev. and cor. 1 p. l., 14 fold. maps. fol. New York, R. Lockwood; Philadelphia, J. Grigg & A. Finley, 1830.  291
NOTE.—Maps same as in 5th edition.

**Homann** heirs.
Schūl-atlas von zwantzig general- und special-landkarten, nach einer neu-verbefferten methode illuminirt, und zum bequemen gebrauch der anfangs-gründe der geographie herrn m. Johann Jacob Schatzens . . . der jugend zum beften alfo eingerichtet . . . Nûrnberg . . . Homånnifchen officin . . . 1743.—Atlas scholastique composé de xx. cartes, tant générales que particulières, le tout nouvellement revû, enluminé et accommodé à l'usage de la jeunesse, suivant les élémens de géographie de mr. Schaz . . . Mis au jour par les héritiers d'Homann. Nuremberg, a. 1743.—Atlas scholasticvs ex xx. mappis generalibvs et specialibvs colorum ope emendativs redditis; compositvs, et ad vsvm elementorvm geographiae dni. m. Ioh. Iac. Schazii . . . 2 p. l., 19 maps, 1 pl. fol. Norimbergae, in officina Homanniana, 1743.  292

NOTE.—Wanting:
no. 10. Polonia, Prussia & Curlandia.
" 13. Suecia & Norvegia.
" 18. America.
" 19. Borussia.
Inserted:
Superioris et inferioris Ducatus Silesiæ.

Mapa geographica complectens i Indiae Occidentalis, partem mediam circvm isthmvm Panamensem. ii Ipsumq, isthmum. iii Ichnographiam praecipuorum locorum & portuum ad has terras pertinentium . . .
Dominia Anglorum in America Septentrionali.
Dominia Anglorum in præcipuis insulis Americæ.
Two plates: Abbildliche geschichte der seethiere.—Abbildliche geschichte der auslandischen land thiere.
The following map relates to America:
no. 1. Planiglobii terrestris cum utroq, hemisphærio cælesti generalis repræsentatio.

Schŭl-atlas von zwantzig general- und special-landkarten, nach einer neu-verbefferten methode illuminirt, und zum bequemen gebrauch der anfangs-grŭnde der geographie, herrn m. Johann Jacob Schatzens . . . der jugend zum beften also eingerichtet zu finden in Nŭrnberg, in der Homånnifchen officin . . . 1745.—Atlas scholastique composé de xx. cartes, tant générales que particulières, le tout nouvellement revû, enluminé et accomodé à l'usage de la jeunesse, suivant les élémens de géographie de mr. Schaz . . . mis au jour par les héritiers de Homann. Nuremberg, 1745 . . . —Atlas scholasticvs ex xx. mappis generalibus et specialibus colorvm ope emendativs redditis, compositvs et ad vsvm elementorvm geographiæ dni. m. Ioh. Iac. Schazii . . . Prostat Norimbergae in officina Homanniana. 1745. 2 p. l., col. front., 20 col. maps. fol. [Nuremberg, Homann heirs, 1745-46] 293

NOTE.—Engraved frontispiece, colored, entitled: Atlas novus terrarum orbis imperia, regna et status exactis tabulis geographicè demonftrans, opera Iohannis Baptistæ Homanni, Norimbergæ.
The following maps, dated 1746, relate to America:
no. 1. Mappe-monde qui représente les deux hémisphères. Tirée des quatre cartes générales de feu mr. le professeur Hasius. Publiée par les héritiers de homann. 1746.
no. 18. Americae mappa generalis, secundum legitimas projectionis ftereographicæ regulas, relationesque recentissimas et obfervationes focioru Acad. reg. sc. quæ Parisiis eft, aliorumque auctorum, nec non secundum mentem d. I. M. Hasii, m. p. p. in partes fuas methodicas divifa, nunc concinnati et delineata ab Aug. Gottl. Boehmio. In lucem proferentibus Homannianis heredibus, a. 1746.

Atlas compendiarivs feu ita dictus scholasticvs minor in ufum erudiendae juventutis adornatus. Excudentibus Homañianis heredibus. A. 1753. 1 p. l., 20 col. maps, 1 col. pl. fol. [Nuremberg, 1753-1790] 294

NOTE.—Engraved title.
The following maps bear a later date than that indicated on the title page:
no. 2. Europa secundum legitimas projectionis stereographicae regulas . . . divisa a Ioh. Matth. Hasio, math. p. p. o. edita curis Homannianorum heredum . . . 1743. Denuo emendata 1789.
" 7. Italia in suos status divisa, ex d'Anvilliano Rizzi Zannonisque prototypis desumta. Curantibus Homannianis haeredibus . . . 1790.

**Homann** heirs—Continued.
  no. 10. Mappa geographica regni Poloniae . . . à Tob. Mayero, s. c. s. Luci publicae tradita per Homannianos heredes. Norinbergae, 1773.
  " 12. General charte vom königreich Dænemark, nebst dem herzogthum Holstein . . . entworfen durch F. L. Güssefeld. Nürnberg bey den Homan: erben, 1789.
  " 13. Scandinavia complectens Sveciæ, Daniæ, et Norvegiæ . . . cura Homanniarum heredum . . . 1776.
  The following map relates to America:
  no. 20. Americae mappa generalis secundum legitimas projectionis stereographicæ regulas relationes que recentisfimas et obfervationes fociorum Acad. reg. fequæ Parisiis eft aliorumque auctorum nec non fecundum mentem d. I. M. Hasii . . . in partes fuas methodicas divifa nunc concinnata et delineata ab Aug. Gottl. Boehmio, phil. magiftro, in lucem preferentibus Homannianis heredibus . . . 1746.

**Huntington, N. G.**
  Huntington's school atlas drawn and engraved expressly to illustrate and accompany the System of modern geography . . . cover-title, 2 l., 11 maps. 4°. Hartford. E. Huntington & co. 1833.
  295
  NOTE.—The following maps relate to America:
  no. [1] The world.
  " [2] North America.
  " [3] United States.
  " [4] New England states.
  " [5] South America.
  " [9] Oceanica and comparative N. America & Asia.
  " [10] Africa and the Atlantic ocean [and part of South America]
  " [11] Chart of climates & productions.

**Johnston, A. K.**
  A school atlas of general and descriptive geography exhibiting the actual and comparative extent of all the countries in the world . . . 3d ed. 2 p. l., 28 pp., 22 maps. 4? Edinburgh & London, W. Blackwood & sons, 1853.
  296
  NOTE.—The following maps relate to America:
  no. 1. The world.
  " 18. North America.
  " 19. United States.
  " 20. Central America & the West Indian islands.
  " 21. South America.

**Lehmann, R.** *and* **Petzold, W.**
  Atlas für mittel-und oberklassen höherer lehranstalten . . . 3 verbesserte aufl. . . . 3 p. l., 80 l. incl. 52 col. maps, 3 col. pl. sm. fol. Bielefeld und Leipzig, Velhagen & Klasing, 1904.
  297

**Lehmann, R.** *and* **Scobel, A.**
  Atlas für höhere lehranstalten mit besonderer berücksichtigung der handelsgeographie . . . 74 haupt-und 66 nebenkarten auf 80 kartenseiten. 2 p. l., 58 maps on 80 l., 2 pl. fol. Bielefeld und Leipzig, Velhagen & Klasing, 1903.
  298

**Lüddecke, R.** *and* **Haack, H.**
  Deutscher schulatlas ... 3. berichtigte und erweiterte aufl.
1 p. l., 42 col. maps, 1 pl.  4°  Gotha, J. Perthes, 1901.  299

**Mitchell, S. A.**
  Mitchell's atlas of outline maps intended to be filled up by pupils studying Mitchell's School geography and atlas.  cover-title, 7 col. maps. 4°. Philadelphia, Thomas, Cowperthwait & co. 1839.
  300
> NOTE.—The following maps relate to America:
> no. [1] North America.
> " [2] United States and Texas.—Inset: Mexico and Guatimala [!]
> " [3] South America.

  Mitchell's new school atlas.  Mitchell's modern atlas ... Drawn and engraved expressly to illustrate Mitchell's New school geography ... 1 p. l., 24 pp., 33 col. maps. 4°.  Philadelphia, E. H. Butler & co. 1865.  301
> NOTE.—The following maps relate to America:
> no. 1. Western hemisphere
> " 2. Eastern hemisphere
> " 3. North America.
> " 4. Canada and New Brunswick.
> " 7. United States.
> " 8. Maine, New Hampshire and Vermont.
> " 9. Massachusetts, Rhode Island and Connecticut.
> " 10. New York, New Jersey, Pennsylvania and Delaware.
> " 11. Maryland, Virginia, West Virginia, North Carolina.
> " 12. South Carolina, Georgia, Florida, Alabama, Mississippi, Louisiana, Tennessee and Arkansas.
> " 13. Texas.
> " 14. Ohio, Kentucky, Indiana, Illinois, Iowa and Missouri.
> " 15. Michigan and Wisconsin.
> " 16–17. Minnesota and Dakota—Nebraska.
> " 18. Kansas, Colorado, New Mexico & Indian Territory.
> " 19. California, Oregon, Idaho, Utah, Nevada, Arizona and Washington.
> " 20. Mexico and Central America.
> " 21. West Indies.
> " 24. South America.
> " 25. Venezuela, United States of Colombia and Ecuador.
> " 27. Peru and Bolivia.
> " 28. Chili, Paraguay, the Argentine Confederation and Uruguay.
> " 36. Asia.
> " 39. India, China, Thibet & Corea.
> " 43. Oceanica ...

  Mitchell's new school atlas.  Mitchell's modern atlas ... Drawn and engraved expressly to illustrate Mitchell's New school geography ...  1 p. l., 24, 41 pp., 34 col. maps. 4°. Philadelphia, E. H. Butler & co. 1871.  302
> NOTE.—Like the edition of 1865 with the following additions:
> no [15] Dakota, Montana & Wyoming.
> At end, an index having a special title-page: An index to Mitchell's New school atlas, containing over 17000 names.  By H. D. Gregory ... Philadelphia, 1871.  For index published separately see title 287.

**Monteith, J.**
    School and family atlas of the world. Descriptive, historical, and statistical . . . 193 pp. incl. 58 maps. 4°. New York and Chicago, A. S. Barnes & co. [1890]      303

**Morse, J.** *and* **Morse, S. E.**
    Modern atlas, adapted to Morse's New school geography. Published according to an act of congress, by Richardson & Lord. cover-title, 8 col. maps. 4°. Boston, J. H. A. Frost, 1822.    304

    Modern atlas, adapted to Morse's School geography. cover-title, 8 col. maps. 4°. New York, Collin & Hannay, 1828.    305

> NOTE.—Like the edition of 1822 except difference of lettering on nos. 1, 3, 6, 7.
> The following maps relate to America:
> no. [1] The world.
> " [2] North America.
> " [3] South America.
> " [5] United States.
> " [7] Asia.

    A new universal atlas of the world . . . 2 p. l., 20 col. maps. 4°. New Haven, Howe & Spalding, 1822.    306

**Nouvel** atlas des enfans, ou principes clairs pour appendre facilement et en fort peu de tems la géographie, suivi d'un Traité méthodique de la sphère, qui explique le mouvement des aftres, les divers systêmes du monde, & l'ufage des globes . . . Nouvelle éd., rev. & corr. xx, 232 pp., front., 22 col. maps, 2 col. pl. 16°. Amsterdam, B. Vlam, 1776.    307

> NOTE.—The following maps relate to America:
> no. 1. [World]
> " 22. [America]

**Olney, J.**
    A new and improved school atlas, to accompany the practical system of modern geography . . . Exhibiting the present empires, kingdoms, states, the principal canals, length of rivers, &c., and all the recent discoveries of Parry, Franklin, Clapperton and others. cover-title, 8 maps. 4°. Hartford, D. F. Robinson & co. 1829.
     308

> NOTE.—The following maps relate to America:
> no. 1. The world on a globular projection.
> " 3. United States.
> " 4. New England.
> " 5. South America.

    Olney's school atlas . . . cover-title, 16 col. maps. fol. New York, Pratt, Woodford & co. [c1844–1847]    309

> NOTE.—Map no. 9 bears copyright date 1847; no. 16, 1845.
> To illustrate Olney's school geography.

The following maps relate to America:
no. [ 1] ... The world on a globular projection ...
" [ 2] ... North America ...
" [ 3] ... United States ...
" [ 4] ... New England and New York ...
" [ 5] ... Central states ...
" [ 6] ... Southern states ...
" [ 7] ... South western and part of the western states ...
" [ 8] ... Michigan, Wisconsin, and part of Iowa ...
" [ 9] Western territories of the United States.
" [10] ... West Indies, Guatimala and part of Mexico ...
" [11] ... South America ...

**Pennesi, G.**
Atlante scolastico per la geografia fisica e politica ... fascicolo 1. 1 p. l., 24 maps, 1 pl. 4°. Roma, 1894. [Istituto cartografico italiano] 310
NOTE.—pt. 2, wanting.

Atlante scolastico per la geografia fisica e politica ... 1 p. l. 49 col. maps, 1 pl. obl. fol. Torino-Roma ... G. B. Paravia & comp. [1897] 311
NOTE.—"New edition [of title no. 310] published in 1894-95 in two parts. Some alterations and additions have been made which add to the value of the atlas."—The geographical journal. London. June 1897. v. 9, no. 6.

**Philip, G. & son.**
Philip's progressive atlas of comparative geography. Edited by P. H. L'Estrange ... 3 p. l., [96], 141-148 pp., 69 col. maps. 4°. London, G. Philip & son [1907] 312

**Smiley, T. T.**
An improved atlas ... cover-title, 8 maps. 4°. Philadelphia, for the author, 1824. 313

A new atlas ... 7th ed. cover-title, 10 maps. 4°. Philadelphia, for the author [1830] 314

A new atlas ... 14th ed. cover-title, 10 maps. 4°. Philadelphia, for the author [1832] 315

A new atlas ... [22d ed.] cover-title, 11 maps. 4°. Philadelphia, Grigg & Elliot [1834] 316
NOTE.—To accompany his: An easy introduction to the study of geography.

A new atlas, intended to illustrate The encyclopædia of geography ... cover-title, 15 maps. 4°. Hartford, Belknap & Hammersly [1838] 317
NOTE.—At head of title: Smiley's Atlas for the use of schools and families.

**Smith, R. C.**

Smith's atlas for schools, academies and families. An atlas to accompany the productive geography . . . cover-title, 12 col. maps on 18 l. 4°. Philadelphia, W. Marshall & co.; Hartford, D. Burgess & co. ᶜ1835. 318

CONTENTS.

no. 1. The world.
" 2. North America.
" 3. United States.
" 4. Eastern states.
" 5. Middle states.
" 6. Southern states.
" 7. Western states.
" 8. South America.
" 9. Europe.
" 10. Asia.
" 11. Africa.
" 12. A chart of the world.

Smith's atlas. cover-title, 13 col. maps on 18 l. 4°. Hartford, Spalding & Storrs [1839] 319

CONTENTS.

no. [ 1] Map of the world.
" [ 2] Map of North America.
" [ 3] Map of the United States.
" [ 4] Map of the eastern states.
" [ 5] Map of the middle states.
" [ 6] Map of the southern states.
" [ 7] Map of the western states.
" [ 8] Map of South America.
" [ 9] Map of Europe . . .
" [10] Map of the British Isles.
" [11] Map of Asia.
" [12] Map of Africa.

Smith's atlas designed to accompany the geography . . . Improved edition. cover-title, 20 col. maps on 22 l. 4°. New York, Cady & Burgess, ᶜ1839. 320

NOTE.—The following maps relate to America:

no. [1] Map of the world.
" [2] Map of North America.
" [3] Map of the United States and Canada.
" [4–12] Maps 1–9. United States.
" [13] Map of the West Indies.
" [14] Map of South America.
" [20] Map of Oceanica.

Smith's atlas designed to accompany the geography . . . Improved ed. 1 p. l., 20 col. maps. 4°. New York, Cady & Burgess, 1850. 321

NOTE.—Maps same as in above edition.

Smith's atlas of modern and ancient geography, corrected and enlarged, to accompany Smith's geography . . . 68 pp. incl. 35 col. maps. 4°. New York, D. Burgess & co. 1853. 322

Smith's atlas of modern and ancient geography, corrected and enlarged, to accompany Smith's geography . . . 8, [6] pp., 24 col. maps. fol. Philadelphia, J. B. Lippincott & co. 1868. 323

NOTE.—Maps irregularly numbered.
The following maps relate to America:
no. 2. Map of the world . . . 1853.
" 3. Map of North America . . . 1853.
" 4. Map of the United States and Canada . . . 1853.
" 24. Map no. 1. United States . . . 1853.
" 26. "     " 2. "     "     "
" 28. "     " 3. "     "     "
" 30. "     " 4. "     "     "
" 34. "     " 5. "     "     "
" 36. Texas.
" 38. Map " 6. United States . . . 1853.
" 40. "     " 7. "     "     "
" 42. "     " 8. "     "     "
" 44. Map " 9. United States. 1853.
" 49. "     " 10. "     "     "
" 51. Map of Mexico.—Map of Central America . . . 1853.
" 53. Map of the West Indies . . . 1853.
" 54. Map of South America . . . 1847.

**Soulier, E.** *and* **Andriveau-Goujon, J.**
Atlas élémentaire simplifié de géographie ancienne et moderne, par E. Soulier (de Sauve) professeur, et J. Andriveau-Goujon . . . 1 p. l., 30 (*i. e.* 33) col. maps, 1 col. pl. fol. Paris, J. Andriveau-Goujon [1838] 324

NOTE.—The following maps relate to America:
no. 3. Mappemonde en deux hémisphères.
" 8. Amérique du Nord.
" 9. Amérique du Sud.

**Stieler, A.**
Atlante scholastico per la geografia politica e fisica. Edizione completa in 48 tavole incise in rame e miniate eseguite sulla trigesima quinta edizione originale dell' Atlante scholastico di Ad. Stieler, Enrico Berghaus, ed Erm. Berghaus. 1 p. l., 45 maps. obl. 4°. Gotha, J. Perthes, 1855. 325

Schul-atlas über alle theile der erde nach dem neuesten zustande und über das weltgebaüde. Nach Stieler's hand-atlas verkleinert. 36te verbesserte und vermehrte aufl. 1 p. l., 32 maps. obl. 4°. Gotha, J. Perthes, 1856. 326

**Sydow, E. von.**
　E. von Sydow's schul-atlas . . . 8. aufl.　1 p. l., 16 pp., 36 maps.　obl.　8°.　Gotha, J. Perthes, 1856.　327

　E. von Sydow's schul-atlas in zwei und vierzig karten.　20. aufl.　2 p. l., 18 pp., 35 maps, 6 pls.　8°.　Gotha, J. Perthes, 1868.　328

**Sydow, E. von** *and* **Wagner, H.**
　Sydow-Wagners methodischer schul-atlas.　Entworfen, bear. und hrsg. von Hermann Wagner . . . 13. berichtigte und ergänzte aufl. 4 p. l., 43 col. maps, 4 col. pl.　sm. fol.　Gotha, J. Perthes, 1908.　329

**Unwin, W. J.**
　Homerton college atlas . . . Hydrographical, physical, and political.　2 p. l., 30 col. maps.　fol.　London, Longmans, 1863.　330
　　Note.—An edition published in 1861.
　　The following maps relate to America:
　　Nos. 1–3. The world.
　　" 25–27. North America.
　　" 28–30. South America.

**Volckmar, F.**
　Universal-atlas für deutsche schulen in Südamerika . . .　1 p. l., 48 col. maps.　fol.　Leipzig, F. Volckmar, 1907.　331
　　Note.—p. 49 [Plan of] Buenos Aires.

**Warne, F. & co.**
　The junior atlas, for schools; fourteen maps selected from the college atlas: with an alphabetical index of the latitudes and longitudes of 12,000 places.　New ed. rev. 24th thousand.　2 p. l., [19] pp., 13 maps, 1 pl.　4°.　London, F. Warne & co. 1868.　332

**Warren, W.**
　Atlas to Warren's System of geography.　1 p. l., 12 maps.　4°. Portland, W. Hyde, 1843.　333

**Willard, E. H.**
　Willard's atlas to accompany geography for beginners . . . Designed as an introduction or first part to a series of geographical works, by W. C. Woodbridge and E. Willard.　cover-title, 6 maps.　8°.　Hartford, O. D. Cooke & co. °1826.　334
　　Note.—The following maps relate to America:
　　no. [1–3] United States.
　　" [6] The world.

**Woodbridge, W. C.**
　School atlas to accompany Woodbridge's Rudiments of geography.—Atlas on a new plan, exhibiting the prevailing religions,

forms of government, degrees of civilization, and the comparative size of towns, rivers and mountains . . . 5th ed.  cover-title, 9 maps.  8°.  Hartford, O. D. Cooke & sons [1821]  335

  NOTE.—On verso of title: Advertisement.—Classification.—Explanations.
  Map no. 4, United States, wanting.
  The following maps relate to America:
  no. 1. The world.
  " 2. Chart of the inhabited world . . .
  " 3. North America.
  " 5. South America.

Woodbridge's larger atlas.  Atlas on a new plan . . .  cover-title, 4 maps.  8°.  Hartford, S. G. Goodrich [1822]  336

  NOTE.—Imperfect: 4 maps wanting.

Modern atlas on a new plan; to accompany the system of universal geography . . . exhibiting in connection with the outlines of countries, the prevailing religions, forms of government, and degrees of civilization . . .  cover-title, 1 l., 9 maps, 4 tab.  fol.  Hartford, O. D. Cooke & sons [1824]  337

  NOTE.—The following maps relate to America:
  no. [1] The world . . . 1821.
  " [2] Chart of the inhabited world . . . 1821.
  " [4] North America . . . 1821.
  " [5] United States . . . 1821.
  " [6] South America . . . 1821.
  " [8] Asia [Philippine islands]

Woodbridge's school atlas . . .—Atlas on a new plan . . .  A new ed., improved . . . 14th ed.  cover-title, 9 col. maps.  4°.  Hartford, O. D. Cooke & co. 1831.  338

Modern atlas, on a new plan, to accompany the system of universal geography; a new ed. improved . . .  3 p. l., 11 maps.  4°.  Hartford, Belknap & Hamersley [1831]  339

Modern atlas, on a new plan; to accompany the system of universal geography . . . 4th ed.  3 p. l., 1 l., 9 maps.  4°.  Hartford, O. D. Cooke & co. 1831.  340

Woodbridge's school atlas . . .—Atlas on a new plan . . .  Improved ed. 1833.  cover-title, 1 p. l., 16 maps.  4°.  Hartford, O. D. Cooke & co. 1833.  341

Woodbridge's school atlas . . .—Atlas on a new plan . . .  Improved ed. 1835. [16th ed.]  cover-title, 10 maps.  4°.  Hartford, Beach & Beckwith, 1835.  342

  NOTE.—To accompany his: Rudiments of geography.

Modern atlas, physical, political and statistical . . .  1 p. l., 18 maps, 3 l.  4°.  Hartford, Belknap & Hamersley [1843]  343

  NOTE.—Copyrighted in 1843.

## SCIENTIFIC.

**Duval, H. L. N.**

Atlas universel des sciences . . . 4 p. l., 50 l., incl. 33 maps, 11 pl. fol. Paris, Terzuolo, 1837. 344

NOTE.—Half-title: Atlas universel des sciences.
Marginal text comprises genealogical, statistical and chronological tables relating to various sciences, including: astronomy, astrology, biology, geography, geology and mathematics.
The following maps relate to America:
no. 7. Mappemonde de géographie moderne . . .
" 30. . . . L'Asie, l'Inde, la Chine, le Japon.
" 32. . . . L'Amérique Septentrionale.
" 33. . . . L'Amérique Méridionale.
" 34. [Polynésie]

## STAMPS.

**Mekeel, C. H.**

Mekeel's stamp collector's maps of the world. Showing location of every stamp-issuing country, colony and city on the globe. From original designs . . . [8] pp. incl. 7 maps. 4°. St. Louis, C. H. Mekeel stamp and publishing co. 1895. 345

## STATISTICAL.

**Hickmann, A. L.**

Prof. A. L. Hickmann's geographical-statistic universal pocket atlas . . . 79 pp., 24 col. maps, 12 pl., 24 tab. 16°. London, Nilsson & co. [1907] 346

NOTE.—Printed in Austria.
English version of his: Geographisch-statistischen universal taschen-atlas.

## VOLCANOES.

**Bylandt Palstercamp, A.**

Théorie des volcans . . . Atlas. cover-title, 13 maps, 4 pl. obl. fol. Paris, F. G. Levrault, 1836. 347

NOTE.—To accompany work of the same title.
The following maps relate to America:
no. 2. Carte générale.
" 4. Carte de foyer occidental.

## WARS.

**Bellin, J. N.**

Teatro della guerra marittima, e terrestre fra la Gran Bretagna, le Colonie Unite, la Francia, la Spagna ed Olanda che comprende la raccolta delle carte nautiche e terrestri di mr. Bellin. Necessario per l' intelligenza de' fogli periodici per uso de' novellisti. 1 p. l., 14, [14] pp., 13 maps, 1 pl. fol. Venezia, V. Formaleoni, 1781. 348

NOTE.—Engraved title.
Atlas to accompany, "Storia delle rivoluzione dell' America inglese;" tr. by V. A. Formaleoni. 1782-84.

Imperfect. Consists of an atlas of 44 charts by Bellin, with description, translated from the french by Formaleoni. *cf.* Tipaldo, Emilio de. Biografia degli italiani illustri. 1834. v. 3, p. 334.
Contains map by d'Anville not called for by index.
Maps taken from "Abrégé de l'Histoire générale des voyages," by J. F. de La Harpe. 1780.
Following is a list of the maps in this copy arranged in the order in which they appear and numbered according to the index:
no. 4. Prospettiva di Gibitterra.
" 24. Carta del Golfo de Messico e dell' isole Antille . . . 1781.
" 27. Carta della Guyana Tratta dalla carta dell' America.
" 43. Carta dell' isola di Santa Lucia.
" 31. Carta della Carolina e Giorgia. Tratta dalle carte inglesi.
" 15. Il paese degli Ottentotti ne' contorni del capo di Buona Speranza. 1781.
" 29. Carta della Virginia della baja Chesapeack e paesi vicini.
" 18. Carta della costa orientale d' Africa dal capo di Buona Speranza fino al capo del Gada. 1781.
" 44. Carta dell' isola della Barbada.
" 41. Carta dell' isola di S. Cristoforo.
Carta del Senegal di m$^r$ d'Anville. 1781.
" 3. Baja di Gibitterra.
" 39. Carta dell' isola della Guadelupa. 1781.

**Kausler, F. G. F.**

Atlas des plus mémorables batailles, combats et sièges des temps anciens, du moyen âge et de l'âge moderne en 200 feuilles . . . Carlsrouhe & Fribourg, B. Herder, 1831.—Atlas der wichtigsten schlachten, treffen und belagerungen der alten, mittlern und neuern zeit in 200 blättern . . . 1 p. l., 215 l. obl. fol. Carlsruhe & Freiburg [B.] Herder, 1831 [–1837] 349

NOTE.—The numbering of leaves 1–48 is irregular. From l. 49 the numbering is as follows: l. 49–78 (nos. 19–48), l. 79 (nos. 49, 50, 51), l. 80 (no. 49), l. 81–193 (nos. 50–161), l. 194 (no. 163), l. 195, 196 (no. 164), l. 197, 198 (no. 165), l. 199, 200 (no. 166), l. 201–215 (nos. 167–181)
Accompanying text in 2 v. 4°. Titles, prefaces, introductions, titles and explanations of maps, etc., are in german and french. Index at end of v. 2 of text. See prospectus in "Kritischer wegweiser", may, 1830. v. 2, p. 192, and review in april 30, 1831. v. 3, pp. 20–23.
No maps relating to America.

# GENERAL.

(Arranged chronologically)

## 12TH CENTURY.

**Ptolemæus, C.**

Géographie de Ptolémée, reproduction photolithographique du manuscrit grec du monastère de Vatopédi au mont Athos, exécutée d'après les clichés obtenus sous la direction de m. Pierre de Séwastianoff et précédée d'une introduction historique sur le mont Athos, les monastères et les dépôts littéraires de la Presqu'ile Sainte. Par Victor Langlois. 2 p. l., viii, 117 pp., 1 l., 1 map; 1 p. l., cviii pp., incl. 42 maps. fol. Paris, Didot frères, fils & c[ie]. 1867. 350

NOTE.—The historical account of Mont Athos, by V. Langlois contains: "I. Histoire de la montagne Sainte.—II. Monastères et skytes.—III. Archives des monastères.—IV. Bibliothèques des monastères: inventaire des manuscrits grecs; inventaire des manuscrits slaves; inventaire des manuscrits géorgiens; notice sur les manuscrits du Mont Athos.—V. Bibliographie: liste des principaux voyages exécutés au Mont Athos depuis le xve siècle et dont il existe des relations". Followed by map entitled: "Carte du Mont Athos, exécutée à l'échelle de 1:22.222. 1866".

Following this, is the photolithographic reproduction of the Ptolemy, preceded by a richly ornamented chromolithographic title-page, adorned with eight views of Mont Athos and the principal monasteries; the title reads:

"Κλαυδιου Πτολεμαιου γεογραφικης υφηγησεως το εν Αθωι κατα το Βατοπεδιον σωζομενον αντιγραφον επιμελεστατα φωτωλιθογραφηθεν."
"F. Kellarhoven del., imp. Lemercier et cie. . . . . ch. Walter lith."

The text of the geography is reproduced in black on paper colored to imitate parchment; each paragraph begins with a capital letter in red. The maps are said to date from the 12th century.

Only 200 copies of this reproduction were issued. *cf.* "Un manuscrit de la géographie de Ptolémée découvert au Mont Athos", and "Remarques sur le manuscrit de la géographie de Ptolémée, trouvé au monastère de Vatopède (Mont Athos), reproduit photographiquement, en entier et en grandeur naturelle par P. de Sévastianoff", in Société de géographie. Paris. Bulletin, 1859. 4e sér. v. 17, pp. 422–431.

## 1475.

[Cosmographia. Translated by Jacobus Angelus of Scarparia, and edited by Angelus Vadius and Barnabas Picardus of Vicenza. *Colophon:*] En tibi lector Cofmographia Ptolemæi ab Hermano leuilapide Colonienfi | Vicenciæ accuratiffime impreffa. Benedicto Triuifano: & Angelo Micha- | ele præfidibus. | M.CCCC.LXXV. Idi. Sept. 351

[142] 1. preceded by 1 blank 1. fol.
(sig. aa₂ in nine; bb in eight; a 2 in nine; b-g in eight; h in ten; A-F in eight; G in ten)
This edition contains no maps.
Modern binding, stamped calf.
Eames-Sabin, no. 66469.

The oldest manuscript of Ptolemy's geography known to be extant, probably made about the year 1200, was published in fac-simile at Paris in 1867 (see title 350). Of the many editions, the 1475 edition, without maps, is the earliest known with the exception of that of 1462, which is evidently misdated.
Many interesting features might be mentioned in connection with the various editions. The two issues of the italian metrical version of Berlinghieri, 1478? are noteworthy as the first books with maps wholly engraved. The edition of 1508 is remarkable for containing the Ruysch map which is the first printed map showing any part of America, with the exception of the Waldseemüller map of 1507, brought to light in 1901. The Waldseemüller map is the oldest map with the name America. The Ruysch map does not give the name. It is sometimes found in the 1507 edition, though it is not supposed to have originally belonged there.
The account of Palestine in the 1535 edition, wrongly attributed to Servetus and which served as one of the pretexts for his execution, was first printed in the edition of 1522. The first edition of Ptolemy's geography in italian, translated by Pietro Andrea Mattioli, appeared in 1548.
The 1578 latin edition was the first with Mercator's series of maps. Of the late editions after 1730 a number were published without maps. The L. C. has recently acquired the Amsterdam, Hondius, 1618 edition containing portrait of Bertius.
The following is a list according to Eames, of the editions of Ptolemy's geography, of which the L. C. has all except the misdated latin edition of 1462, the latin editions of 1478, 1514 (no maps) 1608, and the re-issue of the metrical italian version of 1478? This list was published in 1886, 50 copies printed, and also in Sabin's Bibliotheca Americana:

Vincenciae 1475.
Romæ 1478.
Firenze 1480? (1478?)
" 1480? (1478?)
Bononiae 1462 (1482?)
Ulmæ 1482.
" 1486.
Romæ 1490.
" 1507.
Romæ 1508.
Venetiis 1511.
Argentinæ 1513.
Nurenbergæ [1514]
Argentorati 1520.
" 1522.
" 1525.
Lugduni 1535.
Basileae 1540.
Lugduni-Viennae 1541.
Basileæ 1542.
" 1545.
Venetiis 1548.

**Ptolemæus, C.**—Continued.
    Basileæ 1552.
    Venetia 1561.
    Venetiis 1562.
        " 1564.
        " 1574.
    Coloniæ Agrippinæ 1578.
        " 1584.
    Venetiis 1596.
    Coloniæ Agrippinæ 1597.
    Venetia 1597–1598.
        " 1598–1599.
    Francofurti & Amsterodammi 1605.
    Coloniae Agrippinæ 1608.
    Arnheimii 1617.
    Lugduni Batavorum 1618–1619.
    Padua. 1620–1621.
    Franequeræ 1695.
    Amstelædami 1730.

Nordenskiöld's list, found in his Facsimile atlas, contains the following editions not noted by Eames, of which the L. C. has the greek edition of 1533 (no maps) the latin editions of 1533 (no maps) 1540 (no maps) 1698, 1838, 1867 and 1883:

    Argentorati 1532.
    Basiliæ 1533.
    Ingolstadii 1533.
    Coloniæ 1540.
    Basileæ 1541.
    Parisiis 1546.
    Venetiis 1564.
    Dusseldorfii 1602.
    Francofurti-Amsterodammi 1624.
    Franequeræ et Trajecti ad Rhenum 1698.
    Trajecti ad Rhenum 1704.
    Paris 1828.
    Essendiæ 1838.
    Leipzig 1843–45
    Paris 1867.
    Parisiis 1883.

### 1478?

[Geographia. Firenze, Nicolo Todescho, 1478?] 352

186 l. comprising: 36 l., 8 maps, 32 l., 6 maps, 15 l., 4 maps, 21 l., 5 maps, 12 l., 5 maps, 10 l., 3 maps. fol.

(sig. 2 l. unsigned; aa in ten; bb–dd in eights; ee in six; ff–gg in eights; hh in six; ii in four; a in six; b in ten; c in eight; d–e in twelves; f in ten) Collation: contents, "In qve | sto volvme | si contengonᴏ sep | te giornate della Geog | raphia di Francesco Berlin | geri | Fiorentino allo Il | lvstrissimo Federi | go Dvca Dvr | bino" | on verso l. 1, recto blank, followed by table "In qvale libro" on recto and a metrical dedication on verso l. 2; prefatory verses "Geographia di Francesco | Berlinghieri Fiorentino | allo illvstrissimo Fedᴏ | rigo dvca dvrbino liber | primvs feliciter incipit," begins on recto sig. aa$^1$ ending on verso,—text begins on recto sig. aa$_2$, with book II ending on

verso dd$_7$, sig. dd$_8$ part of blank leaf, (sig. aa–dd.); 8 maps on 16 l.; book III, 31 l. followed by 1 blank l., (sig. ee–ii); 6 maps on 12 l.; book IV, 15 l. (sig. a–b$_9$); 4 maps on 8 l.; book V, 21 l., (sig. b$_{10}$–d); 5 maps on 10 l.; book VI, 11 l., verso e$_{11}$ blank, followed by 1 blank l., (sig. e); 5 maps on 8 l; book VII, 10 l. incl. sig. f$_8$ blank, (sig. f); 3 maps on 6 l.
Without place, date, printer's name, pagination, or catch words.
Text in double columns, 51 lines to full column. Roman type; initials indicated by small letter.
First issue, without the title in red on recto of first leaf which appears in copies of the second issue: "Geographia di | Francesco Berlinghieri | Fiorentino in terza | rima et lingva Toscana di stincta con le sve tavo | le in varii siti et pro | vincie secondo la | Geographia | et destin | ctione dele | tauole di Ptolomeo." and without the extra leaf added at end in the second issue giving the register, and colophon: "Impresso infirenze per Nicolo Todescho | & emendato con somma dili | gentia dallo auctore." |
Paraphrase in italian verse, by Francesco Berlinghieri, of probably the latin version by Jacobus Angelus, of Ptolemy's geography (. . . "lavoro intieramente dal Berlinghieri, il quale per altro moltissimo si è servito di Tolomeo nelle cose antiche, e di Flavio Biondo nelle moderne."—Mazzuchelli, Scrittori, v. 2, pt. 2, 1760, p. 957)
Supposed to be the first book with maps wholly engraved on copper, the legends upon the engraved maps of the Ptolemy of 1478 having been stamped upon the plates. Second book with engraved illustrations. Figures representing the winds on the map of the world.
"The plates are of importance as the only copies of Ptolemy's maps printed on their original projection, with equidistant parallels and meridians . . .
Berlinghieri's work, however, derives its greatest value from the modern maps it contains: "*Novella Italia,*" "*Hispania novella,*" "*Gallia novella*" and "*Palestina moderna et Terra Sancta.*" With the exception of the coarse drawing of the Holy Land . . . published in *Rudimentum novitiorum* . . . these "Tabulæ novellæ" are the first printed modern maps, the first germ of modern cartography . . . Nor have I found any statements regarding the source or origin of these maps . . . Probably they belonged to that latin manuscript of Ptolemy which Berlinghieri used for his translation. If they are compared with the corresponding *Tabulæ Novæ* in the editions of Ptolemy printed in Ulm 1482 and 1486, and with the maps of the codex in Brussels . . . considerable differences will certainly be found. But probably all these maps ultimately derive from the same original . . . " *cf.* Nordenskiöld, A. E. Facsimile-atlas. Stockholm, 1889. p. 13–14.
Nordenskiöld supplies the date 1478 ? to his copy of this work.
Copy from Sobolewski's library (no. 1625 of his catalogue, 1873) with his autograph notes and collation prefixed. The first leaf, with title on verso, in excellent facsimile. On fo. 2 and 3, the arms of Bartholomaeus Thurus, presbicterus emporiensis, with two latin distichs, and ms. marginal notes.
Modern binding, full brown morocco.
Eames—Sabin, no. 66500.

## 1482

[Cosmographia. Translated by Jacobus Angelus. Edited by Dominus Nicolaus Germanus. *Colophon:*] Clavdii Ptolomei viri A | lexandrini Cosmographie | octavvs et vltimvs liber | explicit | Opvs Donni Nicolai Germa | ni secvndvm Ptolomevm | finit+ | Anno

**Ptolemæus, C.**—Continued.

MCCCCLXXXII.₊ Avgv | sti vero Kalendas₊ XVII.₊ | Imprssvm [!] Vlme per Ingeni | osvm virvm Leonardvm | Hol prefati oppidi civis+‡+ |                                                                                353

    133 l. comprising: [69] l., 32 maps on [63] l., [1] l. fol.
    (sig. a in ten; b–g in eights; h in eleven; 1 l. unsigned)
    Collation: dedication, "Beatissimo Patri Pavlo Se | cvndo Pontifici Maximo. | Donis Nicolavs Germanvs" | begins on recto l. 1, with a colored woodcut initial N representing Donis on his knees presenting the book to pope Paul II and ends on recto l. [2]; Ptolemy's text begins on verso l. [2] with a colored initial vignette, ends on verso l. [69] with "Hinc seqvntvr tabvle," [69] l., (sig. a–h); 31 double page and 1 single, colored maps on [63] l., 1 l. with colophon on verso.
Text in double columns with 44 lines to a full column.
Initials, borders, maps and headings colored.
"In accordance with what seems to have been the original intention of the author, that part of the eighth book which contains the explanatory remarks regarding the maps, is printed on the reverse of each corresponding map . . . Besides the new maps of Spain . . . Italy . . . and the countries of the North . . . the edition contains a new map of Gallia and one of Palestine. There are no explanatory remarks to these maps, excepting on the reverse of the map of Italy, where a short text is printed . . . The maps are rough, though clear and distinct wood-cuts, according to the legend on the upper border of the map of the world . . . sculptured by Johannes Schnitzer de Armssheim . . . This is the first printed map which is *signed*. It is further remarkable because the geographer for the first time has ventured to make some changes in Ptolemy's picture of the world, though as yet only for the distant north . . . To indicate these editions [1482, 1486] by the name of Donis . . . is incorrect. The text of the edition follows the translation of Jacobus Angelus. As original for the maps has served the reproduction of Ptolemy's maps in a new projection, first executed by Dominus Nicolaus Germanus. But these very maps were already engraved on copper by Arnold Buckinck in 1478 . . . The edition Ulmæ 1482 contains nothing particularly belonging to Donis which is not found in the Rome edition, except the dedication to the pope and principally its initial N, faithfully copied from the manuscript of Donis. The name Nicolaus Donis . . . is . . . incorrect. The writer of the codex for the Ulm edition was called Nicolaus. He was a native of Germany and accordingly designated as *Germanus*, and to him belonged the title of *Dominus*. His complete name and title were therefore *Dominus Nicolaus Germanus* . . . .
The frequently repeated assertion that the first *Tabulæ novæ* were printed in the edition of Ulm 1482, and the supposition that Nicolaus Germanus or "Donis" was their author, is doubly misleading with regard to a question particularly important to the history of geography . . . The first *Tabvlæ novæ* were drawn, not on the projection of Donis, but on an equidistant cylindrical projection and were printed in about 1478, in the *Septe giornate della Geographia* of Berlinghieri . . . And that Donis was not their author is shown by the fact that for the new maps of Spain, France and the Holy Land, the same original has served for the edition Firenze 1478 and for that of Ulm 1482 and 1486. But, if the merit of having communicated the first *tabulæ novæ* in print does not belong to the editions of Ulmæ 1482 and 1486, these however are, in another respect, very remarkable and important. In the former edition printed ten years before the first voyage of Columbus, a map is given, embrac-

ing not only the North of the Old World, but also that part of the New World (Greenland) which, half a millenium before Columbus, was discovered by the Scandinavians." *cf.* Nordenskiöld.
Modern binding, full russia tooled back and edges.
Eames-Sabin, no. 66472.

## 1486

[Cosmographia. Translated by Jacobus Angelus. Edited by Dominus Nicolaus Germanus. *Colophon:*] Impressvm Vlme opera et | expensis Ivsti de Albano | de Venetiis per provisorem | svvm Iohannem Reger. An | no. Domini. M.CCCC.LXXXVI. | XII. Kalendas. Avgvsti. | 354
204 l., comprising: 116 l., 32 maps on 64 l., 24 l. fol.
(sig. A-B in eights; C in ten; D-E in eights; a in ten; b-i, a-c in eights)
Collation: index, beginning "Nota ad inueniendum igitur regiones" on verso l 1, recto blank, "Registrvm Alphabeticvm" begins on recto $A_2$, ends on verso $E_8$, 42 l. (sig. A-E); dedication "Beatissimo Patri Pavlo Se | cvndo Pontifici Maximo. | Donis Nicolavs Germanvs" | begins on recto $a_1$, followed on next leaf by text in double columns, 74 l. (sig. a-i); 32 colored maps on 64 l.; treatise of Donis, "Incipit regiftrum" on verso sig. a $_1$, recto blank, "De locis ac mirabilibvs | mvndi. Et primo de tri | bvsorbis partibvs" | begins on recto $a_2$, ending with colophon, printer's mark and initials "I R" on recto $c_8$, verso blank, 24 l. (sig. a-c)
Second edition of Donis's Ptolemy, being a reprint of the 1482 edition with corrections and additions.
Without title, pagination, or catchwords.
Text in double columns, 44 lines to a full column. The text has, topographically, been somewhat changed, the woodcut borders to the descriptive text on the back of the maps have been omitted, and the initials varied. The initial on the back of the second map of Europe has been omitted; the initial N of the dedication and C of the text are similar to those in the 1482 edition, as are the diamgrams on l. 53, 54.
The maps are the same as those in the 1482 edition having been printed from the same blocks.
"*De locis ac Mirabilibvs Mundi*, follows the maps and ends the book . . . Everything shows that, under the name of Donis, a mediæval work has been added to the edition of 1482 by the editor of the edition 1486 'Justus de Albano *de Venetiis per provisiorem suum* Johannem Reger,' in order to make it more attractive to the buyer. This is also confirmed by the fact, that the sheets in the 'De locis ac mirabilibvs mundi' are marked with special signatures, from which it appears that the original intention had been to publish it as a separate work. It must have been very popular, as it is also inserted into the editions Romæ 1507 and 1508." *cf.* Nordenskiöld.
Modern binding, half american russia.
Eames-Sabin, no. 66473.

## 1490

[Geographia. Translated by Jacobus Angelus. *Colophon:*] Hoc opvs Ptholomei memo | rabile qvidem et insigne ex | actissima diligentia casti | gatvm ivcondo qvodam ca | ractere impressvm fvit

**Ptolemæus, C.**—Continued.

et completvm Rome anno a na | tivitate Domini. M.CCCC.LX⁄ | xxx. Die. iv. Novembris. Arte | ac impensis Petri de Tvrre. | 355 174 l., (preceded by 2, and followed by 1, blank leaves) comprising: 60 l., 4 blank l., 34 l., 1 blank l., 27 maps on 54 l., 21 l. fol.

(sig. a in ten; b–g in eights; h in six; A–C in eights; D–E in sixes; a–b in eights; c in six)

Collation: text, preceded by 2 bl. l., begins on recto a$_2$, ends with "Hinc seqvvntvr tabvle" on recto, h$_3$, verso blank, followed by 3 bl. l., 60 l. (sig. a–h); index, "Registrvm Alphabeticvm," preceded and followed by 1 bl. l., begins on recto A$_2$, ends verso E$_5$, 34 l. (sig. A–E); 27 maps on 54 l.; treatise of Donis begins verso a$_1$, recto blank, with "Incipit Regiftrvm" followed on recto a$_2$ by "De locis acmirabilibvs mvn | di. Et primo de tribvs orbis partibvs," ends with colophon on recto c$_5$ followed by 1 bl. l., 21 l. (sig. a–c) Without title page, pagination or catch words.

Text in double columns, 53 lines to a full column.

Second roman edition.

Maps are said to be the same, having been printed from the same plates, as those in the 1478 ed.

Sig. a–h to be correctly placed, should follow sig. E.

Leaves [153–160] (sig. a 1–8), [169–173] (sig. C 1–5) repaired and inlaid into new paper.

Binding repaired with one quarter calf and original wooden sides.

Eames–Sabin, no. 66474.

## 1507

In hoc operae | haec continē | tvr | Geographia Cl. Ptholemaei A plurimis uiris utriufq̃ linguæ doctiff. | emendata: & cum Archetypo græco ab ipfis collata. | Schemata cum demonftrationibus fuis correcta a Marco monacho Cæleftino Beneuen⁄ | tano: & Ioanne Cota Veronenfi uiris Mathematicis confultiffimis. | Figura de proiectione Sphæræ in plano quæ in libro octauo defiderabantur ab ipfis nō⁄ | dum inftaurata sed fere adinuenta: eius. n. ueftigia in nullo etiā græco codice extabant. | Sex tabulæ nouiter cōfectæ v̧ Hifpaniæ: Galliæ: Liuoniæ: Germāiæ: Poloniæ: | Vngariæ: | Ruffiæ: & Lituaniæ: Italiæ: & Iudeæ: | Maxima quantitas dierum ciuitatum: & diftantiæ locorum ab Alexandria Aegypti | cuiufq̧ ciuitatis quæ in aliis codicibus non erant. | Planifphærium Cl. Ptholemæi nouiter recognitum & diligentiff. emendatum a Marco | monacho Cæleftino Beneuentano. | Cavtvm est edicto Ivlii. ii. Pont. Max. | ne qvis imprimere avt imprimi | facere avdeat hoc ipsvm opvs | pena excommvnicationis latæ sententiae | his qvi contra mandatvm ivssvmqve | conari avdebvnt. | [*Colophon*]: Explicit Planifphærium Ptholemæi recognitum diligentiffime | a Marco Beneuentano Monacho Cæleftinorum quod antea in | multis etiā antiquis exemplaribus latinis corruptiffimum repe⁄ | riebantur. Nec nō Claudii Ptholemæi a plurimis uiris utriufq̧ | linguæ doctiff. emendatū cum multis additionibus Romę No⁄ | uiter impreſſum per Bernardinū Venetū de Vitalibus. Expēſis | Euāgeliſta Tofino Brixiano Bibliopola. Impante Iulio. II. Pont. | Max. Anno. III. Pōtificatus fui. Die. VIII. Septēbr. M.D.VII. | 356

210 l. (preceded and followed by 2 blank l.) comprising: title, [142] l. (text) 1 blank l., 34 col. maps on 68 l. fol.
(sig. A-C in eights; D-E in sixes; F-O, Aa-Bb in eights; Cc in four; a in six; b in eight)
Collation: title, verso containing dedication by Tosinus dated "Romæ Eidibus Augusti. M.D.VII", "Registrvm Alphabeticvm" [67] pp., text, followed by epistle from Beneventanus to Baduarius [130] pp. (sig. A-N); "Planisphere" ending with the colophon on recto sig. O$_7$ and the "Privilege" on verso O$_7$ followed by 1 blank l. [14] pp. (sig. O); treatise of Donis beginning "Incipit Regiſtrum" on recto and "De locis ac mirabilibvs mvndi" . . . on verso sig. Aa$_1$, ending on recto Cc$_4$, verso blank, [40] pp. (sig. Aa-Cc); dedicatory epistle by Tosinus recto a$_1$, epistle by the author verso a$_1$, treatise of Beneventanus begins on recto a$_2$, ending on recto b$_8$, verso blank, [28] pp. (sig. a-b); 34 double page copperplate, colored maps, followed by 2 blank l.
Text, with exception of sig. a and b, in double columns, 52 lines to a full column, is without the addenda to the tenth chapter of the second book and fifth chapter of the third book inserted in the 1486 Ulm ed. A new edition of the translation of Jacobus Angelus, revised and edited by Marcus Beneventanus and Joannes Cota of Verona and sold by the bookseller Tosinus to whom pope Julius II gave, july 28, 1506, a patent to the exclusive sale for six years on condition that the price be fixed by the pope's librarian.
In addition to the material usually contained in this edition, there are the Ruysch map and the treatise by Beneventanus. The map has been found, inserted in several copies of the 1507 ed. (cf. B. M., Murphy and Verona library copies) and in separate sheet form showing no evidence of binding (cf. Murphy and Harvard library copies) The treatise, however, first appeared in the 1508 edition.
In the dedication Tosinus enumerates his assistants and commends the addenda, especially of the planispherium and the "tabula novae" enumerated on the title page.
The "Registrvm Alphabeticum" is a slightly altered reprint from the Ulm edition of 1486.
The "Planisphærium Ptolemæi" has a dedication to Johannes Baduarius who had presented a ms. of the planisphere to Marcus Beneventanus.
Twenty seven of the thirty four maps are printed from the plates of the 1478 and 1490 editions. The six new maps are: Tabvla moderna Prvssię, Livonię, Norvegię et Gottię; Tabvla moderna Hispanie; Tabvla moderna Francię; Tabvla moderna Polonie, Vngarie, Boemie, Germanie, Rvssie, Lithvanie; Tabvla moderna Terre-Sanctę; Tabvla nova Italie. Nordenskiöld states that of these six maps all but the Tabvla moderna Polonie . . . are only slightly altered editions of corresponding maps in the works of Berlinghieri, of the editions printed in Ulm in 1482 and 1486. The "Tabvla moderna Prussię, Livonię, Norvegię et Gottię" contains a representation of Greenland as a peninsula of northern Europe under the name of Evgrovelant which is also given to the country adjoining Norway.
Original vellum binding.
Eames-Sabin, no. 66475.

## 1508

**Ptolemæus, C.**—Continued.

In hoc opere | haec conti | nentvr | Geographiæ Cl. Ptolemæi a plurimis uiris utriufq̃ linguæ doctiff. | emēdata: & cū archetypo græco ab ipſis collata. | Schemata cū demonſtrationibus ſuis correcta a Marco Beneuentano | Monacho cæleſtino | & Ioanne Cotta Veronenſi uiris Mathematicis | confultiſſimis. | Figura de proiectione ſphęræ in plano quæ in libro octauo deſidera | batur ab ipſis nōdum inſtaurata ſed fere ad inuenta eius. n. ueſtigia | in nullo etiam græco codice extabant. | Maxima quantitas dieʀ ciuitatū: & distantiæ locoʀ ab Alexādria | Aegypti cuiuſq̃ ciuitatis: quæ in alijs codicibus nō erant. | Planiſphærium Cl. Ptolemęi nouiter recognitū & diligentiſſ. emen⁄ | datum a Marco Beneuentano Monacho cęleſtino. | Noua orbis defcriptio ac noua Oceani nauigatio qua Liſbona ad | Indicū peruenitur pelagus Marco Beneuentano monacho cæle⁄ | ſtıno ædita. | Noua & uniuerſalior Orbis cogniti tabula Ioā. Ruyſch Germano | elaborata. | Sex Tabulæ nouiter confectæ uideiicet Liuoniæ: Hyſpaniæ: Galliæ: | Germaniæ: Italiæ: & Iudeæ. | Cavtvm est edicto Ivlii. II. Pont. Max. | ne qvis imprimere avt imprimi | facere avdeat hoc ipsvm opvs | pena excommvnicationis latae sententiae | his qvi contra mandatvm ivssvmqve | conari avdebvnt. | Anno Virginei partvs | MDVIII. | Rome. | [*Colophon*:] Explicit Planiſphærium Ptholemæi recognitum diligentiſſime | a Marco Beneuentano Monacho Cæleſtinorum quod antea in | multis etiā antiquis exemplaribus latinis corruptiſſimum repe⁄ | riebantur. Nec nō Claudii Ptholemæi a plurimis uiris utriuſq̃ | linguæ doctiſſ. emendatū cum multis additionibus Romę No⁄ | uiter impreſſum per Bernardinū Venetū de Vitalibus. Expēſis | Euāgeliſta Toſino Brixiano Bibliopola. Impante Iulio. II. Pont. Max. Anno. III. Pōtificatus ſui. Die. VIII. Septēbr. M. D. VII. 357

209 l. comprising: title, [120] l., 34 maps on [68] l., [20] l. fol.
sig. A-C in eights; D-E in sixes; F-O in eights; a in six; b, Aa-Bb in eights; Cc in four. sig. O₈ (blank) wanting.
Collation: title, verso containing dedication by Tosinus, dated "Romæ Eidibus Augusti. M. D. VIII", "Registrvm Alphabeticvm" [67] pp., text, followed by epistle from Beneventanus to Baduarius [130] pp. (sig. A-N); "Planisphere" ending with the colophon on recto sig. O₇ and the "Privilege" on verso, blank l., O₈ wanting, [14] pp. (sig. O); dedicatory epistle by Tosinus on recto a₁, epistle by the author verso a₁, treatise of Beneventanus begins on recto a₂ ends on recto b₆, verso blank, [28] pp. (sig. a-b); 34 double page copperplate maps on 68 l.; treatise of Donis begins with "Incipet registrum" on recto and "De locis ac mirabilibvs mvndi" . . . on verso sig. Aa₁, ending on recto Cc₄, verso blank, [40] pp. (sig. Aa-Cc)
A re-issue of the 1507 edition with a new title page and the addition of the Ruysch map, "Vniversalior cogniti orbis tabvla, ex recentibvs confecta observationibvs" and the . . . "Orbis noua defcriptio" by Beneventanus.

The maps are uncolored and some of the signatures differently placed, otherwise there is no difference between the two editions. This edition is remarkable for containing, with the exception of the Waldseemüller map, the first printed map showing any part of America. Johann Ruysch, a german, visited America and is supposed to have first published his map in this edition although there exist separate copies, showing no evidence of binding, which may have been issued a short time previous. Nordenskiöld, Facsimile-atlas, p. 63, states: "This map was published among the *tabulæ novæ* in the edition of Ptolemaeus, Romae 1508, and its engraving was hardly finished before that year, as may be concluded from the following legend at Trapobane: *Ad hanc Lusitani naute navigarunt anno salutis* MDVII. Sometimes it is also inserted in the edition of 1507, without however, being mentioned on the title page, on which, according to the custom of the period, a synopsis of the contents of the work is given. But on the new title page, with which the edition of 1508 was provided, this passage is printed: *In hoc opere haec continentur: . . . Nova et universalior orbis cogniti tabula Ioa Ruysch Germano elaborata . . .*" p. 66. ". . . The text of Beneventanus is introduced by a letter to the roman patrician Marianus Alterius, from which the remarkable information is obtained that Ruysch's map was printed before it was incorporated with the Ptolemy of 1508. At least this seems to be deducible from the . . . passage in Tosinus' letter, from which we also find that Beneventanus only wrote commentaries on the map and had nothing to do with its authorship . . ."
The separate (Harvard, Barlow) copies of this map, showing no signs of ever having been bound, may refer to the above statement. There are two distinct copies of this map, one of which does not contain the legend, "Plisacvs Sinvs" off the eastern coast of Asia. This copy, unlike the Stevens, Santarem and Nordenskiöld reproductions, does not contain the legend. Nordenskiöld notes, on the various copies examined by him, traces of successive corrections and emendations, *e. g.* on the long legend identifying Hispaniola with Sipangu.
This map is sometimes found inserted in the 1507 ed. "The map of Ruysch forms an epoch in the development of cartography. [In addition to its American features] it is:
(1) The first printed map of the world on which the discoveries of the Portuguese along the coasts of Africa are laid down . . .
(2) First published in print on which India is drawn as a triangular peninsula projecting from the south coast of Asia . . .
(3) First printed map on which the delineation of the interior and eastern parts of Asia is no longer based exclusively on the material collected by Marinus of Tyre and Ptolemy more than a millenium previously . . .
(4) First printed map on which, in conformity with the drawings on the portolanos, a tolerably correct direction is given to the northern coast of Africa . . .
(5) First map published in print, which, following a correction made in the portolanos since the beginning of the 14th century, leaves out that excessive projection toward the east, which characterizes Ptolemy's map of the northern part of Scotland . . .
(6) Greenland is here for the first time drawn without being connected with Europe by a vast polar continent. The legends on the map are . . . of a very high interest and form a more important contribution to the history of geography than many a bulky volume . . ." *cf.* Nordenskiöld, pp. 63-67.
The "Orbis noua defcriptio" is an extensive though not very important supplement consisting principally of a commentary on the Ruysch map and accounts of discoveries in the new world.

**Ptolemæus, C.**—Continued.
On this new title page the ordinary initial "I" of the 1507 edition is replaced by a large ornamental letter.
Modern binding, half morocco.
Eames-Sabin, no. 66476.

## 1511

Clavdii Ptholemaei Alexandrini Li | ber Geographiae cvm Tabvlis et | vniversali figvra et cvm ad | ditione locorvm qvae a | recentioribvs reper | ta svnt diligenti | cvra emenda | tvs et im | pressvs. | [*Colophon:*] Venetiis per Iacobum Pentium de leucho | Anno domini. M.D.XI. Die. xx. | Menſis Martii. | 358

92 l. (preceded by 1 blank l.) comprising: title, [61] l., 28 maps on [30] l. fol. (sig. ✠ in four; A in eight; B–H in sixes; I in eight)
Collation: title, verso containing poem headed "Ioannes Aurelius Augurellus;" and dedication, "Bernardus Syluanus Ebolienſis: ad Illuſtriſſimum Andream Mathevm. Aqvaevivvm Adriæ Ducem" . . . on recto l. [1], followed by "Bernardi Syluani Eboliēſis ānotationes in Ptholemæi geographiam" . . . which ends on recto l. [4], "Tabula primi Libri Geographiæ Ptholemæi," on verso, (sig. ✠); text incl. 4 diagr. ends with colophon, and "Regiſtrum" on recto of l. [61] verso blank, [61] l., (sig A–I); 28 double page maps on [30] l.
Text in double columns, 60 lines to a full column.
Latin version of Jacobus Angelus, edited with many corrections by Bernardus Sylvanus of Eboli, the principles of which are developed in the introduction. "As an edition of Ptolemy, the work of Sylvanus is quite worthless on account of the arbitrary alteration of Ptolemy's data for longitude and latitude. Nor has his attempt to transform the work of the Alexandrian geographer into a modern atlas been attended with better success. Sylvanus for instance leaves the old names unchanged in maps, pretended to be modernized. The merit, however, must be conceded to Sylvanus, that he was the first to break with the blind confidence that almost every scholar in the beginning of the 16th century had in the atlas of the old Alexandrian geographer. Sometimes also the corrections and modifications by Sylvanus were real improvements. In this edition . . . the usual addenda is omitted . . . For the first time we here meet with maps printed in two colours, and contrary to what generally was and yet is the custom, both sides of the paper are used for the map print; excepting for the new map of the world, where the reverse is left blank. The maps are from woodcuts, for which the legends in black are produced by types fitted into blocks. . . . But the greatest importance of this edition to the history of cartography, consists in the cordiform map of the world . . . the first on this projection. This is the second printed map of the world, in the delineation of which some attention has been paid to the great geographical discoveries of the preceding years." Selected from Nordenskiöld. [This map] "contains the first printed delineation of any portion of the North American continent, under the names of *regalis domus* . . . and *terra laboratorus*—the former a fragmentary coast line and the latter as a large island. Below these are *ispaniar insu.*, *terra cube*, and a part of the southern continent with the inscription *Terra sanctae crucis*. Greenland (*engronelāt*) is put down as part of northern Europe." *cf.* Eames, List of editions of Ptolemy's geography.
Modern binding, quarter american russia. Eames-Sabin, no. 66477.

## 1513

Claudii Ptolemei | viri Alexandrini | Mathematicę difciplinę Philofophi | doctiffimi Geographię opus nouiffima traductione e Gręco= | rum archetypis caftigatiffime preffum: cęteris | ante lucubratorum multo pręftantius. | Pro Prima parte continens | 1 Cl. Ptolemęi Geographiam per octo libros partitam, | ad antiquitatē fuam , integre & fine ulla corruptione. | 2 Vna cum collatione dictionum gręcarum e regione | ad latinas certiffima graduum calculatione. | 3 Regiftrationem item nouam regionum, præfecturarum, | ciuitatum, | fluminum, marium, lacuum, portuum, filua= | rum, oppidorum, villa- .rum ac gentium, ad ordinem | chartarum & columnarum fingula certiffimo mon= | ftrans indice. | 4 Quā breuis & doctiffima Gregorij Lilij fubfequitur in= | ftructio de GręcoR numerali fupputatione, in tradu= | ctione gręca res fcitu aurea. | 5 Tabularum dein Auctoris vigintifeptem ordo hic eft | Generale orbis iuxta defcriptionē Ptolemęi Vna. | Europę tabulę Decem. | Aphricę tabulę Quattuor. | Afię tabulę Duodecim. | Eft & una corporis Spherici in plano iuxta finē. 7. li. | Pars Secunda moderniorum luftrationum Viginti tabu | lis, veluti fupplementum quoddam antiquitatis obfo | letę, fuo loco quę vel abftrufa, vel erronea videban= | tur refolutiffime pandit. | Adnexo ad finem tractatu ficuti lectu iucundiffimo, | ita & utiliffimo de varijs moribus & ritibus gen= | tium: eorundemqʒ ac localium nominū originibus. | Breuis continentia Libri. | Oppida, regna, lacus, montes, & ęquora, filuas | Ac hominum mores hic Ptolemęus habet. | Cum gratia & priuilegio Imperiali | per 4 annos. | [*Colophon:*] Anno Christi Opt. Max. mdxiii. Marcii xii. | Preffus hic Ptolemęus Argentinę vigilantiffima cafti= | gatione | induftriaqʒ Ioannis Schotii ur= | bis indigenę. | Regnante Maximiliano Caesare | Semper Avgvsto. | 359

180 l. (followed by 1 blank l.) comprising: .2 p. l., 5-60 numb. l. incl. diagr., 14 l., 27 maps on 53 l., 1 l., 20 maps on 39 l., 15 l., 1 bl. l. fol.
(sig. 2 l. unsigned; B–L in sixes; M in four; N, a in sixes; b in four; c in six) Collation: title on recto l. 1, verso containing epistle from Ioannes Francifcus Picus Mirandulę ending with "Noui quarto Calendas Septemb. Anno a partu virginis mdviii," dedication to the emperor Maximilian by Jacobus Aeschler and Georgius Übelin, concluding with "Datū Argentinę sub Annū Dñi mdxiii Marcij xv," on recto l. 2, table of contents on verso (2 l. unsigned); text on numb. l. 5-60, with "Sphera in Plano" on verso l. no. 53, index in 14 l. beginning on verso l. 60 ending on recto N₆, verso containing epistle "Ad Lectorem" from Lilius Gregorius Ziraldus to Philesius, and the colophon, 70 l. (sig. B–N); 27 maps on 53 l. comprising "Generale Ptolemei," 10 of Europe, 4 of Africa, and 12 of Asia, no. 1 of Europe being colored; title to supplement " In Claudii Ptolemei | Supplementum | modernior luftratio terrę, marifqʒ | singula pofitiōibus certiffimis re, | gulatius tradens ad fęculi noftri | peragratiōes. Pars Secunda | " . . . on recto and "Ad Lectorem" on

**Ptolemæus, C.**—Continued.

verso 1 l. unsigned; 20 modern maps on 39 l.; Donis's treatise "De locis ac mirabilibvs mvndi," headed "Locorvm ac mirabilivm mvṇdi descriptio," on 15 l., with the "Index Capitum" on verso sig $c_5$, followed by 1 bl. l., (sig. a–c)

Text in double columns, 66 lines to a full column.

Colophon to supplement, described by Eames, "Secundę partis Ptolemæi finis: opera Ioannis Schotti Argentineñ. | Anno Christi Opt. Max. 1513," does not appear on the margin of the last map, "Lotharingia" which is a single sheet surrounded on two sides by escutcheons and printed in colors.

"Commenced by the Saint-Dié geographer Martin Waltzmüller ('Hylacomylus') about the year 1505 partly at the expense of Duke René of Lorraine, who also contributed the celebrated 'Hydrographia,' or Admiral's map. Mathias Ringmann (Philesius) was also employed on the work. The modern maps were prepared by Waltzemüller, and most of these—perhaps all—engraved as early as 1507. The completion of the text, however, was delayed; and in 1508 all of the material passed into the hands of Jacobus Eszler and Georgius Ubelin . . . who edited and finally published the work in 1513 . . . Under their care, assisted by Ringmann, the version of Angelus was compared with an important Greek manuscript furnished by Mirandula, the Greek names of places were added, [for the first time] and the text revised and corrected throughout" . . . cf. Eames.

With reference to the authorship of the new maps which he attributes to the learned coteries at St. Dié, Nordenskiöld, p. 69, states "the argument generally quoted for regarding Waltzeemüller as the author of the twenty new maps in this edition depends . . . on an incorrect interpretation of a passage in the edition of 1522 . . ."

"On five of these new maps the discoveries of the Spaniards and Portuguese during the preceding century are represented . . . Isolated new maps had already been published in several works before 1513. But in the addenda of Aeschler's and Übelin's edition of Ptolemy we for the first time obtain a modern atlas with maps of all the parts of the globe of which new geographical data could be had. To some extent this atlas may therefore be regarded as the opening chapter of the modern literature of atlases . . . Its maps, as regards their execution, cannot compete either with the copper-plates of Buckinck-Schweinheim, with the woodcuts of Johannes Schnitzer von Armsheim, or with those in the Ptolemy of Bernardus Sylvanus."

The maps are mounted on vellum strips from a latin ms., 15th ? cent. (theological treatise) in a beautiful regular hand, rubricated, initials in red and blue, notes in a later 16th ? cent. hand. They have been slightly emendated and supplemented by the following modern maps:

Orbis Typvs Vniversalis ivxta Hydrographorvm Traditionem; Tabvla Terre Nova; Tabvla Nova Hibernie Anglie et Scotie; Tabvla Moderna et Nova Hispanie; Tabvla Moderna Gallie; Tabvla Moderna Germanie; Tabvla Moderna Sarmatie Evr. sive Hvngarie Polonie Rvssie Prvssie et Valachie; Tabvla Moderna Norbegie et Gottie; Tabvla Moderna et Nova Italie ac Sicilie; Tabvla Moderna Italie; Tabvla Moderna Bossine Servie Gretiae et Sclavonie; Tabvla Moderna Prime Partis Aphricae; Tabvla Moderna seconde Porcionis Aphrice; Tabvla Nova Asie Minoris; Tabvla Moderna Terre Sancte; Tabvla Moderna Indiae; Tabvla Nova Heremi Helvetioṽ; Tabvla Nova Particvlaris Provincie Rheni Svperioris; Tabvla Necterica Crete sive Candie Insvle; Lotharingia.

The following relate to America:

no. [28] "Orbis Typvs Vniversalis." A new map of the world, first appearing in this edition, by some attributed to columbus, hence the name "the Admiral's map" and by others to Vespuccius. Nordenskiöld states that this map is evidently of portuguese origin and shows little advancement over the maps of Ruysch, Sylvanus and Stobnicza.

" [29] "Tabvla Terre Nova." First appears in this edition and is one of the earliest printed maps devoted entirely to the new world.

" [35] "Tabvla moderna Norbegie et Gottie." Shows "Engronelandt" and "Engronelād."

Copy in original (?) binding: beveled beach boards half covered with stamped pig-skin.

On title page: "Monasterij Schyrensis" (Scheyern, Bavaria)

Bookplate: arms, with the initials B. G. A., dated 1587.

"Duplum Biblioth. regiae Monacensis."

Eames-Sabin, no. 66478.

## 1520

Ptole | maevs | avctvs | restitvtvs. | Emacvlatvs. | Cvm tabvlis | veteribvs | ac novis | [*Colophon:*] Caroli v. | Imperii Anno 1. | Vim vi repellere licet | Ioannes Scotus, Argentorati literis excępit. 1520. 360

149 l. comprising: 57 l., 47 maps on 92 l. fol.

(sig. A-I in sixes; K in three)

Collation: title, verso blank, l. 1; "Lectori Salvs," followed by contents, recto and verso l. 2; text including 5 diagr. ending with colophon on verso of l. 52, 3-52 l. (sig. A—K)

Text in double columns, 65 lines to a full column.

"This edition was published under the supervision of Georgius Ubelin, one of the editors of the edition of 1513, of which it is mainly a reprint, with the omission of the index, the treatise "Di locis," and the greek names of places in the text." *cf.* Eames.

The title-page is surrounded by an elaborate woodcut border printed in red; the same border in black surrounds the colophon, on the verso of the last page of text, which is further ornamented by a woodcut representing two dogs biting each other's backs.

Folios I$_5$ and I$_6$ have been transposed.

The maps are the same as in the 1513 edition with the exception of "Tabvla prima Evropae," which shows slight changes and lacks title, and "Tabvla Nova Eremi Helvetiorivm," which differs from the corresponding map.

Of the following maps which relate to America, nos. [29-30] are described in the 1513 edition:

no. [29] Orbis typvs universalis ivxta hydrographorvm.

" [30] Tabvla Terre Nove.

" [36] Tabvla moderna Norbegie et Gottie. [Shows Engronelandt]

Modern binding, full stamped morocco.

Eames-Sabin no. 66480.

## 1522

Clavdii Ptolemæi | Alexandrini Mathematicoȓ principis. opus Geographię | nouiter caftigatū & emaculatū additiōibus. raris et inuifis. necnon | cū tabularum in dorfo iucunda explanatione.

**Ptolemæus, C.**—Continued.

Regiſtro quoq̨ totius | operis. tam Geographico. q̃ etiã hiſtoriali. facillimũ introitũ prebēti. | Ordo contento | rvm in hoc libro totali. | Octo libri Geographię ipſius Autoris adantiquitatē ſuam in= | tegri & ſinevlla corruptiōe. cum collatione dictionũ grecarũ e regiōe | ad latinas. certiſſima graduũ calculatiōe examinati. | Registrvm Item alphabeticũ omniũ regionũ. prefecturarũ | ciuitatũ. Fluuio. mariũ. lacuũ. portuũ Siluaꝶ. oppidoꝶ. villaꝶ. gen | tiũ & hiſtoriarũ. ſingula certiſſimo indice monſtrans. | Post hoc Sequũtur tabule. quaꝶ nũero. xxvij erũt. Prima ſcz | Generalē orbis deſcriptiōne tradens iuxta mentē Ptolemęi. Europę | poſt hīc tabule. &. Aphricę. iiij. aſię. xii. et vna corporſ ſperici inplāo. | Has ſuccedũt neotericoꝶ perluſtratiōes. ea que abantiqs. emiſſa | xx. tabulis ad implentes. Et in harũ omnium. tã vetuſtioꝶ q̨ recen / | tioꝶ tergis expoſitões vni lateri. alteri vero lucubratiōes iucũdiſſime | rituũ. easdã plagas inhabitantiũ (cũ varijs mirabilib⁹ mũdi) incũbũt. | Tandem breuis ſub oritur doctrina. ignorãtibus viam pr꞉ | bens fructũ auſcultandi Geographicũ / Quę huc vsq̨ multis in// | cognita / & ſepulta delituit Gaudeat igit' Lector optimus. | Hec bona mente Laurētius Phriſius artis Appolineę, doctor & | mathematicaꝶ artium clientulus. in lucem iuſſit prodire. | Agammemnonis puteoli plurimũ delicati: | [*Colophon:*] Ioannes Grieninger ciuis Argentorateñ | opera et expenſis proprijs id opus inſigne, ęreis | notulis excepit, Laudabiliq̨ fine perfecit xii. die | Marcij Anno | M. D. XXII.                                                                    361

196 l. comprising: 2 p. l.; 3-22, 37-100 (*i. e.* 84) irreg. numb. l., [2] l.; 1 map on [2] l., [1] l., 1 map on [2] l., [1] l., 48 maps on [94] l, [8] l. fol.
(sig. A-B, C/D, in six, E/F in four, G-R in sixes, S in eight)
Collation: title in red and black within woodcut border, verso blank,—l. 2, preface, dated "Argentoraci ex Edibus noſtris Die. x. Menſis Ianuarij. Anno Chri. M. D. XXIJ.,"—Registrvm Alphabeticv̄" comprises leaves 3, 4, [5, 6], 7-18, 22, [*i. e.* 19], [20],—"Erro Tochi Ope." l. [21],—"Directori," l. 22, in all 20 l. (sig. A-E/F); text, books I-VII, leaves 37-70, 77 [*i. e.* 71], 72-85, 89 [*i. e.* 86], 87-100, with "Sphera in Plano" on verso l. 99, "Cvmplementum," l. [101], "Finis VIII & vltimi libri," verso l. [102] recto blank, in all 66 l. (sig. G-R); 50 maps on 98 l., with book VIII of text, with additions by the editor, continued on back of maps,—1 l., verso blank, bet. maps I and II of Europe,—1 l., recto blank, bet. maps II and III of Europe; "Introdvctiorvm Isagogae in Libros Geographiae Ptolemaei," by Laurentius Phrisius, ends with colophon on recto last leaf (sig. S)
Text in double columns with 55 lines to a full column.
"Laurentius Fries or Phrisius, a physician and mathematician of Metz, was the editor of this edition, to which he added an index of places, annotations on the backs of the maps and a mathematical appendix. The text, however, was the translation of Jacobus Angelus. The introductory epistle of Aucuparius refers to America in the following words: 'Quorũ omniũ Imprimis et nõ vulgari celebrãdus eſt honore. Americ⁹ ille Veſputi⁹: Americę terrę. Quã hodie Américã: Nouũ mundũ vel Quartã mũdi parte vocãt . . .' The account of Palestine, wrongly attributed to Servetus and which served as one of

the pretexts for his execution, was first printed in this edition on the map of the Holy Land." *cf.* Eames.

This edition is of special interest as it is the first of Ptolemy's works to contain a map bearing the name America.

The maps are each on two leaves with the exception of "Lotharingia" (printed on reverse of second leaf of "Tab. Nova Nor. & Gott.") with borders and woodcuts on the reverse illustrating the manners and customs of the inhabitants. Scrolls containing headings surmount maps and text.

Maps of Ptolemy, comprising ten of Europe, four of Africa, twelve of Asia, Generale Ptho., are, with the exception of "Tab. v Asie", badly executed copies most of them on a reduced scale of those in the 1513 edition.

Nordenskiöld considers that the statement on verso fo. 100 indicates that Waltzemüller was not the author of the new maps but that he copied the maps of the 1513 ed. on a reduced scale for this edition. Both the old and new maps were reprinted in the editions of 1525, 1535 and 1541 with differences only in borders and titles. To the "tabulæ novæ", three new maps, one general and two of eastern Asia, have been added in this edition.

The modern maps are: Tabvla Terre Nova; Tabv Hiberniæ Sco; Tabv Moder Hispa; Tabv Moder Galie; Tabv Moder Germ; Tabv mode Vvala; Tab Nova Nor & Goti; Lotharingia; Tabv Nova Itali; Tabv Mo Italiæ; Tabvla Mo Bossin; Tabvla Moderna Portionis Aphrice; Tabvla Moderna Aphrice; Tabv Minor Asiæ; Tabv Mo Ter Sanctæ; Tabvla Moderna Indiæ; Tabv Mo Jn orig; Tabvla; Tabv Here[ml]. Helvet[iorum]; Tabv Nova Can; Tabv Provi Rhen; Tabv Gran Rvssie; Orbis. Typvs. Vniversalis. Ivxta. Hydrographorvm. Traditionem. Exactissime. Depicta. 1522. L. F.

The following maps relate to America:

no. [28] Tabvla Terre Nova. Practically the same as that in 1513 edition, with slight changes and the addition of inscriptions, a woodcut representing natives, etc., added to South America. The reverse contains an account of the voyages and discoveries of Columbus.

" [34] Tab. Nova Nor. & Goti. Represents "Engronelandt" as a peninsula of Europe.

" [49] Tabv. Gran. Rvssie. Map of the world resembling the "Orbis Typvs" in 1513 edition.

" [50] Orbis. Typvs. Universalis. Ivxta. Hydrographorvm. Traditionem. Exactissime. Depicta. 1522. L. F. "The new map of the world . . . was the production of Laurentius Fries . . . It is a revision, with alterations, of that of the preceding editions and is remarkable as the first map with the name America that appeared in Ptolemy's work. This name is inscribed on a portion of the South American continent."—*cf.* Eames.

Partly rebound. Original boards covered with brown russia.
Eames-Sabin, no. 66481.

## 1525

Clavdii Pto | lemaei Geo | graphicae | Enarrationis | Libri Octo | Bilibaldo Pirckeym | hero Interprete | Annotationes Ioannis de Regio Monte | in errores commiſſos a | Iacɔbo Angelo | in tranſlatione ſua. | [*Colophon:*] Argentoragi, Iohannes Grieningerus, communibus | Iohannis Koberger impenſis excudebat. | Anno a Chriſti Natiuitate M.D.XXV. Tertio Kal'. Apriles. | 362

228 l. comprising: 82, [48] l., 50 maps on [98] l. fol.

(sig. A–M in sixes; N in four; O–P in sixes; Q in eight; a–e in sixes; f in four)

Collation: title, verso dedication, "Ampliſſimo Principi ac Reverendiſſimo

**Ptolemæus, C.—Continued.**

Domino Sebastiano Episcopo Brixinensi, Bilibaldvs Pirckeymhervs S. D.," dated M.D.XXIV, ending on verso l. 2, followed by "Clavdii Ptolemaei Geographicae Enarrationis Liber Primvs, in qvo haec continentvr," 2 l.,—text incl. 6 diag. with verso l. 71, 82 blank, 3–82 l., (sig. A–O); "Clarissimi Aetatis noſtræ Mathematici, Iohannis de Monte Regio, fragmenta quædam annotationū, in errores quos Iacobus Angelus in tranſlatione Ptolemæi commiſit," ending with the colophon on recto sig. $Q_8$, verso blank, [14] l. (sig. P–Q); "Index Ptolemaei" . . . [34] l., (sig. a–f); 50 woodcut maps. Text in double columns, 52 lines to a full column.

New translation by W. Pirckheimer, with annotations by Regiomontanus. The maps are generally without the scrolls at the top, and nearly all have descriptive text on the back. Title, text, and nearly all descriptions of maps are within ornamental woodcut borders similar to those of the edition of 1522. "The maps are all, with the exception of the "Tabula v. Asiæ," printed from the same blocks as the maps of ed. 1522, and, like these, are almost unaltered copies, on a reduced scale of the maps in the edition of 1513." *cf.* Nordenskiöld.

The maps which relate to America, nos. 28, 34, 49, and 50, are described in the 1522 edition.

Original binding, stamped pigskin.

Eames-Sabin, no. 66482.

## 1533

Κλαυδιον Πτολεμαίον Αλεξανδρεως φιλοσοφον . . . περὶ της γεωγραφίας βιβλία οκτώ . . . Clavdii Ptolemaei Alexandrini philoſophi cum primis eruditi, De Geographia libri octo, ſumma cum uigilantia excuſi. Fro [*vignette*] ben. Basileae Anno MDXXXIII.

**363**

247 l. comprising: 2 p. l., 542, [2] pp. 8°.
Without maps.
"The first complete greek edition of the text of Ptolemy's geography, published by Erasmus." *cf.* Nordenskiöld.

## 1535

Clavdii Ptole- | mæi Alexandrini | Geographicæ Enar- | rationis | Libri Octo. | Ex Bilibaldi Pirckeymheri | tralatione, ſed ad Græca & priſca exemplaria à Mi- | chaële Villanouano iam primum recogniti. | Adiecta inſuper ab eodem Scholia, | quibus exoleta urbium no- | mina ad noſtri ſecu | li morē expo | nuntur. | Qvinqvaginta illæ qvoqve cvm | ueterum tum recentium tabulæ adnectuntur, uarijq́; | incolentium ritus & mores | explicantur. | [*Vignette*] Lvgdvni | Ex Officina Melchioris et | Gasparis Trechsel Fratrvm. | M.D.XXXV. | [*Colophon:*] Excvdebant Lvgdvni | Melchior et Gaspar | Trechsel Fratres. | M.D.XXXV. |

**364**

212 l. (followed by 1 blank l.) comprising: [2] l. 149, [1] pp., [1] l., 50 maps on [98] l., [38] l., 1 blank l. fol.

(sig. a–m in sixes; n in four; A–E in sixes; F in eight)

Collation: title, with "Michael Villanovanvs Lectori s." on verso, "Ampliſsimo Principi ac Reverendissimo Domino Sebaſtiano epiſcopo Brixinenſi, Bilibaldus Pirckeymherus S. D.," beginning on recto and ending on verso l. [2] with "Norēbergæ Kal.ēdis ſeptēbris, Anno Salutis noſtræ M D.XXIIII," followed by "Primo libro haec continentur, 2. l.,—text incl. 6 diagrs., 5-149, [1] pp., 1 l. with colophon on recto, verso blank, (sig. a-n); 49 double page (and one single) maps on 98 l., 35 of which have text on the reverse; "Index Ptolemaei," [35] l., "Regionvm civitatvm," 1 l., two tables on 1 l., and "Errata," 1 l. verso blank, (sig. A-F)

Text in double columns, 56 lines to a full column.

"The woodcut borders and ornaments which surround the descriptions are supposed by some critics to be the work of Hans Holbein and graf of Basle. The 50 woodcut maps . . . are the same as those in the preceding [1525] edition, having been printed from the same blocks, and are arranged and numbered in the same order." *cf.* Eames.

The maps relating to America, nos. 28, 34, 49, and 50, are described in the 1522 edition.

On the reverse of map 41 of this edition is found the passage which was used in one of the charges against Servetus when he was burned. This passage was, however, not original with Servetus but was copied from the editions of 1522 and 1525.

Title vignette and shield below imprint in colors, executed by hand.

Modern binding, quarter calf with tooled back.

Eames-Sabin, no. 66483.

### 1540

Geographia | vniversalis, vetvs et nova, | complectens | Clavdii Pto- | lemæi Alexandrini enarratio- | nis libros viii. | Quorum primus noua translatione Pirckheimheri et | acceffione commentarioli illuftrior quàm hacte- | nus fuerit, redditus eft. | Reliqui cum græco & alijs uetuftis exēplaribus col- | lati, in infinitis ferè locis caftigatiores facti funt. | Addita funt infuper Scholia, quibus exoleta urbium | montium, fluuiorumq̨ nomina ad noftri feculi mo- | rem exponuntur. | Succedunt tabulæ Ptolemaicę, opera Sebaftiani Mun | fteri nouo paratæ modo. | His adiectæ funt plurimę nouæ tabulæ, modernā or- | bis faciem literis & pictura explicantes, inter quas | quædam antehàc Ptolemæo non fuerunt additæ. | Vltimo annexum eft compendium geographicę de- | fcriptionis, in quo uarij gentium & regionum ri- | tus & mores explicantur. | Pręfixus eft quoq̨ uniuerfo operi index memorabiliū | populorum, ciuitatum, fluuiorum, montium, ter- | rarum, lacuum &c. | Basileæ apvd Henricvm Petrvm | Mense Martio Anno M. D. XL. [*Colophon:*] Basileæ apvd Henricvm Petrvm | Menfe Martio An. M. D. XL. 365

222 l. (incl. 1 blank l. and preceded by 1 blank l.) comprising: title, [52] pp., 1 blank l., 155 pp., 48 maps on [96] l., 157-195 pp. fol.

(sig. aa in four; *, a-c, A-N, Aa-Bb in sixes, Cc in eight)

Collation: title, verso blank, "Epistola Nvncvpatoria" of Münster, 2 l., "Errata," 1 l., recto blank, (sig. aa); "Index," followed by "Primo libro hæc con tinentur," 6 l., (sig. *); book I of text with Münster's annotations, incl. 4 diagr. 17 l. followed by 1 blank l. (sig. a-c); books II-VIII of text, incl. 3 diagr., 155 pp., verso p. 155 blank (sig. A-N); 48 maps on [96] l.; "Appendix Geographica" of Münster, pp. 157-195, colophon on recto p. 195, printer's mark on verso (sig. Aa-Cc)

Text in double columns, 50 lines to a full column.

"A new and important edition, revised and edited by the geographer Sebastian Münster who designed the maps anew and added an appendix." *cf.* Eames

**Ptolemæus, C.**—Continued.

The 48 wood-cut maps are as follows: Mappemonde; ancient maps, re-designed by Münster, no. 2-28; twenty modern maps, "novæ tabulæ," designed by Münster, nos. I-XX. The recto of the first leaf of these contains descriptive text with ornamental borders, by some ascribed to Holbein.
The following maps relate to America:
no. 1. Typvs Orbis Vniversalis.
" 41. Schonlandia XIII Nova Tabvla.
" 45. Novae Insvlae, XVII Nova Tabvla. Represents the american lands and islands with an account of their discovery by Columbus printed on the back.
Accompanied by Munster's "Organum Uranicum, Basileae, 1536."
Modern binding.
Eames—Sabin, no. 66484

### 1541

Clavdii | Ptolemaei | Alexan- | drini | Geographicæ Enarrationis, | Libri Octo. | Ex Bilibaldi Pircke- | ymheri tralatione, fed ad Græca & prifca exemplaria à Michaële Villanouano | fecundò recogniti, & locis innumeris denuò caftigati. Adiecta infuper ab eodem Scho | lia, quibus & difficilis ille Primus Liber nunc primum explicatur, & exoleta Vrbium | nomina ad noftri feculi morem exponuntur. Quinquaginta illæ quoque cum ueterum tum | recentium Tabulæ adnectuntur, uarijq̸ incolentium ritus & mores explicantur. | Accedit Index locupletifsimus hactenus non uifus. | [*Vignette*] Proftant Lugduni apud Hugonem à Porta. | M.D.XLI. | [*First colophon:*] Gaspar Trechsel | Excvdebat | Viennae. | M.D.XLI. | [*Second colophon:*] Excudebat | Gafpar Trechfel | Viennæ | M.D.XLI.

366

222 l. comprising: [2] l., 5-149, [1] pp., [1] l., 50 maps on [98] l., [48] l. fol.
(sig. a-m in sixes; n in four; a-h in sixes)
Collation: title, preface on verso, dedication l. 2, with "Primo libro hæc continentvr," on verso, 2 l., text incl. 6 diagr. with table on verso of last page, 5-149 pp. followed by 1 l. colophon on recto, verso blank (sig. a-n); 49 double page and 1 single woodcut maps on 98 l.; "Index," 45 l., "Regionum, Ciuitatum," 1 l., 2 tables on 1 l., followed by 1 l. containing second colophon on recto, verso blank (sig. a-h)
Text in double columns, 57 lines to a full column.
"A new edition of the Ptolemy of Servetus . . . very inferior to the first one owing to the omission of the interesting, although often offensive legends to the new maps, in the edition of 1535. Text and maps are otherwise unaltered . . . from the same blocks . . . used for the editions of 1522, 1525 and 1535."
*cf.* Nordenskiöld.
The maps which relate to America, nos. 28, 34, 49 and 50, are described in the edition of 1522.
Modern binding, boards.
Eames-Sabin, no. 66485.

### 1542

Geographia | vniversalis, vetvs et nova, | complectens | Clavdii Pto- | lemæi Alexandrini enarratio- | nis libros VIII. | Quorum primus noua translatione Pirckheimheri et | acceffione commentarioli illuftrior quàm hacte- | nus fuerit, redditus eft. | Reliqui cum græco & alijs uetuftis exēplaribus col- | lati, in infinitis ferè locis caftigatiores facti funt. | Addita funt infuper Scolia, quibus exoleta urbium, | montium, fluuiorumq̇, nomina ad noftri feculi mo- | rem exponuntur. | Succedunt tabulæ Ptolemaicæ, opera Sebaftiani Mun- | fteri nouo paratæ modo. | His adiectæ funt plurimæ nouæ tabulæ, | modernā or- | bis faciem literis & pictura explicantes, inter quas | quædam antehàc Ptolemæo non fuerunt additæ. | Vltimo annexum eft compendium geographicæ de- | fcriptionis, in quo uarij gentium & regionum ri- | tus & mores explicantur. | Præfixus eft quoq̇, uniuerfo operi index memorabiliū | populorum, ciuitatum, fluuiorum, montium, ter- | rarum, lacuum &c. | Basileæ apvd Henri- | cvm Petrvm. | [*Colophon:*] Basileæ apvd Henricvm Petrvm | Mense Martio, An M.D.XLII. | 367

223 l. (preceded by 1, incl. 3, and followed by 2 blank l.) comprising: title, [54] pp., 1 bl. l., 155 pp., 48 maps on [96] l., 157-195 pp. fol.
(sig. a a in four; *, a-c, A-N, Aa, Bb, in sixes; Cc in eight)
Collation: title, verso blank, "Epistola Nvncvpatoria" of Münster, 2 l., 1 blank l. (sig. a a); 1 blank l. unsigned; "Index," followed by "Primo libro hæc continentur," 6 l., (sig. *); book I of text with Munster's annotations, (incl. 4 diagr.) 17 l. followed by 1 blank l., (sig. a-c); books II-VIII of text, (incl. 3 diagr.) pp. 1-155, verso p. 155 blank, (sig. A-N); 48 maps on [96] l. "Appendix Geographica" of Münster, pp. 157-195, colophon on recto p. 195, printer's mark on verso, (sig. Aa-Cc)
Text in double columns, 50 lines to a full column.
Second edition of Münster's Ptolemy reprinted from the edition of 1540, with slight corrections, alterations of punctuation, of the types in the rubrics, etc.
"The 48 double-page woodcut maps are the same as those in the 1540 edition, having been printed from the same blocks, but some of the inscriptions are in a different style of type. They are also numbered and arranged in the same order, and have the same names, excepting the first, which is entitled "Typvs Vniversalis . . . [Some of] the ornamental borders which surround the text on the backs of the maps are similar to those in the 1540 edition, but vary in the order of arrangement."—*cf.* Eames.
"Holbein is said by some to have engraved the borders; but doctor Trumbull thinks they were blocks,—perhaps in some cases designed by Holbein,—evidently used from the publisher's stock; and that they had done earlier service in other books. The border to tabula x is dated 1523; while that used both in III and XXVIII shows the monogram of Adam Petri. Groups of boys like Holbein's are in nos. I, V, XIV, XIX, XXIV, XXVII. *cf.* C. F. v. Rumohr's Holbein, Leipsic, 1836, p. 114."—*cf.* Winsor.
The following maps relate to America:
no. 1. Typvs Vniversalis.
" 41. Schonlandia XII nova tabvla.
" 45. Novae insvlae XVII nova tabvla.
Bound in full sheep, with tooled back.
Eames-Sabin, no. 66486.

**1545**

**Ptolemæus, C.**—Continued.

Geographia | vniversalis, vetvs et nova, | complectens | Clavdii Pto- | lemæi Alexandrini Enarratio⁄ | nis libros VIII. | Quorum primus noua translatione Pirckheimheri & | acceffione commentarioli illuftrior quàm hactenus | fuerit, redditus eft. | Reliqui cum græco & alijs uetuftis exemplaribus col⁄ | lati, in infinitis ferè locis caftigatiores facti funt. | Addita funt infuper Scholia, quibus exoleta urbium, | montium, fluuiorumq̃; nomina ad noftri feculi mo⁄ | rem exponuntur. | Succedunt tabulæ Ptolemaicæ, opera Sebaftiani Mun | fteri nouo paratæ modo. | His adiecta funt plurimæ nouæ tabulæ, modernam or⁄ | bis faciem literis & pictura explicantes, inter quas | quędam antehàc Ptolemęo non fuerunt additæ. | Vltimo annexum eft compendium geographicæ de⁄ | fcriptionis, in quo uarij gentium & regioonum ritus | & mores explicantur. | Præfixus eft quoq̃; uniuerfo operi index memorabiliũ | populorum, ciuitatum, fluuiorum, montium, terra⁄ | rum, lacuum &c. | Adiectæ funt huic pofteriori editioni nouæ quædam tabulæ, quæ hactenus apud nul= | lam Ptolemaicam impreffuram uifæ funt. | Basileæ per Henrichvm Pe⁄ | trum, Anno MD. XLV. | [*Colophon:*] Basileae per Henrichvm Petrvm | Mense Avgvsto, An. M. D. XLV: | 368

234 l. (including 1 blank l. and followed by 1 blank l.) comprising: title, [52] pp., 1 blank l., 155 pp., 54 maps on [108] l., 157-195 pp. fol. 234 l. (including 1 blank l. and followed by 1 blank l.) fol.

(sig. aa in four; \*, a-c, A-N, Aa-Bb in sixes; Cc in eight)

Collation: title, with inscription and woodcut figure of Ptolemy on verso, "Epistola Nvncvpatoria," dated on recto l. [4] "Bafsleæ anno M. D. XLV. menfe Maio," 3 l., verso l. 4 blank, (sig. aa); "Index" followed by "Primo libro hæc continentur," 6 l., (sig. \*); book I of text incl. 4 diagr., and followed by blank leaf, 18 l., (sig. a-c); books II-VIII of text incl. 3 diagr.,—155 pp., verso p. 155 blank, (sig. A--N); 54 double page maps on [108] l.; "Appendix Geographica,'' with colophon on recto of p. 195, printer's mark on verso, 157-195 pp., (sig. Aa-Cc)

Text in double columns, 50 lines to a full column.

Third edition of Münster's Ptolemy, Pirckheimer's translation.

The maps are from the same blocks as those in the editions of 1540 and 1542 with the exception of six, which are as follows: Valesiae Charta Prior et VI. Nova Tabvla; Valesiae Altera et VII. Nova Tavula; Nigra Sylva XI. Nova Tabvla; Slesiae Descriptio XV. Nova Tabvla; Descriptio totivs Illyridis XVI. No. Tab.; Bohemiæ Nova Descriptio Tabvla; Transsylvania XXI. Nova Tabvla; and Nova Graecia XXII. Nova Tabvla.

Each map contains descriptive text on the reverse, generally printed within ornamental woodcut borders, designed in the Holbein style. Maps 25, 26, 27 are misplaced (*i. e.* 27, 26, 25)

The following maps relate to America:

no. 1. Typus Vniversalis.

" 46. Septentrionales Regiones. XVIII. No. Tab.

" 54. Novae Insvlae XXVI. Nova Tabvla.

Modern binding, stamped calf.

Eames-Sabin, no. 66487.

### 1548

Ptolemeo | La Geografia | di Clavdio Ptolemeo | Alessandrino, | Con alcuni comenti & aggiunte fat | teui da Sebaſtiano munſtero Ala | manno, Con le tauole non ſolamente antiche & moderne ſolite di ſtāpar⁄ | ſi, ma altre nuoue aggiunteui di Me | ſer Iacopo Gaſtaldo Piamōteſe coſ⁄ | mographo, ridotta in uolgare Italia | no da M. Pietro Andrea Mat⁄ | tiolo Seneſe medico Eccellētiſsimo. Con l'aggivnta d' infiniti | nomi moderni, di Cittá, Prouincie, Castella, et | altri luoghi, fatta cō grandiſſima diligenza | da eſſo Meſer Iacopo Gaſtaldo, il che in | niſſun altro Ptolemeo ſi ritroua. | Opera ueramente non meno utile | che neceſſaria. | In Venetia, per Gioā. Baptiſta Pedrezano. | Co'l priuilegio dell' Illuſtriſs. Senato Veneto per | Anni. x. M.D.XLVIII. | [*Colophon:*] In Venetia, ad Inſtantia di meſſer Giouābattiſta Pedrezano | libraro al ſegno della Torre a pie del ponte di Rialto. | Stampato per Nicolo Baſcarini nel Anno del | Signore. 1547. del meſe di Ottobre. | 369

406 l. (including 1 blank l.) comprising: 8 p. l., 214, [2], [64] l., 59 maps on [118] l. 12°.
(Sig. †, A–T, V, X–Z, AA–DD, a–h in eights)
Collation: title, verso blank, sketch of Ptolemy with woodcut, 1 l., dedication, 1 l., "A li Lettori," 5 l., contents of book I on verso l. 5., (sig †); text, 214 l., "Registro," colophon, and printer's mark, 1 l. verso blank, followed by 1 blank l., (sig. A–DD); "Tavola," [64] l., printer's mark on verso l. [64] (sig. a–h); 59 double page maps on [118] l.
"The first edition of Ptolemy's Geography in italian. The translation was made by Pietro Andrea Mattioli, a learned physician of Siena, and the maps were designed and added by Jacobo Gastaldo, who also wrote the dedication, which is dated 'Di Vinetia a due di Giennaio MDXLVIII.' The 60 double page copperplate maps were mostly based on those of Münster in the Latin edition of 1540, but contain many important additions." *cf.* Eames.
Nordenskiöld states that 26 of the maps "are Ptolemy's (his map of the world is excluded) and there are 34 new ones, namely: Inghilterra; Spagna; Francia; Brabantia, Fiandra & Holandia; Germania; Schiavonia et Dalmatia; Italia; Piemonte; Marcha Trevisana; Marcha de Anchona; Sicilia et Sardegna; Prusia et Livonia; Scholandia (after Ziegler); Polonia et Ungheria; Grecia; Mauritania; Aphrica minore; Marmaricha; Egritto; Aphrica; Natolia; Moschovia; Soria; Persia; Arabia Felice; Calecut; India Tercera; Terra nuova (South America); Nova Hispania (Central America); Terra nova de Bacalaos; Isola Cuba; Spagnola; Universale nuovo; Carta marina universale. A whole series of plates of the New World is here met with, for the first time, and some of them are of no slight interest to the history of geography."
Map no. 60, Carta marina universale, is wanting in this copy.
Modern binding, half sheep.
Eames–Sabin, no. 66502.

### 1552

Geogra | phiae | Clavdii Ptole- | mæi Alexandrini, Philoſophi ac Mathema | tici præſtātiſſimi, Libri viii, partim à Bilibaldo Pirckheymero tranſ= | lati ac commentario illuſtrati, partim etiam Græcorum an= | tiquiſſimorunmq̃ exemplariorum collatione emen | dati

**Ptolemæus, C.**—*Continued.*

atque in integrum reſtituti. | His accesservnt, | Scholia, quibus exoleta locorum omnium nomina in Ptolemæi | libris ad noſtri ſeculi morem exponuntur. | Indices duo hactenus à multis deſiderati, quorū adminiculo, ue | terum ſimul ac recentiorum locorum (utpote regionum, ma= | rium, inſularum, promontorium, montium, fluminorum, ur= | bium, &c.) ſitus, facillimaratione in tabulis depictis deprehen | dūtur, Conradi Lycoſthenis Rubeaquēſis opera adiecti. | Quibus præfixa eſt epiſtola in qua de utilitate tabularum Geo= | graphicarum ac duplicis indicis uſu latè differitur. | Tabulæ nouæ quæ hactenus in nulla Ptolemaica editione uiſæ | ſunt, per Sebastianvm Mvnstervm. | Geographicę deſcriptionis compendium, in quo uarij gentium | ac regionum ritus, mores atqȝ conſuetudines per eundem ex= | plicantur. | Cum Regiæ Maieſtatis Gratia & Priuilegio ad ſexennium. | [*Colophon:*] Basileæ ex offi= | cina Henrichi Petri, | Mense Martio, Anno | M.D.LII. | 370

312 l. (incl. 3 blank l.) comprising: title, [107] l., 195 pp., 53 maps on 106 l. fol.

(sig. *-a in fours; b-o in sixes; p in four; AA-QQ. Aa-Bb in sixes; Cc in eight)

Collation: title, with inscription and woodcut figure of Ptolemy on verso,—"Epistola Nvncvpatoria," 2 l., royal license on verso l. 4, recto blank, (sig. *); "De Vtilitate Tabularum Geographicarum," followed by a blank leaf, 4 l., (sig. a); "Index in vniversas tabvlas Ptolemaicas" . . . followed by a blank leaf, [82] l. (sig. b-p); book I of text, incl. 4 diagr., followed by blank leaf, [18] l., (sig. AA-CC); books II-VIII of text, incl. 3 diagr., 155 pp., verso p. 155 blank, (sig. DD-QQ); "Appendix Geographica," pp. 157-195, verso p. 195 blank, (sig. Aa-Cc; 53 double page maps on 106 l., printer's mark and colophon on reverse of last map.

Text in double columns, 50 lines to a full column.

The 4th edition of Münster's Ptolemy, with an additional treatise, and enlarged indexes by Conradus Lycosthenus, *i. e.* Konrad Wolffhart.

"The plates are the same, and printed from the same blocks as those of the edition of 1545, with the exception of the map of *Lacus Constantinensis* being left out, instead of which a map of *Pomerania* (map 42) is inserted." *cf.* Nordenskiöld.

Descriptive text on the reverse of maps, generally within woodcut borders.

Map no. 44, Sclavonia, wanting.

The following maps relate to America:

no. 1. Typvs Vniversalis. Slightly altered from that in 1545 edition.
" 46. Septentrionales Regiones XVIII. No. Tab.
" 54. Novae Insvlae XXVI. Nova Tabvla.

Modern binding, half brown, american russia.

Eames-Sabin, no. 66488.

## 1561

La Geografia | di Clavdio Ꞇolomeo | Alessandrino, | Nuouamente tradotta di Greco in Italiano, | da Girolamo Rvscelli, | Con Eſpoſiᵗioni del medeſimo, particolari di luogo in luogo, & uni- | uerſali

fopra tutto il libro, et fopra tutta la Geografia, ò modo | di far la
defcrittione di tutto il mondo. | Et con nuoue & belliffime figure in
iftampe di rame, oue, oltre alle xxvi antiche | di Tolomeo, fe ne
fon' aggiunte xxxvi altre delle moderne. Con la carta | da naui-
care, & col modo d' intenderla, & d' adoperarla. | Aggiuntoui vn
pieno difcorfo di M. Gioseppe Moleto Matematico. Nel quale
fi | dichiarano tutti i termini & le regole appartenenti alla Geo-
grafia. | Et con vna nuoua & copiofa Tauola di nomi antichi, dichiarati
co i nomi moderni, & con molte altre | cofe vtilifsime & neceffarie,
che ciafcuno leggendo potrà conofcere. | Al sacratissimo et sempre
felicissimo | Imperator Ferdinando Primo. | Con priuilegio dell'
Illuftrifsimo Senato Veneto, et | d' altri Principi per anni xv. |
[*Vignette*] In Venetia, | Appreffo Vincenzo Valgrifi, M.D.LXI. |
[*Title to second part:*] Espositioni | et Introdvttioni | Vniversali, di
Girolamo Rvscelli | fopra tutta la Geografia di Tolomeo. | Con
xxxvi. nuoue Tauole in iftampe di rame, così | del mondo conof-
ciuto da gli antichi, come del nuouo. | Con la carta da nauicare, &
con più altre cofe | intorno | alla Cofmografia, così per mare, come
per terra. | Con priuilegio dell' Illuftriffimo Senato Veneto, & | d'
altri Principi per anni xv. | [*Vignette*] In Venetia, | Appreffo Vin-
cenzo Valgrifi. MDLXI. | 371

364 l. comprising: 4 p.l., 358 pp., 1 l., 28 maps on [56] l., [28] l., 36 maps on
[72] l., [24] l. 8°.
(sig. *, A-Z, AA-YY in fours; ✠, A-D, F, F-Z, A1, B2, C3, D4 in twos; α-η
in fours; A-E, F, F-K, K, N-Q, [R] S-Z, Aa-Nn in twos; A-F in fours)
Collation: title, verso blank, dedication, 2 l., preface, 1 l., (sig. *); text, incl. 9
diagr., 358 pp., followed by "Il Regiftro," 1 l. verso blank, (sig. A-YY); 28
double page, copperplate maps on [56] l., (sig. ✠-D4); "Espositioni et Intro-
dvttioni Vniversale, di Girolamo Rvscelli" . . . [28] l. incl. 2 diagr. (sig.
α-η); 36 double page copperplate maps on [72] l., printer's mark on verso
l. [72], (sig. A-Nn); "Tavola de' nomi" . . . [24] l., (sig. A-F)
"A new translation into italian with numerous remarks and extensive addenda
by Ruscelli. It is notified on the title-page that the work was to contain 26
old and 36 new maps, but there are in reality 27 old and 37 new plates. The
maps are enlarged copies of Gastaldi's maps in the edition of 1548, excepting:
"*Universale Novo*" drawn on a new projection, and called "*Orbis descriptio*";
the map of Britain, for the northern part of which the author has modified
the type hitherto followed of the "*Tabula nova Hiberniae, Angliae et Scotiae*"
in the Ptolemy of 1513; and the map of Central America (*Neuva Hispania*),
where Yucatan is drawn as a peninsula, and not separated from the main by a
strait as in the map of 1548. Four maps are added, vis: *Toscana, nova tabula;*
Zeno's map or "*Septentrionalium partium tabula nova*"; *Brasil, nova tavola*, and
the old map of the world by Ptolemy, excluded from the edition of 1548, is
here re-inserted". *cf.* Nordenskiöld.
Maps have descriptive text on the reverse.
The "Discorso" of Moleto, pp. 1–47, (sig. A-F), is wanting in this copy. It
is not mentioned in the general register at end of volume, but should precede
the "Tavola."

**Ptolemæus, C.**—Continued.
The following maps relate to America:
Orbis Descriptio.
no. VI. Schonladia Nvova.
" XXIX. Tierra Nova.
" XXX. Brasil Nvova Tavola.
" XXXI. Nveva Hispania Tabvla.
" XXXII. Tierra Nveva.
" XXXIII. Isola Cvba Nova.
" XXXIV. Isola Spagnola Nova.
" XXXV. Septentrionalivm Partivm Nova Tabvla.
" XXXVI. Carta Marina Tavola.
Modern binding, half red morocco, original vellum covers bound in.
Eames-Sabin, no. 66503.

## 1562

Geographia | Cl. Ptolemaei | Alexandrini | Olim a Bilibaldo Pirckheimherio traslata, at nunc multis co- | dicibus græcis collata, pluribusque in locis ad pri- | ftinam ueritatem redacta | A Iosepho Moletio Mathematico. | Addita funt in primum, & feptimum librum amplifsima eiufdem commentaria, | quibus omnia, quæ ad Geographiam attinent, & quæ prætermiffa funt a Pto- | lemæo declarantur: atque nominibus antiquis regionum, ciuitatum, oppido- | rum, montium, fyluarum, fluuiorum, lacuum, cæterorumque locorum, appo- | fita funt recentiora. | Adfunt LXIIII. Tabulæ XXVII. nempe antiquæ, & reliquæ nouæ, quæ totam continent | terram, noftræ, ac Ptolemæi ætati cognitam, Tipisq́; æneis excuffæ. | Indices rerum quæ tractantur copiofifsimi. Cvm privilegiis. | [*Vignette*] Venetiis,—Apvd Vincentivm Valgrisivm. | MDLII. | 372

364 l. comprising: 4 p. l., 112, 286 pp., 1 l., 64 maps on [128] l., [32] l. 8°.
(sig. *, A-O in fours; A-S in eights; A-H in fours)
Collation: title, verso blank, dedication, 3 l., verso l. 4, blank, (sig. *); book I of text incl. 7 diagr., 112 pp. (sig. A-O); books II-VIII of text incl. 6 diagr., 286 pp., 1 blank l., (sig. A-S); 64 double page, copperplate maps on [128] l.; Index, 31 l., Errata, 1 l., verso blank, (sig. A-H)
"New edition, revised and annotated by Josephus Moletius . . . The 64 maps, ten of which relate to America, are from the same plates as those in the italian version printed at Venice in 1561." *cf.* Eames.
Descriptive text on reverse of maps.
Title-page mutilated and remounted.
Original binding, full vellum.
Eames-Sabin, no. 66489.

## 1564

La Geografia | di Clavdio Tolomeo | Alessandrino, | Nuouamente tradotta di Greco in Italiano | da Ieronimo Rvscelli, | Con Espositioni del medefimo particolari di luogo in luogo, & | uniuerfali fopra tutto il libro, & fopra tutta la Geografia, ò modo | di far la defcrittione di tutto il mondo. | Et con nvove & belliffime figure in iftampe di rame, oue, oltre alle | xxvi antiche di Tolomeo, fe ne son' aggiunte xxxvi altre delle moderne | Con la carta da nauicare, & col modo d'intenderla, & d'adoperarla. | Aggivntovi un pieno difcorfo di M. Gioseppe Moleto Matematico. Nel | quale fi dichiarano tutti i termini & le regole appartenenti alla Geografia. | Et con vna nuoua & copiofa Tauola de' nomi antichi, dichiarati co i nomi | moderni, & con molte altre cofe vtiliffime & neceffarie, che ciafcuno leggendo po- | trà conofceré. | Al facratiffimo & fempre feliciffimo Imperator | Ferdinando Primo. | Con priuilegio di N. S. Papa Pio iiii. & dell' Illustiffima | Signoria di Venetia per anni xv. | In Venetia, | Appreffo Giordano Ziletti, al fegno della Stella, | M.D.LXIIII. | [*Title to second part:*] Espofitioni | et Introdvttioni | Vniversali, | di Ieronimo Rvscelli | fopra tutta la Geografia di Tolomeo. | Con xxxvi. nuoue Tauole in iftampe di rame, cosî | del mondo conofciuto da gli antichi, come del | nuouo. Con la carta da nauicare, & con più | altre cofe intorno alla Cofmografia, cosî | per mare, come per terra. | Con priuilegio dell' Illustriffimo Senato Veneto, & | d' altri Principi per anni xv. | In Venetia, | Appreffo Giordano Ziletti, al fegno della Stella. | MDLXIIII. | [*Title to third part:*] Discorso | Vniversale | di M. Gioseppe Moleto | Mathematico. | Al signor Federigo Morando, | Nelquale fon raccolti, & dichiarati tutti i ter- | mini, & tutte le regole appartenen= | ti alla Geografia. | Con priuilegio dell' Illustrifsimo Senato Veneto, & | d' altri Principi per anni xv. | In Venetia, | Appreffo Giordano Ziletti, al fegno della Stella. | MDLXIIII. | 373

390 l. (preceded and followed by 1 blank l.) comprising: 4 p. l., 358 pp., [1] l., 27 maps on [54] l.; [28] l., 38 maps on [76] l.; 47 pp., [24] l. 8°.
(sig. *, A-Z, AA-YY in fours; A-D, F, F-Z, $A_1$, $B_2$, $C_3$, $D_4$, in twos; $\alpha$-$\eta$ in fours; A-F, F-K, K-Q, [R], S-Z, Aa-Nn, in twos; A-F, A-F, in fours) a)
Collation: title, verso blank, sketch of Ptolemy with woodcut on recto, —1 l., preface, "A i Lettori," —2 l. with same woodcut on verso l. 4, (sig. *); text with annotations of Ruscelli, incl. 11 diagr., 358 pp.,—"Il Regiftro," 1 l., verso blank, (sig. A-YY); 27 maps on [54] l., description on reverse (sig. A-Z, $A_1$-$D_4$); "Espositioni" of Ruscelli, [28] l., verso l. 28 blank, (sig. $\alpha$-$\eta$); 38 maps on [76] l., printer's mark on verso sig. $Nn_2$, (sig. A-Z, Aa-Nn); "Discorso" of Moleto, 47 pp., reverse of p. 1 and 47, blank, (sig. A-F); "Tavola," [24] l., (sig. A-F)
Second edition of Ruscelli's Ptolemy.
Maps the same as those in italian edition of 1561 and latin edition of 1562.
Maps (sig†) "Orbis descriptio," wanting.
Eames states in describing this edition that "The same irregularity in the numbering [of the maps] occurs in the edition of 1561 and is not an imperfection." In connection with the 1561 edition he states that "The apparent deficiency of two maps (nos. xi L and xii M) both of which are included in the register with the two extra numbers vi F and x K, occurs in all the copies that I know of, and also in the edition of 1564." In this copy two maps, signed xi L and xii M have evidently been inserted. xi L is a duplicate of the "Sep-

**Ptolemæus, C.**—Continued.

tentrionalivm Partivm Nova Tabvla" in this copy signed xxv Mm; xii M, "Territorio di Roma," is the new map appearing in the 1574 edition.
The following maps relate to America:
- no. vi. Schonladia Nvova.
- " xxix. Tierra Nova.
- " xxx. Brasil Nvova Tavola.
- " xxxi. Nveva Hispania Tavola Nova.
- " xxxii. Tierra Nveva.
- " xxxiii. Isola Cvba Nova.
- " xxxiiii. Isola Spagnola Nova.
- " xxxv. Septentrionalivm Partivm Nova Tabvla.
- " xxxvi. Carta Marina Nvova Tavola.

Modern binding, full.
Eames-Sabin, no. 66504.

### 1570

**Ortelius, A.**

Theatrvm orbis terrarvm. 1 p. l., [143] l. incl. 53 col. maps. fol. [*Colophon:*] apud Ægid. Coppenium Diefth, Antverpiae, 1570.

374

NOTE.—Collation: sig. [A] in eight.—Maps 1-53; with text on front page.—sig. a–e in sixes.

sig. [A] recto: col. eng. title; verso: Epigramma Danielis Rogerii . . . sig. Aij recto: D. Philippo Avstriaco Caroli V . . . verso—Aiij verso: Adolphi Mekerchi Brvgensis . . . frontispicii explicatio. sig. Aiiij recto-Av recto: Abrahamvs Ortelivs Antverpianvs, benevolis lectorib. S. D. (dated: Antverpiæ 1570. sig. Av recto—Avj verso: Catalogvs avctorvm tabvlarvm geographicarvm qvotqvot ad nostram cognitionem hactenvs pervenere; quibvs adidimvs, vbi locorvm, qvando, et a qvibvs excvsi svnt. (92 names). sig. Avij recto—Aviij recto: Index tabularum huius operis, fiue infcriptionum earundum. sig. Aviij verso: blank.—maps 1-53. sig. a recto — aiij verso: De Mona drvidvm insvla . . . (dated 1568; signed Humfredus Lhuyd). sig. a iiij recto—[c vj] recto: Antiqva regionvm, insvlarvm, vrbium, oppidorum . . . recentibus eorundem nominibus explicata; auctoribus quibus fic vocantur, adiectis. sig. [c vj] recto—[e vj] recto: Indice hoc primo ad finem perducto . . . sig. [e vi] verso: Signa et series foliorvm.—Tenor privilegii (dated 1569)—Colophon.

The following is the list of maps contained in the atlas:
- no. 1. Typvs orbis terrarvm.
- " 2. Americae sive novi orbis, nova descriptio.
- " 3. Asiae nova descriptio.
- " 4. Africae tabvla nova. 1570.
- " 5. Evropae.
- " 6. Angliae, Scotiae et Hiberniae . . . descriptio.
- " 7. Regni Hispaniae post omnivm editiones locvple[t]issima descriptio.
- " 8. Portvgalliae quę olim Lufitania, nouifsima . . . defcriptio auctore Vernando Aluaro Secco. 1560.
- " 9. Galliae regni potentiss: nova descriptio Ioanne Ioliveto avctore.
- " 10. Regionis Bitvrigvm exactiss: descriptio per D. Ioannem Calamaevm.— Limaniae topographia Gabriele Symeoneo avct.
- " 11. Caletensivm et Bononiensivm ditionis . . . delineatio.—Veromandvorvm eorvmqve confinivm . . . descriptio. Johanne Surhonio auctore.

no. 12. Galliae Narbonensis ora marittima recenter defcripta.—Sabavdiae et Bvrgvndiae comitatus defcriptio; auctore Aegidio Bulionio Belga.
" 13. Germania.
" 14. Descriptio Germaniae inferioris.
" 15. Gelriae, Cliviae . . . descriptio. Chriftiano Schrot. auctore.
" 16. Brabantiæ, Germaniae inferioris . . . descriptio. Jacobo a Dauētria auct.
" 17. Flandria. Gerardus Mercator Rupelmundanus defcribebat.
" 18. Zelandicarvm insvlarvm exactissima . . . descriptio, avctore d. Iacobo a Daventria.
" 19. Hollandiae antiqvorvm catthorvm sedis nova descriptio, avctore Iacobo a Daventria.
" 20. Ooft ende weft Vrieflandts befchrÿuinghe . . . 1568.
" 21. Daniae regni typvs.
" 22. Thietmarsiae, Holsaticae regionis partis typvs. Auctore Petro Boeckel.—Prvssiae descriptio ante aliquot annos ab Henrico Zellio edita . . .
" 23. Saxoniae, Misniae, Thvringiae . . . descriptio.
" 24. Franciæ orientalis . . . descriptio, avctore Sebast. a Rotenhan.— Monasteriensis et Osnabvrgensis episcopatvs descriptio. Auctore Godefrido Mafcop Embricenfe.
" 25. Regni Bohemiae descriptio.
" 26. Silesiae typvs defcriptus et editus a Martino Heilwig Neifense . . . 1561.
" 27. Avstriae dvcatvs chorographia, Wolfgango Lazio avctore.
" 28. Salisbvrgensis ivrisdictionis . . . defcriptio auctore Marco Secznagel Salisburgense.—Vrbis Salisbvrgensis . . . descriptio.
" 29. Tipus Vindeliciæ sive vtrivsqve, Bavariae secvndvm antiquum et recentiorem fitum, ab Joanne Auentino olim defcriptus . . . 1533.
" 30. Palatinatvs Bavariae descriptio Erhardo Reych . . . avctore.— Wirtenbergensis dvcatvs vera descriptio . . . 1558.
" 31. Helvetiae descriptio. Aegidio Tschvdo avct.
" 32. Italiae novissima descriptio avctore Iacobo Castaldo Pedemontano.
" 33. Dvcatvs Mediolanensis . . . descriptio, avctore Ioanne Georgio Septala Mediolanense.
" 34. Pedemontanae vicinorvmqve regionvm avctore Iacobo Castaldo descrip.
" 35. Larii lacvs vvlgo Comensis descriptio. Avct. Pavlo Jovio.—Territorii Romani descrip.—Fori Ivlii, vvlgo Frivli typvs.
" 36. Thvsciae descriptio avctore Hieronymo Bellarmato.
" 37. Regni Neapolitani verissima . . . descriptio Pyrrho Ligorio avct.
" 38. Insvlarvm aliqvot maris Mediterranei descriptio.
" 39. Cyprvs insvla.—Candia, olim Creta.
" 40. Iacobo Castaldo . . . Graeciae vniversae secvndvm hodiernvm sitvm neoterica descriptio auctore.
" 41. Schlavoniae, Croatiae, Carniae . . . descriptio, avctore Avgvstino Hirsvogelio.
" 42. Hvngariae descriptio, Wolfgango Lazio avct.
" 43. Transilvania . . . —edidit Viennę aº 1566 nobilifs. atq̨ doctifs Ioēs Sabucus Pannonius.
" 44. Poloniae finitimarumque locorum defcriptio auctore Wenceslao Godreccio Polono.
" 45. Septentrionalivm regionvm descrip.
" 46. Rvssiae, Moscoviae et Tartariae descriptio. Auctore Antonio Ienkenfono . . . edita Londini anno 1562.
" 47. Tartariae sive magni chami regni typus.

**Ortelius, A.**—Continued.
  no. 48. Indiae orientalis insvlarvmqve adiacientivm typvs.
  " 49. Persici sive Sophorvm regni typvs.
  " 50. Tvrcici imperii descriptio.
  " 51. Palestinae sive totivs terrae promissionis nova descriptio avctore Tilemanno Stella Sigenens.
  " 52. Natoliae, qvae olim Asia minor . . . descriptio.—Aegypti recentior descriptio.—Carthaginis . . . sinvs typvs.
  " 53. Barbariae et Biledvlgerid . . . descriptio.
The first edition of the "Theatrvm orbis terrarum" was published may 20, 1570, by Egidius Coppens Diesth at Antverp. The circumstances which led to the compilation of the atlas are set forth in a letter (dated july 25, 1603) of Radermacher, Ortelius' friend to the latter's nephew Jacob Cools: " . . . My master [Aegidius Hooftman, well-known merchant of Antverp] though not a man of letters himself, had a great esteem for literature, for scholars and for the arts . . . In nautical experience he surpassed the Antverp merchants of his time . . . He also bought all the geographical maps that could be had . . . but as the unrolling of the large maps of that time proved to be very inconvenient, I suggested to obviate this difficulty by binding as many small maps as could be had together in a book which might easily be handled. Hence the task was entrusted to me, and through me to Ortelius, of obtaining from Italy and France as many maps as could be found printed on one sheet of paper. In this way originated a volume of about thirty maps which is still in the possession of Hooftman's heirs, and its use proved to be so convenient that it induced our friend Abraham to extend its benefit to scholars in general, and to collect the maps of the best authors in a volume of uniform size." cf. Hessel's Abrahami Ortelii . . . epistvlae. 1887. p. 772. Wauvermans states in his "Histoire de l'école cartographique" that this first compilation, which served as a model for the "Theatrum," could not be located.
A second edition of the "Theatrum," of which the Library of Congress has three different impressions appeared in the same year (i. e. 1570); the alterations are noted further on. Another edition was issued in 1571 and then edition followed edition until 1612 when the last was published. These editions appeared in latin, dutch, french, german, spanish, italian and english. In order to increase the usefulness of his atlas, Ortelius published 5 supplements (Additamenta) dated 1573, 1580, 1584, 1590 and 1595. The maps of these supplements were incorporated the same years into new editions of the "Theatrum." In 1579, Ortelius added to his atlas a collection of maps relating to ancient history and geography, under the title of "Parergon theatri;" this parergon at first had 3 maps, but was so increased that in 1612 it contained 38 maps. It was also published separately in 1624.
The names of the cartographers and authors consulted by Ortelius are found listed in several editions of the "Theatrum." A full list has been reprinted with additional notes by Nordenskiöld in his Facsimile atlas.
Besides the "Theatrum" in folio size, there have been published numerous smaller editions. "So early as 1576 appeared the reduced maps of Philip Galle, with the dutch text, in rhyme, by Peeter Heyns (Spieghel der werelt, ghestelt in rijme, Antwerpen. Chr. Plantin. obl. 8°) This work was composed of 73 leaves, 12 of which were double, and was destined as a guide for travellers; it contained 72 maps, of which 66 on single leaves." Hessel, op. cit., p. xli.
On the eng. title "there are four female figures, representing the four divisions of the world, and thus in this book we have America for the first time admitted into the realm of symbolism as the equal of the other three parts of the globe." cf. J. B. Thacher's The continent of America. New York, 1896, p. 254.

Chronological list of the folio editions of the "Theatrum," as found in Hessel's Abrahami Ortelii epistvlae.

1570. Latin. Dated xx maji. (Verso of t. p. blank)
1570. Latin (3 impressions, not dated as above)
1571. Latin.
1571. Dutch.
1572. German.
1573. Additamentum. (Perhaps also with dutch and german text)
1573. Latin.
1573. German.
1574. Latin.
1575. Latin.
1578. French.
1579. Latin.
1580. Additamentvm II.
" German.
1581. French.
1584. Additamentum III.
1584. Latin.
1585. Additamentum III. (With french text)
1587. French.
1588. Spanish.
1589. Latin.
1590. Additamentum IV. (Also in german)
1591. Latin.
1592. "
1595. Additamentum V.
1595. Latin.
1598. Dutch.
" French.
1601. Latin.
1602. Spanish.
" German.
1603. Latin.
1606. English.
1607. Latin.
1608. Italian.
1609. Latin.
1612. Latin.
" Italian.
" Spanish.
1624. Parergon.

Chronological list of the small editions.

1576. Dutch.
1577. Dutch.
" French.
1579. Dutch?
" French.
1583. Dutch.
" French.
1585. Latin.
1588. French.
1589. Latin.
1590. French.
" Latin.
1593. Italian.
1595. Latin.
1596. Dutch.
1598. French.
" Italian.
1601. Latin.
1602. French.
1603. English.
1604. German.
1609. French.
1610? English (J. Norton, London) see title 418, where date is given, 1602?
1612. Latin.
' Italian.
1655. Italian.
1667. "
1679. "
1683. "
1684. "
1697. "

Of the above-mentioned editions the Library of Congress has the following:

Folio editions.

1570 (2d ed. 3 imp.)
1571. Latin.
1572. German.
1573. German.
" Latin.
1574. Latin.
1575. Latin.
1579. Latin.
1584. Additamentvm III (Latin)
" Latin.
1587. French.
1588. Spanish.
1590. Additamentvm IV (Latin)
1592. Latin.
1595. Latin.
" Additamentvm V (Latin)
1598. French.
1601. Latin.
1603. Latin.
1609. Latin.
1612. Italian.
1624. Parergon.

**Ortelius, A.**—Continued.

Small editions.

| | |
|---|---|
| 1589. Latin. | 1604. German. |
| 1593. Italian. | 1612. Latin. |
| 1595. Latin. | 1667. Italian. |
| 1598. Italian. | 1679. Italian. |
| 1601. Latin. | 1683. Italian. |
| 1602. French (Vrients). | 1684. Italian. |
| " French (Coignet). | 1697. Italian. |
| 1602? English. | |

The Library of Congress has three impressions of the 2d ed. 1570; they differ as follows:

| Copy 1. (Described above) | Copy 2. | Copy 3. |
|---|---|---|
| | *On verso of t.-p.:* Gerartvs Falkenbvrgivs noviomagvs (4 lines of Greek verses) added to the Epigramma D. Rogerii. | |

*Different typesetting in the A. Ortelius . . . lectorib. S. D.*

Sig. Aiiij recto ends:

| "in eamen tamen" | "ne vel" | "ne vel" |
|---|---|---|

Sig. Aiiij verso ends:

| "in Sclauoniam" | "Tanais &c" | "ad Ifthmum qui." |
|---|---|---|

*Catalogvs avctorvm.*

| 92 names. | 94 names | 91 names. |
|---|---|---|
| | "Andreas Pogradus Pilsnenfis." | |
| | "Paulus Fabritius medicus." | |
| | "Sigifmundvs ab Herberftein" (Not in the other copies). | |
| "Joannes Hafelbergius à Reichenau" (Not in the other copies) | | |
| | After "Tilemanvs Stella Sigenenfis" has been added: "Idem Comitatum Mansueldiensem Coloniae apud Franc. Hogenbergem." (Not in the other copies) | |

*"Ferdinandvs à Lannoy"* ends:

| "Sed nondum edita." | "Sed non dum edita est [!]" | "Sed non dum edita eft." |
|---|---|---|
| "Jacobus à Dauentria" | "Jacobus Dauentria" | Same as in copy 1. |
| "Marcus Zecfnagel" | spelled "Secfnagel." | " " " " |
| "Stephanus Geltenhofer." | spelled "Keltenhofer" | " " " " |

*On front page of map no. 1.*

"Hartmannvs Scheydel"
(Not in the other copies)

"Hieronymvs Girava"
(Not in the other copies)

*On front page of map no. 47 letterpress ends:*

"libro 18. Cap. 30."  "libro 18. Cap. 30.  Same as in copy 1.
Habet & Laonicus de
Tartaris fub Schytarum
nomine variis in locis
multa; vt & Gregoras
alius fcriptor Græcus."

Inserted between the 53 maps of copy 3 are found 79 maps dated 1572–1590; bound with this copy are the "Parergon theatri" containing 26 maps dated 1579–90, and the "Additamentvm qvintvm, 1595, with 17 maps."

## 1571

Theatrvm orbis terrarvm.   1 p. l., [144] l. incl. 53 col. maps. fol.   [*Colophon:*] apud Ægid. Coppenium Diefth, Antverpiae, 1571.   375

NOTE.—Collation: sig. [A] in eight.—Maps 1–53, with text on front page.—sig. a–d in sixes, e in eight.
sig. [A1] recto: col. eng. title; verso: Epigramma Danielis Rogerii . . . sig. Aij recto: D. Philippo Avstriaco Caroli V. . . verso–Aiij verso: Adolphi Mekerchi Brvgensis . . . frontispicii explicatio. sig. Aiiij recto—Av recto: Abrahamvs Ortelivs Antverpianvs, beneuolis lectoribus S. D. sig. Av recto—Avj verso: Catalogvs avctorvm tabvlarvm geographicarvm (94 names). sig. Avij recto–Aviij recto: Index tabularum. sig. Aviij verso: blank.—Maps 1–53. sig. a recto—a iij verso: De mona drvidvm insvla . . . sig. a iiij recto—[c vj] verso: Synonymia locorvm geographicorvm . . . sig. [c vj] verso—e vij recto: Indice hoc primo ad finem perducto . . . sig. e vij verso: Signa et series foliorvm. Tenor privilegii (dated 1569).—Colophon.—Blank leaf.
Maps are the same as in the editions of 1570, with the exception of no. 29 entitled: "Bavariae, olim Vindeliciae, delineationis compendivm ex tabula Philippi Apiani math."

## 1572

Theatrvm oder schawplatz des erdbodems, warin die landttafell der gantzen weldt, mit fambt aine der felben kurtze erklarüg zu fehen ift.   1 p. l., [192] l. incl. 92 col. maps. 1 col. pl. fol. [*Colophon:*] . . . Gielis von Diest geschworner buchtruckher der kuniglicher maieftat tzo Antorff.   1572.   376

NOTE.—Collation: 2 l., sig. [A] in six.—92 maps, with text on front page.—sig. aj–aiij.
L. [1 & 2]: Colored engraving representing inhabitants of the four continents, in their costumes, sports, etc. Europe, the largest engraving, occupies the upper half of the plate; on the lower half are Africa, America and Asia. In the center is an inscription signed: "Georgmacken, illuminiften zu Nurmberg." sig. [A1] recto: col. eng. title; verso: M. Tvllivs Cicero. Das rofs ift zum ziehen . . . sig. Aij recto: Dedicatio operis; verso—Aiij verso: Adol-

**Ortelius, A.**—Continued.
>phi Mekerchi Brvgensis . . . frontispicii explicatio. sig. Aiiij recto—[A5] verso: Abraham Ortelius zum guetwilligen lefer. sig. [A6] recto: Epigramma Danielis Rogerii . . . verso: blank.—92 col. maps.—sig. a.j. recto: Urlaub des authors tzu feinem lefer; verso—aiij recto: Regifter oder zeyger der tittel von den landtaffelen difes buechs. sig. aiij verso: Regifter vnd zeichen der bogen.—Privilege, colophon and approbation.
>Contains the same maps (1–53) as the 1570 edition, between which have been inserted 16 maps of the 1st Additamentum (1573) and 23 of the 2d (1580)
>The following inserted maps relate to America:
>no. 2*a*. Hispaniae novae . . . descriptio. 1579.
>" 2*b*. Cvliacanae, Americae regionis descriptio.—Hispaniolae, Cvbae aliarvmqve insvlarvm . . . delineatio.

### 1573

Theatrvm oder schawplatz des erdbodems, warin die landttafell der gantzen weldt, mit fambt aine der felben kurtze erklarūg zu fehen ift. Ihietz mitt vielen neuwen landtafflen gemehret. M.CCCCC.LX [XIII] 1 p. l., [142] l. incl. 67 col. maps. fol. [*Colophon:*] . . . Gielis von Diest gefchworner buchtruckher der kuniglicher maieftat tzo Antorff. 1572. 377

>NOTE.—Collation: sig. [A] in six.—67 maps with text on front page.—sig. aj-aiij.
>sig. [A1] recto: col. eng. title; verso: M. Tvllivs Cicero. Das rofs ift zum ziehen . . . sig. Aij recto: Dedicatio operis; verso—Aiij verso: Adolphi Mekerchi Brvgensis . . . frontispicii explicatio. sig. Aiiij recto—[A5] verso: Abraham Ortelius zum guetwilligen lefer. sig. [A6] recto: Epigramma Danielis Rogerii . . . verso: blank.—67 col. maps, with text on front page. sig. a. j. recto: Urlaub des authors tzu feinem lefer; verso—aiij recto: Regifter oder zeyger der tittel von den landtaffelen difes buechs; verso: Regifter vnd zeichen der bogen.—Privilege, colophon and approbation.
>Maps 24 and 44 wanting.
>Contains same maps as edition of 1570 (excepting no. 29) between which have been inserted 16 maps of the Additamentum (1573)
>Although the colophon is dated 1572, this edition is described by Tiele and Hessel as having the date 1573 on the t. p.; on L. C. copy the last XIII of the date have been erased.

### 1573

Theatrvm orbis terrarvm. Opus nunc denuò ab ipso auctore recognitum, multisquè locis castig[atum] & quamplurimis nouis tabulis atquè commentarijs auctum. 1 p. l., [192] l. incl. 69 col. maps. fol. [*Colophon:*] apud Ant. Coppenium Diesth, Antverpiae 1573. 378

>NOTE.—Collation: sig. [A] in six; B in four.—Maps 1–27, 29–70.—sig. a–h in sixes.
>sig. [A1] recto: col. eng. title; verso: Epigramma Danielis Rogerii . . .—Hadriani Ivnii Hornani in idem. sig. Aij recto: Dedication, D. Philippo Avstriaco Caroli V . . . verso—Aiij verso: Adolphi Mekerchi Brvgensis . . . frontispicii explicatio. sig. Aiiij recto—[A5] recto: Abrahamvs Ortelivs Antverpianvs, beneuolis lectoribus S. D., (dated Antverpiæ M. D. LXX). sig. [A5]

verso—B recto: Catalogvs avctorvm ... (103 names). sig. B verso—Bij recto: Index tabularum huius operis ... sig. Bij verso—Biij recto: Qvoniam vero plvres regiones ... sig. Biij verso: D. Abrahamo Orthelio (signed Daniël Rogerius).—Gerartvs Falkenbvrgivs noviomagvs (in Greek). sig. [B4] recto: Ornatissimo viro D. Abrahamo Ortelio, amico cùm primis caro (dated: Duysburgi 22. Nouembris 1570; signed: Gerardus Mercator).—Tabulæ quæ recenter accefferunt. sig. [B4] verso: blank.—Maps 1-27, 29-70, with text on front page, on verso of last map: Errata aliqvot typographica ... sig. aj recto—[dvi] recto: Synonymia locorvm geographicorvm ... sig. [dvi] verso—hij verso: Indice primo ad finem perducto, hunc alterum in ftudioforum gratiam fubiungere placuit ... sig. hiij recto—[hv] verso: De Mona Drvidvm insvla ... sig. [hvi] recto: Privilegivm rom. imperii.—Tenor privilegii regis Hispaniæ; verso: Ad libri compactorem.—Approbation and colophon. Map 28, Mansfeldiæ comitatus descriptis; wanting. One sheet from maps 35, 47 and 61 wanting.

The following maps relate to America:
no. 1. Typvs orbis terrarvm.
" 2. Americae sive novi orbis, nova descriptio.
" 4. Africae tabvla nova ... 1570.
" 5. Evropae.
" 60. Septentrionalivm regionvm descrip.
" 62. Tartariae sive magni chami regni tÿpus.
" 63. Indiae orientalis, insvlarvmqve adiacientivm typvs.

## 1574

Theatrvm orbis terrarvm. Opus nunc denuò ab ipso auctore recognitum, multisquè locis castigatum, & quamplurimis nouis tabulis atquè commentarijs auctum. 1 p. l., [197] l. incl. 70 col. maps. fol. [*Colophon*:] apud Ant. Coppenium Diefth, Antverpiæ, 1574. 379

NOTE.—Collation: sig. [A] in six; B in four.—Maps 1-70.—sig. a-h in sixes.
sig. [A1] recto: col. eng. title; verso: Epigramma Danielis Rogerii ...—Hadriani Ivnii Hornani in idem. sig. A2 recto: Dedication, D. Philippo Avstriaco Caroli V ... verso—A3 verso: Adolphi Mekerchi Brvgensis ... frontispicii explicatio. sig. Aiiij recto—[Av] recto: Abrahamvs Ortelivs Antverpianvs ... beneuolis lectoribus S. D. (dated Antverpiæ M. D. LXX). sig. [Av] verso—B recto: Catalogvs avctorvm ... (103 names). sig. B verso—Bij recto: Index tabularum huius operis ... sig. Bij verso—Biij recto: Qvoniam vero plvres regiones ... sig. Biij verso: Ornatissimo viro d. Abrahamo Ortelio, amico cùm primis caro (dated: Duysburgi 22 Nouembris 1570; signed: Gerardus Mercator).—Io. Vivianvs Valentianvs Abrahamo Ortelio svo. sig. [Biv] recto: D. Abrahamo Orthelio (signed Daniël Rogerius).—Gerartvs Falkenbvrgivs noviomagvs (in greek). sig. [Biv] verso: In theatrvm Abrahami Ortelii.—Maps 1-70, with text on front page; on verso of last map: Errata qvaedam fic corrigentur. sig. aj recto—[dvi] recto: Synonymia locorvm geographicorvm ... sig. [dvi] verso-hij verso: Indice primo ad finem perducto, hunc alterum in ftudioforum gratiam fubiungere placuit ... sig. hiij recto—[hv] verso: De Mona drvidvm insvla ... sig. [hvi] recto: Privilegivm rom. imperii.—Tenor privilegii regis Hispaniæ; verso: Ad libri compactorem—Approbation & colophon.
Maps same as in edition of 1573.

## 1574

**Ptolemæus, C.**
La | geografia | di Clavdio Tolomeo | Alessandrino, | Già tradotta di Greco in Italiano da M. Giero. Rvscelli: | & hora | in queſta nuoua editione da M. Gio. Malombra | ricorretta, & purgata d'infiniti errori: | come facilmente nella Prefatione a' Lettori | può ciaſcuno vedere. | Con L'Espositioni del Rvscelli, particolari di luogo in luogo, & vniuerſali, | ſopra tutto il libro, & ſopra tutta la Geografia, o Modo di fare la de- | ſcrittione del Mondo. | Con vna copioſa Tauola de' Nomi antichi, dichiarati co' Nomi | moderni: dal Malombra riueduta, & ampliata. | Et con vn Diſcorſo di M. Gioseppe Moleto, doue ſi dichiarano tutti i termini | appartenenti alla Geografia. Accreſciuto di nuouo del modo di fare i Mappamondi, le Balle, | le Tauole di Geografia, & di molte figure neceſſarie. | Al Clariss. S.r Giacomo Contarini. | Con Pri [*Vignette*] vilegi. | In Venetia, Appreſſo Giordano Ziletti. | MDLXXIIII. | [*Title to second part:*] Espositioni | et Introdvttioni | Vniversali, | di Girolamo Rvscelli | ſopra tutta la Geografia di Tolomeo. | Con XXXVII. noue Tauole in iſtampe di rame, così | del mondo conoſciuto da gli antichi, come del nuouo. | Con la carta da nauicare, & con più altre coſe intorno alla Coſmografia, così par mare, come per terra. | Con priuilegio dell' Illuſtriſſimo Senato Veneto, | & d'altri Principi. | [*Vignette*] In Venetia, | Appreſſo Giordano Ziletti. MDLXXIII. | [*Title to third part:*] Discorso | di M. Gioseppe Moleto | Medico, Filosofo, et Mate- | matico eccellentissimo. | Nel quale con uia facile & brieue, ſi dichiarano & | inſegnano tutti i termini, & tutte le regole | appartenenti alla Geografia. | Di nuouo dal proprio autore ricorretto, & accreſciuto | del modo di far i Mappamondi, le Balle, le Tauole | di Geografia; di trouar le differenze delle lun- | ghezze, & delle laŕghezze, di molte Figure; | & di molte, & molte coſe neceſſarie | alla perfettione della ſcienza, che | nell' altro mancauano. | [*Vignette*] | In Venetia, Appreſſo Giordano Ziletti, al ſegno | della Stella, MDLXXIII. | 380

407 l. comprising: 8 p. l., 32 l., 350 (*i. e.* 352) pp., 27 maps on [54] l., 38 maps on [76] l., [28] l., 57-65, 55 [1] pp. 8°.

(sig. *, **, A-H, A-Z, Aa-Xx in fours, A-Z, Aa-Dd, ▓, A-Z, Aa-Oo in twos, $\alpha$-$\eta$ in fours, H in six, A-G in fours)

Collation: title, verso blank—sketch of Ptolemy with woodcut on recto, 1 l., preface "A i "Lettori," 2 l. with same woodcut on verso l. 4, (sig. *); dedication, dated "Il primo di Gennaio 1574," 4 l., (sig. **); "Tavola", [31] l., 1 blank l., (sig. A-H); text, incl. 11 diagr., 251, 250-350 pp. (sig. A-Z, Aa-Xx); 27 maps on [54] l., description on reverse, (sig. A-Z, Aa-Dd); 38 maps on [76] l., (sig. ▓, A-Z, Aa-Oo); "Espositioni" of Rvscelli, [27] l., 1 blank l., (sig. $\alpha$-$\eta$); "Discorso" of Moleto, incl. 3 diagr., pp. 57-65, blank l. completing sig. wanting, (sig. H); pp. [1]-55 [1] incl. 5 diagr., (sig. A-G)

Third edition of Ruscelli's translation, revised and corrected by Gio. Malombra. Maps the same as those in italian edition of 1564 with different numbering for the new maps and the following exceptions:

no. 1. "Ptolemaei Cognita" for which Malombra returned to the original conical projection of Ptolemy.
" 11. "Territorio di Roma"; a new map for this edition. Inserted in L. C. copy of 1564 italian edition.

The following maps relate to America:
no. 1. Orbis Descriptio.
" 15. Schonladia Nvova.
" 16. Septenirionalivm [!] Partivm Nova Tabvla.
" 31. Tierra Nveva.
" 32. Nveva Hispania Tabvla Nova.
" 33. Tierra Nova.
" 34. Brasil Nvova Tavola.
" 35. Isola Cvba Nova.
" 36. Isola Spagnola Nova.
" 37. Carta Marina Nvova Tavola.

Modern binding, half vellum.
Eames-Sabin, no. 66505.

## 1574

——— Same. 381

404 l. comprising: 8 p. l., 32 l., 350 (*i. e.* 352) pp., 27 maps on [54] l., [27] l., 37 maps on [74] l., 65 pp. 8°.
(sig. *, * *, A–H, A–Z, Aa–Xx in fours, A–Z, Aa–Dd in twos, $\alpha$–$\eta$ in fours, A–Z, Aa–Oo in twos, A–G in fours, H in six)
Collation: title, verso blank—sketch of Ptolemy with woodcut on recto, 1 l., preface "A i Lettori" 2 l., with same woodcut on verso l. 4, (sig. *); dedication, dated "Il primo di Gennaio 1574," 4 l., (sig. * *); "Tavola", [31] l., 1 blank l., (sig. A–H); text, incl. 11 diagr., 251, 250–350 pp. (sig. A–Z, Aa–Xx); 27 maps on [54] l., description on reverse, (sig. A–Z, Aa–Dd); "Esposition" of Rvscelli, [27] l., blank l. completing sig. $\eta$ wanting, (sig. $\alpha$–$\eta$); 37 maps on [74] l., (sig. A–Z, Aa–Oo); "Discorso of Moleto, incl. 8 diagr., 61, 60–65 pp., verso p. 65 blank, blank l. completing sig. H wanting, (sig. A–H)
Map entitled "Orbis Descriptio" wanting.
Modern binding, half red morocco.

## 1575

**Ortelius, A.**

Theatrvm orbis terrarvm. Opu[s] nunc denuò ab ïpso auctore recognitum, multisquè locis castigatum, & quamplurimis nouis tabulis atquè commentarijs auctum. 1 p. l., [197] l. incl. 70 col. maps. fol. [*Colophon:*] apud Ægidium Radæum Gandenſem, Antverpiae, 1575. 382

NOTE.—Collation: sig. [A] in six; B in four.—Maps 1–70.—sig. a–h in sixes. sig. [A1] recto: col. eng. title; verso: Epigramma Danielis Rogerii . . .— Hadriani Ivnii Hornani in idem. sig. A2 recto: Dedication, D. Philippo Avstriaco Caroli V . . . verso—A3 verso: Adolphi Mekerchi Brvgensis . . . frontispicii explicatio. sig. Aiiij recto—[Av] recto: Abrahamvs Ortelivs Antverpianvs . . . beneuolis lectoribus S. D. (dated Antverpiæ M.D.LXX). sig.

**Ortelius, A.**—Continued.
[Av] verso—B recto: Catalogvs avctorvm . . . (106 names) sig. B verso—Bij recto: Index tabularum huius operis . . . sig. Bij verso—Biij recto: Qvoniam vero plvres regiones . . . sig. Biij verso: Ornatissimo viro D. Abrahamo Ortelio, amico cùm primis caro (dated: Duysburgi 22. Nouembris 1560 [!] signed: Gerardus Mercator).—Io. Vivianvs Valentianvs Abrahamo Ortelio 8vo. sig. [Biiij] recto: D. Abrahamo Ortelio (signed: Daniël Rogerius).— Gerartvs Falkenbvrgivs noviomagvs (in greek) verso: In theatrvm Abrahami Ortelii.—Maps 1-70, with text on front page; on verso of last map: M. Tvllivs Cicero. Eqvvs vehendi cavsa . . . sig. aj recto—[dvj] recto: Synonymia locorvm geographicorvm . . . sig. [dvj] verso—sig. hij verso: Indice primo ad finem perdvcto, hunc alterum in ſtudioforum gratiam ſubiungere placuit . . . sig. hiij recto—[hv] verso: De Mona drvidvm insvla . . . sig. [hvi] recto: Privilegivm rom. imperii.—Tenor privilegii regis. Hispaniæ verso: Ad libri compactorem.—Approbation and colophon.
Maps same as in the 1574 edition.

### 1578
**Jode, G. de.**
Specvlvm orbis terrarvm. 2 v. in 1. 4 p. l., [4] pp., 27 sheets numb. I-XXVII incl. 27 maps; 1 p. l., 1 numb. l., 38 sheets numb. I-XXXVIII incl. 38 maps, 1 l. fol. [*Colophon:*] Antverpiæ . . . in ædibus Gerardi de Iode. Typis Gerardi Smits [1578] 383

NOTE.—Collation: v. 1. l. 1 recto: eng. title, (verso blank).—l. 2 recto—verso: Illvstrissimo d. Philippo . . . Daniël Cellarius Ferimontanus S. P. D. (dated 1578). sig. *recto-verso: Daniel Cellarius Ferimontanus lectori s. — sig. [*2] recto-verso: Catalogus authorum, quorum ſcriptis in hoc opere vſi ſumus.—Index tabvlarvm primi volvminis.—sig. a-c in twos: sheets I-III.—sig. c² in two: Sequitur Libya . . . (4 pp.) — sig. d-i in twos: sheets IIII-IX.—sig. k-s, v, z, x, y, Z, aa, bb, in twos: sheets x-xxv.—sig. cc in two: sheet no. XXVII.—Sheet no. XXVI not signed.—v. 2, l. 1 recto: eng. title: Specvlvm geographicvm totivs Germaniæ imperivm repræsentans. 1578. (verso blank).— Sig. A2 recto-verso: Germaniae vniversalis tabvla I.—sig. A2 [!], B-I in twos: sheets I-IX.—sig. K-T V, X-Z, Aa-Ii in twos: sheets x-xxxII.—sig. KK-PP in twos: sheets XXXIII-XXXVIII. 1 l. unsig. recto: Privilege (dated 1577) and colophon (verso blank). See also title 398.
Maps have text on reverse.
The following maps relate to America:
   no. 1. Vnìversi orbis sev terreni globi in plano effigies.—Insets: Cvsco regionis Perv metropolis.—Messico Hispaniæ novæ metropolis.
" 2. Americæ Pervvi . . . recens delineatio.
" 4. Asiae novissima tabvi. a. [!]

### 1578
**Ptolemæus, C.**
Tabvlae ge | ographicae Cl: Ptolemẹi ad | mentem autoris | reſtitutæ & | emendatẹ. | Per Gerardum Mercatorem | Illuſtriſſ: Ducis Cliuiẹ &c: | Cofmographū. | [*Colophon:*] Coloniae Agrippinae | Typis Godefridi Kempensis. | Anno Virginei Partvs, | M.D.LXXVIII. | 384

74 l. (preceded by 1 and followed by 3 blank l.) comprising : 4 p. l., 28 maps on [55] l., [15] l. fol.
(sig. 1 l. unsigned; (?) in two; (?) (? ) in one; * *, A-N in twos; 1 l. unsigned; O-Z, Aa-Cc, a-h, in twos)
Collation: title, verso blank, (unsigned); dedication, signed Gerardus Mercator, dated "Duysburgi menſe febr: 1578" on recto l. [2], "Praefatio" begins on verso l. [2] and ends on recto l. [4], diagram on verso l. [4], (sig. (?), (?) (?)); 27 double-page and 1 single maps on [55] l., (sig. * *, A-Cc); "Indecem," ending with colophon, [15] l., 1 blank l., (sig. a-h)
First edition of Mercator's maps for Ptolemy's geography.
Without "Privileges" on 1 l. following "Indecem."
"Les premiérs exemplaires parurent sans privilége: Mercator avait oublié d'en faire la demande à temps et n'avait pu attendre l'octroi 'J'ai été obligé—écrit-il—de publier mon ouvrage de Ptolémée avant même d'avoir obtenu, de sa majesté impériale, le privilége sollicité un peu tard par négligence'. Ce ne fut qu'en octobre 1578, qu'un privilége pour dix ans du roi Philippe, daté de Bruxelles du 3 février de cette année et un autre pour un pareil terme de l'empereur Ferdinand, daté de Vienne du 26 mai suivant lui parvinrent et furent joints à son livre." *cf.* Raemdonck, J. van. Mercator, pp. 158-159.
In this edition the text of Ptolemy has been omitted. The reverse of all the maps except one, carry annotations explaining the corrections which Mercator made in the accepted Ptolemaic types.
The maps, comprising only the 27 old maps of Ptolemy and a small one of the Delta of the Nile, were engraved on copper, each with an elaborate cartouche but without ornamental borders. They were reprinted in 1584, 1605 and 1619 and are considered the finest ever prepared for the work.
Original binding, full vellum.
Eames-Sabin, no. 66490.

**1579**

**Heyns, P.**

Le miroir dv monde, redvict premièrement en rithme Brabaçonne, par m. P. Heyns; et maintenant tourné en prose françoise: auquel se représente clairemont & au vif, tant par figures, que caracteres, la vraye situation, nature, & propriété de la terre vniverselle: non moins dvisant par chemin à tous voyagers curieux, que l'excellent Théatre d'Abraham Ortelius, est vtile & conuenable à l'estude de tous estudiants ingénieux . . .    8 p. l., 23, [1] l. incl. 72 maps, 1 pl.   obl. 24°.   à Anvers, de l'imprimerie de Christophle Plantin, pour Philippe Galle, 1579.                                             385

NOTE.—(sig. †-A in eights, B in four, C in twelve, D-K in eights)
Maps and descriptions reduced from the early editions of Ortelius. The maps of America are accurate copies of those in the original Ortelius. "So early as 1576 appeared the reduced maps of Philip Galle, with dutch text, in rhyme, by Peeter Heyns (Spieghel der werelt, ghestelt in rijme. Antwerpen, Chr. Plantijn . . .) This work was destined as a guide for travellers . . .— Reprints with dutch text were published by Plantin iu 1577, 1579(?) and 1583;—with french text (Le Miroir du monde . . . tourné en prose Françoise) by Plantin in 1577, 1579 and 1583 . . ." *cf.* Hessels, J. H. Abrahami Ortelii . . . Cantabrigiae, 1887, p. xli.
Six of the numbered leaves are folded.
See title 387.
The following maps relate to America:
no. [1] Typus orbis terrarum . . . 1574.
 " [2] Americae siue noui orbis noua descriptio.
 " [6] Evropae [showing] Gronlandiae pars.

## 1579

**Ortelius, A.**

Theatrvm orbis terrarvm. Opus nunc denuò ab ipso auctore recognitum, multisquè locis castigatum, & quamplurimis nouis tabulis atquè commentarijs auctum. 1 p. l., [235] l., 77 [9] pp., incl. 113 maps, 1 port. fol. [*Colophon:*] Antverpiæ . . . apud Christophorum Plantinum, 1579. 386

NOTE.—Collation: sig. [A] in six; B in four.—113 maps.—sig. A-F in sixes, G in eight.

sig. [A1] recto: eng. title; verso: Daniel Rogersivs ad theatrvm orbis, Abrahami Ortelii, denvo ab auctore recognitum. sig. A2 recto: Dedication: D. Philippo Avstriaco Caroli V . . . verso—A3 verso: Adolphi Mekerchi Brvgensis . . . frontispicii explicatio. sig. A4 recto—[A5] recto: Abrahamvs Ortelivs Antverpianvs . . . benevolis lectoribvs S. D. (dated: Antverpiæ M.D.LXX)—Hadriani Ivnii Hornani in hoc theatrvm. sig. [A5] verso—B recto: Catalogvs avctorvm tabvlarvm . . . (127 names). sig. B verso—B2 recto: Index tabvlarvm hvivs operis . . . sig B2 verso: Qvoniam vero plvres regiones . . . sig. B3 recto: Ornatissimo viro D. Abrahamo Ortelio, amico cvm primis caro (dated: Duysburgi 22 Nouembris 1570; signed: Gerardus Mercator).—Io. Vivianvs Valentianvs Abrahamo Ortelio svo. sig. B3 verso: D. Abrahamo Ortelio (signed: Daniel Rogerfius).—Gerartvs Falkenbvrgivs Noviomagvs (in greek).—sig. [B4] recto: Epigramma Danielis Rogersii . . .—In idem Ioan. Vivianvs Valentianvs; verso: portrait of Ortelius.—113 maps, i. e. maps numbered 1-93 between which have been inserted 20 unnumbered or unsigned maps appearing in the Additamentum of 1580 and the atlas of 1584; several of these inserted maps are dated 1584.—On the recto of map 91 is the following title: "Parergon theatri" to which has been added in mss.: "in quo veteris geographię aliquot tabulæ." The Parergon contains 10 maps; the first three are numbered: 91, 92, 93; the others are not numbered.—Maps have text on front page.

sig. a1 recto: "Nomenclator Ptolemaicvs; omnia locorvm vocabvla qvæ in tota Ptolemæi geographia occurrunt . . . Antverpiæ, C. Plantinus, 1579", verso: Abrahamvs Ortelivs candido lectori. sig. a2 recto— g3 recto [Nomenclator Ptolemaicvs] sig. g3 verso—[g6] verso: De Mona drvidvm insvla. sig. [g7] recto: Imp. Rvdolphi Philippi Hisp. regis, et cancellariæ Brabanticæ privilegiis sancitvm est . . .—By privilegien des keyfers . . . verso: Ad libri compactorem . . .—Approbation.—Colophon.

At the foot of the t.-p. is found the following mss. dedication, written by the author: "Ornatifsimo viro Dno. I. Baptisti Favolio, homini bono, et amico suo vero, auctor D. D." The text of the atlas also contains many mss. corrections and additions, which have been printed in later editions. The handwriting of these corrections and additions is the same as that of the dedication on the t.-p.

Map no. 51 contains view of Salzburg: "Vrbis Salis bvrgensis genvina descriptio. The following maps relate to America:

no. 1. Typvs orbis terrarvm.
" 2. Evropæ.
" 4. Africae tabvla nova . . . 1570.
" 5. Americae sive novi orbis . . . descriptio.
" 6. Hispaniae novae . . . descriptio. 1579.
" 7. Pervviae avriferæ regionis typvs. Didaco Mendezio auctore.—La Florida. Auctore Hieron. Chiaues.—Gvastecan reg . . .
" 81. Septentrionalivm regiorvm descrip.
" 83. Tartariae sive magni chami regni typus.
" 84. Indiae Orientalis, insvlarvmqve adiacientivm typvs.

## 1583

**Heyns, P.**

Le miroir dv monde, redvit premièrement en rithme Brabançonne, par m. P. Heyns; et maintenant tourné en prose Françoise: auquel se représente clairement & au vif, tant par figures, que caractères, la vraye situation, nature, & propriété de la terre vniuerselle: non moins dvisant par chemin à tous voyagers curieux, que l'excellent Théâtre d'Abraham Ortelius, est vtile & conuenable en la bibliothèque de tous estudiants ingénieux. Revev, corrigé & augmenté de plusieurs belles cartes . . .   10 p. l., 84, [1] l. incl. 83 maps, 1 pl. obl. 24°.  à Anvers, de l'imprimerie de Christofle Plantin. pour Philippe Galle, 1583. 387

NOTE.—(sig. †-†† in fours, ††† in two, A-Z in fours)
Third french edition. See 1579 edition, title 385.
Six of the numbered leaves are folded.
The following maps relate to America:
no. [1] Tipus orbis terrarum . . . 1574.
" [2] Americae siue noui orbis noua descriptio.
" [6] Evropae [showing] Gronlandiae pars.

## 1584

**Ortelius, A.**

Theatrvm orbis terrarvm. Opus nunc tertio ab ipso auctore recognitum, multisquè locis castigatum, & quamplurimis nouis tabulis atquè commentarijs auctum.   1 p. l., [279] l. incl. 112 col. maps, 1 por. fol. [*Colophon:*] Antverpiæ . . . apud Chriftophorum Plantinum, 1584] 388

NOTE.—Collation: sig. [A], B in sixes.-maps 1-100.-l. 101, 102.-maps 103-114.-sig. [A]-F in sixes, G in eight.
sig. [A1] recto: col. eng. title; verso: Daniel Rogersivs ad theatrvm orbis Abrahami Ortelii, denvo ab auctore recognitum. sig. A2 recto: Dedication; D. Philippo Avstriaco Caroli V . . . verso—A3 verso: Adolphi Mekerchi Brvgensis . . . frontispicii explicatio. sig. [A4] recto—[A5] recto: Abrahamvs Ortelivs Antverpianvs . . . benevolis lectoribvs S. D. (dated: Antverpiæ M.D.LXX).—Hadriani Ivnii Hornani in hoc theatrvm. sig. [A5] verso—B1 verso: Catalogvs avctorvm tabvlarvm . . . (134 names). sig. B2 recto—B3 recto: Index tabvlarvm hvivs operis . . . sig. B3 verso—B4 recto: Qvoniam vero plvres regiones . . . sig. B4 verso: Ornatissimo viro D. Abrahamo Ortelio, amico cvm primis caro. (dated Duysburgi 22 Nouembris 1570; signed Gerardus Mercator). Io. Vivianvs Valentianvs Abrahamo Ortelio svo. sig. [B5] recto: D. Abrahamo Ortelio (signed: Daniel Rogerfius.)—Gerartvs Falkenbvrgivs noviomagvs (in greek). sig. [B5] verso: Epigramma Danielis Rogersii . . .—In idem Ioan. Vivianvs Valentfanvs. sig. [B6] recto: portrait of Ortelius (colored engraving); verso: blank.—Maps 1-100.—L. 101 recto: Parergon, in quo veteris geographiæ aliquot tabulæ; verso—l. 102 verso: Ornatissimo viro d. Abrahamo Ortelio (signed: Coloniæ Agripp. pridie kal. Ian. cIɔ. IɔlxxvIII. A. Graphevs)—Maps 103-114. Maps have text on front pages. Sig. [A1] recto: Nomenclator Ptolemaicvs; omnia locorvm vocabvla qvæ in tota Ptolemæi geographia occurunt . . . Antverpiæ, C. Plantinus, 1584; verso: Abrahamvs Ortelivs candido lectori. sig. A2 recto—G3 recto: [Nomenclator Ptolemaicvs] sig. G 3 verso—[G6] verso: De Mona drvidvm insvla . . .

**Ortelius, A.**—Continued.

 sig. [G7] recto: Imp. Rvdolphi, Philippi Hisp. regis, et cancellariæ Brabanticæ privilegiis sancitvm est . . .—By privilegien des keysers . . . verso: Ad libri compactorem . . .—Approbation.—Colophon.—Blank leaf.

 Map no. 57 contains a view of Salzburg: "Vrbis Salisbvrgensis genvina descriptio."

 The following maps relate to America:

 no. 1. Typvs orbis terrarvm . . .
 " 2. Evropae.
 " 4. Africae tabvla nova . . . 1570
 " 5. Americae sive novi orbis . . . descriptio.
 " 6. Hispaniae novae . . . descriptio. 1579.
 " 7. Cvliacanae, Americae regionis, descriptio.—Hispaniolae, Cvbae, aliarvmqve insvlarvm circvmiacientivm, delineatio.
 " 8. Pervviae avriferæ regionis typvs. Didaco Mendezio auctore.—La Florida. Auctore Hieron. Chiaues—Gvastecan reg.
 " 90. Septentrionalivm regionvm descrip.
 " 92. Tartariæ sive magni chami regni tÿpus.
 " 94. Indiae Orientalis, insvlarvmqve adiacientivm typvs.

## 1584

Additamentvm III. Theatri orbis terrarvm. 1 p. l., (1 blank l.) 24 maps. fol. Antuerpiæ Ambivaritorum, 1584.   389

 NOTE.—Maps have text on front pages.

 On the t. p. are the following:

 Abrahamvs Ortelivs geographiæ ftudiofis.—Index tabularum huius additamenti.—In Abrahami Ortelij diligentiam inuictam.

 map no. [14] entitled: Valentiæ regni . . . 1584 is not mentioned in the index on the t. p.

 The following map relates to America:

 no. [10] Pervviae avriferæ regionis typvs. Didaco Mendezio auctore.—La Florida. Auctore Hieron Chiaues.—Gvastecan reg.

## 1584

**Ptolemæus, C.**

 Cl. | Ptolemaei | Alexandrini, | Geographiae | Libri Octo, | recogniti iam et diligenter emendati cum tabulis ge- | ographicis ad mentem auctoris restitutis ac emen- | datis, per Gerardvm Mercatorem, Illus- | trifs. Ducis Cliuensis etc. Cofmographum. | Cum gratia & Priuilegio Sac Cæf. | Maiestat. | M. D. LXXXIV. | [*Colophon:*] Coloniae Agrippinae | Typis Godefridi Kempensis. | Anno Virginei Partvs, | M. D. LXXXIIII. |   390

 145 l. (followed by 1 blank l.) comprising: 2 p. l., 106, [2] pp., [19] l., 28 maps on [55] l., [15] l. fol.

 (sig. 2 l. unsigned; A–L in sixes; M in four; (?) in four; A–L, K, M₂, O, N–Y, Zz, Aa–Bb, in twos; a–b in sixes; c in four)

 Collation: title, ornamented with a map, verso blank (unsigned); dedication by Mylius, dated "Coloniæ Calendis Iulij, Anno D. 1583," followed by commendatory verses by Isselt, 1 l. (unsigned); text incl. 6 diagr., 106, [2] pp., (sig. A–I); "Index Eorvm Qvae in Octo Libris Ptolemæi" with table on verso l. [15], blank l. completing sig. M wanting, [15] l., (sig. K–M); title, "Tabvlae Geo= | graphicae Cl. Ptole | maei ad mentem Avcto≠ | ris restitvtae et emendatae, | per Gerardvm Mercatorem | Illvstriss. Dvcis Cliviæ &c. | Cosmogra- | phvm" | , verso contains privileges subscribed "Datum Viennæ Auftriæ 26. Maij 1578" and "Datum 3. Februarij 1578. Bruxellæ," l. [1], dedication to Ortelius dated "Duysburgi menfe Febr: 1583" signed by Mercator, on recto l. [2], preface beginning on verso l. [2], ending on recto l. [4], diagr. on verso, (sig. (?)); 27 double page, and 1 single copperplate, maps with descriptive text on reverse, the single leaf map "Appendix III Tabvlae Afr" is attached to "Afr: III Tab.," which appears on sig. $M_1$ incorrectly signed O, [55] l, (sig. A–L, K, $M_2$, O, N–Y, Zz, Aa–Bb); "Indicem ending with colophon on l. [15], [15] l., 1 blank l., (sig. a–c)

Ptolemy's geography with Mercator's maps. Pirckheymer's translation edited by Arnoldus Mylius.

Maps same as those published without the Ptolemy text in 1578 and reprinted in the editions of 1605 and 1619.

This edition corresponds to that in the Boston Athenæum with the exception of sig. F which is not incorrectly signed E.

Modern binding, half morocco.

Eames-Sabin, no. 66491.

## 1585

**Favoli, U.**

Theatri orbis terrarvm enchiridion, minoribvs tabvlis per Philippvm Gallævm exaratvm: et carmine heroico, ex variis geographis & poëtis collecto, per Hvgonem Favolivm illustratum. 4 p. l., 170 [2] (*i. e.* 184) pp. incl. 83 maps, 1 pl. 12°. Antvverpiæ, excudebat Philippo Gallæo Christophorus Plantinus, 1585. 391

NOTE.—The following maps relate to America:
no. 1. Tiipus orbis terrarum. 1574.
" 2. Americae siue noui orbis noua descriptio.

## 1587

**Ortelius, A.**

Théâtre de l'vnivers, contenant les cartes de tovt le monde. Avec vne brieve déclaration d'icelles. Le tout reveu, amendé, & augmenté de plufieurs cartes & declarations par le mefme autheur. 1587. 1 p. l., [234] l. incl. 112 col. maps, 1 por. fol. [*Colophon:* A Anvers, C. Plantin] 392

NOTE.—Collation: 1 l., sig.* in five.—Maps 1–102, 104, 103, 105–112.—sig. A in five, (last l. wanting).

l. 1 recto: col. eng. title; verso: M. Tvllivs Cicero. Le cheual eft créé pour porter,& tirer . . . sig.* recto: Av prvdent senat, et pevple d'Anvers, Christophle Plantin; verso—*3 recto: Abraham Ortelivs av lectevr débonnaire (dated: D'Anuers l'an M.D.LXXII) sig. *3 verso—[* 4] verso: M. Gerard dv Vivier svr le frontispice de ce present livre. sig. [* 5] recto: Av débonaire spectatevr et lectevr dv théâtre d'Abraham Ortel . . . verso: col. eng. portrait of Ortelius.—Maps 1–100. On the front page of map 101 is the title: "Parergon dv théâtre".—Maps 102, 104, 103, 105–112 (with text in French on the front pages). sig. A1 recto: L'adiev de l'avctevr av lectevr; verso—A2 recto: Voyes, chemins et addresses par ov, et en qvelle manière les pierreries . . . font amenées en Europe. sig. A2 verso—A3 recto: Noms d'avcvnes marchandises . . . sig. A3 verso—A4 verso: La table, ou indice des tiltres des cartes com-

35799—08——10

**Ortelius, A.**—Continued.
prifes en ce liure. sig. [A5] recto—verso: Povrce qv'en ces cartes est faict la description de plvsievrs pays . . .—The last l. containing the Privilège and the colophon is wanting.

Map no. 57 contains a view of Salzburg: "Vrbis Salisbvrgensis genvina descriptio."

The following maps relate to America:
no. 1. Typvs orbis terrarvm. (The words: "Cum priuilegio. Franciscus Hogenbergus sculpsit", left out)
" 2. Evropae.
" 4. Africae tabvla nova . . . 1570.
" 5. Americae sive novi orbis . . . descriptio. On this map the delineation of South America has been altered.—In the S. E. corner the following has been added to "Cum priuilegio": decennali Ab. Ortelius delineab. et excudeb. 1587.
" 6. Hispaniae novae . . . descriptio. 1579.
" 7. Cvliacanae . . . descriptio.—Hispaniolae, Cvbae, aliarvmqve insvlarvm circvmiacientivm delineatio.
" 8. Pervviae avriferæ regionis typvs. Didaco Mendezio auctore.—La Florida. Auctore Hieron. Chiaues.—Gvastecan reg.
" 90. Septentrionalivm regionvm descrip.
" 92. Tartariae sive magni chami regni typus.
" 94. Indiae orientalis . . . typvs.

### 1588

Theatro de la tierra vniversal . . . con sus declaraciones traduzidas d' el latin. 1 p. l., [209] l. incl. 100 col. maps, 1 por. fol. Impreffo en Anueres por Christoual Plantino, prototypographo d' el rey nuestro señor en fus Eftados Baxos. Año 1588. 393

NOTE.—Collation: sig.* in six.—Maps 1-100.—sig. A in four.

Sig. [*1] recto: col. eng title; verso: blank.—sig. *2 recto—verso: Al principe de España don Filippe d'Avstria (dated De Anuers, a II. d' el mes de mayo. M. D. LXXXVIII). sig. *3 recto—*4 recto: Abraham Ortelio Antverpiano, geographo d' el rey . . . a los benevolos lectores salvd. sig. *4 verso—[*6] recto: Tabla de las cartas d' esta obra, o de los titvlos d' ellas.—Por qve se hallaran mas regiones o islas declaradas en estas cartas qve las qve los titvlos d' ellas contienen . . . sig. [*6] verso: col. eng. portrait of Ortelius.—Maps 1-100 (with text on front pages). sig. A1 recto: La despedida d' el avctor al lector. sig. A1 verso—A2 verso: Navegacion, caminos y medios por donde y en qve modo las pedrerias . . . y otras cosas peregrinas de los Afianos . . . folian venir à nueftras prouincias . . . sig. A3 recto—verso: Nombres de algvnas mercaderias peregrinas . . . de donde nos las traen. sig. [A4] recto: Imp. Rvdolphi, Philippi Hisp. regis, et cancellariæ Brabanticæ privilegiis sancitvm est; verso: blank.

Not mentioned by Tiele in his bibliographical essay on Ortelius' Theatrum (1876); Hessel in Epistvlae Ortelianæ (1887) describes a copy of this edition in the British Museum.

The following maps relate to America:
no. 1. Typvs orbis terrarvm.
" 2. Evropae.
" 4. Africae tabvla nova. 1570.
" 5. Americae sive novi orbis, nova descriptio. 1587.
" 6. Hispaniae novæ . . . descriptio. 1579.

no. 7. Cvliacanae, Americae regionis, descriptio.—Hispaniolae, Cvbae, aliarvmqve insvlarvm circvmiacientivm delineatio.
" 8. Pervviae avriferæ regionis typvs. Didaco Mendezio auctore.—La Florida. Auctore Hieron. Chiaues.—Gvastecan reg.
" 90. Septentrionalivm regionvm descrip.
" 92. Tartariae sive magni chami regni tÿpvs.
" 94. Indiae Orientalis, insvlarvmqve adiacientivm typvs.

Map no. 57 contains a view of Salzbourg: "Vrbis Salisbvrgensis genvina descriptio."

## 1589

Epitome theatri Orteliani, præcipuarum orbis regionum delineationes, minoribus tabulis expreffas, breuioribufque declarationibus illuftratas, continens. 1 p. l., [103] l. incl. 94 maps, 1 pl. obl. 32°. Anverpiæ, Philippo Gallæo excudebat Chriftophus Platinus, 1589. 394

NOTE.—Collation: sig. A-N (in eights). sig. [A1] recto title, verso blank. sig. A2 recto—A3 verso, text, headed Candido lectori et spectatori Philippvs Gallævs S. sig. A4 recto—[A7] recto, text, headed De natvra maris. sig. [A7] verso, comment on Psalm 45. sig. [A8] recto, engraved plate, verso, descriptive text. sig. B-[N6] 94 l. incl. 94 maps on recto, text on verso. sig. [N6] verso, Approbatio, signed M. H. B., dated 26 Maij, Anno MDLXXXIX. sig. [N7] recto—[N8] recto, Index tabvlarvm. sig. [N8] verso, blank.

Leaves nos. 50 and 52 have been transposed.

The following maps relate to America:—
no. 1. Typvs orbis terrarvm.
" 2. Evropa.
" 4. Africae ta bula nou a. [!]
" 5. Americae fiue noui orbis noua defcriptio.
" 82. Septentrionalium regionum descriptio.
" 84. Tartariae fiue magni chami regni tÿpus.
" 86. Indiae orientalis insularumque adiacientium tÿpus.

## 1590

Additamentum IV. Theatri orbis terrarvm. 1 p. l., [50] l., incl. 25 col. maps. fol. Antverpiæ, ex officina Plantiniana, 1590. 395

NOTE.—Maps have text on front pages.

The 3 following maps belonging to the Additamentvm v, 1595, have been inserted in this copy:
no. [2] Aeneae Troiani navigatio. 1594.
" [4] Evropam, sive Celticam veterem fic defcribere conabar Abrah. Ortelius. 1595.
" [13] Galliæ veteris typvs. 1594.

On the t.-p. are the following:

Abrahamvs Ortelivs geographiæ ftudiofis.—Index tabularum huius Additamenti.—In Abrahami Ortelij diligentiam inuictam.

The following map relates to America:
no. [22] Maris Pacifici (quod vulgò Mar del Zur) cvm regionibus circumiacentibus, infulisque in eodem pafsim fparsis, novifsima descriptio. 1589.

It is the earliest map in which the two divisions of America are named "Americae septemtrionalior pars" "Americae meridionalior pars."

## 1592

**Ortelius, A.**—Continued.

Theatrvm orbis terrarvm. Opus nunc denuo ab ipso auctore recognitum, multisquè locis castigatum, & quamplurimis nouis tabulis atquè commentarijs auctum. 1 p. l., [326] l. incl. 134 maps, 1 por. fol. [*Colophon*]*:* Antverpiæ, in officina Plantiniana, 1592]. 396

NOTE.—Collation: sig. A, B in sixes.—Maps 1-108.—sig. a in four.—Maps 1-26.—sig. A-F in sixes; g in seven.

sig. [A1] recto: eng. title; verso: In theatrvm orbis terrarvm Abrah. Ortelii Antverp (signed And. Schottus . . .)—Gerartvs Falkenbvrgivs Noviomagvs. sig. A2 recto: Dedication: D. Philippo Avstriaco Caroli V . . . verso–A3 verso: Adolphi Mekerchi Brvgensis . . . frontispicii explicatio. sig. [A4] recto–[A5] recto: Abrahamvs Ortelivs Antverpianvs . . . benevolis lectoribvs S. D. (dated Antverpiæ Ambivaritorum M.D.LXX).—Ornatissimo viro D. Abrahamo Ortelio, amico cvm primis caro (signed Gerardus Mercator). sig. [A5] verso–B2 recto: Catalogvs avctorvm tabvlarvm . . . (153 names). sig. B2 recto—B3 recto: Index tabvlarvm hvivs operis . . . sig. B3 verso-B4 recto: Qvoniam vero plvres regiones . . . sig. B4 verso–[B5] recto: Epigrammata Danielis Rogersii . . .—In Abrahami Ortelii theatrvm orbis (signed Paulus Meliffus Francus); verso: Hadriani Ivnii Hornani . . .—Io. Vivianvs Valentianvs Abrahamo Ortelio svo. sig. [B6] recto: eng. portrait of Ortelius; verso: Immenfum exiguo . . . (signed Io. Pofthius med. d.)—maps 1–108. sig. [ai] recto: Parergon, sive veteris geographiæ aliqvot tabvlæ; verso: blanc. sig. aij recto–[aiij] recto: Ornatissimo viro D. Abrahamo Ortelio (signed: Coloniæ Agripp. pridie Kal. Ian. CIƆ.IƆ.LXXV'II. A. Graphevs). sig. [aij] verso–[aiv] recto: In regivm geographvm Dn. Abrahamvm Ortelivm. . . . Iacobvs Colivs Ortelianvs.—Regionvm sive insvlarvm hvivs parergi index; verso: blanc.—Maps 1–26. sig. [A1] recto: Nomenclator Ptolemaicvs; omnia locorvm vocabvla qvæ in tota Ptolemæi geographia occurrunt . . . Antverpiæ, in officina Plantiniana . . . 1591; verso: Abrahamvs Ortelivs candido lectori. sig. A2 recto–g3 recto [Nomenclator Ptolemaicvs]. sig. g3 verso–[g6] verso: De Mona drvidvm insvla . . . sig. [g7] recto: Imp. Rvdolphi, Philippi Hisp. regis, et cancellariæ Brabanticæ privilegiis sancitvm est . . .—By privilegien des keysers . . . verso: Ad libri compactorem.—Approbation.—Colophon.

Maps have text on front page.

Several alterations and corrections have been made to the maps of this edition; they are noted in Tiele's Het Kaartboek van Abraham Ortelius and in Hessel's Ecclesiae Londino-Batavæ archivum. Epistulae Ortelianæ.

Map of the Pacific ocean (no 6), dated 1589 is the earliest in which the two divisions of America are named: "Americæ septemtrionalior pars"—"Americæ meridionalior pars." See also note to title no. 395.

The following maps relate to America:

    no. 1. Typvs orbis terrarvm.—On this map the delineation of the western coast of South America has been changed; the Solomon Islands have been added.—In the S. E. corner the following appears: Ab. Ortelius defcrib. cum priuilegio decennali 1587.—The decoration of the title and the quotations are different from the earlier editions, and in the four corners of the map quotations from Seneca and Cicero have been inserted.

    " 2. Evropae.

    " 4. Africae tabvla nova . . . 1570.

no. 5. Americæ sive novi orbis . . . descriptio . . . 1587.
" 6. Maris Pacifici (quod vulgò Mar del Zur) cum regionibus circumiacentibus . . . novifsima descriptio. 1589.
" 7. Hispaniae novae . . . descriptio. 1579.
" 8. Cvliacanae, Americae regionis, descriptio.—Hispaniolae, Cvbae, aliarvmqve insvlarvm circvmiacientivm, delineatio.
" 9. Pervviae avriferæ regionis typvs. Didaco Mendezio auctore.—La Florida Auctore Hieron. Chiaues.—Gvastecan reg.
" 97. Septentrionalivm regionvm descrip.
" 100. Tartariae sive magni chami regni tÿpus.
" 102. Indiae Orientalis, insvlarvmqve adiacientivm typvs.
Map 61 contains a view of Salzburg.

### 1593

Theatro . . . ridotto in forma piccola, augumentato di molte carte nuoue . . . Tradotto in lingua italiana da Giouanni Paulet. Al. ill$^{mo}$ s$^{or}$ il s$^{or}$ Pietro di Hennin conte di Bovssv. 1 p. l., [116] l. incl. 107 maps. obl. 32°. In Anversa, nella stamparia Plantiniana, a le fpefe di Philippo Gallo, 1593. 397

NOTE.—Collation: sig. A-I, K-O in eights, P in five.
sig. [A1] recto: title; verso: engraving representing two women "Geometria" and "Geographia" on either side of a heraldic shield. sig. A2 recto-A3 verso: Al . . . signor Pietro di Hennin Lietard, conte di Bouffu . . . (signed Giouan Paulet). sig. A4 recto-verso: Filippo Gal alli benigni lettori. sig. A5 recto-[A7] recto: Descrittione del mare. sig. [A7] verso: Il mondo. sig. [A8] recto: Typvs orbis terrarvm; text on verso. sig. B recto-P2 recto: maps 1-106 on recto of leaves, with text on verso. sig. P2 verso-P3 recto: Giovan Pavlet alli lettori. sig. P3 verso-[P5] recto: Tavola. sig. [P5] verso: Quefto theatro piccolo . . . non contiene cofa alcuna contraria a la S$^{ta}$ fede o religione catholica romana . . . effendo vtiliffimo a tutti li ftudiofi, dato in Anverfa, a di XII. di nouembre, 1592, signed: d. Henrico Seberto Dungheo, dottore theologo . . .
The following maps relate to America:
[A8] Typvs orbis terrarvm.
no. 1. Evropa.
" 3. Africae ta bula nou a [!].
" 4. Americae fiue noui orbis noua defcriptio.
" 94. Septentrionalium regionum descriptio.
" 96. Tartariae fiue magni Chami regni tÿpus.
" 98. Indiae orientalis insularumque adiacientium tÿpus.

### 1593-1613

**Jode, G. de** *and* **Jode, C. de.**

Specvlvm orbis terræ. 2 v. in 1. 3 p. l., [17] pp., 2 l., front (port.) 34 sheets numb. 1-10, (1 sheet unnumb.), 11-33 incl. 34 col. maps; 1 p. l., [2] pp., 1 l., 51 sheets numb. 1-38, 45, 40-51 incl. 49 col. maps, 2 col. pl. fol. Antverpiæ, sumptibus viduæ et hęredū Gerardi de Iudæis [1593-1613] 398

NOTE.—Map no. 7 is dated 1613. See also title 383.
Collation: v. 1, l. 1 recto: "Boetius de Philosoph. consol. lib. 2. pros. 7," verso: col. eng. portrait of the bishop Neidhard of Bamberg.—l. 2 recto:

**Jode, G. de** *and* **Jode, C. de**—Continued.

col. eng. title, (verso blank).—l. 3 recto: "Illvstrissimo . . . D. Neidhardo D. G. Bambergensi" . . . (verso blank).—sig. ☙) 2 recto-verso: "Benevolis geographiæ stvdiosis Cornelivs de Ivdæis s. optat." sig. \*,\*\*,\*\*\*,\*\*\*\*, (in twos) (verso of last leaf blank): Introdvctis mathematica." . . . . followed by two unsig. leaves: 1st l. (recto blank) verso: "Catalogvs avthorvm qvorvm scriptis in hoc opere vsi svmvs,"—2nd l. recto: Index tabvlarvm qvae in hoc primo volvmine continentvr." (verso blank).—sig. A-D (in twos), sheets 1-4.—sig D² 1 l. (2 pp. of text).—sig. E-[I], K (in twos) sheets 5-10.—sig. KK² (in two) "China qvae et Sina" (unnumb. sheet).—sig. L-T, V, X-Z, AA-II, KK (in twos) sheets 11-33.—v. 2. l. 1 recto: col. engr. title: "Germania geographicis tabvlis illvstrata. Per Cornelium de Iudæis Antverpianū." sig. Bb, Cc (in twos) sheets, 1, 2: "De institvtione et ordine imperii Germanici tabvla" I, II incl. 2 pl.—sig. Dd (in two) sheet 3.—sig. Dd 1 l. numb. 3 (2 pp. of text.)—sig. Ee-Ii, Kk-Tt, Vv, Xx-Zz, Aaa-Iii, Kkk-Ppp (in twos) sheets 4-37.—sig. Qqq, 1 l. numb. 38.—sig. Zzz (in twos) sheet 45.—sig. Sss, Ttt, Vvv, Xxx-Zzz Aaaa-Ffff (in twos) sheets 40-51.—1 l. unsig. recto: Privilege and colophon, (verso blank)

See also note following the description of the following copy, no. 399.

The following maps relate to America:

no. 1. Totivs orbis cogniti vniversalis descriptio.
" 2. Hemispheriv̄ ab æqvinoctiali linea, ad circvlv̄ poli arctici; Hemispheriv̄ . . . ad circvlv̄ poli ātarctici.
" 3. Brasilia et Pervvia.
" 7. Nova totivs Evropæ tabvla. 1613.
" 11. Americæ pars borealis.
" 12. Qvivirae regnv̄.

## 1593-1613

Specvlvm orbis terræ. 2 v. in 1. 7 p. l., [17] pp., 34 sheets numb. 1-2, (1 sheet unnumb.), 3-33 incl. 34 maps; 1 p. l., [2] pp., 51 sheets numb. 1-38, 45, 40-51 incl. 49 maps, 2 pl. fol. Antverpiæ, sumptibus viduæ et hęredū Gerardi de Iudæis [1593-1613]   399

Note.—This copy uncolored, and without portrait. Map no. 7 is dated 1613. Collation: v. 1. 1 l. recto: eng. title (verso blank).—l. 2 recto: "Boetius de Philosoph. consol. lib. 2. pros. 7" (verso blank).—l. 3 recto: Privilege and colophon dated 1593 (verso blank), followed by a blank leaf.—l. 4 (recto blank) verso: "Catalogvs avthorvm qvorvm scriptis in hoc opere vsi svmvs."—l. 5 recto: "Index tabvlarvm qvae in hoc primo volvmine continentvr." (verso blank).—l. 6 recto: " Illvstrissimo . . . D. Neidhardo D. G. Bambergensi" . . . (verso blank).—sig. ☙2 recto-verso: "Benevolis geographiæ stvdiosis Cornelivs de Ivdæis s. optat."—sig. \*, \*\*, \*\*\*, \*\*\*\*, (in twos) (verso of last leaf blank): "Introdvctio mathematica" . . .— sig. A, B (in twos), sheets 1, 2.—sig. K K² (in two), " China qvae et Sina" (unnumb. sheet).—sig. C, D (in twos), sheets 3, 4.—sig. D², 1 leaf, (2 pp. of text).—sig. E-I, K-T, V, X-Z, AA-II, KK (in twos), sheets 5-33.—v. 2: l. 1 (recto blank) verso: eng. title "Germania geographicis tabvlis illvstrata. Per Cornelium de Iudæis Antverpianū.—sig. Bb, Cc (in twos), sheets 1, 2: "De institvtione et ordine imperii Germanici tabvla" I, II. incl. 2 pl.—sig. Dd in two, sheet 3.—sig. Dd, 1 leaf, numb. 3 (2 pp. of text).—sig. Ee-Ii, Kk-Tt, Vv, Xx-Zz, Aaa-Iii, Kkk—Ppp (in twos), sheets 4-37.—sig. Qqq, 1 leaf, numb. 38.—sig. Zzz, sheet 45.—sig. Sss, Ttt, Vvv, Xxx-Zzz, Aaaa-Ffff (in twos) sheets 40-51.

Cornelis de Jode completed the work of his father by inserting several maps (signed by himself) in the Specvlvm ; the more important are: "Totivs orbis . . . descriptio;" "Americæ pars borealis;" "China regnvm." The engraved titles and the plates are attributed to Antoine Wiericx, and the explanatory text on the reverse of the maps to Cornelis de Jode.

Maps same as in copy, no. 398, but not colored.

## 1595

**Ortelius, A.**

Theatrvm orbis terrarvm. Opus nunc denuo ab ipso auctore recognitum, multisquè locis castigatum, & quamplurimis nouis tabulis atquè commentarijs auctum. 1 p. l., [337] l. incl. port., 145 maps, 2 pl. fol. [Antverpiæ, ex officina Plantiniana, 1595] 400

NOTE.—Collation: sig. A-B in sixes, numb. sheets 1-115 (i. e. [230] pp.); [4] l.; sig. A-T, V, X-Z, a-i in twos, sig. A-C in sixes.
sig. [A1] recto title, verso: In theatrvm orbis terrarvm. Abrah. Ortelii Antverp (signed And. Schottus Antverp). Gerartvs Falkenbvrgivs Noviomagvs, greek epigram. sig. A2 recto, dedication: D. Philippo Avstriaco Caroli V . . . sig. A2 verso-A3 verso: Adolphi Mekerchi Brvgensis I. C . . . frontispicii explicatio. sig. [A4] recto-[A5] recto: preface dated 1570, and letter from Mercator dated 22 nouembris, 1570. sig. [A5] verso-B verso: Catalogvs avctorvm tabvlarvm geographicarvm (170 names). sig. B2 recto-B4 recto, Index. sig B4 verso-B5 verso: Epigrammata Danielis Rogersiis—In Abrahami Ortelii theatrvm orbis (signed Paulus Melissus Francus). Hadriani Ivnii Hornani in hoc theatrum.—Io. Vivianvs Valentianvs Abrahamo Ortelio svo. sig. [B6] recto, portrait of Ortelius, verso: Epigram signed Io. Pofthius med. d; sheet 1-115 maps text on the reverse; [4] l. Parergon; Ad Abrahamvm Ortelivm . . . Michaelis Vander-Hagen . . . Epigramma; Ornatissimo viro, dated 1578, signed A. Graphævs; In regivm geographvm dn. Abrahamvm Ortelivm . . . Iacobi Colii Orteliani . . . Regionvm insvlarvmqve hvivs Parergi index. sig. A-T, V, X-Z, a-g, 30 maps with text on the reverse. sig. h-i 2 pl. sig. [A1] recto: Nomenclator Ptolemaicvs . . . 1595, verso: Abrahamvs Ortelivs candido lectori. sig. A2 recto-[C6] recto: Ptolemaeo geographorvm primario avctore, orbis terrarvm dividitvr in partes tres. sig. [C6] verso: blank.

The following maps relate to America:

no. 1. Typvs orbis terrarvm . . . 1587.
" 2. Evropæ.
" 4. Africae tabvla nova . . . 1570.
" 5. Americae sive novi orbis, nova descriptio 1587.
" 6. Maris Pacifici . . . 1589.
" 7. Hispaniae novae sivæ magnae récens et vera descriptio. 1579.
" 8. Cvliacanae, Americae regionis, descriptio.—Hispaniolae, Cvbae, aliarvmqve insvlarvm circvmiacientivm, delineatio. 1579.
" 9. Pervviae avriferæ regionis typvs. Didaco Mendezio auctore.—La Florida, auctore Hieron. Chiaues.—Gvastecan reg.
" 102. Septentrionalivm regionvm descrip.
" 105. Tartariae sive magni chami regni typus.
" 108. Indiae orientalis, insvlarvmqve adiacientivm typvs.

## 1595

**Ortelius, A.**—Continued.

Additamentvm qvintvm, theatri orbis terrarvm. 1 p. l. (1 blank l.), 17 col. maps. fol. Antverpiæ, ex officina Plantiniana, 1595.

401

[*With his* Theatrvm . . . 1570. Copy no. 3]

NOTE.—Maps have text on front pages.
On the t. p. are the following: Abrahamvs Ortelivs geographiæ ftudiofis.— Index tabularum huius Additamenti.—In Abrahami Ortelij diligentiam inuictam.
Differs from copy described by Tiele in Bibliographische Adversaria, v. 3, which contains 28 maps. According to the index on the t. p., the copy in the Library of Congress is complete.

## 1595

Epitome theatri Orteliani. Præcipuarum orbis regionum delineationes, minoribus tabulis expreffas . . . continens. Noua editio, multis locis emendata, & octodecim nouis tabulis aucta. 1 p. l., [118] l. incl. 109 maps, 1 pl. obl. 32°. Antverpiæ, Philippo Gallæo excudebat Arnoldus Connix, 1595.

402

NOTE.—Collation: sig. A–I, K–O in eights, P in seven.
sig. [A1] recto: title; verso: blank. sig. A2 recto–A3 verso: Candido lectori et spectatori Philippvs Gallævs S. sig. A4 recto–[A7] recto: De natvra maris. sig. [A7] verso: engraving, three figures representing "Prudentia Dei, Omnipotentia Dei, Veritas Dei." sig. [A8] recto: Reqviescens a creatione omnipotens . . . Pfalm 45; verso: letterpress "Orbis terrarvm." sig. B recto–P5 recto: maps 1–109; maps are on the recto of the leave; the letterpress is on the verso. sig. P5 verso: Approbatio (dated: Antuerp . . . M. D. LXXXIX. Signed: M. H. B.) sig. [P6] recto–[P7] recto: Index tabvlarvm. sig. [P7] verso: blank. Throughout the book there are numerous mss. notes.
The following maps relate to America:
no. 1. Typvs orbis terrarvm.
" 2. Evropa.
" 4. Africae ta bula nou a. [!]
" 5. Americae fiue noui orbis noua defcriptio.
" 97. Septentrionalium regionum descriptio.
" 99. Tartariae fiue magni chami regni typus.
" 101. India orieṅt.

## 1596

**Ptolemæus, C.**

Geographiae | vniuersae | tvm veteris tvm novae absolvtissimvm opvs | dvobvs volvminibvs distinctvm, | In quorum priore habentur | Cl. Ptolemaei Pelvsiensis | Geographicæ enarrationis Libri octo: | Quorum primus, qui præcepta ipfius facultatis omnia complectitur, | commentarijs vberrimis illustratus est à | Io. Antonio Magino Patavino. | In fecundo volumine infunt | Cl. Ptolemæi antiquæ orbis tabulæ XXVII. ad prifcas hiftorias intelligendas fummè neceffarię. Et tabulę XXXVII. recentiores, quibus vniuerfi orbis pictura, | ac facies, fingularumq; eius partium, regionum, ac prouinciarum | ob oculos patet noftro sæculo congruens. | Vnà cum ipfarum tabularum copiofiffimis expofitionibus, quibus fingulæ orbis partes, prouinciæ, | regiones, imperia, regna, ducatus, & alia dominia, pro ut noftro tempore | fe habent, exacte defcribuntur. Auetore eodem Io. Ant. Magino Patavino Mathematicarum | in Almo Bononienfi Gymnafio publico profeffore. | Cvm Privilegio. Venetiis, cIɔ.Iɔ.xcvi. | Apud Hæredes Simonis Galignani de Karera. | [*Title to second part:*] Geographiae | Cl. Ptolemaei | Pars Secunda, | continens praeter antiqvas ipsivs | Ptol. recentiores etiam Tabulas, quæ Vniuerfæ terræ | faciem noftro æuo cognitam exhibent. | A Hieronymo Porro Pat. incisas. | Vnà cum ipfarum Tabularum vberrimis expofitionibus, quibus | fingulæ Orbis Prouinciæ, Regiones, Imperia, Regna, Ducatus, & alia Dominia defcribuntur. | Auctore. | Io. Antonio Magino Patavino | Almi Bonon. Gymnafij Publico Mathematico. | Cvm Privilegio. | Venetiis, Apud Hæredes Simonis Galignani de Karera. | cIɔ.Iɔ.xcIv. [Date altered by hand to cIɔ.Iɔ.xcvi] 403

460 l. (preceded and followed by 1 blank l.) comprising: 6 p. l., [20] l., 184, 47 pp., 292 (*i. e.* 288) l. incl. 62 maps, 1 map on [2] l., [28] l. fol.

(sig. † in six; A–E in fours; A–L in eights; M, A–F in fours; A–C in eights; D in four; E–P in eights; Q in four; R–Z, Aa–Oo in eights; a–f in fours; g,* in twos)

Collation: title, verso blank,—dedication subscribed "Datum Bonon. Kal. Aprilis, 1596," [2] l., preface, [3] l. (sig. †); "Index," [19] l. followed by 1 blank l. (sig. A–E); text incl. 7 diagr., 184 pp. (sig. A–M); "Io. Antonii Magini Patavini in Primvm Librvm Geographiæ Clavdii Ptolemaei Commentaria, & Annotationes," incl. 10 diagr., 47 pp., verso p. 47 blank (sig. A–F); [27] maps on 27 l. with title, "Geographiae Cl. Ptolemaei Pars Secunda," on recto of first map,—l. 28 text, verso blank (sig. A–D); "Novae Geographicae Tabvlae," l. [29] containing map "Vniversi Orbis Descriptio" on verso, followed by 1 (unsigned) double page map, "Orbis Terrae Compendiosa Descriptio,"—text "Vniversi Orbis Terreni Secvndvm Recentiorem Nostri Temporis rationem Defcriptio," 30–32, [33] 34–67, [68] 69–75, 75, 77–84, 91–117, 120, 119, 122, 121, 122, 125–139, 132, 141, 134, 143–166, 168, 168–184, 181–182, 187–190, 187–259, 259–262, 253, 264–269, 269, 271–273, 278, 275, 275, 277–281, 283, 278, 285–292 l., in all 259 l. incl. [35] single page maps (sig. E–Oo); "Index," 25 l. followed by 1 blank l., (sig. a–g); "Errata," [2] l. verso last l. blank (sig. *)

"A new edition, with new maps, and edited by Giovanni Antonio Magini, of Padua. . . The 64 copperplate maps prepared for this edition, and engraved by Girolamo Porro, are on a smaller scale, and somewhat better executed than those in the editions of 1562." *cf.* Eames.

In this copy, maps, "Tabvla Africae III," and "Tabvla Evropae VIII, which should appear on l. 15 and l. 9 respectively, have been transposed. To rectify this mistake, copies of the correct maps were pasted over the misprints.

The maps were reprinted in the latin editions of 1597, 1608 and 1617, and the italian editions of 1598 and 1621.

The illustration on the titles to first and second parts is the same.

**Ptolemæus, C.**—Continued.
The following maps relate to America:
1. [29] Vniversi Orbis Descriptio.
— Orbis Terrae Compendiosa Descriptio.
" [33] Evropa. [Showing] Gronlandiæ.
" 35. Scandia, sive Regiones Septentrionales.
" 184. Africa.
" 229. Tartariae Imperivm.
" 251. India Orientalis.
" 278. America.
" 291. Vniversi Orbis Descriptio ad vsvm Navigantivm.
Original binding (?) full vellum.
Eames Sabin, no. 66492.

## 1597

Geo- | graphiae | vniversae | tvm veteris, tvm | novae absolvtissimvm | opus, duobus voluminibus diftinctum, | In quorum priore habentur | Cl. Ptolemaei Pelvsiensis | Geographicæ enarrationis Libri octo: | Quorum primus, qui præcepta ipfius facultatis omnia complectitur, | commentarijs vberrimis illustratus est à | Io. Antonio Magino Patavino. | In fecundo volumine infunt | Cl. Ptolemaei, antiquæ orbis tabulæ xxvii. ad prifcas hi- | ftorias intelligendas fummè neceffariæ. Et tabulæ xxxvii. recen- | tiores, quibus vniuerfi orbis pictura, ac facies, fingularumq̃ | eius partium, regionum, ac prouinciarum ob ocu- | los patet noftro fæculo congruens. | Vnà cum ipfarum tabularum copiofifsimis expofitionibus, quibus fingulæ | Orbis partes, prouinciæ, regiones, imperia, regna, ducatus, & | alia dominia, prout nostro tempore fe habent, | exactè defcribuntur. | Auctore eodem Io. Ant. Magino | Patavino, Mathematicarum in | Almo Bononienfi Gymnafio | publico profeffore. | Anno 1597. | In celeberrima Agrippinensivm Colonia excvdebat | Petrvs Keschedt. | [*Title to second part:*] Geogra- | phiae | Cl. Ptolemæi | Pars Secvnda, | continens prae- | ter antiqvas ipsi- | vs Ptol. recentio- | res etiam Tabulas, quæ | Vniuerfæ terræ fa- | cié noftro æuo | cognitā ex- | hibent. | A Hieronymo Porro | Pat. incisas. | Vnà cum ipfarum Tabularum vberrimis expofitio- | nibus, quibus fingulæ Orbis Prouinciæ, Regio- | nes, Imperia, Regna, Ducatus, & | alia Dominia defcri- | buntur. | Avthore | Io. Antonio Magi- | no Patauino, Almi Bo- | non. Gymnafij Pu- | blico Mathe- | matico. | In celeberrima Agrippinensivm Colonia excvdebat | Petrvs Keschedt. | [*Colophon:*] Arnhemii, | Apud Ioannem Ianfonium | Bibliopolam. | Anno M.D.XCVII. | 404

456 1. (preceded and followed by 1 blank l.) comprising: 4 p. l., 47, 184 pp., [20] l., 292 (*i. e.* 288) l. incl. 62 maps, [28] l. fol.
(sig.)( , A–F in fours; A–L in eights; M, A–E in fours; A–C in eights; D in four; E–P in eights; Q in four; R–Z, Aa–Oo in eights; a–g in fours)
Collation: title, verso blank, dedication, dated "Anno à partu Virgineo cɪɔ. ɪɔ. xcvɪɪ. xɪɪɪ. Sept. ftylo Gregoriano," beginning on recto of l. [2] end-

ing on recto of l. [3], preface beginning on verso l. [3] ending on verso l. [4], (sig.)( ); "Io. Antonii Magini Patavini in Primvm Librvm Georgraphiae Clavdii Ptolemaei Commentaria, et Annotationes," incl. 10 diagr., 47 p., verso p. 47 blank, (sig. A–F); books i–viii of text incl. 7 diagr., 184 pp., (sig. A–M); Index, [19] l. followed by 1 blank l., (sig. A–E); [27] copperplate maps on 27 l. with title, "Geographiae Cl. Ptolemæi Pars Secvnda," on recto of first map, followed by l. 28, text, verso blank, (sig. A–D); "Novae Geographicae Tabvlæ", l. [29] containing map "Vniversi Orbis Descriptio" on verso, text "Vniversi Orbis Terreni Secundvm Recentiorem Nostri Temporis rationem Defcriptio," 30–32, [33], 39, 35–67, [68] 69–84, 91–122, 125–184, 181–292 l. in all 259 l. incl. 35 single page copperplate maps, (sig. E–Oo); "Index" ending with colophon, [28] l. (sig. a–g)

Second edition of Magini's Ptolemy.

Maps are the same as those in the 1596 edition.

The double page map, "Orbis Terrae Compendiosa Descriptio," appearing in edition of 1596 between leaves 1 and 2 of the second part, and spoken of by Eames as appearing in this edition with a slight difference in title, is wanting.

Engraved border on the title-pages to the first and second parts are the same.

Maps relating to America given in 1596 edition.

Modern binding with old stamped calf sides.

Eames-Sabin, no. 66493.

**1598**

Geografia | cioè | Descrittione Vniversale | della Terra | Partita in due volumi, | Nel Primo de' quali fi contengono gli Otto Libri della Geografia | di Cl. Tolomeo, | Nuouamente con fingolare ftudio rincontrati, & corretti | dall' Eccell.mo Sig. Gio. Ant. Magini Padovano | Publico Matematico nello Studio di Bologna, | Con vna larghif-sima & copiofifsima fpofitione del medefimo fopra'l Primo de' detti Libri | d'intorno a' precetti & alle regole della Geografia. | Nel Secondo vi fono pofte xxvii. Tauole Antiche di Tolomeo, & xxxvii. altre Moderne, tutte reuifte | & in alcuni luoghi accrefciu-te & illuftrate da ricchifsimi Commentarij di detto Sig. Magini, | Liquali non pur di minuto rapprefentano fiti, qualità, diuifioni, monti, fiumi, porti, città, caftella di tutte le parti | & Prouincie del Mondo, co' loro nomi Antichi & Moderni; ma pieniffimamente informano | della natura, de' coftumi, delle fignorie, delle ragioni de' gouerni, & interamente dello ftato | di tutte le nationi dell' vni-uerfo, cofi ne' tempi pafsati, come ne' prefenti. | Opera vtiliffima & fpecialmente neceffaria allo ftudio dell' Hiftorie, | Dal Latino nell' Italiano Tradotta | Dal R. D. Leonardo Cernoti Vinitiano | Canonico di S. Salvadore. | Con due Indici copiofiffimi. | Con licenza de' Superiori, & Priuilegi. | In Venetia, m.d.xcviii. | Appreffo Gio. Battifta, Giorgio Galignani Fratelli. | [*Title to second part:*] La Seconda Parte | della Geografia | di Cl. Tolomeo, | La quale, oltra l'Antiche Tauole d'effo Tolomeo, contiene le | Moderne ancora, che moftrano la faccia di tutta la Terra, | infino à quefta noftra età conofciuta, | Intagliate da Girolamo Porro. | In-fieme con le loro copiofiffime efpofitione fatte | Dall' Eccellen-

**Ptolemæus, C.**—Continued.

tiss. | Sig. Gio. Ant. Magini Padovano | Lettore delle Matematiche | nel Pvblico Stvdio di Bologna. | Tradotte dal R. D. Leonardo Cernoti Vinitiano | Canonico di S. Salvadore. | Con Privilegi. | In Venetia, M.D.XCVII. | Appreſſo Gio. Battiſta, & Giorgio Galignani Fratelli. | 405

 342 l. (preceded by 2 and followed by 3 blank l.) comprising: 2 p. l., 62, 21, [15] l., 18 l. incl. [27] maps, [1] l., 1 fold. map, 20–212 l. incl. 36 maps, [30] l. 4°.
 (sig. 2 l. unsigned; a–i in sixes; k in eight; aa–cc in sixes; dd in four; A in six; B–C in fours; A–Z, Aa–Ll in sixes; Mm in eight; a–e in sixes)
 Collation: title, verso blank, dedication, verso blank, 2 l. (unsigned); books I–VIII of text incl. 5 diagr., 62 l., (sig. a–k); "Commentarii, et Annotationi dell' Eccell ᵐᵒ. Sig. Gio. Antonio Magini Padouano, nel Primo Libro della Geografia di Claudio Tolomeo. Tradotte dal R. D. Leonardo Cernoti Vinitiano" . . . incl. 10 diagr., 21 l., followed by 1 blank l., (sig. aa–dd); "Tavola," [14] l., (sig. A–C); "La Seconda Parte della Geografia di Cl. Tolomeo" . . . 18 l. incl. 27 maps, verso of l. [1] and l. 18 blank, (sig. A–C); the title "Moderne Tavole di Geografia" . . . 1 l., verso blank, 1 fold. map (unsigned) "Orbis Terræ Compendiosa Descriptio," followed by "Descrittione di tvtto'l mondo terreno al piv moderno stile del nostro tempo," incl. 36 maps, 20–212 l., verso l. 212 blank, (sig. D–Mm); "Indice", [30] l., verso l. [30] blank, (sig. a–e)
 "A translation by Leonard Cernoti of Magini's edition of Ptolemy printed at Venice in 1596 . . . The 64 copperplate maps are the same as those in the latin editions of 1596 and 1597, having been printed from the same plates." *cf.* Eames.
 The maps appear on upper half of the page, followed by text.
 Maps relating to America are noted in the 1596 edition.
 Modern binding, full calf.
 Eames-Sabin, no. 66506.

### 1598

**Ortelius, A.**

Théâtre de l'vnivers, contenant les cartes de tovt le monde. Avec vne brieve déclaration d'icelles. . . . Le tout reveu, amendé, & augmenté de pluſieurs cartes & déclarations par le meſme autheur. 1598.  1 p. l., [249] l. incl. 119 col. maps, & 1 por. fol. [*Colophon:*] À Anvers, de l'imprimerie Plantinienne . . . 1598.  406

 NOTE.—Collation: 2 l.—sig.* in four.—Maps 1–119. sig. A in six.
 L. [1] recto: Col. eng. title; verso: M. Tvllivs Cicero. Le cheual eſt créé pour porter & tirer. l. [2] recto: Av débonaire spectatevr et lectevr dv théâtre . . . verso: col. eng. portrait of Ortelius. sig. * recto: Av prvdent sénat, et pevple d'Anvers, Christophle Plantin. sig.* verso—*3 recto: Abraham Ortelivs av lectevr débonnaire. (dated: D'Anuers l'an M.D.LXXII). sig.* 3 verso–[*4] verso: M. Gerard dv Vivier svr le frontispice de ce present livre.— maps 1–119 (with text on front pages). sig. A1 recto: L'adiev de l'avctevr av lectevr. sig. A1 verso–A2 recto: Voyes, chemins et addressses par ov et en qvelle manière les pierreries . . . font amenées en Europe. sig. A2 verso–A3 recto: Noms d'avcvnes marchandises . . . et des places d'ov elles novs sont icy amenées. sig. A3 verso–[A5] verso: La table . . . des cartes compriſes en ce liure. sig. [A6] recto: Privilège.—Colophon; verso blank.
 On the front page of map 117 is the following: Av lectevr salvt. Après auoir acheué la deſcription de tout le monde; voicy, amy lecteur ces troys cartes

fuyuantes . . . ie les ay adiouftées à la fin de ceft œuure comme Parergon.
The three blank leaves preceding the title and one following the last leaf of the atlas are covered with mss. notes on geography, mineralogy, etc.
The following maps relate to America:
no. 1. Typvs orbis terrarvm . . . 1587.
" 2. Evropae.
" 4. Africae tabvla nova . . . 1570.
" 5. Americae sive novi orbis, nova descriptio . . . 1587.
" 6. Maris Pacifici (quod vulgò mar del Zur) . . . novifsima descriptio . . . 1589.
" 7. Hispaniae novae . . . descriptio. 1579.
" 8. Cvliacanae, Americae regionis, descriptio.—Hispaniolae, Cvbae, aliarvmqve insvlarvm circvmiacientivm delineatio.
" 9. Pervviae avriferæ regionis typvs. Didaco Mendezio auctore.—La Florida. Auctore Hieron. Chiaues.—Gvastecan reg.
" 103. Septentrionalivm regionvm descrip.
" 106. Tartariae sive magni chami regni typus.
" 109. Indiae orientalis, insvlarvmqve adiacientivm typvs.

## 1598

Theatrvm orbis terrarvm Abrahami Orteli Antverp. geographi regii. Dit tonneel des aert-bodems van Abraham Ortelivs, is te koope t' Antvverpen, inden Plantijnfchen Winckel, by de vveduvve ende sonen van Ian Moerentorf. 1 p. l., [187] l. incl. 91 maps. fol. [*Colophon:*] Ghedruckt voor Abraham Ortelius, anno 1598. 407

NOTE.—Collation: sig. A in four.—Map 1-91.—sig. a in two.
sig. [A1] recto: eng. title; verso: M. Tvllivs Cicero. Het peerdt is tot voeren ende trecken ghefchapen . . . sig. Aij recto-verso: M. Peeter Heyns op den figvrliicken titel van desen boecke. sig. [Aiii] recto-[Aiv] recto: Abraham Ortelivs totten goet-vvilligen leser (dated Antwerpen, 1571); verso: blank.—Maps 1-91, with text on front pages. sig. a recto: Adiev vanden avtevr tot siinen lesere. sig. a verso-[a 2] recto: Tafel van desen tegenwordighen caertboeck; verso: Register.—Privilegie.—Colophon.
The following maps relate to America:
no. 1. Typvs orbis terrarvm . . . 1587.
" 3. Africae tabvla nova . . . 1570.
" 4. Evropae.
" 5. Americae sive novi orbis . . . descriptio. 1587.
" 6. Maris Pacifici (quod vulgò Mar del Zur) cum regionibus circumiacientibus . . . novifsima descriptio. 1589.
" 7. Hispaniae novae . . . descriptio. 1579.
" 8. Cvliacanae, Americae regionis, descriptio.—Hispaniolae, Cvbae, aliarvmqve insvlarvm circvmiacientivm delineatio.
" 9. Pervviae avriferæ regionis typvs. Didaco Mendezio auctore.—La Florida. Auctore Hieron. Chiaues.—Gvastecan reg.
" 71. Septentrionalivm regionvm descrip.
" 74. Tartariae sive magni chami regni typus.
" 77. Indiae orientalis, insvlarvmqve adiacientivm typvs.

## 1598

Il theatro del mondo . . . Nel qvale distintamente si dimostrano in tauole tutte le prouincie, regni, & paefi del mondo, al prefente

**Ortelius, A.**—Continued.

conosciuti; con la descrittione delle città, castelli, monti, mari, laghi, & fiumi di essi; le popolationi, i costumi, le ricchezze, & altri particolari desiderabili. Ridotto dalla forma grande in qvesta piccola, per maggior commodità di ogniuno. Con vna tavola delle cose piv degne che nell' opera si contengono. 4 p. l., 215 (*i. e.* 217), [12] pp. incl. 109 maps. 12°. In Brescia, appresso la compagnia Bresciana, 1598. 408

> NOTE.—Collation: sig. † in four, A–I, K–N in eights, O in five, P in six.
> sig. [†1] recto: title; verso: blank.  sig. †2 recto-verso: All' eccellentiss... Givlio Cesare Inzaghi (signed Pietro Maria Marchetti).  sig. [†3] recto-verso: A benigni lettori.  sig. [†4] recto–[O5] recto: Theatro del mondo.  sig. [O5] verso: Registro.—[Colophon]: In Brescia, appresso la compagnia Bresciana, 1598.
> sig. P does not appear in the "Registro," and must have been added after the book had been completed: sig. P recto–[P6] recto: Tavola delli nomi, et particolarita contenute nella presente opera.  sig. [P6] verso: blank.
> Pagination irregular; pp. 145 & 146 repeated; 2 pages are numbered 188 following p. 189.
> Maps are printed on the upper part of the recto pages, with text on the lower part and on the verso.
> The following maps relate to America:
> no. 1. Carta marina.
> "    3. Typvs orbis terrarvm.
> "    5. Evropa.
> "    9. Africae tabvla nova.
> "   11. Americae sive novi orbis nova descriptio.
> " 191. Septentrionalivm regionvm descriptio.
> " 195. Tartariae sive magni chami regni tipvs.
> " 199. Indiae orientalis insvlarvmqve adiacientivm tiipvs.

### 1599

**Ptolemæus, C.**

Geografia | di | Clavdio Tolomeo | Alessandrino, | Tradotta di Greco nell' Idioma Volgare Italiano | Da Girolamo Rvscelli, | Et hora nuouamente ampliata | Da Giosesso Rosaccio, | Con varie Annotationi, & Espositioni, & Tauole di Rame, che nelli stampati altre | volte non erano, hauendo etiandio poste à i lor luoghi le Tauole | vecchie, che prima confusamente giaceuano, | Et vna Geografia vniuersale del medesimo, separata da quella di Tolomeo; | Nella quale secondo il parere de' più Moderni Geografi, fedelmente sono poste le Pro- | uincie, Regni, Città, Castelli, Monti, Fiumi, Laghi, Porti, Golfi, Isole, | Penisole, Popoli, Leggi, Riti, & Costumi di ciascuna Città. | Et vna breue Descrittione di tutta la Terra, distinta in quattro Libri, | Nel Primo de' quali si tratta dell' Europa; | Nel Secundo dell' Africa, | Nel Terzo dell' Asia, | Nel Quarto dell' America. | Con due Indici Copiosissimi di tutto quello, che di notabile si contiene nell' Opera. | Con licentia, et privilegio. | In Venetia, MDXCIX. | Appreffo gli Heredi di Melchior Seffa. 409

    435 l. (followed by 1 blank l.) comprising: 4 p. l., [32] 42, 186 l. incl. [27] maps, 144 l. incl. [42] maps, [27] l. 4°.

    (sig. *, a–f in fours; g in two: * in four; * * in two; A–K in fours; L in two; A–Z, Aa–Zz, Aaa–Ppp, A–Z, Aa–Zz, Aaa–Nnn in fours and twos; a–e, e–f in fours) Collation: title, verso blank, dedication beginning on recto of l. [2] ending on recto of l. [3], preface "A i Lettori" beginning on verso l. [3] ending on verso l. [4], (sig. *); "Tavola de' nomi antchi" . . . [26] l., (sig. a–g); "Tavola delle cose piv notabili" . . . [6] l., verso of l. [6] blank, (sig. *, * *); book I of text incl. 6 diagr., 42 l., (sig. A–L); books II–VIII of text incl. [27] double page copperplate maps and 2 diagr., 186 l., verso l. 186 blank, (sig. A–Ppp); "Descrittione | della Geografia | Vniversale, | con tavole qvarantadve" | . . . 144 l. incl. [42] double page copperplate maps, (sig. A–Nnn); Espositioni, | et Introdvttioni | Vniversali | di Girolamo Ruscelli | sopra la Geografia | di Clavdio Tolomeo | Alessandrino. | In Venetia, MDXCVIII". | . . . incl. 1 diagr., [27] l., followed by 1 blank l., (sig. a–f)

    Fourth edition of Ruscelli's Ptolemy, edited by Gioseppe Rosaccio. Eames states that five of the maps in this edition are entirely new. They are: "Evropa", "Hvngaria et Transilvania", "Africa", "Asia", and "America". The fourth book of the second part, l. 125–140, contains description and maps of America. These maps together with three general maps are as follows:

l. 2. Orbis Terrae Compendiosa Descriptio.
" 10. Orbis Descriptio.
" 126. America.
" 128. Tierra Nveva.
" 130. Nveva Hispania Tabvla Nova.
" 132. Tierra Nova.
" 134. Brasil Nvova Tavola.
" 136. Isola Spagnola Nova.
" 138. Isola Cvba Nova.
" 142. Septentrionalivm Partivm Nova Tabvla.
" 144. Carta Marina Nova Tavola.

Modern binding, full vellum.
Eames-Sabin, no. 66507.

## 1599

**Langenes, B.**

    Caert-thresoor, inhoudende de tafelen des gantfche werelts landen, met befchryvinghen verlicht, tot luft vanden lefer, nu alles van nieus met groote coften eñ arbeyt toegereet. 8 p. l., 462 pp., [1] l., 196, [4] pp. incl. 165 maps, 5 pl. obl. 24°. Amfterdam, by Cornelis Claefz, 1599. 410

    NOTE.—Engraved title. First published 1598. *cf.* Tiele, P. A. Nederlandsche bibliographie van land- en volkenkunde. p. 56. See titles 415, 424 and 428. Pages 75 and 187 blank.

    Maps by various cartographers including: Hondius, Keer, Wright and Pigafetta.

**Langenes, B.**—Continued.
   The following maps relate to America:
   pt. 1, p.  1. Typus orbis terrarum.
   "    "   17. De Cloot der aerden.
   "    "   21. Europa oft Kerſtenrijck.
   "    "   25. Asien.
   "    "   31. Africa.
   "    "   35. De nieuvve vverelt.
   " 2,  "   49. China.—China regio Afię.
   "    "  143. America. (Same as p. 35)
   "    "  145. Tercera.
   "    "  149. Cuba Hiſpaniola Iucatan, &c.—Inſularum Cubae, Hiſpaniolæ, Iucatanæ . . . descriptio.
   "    "  150 (i. e. 151) Cuba ende Iamaica.—
   "    "  153. Hiſpaniola.—Aity sive Spaniola.
   "    "  155. America aen het Zuyden.
   "    "  157. Braſilien.
   "    "  163. Chili.—Cbili et Patagonum regio.
   "    "  167. Mynen van Potoſi.
   "    "  169. Peru.
   "    "  179. Nieu Hiſpanien.—Mexicana.
   "    "  183. Terra Nova, &c.
   "    "  189. Engte van Magellanes.—Fretum Magellanicum.

## 1600

**Quad, M.**

Geographisch handtbuch in welchem die gelegenheit der vornembſten lantſchafften des gantzen erdtbodems in zwej und achtzig in kupffer geſchnittenen taffeln furgebildt. Mit beygefügter notwendiger beſchreibung und auslegung derselben: also das jedes landes art, natur, gelegenheit, ſitten, völcker, fruchtbarkeit, handtirung, sampt andere zu wiffen nutzliche ſachen, schrifftlich und augenſcheinlich nach notturfft daraus mögen erlernet werden. Zugericht durch Matthis Qvaden kupfferschneider.  4 p. l., [328] pp. incl. 82 maps.  4°.  Coln am Rein, bey Iohan Buxemacher kunstdrucker vff. s. Maximini ſtraſs daſelbſt, 1600.  **411**

NOTE.—Collation: 4 p. l. comprising illus. title, verso blank, l. 1; "Inhalt der charten dieses buchlins," l. 2; plate signed Q, inscription, "Zu ehren und wolgefallen," signed Johan Bussmacher, recto l. 3; "Vorredahndengunstigen leser," dated 1600, signed Matthis Quad, verso l. 3–verso l. 4; 82 numb. maps on 164 l., with descriptive text on the reverse.
Nearly all the maps are copied from the "Theatrum orbis terrarum" of Ortelius, 46 having been used in Quad's Atlas, 1594. They contain the names of many early cartographers.
The title-page is copied from the title-page of the "Theatrum," with figures representing Europe at the top, Africa at the right, Asia at the left, and America at the foot of the design, slight changes having been made in both figures and back ground.  cf. Hilbenbrand, F. J. Matthis Quad und dessen Europae universalis et particularis descriptio. 1893.

The following maps relate to America:
no. 1. Typvs orbis terrarvm, ad imitationem vniversalis Gerhardi Mercatoris.
" 77. Polvs Arcticvs fiue tract9 septentrionalis. Coloniæ, ex officina typographica Jani Buffemechers.
" 78. Novi orbis pars borealis, America scilicet, complectens Floridam, Baccalaon, Canadam, Terram Corterialem, Virginiam, Norombecam, pluresque alias prouincias . . . Coloniæ, laminis Jani buxemeohers.
" 79. Hispaniae Novae sive magnae vera descriptio.
" 80. Pervvia id est, Noui orbis pars meridionalis à præstantifsima eius in occidetem regione sic appellata. 1598. Coloniæ excudit Johan Buffemecher.
" 81. Chica sive Patagonica et australis terra. 1600. Coloniæ Agrippinæ formulis Jani buxemacheri in platea maximinia.

## 1601
**Ortelius, A.**
Theatrvm orbis terrarvm, Abrahami Orteli. Quod ante extremum vitæ fuæ diem, poftremum recenfuit, nouis tabulis et commentarijs auxit atque illuftrauit. 1 p. l., [321] l. incl. 153 maps, 1 por., 30, [5] pp. fol. Antverpiae, ex officina Plantiniana, apud Ioannem Moretum. Anno 1601. 412

NOTE.—Collation: sig. A, B in sixes.—Maps 1-25, 25*, 25**, 25***, 26-115.—sig. a in four.—Maps I-x, xI & xIj, xIII, xIv, xv & xvj, xvIj-xxxvIj.—sig. A-C in sixes. sig. [A1] recto: eng. title; verso: In theatrvm orbis terrarvm Abrah. Ortelii Antverp. (signed And. Schottus Antverp).—Gerartvs Falkenbvrgivs Noviomagvs. sig. A2 recto: Dedication, D. Philippo Avstriaco Caroli V . . . sig. A2 verso-A3 verso: Adolphi Mekerchi Brvgensis . . . frontispicii explicatio. sig. [A4] recto-[A5] recto: Abrahamvs Ortelivs Antverpianvs . . . benevolis lectoribvs S. D.—Ornatissimo viro d. Abrahamo Ortelio, amico cvm primis caro. (signed: Duysburgi, 22. nouembris, 1570 . . . Gerardus Mercator.) sig. [A5] verso-B1 verso: Catalogvs avctorvm . . . (183 names). sig. B2 recto-B3 recto: Index tabvlarvm hvivs operis . . . sig. B3 recto-B4 recto: Qvoniam vero plvres regiones avt insvlæ in his tabvlis descriptæ svnt . . . sig. B4 verso-[B5] recto: Epigrammata Danielis Rogersii . . .—In Abrahami Ortelii theatrvm orbis (signed: Paulus Meliffus Francus). sig. [B5] verso: Hadriani Ivnii Hornani in hoc theatrvm.—Ioannis Posthii med. d.—Io. Vivianvs Valentianvs Abrahamo Ortelio 8vo. sig. [B6] recto: eng. portrait of Ortelius; verso: Epitaphium Abrahami Ortelii Antuerpiæ ad D. Michaëlis.— Maps 1-25, 25*, 25**, 25***, 26-115.—sig. [a] recto: Parergon, sive veteris geographiæ aliqvot tabvlae. Lector S.; verso: Ad Abrahamvm Ortelivm enthevm geographorvm principem Michaelis Vander-Hagen Antverpiani epigramma. sig. aij recto-[aiij] recto: Ornatissimo viro d. Abrahamo Ortelio. (signed: Coloniæ Agripp. pridie kal. Ian. cIɔ.Iɔ.LXXVIII. A. Graphævs); verso-[a Iv] recto: In regivm geographvm dn. Abrahamvm Ortelivm . . . Iacobi Colii Orteliani Carmen ΑΝΑΓΡΑΜΜΑΤΙΚΩΣ.—Regionvm insvlarvmqve hvivs parergi index. sig. [AIv] verso: A Iove principivm inquit vetuftas.—A sacris itaqve avspicandvm hvnc nostrvm laborem duximus.— maps I-x, xI & xIj, xIII, xIv, xv & xvj, xvIj-xxxvIj. sig. [A1] recto: Nomenclator Ptolemaicvs . . . Antverpiæ . . . apud Ioannem Moretum, 1601; verso: Abrahamvs Ortelivs candido lectori. sig. A2 recto-C3 verso: [Nomenclor Ptolemaicvs]. sig. C4 recto-[C5] verso: De Mona drvidvm insvla . . .— Approbatio. sig. [C5] recto: Imp. Rvdolphi, Philippi Hisp. regis . . .— Ad libri compactorem . . . verso: blank.

**Ortelius, A.**—Continued.

The following maps relate to America:
no. 1. Typvs orbis terrarvm . . . 1587.
" 2. Evropae.
" 4. Africae tabvla nova . . . 1570.
" 5. Americae sive novi orbis . . . descriptio. 1587.
" 6. Maris Pacifici, (quod vulgò Mar del Zur) cum regionibus circumiacentibus . . . novifsima descriptio. 1589.
" 7. Hispaniae novae . . . descriptio. 1579.
" 8. Cvliacanae, Americae regionis, descriptio.—Hispaniolae, Cvbae aliarvmqve insvlarvm circvmiacientivm, delineatio.
" 9. Pervviae avriferæ regionis typvs. Didaco Mendezio auctore.— La Florida. Auctore Hieron. Chiaues.—Gvastecan reg.
" 102. Septentrionalivm regionvm descrip.
" 105. Tartariae sive magni chami regni typus.
" 108. Indiae orientalis, insvlarvmqve adiacientivm typvs.

## 1601

Epitome theatri Orteliani, præcipuarum orbis regionum delineationes, minoribus tabulis expreffas, breuioribufque declarationibus illuftratas, continens. Editio vltima, multis locis emendata, & nouis aliquot tabulis aucta. 1 p. l., [134] l. incl. 124 maps, 3 pl. obl. 32°. Antverpiæ, apvd Ioannem Bapt. Vrientivm, 1601. 413

NOTE.—Collation: sig. A-I, K-Q in eights, R in ten. sig. [A1] recto: title; with a hemisphere in the center of the page. Around the hemisphere is Ortelius' motto: "Contemno, et orno:mente, manv" with his monogram; verso: engraved coat of arms. sig. A2 recto–A3 verso: Sereniʃsimis principibvs Alberto et Isabellæ . . . (signed: Ioan. Bap. Vrientius). sig. A4 recto–[A5] recto: Ioannes Baptista Vrientivs candido lectori S. D.—Ad Io. Baptistam Vrientivm Antverpianvm. sig. [A5] verso: Vtrivsqve hemisphaerii tam coelestis qvam terrestris . . . declaratio. sig. [A6] recto, plate: "Globvs coelestis"; verso: Elementaris regio, ab infimo planetarvm orbe . . . sig. [A7] recto, map: "Globvs terrestris," verso: Ad Philippvm II. Hispaniarvm . . . sig. [A8] recto, plate: Scenographia totivs fabricæ S. Lavrentii in Escoriali; verso: Orbis terrarvm (letterpress). sig. B recto–[P6] recto: Maps 1–110, printed on the recto pages of the leaves, with letterpress on the verso. sig. [P6] verso: Approbatio. (Dated, Antuerp. hac 26 maij, anno M. D. LXXXIX; signed, M. H. B.) sig. [P7] recto–[P8] recto: Index tabvlarvm; at end: Typis Henrici Swingenij. sig. [P8] verso, blank. sig. Q recto: Additamentvm epitomæ theatri minoris Abr. Ortelii geographi regij; verso: Lemovicvm, (letterpress). sig. Q2 recto–[R6] recto: Maps 1—13 (with letterpress on reverse.) sig. [R6] verso: blank. sig. [R7] recto: Index tabvlarvm additamenti; verso: blank, with the following in mss.: Jacobus de la Fontaine . . . Rhemis, A? 1630.—Three blank leaves, one attached to cover.

The following maps relate to America:
no. [A7] Globvs terrestris.
" 1. Typvs orbis terrarvm.
" 2. Evropa.
" 4. Africa.
" 5. America five novvs orbis.
" 97. Septemtrionales reg.
" 99. Tartaria five magni chami imperivm.
" 101. India orient.

## 1602

**Bertius, P.**
P. Bertii Tabvlarvm geographicarvm contractarvm libri quinque, cum luculentis fingularum tabularum explicationibus. Editio secvnda. 8 p. l., 679, [9] pp. incl. 171 maps, 4 pl. obl. 32°. Amsterlodami, apud C. Nicolai, 1602.  414

NOTE.—The following maps relate to America:
p. 6. Typus orbis terrarum. I. Hondius cælavit.
" 32. De globo terræ. Jodocus Hondius.
" 44. Europæ . . . Iodocus Hondius cæla. Shows "Americae pars."
" 48. Descriptio hyperboreorvm. Petrus Kærus fecit et cælavit. Shows "Groenland."
" 615. Infulæ Philippinæ. Petrus Kærius.
" 620. Descriptio Americæ.
" 626. Terra Nova.
" 634. Infularum Cubæ, Hispaniolæ Iucatanæ & circumijacentium descriptio.
" 637. Cuba insula. Petrus Kærius cæla.
" 639. Aity sive Spaniola. P. Kæri caelavit.
" 642. Mexicana.
" 646. Descriptio Americæ Avstralis.
" 650. Peru.
" 660. Cerro de Potosi.
" 662. Chili et Patagonum regio.
" 664. Brasilia.
" 672. Fretum Magellanicum. Petrus Kærius cælavit.

## 1602

**Langenes, B.**
Thrésor de chartes, contenant les tableavx de tovs les pays dv monde, enrichi de belles defcriptions, & nouvellement mis en lumière. 8 p. l., 472, 202, [5] pp. incl. 164 maps, 5 pl. obl. 24°. [Amsterdam] A la Haye, de l'imprimerie d'Albert Henry, pour Corneille Nicolas [1602]  415

NOTE.—Engraved title.
A translation into french by Jean de La Haye, from Langenes' Caert-thesoor, inhoudende de tafelen des gantsche werelts landen . . . 1598. cf. Tiele, P. A. Nederlandsche bibliographie van land- en volkenkunde. p. 56. See titles 410, 424 and 428.
Maps by various cartographers including: Hondius, Keer, Wright and Pigafetta.
The following maps relate to America:
p. 1. Typus orbis terrarum.
" 19. Le globe terrestre.
" 29. Asie. (Shows North America)
" 33. Afrique. (Shows South America)
" 39. Le nouveau monde.
" 51. La Chine. (Shows America)
" 149. Tercere.
" 153. Cuba, Hispaniola, Iucatan.
" 155. Cuba & Iamaica.
" 157. Hispaniola.
" 159. L'Amérique du coste du midi.

**Langenes, B.**—Continued.
- p. 163. Brésil.
- " 169. Chile.
- " 175. Peru.
- " 185. La Nouvelle Espaigne.
- " 189. Terre Neuve.
- " 195. Destroit de Magellan.

**1602**

**Ortelius, A.**

Abrégé dv théâtre, contenant la defcription des principales parties & régions du monde, repréfentées en petites cartes, & illuftrées de fommaires expofitions. Dernière édition, corrigée en plufieurs lieux, & augmentée de quelques cartes nouvelles. 1 p. l., [134] l., incl. 125 maps, 1 pl. obl. 32°. À Anvers, I. B. Vrients, 1602.    416

NOTE.—Collation: sig. A, A–Q. in eights.

sig. [A1] recto: title, with a hemisphere around which is Ortelius' motto: "Contemno et orno: mente, manv" and his monogram, verso: engraved coat of arms.  sig. A 2 recto–A 3 verso: Avx altesses serenissmes Albert et Isabeav d'Avstriche . . . (signed: Baptiste Vrients).  sig. A4 recto–A5 recto: Iean Baptiste Vrients av lectevr salvt.—A Iean Baptiste Vrients Bovrgeois d'Anvers epigramme.  sig. A5 verso: Brieve description des devx globes . . .  sig. [A6] recto, plate: Globe céleste; verso: La région élémentaire est comprise . . . par le dernier ciel des sept planètes . . .  sig. [A7] recto, map: Globe terrestre; verso: A Philippe II. catholiqve . . .  sig. [A8] recto, plate: Scenographia totivs fabricæ, S. Lavrentii in Escoriali; verso: La terre vniverselle.  sig. A recto–[P6] recto: maps 1–118, printed on the recto of the leaves, the verso contains the letterpress.  sig. [P6] verso: Approbation (dated 1588, signed: Michaël Breughel . . .)—Privilege (signed: Iac. Blyleuen).  sig. [P7] recto–[P8] recto: Table des cartes; verso: blank.  sig. Q recto: Addition d'avlcvnes cartes, verso: blank.  sig. Q2 recto: Av lectevr; verso: Corse (letterpress).  sig. Q 3 recto–[Q7] recto: 5 maps, with text on reverse.  sig. [Q7] verso: L'adiev de l'avctevr av lectevr; 2 blank l.

The following maps relate to America:

- no. [A7] Globe terrestre.
- "     1. Typvs orbis terrarvm.
- "     2. Evropa.
- "     4. Africa.
- "     5. America five novvs orbis
- " 104. Septemtrionales reg.
- " 106. Tartaria . . .
- " 109. India orient.

**1602**

L'Epitome dv théâtre de l'vnivers nouuellement recogneu, augmentè [!] et reftraurè [!] de mefeure géographique, par Michel Coignet.  8 p. l., 110 numb. l., [2] pp., 13 numb. l., [3] l., incl. 123 maps.  obl. 24°.  Antverpiae svmptibvs Ioannis Keerbergii, 1602.    417

NOTE.—Collation: sig. +, A–Q (in eights)

sig. [+1] recto-title ornamented with medallions of Strabo, Plinivs, Solinvs, Ptolemaevs, Volaterranvs, G. Mercator, and Ab. Ortelivs; verso-blank.  sig. [+2] recto-verso, quotation from Cicero.  sig. +3–[+8], text and 2 diagrams.

sig. A-[O6], 110 l. incl. 110 maps on recto, text on verso. sig. [O7] recto, title: Addition a l'Epitome . . . text on verso. sig. [O8]-Q4, 13 l. incl. 13 maps on recto, text on verso. sig. Q4 verso-[Q6] recto, La table des cartes. sig. [Q6] verso, Approbatio (signed Guilielmus Lucas, dated 19 septemb. 1601). sig. [Q7] recto, Le sommaire du priuilège (signed I. de Bufchere, dated 12 may 1601) sig. [Q8] and 3 extra blank l.
The last three leaves of each sig. unp.
The following maps relate to America:
no. 1. Typus orbis terrarvm.
" 4. Africa.
" 5. America.
" 97. Septentrionales reg.
" 101. India orient.

## 1602 (?)

An epitome of Ortelivs, his theatre of the vvorld, vvherein the principal regions of the earth are defcribed in fmalle mappes. VVith a brief declaration annexed to ech [!] mappe . . . It is alfo amplyfied with new mappes, wanting in the latin editions. 1 p. l., [129] l. incl. 123 maps, 1 pl. obl. 32°. At London, printed by Iohn Norton [1602?] 418

NOTE.—Collation: 4 l. unsigned, followed by sig. B, A$^2$, B$^3$, A$^4$, B$^5$, 2 l. unsigned.—sig. C-I, K-Q in eights, R in seven.
L. [1] recto, title, with hemisphere, around which is the following motto: "Contemno, et orno: mente, manv," and Ortelius' monogram; verso: coat of arms of Richard Gargrave. l. [2] recto, dedication; verso: A brief defcription of the 2 half globes . . . l. [3] recto, plate: The celestial globe; verso: letterpress. l. [4] recto, map: The terrestrial globe; verso: A brief description of the vvhole vvorld. . . M. Tullius Cicero. The horfe is created to beare and to dravv . . . sig. B recto-B 5 recto: maps 1-5.—map no. 6 of England is wanting.—2 l. unsigned: maps no. 7 & 8.—sig. C recto—[P6] recto: maps no. 9-110, printed on the recto of the leaves, with letterpress on the verso. sig. [P6] verso: vignette. sig. [P7] recto-[P8] recto: The table. sig. [P8] verso: blank. sig. Q recto: An addition of certaine maps vnto this epitome of the theatre of Abraham Ortelivs; verso: letterpress. sig. Q 2 recto-[R6] recto: maps 1-13 with letterpress on reverse. sig. [R6] verso: blank. sig. [R7] recto: The table vnto the addition.—Typis Henrici Svvingenij; verso: blank. Maps are the same as those of the latin edition of the epitome published at Antwerp in 1601. Date of publication given as 1602?, as in 1603 "Mr. Richard Gargrave," to whom the work is dedicated, was knighted by James I, and became "Sir Richard Gargrave." An edition was published in London, by Ieams Shawe, dated 1603. The titles on the maps are in latin, but english titles have been printed in the upper margin.

## 1603

Theatrvm orbis terrarvm Abrahami Orteli Antverp. geographi regii. Tabvlis aliqvot novis vitaq. avctoris illvstratvm. editio vltima. 1 p. l. [341] l. incl. 154 maps, 3 pl., 1 por., 30, [5] pp. fol. Antverpiæ, apvd Ioannem Bapt. Vrintivm, 1603. 419

NOTE.—Collation: sig. A-C in sixes, D in four.—maps 1-68, 68½ (numb. in ink), 69-118.—sig. a in four.—maps j-xj, l. xij, maps xiij-xv, l. xvj; pl. xvij, xviij. maps xix-xxxix. pl. XL.—sig. A-C in sixes.
sig. [A] recto eng. title; verso: Arms of the King of Spain. sig. A2 recto: dedication: D. Philippo Avstriaco Caroli V . . . sig. A2 verso-A3 verso:

**Ortelius, A.**—Continued.
Adolphi Mekerchi Brvgensis I. C. . . . frontispicii explicatio.—In theatrvm orbis terrarvm Abrahami Ortelii, R. P. Andreas Schottvs Antverp . . . sig. A4 recto–[A5] recto–Abrahami Ortelii Antverpiensis . . . vita, Francisco Svveertio F. Antverp. avctore. sig. [A5] verso: Abrahami Ortelii qvem vrbs vrbivm Antverpia edidit rex regvm Philippvs geographvm habvit monvmentvm hic vides . . . (within engr. borders). sig. [A6] recto–C recto: Insignivm aliqvot hvivs ævi poetarvm carmina ex lacrymis Francisci Sweerti F. in Abrahami Orteli obitum. . . . sig. C verso–C2 verso: Abrahamvs Ortelivs Antverpianvs . . benevolis lectoribvs S. D.—Ornatissimo viro D. Abrahamo Ortelio, amico cvm primis caro. (signed: Duysburgi, 22. Nouembris, 1570 . . . Gerardvs Mercator). sig. C3. recto–[C5 recto]: Catalogvs avctorvm tabvlarvm geographicarvm . . . (183 names). sig. [C5] verso–[C6] verso: Index tabvlarvm hvivs operis . . . sig. D recto–verso: Qvoniam vero plvres regiones avt insvlæ in his tabvlis descriptæ svnt . . . sig. D2 recto–verso: Epigrammata Danielis Rogersii Albimontani . . .—In Abrahami Ortelii theatrvm orbis (signed Paulus Meliffus Francus). sig. D3 recto–verso: Hadriani Ivnii Hornani in hoc theatrvm.—Ioannis Posthii med. d.—Io. Vivianvs Valentianvs—Abrahamo Ortelio svo.—In eivsdem theatrvm (signed Maximus Æmylianus de Vriendt . . .) sig. [D4] recto: Nicolavs Rhedinger . . .—Ioan. Matthævs Vackervs . . .—Ex elogiis . . . Avberti Miraei . . . verso: eng. portrait of Ortelius.—Maps 1-68, 68½, 69-118. sig. [ai] recto: eng. title. Parergon, sive veteris geograpiæ [!] aliqvot tabvlæ . . . verso: Ad Cl. V. Abrahamvm Ortelivm Iani Lernvti epigramma.—Ad Abrahamvm Ortelivm enthevm geographorvm principem Michaelis Vander-Hagen . . . epigramma. sig. aij recto–[aiij] recto: Ornatissimo viro D. Abrahamo Ortelio. (signed: Coloniæ Agripp. pridie Kal. Ian. CIƆ.IƆ. LXXVIII. A. Graphaevs.) sig. [aiij] verso–[aiv] recto: In regivm geographvm dn. Abrahamvm Ortelivm . . . Iacobi Colii Orteliani Carmen *ANAΓPAMMATIKΩΣ*.—Regionvm insvlarvmqve hvivs parergi index. sig. [aiv] verso: A Iove principivm, inqvit vetvstas.—A sacris itaqve avspicandvm hvnc nostrvm laborem dvximvs. maps j–xj, l. xij (2 pp. of text.) maps xiij–xv.-l. xvj (2 pp. of text). pl. xvij, xviij: De institvtione et ordine imperii germanici tabvla I–II. maps xix–xxxix.—pl. XL: Scenographia totivs fabricæ S. Lavrentii in Escoriali. sig. [A] recto: Nomenclator Ptolemaicvs; omnia locorvm vocabvla qvae in tota Ptolemaei geographia occurrunt . . . Antverpiæ, typis Roberti Brvneav, 1603; verso: Abrahamvs Ortelivs candido lectori. sig. A2 recto–C3 verso: [Nomenclator Ptolemaicvs] sig. C4 recto–[C5] verso: De Mona drvidvm insvla . . .—Approbatio. sig. [C6] recto: Imp. Rvdolphi, Philippi Hisp. regis . . .—Ad libri compactorem; verso: blank. Maps and plates have text on front pages, and several also on the last.

The following maps relate to America:
- no. 1. Typvs orbis terrarvm . . . 1587.
- " 2. Evropae.
- " 4. Africae tabvla nova . . . 1570.
- " 5. Americae sive novi orbis . . . descriptio . . . 1587.
- " 6. Maris Pacifici, (quod vulgò Mar del Zur) . . . novifsima descriptio . . . 1589.
- " 7. Hispaniae novae . . . descriptio. 1579.
- " 8. Cvliacanae, Americae regionis descriptio.—Hispaniolae, Cvbae, aliarvmqve insvlarvm circvmiacientivm delineatio.
- " 9. Pervviae avriferæ regionis typvs. Didaco Mendezio auctore.—La Florida. Auctore Hieron. Chiaues.—Gvastecan reg.
- " 105. Septentrionalivm regionvm descrip.
- " 108. Tartariae sive magni chami regni typvs.
- " 111. Indiae orientalis, insvlarvmqve adiacientivm typvs.

## 1604

Aūfszūg aūfs des Abrahami Ortelÿ Theatro orbis teūtſch beſchriben dūrch Levinvm Hvlsivm. 45, [1] pp., [134] l. incl. 128 maps, 2 diagr. obl. 32°. Francfort am Main, 1604.    420

NOTE.—Collation: sig. A, B in eights, C in ten, D–I, K–T in eights, V in eight. sig. [A] recto: eng. title; at foot of title: Prostant apvd Iohañem Keerbergivm et Levinvm Hvlsivm; verso: eng. coat of arms. sig. Aij recto–A4 recto: Dem durchleuchtigen . . . herrn Joachim Ernſt, marggraffen zu Brandeburg, in Preuſſen . . . (signed: Leuinus Hulſius). sig. A4 verso–[C7] recto: Leuini Hulſii anleitung der geographiæ . . . sig. [C7] verso–[C8] recto: folded map 1: Descriptio totivs orbis terræ. ex varÿs recentior: aŭtoribŭs in hanc formam redacta. An°. 1598. exc: Leŭin: Hŭlsiŭs f.; verso: letterpress. sig. [C9] recto–[E7] recto: maps 2–18. sig. [E7] verso–[E8] verso: letterpress. sig. F recto–Fiij recto: maps 19–21. sig. Fiij verso–[F6] verso: letterpress. sig. [F7] recto–V recto: maps 22–128. sig. V verso–V3 recto: Register der landcharten. sig. V3 verso: blank.

Maps are printed on the recto of the leaves, the letterpress on the verso.

Maps are the same (except no. 1, 7, 20 & 77) as those of the epitome published at Antwerp in 1602 by Michel Coignet.

## 1605

**Ptolemæus C.**

Claudii | Ptolemæi | Älexandrini | Geographiae | Libri Octo | Græco-Latini | Latinè primùm recogniti & emendati, | cum tabulis geographicis ad mentem | auctoris restitutis per | Gerardum Mercatorem: | Iam verò ad Græca & Latina exemplaria | à Petro Montano iterum recogniti, et | pluribus locis castigati. | Adjecta inſuper ab eodem nomina recentia et æquipollentia | ex varijs auctoribus veteribus et recentiorib. magna cura coĺ | lecta, in gratiam et uſum Geographiæ ſtudioſorum. | Iodocus Hondius excudit ſibi et Cornelio | Nicolai, in cujus officina proſtant, Frācofurti, | Amſterodammi. | 1605 |    421

201 l. (preceded and followed by 1 blank l.) comprising: 6 p. l., [16] l., [28] maps on [55] l., 215 pp., [16] l. fol.

(sig. 6 l. unsigned; a–b in sixes; c in four; A–O in twos; 1 l. unsigned; P–V, V₂, X, X altered to Y, Z, Zz, Aa–Bb in twos; A–V in sixes; X in four) Collation: engraved title colored, verso blank,—preface by Hondius, dated M.DI.V, 1 l., with greek verse by Daniel Heinsivs on verso,—latin verses signed "P. Bertivs" and "Iacobvs Grvtervs" followed by catalogue of authors, 1 l., verso blank,—"Praefatio Inseqvens Tabvlarvm Ptolemaei Opvs, 2 l.,—diagram, followed by latin verse by Michael Isselt, 1 l., on verso a colored engraved portrait of Mercator entitled "Gerardi Mercatoris Rvpelmvndani effigiem Annor. dvorvm et sex-aginta, svi erga ipsvm stvdii cavsa depingi cvrabat Franc. Hog. CIƆ. IƆ. LXXIV," with latin verses by Bernardus Fermerius beneath, (unsigned); "Indicem," [15] l., followed by 1 blank l., (sig. a–c); [27] double page and 1 single copperplate colored maps, text on first reverse, on [55] l., (sig. A–Bb); text incl. 6 diagr., 215 pp., verso p. 215 blank, (sig. A–S); "Index Eorvm qvae in Octo Libris Ptolemæi Continentvr" . . . [16] l., (sig. T–X)

First edition of the greek and latin text together, accompanied by Mercator's maps and edited by Petrius Montanus. The plates of the Mercator maps

**Ptolemæus, C.**—Continued.

which appeared in the editions of 1578 and 1584, were purchased by Hondius from the heirs of Mercator. They are "Vniversalis Tabvla ivta Ptolemevm," ten of Europe, five of Africa, and twelve of Asia. *cf.* Eames.

There are a number of variations in different copies of this edition including the place of publication, some giving Frankfort, others Amsterdam, and still others both.

Original binding, full vellum.
Eames-Sabin, no. 66494.

**1607**

**Mercator, G.**

Gerardi Mercatoris atlas sive cosmographicæ meditationes de fabrica mvndi et fabricati figvra. Iam tandem ad finem perductus, quamplurimis æneis tabulis Hispaniæ, Africæ, Afiæ & Americæ auctus ac illuftratus á Iudoco Hondio. Quibus etiam additæ, præter Mercatoris, dilucidæ & accuratæ omnium tabularum defcriptiones novæ, ftudio et opera Pet. Montani. Editio secunda qua et ampliores defcriptiones & novæ tabulæ geographicæ accefserunt. 8 p. l., 356 (*i. e.* 357), [35] pp., [4] l., 146 maps. fol. Amfterodami, excufum in ædibus Iudoci Hondij, 1607. 422

NOTE.—Collation: engraved title, verso blank, p. l., [1].—Dedication, signed Jodocus Hondius, dated 1607, recto and verso p. l. [2].—Vita celeberrimi clarissimiq́; viri Gerardi Mercatoris Rupelmundani, à domino Gualtero Ghymmio . . . recto p. l. [3]-verso p. l. [4].—Latin verse: Epitaphivm in obitum Gerardi Mercatoris . . .; Epistolæ dvæ, duorum doctifsimorum virorum, doctris Reinhardi Solenandri . . . & d. Jacobi Sinstedij . . . in laudem atlantis confcriptæ; In atlantem Gerardi Mercatoris avi fui, signed Iohannes Mercatoris, recto p. l. [5]-recto p. l. [6].—Præfatio in atlantem, verso p. l. [6].—Iodocvs Hondivs lectoris., dated 1607, recto p. l. [7].—Latin verse: Gerardo Mercatori et Ivdoco Hondio cofmographis, signed Petrus Bertius; verse in Latin and in Greek: In Gerardi Mercatoris Flandri atlantem . . . signed Daniel Heinsius; Latin verse, signed Jacobus Gruterus; followed by Greek verse, verso p. l. [7].—Index, recto & verso p. l. [8].—Stemma Atlantis, p. [1].—De mvndi creatione, ac fabrica liber, pp. 2-26.—Blank, pp. 27-28.—Text and 43 maps, pp. 29-120.—Engraved title: Galliæ tabulę geographicæ. Per Gerardum Mercatorem . . . verso blank.—Stvdioso et benevolo lectori, pp. 121-123.—De politico statv regni Galliæ, pp. 123-127.—In vsvm tabvlarvm admonitio, p. 127.—Index tabvlarvm Galliæ, p. 128.—Text and 20 maps, pp. 129-170.—Engraved title: Belgii inferioris geographicæ tabulę. Per Gerardum Mercatorem . . . verso blank.—Ad stvdiosvm lectorem; followed by, Politia Belgii sub Bvrgvndionibvs, pp. 171-173.—Index tabvlarvm Eelgii inferioris, p. 173.—Belgii inferioris tabvla, p. 172.—Text and 10 maps, pp. 175-198.—Engraved title: Germaniae tabulę geographicæ. Per Gerardum Mercatorem, verso blank.—In Germanicas tabvlas vtilis et praenoscenda instrvctio, pp. 199-202.—Catalogvs tabvlarvm Germaniæ, p. 202.—Text and 28 maps, pp. 203-265.—Engraved title: Italiae, Sclavoniæ, et Græcæ tabulę geographicę. Per Gerardum Mercatorem, verso blank.—Text and 45 maps, pp. 263-356.—Index, [35] pp.

Pagination irregular.

Text on reverse of maps.

The L. C. has the following editions of the Atlas "Major:"

| | | |
|---|---|---|
| 3rd Latin | ed | 1607. |
| 1st French | " | 1609. |
| 6th Latin | " | 1613. |
| 8th Latin | " | 1619. |
| 4th French | " | 1628. |
| 12th Latin | " | 1630. |
| 1st German | " 2 v | 1633. |
| 6th French | " 2 v | 1633. |
| 1st Dutch | " | 1634. |
| English | " | 1636. |
| (Hexham) | | |
| 2nd English ed | | 1637. |
| (Historia mundi) | | |

Also the following editions of the Atlas "Minor":

| | | |
|---|---|---|
| 1st Latin ed | | 1607. |
| German | " | 1609. |
| Latin | " | 1610. |
| " | " | 1621. |
| " | " | 1628. |
| Dutch | " | 1630. |
| Latin | " | 1634. |
| German | " | 1651. |

No text to "Asiæ Nova," and to general map of America.
The following maps relate to America:
no. [1] Orbis terrae compendiosa descriptio. 1587.
" [2] Evropa.
" [3] Nova Europæ descriptio. Auctore Iodoco Hondio.
" [4] Africa.
" [5] Asia.
" [6] America fiue India Nova . . . Per Michaelem Mercatorem.
" [7] Septentrionalivm terrarum defcriptio.
" [129] Asiæ Nova defcriptio. Auctore Iodoco Hondio.
" [135] Tartaria.
" [136] China.
" [138] Insulæ Indiæ Orientalis præcipuae . .
" [141] America. Jodocus Hondius excudit. (First general map of America by Hondius which gives North and South America their respective names. The map entitled: Maris Pacifici . . . in the "Additamentum" of Ortelius, 1590, is the first map upon which the two continents are thus designated)
" [142] Hispaniæ Novæ nova descriptio.
" [143] Virginiae item et Floridae Americæ provinciarum, nova descriptio.
" [144] Cuba insula. Inset: Havana portus.—Hispaniola insula.—Insula Iamaica.—Ins. S. Ioannis.—I. s. Margareta cum confiniis.
" [145] America Meridionalis.
" [146] Exquifita & magno aliquot menfium periculo luftrata et iam retecta Freti Magellanici facies.

Only parts of Mercator's atlas had been published before his death. "Gallia" and "Germania" in 1585, and "Italia" in 1590. The collection of maps on the northern countries was ready for publication at the time of his death and was published by his son Rumoldus in 1595. Rumoldus died in 1600. The three

**Mercator, G.**—Continued.

parts of the Atlas of Mercator were published in one volume for the heirs, by Bernard Busius at Dusseldorf in 1602. Jodocus Hondius brought out an edition in 1606, augmented by fifty new maps by himself and others, Petrus Montanus being the author of the text. This was the 1st edition of Hondius. The edition of 1607 was still further augmented and was the "Editio secunda" of Hondius, but the 3rd edition of Mercator's atlas. The imprint of a copy of this edition quoted by Raemdonck reads: Sumptibus Cornelij Nicolaï & Jodoci Hondij Amsterodami, 1607. Many editions in the various european languages followed. At the death of Jodocus Hondius in 1611 the publication of the atlases was carried on by his son Henrick and his son-in-law Jan Janssen. New maps were gradually added and those of Mercator withdrawn or altered.

Among the examples of Mercator's Atlas in the L. C., a noteworthy one is the latin edition of 1619. None of the authorities on Mercator mention this edition; even Raemdonck does not seem to know of its existence. The same is true of the 1636 french edition of the larger reduced atlas. The fact that this edition has not been noted shows that it is rare, but it is of no special interest as it is exactly the same as the 1630 edition of this series except for the change of dates.

The L. C. has recently acquired the 1613 latin edition.

The following is a list of the various editions of Mercator's Atlas Major:

| | |
|---|---|
| Latin text.........pt. 1...... | 1585. |
| "      "  ........." 2...... | 1590. |
| "      "  ........." 3...... | 1595. |

Published as a whole:

| | |
|---|---|
| 1st Latin ed ........ | 1602. |
| 2nd  "    " ........ | 1606. |
| 3rd  "    " ........ | 1607. |
|   (2nd of Hondius) | |
| 4th Latin ed ........ | 1608. |
|   (A reprint of 1607) | |
| 1st French ed ........ | 1609. |
| 5th Latin  "  ........ | 1611. |
| 6th   "    "  ........ | 1613. |
| 2nd French "  ........ | 1613. |
| 7th Latin  "  ........ | 1616. |
| 3rd French "  ........ | 1619. |
| 8th Latin  "  ........ | 1619. |
| 9th   "    "  ........ | 1623. |
|   (Called by error 5th ed.) | |
| 10th Latin ed ........ | 1627. |
| 11th   "    "  ........ | 1628. |
| 4th French "  ........ | 1628. |
| 12th Latin "  ........ | 1630. |
| 5th French "  ........ | 1630. |
|   (Last four editions all have same title-page and are by error all called the 10th) | |
| 13th Latin ed ........ | 1631. |
|   (Also has same title as 1638, 1630) | |
| 1st German ed. 2 v ........ | 1633. |
| 6th French " 2 v ........ | 1633. |
| ? Latin    "  ........ | 1633. |
| 1st Dutch  "  ........ | 1634. |
| 7th French " 2 v ........ | 1635. |

1st English " ............................................................1635.
   (Historia mundi)
2nd English ed...................................................... 1637.
   (Same)
English ed.............................................................. 1636.
   (Hexham)
14th Latin   ed. 3 v...................................................... 1638.
2nd Dutch   " 2 v........................................................ 1638.
2nd German " .................................................... 1638.

Lelewel assumes the existence of editions of 1620, 1637 and 1640. No editions of these dates seem to be mentioned elsewhere. Lelewel gives a turkish edition brought out by Moustafa ben Abdallah.

In 1596 Girolamo Porro reproduced at Venice the maps of Mercator on a small scale. This was the first reduction of the maps.

The editions of the regular Atlas "Minor" were:
1st Latin ed.................................................................. 1607.
French   "   ............................................................ 1608.
Latin   "   ............................................................ 1609.
French   "   ............................................................ 1609.
German   "   ........................................................... 1609.
Latin   "   ............................................................ 1610.
  "   "   ............................................................ 1621.
1st Dutch "   ............................................................ 1621.
Latin   "   ............................................................ 1628.
French   "   ............................................................ 1628.
? German "   ............................................................ 1629.
Dutch   "   ............................................................ 1630.
French   "   ............................................................ 1630.
German   "   ........................................................... 1631.
Latin   "   ............................................................ 1634.
? Dutch   "   ............................................................ 1636.
German   "   ........................................................... 1651.

Of the larger reduced edition of Mercator's Atlas, the following are known:
French ed........................................................................ 1630.
Latin   "   ............................................................ 1632.
French   "   ............................................................ 1636.

## 1607

Atlas minor Gerardi Mercatoris à I. Hondio plurimis æneis tabulis auctus atque illustratus. 4 p. l., [678] pp. incl. 151 maps, 1 pl. obl. 12°. Amsterodami, excusum in ædibus Iudoci Hondij. Veneunt etiam apud Corneliũ Nicolai item apud Ioannem Ianſoniũ Arnhemi [1607]    423

   NOTE.—Collation: engraved title, verso blank, p. l. [1].—Iodocus Hondius lectori s. d., dated 1607, recto and verso p. l. [2].—In uſum tabularum, recto and verso p. l. [3].—Index tabularum, recto and verso p. l. [4].—Engraved pl. representing the three fates, p. [1].—Text incl. 152 maps, p. [2-678] Jodocus Hondius reduced the large atlas of Mercator to small quarto, and first published it, with latin text in 1607. It passed through many editions in latin, french, german and dutch. *cf.* Raemdonck, J. van. Gérard Mercator. 1869. p. 269.

**Mercator, G.**—Continued.
The following maps relate to America:
no. [2] Typus orbis terrarum.
" [3] Europa.
" [4] Asia.
" [6] Americæ descrip.
" [7] Polus Arcticus cum vicinis regionibus.
" [135] Tartaria.
" [140] Insulæ Indiae orientalis.
" [144] Hispania Nova.
" [145] Virginia et Florida.
" [146] Cuba insul.— Hispaniola.— Havana portvs.— I. Iamaica.— I. S. Ioannis.— I. Margareta.
" [147] America Meridionalis.
" [148] Fretum Magellani.
" [151] Designatio orbis Christiani.

### 1609
**Langenes, B.**

Hand-boeck; of cort begrijp der caerten ende beschryvinghen van alle. landen des werelds. Van nieuvvs oversien ende vermeerdert. 8 p. l., 761 (*i. e.* 759), [4] pp. incl. 172 maps, 5 pl. obl. 32°. 't Amstelredam, Cornelis Claesz, 1609. 424

NOTES.—Engraved title. See also titles 410, 415 and 428.
Incorrect pagination at pp. 606, 607.
The pages 314, 315, 318, 319, 700, 701, 740 are numbered 114, 115, 118, 119, 100, 101, 340.
An engraving of Magellan's ship appears on page 21.
The same map of "America" is found on pp. [701] and 39.
The following maps relate to America and to the Philippines:
p. 39. De nieuvve vvereld.
" 605. Infulæ Philippinae.
" 707. Infularum Cubæ, Hifpaniolæ, Iucatanæ, & circumjacentium descriptio.
" 711. Cuba insula.
" 713. Aity sive Spaniola.
"[715] [America in't Zuyden]
" 719. Brasilia.
" 729. Chili et Patagonum regio.
" 733. Peru.
" 743. Cerro de Potosi.
" 745. Mexicana.
" 749. Terra Nova.
" 753. Fretum Magellanicum.

### 1609
**Mercator, G.**

Atlas minor, das ift ein kurtze jedoch gründtliche befchreibung der gantzen welt vnd aller ihrer theyl: erftlich von Gerardo Mercatore in Latein befchrieben: folgendts durch Iodocvm Hondivm mit vielen kupffern gebeffert vnd vermehrt: vnd endtlich in vnfere hoch Teutfche sprach verfetzt. 7 p. l., 676 (*i. e.* 686), [18] pp. incl. 150 maps, 1 pl. obl. 12°. [Franckfurt am Mayn, 1609] 425

NOTE.—Collation: engraved latin title, verso blank, p. l. [1].—German title, verso blank, p. l. [2].—Dedication and "Vorred," signed Peter Vffenbach, dated 1609, recto p. l. [3]-verso p. l. [5].—Ein kurtze und nützliche vnterrichtung . . . recto p. l. [6]-recto p. l. [7] verso blank.—Engraved pl. representing the three fates, p. [1].—Text incl. 149 maps, pp. [2]-676.—1 map.—Register, 17 pp.

German title-page is preceeded by engraved title of latin edition of 1607, reading: Atlas minor Gerardi Mercatoris à I. Hondio plurimis æneis tabulis auctus atque illustratus. Amsterodami, excusum in ædibus Iudoci Hondij. Veneunt etiam apud Corneliū Nicolai item apud Ioannem Iansoniū Arnhemi.

Paging omitted on first 19 pages and on all maps.

Contains all maps in first edition except the following:

no. [73] Lyonnois Foreft et Beaujolois.
" [86] Alsatia Inferior.
" [127] Marocchi regnum.
" [153] Aeneae troia ni navigatio.

Also contains one map not in first edition:

p. [75] Cambria five Wallia.

Instead of map entitled Alsatia Inferior, which is called for by index, and which is found in first edition, a duplicate of Alsatia Superioris appears in this copy.

The following maps relate to America:

p. [3] Typus orbis terrarum.
" [7] Europa.
" [17] Asia.
" [21] Americae descrip.
" [25] Polus Arcticus cum vicinis regionibus.
" [619] Tartaria.
" [630] Insulæ Indiae orientalis.
" [645] Hispania Nova.
" [649] Virginia et Florida.
" [653] Cuba Insul.—Hispaniola.—Havana portvs.—I. Iamaica.—I. S. Ioannis.—I. Margareta.
" [659] America Meridionalis.
" [662] Fretum Magellani.
" [671] Designatio orbis Christiani.

## 1609

L'Atlas ou meditations cosmographiqves de la fabriqve du monde et figure dicelvy. Commencé en latin par le tref-docte Gerard Mercator, parachevé p. Iodocus Hondius. Traduit en françois par le sieur de la P[opelinière] Editio secunda qua et ampliores defcriptiones & novæ tabulæ geographicæ accefserunt. 4 p. l., 358 (*i. e.* 361), [35] pp., [4] l., 146 maps. fol. Amfterodami sumptibus & typis æneis Iudoci Hondij, 1609. 426

NOTE.—Collation: engraved title, verso blank, p. l. [1].—Iodocvs Hondivs av lectevr salvt, dated 1609, recto p. l. [2].—Latin verse, Gerardo Mercatori et Ivdoco Hondio, signed Petrus Bertius; verse in latin and in greek, In Gerardi Mercatoris Flandri atlantem, signed Daniel Heinfius; latin verse, signed Iacobus Gruterus; followed by greek verse, verso p. l. [2].—Indice des tables de cest oevvre, recto and verso p. l. [3].—A monsignevr . . . le davphin, signed Iodocus Hondius, recto p. l. [4].—Latin verse, Ad Iodocvm Hondivm . . . signed Maxæmylianus Vrientius, dated 1609, verso p. l. [4].—La race d'Atlas, p. 1.—Livre de la creation & fabrique du monde, pp. 2-28.—Text and 43 maps, pp. 29-120.—Engraved title: Galliae tabulę geographicæ. Per Gerardum Mercato-

**Mercator, G.**—Continued.

rem . . . verso blank.—Av favorable lectevr, pp. 121-123.—L'estat politic dv royavme de France, pp. 123-127.—Advis povr l'vsage des tables, pp. 127-128.—Rolle et indice des tables de la Gavle, p. 128.—Text and 20 maps, pp. 129-170.—Engraved title: Belgii inferioris geographicæ tabulę. Per Gerardum Mercatorem . . . verso blank.—Au bien affectionné lecteur; La police dv Pays Bas sovs les Bovrgognons, pp. 171-173.—Lifte de la table des Pays bas, p. 173.—La table de la Germanie Inferievre, p. 174.—Text and and 10 maps, pp. 175-198.—Engraved title: Germaniae tabulę geographicæ. Per Gerardum Mercatorem . . . verso blank.—Advertissement vtile et necessaire svr les tables de la Germanie, pp. 199-202.—Le catalogve et recveil des tables de la Germanie porte, p. 202.—Wanting, pp. 203-204.—Text and 28 maps, pp. 209-264.—Engraved title: Italiae, Sclavoniæ, et Græciæ tabulę geographicę. Per Gerardum Mercatorem . . . verso blank.—Text and 45 maps, pp. 265-358.—Index, [35] pp. French title on a flap over title of latin edition of 1607. The words "Editio secunda" . . . refer to the 1607 latin edition.

Pagination irregular.

Text on the reverse of maps.

No text to Asiæ Nova, and to general map of America.

The first french edition translated from latin edition of 1607 by Lancelot de Voysin, seigneur de la Popelinière. *cf.* Raemdonck (J. van) Gérard Mercator . . . 1869. p. 189, 269.

The following maps relate to America:

no. [1] Orbis terrae compendiosa descriptio . . . 1587.
" [2] Evropa.
" [3] Nova Europæ descriptio. Auctore Iodoco Hondio.
" [4] Africa.
" [5] Asia.
" [6] America fiue India.
" [7] Septentrionalivm terrarum descriptio.
" [129] Asiæ nova descriptio. Auctore Iodoco Hondio.
" [135] Tartaria.
" [136] China.
" [138] Insulæ Indiæ orientalis praecipuæ . . .
" [141] America.
" [142] Hispaniæ Novæ nova descriptio.
" [143] Virginiae item et Floridae Americæ provinciarum, nova descriptio.
" [144] Cuba insula. Inset: Havana portus.—Hispaniola insula.—Insula Jamaica.—Ins. S. Joannis. I. s. Margareta cum confiniis.
" [145] America Meridionalis.
" [146] Exquifita & magno aliquot menfium periculo luftrata et iam retecta Freti Magellanici facies.

## 1609

**Ortelius, A.**

Theatrvm orbis terrarvm Abrahami Orteli Antverp. geographi regii.   1 p. l., 376 l. incl. [5], 163 col. maps, 6 pl., 1 por., 30, [5] pp.  fol.  Antverpiæ, apvd Ioannem Bapt. Vrintivm, anno 1609.

427

Note.—Collation: sig. A-D in sixes, E in four.—Maps 1-22, l. 22*, maps 23-128.—sig. a in four.—maps i-xj, l. xij (2 pp. of text).—maps xiij-xv, l. **xvj** (1 p. of text, verso blank), pl. xvij, xviij.—maps xix-xxxix.—pl. xl.—sig. a-c in sixes.

sig. [A¹] recto: col. eng. title; verso: arms of the King of Spain (colored). sig. A² recto, dedication: D. Philippo Avstriaco Caroli V . . . sig. A² verso– A³ verso: Adolphi Mekerchi . . . frontispicii explicatio. In theatrvm orbis terrarvm Abrahami Ortelii, R. P. Andreas Schottvs . . . sig. A4 recto– [A5] recto: Abrahami Ortelii . . . vita, Francisco Svvertio F. Antverp. auctore. sig. [A5] verso: Abrahami Ortelii qvem vrbs vrbivm Antverpia edidit, rex regvm Philippvs geographvm habvit monvmentvm hic vides . . . (within eng. border). sig. [A6]–C recto: Insignivm aliqvot hvivs ævi poetarvm carmina ex lacrymis Francisci Sweerti F. in Abrahami Orteli obitum. sig. C verso–C2 verso: Abrahamvs Ortelivs Antverpianvs . . . beneγolis lectoribvs S. D.—Ornatissimo viro D. Abrahamo Ortelio, amico cvm primis caro. (signed: Gerardvs Mercator). sig. C3 recto–[C5] recto: Catalogvs avctorvm tabvlarvm geographicarvm qvotqvot ad nostram cognitionem hactenvs peruenêre . . . (183 names). sig. [C5] verso: Index tabvlarvm hvivs operis, sive inscriptionvm earvndem. sig. D recto–D2 recto: Qvoniam vero plvres regiones avt insvlæ in his tabvlis descriptæ svnt . . . sig. D2 verso– [D3] recto: Epigrammata Danielis Rogersii Albimontani . . . In Abrahami Ortelii theatrvm orbis (signed Paulus Meliffus Francus) sig. [D3] verso–[D4] verso: Hadriani Ivnii Hornani in hoc theatrvm.—Ioannis Posthii med. d.— Io. Vivianvs Valentianvs Abrahamo Ortelio svo.—In eivsdem theatrvm (signed Maximus Æmylianus de Vriendt . . .)—Nicolavs Rhedinger . . .— Ioan. Matthævs Vackervs . . .—Ex elogiis . . . Auberti Miraei . . . sig. [D5] recto: In atlantem Gerardi Mercatoris a Ivdoco Hondio fuppletum & divulgatum epigramma (signed P. Scriverius).—In tabvlas geographicas Gerardi Mercatoris avthore et avspice Cl. V. Ivdoco Hondio avctivs et illvstrius e vulgatos (signed: Ioh. Isacius Pontanus). sig. [D5] verso–[D6] recto: eng. pl. (colored) with portraits of Mercator and Hondius (same as in Mercator's atlas) sig. [D6] verso: Atlas Gerardi Mercatoris et Ivsti Hondii cosmographorvm mortem dolens (signed Petrus Montanus).—In obitvm cl$^{mi}$. V. Iudoci Hondii cofmographi (signed: Maxæmylianus Vrientius . . .) sig. E recto—[E4] recto: Introdvctio mathematica, ad pleniorem intellectvm tabvlarvm geographicarvm, qvae svnt in theatro orbis terrarvm Abrahami Ortelii . . . auctore Michaële Coigneto mathematico, &c. (with 5 col. maps in text). sig. [E6] verso: eng. portrait of Ortelius (colored).—maps 1–22, l. 22*, maps 23– 128. sig. [a] recto: col. eng. title: Parergon, sive veteris geograpiæ[-]aliqvot tabvlæ. sig. [a] verso: Ad. Cl. V. Abrahamvm Ortelivm Iani Lernvti epigramma.—Ad Abrahamvm Ortelivm enthevm geographorvm principem, Michaelis Vander-Hagen . . . epigramma. sig. a ij recto–[a iij] recto: Ornatissimo viro d. Abrahamo Ortelio (dated: Coloniæ Agripp. pridie Kal. Ian. CIƆ.IƆ.LXXVIII. Signed: A. Graphaevs). sig. [a iij]–verso [a iv] recto: In regivmgeographvm dn. Abrahamvm Ortelivm Antverpianvm avunculum fuum carifsimum, Iacobi Colii Orteliani carmen *ANAΓPAMMATIKΩΣ*.—Regionvm insvlarvmqve hvivs parergi index. sig. [a iv] verso: A Iove principivm inqvit vetvstas.—A sacris itaqve avspicandvm hvnc nostrvm laborem dvximvs.— maps j–xj, l. xij (2 pp. of text). maps xiij–xv.—l. xvj (1 p. of text, verso blank). pl. xvij, xviij: De institvtione et ordine imperii germanici tabvla I.-II.—maps xix–xxxix.—pl. xl: Scenographia totivs fabricæ S. Lavrentii in Escoriali. maps have text on front pages, several on the last pages also. sig. [A] recto: Nomenclator Ptolemaicvs; omnia locorvm vocabvla qvæ in tota Ptolemaei geographia occurrunt . . . Antverpiæ, typis Roberti Brvneav, anno M.DC.IX; verso: Abrahamvs Ortelivs candido lectori. sig. A2 recto– C3 verso: Ptolemaeo geographorvm primario avctore orbis terrarvm dividitvr in tres partes . . . sig. C4 recto—[C5] verso: De Mona drvidvm insvla . . . (sig. Humfredus Lhuyd . . . )—Approbatio. sig. [C6] recto: Approbatio

**Ortelius, A.**—Continued.
novarvm descriptionvm.—Imp. Rvdolphi, Philippi Hisp. regis et cancellariae Brabanticae privilegiis sancitvm est.—Svmma privilegii.—Ad libri compactorem; verso blank.
The following maps relate to America:
no. 1. Typvs orbis terrarum. 1587.
" 2. Evropae.
" 4. Africae tabvla nova . . . 1570.
" 5. Americae sive novi orbis, nova descriptio. 1587.
" 6. Maris Pacifici (quod vulgò Mar del Zur) . . . novifsima descriptio. 1589.
" 7. Hispaniae novae . . . descriptio. 1579.
" 8. Cvliacanae, Americae regionis, descriptio.—Hispaniolae, Cvbae aliarvmqve insvlarvm circvmiacientivm delineatio.
" 9. Pervviae avriferæ regionis typvs. Didaco Mendezio auctore.—La Florida. Auctore Hieron. Chiaues.—Gvastecan reg.
" 115. Septentrionalivm regionvm descrip.
" 118. Tartariae sive magni chami regni typus.
" 121. Indiae orientalis, insvlarvmqve adiacientivm typvs.
The copy described by Hessel in "Epistvlae Ortelianae," contains 118 maps numbered 1–25, 25*, 25**, 25***, 26–115 and 40 in the Parergon; the "Nomenclator Ptolemaicvs" is dated 1603.

## 1610?
**Langenes, B.**

Thrésor de chartes, de tovs les pays dv monde, enrichi de belles defcriptions, reveu & augmenté. 8 p. l., 496, 202, [5] pp. incl. 160 maps, 5 pl. obl. 32°. [Francfort?] M. Becker, pour H. Lavrentz [1610?] 428

NOTE.—Translated from the dutch edition, 1598, by J. de la Haye. See also titles 410, 415, 424. There are three french editions, one brought out by Chr. Guyot for Corneille Nicolas, 1602; another by Albert Henry for Corneille Nicolas [1602?]; and this edition which Muller states was published about 1610.

The maps were mostly engraved by Keer and Hondius, and were reduced from the maps of Ortelius.

Map in pt. 2, p. 27, Sancta Helena, bears the inscription Benjamin W[right] caelator.

Contains nine "Descriptions," and six maps not found in french edition published by Albert Henry, for Corneille Nicolas.

The following maps relate to America:
pt. 1. p. 1. Typus orbis terrarum.
" " 19. Le globe terreftre.
" " 39. Le nouveau monde.
" 2. " 55. Infulæ Philippinae.
" " 149. Tercere.
" " 153. Infularum Cubæ, Hifpaniolæ, Iucatanæ & circumjacentium describtio [!]
" " 155. Cuba insula.
" " 157. Aity sive Spaniola.
" " 159. L'Amérique du cofte du Midi.
" " 163. Brasilia.
" " 169. Chili et Patagonum regio.
" " 171. Cerro de Potosi.

pt. 2. p. 175. Peru.
"   " 185. Mexicana.
"   " 189. Terra Nova.
"   " 195. Fretum Magellanicum.

## 1610
**Mercator, G.**

Atlas minor Gerardi Mercatoris à I. Hondio plurimis æneis tabulis auctus atque illustratus. Amsterodami, Excusum in ædibus Judoci Hondij. Veneunt etiam apud Corneliū Nicolai item apud Ioannem Ianſsoniū Arnhemi. 4 p. l., 684 pp. incl. 153 maps, 1 pl. obl. 12°. [ *Colophon:*] Dordrechti, excudebat Adrianus Bottius, 1610.

429

NOTE.—Collation: engraved title, verso blank, p. l. [1].—Iodocus Hondius lectori s. d., dated 1607, recto and verso p. l. [2].—In uſuni tabularum, recto and verso, p. l. [3].—Index tabularum, recto and verso p. l. [4].—Engraved pl. representing the three fates, p. l.—Text incl. 153 maps, ending with vignette and colophon on p. 684, pp. 2–684.

Jodicus Hondius reduced the large atlas of Mercator to a small quarto, and first published it, with latin text in 1607. Several other editions in latin, french and german followed, this edition appearing in 1610 with the same title as the first latin edition in 1607. The 1613 latin edition was acquired too late for a detailed description.

The following maps relate to America:

p.  3. Typus orbis terrarum.
"   7. Europa.
"  15. Asia.
"  19. Americae descrip.
"  23. Polus Arcticus cum vicinis regionibus.
" 627. Tartaria.
" 639. Insulæ Indiae orientaliʜ.
" 651. Hispania Nova.
" 655. Virginia et Florida.
" 659. Cuba insul.—Hispaniola—Havana Portvs.—I. Iamaica.—I. S. Ioannis.—I. Margareta.
" 663. America Meridionalis.
" 667. Fretum Magellani.
" 675. Designatio orbis Christiani.

## 1612
**Ortelius, A.**

Theatro del mondo . . . da lui poco inanzi la ſua morte riueduto, & di tauole nuoue, et commenti adorno, & arricchito, con la vita dell' autore. Traslato in lingua toscana dal sig$^r$. Filippo Pigafetta. 1 p. l., [371] l. incl. [5], 163 maps, 3 pl., 2 por., 30, [6] pp.   fol. In Anversa, si vende nella libraria Plantiniana, 1612.

430

NOTE.—Collation: sig. A–D in sixes, E in three.—Maps 1–19, 21–23. l. 23*.—Maps 24–84.—l. 84*—maps 85, 85*, 86–91, 91*–127.—sig. a in four.—maps j–**xv**, sheet xvi (4 pp. of text).—pl. xvij, xviij.—maps xix–xxxix.—pl. xl.—sig. **A** in six (i. e. A$^2$, A$^3$, A$^4$, 3 l. unsig.), B, C in sixes.

sig. [A$^1$] recto: col. eng. title; verso: engr. portrait of pope Clement vııı.
sig. A$^2$ recto-verso: Alla S$^{ta}$. di . . . papa Clemente vııı. (signed: Gio.

**Ortelius, A.**—Continued.
> Baptiſta Vrintzio). sig. A3 recto: All' illvstrissimo . . . il sig<sup>r</sup>. card<sup>l</sup>. Piet. Aldobrandino (signed: Gio. Bap<sup>ta</sup>. Vrintzio); verso: Espositione della facciata del theatro di Filippo Pigafetta. sig. A4 recto-[A5] recto: La vita d' Abrahamo Ortelio d' Anversa . . . scritta da Francesco Svveertio. sig. [A5] verso: Abrahami Ortelii qvem vrbs vrbivm Antverpia edidit, rex regvm Philippvs geographvm habvit monvmentvm hic vides . . . (within eng. border). sig. [A6] recto-C recto: Insignivm aliqvot hvivs ævi poetarvm carmina ex lacrymis Francisci Sweerti F. in Abrahami Orteli obitvm [etc.] sig. C verso-C2 verso: Abrahamo Ortelio d' Anversa . . . salvta li benevoli lettori. sig. C3 recto-[C5] recto: Tavola di tvtti li nomi de gli avtori delle carte di geografia che siano insin ad hora alla conoscenza nostra pervenvti . . . (183 names). sig. [C5] verso-D2 recto: Tavola delle carte di geografia et de paesi di qvest' opera . . . sig. D2 verso-D3 verso: Adolphi Mekerchi Brvgensis . . . frontispicii explicatio.—In theatrvm orbis terrarvm Abrahami Ortelii, R. P. Andreas Schottvs Antverp . . . sig. D4 recto-verso: Epigrammata Danielis Rogersii Albimontani . . .—In Abrahami Ortelii theatrvm orbis. (signed Paulus Meliſſus Francus). sig. [D5] recto-verso: Hadriani Ivnii Hornani in hoc theatrvm.—Ioannis Posthii med. d.—Io. Vivianvs Valentianvs Abrahamo Ortelio svo.—In eivsdem theatrvm (signed Maximus Æmylianus de Vriendt). sig. [D6] recto: Nicolavs Rhedinger . . .—Ioan. Matthævs Vackervs . . . Ex elogiis . . . Avberti Miraei . . . verso: engr. portrait of Ortelius. sig. E recto-[E3] verso: Introduttione mathematica . . . per Michele Coigneto . . . (with 5 maps in text).—maps 1-19, 21-23. l. 23*, maps 24-84. l. 84*. maps 85, 85*, 86-91, 91*-127.—sig. [a] recto: Parergon, cioe fvor d' opera, et givnta, overo alcvne tavole dell' antica geografia; verso: Ad Cl. V. Abrahamvm Ortelivm Iani Lernvti epigramma.—Ad Abrahamvm Ortelivm enthevm geographorvm principem Michaelis Vander-Hagen Antverpiani epigramma. sig. a ij recto-[aiij] recto: Ornatissimo viro D. Abrahamo Ortelio (signed: Coloniæ Agripp. pridie kal. Ian. cIƆ.IƆ. LXXVIII. A. Graphaevs). sig. [aiij] verso—[aiv] recto: In regivm geographvm dn. Abrahamvm Ortelivm . . . Iacobi Colii Orteliani carmen Αναγραμματικος.—Tauola delle regioni & dell' isole di questo Parergo.—sig. [aiv] verso: Da Giove il principio dice l' antichita.—Onde vogliamo prender il cominciamento di qvesta fatica nostra dalle cose sacre.—maps j-xv; sheet xvj (4 pp. of text), pl. xvij, xviij: Della constitvtione et ordine dell' imperio thedesco tavola I-II.—maps xix-xxxix.—pl. xl: Scenographia totivs fabricæ S. Lavrentii Escoriali.—Maps have text on front pages. sig. A2 recto-C3 verso: Nomenclator Ptolemaicvs. sig. [A1] containing the title has been inserted after the leaf following sig. A5, the title reads: Nomenclator Ptolemaicvs; omnia locorvm vocabvla qvae in tota Ptolemaei geographia occurrunt . . . Antverpiæ, typis Roberti Brvneav, 1607; on the reverse: Abrahamvs Ortelivs candido lectori. sig. C4 recto-[C5] verso: Epistola del . . . gentil'hvomo Hvmfredo Lvid, dell' isola mona delli druidi . . .—Approbatio. sig. [C6] recto: Approbatio.—Imp. Rvdolphi, Philippi Hisp.—Svmma privilegii; verso: Gli errori della ſtampa ſi hanno da correggere come ſegue.—Ad libri compactorem.
> NOTE.—Map no. 20 wanting.
> The following maps relate to America:
> no. 1. Typvs orbis terrarvm . . . 1587.
> " 2. Evropae.
> " 4. Africae tabvla nova . . . 1570.
> " 5. Americae sive novi orbis . . . descriptio . . . 1587.
> " 6. Maris Pacifici (quod vulgò Mar del Zur) . . . noviſsima descriptio.

no. 7. Hispaniae novae . . . descriptio. 1579.
" 8. Cvliacanae, Americae regionis descriptio.—Hispaniolae, Cvbae, aliarvm qve insvlarvm circvmiacientivm delineatio.
" 9. Pervviae avriferæ regionis typvs. Didaco Mendezio auctore.—La Florida. Auctore Hieron. Chiaues.—Gvastecan reg.
" 114. Septentrionalivm regionvm descrip.
" 117. Tartariae sive magni chami regni tÿpus.
" 120. Indiae orientalis, insvlarvmqve adiacientivm typvs.

## 1612

Epitome theatri orbis terrarvm . . . de nouo recognita, aucta, et geographica ratione reftaurata, a Michaele Coigneto mathem. Antuerpiano.   1 p. l., [146] l. incl. 135 col. maps, 2 pl., 2 diagr. obl. 32°.   Antverpiae, exstat in officina Plantiniana, 1612.   431

NOTE.—Collation: sig. A–S in eights (O3 wanting) T in four.
sig. [A] recto: eng. title; verso: Serenissimo Alberto archid. Avstriæ . . . Michael Coignetvs . . . sig. [A2] recto—verso: Michael Coignetvs Antverp. benevolis lectoribvs S. D.   sig. A3 recto—[A8] recto: De geographiæ principijs . . . sig. [A8] verso: Vtrivsqve hemisphaerii tam coelestis qvam terrestris . . . declaratio.   sig. B recto, plate; Globvs coelestis; verso: Elementaris regio, ab infimo planetarvm orbe . . .   sig. B2 recto, map: Globvs terrestris; verso: Ad Philippvm II Hispaniarvm &c.   sig. B3 recto, plate-Scenographia totivs fabricæ S. Lavrentii in Escoriali; verso: Orbis terrarvm (letterpress).   sig. B4 recto—O2 recto: maps 1–95.   (sig. O3, map no. 96, Neapolitanum regnum wanting).   sig. O4 recto—T recto: maps 97–134.—Maps are printed on the recto of the leaves, the letterpress on the verso.   sig. T verso—T2 verso: Index tabvlarvm.   sig. T3 recto: Index tabvlarvm qvæ recenter hvic operi accesservnt.   sig. T3 verso: Approbatio (dated: 1601, signed: Guilielmus Lucas s. theol. licentiatus . . .)—[Approbatio] (dated: 1609, signed: Ioannes Hemelarius).   sig. T4 recto: Svmma privilegii (dated 1601, signed: I. de Bufchere); verso: blank.
Interleaved copy with manuscript notes.
Maps are from the same plates as those in the Coignet's french edition of the Epitome, 1602, and the same maps relate to America.

## 1617

**Ptolemæus, C.**
Ioannis | Antonii Magini | Patavini, Mathefeos in Almo | Bononienfi Gymnafio Profefsoris, | Geographiae, tum veteris, | tum novae, volumina duo. | In quorum priore, | Cl: Ptol: Pelufiensis Geographicæ Enarrationis | libri octo: quorum primus commentarijs | uberrimis illuftratur. | In pofteriore, | Eiufdem Ptol: antiqui Orbis tabulæ 27. quibus ac- | cedunt 37 recentiores, univerfum Orbem, et | fingularum ejus Regionum Faciē repræfētātes. | Additæ funt copiofiifsimæ ipfarum tabularum ex- | plicationes, quibus fingulæ Orbis partes, Impe- | ria, Regna, Ducatus, aliaque Dominia, | prout noftro tempore fe habent, exa- | ctifsimè defcribuntur. | Arnhemii Excudebat | Ioannes Ianssonius. | Anno 1617 | [*Title to second part:*]   Geogra- | phiae | Cl. Ptolemæi | Pars Secvnda, | continens præ- | ter antiqvas ip- | fius Ptol. recentiores etiam

**Ptolemæus, C.**—Continued.

Ta- | bulas, quæ Vniverſæ terræ | faciem noſtro ævo co- | gnitam exhibent. | A Hieronymo Porro | Pat. incisas. | Vnà cum ipſarum Tabularum uberrimis expoſitioni- | bus, quibus ſingulæ Orbis Provinciæ, Regiones, Im- | peria, Regna, Ducatus, & alia Dominia | deſcribunter. | Avthorae | Io. Antonio Magi- | no Patavino, Almi Bonon. | Gymnaſij Publico | Mathematico. | Arnhemi, | Apud Ioannem Ianſzonium. | Anno 1617. | 432

    458 l. comprising: 4 p. l., 47, 184 pp., [20], 284 (i. e. 288) l. incl. [63] maps, 1 map on [2] l., [28] l. 8°.

    (sig. )(, A–F in fours; A–L in eights; M, A–E in fours; A–C in eights; D in four; E–P in eights; Q in four; R–Z, Aa–Oo in eights; a–g in fours) Collation: title, verso blank,—dedication, signed by Gasparvs Ens, beginning on recto l. [2] and ending on recto l. [3],—preface beginning on verso l. [3] and ending on verso l. [4], (sig. )( ); Io. Antonii Magini Patavini in Primvm Librvm Geographiae Clavdii Ptolemaei Commentaria, et Annotationes", incl. 10 diagr., 47.pp., verso p. 47·blank, (sig. A–F); text incl. 6 diagr., 184 pp., (sig. A–M); "Index Capitvm, qvae in Libro Primo Ptolemaei Continentvr", 19 l., followed by 1 blank l. (sig. A–E); title, "Geographiae Cl. Ptolemæi Pars Secvnda" . . . with map on verso,—1 (unsigned) double page map,—text incl. 63 maps, 2–28, [29], 30–32, [33], 39, 35–49, [50], 51, 52, 35, 54–67, [68], 69–98, 76, 100–110, [111] 111, 137, 113, 115–126, 137, 128, 129, 133, 131–134, 235, 136–164, 166, 165, 167–184, 181–190, 195–198, 195, 238, 139–140, 241–244, 145, 246–259, 250, 261, 162–163, 264–268, 169, 270–284 l. in all 288 l., (sig. A–Oo); "Index, sev Tabvla Nominvm Antiqvorvm et Recentivm", [28] l., (sig. a–g). Fourth edition of Magini's Ptolemy, edited by Gaspar Ens.

    Maps the same as those in the latin editions of 1596, 1597 and 1608 and in the italian editions of 1598 and 1621.

    The nine maps of America are noted in the 1596 edition.

    New engraved border to first title-page. Engraved border to second title-page same as in 1597 edition.

    Bound in full calf, elaborately tooled.

    Eames-Sabin, no. 66496.

## 1618

Theatrvm | Geographiæ | Veteris, | Duobus Tomis diſtinctum, | Edente | Petro Bertio Bevero. | Chriſtianiſsimi Galliarum Regis· Lvdovici xiii. | Cosmographo. | [Engraved title] Theatri | Geographiae Veteris | Tomus prior | in quo | Cl. Ptol. Alexandrini | Geographiæ libri viii | Græcé et Latiné | Græca ad codices Palatinos collata | aucta et emendata ſunt | Latina infinitis locis correcta | opera | P. Bertii Chriſtianiſſimi Galli- | arum Regis Coſmographi. | [*Colophon:*] Lvgdvni Batavorvm, | Excudebat typis ſuis Isaacvs Elzevirivs, | Sumptibus Ivdoci Hondii. | Anno | cIɔ Iɔ cxviii. | 433

    304 l. comprising: 8 p. l., 253 pp., 1 l., [28] maps on [55] l., 28, [40] pp., 2 l., 46 pp., 1 map on [8] l., 20 pp., [36] l. incl. 14 maps. fol.

    (sig. 2 l. unsigned, *,**,*** in twos; A–V in sixes; X in four; Y–Z in twos; A–O in twos; 1 l. unsigned; P–V, V², X–Z, Z², Aa–Bb in twos; Cc–Dd in sixes; Ee in two; AA–GG in sixes, 1 l. unsigned between DD² and DD³; HH–MM in

twos; NN in six, 1 l. unsigned between NN$^2$ and NN$^3$; OO in four; PP in one; QQ-SS in twos; TT in one; VV in two; XX in three; YY-ZZ in twos; AAA-BBB in ones; CCC-KKK in twos; LLL in one)
Collation: title, verso blank; engraved title to v. 1, showing figures of Ptolemaeus and Marinus, verso blank; dedication to Louis XIII, 1 l. verso blank; P. Bertii. In Theatrum Geographicæ Veteris Præfatio, 5 l., (sig. *,**,***); title to text in greek and latin . . . "Clavdii | Ptolemæi | Alexandrini | Philofophi eruditiffimi | De Geographia Libri octo" | with Greek verses on the verso, text in greek and latin in parallel columns, incl. 7 diagr., 253 pp., verso p. 253 blank; title to maps in greek and latin . . . "Ex Clavdii Ptolemæi Geogrophicis [!] libris octo orbem | totum habitabilem Agathodæmon Alexandrinus | mechanicus delineauit. | Has verò tabulas defcripfit Gerardvs Mercator Rupelmundanus. | Recenfuit variè, correxit, auxitq̊, | Petrvs Bertivs Bevervs, | Cbriftianiffimi Galliarvm Regis—Cofmographus". | Greek and latin verses on verso, (sig. A-Z); [27] double page and 1 single maps on [55] l. with descriptions on first reverse, (sig. A-Bb); "Gerardi Mercatoris | Rvpelmvndani | In Tabulas Ptolemaicas | a se | Delineatas | Annotationes" | , portrait of Mercator on verso, [1-2] pp., preface incl. 2 diagr., followed by "Annotationes" on p. 9, 3-28 pp., (sig. Cc-Ee); Index, [40] pp., (sig. AA-DD$_2$); engraved title to v. 2: Geographia | Ocvlvs | Historiarvm | Theatri | Geographiæ | Veteris | Tomvs Posterior | in quo | Itinerarivm Antonini Imperatoris | Terreftre & maritimum | Provinciarvm Romanarvm Libellus | Civitates Provinciarvm Gallicarvm | Itinerarivm a Burdigala Hierofolymam vfq̊ | Tabvla Pevtingeriana cum Notis | Marci Velferi ad Tabulæ eius partem | Parergi Orteliani Tabulæ aliquot | edente | P. Bertio Chriftianiffimi Galliarum | Regis Cofmographi | Amstelodami | Ex officina Iudoci Hondij | Anno 1619 | , verso blank; Itineraria Dvo Antonini Pii . . . [2], 46 pp., (sig. DD$_3$-HH); Tabvla itineraria, ex illustri Pevtingerorvm Bibliotheca, on 8 l., the text on recto of first l., (sig. II-MM); Præfatio in Fragmenta Tabulæ itinerariæ antiquæ, 4 pp., 1 map, Scheda Prior on 1 l., verso blank, Prioris Schedæ Explicatio, Posterioris Schedæ Explicatio, 5-20 pp., (sig. NN-OO); title, Abrahami Ortelii | Geographiæ veteris | Tabvlæ aliqvot | . . . verso blank, [35] l. incl. 14 double-page maps, (sig. PP-KKK); Ad Lectorem, [1] l., with colophon on verso, (sig. LLL)
"The 28 maps in the first part . . . were evidently printed from the same plates as those in the editions of 1578, 1584, and 1605. They comprise the "Vniversalis Tabvla ivxta Ptolemæum," ten of Europe, five of Africa (one of which is on a single leaf entitled "Appendix. III. Tabvlæ Afr:" verso blank), and twelve of Asia. The Peutingerian tables in 4 four double-page plates were engraved and published for the first time nearly twenty years before, and contain the imprint *Antverpiae è Typographeio nostro kal. Decemb. CIƆ IƆ. XCVIII.* In some copies the map "Scheda Prior" is accompanied by another entitled "Scheda Posterior," probably taken from another work. The 14 maps of Ortelius comprise: Evropa; Britannicæ Insvlæ; Hispania; Gallia Strabonis; Belgivm; Germania; Italia; Sicilia; Dacia et Moesia; Pontvs Evxinvs; Thracia; Græcia; Africa Propria; and Palæstina. The backs of these maps and the intervening leaves contain the descriptive text. Most of them had been engraved for earlier editions of Ortelius's Atlas, and some are dated 1590, 1595, 1596, 1603, etc. In some copies the maps "Britannicæ Insvlae, " "Hispania," "Germania," "Sicilia," and "Palaestina" are slightly different, and have the descriptive text on the backs in double columns, and in larger type—perhaps taken from the 1624 edition of the "Theatri Orbis Terrarvm Parergon" of Ortelius. The portrait of Mercator is the same as in the edition of 1605. Brunet describes a copy in which the verso of the dedication  contained a por-

**Ptolemæus, C.**—Continued.

trait of Petrus Bertius. According to Hoffmann and Graesse, some copies have only the brief colophon "Anno MDCXVIII," and instead of the extra map "Appendix. III. Tabvlae Afr:" contain another entitled "Petri Kaerii Germania Inferior." Other copies are without date, and instead of "Abrahami Ortelii Geographiæ veteris Tabvlæ aliquot," have appended the "Theatri Orbis Terrarvm Parergon" of the same author, dated "1624." *cf.* Eames. The L. C. has another copy of this edition in which the dedication on one leaf following the engraved title to v. 1, and the engraved title to v. 2, which should precede the "Itineraria Dvo Antonini Pii," are wanting. The second copy is in the original full vellum binding. Third copy recently purchased: imprint "Amstelodami ex officina. Hondij, anno 1618," contains portrait of Bertius. Modern binding, full russia.

Eames-Sabin, no. 66497.

### 1619
**Mercator, G.**

Gerardi Mercatoris atlas sive cosmographicæ meditationes de fabrica mvndi et fabricati figvra. Denuò auctus. 11 p. l., 365 (*i. e.* 367), [35] pp., [4] l., 150 col. maps. fol. Amſterodami, sumptibus & typis æneis Iudoci Hondij, an. d. 1619. 434

NOTE.—Collation: engraved title colored, verso blank, p. l. [1].—Dedication, signed Iudocus Hondius, dated 1607, recto and verso p. l. [2].—Latin verse signed P. Scriverivs; followed by one signed Ioh. Isacivs Pontanvs, recto p. l. [3].—Engraved colored pl. representing Mercator and Hondius, verso p. l. [3]-recto p. l. [4].—Latin verse: Atlas Gerardi Mercatoris et Ivsti Hondii cosmographorvm mortem dolens, signed Petrvs Montanus; latin verse: In obitvm cl[mi] v. Ivdoci Hondii coſmographi, signed Maxæmylianus Vrientivs, verso p. l. [4].—Ivdocvs Hondivs lectoris, dated 1607, recto p. l. [5].—Latin verse: Gerardo Mercatori et Ivdoco Hondio coſmographis, signed Petrus Bertius; verse in latin and in greek: In Mercatoris Flandri atlantem, signed Daniel Heinſius; latin verse, signed Iacobus Gruterus, followed by greek verse, verso p. l. [5].—Index tabvlarvm, recto and verso p. l. [6].—Vita celeberrimi clarissimiqve viri Gerardi Mercatoris Rvpelmvndani, à domino Gualtero Ghymmio . . . recto p. l. [7]-verso p. l. [8].—Celeberrimi clarissimiqve viri Ivdoci Hondii vita, per P. M., followed by latin verse: Epitaphivm in obitum Ivdoci Hondii . . . signed Ioh. Montanus, recto and verso p. l. [9].— Latin verse: Epitaphivm in obitum Gerardi Mercatoris . . . signed Ioannes Mercator; Epistolæ dvæ, duorum doctiſsimorum virorum doctoris Reinhardi Solenandri . . . & d. Iacobi Sinſtedij . . . in laudem atlantis conſcriptæ; latin verse: In atlantem Gerardi Mercatoris avi sui, signed Iohannes Mercator, recto p. l. [10]-recto p. l. [11].—Praefatio in atlantem, verso p. l. [11].— Stemma Atlantis, p. 1.—De mvndi creatione, ac fabrica liber, pp. 2-26.— Blank, pp. 26-27.—Text and 45 col. maps, pp. 29-126.—Engraved title colored: Galliae tabulę geographicae. Per Gerardum Mercatorem . . . verso blank.—Stvdioso et benevolo lectori, pp. 127-129.—De politico statv regni Galliæ, p. 129-133.—In vsvm tabvlarvm ad monitio, p. 133.—Index tabvlarvm Galliae, p. 134.—Text and 20 col. maps, pp. 135-177.—Engraved title colored: Belgii Inferioris geographicæ tabulę. Per Gerardum Mercatorem . . . verso blank.—Ad studioſum lectorem; Politia Belgii svb Bvrgvndionibvs, pp. 178-180.—Index tabvlarvm Belgii Inferioris, p. 180.—Belgii Inferioris tabvla, p. 181.—Text and 11 maps, pp. 182-211.—Engraved title, colored: Germaniae tabulę geographicæ. Per Gerardum Mercatorem . . . verso blank.—Text and 29 col. maps, pp. 212-271.—Engraved title colored: Italiae, Sclavoniæ, et

Græciæ tabulę geographicę. Per Gerardum Mercatorem . . . verso blank.—
Text and 22 col. maps, pp. 272-319.—Text and 23 col. maps of Africa, Asia and
America, pp. 320-365.—Index, [35] pp.
Pagination irregular.
Text on the reverse of maps.
No text to "Asiæ Nova," and to general map of America.
Title-page is that of the 1611 edition, dated 1619. The first edition of Mercator's atlas in one volume was published with latin text in 1602.
The edition of 1611 was the 5th latin edition or the 4th of Hondius, the edition of 1606 being the first edited by him.
At the death of Jodocus Hondius in 1611, the publication of the atlases was carried on by his son Henrick and his son-in-law Jan Jansson. New maps were gradually added and those of Mercator withdrawn or altered.
This copy of the 1619 edition contains 44 maps which do not bear the name of Mercator.
Raemdonck, Tiele, Lelewel, and others do not mention this edition of 1619 with latin text. In his list of the editions of Mercator's Atlas, Wauwermans gives the latin edition of 1616 as the 7th edition, and the edition of 1623 as the 8th. The 1619 edition, however, must have been the 8th edition.
The following maps relate to America:

no. [1] Orbis terrae compendiosa descriptio . . . 1587.
" [2] Evropa.
" [3] Nova Evropæ descriptio. Auctore Iodoco Hondio.
" [4] Africa.
" [5] Asia.
" [6] America five India Nova.
" [7] Septentrionalivm terrarum defcriptio.
" [133] Asiæ Nova defcriptio. Auctore Jodoco Hondio.
" [139] Tartaria.
" [140] China.
" [142] Insulæ Indiæ Orientalis praecipuæ . . .
" [145] America.
" [146] Hispaniæ Novæ nova descriptio.
" [147] Virginiae item et Floridae Americæ provinciarum, nova descriptio.
" [148] Cuba insula.—Inset: Havana portus.—Hispaniola insula.—Insula Iamaica.—Ins. S. Ioannis.—I. s. Margareta cum confiniis.
" [149] America Meridionalis.
" [150] Exquifita & magno aliquot menfium periculo luftrata et iam retecta Freti Magellanici facies.

## 1621

Atlas minor Gerardi Mercatoris à I. Hondio plurimis æneis tabulis auctus atque illustratus. 4 p. l., 683, [1] pp. incl. 153 maps, 1 pl. obl. 12°. Arnhemii apud Ioannem Ianfsoniū 1621. [*Colophon:*] Arnhemiæ, ex officina Ioannis Janssonii, bibliopolæ. Anno MDCXXI. 435

NOTE.—Collation: engraved title, verso blank, p. l. [1].—Iodocus Hondius lectori s. d., recto and verso p. l. [2].—In ufum tabularum, recto and verso p. l. [3].—Index tabularum, recto and verso p. l. [4].—Engraved pl. representing the three fates, p. 1.—Text incl. 153 maps, ending with vignette and colophon on p. [684], pp. 2-[684]
First latin edition published 1607.

**Mercator, G.**—Continued.
The following maps relate to America:
p. 3. Typus orbis terrarum.
" 7. Europa.
" 11. Asia.
" 19. Americae descrip.
" 23. Polus Arcticus cum vicinis regionibus.
" 627. Tartaria.
" 639. Insulæ Indiae orientalis.
" 651. Hispania Nova.
" 655. Virginia et Florida.
" 659. Cuba insul.—Hispaniola.—Havana portvs.—I. Iamaica.—I. S. Joannis.—I. Margareta.
" 663. America Meridionalis.
" 667. Fretum Magellani.
" 675. Designatio orbis Christiani.

### 1621

**Ptolemæus, C.**

Geografia | cioè | Descrittione Vniversale | della Terra | Partita in due volumi, | Nel primo de' quali fi contengono gli Otto Libri della Geografia | di Cl. Tolomeo, | Nuouamente con fingolare ftudio rincontrati, & corretti | Dall' Eccell.$^{mo}$ Sig. Gio. Antonio Magini Padovano | Publico Matematico nello ftudio di Bologna. | Con vna larghifsima & copiofifsima fpofitione del medefimo fopra' l Primo de' detti Libri | d' intorno a' precetti & alle regole della Geografia. | Nel Secondo vi fono pofte XXVII. Tauole Antiche di Tolomeo, & XXXVII. altre Moderne, tutte reuifte, & in alcuni luoghi | accrefciute, & illuftrate da ricchiffimi Commentarij di detto Sig. Magini, | Liquali non pur di minuto rapprefentano fiti, qualità, diuifioni, monti, fiumi, porti, città, caftella di tutte le | parti & Prouincie del Mondo, co'loro nomi Antichi & Moderni; ma pieniffimamente informano | della natura, de' coftumi, delle fignorie, delle ragioni de' goueini, & interamente dello ftato | di tutte le nationi dell' vniuerfo, così ne' tempi paffati, come ne' prefenti. | Opera vtiliffima & fpecialmente neceffaria allo ftudio dell' Hiftorie, | Dal Latino nell' Italiano Tradotta | Dal R. D. Leonardo Cernoti Vinitiano | Canonico di S. Salvadore. | Con due Indici copiofiffimi. | Nvovamente corretto, et accrescivto. | Con licenza de' Superiori, & Priuilegi. | In Padova, M.DC.XXI. | Appreffo Paolo, & Francefco Galignani, Fratelli. | [*Title to the second part:*] La Seconda Parte | della Geografia | di Cl. Tolomeo, | La quale, oltra l' Antiche Tauole d' effo Tolomeo, contiene le Moderne | ancora, che moftrano la faccia di tutta la Terra, infino | à quefta noftra età conofciuta, | Intagliate da Girolamo Porro. | Infieme con le loro copiofiffime efpofitioni fatte | Dall' Eccellentiss.$^{mo}$ Signor Gio. Antonio Magini Padovano | Lettore delle Matematiche | nel pvblico stvdio di Bologna. | Tradotte | Dal R. D. Leonardo Cernoti Vinitiano | Canonico di S. Salvadore. | Con Priviiegi. | In Padova, M.DC.XX. | Appreſſo Paolo, & Franceſco Galignani Fratelli. |    436

> For collation and description, see edition of 1598 of which this edition is an exact reprint except that the dedication of the earlier edition signed by Gio. Battista, & Giorgio Galignani, dated M.D.XCVII, appears in this on the verso of the title and a new dedication signed by Paolo, & Francesco Galignani, dated M.DC.XXI, appears on the recto of the first leaf, verso blank.
> The double page map, "Orbis Terrae Compendiosa Descriptio," between leaves 19 and 20, is wanting.
> Modern binding, full vellum.
> Eames-Sabin, no. 66508.

## 1628

**Mercator, G.**

Atlas minor Gerardi Mercatoris à I. Hondio plurimis æneis tabulis auctus et illustratus: denuo recognit[9], additiſque novis delineationibus emendatus.   4 p. l., 656 (*i. e.* 644), [16] pp. incl. 143 maps. obl. 12°.   Amsterodami, ex officina Ioannis Ianssonii, 1628.   437

> NOTE.—Collation: engraved title, verso blank, p. l. [1].—Ad candidvm lectorem praefatio, dated 1627, recto p. l. [2]-verso p. l. [3].—In usum tabularum, recto and verso p. l. [4].—Text incl. 143 maps, pp. 1-656.—Index, [16] pp. Pagination irregular.
> First latin edition published 1607.
> Maps differ from those in the earlier editions, and were engraved by Abraham Goos and Peter Keer.
> The following maps relate to America:
> p.   3. Typus orbis terrarum.
> "    7. Europæ nova tabula.
> "   15. Asia.
> "   19. Americæ descriptio.
> "   23. Septentrionalium terrarum defcript.
> "  615. Tartaria.
> "  619. China.   .
> "  627. Insulæ Indiae orientalis.
> "  639. Hispaniæ novæ nova descriptio.
> "  643. Nova Virginiæ tabvla.
> "  647. Cuba insvla.—Hispaniola infula.—Ins. Iamaica.—Ins. S. Ioannis.—I. S. Margareta.
> "  651. America Meridionalis.
> "  655. Freti Magellanici ac novi freti vulgo Le Maire exactiſſima delineatio.

## 1628

Gerardi Mercatoris atlas sive cosmographicæ meditationes de fabrica mvndi et fabricati figvra. Primum à Gerardo Mercatore inchoatæ, deindè à Iudoco Hondio piæ memoriæ ad finem perductæ, iam verò multis in locis emendatæ, et de novo in lucem editæ.

**Mercator, G.**—Continued.

Editio decima.   712 (*i. e.* 710), [35] pp. incl. 155 col. maps, [3] l., 1 pl.   fol.   Amſterodami, sumptibus typis æneis Henrici Hondij, an. d. 1628.   438

NOTE.—Collation: colored engraved title, verso blank, 1 l.—Dedication to Louis XIII, signed Henricus Hondius, p. 3.—Latin verse Ad Ivdocvm Hondium . . . signed Maximilianus Vrientius, dated 1609, p. [4].—Ivdocvs Hondivs av lectevr salvt, dated 1609, p. [5].—La vie du célèbre et illvstre Gerard Mercator, followed by latin verse: Epitaphivm in obitvm Gerardi Mercatoris . . . signed Ioannes Mercator, pp. [6-7].—Latin verse: In atlantem Gerardi avi svi, signed Iohannes Mercator, followed by latin verse: Gerardo Mercatori et Ivdoco Hondio . . . signed Petrvs Bertivs, p. [8].—La vie dv . . . Ivdocvs Hondivs, followed by Latin verse: Epitaphivm in obitvm Ivdoci Hondii . . . signed Ioh. Montanus, pp. [9-10].—Indice des tables . . . pp. [11-12].—Latin verse to Mercator and Hondius, signed P. Scriverius, followed by one signed Ioh. Isacius Pontanus, p. [13].—Colored engraved pl. containing portraits of Mercator and Hondius, p. [14-15].—Latin verse: Atlas Gerardi Mercatoris et Ivsti Hondii cosmographorvm mortem dolens, signed Petrus Montanus, followed by latin verse: In obitvm clarifsimi viri, Ivdoci Hondii cosmographi signed Maximilianus Vrientius, p. [16].—Preface svr l'Atlas, p. [17].—La race d'Atlas, p. [18].—Livre de la creation et fabriqve dv monde, pp. 19-47.—Blank, p. 48.—Text incl. 45 col. maps, pp. 49-236.—Engraved title colored: Galliae tabulę geographicæ.   Per Gerardum Mercatorem . . . verso blank.—Av favorable lectevr, pp. 237-239.—L'estat politic dv royavme de France, pp. 239-243.—Advis l'vsage des tables, pp. 243-244.—Rolle et indice des tables de la Gavle, pp. 244.—Text incl. 26 col. maps, pp. 245-352.—Engraved title colored: Belgii inferioris geographicæ tabulę.   Per Gerardum Mercatorem . . . verso blank.—Au bien affectionné lecteur; La police dv Pays Bays sovs les Bovrgoignons, pp. 353-355.—Lifte des tables des Pay bas; La table de la Germanie inferievre, p. 356.—Text incl. 11 col. maps, pp. 357-404.—Engraved title colored: Germaniae tabulę geographicæ.   Per Gerardum Mercatorem, verso blank.—Text incl. 29 col. maps, pp. 405-528.—Engraved title colored: Italiae, Sclavoniæ, et Græciæ tabulę geographicę   Per Gerardum Mercatorem . . . verso blank.—Text incl. 45 col. maps, pp. 529-712.—Index, [35] pp.

Pagination irregular.

Text on the reverse of maps.

No text to "Asiæ Nova," and to general map of America.

Fourth french edition.

In 1628 and 1630, two french and two latin editions were published all with the above title. These editions are by error, all called the tenth. *cf.* Raemdonck.   Gérard Mercator.   1869.   p. 265.

Maps are by various cartographers including Hondius, Lhuyd, Fayen, Bomparius, Martin and Lubin.

The following maps relate to America:

pp.  [50-51] Orbis terrae compendiosa descriptio . . . 1587.
"    [54-55] Evropa.
"    [58-59] Nova Europæ descriptio.   Auctore Iodoco Hondio.
"    [64-65] Africa.
"    [66-67] Asia.
"    [70-71] America fiue India Nova.
"    [73-74] Septentrionalivm terrarum defcriptio.
"    [642-643] Asiæ Nova defcriptio.   Auctore Iodoco Hondio.
"    [666-667] Tartaria.

pp. [670–671] China.
" [678–679] Insulæ Indiæ Orientalis praecipuæ . . .
" [690–691] America.
" [694–695] Hispaniæ Novæ nova descriptio.
" [698–699] Virginiae item et Florida.
" [702–703] Cuba insula. Inset: Havana portus.—Hispaniola insula.—Insula Iamaica.—Ins. S. Ioannis.—I. s. Margareta cum confiniis.
" [706–707] America Meridionalis.
" [710–711] Exquiſita & magno aliquot menſium periculo luſtrata et iam retecta Freti Magellanici facies.

## 1630

Atlas minor, ofte een korte doch grondige beſchrijvinge der geheeler werelt met alle hare gedeelten: Eerſtlijc van Gerardo Mercatore in't Latijn beſchreven, ende volghens door Ivdocvm Hondivm met vele caerten verbetert ende vermeerdert, ende nu in onſe Nederlantſche ſpracke overgeſet door Ernstvm Brinck. 8 p. l., 763, [12] pp. incl. 143 maps. obl. 12°. t'Amsterdam, ghedruckt by Jan Janssen, 1630. 439

NOTE.—Collation: engraved title, verso blank, p. l. [1].—Aen den doorluchtighen hooch-geboren vorſt ende heere Frederick Henrich . . . dated 1629, signed Ernst Brinck, recto p. l. [2]–recto p. l. [6].—Epigramma . . . signed Joh. Isacivs Pontanvs, verso p. l. [6].—Een korte ende nootwendighe onderrichtinghe . . . recto p. l. [7]–recto p. l. [8] verso blank.—Text incl. 143 maps, pp. 1–763.—Register . . . [12] pp.
First latin edition was published 1607.
Dutch title pasted over the latin of the 1628 edition.
Maps are the same as those in the 1628 edition.
The following maps relate to America:
p. 3. Typus orbis terrarum.
" 7. Europæ nova tabula.
" 17. Asia.
" 23. Americæ descriptio.
" 27. Septentrionalium terrarum defcript.
" 717. Tartaria.
" 723. China.
" 731. Insulæ Indiae orientalis.
" 745. Hispaniæ novæ nova descriptio.
" 749. Nova Virginiæ tabvla.
" 753. Cuba insvla.—Hispaniola infula.—Ins. Iamaica.—Ins. S. Ioannis.— I. S. Margareta.
" 763. Freti Magellanici ac novi freti vulgo Le Maire exactiſſima delineatio

## 1630

Gerardi Mercatoris atlas sive coſmographicæ meditationes de fabrica mundi et fabricati figura. De novo multis in locis emendatus et Appendice auctus studio Iudoci Hondij. 4 p. l., 676, 46, [1] pp. incl. 180 maps. obl. 8°. Amſterodami, sumptibus Iohannis Cloppenburgij, 1630. 440

NOTE.—Collation: half title: L'atlas de Gerard Marcator [!] de nouveau reveu, toutes les cartes corrigéz, & en outre augmenté d'vn Appendix, par Joſse

**Mercator, G.**—Continued.

Hondius, recto p. l. [1], verso blank.—Engraved title, verso blank, p. l. [2].—Dedication, signed I. E. Cloppenbvrgh, dated 1630, recto and verso p. l. [3].—Cartes de l'Atlas Marcatoris [!] recto and verso p. l. [4].—Text incl. 150 maps, 676 pp.—Appendix, incl. 30 maps, 47, [1] pp.
Latin title-page with french text.
Pagination irregular.
A reduced edition but entirely different from the Atlas minor.
Most of the maps were engraved by Petrus Keer. *cf.* Tiele, P. A. Nederlandsche bibliographie van land- en volkenkunde. 1884. p. 168.
Maps by various cartographers including Hondius, Beins, Surhon, Lhuyd and Martin.
The following maps relate to America:

p. 3. Typus orbis terrarum.
" 7. Nova Evropæ defcriptio.
" 15. Asia.
" 19. America noviter delineata.
" 23. Septentrionalivm terrarum defcriptio.
" 635. Tartaria.
" 641. China.
" 647. Insulæ Indiæ Orientalis.
" 659. Hispaniæ Novæ nova descriptio.
" 663. Virginiae item et Floridae Americæ provinciarum nova descriptio.
" 667. Cuba insula. Inset: Havana portus.—Hispaniola insula.—Ins. Iamaica.—Ins. S. Ioannis.—I. s. Margareta.
" 671. America Meridionalis.
" 675. [Du destroit de Magellan]
" 39. Perv.
" 41. Terra Firma et novum regnum Granatense et Popaian.
" 43. De groote ende kleyne eylanden van West-Indien.
" 45. Mappa Æstivarum infularum alias Bermudas dictarum . . .
" 47. Nova Virginiæ tabvla.

## 1630

Gerardi Mercatoris atlas sive cosmographicæ meditationes de fabrica mvndi et fabricati figvra. Primum à Gerardo Mercatore inchoatæ, deindè à Iudoco Hondio Piæ memoriæ ad finem perductæ, iam verò multis in locis emendatæ, et de novo in lucem editæ. Editio decima. 11 p. l., 391 (*i. e.* 395), [35], 4 l., 164 maps. fol. Amfterodami, sumptibus & typhis æneis Henrici Hondij, an. d. 1630. 441

NOTE.—Collation: engraved title, verso blank, p. l. [1].—Dedication, signed Iudocus Hondius, dated 1607, recto and verso p. l. [2].—Latin verse, signed P. Scriverius; followed by one signed Ioh. Isacius Pontanus, recto p. l. [3].—Engraved pl. representing Mercator and Hondius, verso p. l. [3]-recto p. l. [4].—Latin verses: Atlas Gerardi Mercatoris et Ivsti Hondii cofmographorum mortem dolens, signed Petrvs Montanus; In obitvm CL[mi]. V. Ivdoci Hondii cosmographi, signed Maxæmylianvs Vrientivs, verso p. l. [4].—Iudocus Hondius lectori S., dated 1604, recto p. l. [5].—Latin verse: Gerardo Mercatori et Ivdoco Hondio cofmographis, signed Petrus Bertius; verse in latin and greek: In Gerardi Mercatoris Flandri atlantem . . . signed Iacobus Gruterus; followed by Greek verse, verso p. l. [5].—Index tabularum . . . recto and verso

p. l. [6].—Vita celeberrimi clariffimique viri Gerardi Mercatoris Rvpelmvndan à domino Gualtero Ghymmio . . . recto p. l. [7]-verso p. l. [8].—Celeberrimi clariffimique viri Judoci Hondii vita; per P. M.; latin verses: Epitaphivm in obitum Ivdoci Hondii . . . signed Ioh. Montanus; Epitaphium in obitum Gerardi Mercatoris avi fui . . . signed Ioannes Mercator, recto and verso p. l. [9].—Epistolae dvæ, duorum doctriffimorum virorum, doctris Reinhardi Solenandri . . . et d. Jacobi Sinftedij . . . in laudem atlantis confcriptæ, recto and verso p. l. [10].—Latin verse: In atlantem Gerardi Mercatoris avi fui, signed Iohannes Mercator, recto p. l. [11].—Præfatio in Atlantem, verso p. l. [11].—Stemma Atlantis, p. [1].—De mundi creatione, ac fabrica liber, pp. 2-27.—Blank, p. 28.—Text and 46 maps, pp. 29-124.—Engraved title: Galliae tabulę geographicae . . . , verso blank.—Stvdioso et benevolo lectori, pp. 125-126.—De politico statv regni Galliæ, pp. 127-130.—In vsvm tobvlarvm admonitio, p. 131.—Index tabvlarvm Galliæ, p. 132.—Galliæ vniversalis tabvla; Text and 27 maps, pp. 133-189.—Engraved title: Belgii inferioris geographicæ tabulę . . . verso blank.—Ad studiofum lectorem; Politia Belgii svb Bvrgvndionibvs, pp. 190-192.—Index tabularum Belgii inferioris, p. 192.—Belgii inferioris tabvla, p. 193.—Text and 17 maps, p. 194-231.—Engraved title Germaniæ tabulę geographicæ . . . verso blank.—In Germanicas tabvlas vtilis, et praenoscenda instrvctio, pp. 232-235.—Camera imperialis; Catalogvs tabvlarvm Germaniae, p. 235.—Text and 29 maps, pp. 236-297.—Engraved title: Italiae, Slavoniæ, et Græciæ tabulę geographicę . . . verso blank.— Text and 45 maps, pp. 298-391.—Index [35] pp.
Pagination irregular.
Text on the reverse of maps.
No text to "Asiæ Nova," and to general map of America.
In 1628 and 1630, two french and two latin editions of Mercator's Atlas were published, all with the above title. These editions are by error all called the 10th, the latin edition of 1628 being really the 10th, and this, the 1630 edition, the 11th latin edition of Hondius, but the 12th edition of the atlas as a whole.
Maps are by various cartographers including, Hondius, Lhuydo, Secco, Fayen, Bomparius, Berckenrode, Martin and Lubin.
The following maps relate to America:
no. [1] Orbis terrae compendiosa descriptio . . . 1587.
" [2] Evropa.
" [3] Nova Europæ descriptio. Auctore Iodoco Hondio.
" [4] Africa.
" [5] Asia.
" [6] America fiue India Nova.
" [7] Septentrionalivm terrarum defcriptio.
" [148] Asiæ Nova defcriptio. Auctore Jodoco Hondio.
" [154] Tartaria.
" [155] China.
" [157] Insulæ Indiæ Orientalis præcipuæ . . .
" [160] America. Jodocus Hondius excudit.
" [161] Hispaniæ Novæ nova descriptio.
" [162] Virginiae item et Floridae Americæ provinciarum nŏva descriptio.
" [163] Cuba insula. Inset: Havana portus.—Hispaniola insula.—Insula Iamaica.—Ins. S. Ioannis.—I. s. Margareta cum confiniis.
" [164] America Meridionalis.
" [165] Exquifita & magno aliquot menfium periculo luftrata et iam retecta Freti Magellanici facies.

## 1631
**Speed, J.**

A prospect of the most famous parts of the world. Viz. Asia, Affrica, Europe, America. . . . Together with all the prouinces, counties, and shires, contained in that large Theator of Great Brittaines empire.   5 pts. in 1 v.; 3 p. l., [216] pp. 3 l., front., 89 maps.   fol.   London, G. Humble, 1631.   442

> NOTE.—Prefaced by engraved title-page of the "Theatre of Great Britaine" . . . 1627. It resembles a facade with statues of a native briton, a roman, dane, saxon and norman, in niches.
> Maps comprising pts. 2–5 were originally published with this title. 1st ed. appeared in 1611; 2d ed., 1614; 3d ed., in 1627 with the title, "A prospect of the most famous parts of the world."
> Engraved frontispiece, the arms of England, with inscription:—The achievement of our soveraigne king James . . . with the armes of the severall kings that have aunciently raigned within his nowe dominions. Iodocus Hondius Flander cælavit. 1614.
> Descriptive text on the reverse of each map.
> Each part has a special title-page:—pt. 1, A prospect of the most famous parts of the world . . . pt. 2, The theatre of Great Britain . . . pt. 3, . . . containing the principalitie of Wales. . . pt. 4, . . . containing a generall view of the kingdome of Scotland: . . . pt. 5, . . . containing the kingdome of Ireland. . . pt. 2 is dedicated to 'James, king of Great Britain, France, and Ireland.' On the reverse of the dedication is an engraved plate, the coat of arms of England. Then follows a notice "To the well-affected and favourable reader," 2 l.; and commendatory verses to the author, 2 l.
> Maps are ornamented with the arms of the country and of the nobility, and have border illustrations of figures in national costumes and of views of cities. Many maps have also plans of cities, views of castles and cathedrals and other interesting features:—pt. 2, no. 13, [map of] Wilshire, with inset showing the druidical monuments at Stonehenge and inscriptions.
> Maps represent the work of the following engravers:—Iodocus Hondius, R. Elstrack, Abraham Goos, Corn. Danckertsz, Dirck Grijp.
> See also title 488.
> The following maps relate to America:
> pt. 1, no. [1] A new and accurat map of the world . . . 1626.
> " " [2] Asia [Philippine islands] Sculptum apud Abrahamum Goos.
> " " [5] America with those known parts in that unknowne worlde both people and manner of buildings discribed and inlarged by I. S. Ano. 1626. Abraham Goos, Amstelodaminsis sculpsit.
> " " [19] The kingdome of China newly augmented by I. S. 1626 [Shows part of the n. w. coast of America]
> " " [20] A newe mape of Tartary . . . 1626 [Part of America]
> " " [21] A mapp of the Sommer islands once called the Bermudas . . .

## 1632
**Mercator, G.**

Gerardi Mercatoris atlas sive cofmographicæ meditationes de fabrica mundi et fabricati figura. De novo multis in locis emendatus novifq; tabulis auctus studio Iudoci Hondij.   3 p. l., 749 (*i. e.* 745) pp. incl. 179 maps.   obl. 8°.   Amfterodami, sumptibus Johannis Cloppenburgij, 1632.   443

NOTE.—Collation: half title: G. Marcatoris [!] atlas de novo plurimis in locis emendatus, multifque novis tabulis auctus. Studio Iudoci Hondij, verso blank, p. l. [1].—Engraved title, verso blank, p. l. [2].—Index tabularum, p. l. [3].—Text incl. 179 maps, 749 pp.
Latin text.
Pagination irregular.
The dedication to this edition, spoken of by Tiele as dated, "prid. Non. aprilis 1632," is wanting.
Date cut from title-page.
Maps are by various cartographers including Hondius, Beins, Surhon and Martin.
Most of the maps were engraved by Petrus Keer.
The following maps relate to America:

- p. 3. Typus orbis terrarum.
- " 7. Nova Europae defcriptio.
- " 15. Asia.
- " 19. America noviter delineata.
- " 23. Septentrionalivm terrarum defcriptio.
- " 695. Tartaria.
- " 699. China.
- " 707. Insulæ Indiæ Orientalis.
- " 719. De groote ende kleyne eylanden van West-Indien.
- " 721. Cuba insula. Inset: Havana portus.—Hispaniola insula.—Ins. Iamaica.—Ins. s. Ioannis.—I. s. Margareta.
- " 725. Virginia item et Floridae Americæ provinciarum nova descriptio.
- " 729. Nova Virginiæ tabvla.
- " 731. Hispaniæ Novæ nova descriptio.
- " 735. Terra Firma et novum regnum Granatense et Popaian.
- " 737. Perv.
- " 739. Mappa Æstivarvm infularum alias Bermudas dictarum . . .
- " 741. America Meridionalis.
- " 745. [Fretum Magellanicum]

## 1633

Gerardi Mercatoris et I. Hondii atlas, das ist abbildung der gantzen welt mit allen darin begriffenen låndern vnd provintzen: sonderlich von Teutschland, Franckreich, Niderland, Ost vnd West Indien: mit beschreibung der selben. 7 p. l., 684, [3] pp. incl. 160 maps. fol. Amsterdam, bey Johan Jansson und Henricus Hondius, 1633. 444

NOTE.—Collation: Engraved title, verso blank, p. l. [1].—Dem durchleuchtigsten, hochgebornen fûrsten vnd herzn, herzn Georg Wilhelm, marggraff zu Brandenburg . . . signed Joannes Janssonivs vnd Henricvs Hondivs, dated 1633, recto p. l. [2] verso blank.—Das leben Gerardi Mercatoris . . . recto and verso, p. l. [3].—Das leben Jodocii Hondii . . . followed by Latin verse: Epitaphium in obitum Jvdoci Hondii . . . signed Joh. Montanvs, recto and verso p. l. [4].—Eine kurtze vnd nutzliche vnterzichtung . . . recto p. l. [5]—verso p. l. [7].—Text incl. 160 maps, 684 pp.—Register, [3] pp.
Text entitled: Engellandts V. tafel begreifft das Gôrtzerland oder Yorcke, Lincolnshire, Darbishire, Staffordshire, Nottinghamshire &c., and the map, pp. 53-56 wanting.
Maps are by various cartographers, including Henrick Hondius, Henneberg, Jansson, Metius, Freitag, Wicheringe Emmius, Gigas, Westenberg, Mellinger,

**Mercator, G.**—Continued.

Laurenberg, Stella, Lubin, Palbitzke, Comenius, Lazio, Beins, Berkenrode, Surhon, Secco, Lavaña, Gerard and Adrichomius.

The title-page of v. 1 of the french edition of 1633 was used for this edition, with german title pasted over the french. Raemdonck states that the first german edition was published in 2 v. in 1633, and was translated by Peter Uffenbach. Tiele also gives the edition in 2 v.; Woltersdorf in his Repertorium, p. 78, in 1 v. The cover of this copy is ornamented in gold, and stamped with the arms of Saxony; the letters "M. S. C. Z. S." which are abbreviations for "Magdalene Sibylle, curfürstin zu Sachsen;" and the date "1642," which is the year the atlas came into the possession of the electress.

The following maps relate to America:

pp. 2-3. Nova totivs terrarvm orbis geographica ac hydrographica tabvla. Auct. Henr. Hondio. 1630.
" 6-7. Europa exactissime descripta. Auctore Henrico Hondio. 1631.
" 14-15. Asia recens summa cura delineata. Auct. Henrico Hondio. 1631.
" 18-19. America noviter delineata. Auct. Henrico Hondio. 1631.
" 658-59. Tartaria.
" 662-63. China.
" 666-67. Indiæ Orientalis nova descriptio.
" 670-71. Nova Virginiæ tabvla.
" 674-75. Peru.
" 678-79. Accuratissima Brasiliæ tabula.
" 682-83. Freti Magellanici ac novi freti vulgo le Maire exactissima delineatio.

## 1633

Gerardi Mercatoris et I. Hondii atlas ou représentation du monde vniversel, et des parties d'icelui faicte en tables et descriptions tresamples, et exactes: divifé en deux tomes. Edition nouvelle. Augmenté d'un appendice de plufieurs nouvelles tables et defcriptions de diverfes regions d'Allemaigne, France, Pays Bas, Italie et de l'une et l'autre Inde, le tout mis en fon ordre. 2 v. fol. A Amsterdam, chez Henry Hondius, demeurant fur le Dam, a l'enfeigne du chien vigilant, a°. d. 1633. **445**

NOTE.—Collation: v. 1, 404 (*i. e.* 592), [17] pp. incl. 127 col. maps; v. 2, 2 p. l., 401-712 (*i. e.* 466), [19] pp. incl. 112 col. maps.

v. 1. Engraved title colored, verso blank, pp. [1-2].—Dedication to Louis XIII, signed Henricus Hondius, p. [3].—Latin verse, Ad Ivdocum Hondivm cofmographum clariffimum, signed Maximilianus Vrientius, dated 1609, p. [4].—Ivdocvs Hondivs au lecteur salut, dated 1609, p. [5].—La vie du célèbre & illuftre Gerard Mercator, p. [6-7].—Latin verse: Epitaphivm in obitum Gerardi Mercatoris . . . signed Ioannes Mercator, p [7].—Latin verses: In atlantem Gerardi Mercatoris avi svi, signed Johannes Mercator; Gerardo Mercatori et Ivdoco Hondio cofmographis, signed Petrus Bertius, p. [8].—La vie du feu très-fameux & illustre Ivdocvs Hondivs, p. [9-10].—Latin verse: Epitaphium in obitum Ivdoci Hondii . . . signed Ioh. Montanus, p. [10].—Latin verse to Mercator and Hondius, signed P. Scriverius, followed by one signed Ioh. Ifacius Pontanus, p. [11].—Engraved colored pl. representing Mercator and Hondius, pp. [12-13].—Latin verses: Atlas Gerardi Mercatoris et Ivsti Hondii cofmographorum mortem dolens, signed Petrus Montanus; In obitvm clariffime viri, Ivdoci Hondii cosmographi, signed Maximilianus Vrientius, p. [14].—Advertissement av lectevr, signed Henricus Hondius &

Ioannes Iansonius, p. [15].—Indice de toutes les tables dv premier tome, p. [16]. Præface svr l'atlas, p. [17].—La race d'Atlas, p. [18].—Livre la creation et fabriqve dv monde, pp. 19-47.—Blank, p. 48.—Introduction à la géographie, pp. 45-50.—Text incl. 47 col. maps, pp. 49-236.—Engraved colored title: Galliae tabulę geographicæ . . . verso blank.—Text incl. 53 col. maps, pp. 237-352.—Engraved col. title: Belgii inferioris geographicæ tabulę . . . verso blank.—Text incl. 27 col. maps, pp. 353-404.—Index [17] pp. v. 2. Engraved title colored, verso blank, p. l. [1].—Avertissement av lectevr, recto p. l. [2].—Registre des cartes contenus dans ce second tome, verso p. l. [2].—Text incl. 52 col. maps, pp. 401-528.—Engraved col. title: Italiae, Sclavoniæ, et Graeciæ tabulę geographicę . . . verso blank.—Text incl. 60 col. maps, pp. 529-712.—Index, 19 pp.

Edition and imprint differs, v. 2: Editio vltima. Sumptibus & typis æneis Henrici Hondij, Amſterodami, an. d. 1633.

Paged continuously.—Pagination irregular.

Text on the reverse of maps.

No text to "Asia recens" . . . and general map of America.

The 6th french edition.

The following maps relate to America:
v. 1, pp. [50-51] Nova totivs terrarvm orbis geographica ac hydrographica tabvla. Auct: Henr: Hondio. 1630.
" " [54-55] Evropa.
" " [58-59] Evropa exactissime descripta. Auctore Henrico Hondio. 1631.
" " [66-67] Asia.
" " [70-71] America fiue India Nova.
" " [74-75] Septentrionalivm terrarum defcriptio.
v. 2 " [644-45] Asia recens ſumma cura delineata. Auct. Henri Hondio. 1631.
" " [666-67] Tartaria.
" " [670-71] China.
" " [674-75] Indiæ Orientalis nova descriptio. Amstelodami Ioannes Ianſsonius excudebat.
" " [678-79] Insulæ Indiæ Orientalis præcipuæ . . .
" " [690-91] America.
" " [694-95] Hispaniæ Novæ nova descriptio.
" " [698-99] Virginiae item et Floridae Americæ provinciarum, nova descriptio.
" " [698-99] Nova Virginiæ tabvla.
" " [702-03] Cuba insula. Inset: Havana portus. Hispaniola insula.—Insula Iamaica.—Ins. S. Ioannis.—I. S. Margareta cum confiniis.
" " [706-07] Mappa Æstivarum infularum, alias Barmvdas dictarum . . . Amſtelodami, apud Henricum Hondium.
" " [706-07] America Meridionalis.
" " [710-11] Venezuela cum parte auſtrali Novæ Andalusiæ. Amstelodami, Henricus Hondius excudit.
" " [714-15] Terra Firma et novum regnum Granatense et Popayan. Amſtelodami, Joannes Janſsónius excudit.
" " [718-19] Gviana fiue Amazonvm regio. Amstelodami, Henricus Hondius excudit.
" " [722-23] Perv. Amstelodami, apud Ioannem Ianſſonium.
" " [726-27] Accuratissima Brasiliæ tabula. Amstelodami, Henricus Hondius excudit.

**Mercator, G.**—Continued.
v. 2, pp. [730–31] Paragvay, ó prov. de Rio de La Plata cum regionibus adiacentibus Tvcvman et S<sup>ta</sup>. Crvz de la Sierra. Amstelodami, excudebat Ioannes Ianſsonius.
" " [734–35] Chili. Amstelodami, Henricus Hondius excudit.
" " [710–11] Freti Magellanici ac novi freti vulgo le Maire exactiſſima delineatio.

### 1634

Atlas minor Gerardi Mercatoris à I. Hondio plurimis æneis tabulis auctus et illuſtratus: denuo recognit⁹ additiſque novis delineationibus emendatus.   1 p. l., 651, [3] pp. incl. 143 maps. obl. 12°.   Amsterdami, ex officina Ioannis Janssonii, 1634.   446

NOTE.—Collation: engraved title, verso blank.—Text incl. 143 maps, pp. 1–651.—Index tabvlavrm, [3] pp.
Pagination irregular.
The map following the title-page, Freti Magellanici should have been placed at page 651.
Title-page and maps same as in 1628 edition.
The following maps relate to America:
p.  3. Typus orbis terrarum.
"   7. Europæ nova tabula.
"  15. Asia.
"  19. Americæ descriptio.
"  23. Septentrionalium terrarum deſcript.
" 611. Tartaria.
" 615. China.
" 623. Insulæ Indiæ orientalis.
" 635. Hispaniæ Novæ nova descriptio.
" 639. Nova Virginiæ tabvla.
" 643. Cvba insvla.—Hispaniola inſula.—Ins. Iamaica.—Ins. S. Ioannis.—I. S. Margareta.
" 647. America Meridionalis.
" [651] Freti Magellanici ac novi freti vulgo. Le Maire exactiſſima delineatio.

### 1634

——— *and* **Hondius, J.**

Atlas ofte afbeeldinghe vande gantſche weerldt: Daer in vertoont worden ſeer velecaerten van alle de voornaemſte coninckrycken, landen en provintien, van Evropa, Asia, Africa en America, met de beſchryvingen van het ghene daer in ghedenckweerdichſt aen te mercken ſtaet.   Nu eerſt uyt het latyn in onſe Nederlantſche tale getranſlateert.   10 p. l., 400, [2] l. incl. 182 maps, 1 pl. fol. [Amſterdam, Jan Janssen, 1634]   447

NOTE.—Collation: Engraved title, verso blank, p. l. [1].—Dedication signed Henricus Hondius en Ioannes Iansonius, recto and verso p. l. [2].—Gonſtige, kon t-lievende leser, signed Henricus Hondius en Ioannes Iansonius, dated 1634, recto and verso p. l. [3].—Het leven vanden ſeer gheleerden . . . Gerardus Mercator, beginning on recto p. l. [4] ending with latin verse Epitaphivm in obitvm Gerardi Mercatoris, signed Joannes Mercator, on verso p. l. [4].—Kort verhael, van het leven des ſeer wijt-beroemden . . . Ivdoci

Hondii, beginning on recto p. l. [5] followed by verse Graf-dicht . . . van den feer vermaerden cosmographus Ivdocvs Hondivs, signed Jacobus Viverius, dated 1612, on verso p. l. [5].—Latin verse to Mercator and Hondius, signed P. Scriverius, followed by one signed Ioh. Ifacius Pontanus, recto p. l. [6].— Engraved pl. containing portraits of Mercator and Hondius, verso p. l. [6]— recto p. l. [7].—Latin verse to Mercator and Hondius, signed Petrvs Montanvs, followed by latin verse, In obitvm clariffimi viri, signed Maximilianvs Vrientivs, verso p. l. [7].—Een corte en profijtelijcke onderwijfinghe, hoe en in wat manieren foo wit die oude als nieuwe generale geographie, ofte aerdtbefchryvinghe to verftaen zu, recto p. l. [8] verso p. l. [10].—Text incl. 182 maps, 400 l.—Register, [2] l.

The title-page is that of the 6th french edition published in 1633, with the dutch title pasted over the french. On a scroll at the lower part of the page the dutch place, publisher, and date have been removed leaving the french. The first dutch edition was translated by Ernest Brinck and published in 1634. *cf.* Raemdonck, J. van. Gérard Mercator. 1869. p. 267.

Maps are by various cartographers including: Jansson, Secco, Lavaña, Hardy, Henricus Hondius, Beins, Sprecher von Berneck, Cluver, Surhon, Berckenrode, Sinck, Visscher, Wicheringe, Metius, Freitag, Emmius, Gigas, Mellinger, Laurenberg, Lubin, Palbitzke, Keer, Comenius, Lazius, and Adrichomius.

The following maps relate to America:

no. [1] Nova totivs terrarvm orbis geographica ac hydrographica tabvla. Auct: Henr: Hondio: 1630.
" [2] Evropa exactissime descripta. Auctore Henrico Hondio. 1631.
" [3] Septentrionalivm terrarum defcriptio.
" [163] Asia recens fumma cura delineata. Auct. Henr. Hondio. 1631.
" [167] Tartaria.
" [168] China.
" [169] Indiæ Orientalis nova descriptio.
" [172] America noviter delineata. Auct: Henrico Hondio. 1631.
" [173] Hispaniæ Novae nova descriptio.
" [174] Virginlae item et Floridae Americæ provinciarum nova descriptio.
" [175] Cuba insula. Inset: Havana portus.—Hispaniola insula.—Insula Iamaica.—Ins. S. Ioannis.—I. S. Margareta cum confinis.
" [176] Mappa Æstivarvm insularum alias Barmvdas. Apud Henricum Hondicum.
" [177] Venezuela, cum parte auftrali Novæ Andalusiæ. Henricus Hondius excudit.
" [178] Terra Firma et novum regnum Granatense et Popayan. Joannes Janssonus excudit.
" [179] Gviana fiue Amazonvm regio. Henricus Hondius excudit.
" [180] Peru. Apud Ioannem Ianssonum.
" [181] Accuratissima Brasiliæ tabula. Henricus Hondius excudit.
" [182] Freti Magellanici ac novi freti vulgo Le Maire.

## 1635

**Blaeu, W. J.,** *and* **Blaeu, J.**

Toonneel des aerdriicx, ofte nievwe atlas, dat is beschryving van alle landen . . . 2 v.    eng. title, 6 p. l., [247] l. incl. 102 maps, 1 fold. map; eng. title, [244] l. incl. 106 maps, 1 fold. map.   fol. Amsterdam, apud Guiljelmum et Iohannem Blaeu, 1635.      448

NOTE.—In 1631, Willem Jansz. Blaeu published an atlas entitled: Appendix theatri A. Ortelii et Atlantis G. Mercatoris continens tabulas geograph. diversarum orbis regionum nunc prim. editas cum descriptionibus. fol. Amster-

**Blaeu, W. J.,** *and* **Blaeu, J.**—Continued.

dami, apud Guilj. Blaeuw, 1631. This atlas contained 103 maps (2 of which relate to America) and has become very rare. Willem J. Blaeu and his son Joan published together in 1635 a larger atlas in 2 vols. The following quotation, taken from the announcement written by Joan Blaeu in the french edition of the atlas explains its origin: "Guillaume mon père étant excité par les exemples des grands géographes s'était résolu de donner la description de ce monde universel, mais en partie occupé à d'autres affaires, et en partie craignant pour la grandeur de cette entreprise il la remit à un autre temps. Comme donc je fus retourné d'Italie, je pris la charge d'une chose si haute et si difficile et joignant mes travaux aux siens, nous imprimâmes l'atlas en deux volumes."

The following is a list of Blaeu's atlases, as found in Tiele's, Nederlandsche bibliographie, 1884:

Het licht der zee-vaert daerinne claerlijck beschreven ende afghebeeldet werden alle de custen ende havenen vande Westersche, oostersche ende middelandsche zeën. 4°. Amst., 1620.

Le flambeau de la navigation . . . 4°. Amst., 1619.

'T derde deel van't licht der zee-vaert . . . 4°. 1621.

Zeespiegel, inhoudende een korte onderwysinghe in de konst der zeevaert . . . fol. Amsterdam, 1623.

Het nieuwe licht der zeevaert . . . fol. Amst., 1634.

Zeespiegel, inhoudende een korte onderwijsinghe in de konst der zeevaert . . . fol. Amst., 1650.

De groote zee-spiegel . . . 3 v. fol. Amst., 1655-58.

1635. Theatrum orbis terrarum. 2 v. latin (first vol. dated 1634), dutch. A dutch edition in 1642.

1638. French edition.

1640. Latin edition in 3 v. by Joan Blaeu and his brother Cornelis. (Also in dutch, french and german)

1646. A fourth volume published in latin, dutch, french and german.

1649-1655. Edition in 6 v.

   CONTENTS: I. Europa septentrionalis, Germania, Germania inferior. 1649.
    II. Gallia, Hispania, Asia, Africa, America. 1650.
    III. Italia, Graecia, Scotia. 1650.
    IV. Anglia. 1648.
    V. Scotia, Hibernia. 1654.
    VI. Mart. Martinii Novus atlas Sinensis. 1655. Also with dutch, german and french text.

1662. Atlas Major. 11 v. (with a second edition of the first part in 1665)

1663. Le grand atlas ou cosmographie Blaviane. 12 v.

 Also in latin, dutch; a spanish edition was published in 1659-72.

1664-65. Grooten atlas. 9 v.

1667. Another edition of the atlas in 12 v.

The following is a list of other atlases published by Blaeu:

Toonneel der steden van de Vereenighde Nederlanden. Amst., J. Blaeu. [1648-49] 2 v. (Also in latin)

Theatrum civitatum et admirandorum Italiae . . . Amstel, J. Blaeu, 1663. 2 v. (Another edition with the imprint: apud haeredes J. Blaeu, 1676)

Theatrum statuum . . . Sabandiae ducis. Amst. haer. J. Blaeu, 1682. 2 v. Other editions in 2 vols. by R. C. Alberts in 1726 at the Hague and by Adr. Moetjens in 1697; a french edition translated by Jacq Bernard, published by Adr. Moetjens, in 1700, another in 1725.

Nouveau théâtre d'Italie ou description exacte de ses villes. Amst. P. Mortier, 1704. 4 v.
Het nieuw stedeboek van Italie . . . Amst. P. Mortier 1704–5. 4 v.
Nieuw vermeerderd en verbeterd groot stedeboek van geheel Italie. 'sGravenh., R. C. Alberts. 1724. 4 v.

Of Blaeu's atlases of the world, the Library of Congress has the following:
1635. Dutch edition. 2 v.
1642. Dutch edition. 3$^{rd}$ v.
1644. French edition. 2$^{nd}$ v.
1648–58. Dutch edition. 6 v. (Not mentioned by Tiele)
1664–65. Dutch edition. 9 v.
1667. French edition. 12 v.

CONTENTS.

v. 1. Contains the descriptions and maps of the countries of Europe, beginning with "Yslandt" and ending with "Yrlandt."—v. 2 continues with Europe, from "Franckryck" to Spain ("Andalvzia"), followed by Africa, Asia, and America.
The maps are by various cartographers, including S. Rogiers, J. Gigas, J. Westenberg, G. Mercator, etc.
Map no. [5], v. 1, contains an inset plan of Moscou; no. [46] one of "Nvrnberg."
The maps of Europe (v. 1, no. [2]), Africa (v. 2, no. [78]), Asia (v. 2, no. [83]), and America (v. 2, no. [93]) have borders containing plans and views of the principal cities of these continents, and drawings of the inhabitants in their national costumes.
Most of the maps are ornamented with heraldic illustrations.
The map of the world (v. 1, no. [1]) has illustrated borders representing the seven planets, the seven wonders of the world, the four elements and the four seasons, all highly colored.
The following maps relate to America:
v. 1. no. [1] [Nova totius terrarium orbis geographica ac hydrographia tabula.
" 2. " [93] Americæ nova tabula.
" [94] Insvlæ Americanæ in oceano septentrionali . . .
" [95] Nova Belgica et Anglia nova.
" [96] Mappa æstivarvm insvlarum, alias Bermvdas dictarum . . .
" [97] Nova Virginiæ tabula. (From J. Smith's map)
" [98] Nova Hispania et Nova Galicia.
" [99] Terra Firma et novum regnum Granatense et Popayan.
" [100] Venezvela . . .
" [101] Gviana . . .
" [102] Novus Brasiliæ typvs.
" [103] Paragvay . . .
" [104] Tabvla Magellanica . . .
" [105] Chili . . .
" [106] Perv . . .

**1636**

**Mercator, G.**

Atlas or a geographicke defcription of the regions, countries and kingdomes of the world, through Europe, Asia, Africa, and America, reprefented by new & exact maps. Tranflated by Henry Hexham,

**Mercator, G.**—Continued.

quartermaister to the regiment of colonell Goring.   2 v. fol. [Amsterdam, by Henry Hondius and John Johnson. Anno 1636]   449

> NOTE.—Collation: v. 1, 9 p. l., 216 (*i. e.* 222), [3] pp., 81 col. maps; v. 2, 1 p. l., 217–462 (*i. e.* 492), [3] pp., 115 col. maps. v. 1. Engraved colored title, verso blank, p. l. [1].—Dedication to Charles I, signed Henry Hexham, recto, p. l. [2].—Latin verse: Atlanti; english verse; followed by english verse signed Philippvs Vincentivs Firsbævs, verso p. l. [2].—Preface, signed Henricus Hondius, Iohannes Iohnsonius, Henry Hexham, dated 1636, recto p. l. [3]–recto p. l. [4].—The life of . . . Gerard Mercator; followed by latin verse: Epitaphivm in obitum Gerardi Mercatoris . . . signed Ioannes Mercator, verso p. l. [4]–recto p. l. [5].—The life of . . . Iudocus Hondivs, followed by latin verse: Epitaphivm in obitum Iudoci Hondii . . . signed Ioh. Montanus, verso p. l. [5]–recto p. l. [6].—Latin verses: In atlantem Gerardi Mercatoris avi svi, signed Iohannes Mercator; Gerardo Mercatori et Ivdoco Hondio cofmographis, signed Petrus Bertius, verso p. l. [6].—Latin verse to Mercator and Hondius, signed P. Scriverius; followed by one signed Ioh Ifacius Pontanus, recto p. l. [7].—Engraved colored pl. representing Mercator and Hondius, verso p. l. [7]–recto p. l. [8].—Latin verses: Atlas Gerardi Mercatoris et Ivsti Hondii cofmographorum mortem dolens, signed Petrus Montanus; In obitvm clariffimi viri Ivdoci Hondii cosmographi, signed Maximilianus Vrientius, verso p. l. [8].—The preface upon Atlas, recto p. l. [9].—The race of Atlas, verso p. l. [9].—The booke of the creation and fabrick of the world, pp. 1–31.—An introduction to vniversall geographie, pp. 31–37.—Blank, p. [38].—Text and 81 col. maps, pp. 39–216.—A rigister [!] of the descriptions and maps, [3] pp.
>
> v. 2. Engraved colored title, verso blank, p. l. [1].—Text and 115 col. maps, pp. 227–462.—A rigister [!] of the defcriptions and maps, [3] pp.
> Paged continuously. Pagination irregular.
> Text on reverse of maps.
> The title-pages of the french edition of 1633 were used for this edition with the english title pasted over the french. The imprint is not covered in this copy, but is the same as the french edition with the dates changed by pen. The words, Gerardi Mercatoris et I. Hondii, are part of the title of the 1633 edition, but do not properly belong to the english title, also the "Editio vltima," which appears on the title-page of v. 2.
> Maps are by various cartographers including, Henry Hondius, Lhuyd, Pont, Massa, Henneberg, Jansson, Laurenberg, Lubin, Palbitzke, Mellinger, Emmius, Gigas, Comenius, Berckenrode, Surhon, Wicheringe, Hardy, Fayen, Gerard, Fer, Secco, Labaña, Sprecher von Berneck.
> The following maps relate to America:
>
> v. 1, no. [1] Nova totivs terrarvm orbis geographica ac hydrographica tabvla. Auct: Henr: Hondio. 1630.
> " " [2] Evropa exactiffime descripta. Auctore Henrico Hondio. 1631.
> " " [3] Poli Arctici, et circumiacentium terrarum descriptio novissima. Sumptibus Henrici Hondy.
> v. 2, " [84] Asia recens fumma cura delineata. Auct. Henr. Hondio. 1631.
> " " [90] Tartaria.
> " " [91] China.
> " " [94] Indiæ Orientalis nova descriptio.
> " " [101] America noviter delineata. Auct: Henrico Hondio. 1631.

v. 2, no. [102] Nova Virginiæ tabvla.
" " [103] Mappa Æstivarvm infularum, aiias Barmvdas dictarum . . .
" " [104] Nova Anglia Novvm Belgivm et Virginia.
" " [105] Virginiae item et Floridae Americæ provinciarum, nova descriptio.
" " [106] Nova Hispania, et Nova Galicia.
" " [107] Terra Firma et novum regnum Granatense et Popayan.
" " [108] Cuba insula. Inset: Havana portus.—Hispaniola insula.—Insula Iamaica.—Ins. S. Ioannis.—I. S. Margareta cum confiniis.
" " [109] Venezuela cum parte auftrali Novæ Andalusiæ.
" " [110] Gviana fiue Amazonvm regio.
" " [111] Accuratissima Brasiliæ tabula.
" " [112] Perv.
" " [113] Paragvayo, 6 prov. de Rio de La Plata cum regionibus adiacentibus Tvcvman et S$^{ta}$ Crvz de la Sierra.
" " [114] Chili.
" " [115] Freti Magellanici ac novi freti vulgo le Maire exactiffima delineatio.

**1636**

Gerardi Mercatoris atlas sive cofmographicæ meditationes de fabrica mundi et fabricati figura. De novo multis in locis emendatus et Appendice auctus studio Iudoci Hondij. 4 p. l., 676, 47, [1] pp. incl. 180 maps. obl. 8°. Amfterodami, sumptibus Iohannis Cloppenburgij, anno 1636. 450

NOTE.—Collation: half title: L'atlas de Gérard Marcator [!], de nouveau reveu, toutes les cartes corrigéz, & en outre augmenté d'vn Appendix, par Jofse Hondius, p. l. [1], verso blank.—Engraved title, verso blank, p. l. [2].—Dedication, signed I. E. Cloppenbvrgh, dated 1636, recto and verso p. l. [3].—Cartes de l'Atlas Marcatoris [!] recto and verso p. l. [4].—Text incl. 150 maps, 676 pp.—Appendix, incl. 30 maps, 47, [1] pp.
Latin title-page with french text.
Pagination irregular.
The same as the 1630 edition with dates changed to 1636.
No mention of this edition is made by the various authorities on Mercator.
The following maps relate to America:
p. 3. Typus orbis terrarum.
" 7. Nova Evropae defcriptio.
" 15. Asia.
" 19. America noviter delineata.
" 23. Septentrionalivm terrarum defcriptio.
" 635. Tartaria.
" 641. China.
" 647. Insulæ Indiæ Orientalis.
" 659. Hispaniæ Novæ nova descriptio.
" 663. Virginiae item et Floridae Americæ provinciarum nova descriptio.
" 667. Cuba insula. Inset: Havana portus.—Hispaniola insula.—Ins. Iamaica.—Ins. S. Ioannis.—I. S. Margareta.
" 671. America Meridionalis.
" 675. [Du destroit de Magellan]
" 39. Perv.

**Mercator, G.**—Continued.
 p. 41. Appendix. Terra Firma et novum regnum Granatense et Popaian.
 " 43. " De groote ende kleyne eylanden van West-Indien.
 " 45. " Mappa Æstivarvm infularum alias Bermudas dictarum . . .
 " 47. " Nova Virginiæ tabvla.

## 1637

Historia mvndi or Mercators atlas. Containing his cosmographicall descriptions of the fabricke and figure of the world. Latelij rectified in divers places as alfo beutified and enlarged with new mapps and tables bij the studious induftrie of Iodocvs Hondy. Englished by W[ye] S[altonstall] generosus & regin: Oxoniæ. 2d ed. 3 p. l., [1032] pp. incl. 183 maps. 4°. London, for Michaell Sparke, and are to be sowld in greene Arbowre, 1637. 451

 NOTE.—Various and irregular paging.
 Contains also the title-page of the english edition of 1635, upon which the imprint reads: London, printed by T. Cotes, for Michael Sparke and Samuel Cartwright, 1635. The publication changed hands two years after its first issue, and the engraved title was re-engraved, having Sparke's name alone, with "Second edytion" added, and the date changed.
 The rare map of Virginia, Ralph Hall sculpsit, 1636, is found in this edition. cf. Phillips, P. L. Virginia cartography, 1896, p. 29. This map was not ready when the book was first published. The Errata states: "There is no map for Virginia in regard there is a more exact map drawing in that country, whofe platforme is not yet come over, but when it comes, every buyer of the booke fhall have it given him gratis." Most of the copies were issued with simply a duplicate of New Spain impressed opposite the text to Virginia. Sometimes an altered copy of the map of New England from Smith's Virginia is substituted. cf. Sabin's Dictionary of books relating to America. 1880. v. 12, p. 51.
 Portrait of captain John Smith, by Pass, mentioned by Sabin, wanting.
 The following maps relate to America:
 Virginia. Ralph Hall sculpsit. 1636.
 p. 5. Typus orbis terrarum.
 " 9. Europa.
 " 19. Asia.
 " 19 (i. e. 23). Americae descrip.
 " 29. Polus Arcticus cum vicinis regionibus.
 " 861. Tartaria.
 " 877. Insulæ Indiae orientalis.
 " 891. The ylandes of the West Indies.
 " 880 (i. e. 895). Cuba insul.—Hispaniola.—Havana portus.—I. Iamaica.— I. S. Ioannis.—I. Margareta.
 " 899. Virginia et Florida.
 " 905. Hispania Nova.
 " 907. Same.
 " 913. Terra Firma et novum regnum Granatense et Popaian.
 " 915. Perv.
 " 919. Mappa Æstivarvm infularum alias Bermudas dictarum . . .
 " 921. America Meridionalis.
 " 927. Fretum Magellani.

## 1639

**Hondius, H.**
Nouveau théâtre dv monde ou novvel atlas comprenant les tables et descriptions de toutes les régions de la terre divisé en trois tomes. 3 v. fol. A Amsterdam, chez Henry Hondius, demeurant fur le Dam, à l'enfeigne du chien vigilant, a°. d. 1639. 452

NOTE.—The three engraved colored title-pages differ from each other and are of elaborate design and workmanship. Titles of v. 2-3 read: Nouveau théâtre dv monde ou novvel atlas; v. 3, Editio vltima. Sumptibus & typis æneis Henrici Hondij, Amſterodami, 1639. Muller mentions an atlas published by J. Jansson which corresponds with this atlas. Jansson was a brother-in-law of Henry Hondius, and associated with him in business. When Hondius died in 1638, Jansson carried on the work, which accounts for the difference in publishers.

Maps are by various cartographers including: Adrichem, Berckenrode, Biens, Cluver, Comenius, Damme, Emmius, Fabert, Fayen Flandro, Freitag, Gigas, Hardy, Henneberger, Jansson, Jubrien, Langren, Laurenberg, Lavaña, Lazius, Lhuyd, Magnus, Massa, Mellinger, Mercator, Metius, Ortelius, Petit, Pont, Scultetus, Bartholomaeus and Jonas, Secco, Sinck, Wicheringe. The maps are engraved by Ende, Goos, Hamersvelt, Keer and Rogiers.

The following maps relate to America:

v. 1, no. 1. Nova totivs terrarvm orbis geographica ac hydrographica tabvla.
" " 2. Poli Arctici, et circumiacentium terrarum descriptio novissima.
" " 5. Evropa exactissime descripta . . . 1631.
" 3, " 75. Asia recens fumma cura delineata . . . 1631.
" " 81. Tartaria.
" " 95. America noviter delineata. 1631.
" " 96. America Septentrionalis.
" " 97. Nova Anglia, Novvm Belgivm et Virginia. Amſtelodami Johannes Janſsonius excudit.
" " 98. Mappa Æstivarvm infularum, alias Barmvdas dictarum . . .
" " 99. Nova Virginiæ tabvla . . .
" " 100. Virginiae item et Floridae Americæ provinciarum, nova descriptio.
" " 101. Nova Hispania, et Nova Galicia.
" " 102. Terra Firma et novum regnum Granatense et Popayan. Amſtelodami Joannes Janſſonius excudit.
" " 103. Insvlæ Americanæ in oceano Septentrionali, cum terris adiacentibus. Amſtelodami, apud Ioannem Ianſsonium.
" " 104. Americæ pars meridionalis . . .
" " 105. Venezuela cum parte auſtrali Novæ Andalusiæ.
" " 106. Gviana fiue Amazonvm regio.
" " 107. Accuratissima Braziliæ tabula . . .
" " 198. Perv. Amstelodami, apud Ioannem Ianſſonium.
" " 109. Paragvay, ó prov. de Rio de la Plata cum regionibus adiacentibus Tvcvman et Sta. Crvz de la Sierra. Amstelodami, excudebat Ioannes Ianfsonius.
" " 110. Chili.
" " 111. Freti Megellanici . . .
" " 112. Polus Antarcticus . . .

## 1640–43

**Tassin, N.**, & *others*.

Les cartes générales de tovtes les prouinces de France, royaumes et prouinces de l'Europe. Reueües corrigées & augmentées . . . 1640. 1 p. l., 100 maps, pl. fol. [Paris, N. Berey, 1640–1643]   453

    Note.—Engraved title-page and plate. Double page plate follows t. p.; the center figure is an equestrian statue of Louis XIII, beneath which his courtiers are represented as homagers. Near the lower right hand corner is the following: N. Picart fecit. À Paris, chez N. Berey au bout du neuf proche les Augustins, avec priuilege du roy. Imprint date is 1640; maps are dated 1625–1643.

    A collection of maps by various cartographers including: Bertius, Hondius, Jansson, Baudouin, Blaeuw, Danquerts, Surhon, Sanson, Almada, Boisseau and Tassin. A number of maps of the various provinces of France, without signature, are probably Tassin's. The presumption is that the atlas contained originally only Tassin's maps, all of which were devoted to Europe. It is probable that the maps by other cartographers, referred to above, were inserted. no. [1] "Le plan de la ville, cité, vnivercité et favxbovrgs de Paris." In the four corners are the portraits of Louis XIII, Anna of Austria, le Dauphin and the duke of Anjou. In the lower right hand corner is the following: À Paris, chez Nicolas Berey enlumineur de la reine demeurant proche les Augustins au bout du pont Neuf. 1641.

    This plan is especially noted and described by m. Edgar Mareuse, in the Bulletin de la société de l'histoire de Paris et de l'Île-de-France. 1900. v. 27. pp. 161–162.

    The following maps relate to America:

    no. [2] Nova totius terrarum orbis geographica ac hydpographica tabula; auct: Iud. Hondio. 1643.

    " [4] Carte de l'Asie, cor. et aug. . . . par P. Bertius. 1640 [Les Philippines]

    " [5] Carte de l'Amérique, cor. et aug. . . . par P. Bertius [1640?]

## 1642

**Blaeu, W. J.** *and* **Blaeu, J.**

Toonneel des aerdycx, oft nievwe atlas. Derde deel met een aenhangsel tot de twee voorgaende deelen.   col. engr. title, 233 l. incl. 86 col. maps. fol. Amsterdam, I., Blaev, 1642.   454

    Note.—Contains: "Italien, Griecken, Candia," "Aenhangsel van't I en 11 deel van't toonneel des aerdryks . . ."

    Maps are highly colored and adorned with heraldic and other illustrations.

    The following map relates to America:

    no. 63. "Regiones svb polo arctico . . ."

## 1644

Le théâtre dv monde, on novvel atlas. Seconde partie. 2 pts. in 1 v.   eng. title, [112] l. incl. 48 maps; eng. title, [105] l. incl. 44 maps. fol. Amsterdam, I., Blaeu, 1644.   455

    Note.—At head of title: "Dvo protegit vnvs."

    Leaves irregularly numbered.—Maps have text on reverse.

The complete work is in 5 vols. dated 1635-54. *cf.* Paris. Bibl. natl., cat. The first pt. of this 2nd vol. contains France; the second part, Spain, Asia Africa and America.
The following maps relate to America:
pt. 2. no. 30. Americæ nova tabula. Auct: Guiljelmo Blaeuw. (With 9 plans of cities.
" " 31. Nova Belgica et Anglia nova.
" " 32. Insvlæ Americanæ in oceano Septentrionali cum terris adiacentibus.
" " 33. Mappa æstivarvm insularum, alias Barmvdas dictarum . . .
" " 34. Nova Virginiæ tabvla.
" " 35. Virginiæ partis australis, et Floridæ partis orientalis, interjacentiumq, regionum nova descriptio.
" " 36. Nova Hispania et nova Galicia.
" " 37. Terra Firma et novum regnum Granatense et Popayan.
" " 38. Venezvela, cum parte Australi novæ Andalvsiæ.
" " 39. Gviano, siue Amazonvm regio.
" " 40. Brasilia.
" " 41. Paragvay, ó prov. de rio de la Plata.
" " 42. Tabvla Magellanica.
" " 43. Chili.
" " 44. Pérv.

### 1646?

**Avity, P. d'.**, *sieur de Montmartin*.
Neŭwe archontologia cosmica, [das ift befchreibung aller kaÿferthumben, kŏnigreichen und republicken der gantzen welt . . . alles . . . verfaffet Johann Ludwig Gottfried [pseud. of J. P. Abelın] . . . und verlegt von Matthæo Merian] 1 p. l., [31] maps, [61] pl. obl. fol. Franckfurt am Maijn, M. Merian [1646?]
456

NOTE.—Engraved title.
These plates, with the exception of the engraved title, accompany the text of the 1646 ed. which also includes a few other plates. For contents see entry under World. Cities. Title 58.
The following maps relate to America:
no. [1] Nova totius terrarum orbis . . .
" [9] America noviter delineata.

### 1646-47

**Dudley, Sir R.**, *styled duke of Northumberland and earl of Warwick*.
Dell' arcano del mare . . . libri sei; nel primo de' quali fi tratta della longitudine praticabile in diuerfi modi, d' inuenzione dell' autore, nel secondo, delle carte fue generali, e de' portolani rettificati in longitudine, e latitudine, nel terzo, della difciplina fua marittima, e militare. Nel quarto, dell' architettura fua nautica di vafcelli da guerra, nel quinto, della nauigazione scientifica, e perfetta, cioè spirale, ò di gran circoli, nel sefto, delle carte fue geografiche, e particolari. Al serenissimo Ferdinando secondo gran dvca di Toscana

**Dudley,** *Sir* **R.**—Continued.
  suo signore.   3 v. in 2.   fol.   In Firenze, nella stamperia di Francefco Onofri, 1646–47.   457

    Note.—First marine atlas in which the maps were drawn on the Mercator protection. Con licenza de' ss. superiori.
    v. 1, bk. 1.   Added ms. title, half title, title, 8, [2], 9–10, [2], 11–28, [6], 29–56 pp., 26, [4] pl.
    Lacks fac-simile of patent from Ferdinand II, grand duke of Tuscany, confirming Dudley, in the use of the title duke of Northumberland, which appears after general title in Grenville copy in the British Museum, Harvard library copy and L. C. 2nd copy.
    pls. numbered 1–27, with four unnumbered pl., two of which have text on the reverse.
    No pl. 25 in Grenville, Harvard, or either of the L. C. copies.
    pl. 27 is not numbered so, but is referred to in the text, p. 53 as "figura 27 numerata 151 e 154."
    v. 1, bk 2.   76 pp., [1] l., [15] maps, 12, [1] pl.
    pls. numbered 1–8, 8–12, 3.
    pls. 1–2 pasted on 1 l.
    "   5–6 printed "   "
    "   8 printed on 2 l.
    "   3 Vlti°. follows p. 66, after the maps.
    At end, 1 l. entitled: "Avvertimenti al lettore."
    v. 2, bk. 3.   Half title, title, 12 pp., [1] l., 13–14 pp., [1] l., 15–16 pp., [1] l., 17–46, [6], 47–55 pp., 8 pl.
    Title reads: Dell' arcano del mare, di d. Rvberto Dvdleo dvca di Nortvmbria, e conte di Warvich, libro terzo, e qvarto; nel terzo, fi contiene la difciplina marittima, e militare dell' autore, e nel quarto, l' architettura sua nautica di vafcelli da guerra. Al serenissimo Ferdinando secondo gran dvca di Toscana suo signore. In Firenze, nella stamperia di Francefco Onofri. 1646. Con licenza de' ss. superiori.
    Two leaves, which appear intact in 2nd L. C. copy, have been cut apart and inserted in varions places as follows:
    "Forma seconda dell' armata . . . car 11," pasted on back of pl. 2.
    "Forma terza dell' armata . . . car 13," and "Forma seconda dell' armata . . . car 13," have been inlaid and the leaf follows pl. 14.
    "Forma seconda dell' armata mifta . . . car 15," pasted on leaf following p. 16.
    Between pp. 46–47 are two unnumbered pages entitled: "Aggivnta di tre altre fogge di sqvadre;" followed by four pages of printed naval formations: Figura 8, e 9; Figura 10, e 11; Figura 12; Figura 13.
    First plate unnumbered, cipher: La pri$^a$. del. 3. li°.; pls. numbered 2, 4, 14–16, 16 f$^{cca}$., 17.
    No pls. 3 or 5–13 in Grenville, Harvard or L. C. copies.
    v. 2, bk. 4.   39 pp., [1] l., 19 pl.
    pl. 1 is a diagram in text on p. 5.
    pl. 19 is pasted at foot of p. 33.
    At end, 1 l. entitled: "Avvertimentia a chi legge."
    v. 3, bk. 5.   Title, 26 pp., [1] l., 27–36 pp., [1] l., 113, [13] pl.
    Title reads: Dell' arcano del mare, di d. Rvberto Dvdleo dvca di Nortvmbria, e conte di Warvich. Parte prima del tomo terzo contenente il libro qvinto. Nel quale fi tratta della nauigazione fcientifica, e perfetta, cioè spirale, ò di gran circoli. Al serenissimo Ferdinando secondo gran dvca di Toscana svo signore. In Firenze, nella stamperia di Francesco Onofri. 1647. Con licenza de' superiori.

Plates not arranged consecutively.
Thirteen plates unnumbered.
pls. numbered 1-2, 7, 16-24, 26-46, 49-52, 54-56, 60, 65-69, 74-82, 87-118, 120-152, 154-160, 162-166, 168-171.
pls. 1-2 printed on 1 l.
Two unnumbered pls. printed on 1 l. following p. 6.
pls. 16-23, 1 pl. on 8 l.
" 26-27 printed on 1 l.
" 28-39, 1 pl. on 12 l.
" 41-42 printed on 1 l.
Three unnumbered pls. on 1 l.
pls. 43-44 printed on 1 l.
" 45-46 pasted on l. above pl. 49.
" 50, 56 pasted on 1 l.
" 52, 51, 55 pasted on 1 l.
" 54, 60   "   "   "
" 65-66 pasted on l. above pls. 67-68.
pl. 80 pasted on 1 l.
pls. 82, 74   "   "   "
" 75-77 printed on 1 l.
" 78-79 pasted on 1 l.
" 89-90 printed on 1 l.
" 91-92 printed on 1 l.
" 93-94   "   "   "
" 95-96   "   "   "
pl. 101 pasted on 1 l. above pl. 102.
pls. 103-104 printed on 1 l.
" 106-107   "   "   "
" 108-109   "   "   "
" 117-118   "   "   "
pl. 120 pasted on l. above pl. 121.
pls. 128-130 printed on 1 l.
" 131-132   "   "   "
" 134-135   "   "   "
" 139-140   "   "   "
Unnumbered pl. pasted on l. below pl. 152.
pls. 159-160 printed on 1 l.
" 170-171   "   "   "
pl. 99 pasted on 1 l.
pls. 168-169 printed on 1 l.
Two unnumbered pl., nos. [116-117] in consecutive order, printed on 1 l.
One leaf follows pl. 144, and is entitled:
"Tavola dell' avtore, per facilitare l'operazione delle quattro figure seguenti, & il quadrante precedente."
One leaf at end: "Avvertimento circa il sesto libro."
v. 3, bk. 6. title, 60, [2] pp., 131 maps.
Title reads: "Dell arcano dell mare, di d. Rvberto Dvdleo dvca di Nortvmbria, e conte di Warvich. Parte seconda del tomo terzo contenente il libro sesto, nel quale fi tratta delle carte fue corografiche, e particolari. Al serenissimo Ferdinando secondo gran dvca di Toscana svo signore. In Firenze, nella stamperia di Francefco Onofri, 1647. Con licenza de' superiori." Ornamented with pl. "Orsa Minore" also contained in v. 3, bk. 1, as pl. 159.
v. 3, bk. 6, [pt. 1] [Europa] 22 pp., 58 maps.
Maps [1-2] unnumbered, no. [3-58] numbered I-LIIII (i. e. 56); no. [8]
. . . "Europa, carta quinta" not marked "seco*" as on Grenville copy; no.

**Dudley, *Sir* R.—Continued.**

[16-20] ... "Carta xiii- ... carta xvii" do not contain the addition, "Euroª," placed below the number on Grenville copies; no. [40] ... "Di Europa carta xxxvi" contains the manuscript addition "secoª" which is engraved on the Grenville copy; no. [58] ... Carta liiii does not contain the addition "d'Euroª"

v. 3, bk. 6, pt. 2. [Affrica] 23-28 pp., 17 maps.
Map no. [59] unnumbered; no. [60-75] numbered ii-xvii.
v. 3, bk. 6, pt. 3. [Asia] 29-40 pp., 23 maps.
map no. [76] unnumbered; no. [77-98] numbered ii-xxiii.
v. 3, bk. 6, pt. 4. [America] 41-58 pp., 33 maps, 59-60, [2] pp.
map no. [99] unnumbered; nos. [100-131] numbered ii-xxxiii; nos. [111-112] "Carta xii- ... xiii," do not contain "d'America" as on the Grenville copies.

v. 3, bk. 6, pt. 4. pp. 59-60, "Alconi erroretti," followed by [2] pp., "Difcorfo delle fcienze mathematiche, che entrano nell' opera dell' Arcano del mare" with imprint at end "In Firenze, nella stamperia di Francefco Onofri. Con licenza de' superiori. mdcxxxiix."

The first edition of which exist only a few copies. The best known are in the Bibliothèque Nationale, the Grenville copy in the British Museum and the manuscript copy in the Royal Library at Munich. In America there are complete copies in Harvard Library and the Library of Congress, and part of a copy in the latter and the Public Library of the city of Worcester. Baron Nordenskiöld states "In how many of the large libraries of Europe one seeks in vain for ... the Arcano dell mare."

The author, Sir Robert Dudley, son of the earl of Leicester, was well qualified by education, travel and the possession of valuable new material, to produce a work of importance and lasting value. His knowledge gained through his experience as a seaman, together with that of his brother-in-law Henry Cavendish the navigator, is amply set forth and accompanied by additional information supplied by Abraham Kendal and John Davis. Three manuscript volumes, the first two dated 1610, preserved in the Specola, or Museo di Storia Naturale at Florence, are perhaps the basis of this work, whereas the manuscript in the Royal Library at Munich is the completed work comprising even more than was finally published.

The work consists of 3 v., comprising 6 bks. bound in 2 v., the first of which contains v. 1, bks. 1-2; v. 2, bks. 3-4; v. 3, bk. 5. The second contains v. 3, bk. 6.

The text of bks. 1-4 is uneven, measuring 14-14¼ x 9½ inches. The plates are of various sizes, the larger ones folded to 16 inches. The text of bk. 5 is 16 inches in height; bk. 6, 18½ x 13½ inches inlaid to 21½ x 16½ inches. The maps, 21½ inches in height, are mostly on double sheets 31 x 21½ inches, guarded in the center. On the plates in the different copies, the pointers and centers vary in pattern and seem to be used indiscriminately.

The manuscript coat of arms, the first leaf in the Grenville copy, here omitted, is of similar workmanship to the illustrated manuscript title in this copy. The title in a scroll at the top, reads "Dell' Arcano del mare. Tomo primo diuifo nel libro primo e secondo." Below is a design consisting of rocks in the sea.

The portolanos and charts are of great interest, many of the American ones being on a larger scale than even those of the dutch "pascaart" of later years. That the american maps may perhaps even claim priority over those of Laet,

may be seen from the statement of Antonio Francisco Lucini, the engraver, who states in the dedicatory epistle to the second edition "Fiorenza, 1661," that he worked on the plates in seclusion for twelve years in an obscure tuscan village, using no less than 5,000 pounds of copper in the making.
It is undoubtedly due to the rarity of the work that the maps of America have been so overlooked, although dr. Winsor calls attention to it and gives several partial reproductions in his "Narrative and critical history of America," v. 3–4. The maps are by english and other pilots and it is generally conceded that the work was both scientific and accurate for the time. Dr. Hale, in his "Notes on Robert Dudley" (American antiquarian society. Proceedings. 1873, v. 61, p. 95) says: "If, as I believe, he used the original charts of Henry Hudson, the manuscript at Munich gives us by far the most accurate account we have of the northern voyages of that discoverer. I have already said that there is reason to suspect that the maps of the Pacific coast were drawn from the original observations of Cavendish . . . ."
Abraham Kendal, the master of Dudley's flagship in the expedition of 1594-95 to explore the "Eldorador," left notes and plans embodied by Dudley, in v. 1, bk. 2. The work of another of this group of famous navigators is represented in a portolano covering the voyage of John Davis to India in 1601.
Maps relating to America are: v. 1, bk. 2, nos. [2–5], [7], [10]; v. 3, bk. 6, nos. [53–58], [64], [83–87, Philippines], [93], [98–131]
The following is a complete list of the maps:

v. 1, bk. 2, no. [1] Carta terza generale di Europa.
" " " [2] Carta prima generale d'Affrica è par.te d'America.
" " " [3] Carta prima generale d'America dell' India occidëtale è Mare del Zur.
" " " [4] Carta terza generale d'America.
" " " [5] Carta secon.da generale del'Asia.
" " " [6] Carta seconda generale d'Affrica.
" " " [7] Carta prima generale dell'Asia.
" " " [8] Asia carta diciasete piu moderna.
" " " [9] Carta terza generale del'Asia.
" " " [10] Carta seconda generale del'America.
" " " [11] Carta quarta generale di Europa.
" " " [12] Carta quinta generale di Europa.
" " " [13] Carta sefta generale del' Europa.
" " " [14] Carta nonna generale di Europa.
" " " [15] Carta di Noruegia piu moderna.
v. 3, bk. 6, no. [1] Vna carta generale del mare Mediterranio. Carta prima generale d' Europa.
" " " [2] Vna carta dell' arcipelago, con parte del mare mediterraneo uerso leuante.
" " " [3] Vna carta del mare oceano, che comincia con il Capo S: Vincenzio in Portogallo, e finisce con lo stretto di Gibilterra. Carta prima particolare d' Europa.
" " " [4] Carta particolare del mare Mediterranio che comincia con lo stretto di Gibilterra e finisce con il porto di Cartagena in Ispagna e del capo Falcone in Barberia. di Europa carta II.
" " " [5] Carta particolare del mare Mediterraneo che comincia con il capo Paulos e finisce con il capo di S. Martino in Ispagns e del capo Bogia in Barberia. Euro.a III.

**Dudley,** *Sir* **R.**—Continued.

v. 3, bk. 6, no. [6] Carta particolare del mare Mediterraneo che cominca con il capo S: Martino e, finisce con il capo Dragone, in Ispagna e, con l isole di Maiorica e, Minorica e, ÿuica. di Europa carta quarta.

" " " [7] Carta particolare del mare Mediterraneo, che comincia con il capo Dragone, in Jspagna e' finisce con il capo Melle nella riuera di Genoua. La longitudine cominca da l isolla di Picho e' di Asores. di Europa a carta quinta.

" " " [8] Europa. Carta quinta [seco$^a$.]

" " " [9] Carta particolare del mare Mediterraneo che comincia con il capo Melle nella riuiera di Genoua è finisce con ciuita uecchia nelo stat$^o$ del Papa. La longitudine comincia da l isolla di Picho di Asores. di Europa carta sesta.

" " " [10] Carta particolare della jsolla di Sardinia e parte della Corsica. La longitudine comincia da l isolla di Picho di Asores. di Europa carta setima.

" " " [11] Carta particolare del mare Mediterraneo che comincia con ciuita uecchia è finisce con il capo S: Maria in Calabria. La longitudine comincia da l isola di Picho di Asores di Europa carta ottaua.

" " " [12] Carta particolare del mare Mediterraneo che comincia con Budua in Dalmatia è finisce con Corfu nelo stato Venetiāo. La longitudine comincia da l isola Picho di Asores. Cartta nona di Europa.

" " " [13] Carta particolare del mare Adriatico che comincia con il capo di Ancona è finisce con l' isola Lesina nello Isteso mare. La longitudine comincia da l' isola di Picho di Asores. Carta x. di Europa.

" " " [14] Carta particolare del mare Mediterraneo che comincia con il capo Spartiuento è finisce con il cap$^o$ Matapan nella Morea. La longitudine comincia da l' isola di Picco di Asores. Carta xi. di Europa.

" " " [15] Carta particolare del Arcipelago. La longitudine comincia da l' iſola di Picco di Aſores. Carta xii. di Europa.

" " " [16] Carta particolare del mare Mediteran$^o$ che comincia con il capo Gironda è finisce con Antiochia in Soria. La longitudine comincia da l isola di Picco di Aſoreſ. Carta xiii.

" " " [17] Carta particolare del mare Mediterraneo che comincia con l' isola di Candia è finisce con il capo Roxatin in Barberia. La longitudine comincia da l' iīola di Picco di Asores. Carta xiiii.

" " " [18] Carta particolare del mare Mediterraneo che comincia con il capo Teti è finisce con Folselli in Barberia. La longitudine comincia de l' isola di Picco di Asores. Carta. xv.

" " " [19] Carta particolare del mare Mediterraneo che comincia con il porto di tre Croce è finisce con il capo Araso. La longitudine comincia da l' isola di Picco di Asores. Carta x.v.i.

v. 3, bk. 6, no. [20] Carta particolare del mare Mediteraneo che comincia con il capo Bogia è finisce con il porto di tre Croce. La longitudine comincia da l' ifola di Picco d' Asores. Carta. x.v.ii.

" " " [21] Carta particolare del oceano che comincia con il capo S: Vincentio è finisce con il capo Roxo in Portogallo. La longitudine comincia da l' ifola di Picco d' Asores. di Europa carta. x.v.iii.

" " " [22] Carta particolare del oceano che comincia con la costa dio. Roxo è finisce con il capo di Mogera ni Portogallo. La longitudine comincia da l' isola di Picco d' Asores di Europa carta x.v.iiii.

" " " [23] Carta particolare che comincia con il capo Mogera in Portogallo è finisce con il capo di Coriano in Ispagna. La longitudine comincia da l' isola di Picco d' Asores. di Europa carta xx.

" " " [24] Carta particolare che comincia con il capo di Coriano è finisce con il capo di Auiles in Ispagnia. La longitudine comincia da d' isola di Picco d' Asores. di Europa carta xxi.

" " " [25] Carta particolare che comincia con il capo di Auiles è finisce con il capo di Oringan in Biscaia sotto posto alla corona di Ispaia. La longitudine comincia da l' isola di Picco d' Asores. di Europa carta xxii.

" " " [26] Carta particolare che comincia con il capo di Oringan in Biscaia è finisce con la costa d' Alcason in Francia. La longitudine comincia da l' isola di Picco d' Asores. di Europa carta xxiii.

" " " [27] Carta particolare della costa di Guasconnia in Francia che comincia con il fiume di Burdeaux è finisce con l'isola di Heÿs. La longitudine comincia da l'isola di Picco d' Asores. di Europa carta xxiiii.

" " " [28] Carta particolare della Brittania bassa in Francia che comincia con il capo Armentice è finisce con il capo Forne. La longitudine comincia da l'isola di Picco d' Asores. di Europa carta xxv.

" " " [29] Carta particolare dell canale fra Inghilterra è Francia che comincia con l'isole di Sorlinges e' finisce con l'isola di Garnseÿ. La longitudine comincia da l'isole di Picco d' Asores. di Europa carta xxvi.

" " " [30] Carta particolare della costa d'Inghilterra è Francia che comincia con l'isola di Garnesÿ è finisce con il C. di Fecam nella costa di Normandia. La longitudine comincia dal' Isola di Picco d'Asores. di Europa carta xxvii.

" " " [31] Carta particolare dell mare di Ierlandia è parte di Inghilterra è della Iscotia. La longitudine comincia da l'isola di Picco d'Asores. di Europa carta xxviii.

" " " [32] Carta particolare dell mare oceano fra l' Ierlandia è l'isole di Asores. La longitudine comincia da l'isola di Picco d' Asores. di Europa carta xxviiii.

" " " [33] Carta particolare dello stretto di Inghilterra tra Douer è Cales con la costa intorno. La longitudine comincia da lisole di Picho d'Asores. di Europa carta xxx.

**Dudley,** *Sir* **R.**—Continued.

v. 3, bk. 6, no. [34] Carta particolare della bocca del Tamigi in Inghi*t*ª è finisce à Ieÿstof nella prouincia di Suffoleh. La longitudine comincia da l'isola di Picho d'Asores. di Europa carta xxxi.

" " " [35] Carta particolare della costa di Inghilterra che comincia con Orfordness è finisce con Flamborow heade. La longitudine comincia da l'isola di Picho d'Asores. di Europa carta xxxii.

" " " [36] Carta particolare della costa di Inghilterra che comincia a Fÿleberg è finisce con il c: di S: Tabs in Ischozia. La longitudine comincia da lisola di Picho Asores. di Europa carta xxxiii.

" " " [37] Carta particolare della costa di Scozia che comincia con il c: di S. Tabs è finisce con il c: d' Comar. La longitudine comincia d' l'isola di Picho d' Asores. di Europa carta xxxiiii.

" " " [38] Carta particolare della costa di Scozia che comincia con il c: di Cromar è finisce con l' isole di Orcades. La longitudine comincia da l' isola di Picho d' Asores. di Europa carta xxxv.

" " " [39] Carta particolare della costa di Zelanda è Frislanda è Olanda che comincia con il porto di Newport è finisce con Messelward. La longitudine comincia da l' isola di Picho d' Asores. di Europa carta xxxvi.

" " " [40] Carta particolare della costa di Zelanda è Frislanda è Olanda che comincia con il porto di Newport è finisce con Messelward. La longitudine comincia da l' isola di Pico d' Asores. Di Europa carta xxxvi.

" " " [41] Carta particolare che comincia con il gran fiume Albis è contende parte dell mare Baltico è Lentrata al sondo di Danemarca. La longitudine comincia da l' isola di Picco d' Asores. di Europa carta xxxvii.

" " " [42] Carta particolare che comincia con la Iutlandia è contiene parte della costa di Suetzia è della Noruegia. La longitudine comincia da l' isola di Picho di Asores. di Europa carta xxxviii.

" " " [43] Carta particolare del mare Baltico che comincia con Colbergen è finisce con il c: di Westuesen in Prusia. La longitudine comincia da l' isola di Picco d'Asores. di Europa carta xxxviiii.

" " " [44] Carta particolare dell mare Baltico che comincia con il capo di Eleeholm in Suezia è finisce con Padus in Liflandia. La longitudine comincia da l' isola di Picco d' Asores. di Europa carta xxxx.

" " " [45] Carta particolare di Liuonia cor una particella della costa che comincia con Lockston è finisce con il P*t*? Derliuen. La longitudine comincia da l' isola di Picco d' Asores. di Europa carta xxxxi.

" " " [46] Carta particolare dell fine del mare Baltico in sino all narue. La longitudine comincia da l' isola di Picho d' Asores. di Europa carta xxxxii.

v. 3, bk. 6, no. [47] Carta particolare della entrata del mare Botnico o' Boddico. La longitudine comincia da l' isola di Picco d' Asores. di Europa carta xxxxiii.

" " · " [48] Carta particolare della parte australe della Noruegia. La longitudine comincia da l' isola di Piho d' Asores. di Europa carta xxxxiiii.

" " " [49] Questa carta contiene l' isolle di Ferro è di Shutland con la Noruegia Settentrionale. La longitudine comincia da l'isola di Pico d' Asores. di Europa carta xxxxv.

" " " [50] Carta particolare della costa di Finlandia con il Capo dell Norto. La longitudine comincia da l' isola di Pico d' Asores. di Europa carta xxxxvi.

" " " [51] Carta particolare del mare settentrionale di Moscouia è Russia con listreto di Wigats è finisce con il fiume obÿ. La longitudine comincia da l' isola di Pico d' Asores. di Europa carta xxxxvii.

" " " [52] Carta particolare della costa di nuoua Zembla. La longitudine comincia da l' isola di Pico d' Asores. di Europa carta xxxxviii.

" " " [53] Carta particolare della terra di Grenlande gia incognita fu scoperta da Inglesi sino a, gradi: 80: di latitudine. La longitudine comincia da l' isola di Pico d' Asores. di Europa carta xxxxviiii.

" " " [54] Carta particolare dell' isole di Islandia è Frislandia, con l' isolette di fare. La longitudine comincia da l' isola di Pico d'Asores. di Europa carta xxxxx.

" " " [55] Carta particolare della Gronlandia orientale. La longitudine comincia da l' isola di Pico d' Asores. di Europa carta li.

" " " [56] Carta particolare della meta inconita con la Gronlandia occidentale: è dell' Estotiland Scop:$^{to}$ dall' Inglesi. La longitudine comincia da l' isola di Pico d' Asores. di Europa carta lii.

" " " [57] Carta particolare della meta incognita australe con una parte della America Settentrionale. La longitudine comincia da l' isola di Pico d'Asores. di Europa carta liii.

" " " [58] Carta particolare dello istreto è mare iseoperto da Ëen.° Hudson Ingilese nel. 1611. La longitudine comincia da l' isola di Pico d' Asores. Carta liiii.

" " " [59] Carta particolare che comincia con li stretto di Gibilterro è finisce con il capo Gruer nella Barberia occide$^{le}$. La longitudine comincia da l' isola di Pico d' Asores. di Affrica carta prima.

" " " [60] Carta particolare dell' isole d'Asores con l' isola di Madera. La longitudine comincia da l' isola di Pico d' Asores. di Affrica carta ii.

" " " [61] Carta particolare della Barberia occidentale che comincia con il capo Gruer è finisce con il capo Matas. La longitudine comincia da l' isola di Pico d' Asores. di Affrica carta iii.

**Dudley,** *Sir* **R.**—Continued.

v. 3, bk. 6, no. [62] Carta particolare della Barberia australe che comincia con il capo Matas è finiscie con il c: Himilas con l' isole di capo Verde. La longitudine comincia da l' isola di Pico d' Asores. di Affrica carta iiii.

" " " [63] Carta dell isole di Capo Verde con l' isole dell Indie occidentale, et parte della terra ferma di Guiana. La longitudine comincia da l' isola di Pico d' Asores. di Affrica carta v.

" " " [64] Carta particolare dell mare oceano fra la costa di Guinea è la Brasilia. La longitudine comincia da l' isola di Pico d' Asores. di Affrica carta. vi.

" " " [65] Carta particolare che comincia con il fiume Iuntas nella Guinea è finisce con il capo di S: Dara è con l' isola d' S. Tomaso. La longit$^{ne}$. comi$^{ca}$. da l' isola d' Pico d' Asores. di Affrica carta vii.

" " " [66] Carta particolare che comincia con l' isola di S: Tomaso ò tome è $^c$: d' S. Clara e' finisce con il c: d' Aldeas. La longitud$^{ne}$. comi$^{ca}$. da l' isola di Pico d' Asores. d' Affrica carta viii.

" " " [67] Carta particolare del mare di Ethiopia con l' isola di S. Elena è parte della costa. La longitu:$^{ne}$ comincia da l' isola di Pico d' Asores. d' Affrica carta viiii.

" " " [68] Carta particolare che comincia con il capo Aldea è finisce con il capo Degortam. La longitud:$^{ne}$ comi$^{ca}$. da l' isola di Pico d' Asores. di Affrica carta x.

" " " [69] Carta particolare che comincia con il capo, Degortam è con il capo Buona Speranza è finisce in gradi 27. di latitudine australe. La longitu:$^{ne}$ comi:$^{ca}$ da l' isola di Pico d' Asores. di Affrica carta xi.

" " " [70] Carta particolare della parte australle della isola S: Lorēzo con la terra ferma dirinpetto è finisce con gradi: 6: di latitudine australe. La longitud$^{ne}$. comin$^a$. da l' isola di Pico d' Asores. di Affrica carta xii.

" " " [71] Carta particolare dell mare dè l indie con la parte tramontana dè l' isola S: Lorenzo. La longitudine comincia da l' isola di Pico d' Asores. di Affrica carta xiii.

" " " [72] Carta particolare della parte tramontana dell isola di San Lorenzo con la costa diripetto sin$^o$. à Monbazza con l' isole è seccagne int$^{no}$. La longitudi$^{ne}$. comin:$^{ca}$ da l' isola di Pico d' Asores. d' Affrica carta xiiii.

" " " [73] Carta particolare dell mare dell Indie con le secaie è alcqune isolle. La longitudine comi:$^{ca}$ da l' isola di Pico d' Asores d' Affrica carta. xv.

" " " [74] Carta particolare che comincia con il capo è l' isola Mombazza è finisce con il capo Baduis. La longitud:$^{ne}$ comi:$^{ca}$ da l' isola di Pico d' Asores. d' Affrica carta xvi.

" " " [75] Carta particolare che comincia con il capo Baduis è finisce con il capo Cumana, è mostra la bocca dell mare Rosso. La longitudine cominca da l' isola di Pico d' Asores. d' Affrica carta. xvii.

v. 3, bk. 6, no. [76] Carta particolare che comincia con il capo Dofar in Arabia è finisce con il capo Cintapora nell Indie. La longitudine comincia da l' isola di Pico d' Asores. d' Asia carta prima.

" " " [77] Questa carta contiene la costa dell' India orientale con la costa di Coromandell è l'isola di Zeilan è finisce con la parte tramont$^{na}$. di Sumatra. La longitudine comincia da l' isola de Pico di Asores. d' Asia carta II.

" " " [78] Carta particolare del mare d' India sino allo stretto di Sunda fra l'isole di Sumatra è di Iaua magg$^{re}$. con altre isolette è scog$^{li}$. scop$^{to}$. d' Inglesi. La longitudine comincia da l' isola di Pico d' Asores. d' Asia carta III.

" " " [79] Carta particolare del stretto di Sunda fra l' isole di Sumatra è Iauamaggre. La longitudine comincia da l' isola di Pico d' Asores. d' Asia carta IIII.

" " " [80] Carta particolare del' golfo di Bengala è Pegu che comincia con il capo Masulipatan è finisce con la punta Domurco. La longitu$^{ne}$. comin:$^a$ da l' isola di Pico d' Asores. d' Asia carta v.

" " " [81] Carta particolare della Malacca con la costa sin' al Pegu è Camboia con l' isole di Sumatra è Burneo parte tramontana con molte altre isole è iso:$^{te}$ intorō. La longitu:$^{ne}$ comic$^a$. da l' isola di Pico d' Asores. d'Asia carta VI.

" " " [82] Carta particolare del' mare di Cocincina con la parte australe della China. La longi$^{ne}$. comin$^{ca}$. da l' isola di Pico d' Asores. d' Asia carta VII.

" " " [83] Carta particolare del' mare è costa di Manilia. La longitud:$^{ne}$ comincia da l' isola di Pico d' Asores. d' Asia carta VIII.

" " " [84] Carta particolare dello stretto di Manilia nel isole Filippine. La longitu$^{ne}$. comin$^{ca}$. da l' isola di Pico d' Asores. d' Asia carta VIIII.

" " " [85] Carta particolare dell' isole Fillipine è di Luzon. La longitu$^{ne}$. comin$^{ca}$. da l' isola di Pico d' Asores. d' Asia carta x.

" " " [86] Carta particolare del' isola Mindano parte australe con Celebes è Gilolo parte tramontana è con l' isole è di Molucchi è altre isolette in tōro. La longitu$^{ne}$. comin$^a$. da l' isola di Pico d' Asores. d' Asia carta XI.

" " " [87] Carta particolare del' isole di Ladrões con l' isole di Gilolo è de Molucchi. La longitud:$^{ne}$ comincia da l' isola di Pico d' Asores. d' Asia carta XII.

" " " [88] Carta particolare delle 6 isole de Molucchi. La longitu$^{ne}$. comin:$^{ca}$ da 1 isola di Pico d' Asores. d' Asia carta XIII.

" " " [89] Carta particolare del' isole di Iaua magg$^{re}$. è minore con la parte Austr$^{le}$. del isole di Sumatra è Burneo. La longi$^{ne}$. comin:$^{ca}$ da l' isola di Pico d' Asores. d' Asia carta XIIII.

" " " [90] Carta particolare dell' isole Celebes è Giliolo parte austr$^{le}$. è di Buttō, Batuliar, Timor, Seram, Banda, è Amboina è altre isolet$^e$. La longitudine comincia da l' isola di Pico d' Asores. d' Asia carta

**Dudley,** *Sir* **R.**—Continued.

v. 3, bk. 6, no. [91] Carta particolare d' una parte della co$^{ta}$. di China con l' isola di Pakas, è altre isole, sino alla parte piu australe del' Giapone. La longitu$^{ne}$. cominc$^{ca}$: da l'isola di Pico d' Asores. D'Asia carta XVI.

" " " [92] Carta particolare della grande isola del' Giapone è di Iezo con il regno di corai et altre isole in torno. La longitud$^{ne}$. cominc$^{ca}$ da l' isola di Pico d' Asores. d'Asia carta XVII.

" " " [93] Carta particolare della parte orientale del' isola di Iezo con li stretto fra America è la detta isola. La longitu$^{ne}$. comincia da l'isola di Pico d' Asores. d'Asia carta XVIII.

" " " [94] Carta particolare della costa australe scoperta dall' Olandesi. La longitud$^{ne}$. cominc$^{ca}$: da l'isola di Pico d'Asores. d'Asia carta XVIIII.

" " " [95] Carta particolare dell' mare è isole scoperte dal capit$^{no}$. Iacomo Maier Olandese nel 1617. con parte della nuoua Guinea. La longitudine comincia da l'isola di Pico d' Asores. D'Asia carta XX.

" " " [96] Isole scoperte da Iacomo le Maier Olandeſe nel 1617. La longitudine comincia da l'isola di Pico d'Asores. d Asia carta XXI.

" " " [97] Isole nel mare di Sur scoperte nel 1617. La longitudine comincia da l' isola di Pico d' Asores. d' Asia carta XXII.

" " " [98] Carta particolare del mare del Sur che comincia con l'isole di Salamone è finisce con la costa di Lima nel' Peru. La longitudine comincia da l'isola di Pico d' Asores. Asia carta XXIII.

" " " [99] Carta particolare della terra nuoua con la gran baia et il fiume grande della Canida. La longitudine comincia da l' isola di Pico d' Asores. D'America car$^{a}$. prima.

" " " [100] Carta particolare della nuoua Belgia è parte della nuoua Anglia. La longitudine comincia da l'isola di Pico d' Asores. D'America carta II.

" " " [101] Carta particolare della Virginia vecchia è nuoua. La longitu$^{ne}$. comic$^{a}$: da l'isole di Pico di Asores: D'America carta III.

" " " [102] Carta particolare della coſta di Florida è di Virginia. La longitudine comincia da l isola di Pico d' Asores. D'America carta IIII.

" " " [103] Carta particolare del' isola di Cuba é di Iamaica con il capo della Florida è l'isole intorno. La longita$^{ne}$ comincia da l'isola di Pico d' Asores. D'America carta V.

" " " [104] Carta particolare dell' isola Ispaniola è S: Gio$^{né}$: nel' India ocident$^{le}$ con l' isole intorno. La longitudine comincia da l' isola di Pico d'Asores. D'America carta VI.

" " " [105] Carta particolare della bara di Messico con la costa. La longitudine comincia de l' isola di Pico d' Asores. D' America carta VII.

v. 3, bk. 6, no. [106] Carta particolare del' India occidentale che contiene il golfo di Veragua, la baia di Honduras nel' mare del' Noort è parte del' mare di Zur. La longitudine comincia da l' isola di Pico d' Asores. D' America carta viii.

" " " [107] Carta particolare del' India occidentale che comincia con il capo S: Romano nel' mare del' norte, è finisce con il Rio Coquele. La longitudine comincia da l' isola di Pico di Asores. D' America carta viiii.

" " " [108] Carta particolare dell' India Ocidentale, con la terra ferma dal' capo di Paria sin al' capo S: Romano. La longitudine comincia da l' isola di Pico d' Asores. D'America carta x.

" " " [109] Carta particolare dell' isola di Bermuda sin all' India occidentale et al' capo S: Romano della Florida. La longitudine comincia de l'isola di Pico d' Asores. D' America carta xi.

" " " [110] Carta particolare del' mare occeano dal' isole d' Asores di Flores, è Coruo sin alla terra nuoua in America. La longitu$^{ne}$ cominc$^a$ da l'isola di Pico d' Asores. D'America carta xii.

" " " [111] Al ser$^{mo}$ Ferdinando II gran dvca di Toscana svo signore don Roberto Dudleo duca di Northumbria. xiii.

" " " [112] Alla ser$^{ma}$ sig$^{ra}$ princip$^{sa}$ d' Vrbino gran dvchessa di Toscana sva sig$^{ra}$ d: Roberto Dvdleo dvca di Northumbria. xiiii.

" " " [113] Carta particolare dell' ri° d' Amazone con la costa sin al' fiume Maranhan. La longitu$^{ne}$: cominc$^a$ da l' isola di Pico d' Asores. D' America carta xv.

" " " [114] Carta particolare della Brasilia settentrionale. La longitud$^{ne}$ comincia da l' isola di Pico d' Asores. D' America carta xvi.

" " " [115] Carta particolare della Brasilia che comincia con il capo S: Antonio et finisce con il porto del' Spirito Sancto. La longitu$^{ne}$ comin$^a$ da l' isola di Pico d' Asores. D' America carta xvii.

" " " [116] Carta particolare che mostra il Capo buona Speranza con il mare uerso ponc$^{te}$ è con l' isole di Tristan d' Acunha è di Mart$^n$ Vaz. La longitudine comincia da l'isola di Pico d' Aasores. D' America carta xviii.

" " " [117] Carta particolare della Brasilia australe che comincia dal' por° del' Spir$^{to}$ Santo è finisce con il capo Bianco. La longitudi$^e$ cominc$^a$ da l' isola d' Asores. D'America carta xviiii.

" " " [118] Carta particolare dell' Rio della Plata che comincia con la costa in gra di 31 di lati$^{ne}$: australe, è finisce con il capo S: Andrea. La longitu$^{ne}$ comi$^{ca}$ da l' isola di Pico d' Asores. D' America carta xx.

" " " [119] Carta particolare che comincia con il capo S: Andrea è finiscie con il capo Matas d' America. La longitudine comincia da l' isola di Pico D' Asores. D'America carta xxi.

**Dudley,** *Sir* **R.**—Continued.

v. 3, bk. 6, no. [120] Carta particolare della costa di America australe che comincia al C: di Matas sin al C: di Galegos. La longitu[ne] cominc[n] da l'isola di Pico d' Asores. D' America ca[ta] xxii.

" " " [121] Carta particolare dello stretto di Magellano è di Maire. La longitudine comincia da l'isola di Pico d' Asores. D' America carta xxiii.

" " " [122] Carta particolare della costa di Chilue è di Chica è parte australe di Cili. La longitudine comincia da l' isola di Pico d' Asores. D' America carta xxiiii.

" " " [123] Carta particolare della cofta di Cili. La longitudine comincia da l' isola di Pico d' Asores. D' America carta xxv.

" " " [124] Carta particolare della costa del' Peru parte australe con parte di Cili. La longitud[ne] cominc[a] da l' isola di Pico d' Asores. D' America carta xxvi.

" " " [125] Carta particolare del' Peru che comincia con il' rio Pigua è finisce con il capo di Guanapo. La longitudine comincia da l' isola di Pico d'Asores. D'America carta xxvii.

" " " [126] Carta particolare del' Peru che comincia con il' capo di Guanapo è finisce con il c: S: Francesco. La longitudine comincia da l' isola di Pico d'Asores. D'America carta xxviii.

" " " [127] Carta particolare del' mare del' Zur che comincia con il capo S: Francesco nel' Peru è finisce con il' capo S: Lazaro nella nuoua Spagnia. La longitu[ne]. comic[a]. da l' isola di Pico d' Asores. D'America carta xxviiii.

" " " [128] Carta particolare dell' mare del' Zur che comincia con il' capo Lucas è finisce con Cagidos nella nuoua Spagnia, è la baia di Honduras. La longitu[ne]: cominc[a]: da l'isola di Pico d'Asores. Di America carta xxx.

" " " [129] Carta particolare della parte ocidentale della nuoua Spagnia, è della California. La longitudine comincia da l' isola di Pico d'Asores. D' America carta xxxi.

" " " [130] Carta particolare della America è parte maestrale dal C: di Cedros. La longitudine comincia da l' isola di Pico d'Asores. D'America carta xxxii.

" " " [131] Carta particolare dello stretto di Iezo fra l'America è l'isola Iezo. La longitudine comincia da l'isola di Pico d'Asores. D'America carta xxxiii.

## 1646–47

—— Another copy of v. 1–2 comprising bks. 1–4, in 1 v. 458

NOTE.—v. 1, bk. 1. Half title, title, fold. fac-simile, 6, [2], 7–10, [2], 11–26, [6] 27–56 pp., 26, [4] pl.

Fac-simile of patent dated 1620, issued by Ferdinand II, grand duke of Tuscany, confirming Dudley's use of the title of duke of Northumberland, follows general title.

Plate entitled: "Description d'vn navire royal . . . Se vend auec le liure au Haure de Grace chez Iacques Gruchet et a Paris chez Iollain" . . . follows p. 4. It is not in the other copies and is probably inserted here.

In this copy, some of the plates of bk. 1 have slips pasted over the numbers.
Plate entitled: Carte generalles de tous lef vens . . . a Paris, chez A. de Fer
. . . 1666," inserted after p. 56.
v. 1, bk. 2. 76 pp., [1] l., [15] maps, 12, [1] pl.
pls. numbered 1-6, [7], 8, 8, 10, [11-12], 3.
pls. 1, 2, 3 pasted on 1 l.
" 5, 6, [7] pasted on 1 l.
pl. 8 printed on 2 l.
" 9 wanting.
v. 2, bk. 3. Half title, title, 16 pp., [2] l., 17-48, [4], 49-55 pp., 8 pl.
Two leaves between pp. 16-17, contain printed naval formations as follows:
"Forma seconda dell' armata . . . car. 11;" "Figura 6;" "Forma seconda
dell' armata . . . car. 13;" "Forma seconda dell' armata . . . car 15;"
"Forma terza dell' armata . . . car. 13."
Of the six extra pages which in copy 1 follow p. 46, the first entitled:
"Aggivnta di tre altre fogge di sqvadre," is wanting, and the [4] pp. of
printed naval formations follow p. 48.
v. 2, bk. 4. 39 pp., [1] l., 19 pl.
pls. "Figura 2. lib°: 4," and "Fig$^{ra}$ 3 li° 4," pasted on 1 l. which follows p. 6.
pl. 5 imperfect; wants pointer.
In all other respects copy 2 of v. 1-2, is the same as copy 1.

## 1646-49

**Jansson, J.**

Ioannis Ianssonii novus atlas, sive theatrum orbis terrarum: in quo tabulæ & descriptiones omnium regionum totius univerfi accuratiffime exhibentur. 4 v. fol. Amstelodami, apud Ioannem Ianssonium, 1646-49. 459

NOTE.—Irregularly paged; Text on the reverse of the maps and upon leaves between them. The maps, by many authors, are brought together and re-ëngraved by the firm "Jansonius." Jan Jansson was originally in business with his brother-in-law, Hendrick Hondius. The three daughters of Jan Jansson married the three sons of Jean von Waesberg. These sons-in-law took the name Jansson. Two of them, Guillaume and Jean Jansson de Waesberg were booksellers. At the death of Hendrick Hondius in 1644 (or 1638?) the business was continued by Jan Jansson who associated with him his two sons-in-law under the firm name Jansonius.

The following maps relate to America:
v. 1, pt. 1, no. 1. Nova totivs terrarvm orbis geographica ac hydrographica tabvla.
" " " 2. Evropa.
v. 3, pt. 2, no. 1. Asia. 1641.
" " " 19. America noviter delineata. 1641.
" " " 20. America Septentrionalis.
" " " 21. Nova Belgica et Anglia Nova.
" " " 22. Nova Virginiæ tabvla.
" " " 23. Virginiæ partis australis, et Floridæ partis orientalis . . . nova descriptio.
" " " 24. Mappa Æstivarvm insularum.
" " " 25. Nova Hispania, et nova Galicia.
" " " 26. Insvlæ Americanæ in oceano Septentrionali . . .
" " " 27. Americæ pars Meridionalis.
" " " 28. Terra Firma et novum regnum Granatense et Popayan.

**Jansson, J.**—Continued.
v. 3, pt. 2, no. 29. Perv.
" " " 30. Venezuela, cum parte australi Novæ Andalusiæ.
" " " 31. Gviana siue Amazonvm regio.
" " " 32. Accuratissima Brasiliæ tabula.
" " " 33. Paragvay ó prov. de Rio de la Plata.
" " " 34. Chili.
" " " 35. Tabula Magellanica . . .

CONTENTS.

v. 1, pt. 1, eng. title (given above), 61 l. incl. 22 maps. 1649. The four leaves of text in front contain, "Introdvctio ad cosmographiam ejusque partes."
" " 2. Atlas novus sive theatrum orbis terrarum: in quo Germaniæ superioris & singularum ejus partium tabulæ geographicæ & descriptiones continentur. 1649. eng. title, 156 l. incl. 74 maps.
v. 2, pt. 1. Atlas . . . in qvo Galliæ, Helvetiæ, universæ & singulorum cantonum; nec non & Belgii universi, tabulæ geographicæ cum suis descriptionibus. 1649. eng. title, 128 l. incl. 62 maps.
" " 2. Atlas . . . in qvo Germaniæ inferioris & singularum ejus partium tabulæ geographicæ & descriptiones continentur. 1649. eng. title, 90 l. incl. 40 maps.
v. 3, pt. 1. Atlas . . . in quo Hispaniæ, Italiæ, Asiæ, Africæ, nec-non Americæ tabulæ & descriptiones luculentissimæ. 1649. eng. title, 189 l. incl. 68 maps.
" " 2. Atlas . . . in quo Asiæ, Africæ, & Americæ, regiones accuratè exhibentur. 1649. eng. title, 75 l. incl. 35 maps.
v. 4. Ioannis Ianssonii novus atlas, sive theatrum orbis terrarum: in quo Magna Britannia, seu Angliæ & Scotiæ nec non Hiberniæ, regna exhibentur. 1646. eng. title, 266 l. incl. 56 maps.

## 1648–58

**Blaeu, W. J.** *and* **Blaeu, J.**

Toonneel des aerdriicx, ofte nievwe atlas, dat is beschryving van alle landen; nu nieulycx uytgegeven. 6 v. fol. Amsterdami, apud Iohannem Guiljelmi F. Blaeu, 1648–58. 460

NOTE.—The present edition in 6 v. with dutch title and text has the same divisions and maps as the french editions with the following exceptions: v. 1, pt. 1, Europe (*i. e.* northern and eastern Europe), 1 map omitted; v. 2, pt. 2, Asia, 1 map omitted; v. 3, Italien, 1 map omitted, and 4 maps of Gt. Britain omitted; v. 4, Britannien, 3 maps omitted; v. 5, Schotlandt, 3 maps added. *cf.* Muller, Frederik. Catalogue of books.

Contains a great number of plates and maps, by various cartographers, beautifully engraved and colored, and ornamented with views, coats of arms, groups of allegorical figures, men and women in the dress of the time, and many other subjects illustrating the history or description of the country. The following maps relate to America:
v. 2, pt. 3, no. [29] Americæ nova tabula.
" " " [30] Insulæ Americanæ in oceano Septentrionali cum terris adiacentibus.
" " " [31] Nova Belgica et Anglia Nova.
" " " [32] Mappa Æstivarum infularum, alias Barmvdas dictarum. . .

v. 2, pt. 3, no. [33] Nova Virginiæ tabvla.
" " " [34] Virginiæ partis auſtralis, et Floridæ partis orientalis, interjacentiumq̄, regionum nova descriptio.
" " " [35] Nova Hispania, et Nova Galicia.
" " " [36] Terra Firma et novum regnum Granatense et Popayan.
" " " [37] Venezvela cum parte auſtrali Novæ Andalvsiæ.
" " " [38] Gviana siue Amazonvm regio.
" " " [39] Brasilia.
" " " [40] Paragvay, ó prov. de Rio de la Plata cum regionibus adiacentibus Tvcvman et S$^{ta}$. Crvz de la Sierra.
" " " [41] Tabvla Magellanica, quâ Tierræ del fuego, cum celeberrimis fretis a F. Megellano et I. Le Maire detectis novisſima descriptio exhibetur.
" " " [42] Chili.
" " " [43] Peru.

CONTENTS.

v. 1, pt. 1. Noord-Pool.—Europe (*i. e.* northern and eastern Europe)—Dvytslandt. 1649.
v. 1, pt. 2. Nederlandt. 1658.
v. 2, pt. 1. Het koningrÿck Vranckrÿck. 1658.
" " 2. Spanjen.--Asia.—America. 1658.
v. 3, Italien.—Griecken. 1658.
v. 4, Britannien. 1648.
v. 5, Schotlandt.—Yrland. 1654.
v. 6, Novvs atlas Sinensis a Martino Martinio.

**1651**

**Mercator, G.**
Atlas minor, das iſt: eine kurtze jedoch gründliche beſchreibung der gantzen welt, in zwey theile abgetheilet . . .   2 v. in 1. obl. 12°.   Amstelodami, ex officina Ioannis Ianssonii, 1651.   461

NOTE.—Collation: v. 1, 6 p. l., 460 (*i. e.* 468), [3] pp. incl., 114 maps; v. 2, 1 p. l., 428 (*i. e.* 436), [2] pp. incl. 101 maps. Engraved title, verso blank, p. l. [1].—Vorrede an den günſtigen leſer, verso p. l. [2]-recto p. l. [5].—Kurtze und nützliche unterrichtung . . . recto and verso p. l. [6].—Text incl. 114 maps, pp. 1-460.—Register, [3] pp.—Engraved title, verso blank.—Text incl. 101 maps, pp. 1-428.—Register, [2] pp.
Pagination irregular.
Of the 215 maps, 120 are the same as those in the 1628 latin edition, the others differ from those in the earlier editions.
Engraved title-page of v. 2 differs from that of v. 1.
The following maps relate to America:
v. 1, p.   3. Typus orbis terrarum.
v. 2, "  327. Tartaria.
"    "  331. China.
"    "  343. Insulæ Indiæ orientalis.
"    "  385. Americæ descriptio.
"    "  389. Virginia.
"    "  393. Hispaniæ Novæ nova descriptio.
"    "  397. Cvba insvla.—Hispaniola inſula.—Ins. Iamaica.—Ins. S. Ioannis.—I. S. Margareta.
"    "  401. America Meridionalis.

**Mercator, G.**—Continued.
v. 2, p. 407. Terra Firma cum novo regno Granatense et Popayan.
" " 411. Perv.
" " 417. Accuratissima Brasiliae tabula.
" " 421. Paragvay, ó prov. de Rio de la Plata cum regionibus adiacentibus Tvcvman et S<sup>ta</sup>. Crvs de la Sierra.
" " 423. Chili.
" " 427. Freti Magellanici ac novi freti vulgo Le Maire exactissima delineatio.

CONTENTS.

v. 1. Grofs Britannien.—Die Mitternåchtige lånder.—Teutfchland und Niederland.
v. 2. Franckreich.—Hispanien.—Italien.—Afia.—Africa und America.

### 1653
**Boissevin, L.**
Trésor des cartes géographiqves des principavx estatz de lvnivers. 38 numb. sheets, incl. 36 maps, 1 pl. 18°. Paris, L. Boiffeuin, 1653. 462

NOTE.—Bound at end of Isaac Du Mas de Fores' work entitled: La clef de la géographie générale ov sommaire discovrs de l'intelligence de la mappemonde droite. 1654.
The following maps relate to America:
3. Typus orbis terrarvm—Description de la terre vniverselle.
4. Pole arctiqve ou terres du Septentrion.
5. Nouuelle defcription de l'Evrope.
38. Nouuelle defcription de l' Amériqve.

### 1653
**Jansson, J.**
Nuevo atlas, o teatro de todo el mvndo de Juan Janssonio en el qual con gran cuydado . . . 4 v. fol. Amsterdam, J. Janssonio, 1653. 463

NOTE.—A translation into spanish of Jansson's Novus atlas, sive theatrum orbis terrarum. Amstelodami, 1640-50. *cf.* Sabin, Joseph. A dictionary of books relating to America. v. 9, p. 223.
Spanish title pasted over latin title.
In v. 3, section and map, El principado de Bearne, is duplicated.
Maps by various cartographers, including: Hondius, Flandro, Massa, Henneberger, Lubin, Magnus, Emmius, Gigas, Scultetus, Comenius, Lazius, Mercator, Secco, Lavaña, Jubrien, Fabert, Templeux, Sanson, Hardy, Du Val, Goulart, Sprecher von Berneck, Langren, Martini, Surhon, Pynacker, Metius, Freitag, and Wicheringe.
The following maps relate to America:
v. 1, no. [1] Nova totius terrarum orbis geographica ac hydrographica tabvla. Auct: Henr: Hondio.
v. 2, " [38] America noviter delineata.
" " [39] America Septentrionalis.
" " [40] Nova Belgica et Anglia Nova.
" " [41] Nova Virginiæ tabvla.
" " [42] Virginiæ partis auftralis, et Floridæ partis orientalis . . .
" " [43] Mappa Æstivarvm infularum . . .
" " [44] Nova Hispania et Nova Galicia.

v. 2, no. [45] Insulæ Americanæ . . .
"      "   [46] Americæ pars meridionalis.
"      "   [47] Terra Firma et novum regnum Granatense et Popayan.
"      "   [48] Perv.
"      "   [49] Venezuela, cum parte auftrali Novæ Andalusiæ.
"      "   [50] Gviana fiue Amazonvm regio.
"      "   [51] Accuratissima Brasiliæ tabula . . .
"      "   [52] Paragvay . . .
"      "   [53] Chili.
"      "   [54] Tabula Magellanica . . .

CONTENTS.

v. 1. Se proponen los mapas y defcripciones de todo el univerfo.
v. 2. En el qual se contienen los mapas, y defcripciones de España, Asia, Africa y America.
v. 3. En el qual se contienen los mapas, y defcripciones de Francia, Helvetia, y el Belgio, o Olanda.
v. 4. En el qual se contienen los mapas, y defcripciones de Italia, de la gran Bretaña, Ingalaterra, Escocia, e Irlanda.

**1656?**

**Colom, A.**
Zee-atlas, ofte water-wereldt. Inhoudende een korte beschryvinge van alle de bekende zee-kusten des aardtrycks. Nieuwelÿcks uyt-ghegheven. 2 p. l., 18 col. maps. fol. t'Amsterdam, in de lichtende Colom [1656?] 464

NOTE.—See title 480. Date on map entitled "Pascaarte nieuwelyx uytgegeven door Arnold Colom tot Amsterdam . . ."
The following maps relate to America:
no. [1] Werelt caarte.
" [13] Pas caerte van Brazil en Nieu Nederlandt van Cuorvo en Flores tot de Barbados.
" [14] Zuy der deel van America.
" [15] De Carybsche eylanden van de Barbados tot de bocht van Mexico.
" [16] Nieuwe Carybsche pascaart.
" [17] Pas caarte van Nieu Nederlandt.
" [18] Mar del Zur Hispanis Mare Pacificum.

**1657**

**Jansson, J.**
Atlantis majoris qvinta pars, orbem maritimum sev omnium marium totius orbis terrarum navigationibus hodierno tempore frequentatorum defcriptionem accuratiffimam continens. Editio secunda priori auctior. 2 p. l., 326 pp., 31 maps. fol. Amstelodami, apud Ioannem Ianssonium, 1657. 465

NOTE.—Jansson first published this, the fifth volume to his great atlas, in 1650.
The following maps relate to America:
no. 45. Nova et accurata Poli Arctici et tarrarum circum iacentium descriptio . . .
" 47. Mar del Nort.
" 55. Insvlarum Hispaniolæ et Cubæ cum infulis circumjacentibus accuratæ delineatio.

**Jansson, J.**—Continued.
  no. 57. Insvla S. Iuan de Puerto Rico Caribes; vel Canibalum Infulæ.
  " 59. Belgii Novi, Angliæ Novæ, et partis Virginiæ . . .
  " 61. Mar di Æthiopia . . .
  " 65. Capitaniarum de Phernambvca, Itamaraca, Paraiba, et Pio Grande . . ·
  " 74. Capitaniæ de Cirii et Parnambvco.
  " 99. Mar del Zvr Hispanis mare Pacificum.
  " 115. [Polvs Antarcticvs]
  " 141. Pafcaerte van Groen-landt.

### 1659
**Lubin, A.**
  Orbis Avgvstianvs siue conventvvm ordinis eremitarvm Sancti Avgvstini chorographica et topographica defcriptio . . .   3 p. l., 60 maps. obl. 12°. Parisiis, P. Bavdovyn, 1659.   **466**

  Note.—Engraved title.
  The following maps relate to America:
  no. 6. America.
  " 43. Mexicana.
  " 44. Pervana [*i. e.* Peru]
  " 45. Insvlarvm Philippinarvm.
  " 46. Mechoacanensis [*i. e.* Mechoacan]
  " 47. Qvitensis [*i. e.* Quito]
  " 48. Granatensis [*i. e.* Granada]
  " 49. Chilensis.
  " 50. Canariensis.

### 1660
**Nicolosi, G. B.**
  Dell' Hercole e studio geografico . . . Nel quale fi defcriue generalmente il globo terreftre fecondo l'effere, che riceuette dalla natura; secondo le formalità, che gli hà dato l'intendimento humano; & secondo il ripartimento dello ftato prefente, datoli dalla guerra, e dalla pace. Con vna prefatione, che ferue d'introduttione per l'intelligenza, ut ufo di queft' opera; vna tauola metodica de' capi del discorso; e due indici, vno de nomi antichi, e latini, e l'altro de' nomi moderni, fecondo la ortografia più vfata, ut riceuuta nelle prouincie, delle quali fi ragiona . . . 2 v. fol. Roma, V. Mascardi, 1660.   **467**

  Note.—Collation: v. 1, 12 p. l., 414, [39] pp; v. 2, 3 p. l., 8 maps on 46 l.
  Engraved half title to each volume.
  v. 2: In Roma, appresso l'avtore, 1660.
  Title heading author's description of atlas: Hercole Siciliano overo studio geografico di Gio-Battista Nicolosi.
  A latin edition of this work: "Hercules siculus sive studium geographicum, auctore Jo-Bapt. Nicolosi . . . 2 v. Rome, 1671," was published shortly after the death of the author, in the care of a nephew of the same name, who inserted a life of his uncle. *cf.* Société de géographie. Paris. 1863. Bulletin. 5th ser. v. 5, p. 342. See also title 482.
  The following maps relate to America:
  no. [16–19] Mexicvm. 4 sheets.
  " [20–23] Perv. 4 sheets.

## 1660—61
**Doncker, H.**
De zee-atlas ofte water-wæereld, vertoonende alle de zee-kusten van het bekende deel des aerd-bodems, met een generale beschrÿvinge van dien. Seer dienftigh voor alle schippers en stuurlieden; mitsgaders koop-lieden om op 't kantoor gebruykt te werden. Nieuwelÿks aldus uytgegeven.   2 p. l., 22 (*i. e.* 24) pp., 27 col. maps.   fol.   t'Amsterdam, H. Doncker, 1660–[1661]   468

NOTE.—Engraved title, colored.   Maps dated 1658, 1659, 1660, 1661.

CONTENTS.

no. [1] Nova totius terrarum orbis tabula auctore F. de Wit . . . 1660.
" [2] Pas-caert van Texel tot aen de Hoofden . . .
" [3] Pas caart van de Noort Zee . . . 1658.
" [4] Pas caart van de zee-cuften van Ruslant, Laplant, Finmarcken, Spitzbergen, en Nova-zemla . . . 1658.
" [5] De cuften van Noorwegen, Finmarken, Laplant, Spitzbergen, Ian Maÿen Eÿlandt, Yslandt, als mede Hitlandt, en een gedeelte van Schotlandt . . .
" [6] Pas-caerte van Groenlandt . . .
" [7] Pas-caart van de Ost Zee . . . 1658.
" [8] Pas-caart van't Canaal vertoonende int' geheel Engelandt, Schotlandt, Yrlandt . . . 1658.
" [9] Pas caart van de Canaal tuffchen Engeland en Vrancrÿck . . . 1661.
" [10] Paskaarte om achter Yrlant . . . 1658.
" [11] Pas caert van 't in komen van de Canaal . . . 1661.
" [12] Pas-caert van de bocht van Vranckrÿck . . . 1661.
" [13] Pas-caart van Hispangien . . . 1658.
" [14] Nieuwe pas-caart; vertoonende, hoemen uyt de Canaal, de cuften van Portugael, Barbarÿen de Canarifche en Vlaemfche eylanden befeylen zal . . . 1661.
" [15] Pas-caart van de Middelandsche zee . . . 1658.
" [16] De cuft van Barbaria . . .
" [17] Paskaart van Gvinea . . . 1659.
" [18] Pas caart van de zee-cuften van Angola en Cimbebas van rivier de Galion tot. c. de Bona Efperanca . . . 1659.
" [19] 't Wefter deel van Oost Indien . . . 1660.
" [20] 't Oofter deel van Oost Indien . . .
" [21–22] Pascaerte vande Caribische eylanden, vande Barbados tot aende bocht van Mexico . . . 1658.
" [23] Pasçaerte van Brazil en Niev Nederlandt van Corvo en Flores tot de Barbados . . .
" [24] Pas caert van Nieu Nederland, Virginia en Nieu Engelant . . . 1660.
" [25] Paskaert van Brasilia van Pernambuco tot C. de S. Antonio.
" [26] Paskaarte van 't zuÿdelijckste deel van America van Cabo St. Antonio, tot Caep de Hoorn en de inde Zuÿd Zee tot b. de Tongoÿ . . .
" [27] Pascaart vertoon ende de zee cuften van Chili, Peru, Hifpania Nova, Nova Granada en California . . .

## 1661
**Cellarius, A.**
Harmonia macrocosmica sev atlas universalis et novus, totius universi creati cosmographiam generalem, et novam exhibens. In quâ omnium totius mundi orbium harmonica conftructio, fecundum

**Cellarius, A.**—Continued.

diverfas diverforum authorum opiniones, ut et vranometria, feu totus orbis cœleftis, ac planetarum theoriæ, et terreftris globus, tàm planis et scenographicis iconibus, quàm defcriptionibus novis ab oculos ponuntur . . . col. engr. title, title, 6 l. 125, 219 pp., 58 l. incl. 29 maps 1 port. (front.) fol. Amstelodami, J. Janssonius, 1661. 469

> NOTE.—The maps following pages 8, 18, 22, 30, 74, 116, 140, 192, 200, 208 & 212 relate to America. All the maps are beautifully colored by hand.

## 1661

**Loon, J. van.**

Klaer lichtende noort-ster ofte zee atlas; waer in vertoont wordt de gelegentheydt van alle de zee-kuften des geheelen aerdtbodems. 1 p. l., 46 col. maps. fol. t' Amsterdam, by Ioannis van Loon . . . ofte by Gillis van Loon, 1661. 470

> NOTE.—Engraved title-page colored.
> First edition.
> The following maps relate to America:
> no. 1. Orbis terrarum nova et accuratissima tabula . . .
> " 2. Nova et accvratissima totius terrarvm orbis tabvla. Auctore Ioanne Blaev.
> " 3. Pas-caerte van Groenland . . .
> " 36. Pascaerte vande Zvyd-zee . . .
> " 37. Pascaerte van Nova Hispania, Perv en Chili . . .
> " 38. Pascaerte van straet van Magalaen . . .
> " 39. Pas caarte van Brasil . . .
> " 40. Pascaerte van 't weftlyckfte deel vande Spaense zee . . .
> " 41. Pascaerte van de cuft van Guaiana . . .
> " 42. Pascaarte vande vafte cuft en eylanden van West Indien . . .
> " 43. Mappa Æstivarvm infularum alias Barmvdas dictarum . . . Amstelodami, apud Ioannem Ianssonium.
> " 44. Pascaerte vande Caribes.
> " 45. Pas caerte van Niev-Nederland en de Engelsche Virginies . . .
> " 46. Pas caerte van Terra Nova, Nova Francia, Nieuw Engeland en de grote rivier van Canada . . .

## 1664–1665

**Blaeu, J.**

Grooten atlas, oft werelt-beschryving, in welcke 't aerdryck, de zee, en hemel, wort vertoont en beschreven. 9 v. fol. [Amsterdam, J. Blaev, 1664–1665] 471

> NOTE.—In describing the 1664–1665 edition, Tiele says that in all the copies he had examined, the first three volumes were of 1664, the 7th without year, the 8th of 1665, and the 9th of 1664. Of the remaining volumes, the 4th of 1646 or 1648 (the preface of 1647), the 5th of 1654 or 1662, the 6th of 1642 or without year. *cf.* Tiele, P. A. Nederlandsche bibliographie van land- en volkenkunde. pp. 35–36. The present copy exactly corresponds with this description, with v. 4, dated 1648, preface 1647; v. 5, 1662; v. 6, n. d.

In v. 1, the general title-page is preceded by engraved plate showing coat of arms, and followed by Aen den leser, 2 pp.; title, Aerkloots beschryving; engraved title, Geographia Blaviana; Voor-reden, 3 pp., dated september 1, 1664, and signed Joan Blaev; verse on new atlas, 1 p., signed J. V. Vondel; followed by title-page to first volume which gives imprint. All other volumes have title-page to volume but no general title-page.

Contains a very complete system of geography and topography, according to the knowledge of the period, together with a great number of maps and plates. The maps are by various cartographers, and are beautifully engraved and ornamented with views, coats of arms, groups of allegorical figures, men and women in the dress of the time, and many other subjects illustrating the history or description of the country.

Muller states that the text of this, the dutch edition, is somewhat abridged.

In v. 1, is found a set of plates illustrating Tycho Brahé's astronomical observatory and instruments. In this volume, Scandien, or Scandinavien, is described by Andreas Buraeus; Groot Polen.—Kleyn Polen, by Simon Starovolski; and Laplandt, by J. Messenius.

In v. 4, the maps and descriptions of England were taken from John Speed and William Camden.

In v. 5, the maps of Scotland were from the maps prepared by Timothy Pont, and purchased by sir John Scot of Scotstavet after Pont's death. At the request of Scot and Charles I, these maps were completed for Blaeu's atlas, by Robert Gordon, of Straloch, and his son James, and taken to Amsterdam in 1645, by Scot, to superintend their publication. They were not finally issued till 1654 when they appeared as Geographiac Bleauaniæ volumen sextem. Gordon also had the assistance of Buchanan. Many descriptions are from Camden, and the description of Galloway is credited to John Maclellan.

In v. 9, the Novus atlas Sinensis à Martino Martinio forms the second part. The following maps relate to America:

v. 1, pt. 1, p. 1. Nova et accvratissima totivs terrarvm orbis tabvla.
" " " 1a. Regiones svb Polo Arctico. Auctore Guiljelmo Blaeu.
v. 7, pt. 3 " 1. Americæ nova tabula. Auct. Guiljelmo Blaeuw.
" " " 3b. Extrema Americæ versvs boream, Terra Nova, Nova Francia, adjacentiaq.
" " " 4. Insvlæ Americanæ in Oceano Septentrionali, cum terris adiacentibus.
" " " 5b. Canibales insvlæ.
" " " 6. Nova Belgica et Anglia Nova.
" " " 7. Mappa Æstivarvm infularum, alias Barmvdas dictarum . . . Amstelodami, Guiljelm. Blaeuw excudet.
" " " 8. Nova Virginia tabvla. Ex officina Guiljelmi Blaeuw.
" " " 9. Virginia partis auftralis, et Floridæ partis orientalis interjacentiumq, regionum nova descriptio.
" " " 10. Nova Hispania et Nova Galicia. Guiljelmus Blaeuw excudit.
" . " " 12b. Yvcatan conventus iuridici Hispaniæ Nova pars occidentalis, et Gvatimala conventus ivridicvs.
" " " 13. Terra Firma et Novum Regnum Granatense et Popayan. Amftelodami Guiljelmus Blaeuw excudit.
" " " 15. Venezvela cum parte auftrali Novæ Andalvsiæ. Amstelodami, Guiljelmus Blaeuw excudit
" " " 19. Brasilia.
" " " 20b. Sinvs Omnium Sanctorv.
" " " 20e. Præfectura de ciriû vel Seregrippe del Rey cum Itâɼuáma.

**Blaeu, J.**—Continued.
   v. 7, pt. 3, p. 20d. Præfectura Paranambucæ pars borealis, una cum præfectura de Itâmaracâ.
   "  "  " 20c. Præfecturæ Paranambucæ pars meridionalis.
   "  "  " 20f. Præfecturæ de Paraiba, et Rio Grande.
   "  "  " 21. Paraquaria vulgo Paragvay. Cum adjacentibus.
   "  "  " 22. Tabvla Magellanica quâ Tierræ del fuego, cum celeberrimis fretis a F. Magellano et I. Le Maire detectis noviffima et accuratiffima descriptio exhibetur.
   "  "  " 23. Chili. Amftelodami Guiljelmus Blaeuw excudit.
   "  "  " 24. Perv. Amftelodami, Guiljelmus Blaeuw excudit.

CONTENTS.

   v. 1. Arctica. — Noorwegen. — Denemarcken. — Sweden. — Russien. — Polen 1664.
   " 2. Duytslandt met Switserlandt, en andere aengrensende landen. 1664.
   " 3. 't Konincklÿck Nederlandt, en 't Veerenighde.
   " 4. Engelandt. 1648.
   " 5. Schotlandt en Yrlandt. 1662.
   " 6. Vranckrijck.
   " 7. Italien met Griecken.
   " 8. Spanje.—Africa.—America. 1665.
   " 9. Asia, 't welck Sina behelst. 1664.

**1665**
**Doncker, H.**
   De zee-atlas of water-wærelt, vertoonende alle de zee-kusten van het bekende des aerd-bodens, met een generale befchrijvinge der felve: seer dienftigh voor schippers en stuur-lieden, mitsgaders koop-lieden om op 't kantoor gebruyckt te worden. Nieuwelÿcks aldus uytgegeben. 1 p. l., 13-24 pp., 32 col. maps. fol. Amsterdam, H. Doncker, 1665.    472

NOTE.—Engraved title, colored.
Text entitled: "Korte verklaringh der afdeelingh, geftaltenis, ende eigenschappen des aerdtbodems."
"Regifter der caerten van de zee atlas," at the end of text, gives 30 maps.

CONTENTS.

   no.   [1] Nova totius terrarum orbis tabula auctore F. de Wit. 1660.
   "   [2] Pas-kaart van Europa, . . . 1665.
   "   [3] Pas-caart van de Zuyder-zee . . . 1664.
   "   [4] Pas-caert van Texel tot aen de Hoofden . . .
   "   [5] Pas caart van de Noort zee . . . 1664.
   "   [6] Pas caart van de zee-cuften van Ruslant, Laplant, Finmarcken, Spitsbergen en Nova-zemla . . . 1664.
   "   [7] De cuften van Noorwegen, Finmarken, Laplanut, Spitsbergen, Ian Maÿen Eÿlandt, Yslandt, als mede Hitlandt, en een gedeelte van Schotlandt . . .
   "   [8] Pas-caerte van Groenlandt . . .
   "   [9] Pas-caart van de Oost zee . . . 1664.
   "   [10] Pas-caart van 't Canaal, vertoonende in 't geheel Engelant, Schotlant, Yrlant . . . 1665.

no. [11] Pas caart van de Canaal tuffchen Engeland en Vrancrÿck . . . 1661.
" [12] Paskaarte om achter Yrlant . . .
" [13] Pas caert van 't in komen van de Canael . . . 1661.
" [14] Pas-caert van de bocht van Vranckrÿck . . . 1661.
" [15] Pas-caart van Hispangien . . .
" [16] Nieuwe pas-caart; vertoonende, hoemen uyt de Canaal, de custen van Portugael, Barbarÿen, de Canarifche en Vlaemfche eylanden befeylen zal . . . 1661.
" [17] Paskaert van 't Westelycke deel der Middelandsche zee . . . 1664.
" [18] Pas kaert van 't Ooftelycke deel der Middelandsche zee . . . 1664.
" [19] De cuft van Barbaria . . .
" [19a] De cuft van Barbaryen van out Mamora tot C. Blanco.—De cuft van Barbaryen van C. Blanco tot C. de Geer . . .
" [19b] Canarifche eylanden Canaria, Tenerifa, Forteventura, etc. . . . 1664.
" [20] Paskaart van Gvinea . . .
" [21] Pascaart van de zee-cuften van Angola en Cimbebas van rivier de Galion tot c. de Bona efperanca . . . 1659.
" [22] 't Wester deel van Oost Indien . . . 1660.
" [23] 't Oofter deel van Oost Indien . . . 1664.
" [24–25] Pascaerte vande Caribische eylanden, vande Barbados tot aende bocht van Mexico . . . 1658.
" [26] Pascaerte van Brazil en Niev Nederlandt van Corvo en Flores tot de Barbados . . .
" [27] Pas caert van Nieu Nederland, Virginia en Nieu Engelant . . . 1660.
" [28] Paskaert van Brasilia van Pernambuco tot C. de S. Antonio . . .
" [29] Paskaarte van 't zuÿdelÿckfte deel van America van Cabo St. Antonio, tot Caep de Hoorn en de inde zuyd zee tot b. de Tongoÿ . . .
" [30] Pascaart vertoonende de zee cuften van Chili, Peru, Hispania Nova, Nova Granada en California . . .

**1666**

**Goos, P.**

De zee-atlas ofte water-weereld, waer in vertoont werden alle de zee-kusten van het bekende des aerd-bodems. Seer dienstigh voor alle heeren en kooplieden, als oock voor alle schippers en stuurlieden . . . 10 p. l., 41 maps. fol. Amsterdam, P. Goos, 1666. 473

Note.—Engraved title, colored. See also title 481a.
The maps are similar to those in edition without title except that these are not numbered in the lower right hand corner as are some in the other copy.
Map no. 32 differs in lettering from same map, no. 31, in other copy and omits engraver's name.
The following maps relate to America:
No. [ 1] Nieuwe werelt kaert.
" [30] Pascaerte van Groen-Landt.
" [31] Paskaert zÿnde de Noordelÿckste zeekuften van America van Groenland . . .
" [32] Pascaerte vande Vlaemfche, Soute en Caribefche Eylanden . . .
" [33] Pas caerte van Nieu Nederlandt en de Engelsche Virginies . . .
" [34] Pascaerte van de Zuÿdt en Noordt Revier in Nieu Nederlandt . . .

**Goos, P.**—Continued.
>no. [35] Pascaerte van West Indien . . .
>" [36] Pascaert vande Caribes Eylanden.
>" [37] Paskaart van Brasil . . .
>" [38] Paskaarte van het zudelÿckfte van America . . .
>" [39] Pascaerte van Nova Hispania, Chili, Perv, en Gvatimala.
>" [40] Paskaerte van Nova Granada en t' Eylandt California.
>" [41] Parcaerte vande Zvyd zee . . .

### 1666

[De zee- atlas ofte water-weereld, waer in vertoont werden alle de zeekusten van het bekende des aerd-bodems . . . Gesneden, gedruckt en uytgeg] 40 maps. fol. [t'Amsterdam, P. Goos, 1666] 474

>NOTE.—Lacks title, text and map of the world; 1666 on many of the maps.
>The following maps relate to America:
>no. [29] Pascaerte van Groen-Landt.
>" [30] Paskaert zÿnde de Noordelÿckste zeekuften van America van Groenland . . .
>" [31] Pascaerte van de vlaemfche, Soute en Caribesche Eylanden . . .
>" [32] Pas caerte van Nieu Nederlandt en de Engelfche Virginies . . .
>" [33] Paskaerte van de Zuÿdt en Nordt Rivier in Nieu Nederlandt.
>" [34] Pascaerte van West Indien.
>" [35] Pascaerte van de Caribes Eylanden.
>" [36] Paskaart van Brasil.
>" [37] Paskaarte van het zuydelÿckfte van America.
>" [38] Pascaerte van Nova Hispania, Chili, Perv en Gvatimala.
>" [39] Paskaerte van Nova Granada en t'eylandt California. Pascaerte van de Zvyd Zee.

### 1666

**Jansson, J.**

Joannis Janssonii atlas contractus, sive atlantis majoris compendium: in quo totum universum velut in theatro quam exactiffimis tabulis ante oculos ponitur, additifque regionum omnium descriptionibus accuratiffime illustratur. 2 v. fol. Amstelodami, apud Joannis Janssonii p. m. hæredes, 1666. 475

>NOTE.—Collation: v. 1, 7 p. l., [355] pp. incl. 84 maps, 1 pl; v. 2, 1 p. l., [355] pp. incl. 87 maps.
>Engraved titles; v. 1, signed J. Viffcher sculpsit. Date 1566, evidently a mistake.
>Many maps are same as in Mercator and Hondius atlas of 1633.
>Among the maps of America the one entitled, "Belgii Novi, Angæ Novæ et partis Virginiæ," after de Laet, and the two of Virginia, are the same as in Jansson's Atlas 1639.
>Maps are by various cartographers including: Henricus Hondius, Massa, Henneberger, Flandro, Emmius, Mellinger, Laurenberg, Palbitzke, Magnus, Comenius, Lazius, Mercator, Pynacker, Wicheringe, Metius, Freitag, Langren, Martini, Surhon, Templeux, Hardy, Samson, Sprecher á Berneck, Lavaña, Ortelius, van Loon, Genevensi.

The following maps relate to America:
v. 2, no. [70] America . . .
" " [71] America Septentrionalis.
" " [72] Belgii Novi, Angliæ Novæ, et partis Virginiæ novissima delineatio.
" " [73] Nova Virginiæ tabvla. Amftelodami, ex officina Henrici Hondii.
" " [74] Virginiæ partis auftralis et Floridæ partis orientalis . . .
" " [75] Nova Hispania et Nova Galicia.
" " [76] Terra Firma et Novum Regnum Granatense et Popayan.
" " [77] Insvlæ Americanæ in Oceano Septentrionale, cum terris adiacentibus.
" " [78] Mappa Æstivarvm infularum, alias Barmvdas dictarum . . .
" " [79] Americæ pars meridionalis.
" " [80] Venezuela, cum parte australi Novæ Andalusiæ.
" " [81] Gviana fiue Amazonvm regio.
" " [82] Perv.
" " [83] Chili.
" " [84] Tabula Magellanica, qua Tierræ del Fuego, cum celeberrimis fretis a F. Magellano et I. Le Maire detectis. Novissima et accuratissima defcriptio exhibetur.
" " [85] Paraguay ó prov. de Rio de La Plata cum regionibus adiacentibus Tvcvman et St<sup>a</sup>. Crvz de la Sierra.
" " [86] Accuratiffima Brasiliæ tabula.
" " [87] Polvs Antarcticvs.

## 1666

**Loon, J. van.**

Klaer-lichtende noort-star ofte zee-atlas; waer in vertoont wordt, de gelegentheydt van alle de zee-kuften des geheelen aerdt-bodems, nieuwelicks uyt-gegeven. 1 p. l., 47 col. maps. fol. t'Amsterdam, J. van Loon, 1666. 476

NOTE.—Title-page colored.
The following maps relate to America:
no. [1] Orbis terrarum nova et accuratissima tabula . . .
" [2] Noorder zeekuften van America van Groenland door de Straet Davis en Hudson tot aen Terra Neuf . . .
" [3] Groenland, Ysland, Straet. Davids en Ian Mayen eyland . . .
" [35] Oost-Indian met alle de eylanden daer onder gelegen van Cabo Comorin tot aen Iapan . . .
" [38] Nova Hispania, Perv en Chili . . .
" [39] Nova Granada, en t'eylandt California . . .
" [40] Straet van Magalaen . . .
" [41] Brasil van Rio Grande tot Rio de la Plata . . .
" [42] Pascaerte van't weftlyckste deel van de Spaense zee . .
" [43] Pascaerte van de cust van Guaiana . . .
" [44] Vafte cuft en eylanden van West Indien . . .
" [45] Caribes . . . Porte Rico . . . I. Spangnola . . .
" [46] Niev-Nederland en de Engelsche Virginies; van Cabo Cod tot Cabo Canrik.
" [47] Terra Nova, Nova Francia, Nieuw Engeland en de grote rivier van Canada . . .

## 1667

**Jollain, C.**

Trésor des cartes géographiqves des principavx estats de lvnivers. 1 p. l., 37 maps. obl. 16°. Paris, chez Jollain [1667]  477

> NOTE.—Engraved title. Map no. 9, "la France," wanting.
> Majority of the maps signed "Jollain excudit 1667."
> The following maps relate to America:
> no. 3. Typus orbis terrarvm description de la terre vniverselle.
> " 4. Pole arctiqve ou terre du septentrion.
> " 38. Nouuelle description de l Amériqve.

## 1667

**Ortelius, A.**

Theatro del mondo. Nel quale diftintamente fi dimoftrano, in tauole, tutte le prouincie, regni, & paefi del mondo. Con la defcrittione delle città, territorÿ, castelli, monti, mari, laghi, & fiumi; le popolationi, i coftumi, le ricchezze, & ogn' altra particolarità. Ridotto à intiera perfectione, & in quefta picciol forma, per maggior commodità de' viaggianti. Con la tavola delle cose piv degne, che nell' opera fi contengono. Al l'illvstrissimo signor Pietro Qverini nobile Veneto. 4 p. l., 232, [15] pp. incl. 108 maps. 24°. Venetia, per Scipion Banca, 1667.  478

> NOTE.—Collation: 4 l. unsig.—sig. A-I, K-P in eights, Q in four.
> L. [1] recto: Theatro del mondo; verso blank.—l. [2] recto: title; verso: blank.—l. [3] recto–verso: Illvstrissimo signor mio, signor, e patron colendiss. (signed: Scipion Banca).—l. [4] recto–verso: Lo stampatore al benigno lettore.—sig. A recto–P4 verso: Theatro del mondo, inc. 108 maps.—sig. [P5] recto–[Q4] recto: Tavola delli nomi et particolarità contenute nella presente opera.—[Q4] verso: blank.
> Maps are on the verso of the leaves; letterpress on the recto.
> The maps of Asia and America have been pasted on pages 8 and 12.
> The following maps relate to America:
> p. 4. Typvs orbis terrarvm.
> " 6. Evropa.
> " 10. Africae tabvla nova.
> " 12. Americae sive novi orbis nova descriptio.
> " 204. Septentrionalivm regionvm descriptio.
> " 208. Tartariae sive Magni chami regne tipvs.
> " 212. Indiae orientalis insvlarvmqve adiacientivm tiipvs.

## 1667

**Blaeu, J.**

Le grand atlas, ov cosmographie Blaviane, en laquelle est exactement descritte la terre, la mer, et le ciel. 12 v. fol. [A Amsterdam, J. Blaeu, 1667]  479

> NOTE.—A very elaborate edition containing descriptions of all the countries of the known world and numerous beautifully engraved, colored maps by various cartographers. With some alterations the same as the latin edition. All volumes have title-page to volume giving imprint and date, v. 1, alone containing the general title. Excepting v. 2, 3, 8, 12, all volumes have engraved colored half titles.

In v. 1, there appears a description of the astronomical observatory of Tycho Brahé at Hven, illustrated with 15 plates. The description of "Danemarqve" is translated from the latin of Jean Isaac Pontan.

In v. 2, the description of "Scandinavie" is from the latin of André Buraeus; description of "Suede" by Buraeus; also of "Suede" and "Lappie" by J. Messenius; general description of "Pologne" from the latin of Salomon Nevgebavere; of "Grand Pologne" and of "Pologne Minevre," from the latin of Simon Starovolsci; and of "Flevve Borysthene" from the french of Guillaume le Vasseur.

In v. 3, the description of "Silesie" is from Nicolas Henelius.

In v. 4, the description of the "Fortresse di Santflite &c." is from Hugo Grotius.

For note on v. 5-6, see note on v. 4-5, Blaeu's Grooten atlas, 1664-1665.

In v. 10, Espagne, 7 fine plates of the Escurial are included.

In v. 11, Asia, the "Novus Sinensis à Martino Martinio . . ." forms the second part, together with "Addition dv royavme de Catay par Jacqves Gool."

In v. 12, America, there appear 23 maps with 309, [2] pp. of descriptive text. The first map, "Americæ nova tabula. Auct. Guiljelmo Blaeuw," is ornamented with 9 views of cities and 10 illustrations of the natives.

The following maps relate to America:

v. 1, pt. 1, p. j. Nova et accvratissima totius terrarvm orbis tabvla . . .
" " " 1. Regiones sub Polo Artico. Auctore Guiljelmo Blaeu.
v. 12, p. j. Americæ nova tabula. Auct. Guiljelmo Blaeuw.
" " 1. Extrema Americæ versus boream, ubi Terra Nova, Nova Francia, adjacentiaq̨.
" " 17. Nova Belgica et Anglia Nova.
" " 21. Nova Virginiæ tabvla. Ex officina Guiljelma Blaeuw.
" " 25. Virginiæ partis auſtralis, et Floridæ partis orientalis, interjacentiumq̨ regionum nova descriptio.
" " 29. Nova Hispania et Nova Galicia. Guiljelmus Blaeuw excudit.
" " 63. Yvcatan conventus iuridici Hispaniæ Novæ pars occidentalis, et Gvatimala conventvs ivridicvs.
" " 83. Insvlæ Americanæ in Oceano Septentriuuali, cum terris adiacentibus . . .
" " 95. Canibales insvlæ.
" " 99. Mappa Æstivarvm inſularum, alias Barmvdas dictarum . . . Amstelodami Guiljelm. Blaeuw excudit.
" " 103. Terra Firma et Novum Regnum Granatense et Popayan. Amſtelodami Guiljelmus Blaeuw excudit.
" " 135. Perv. Amſtelodami, Guiljelmus Blaeuw excudit.
" " 191. Chili. Amſtelodami Guiljelmus Blaeuw excudit.
" " 199. Tabvla Magellanica, quâ Tierræ del fuego, cum celeberrimis fretis a F. Magellano et I. Le Maire detectis noviſſima et accuratiſſima descriptio exhibetur.
" " 211. Paraqvaria vulgo Paragvay. Cum adjacentibus.
" " 225. Brasilia.
" " 257. Sinvs Omnium Sanctorv.
" " 259. Præfectura de Cirliû vel Seregrippe del Rey cum Itâpuáma.
" " 261. Præfecturæ Paranambucæ pars borealis, una cum præfectura de Itâmaracâ.
" " [262a] Præfecturæ Paranambucæ pars meridionalis.
" " 263. Præfecturæ de Paraiba, et Rio Grande.
" " 277. Gviana siue Amazonvm regio. Amstelodami Guiljelmus Blaeuw excudit.
" " 299. Venezvela, cum parte auſtrali Novæ Andalvsiæ. Amstelodami, Guiljelmus Blaeuw excudit.

**Blaeu, J.**—Continued.

CONTENTS.

v. 1. Arctiqve.—Norvege.—Danemarqve.
" 2. Scandinavie.—Russie.—Pologne.—Regions orientales av delà de l'Alemagne pres le Danvbe.—Grece.
" 3. Alemagne.
" 4. Belgique royale.—Belgique confédérée.
" 5. Angleterre.
" 6. Escosse.—Yrlande.
" 7. France.
" 8. " Suisse.
" 9. Italie.
" 10. Espagne.—Afriqve.
" 11. Asie.
" 12. Ameriqve.

### 1669

**Colom, J.**

Atlas maritimo o mundo aquatico, o qual conteimhua breve descripsao. De todas as conoçidas costas maritimas da terra. Novamenta facado aluz.   4 p. l., 52 maps.   fol.   Amsterdam, insignia da Colonna Ardente, 1669.   480

NOTE.—First title engraved and colored. Maps also by Arnold Colom, Jacob Aertsz Colom, and Dirck Davidſz.
Contains second title-page without date, reading exactly same as first, with Arnold Colom instead of Jacob as author. See title 464.
The following maps relate to America:
no. 1. Nova totivs terrarvm orbis geographica ac hydrographica tabvla . . .
" 42. Pas caerte van Groenland . . .
" 43. Paskaert van de Noordelijckſte kuſte van America . . . 1668.
" 44. Pas caerte van Terra Nova, Nova Francia, Nieuw Engelandt en de grote rivier van Canada . . .
" 45. Pas-caarte van de vlaemſe, en Groeneylanden, tot de Caribſe eylanden, mitsgaders de zeecusten vant vaste lant . . .
" 48. [Virginia, Nieu Nederlant, Nieu Englant]
" 49. De eylanden ende vaſtelanden van Weſtindien op de Noordzee.
" 50. [Las islas de los Caribes, con mucha dilatacion]
" 51. Zuyder deel van America uytgegeven door Arnold Colom.
" 52. Mar del Zur Hispanis Mare Pacificum.   Arnold Colom.

### 1670

**Du Val, P.**

Le monde ov la géographie vniverselle, contenant les descriptions, les cartes & le blaſon des principaux païs du monde . . .   2 v.   24°.   Paris, l'auteur, N. Pepingue, 1670.   481

NOTE.—Paged continuously.
Engraved title to each volume.

CONTENTS.

v. 1. [America, Africa, Asia]   5 p. l., 336 pp., 51 maps.
v. 2. [Europe]   3 p. l., 337–650 pp., 31 maps.

The following maps relate to America:
v. 1. no. [ 1] Le monde en planisphere . . .
" " [ 2] Terres arctiqves.
" " [ 4] Terres antartiqves.
" " [ 5] Amériqve . . .
" " [ 6] Canada.
" " [ 7] Carte de la Virginie . . .
" " [ 8] La Floride . . .
" " [ 9] Novveav Méxiqve.
" " [10] Méxiqve ou N$^{le}$ Espagne.
" " [11] Isles Antilles.
" " [12] Castille d'Or.
" " [13] La Gviane ou France éqvinoctiale.
" " [14] Pérov.
" " [15] Chili.
" " [16] Magellaniqve.
" " [17] Tvcvman.
" " [18] La Plata.
" " [19] Brésil.

**1670**

**Goos, P.**

The sea-atlas or the watter-world, wherein defcribed all the sea coasts of the knowne world. Very ufefull and neceffary for all shipmafters, pilots . . .   1 p. l., [7] pp., 20 maps. fol. Amsterdam, P. Goos, 1670. 481a

NOTE.—Engraved title. See title 473.
"A short declaration of the divifion, fituation, & qualities of the earth" in english; map of the world in latin, with latin and dutch titles, and border illustrations. The other maps are in dutch.
Several maps dated 1669.
The following maps relate to America:
no. [ 1] Nieuwe wereit kaert.—Orbis terrarvm nova . . . tabvla.
" [14] Pafcaerte vande vlaemfche, soute en caribefche eylanden, als mede Terra Nova, en de cuften van Nova Francia. Abraham Deur fecit.
" [15] Pas-caerte van Nieu Nederlandt en de engelfche Virginies.
" [16] Pascaerte van Westindien, de vafte kuften en de eylanden.
" [17] Pafcaert vande Caribes eylanden.

**1670-1671**

**Nicolosi, G. B.**

Hercvles, Sicvlvs sive stvdivm geographicvm . . .   2 v.   fol. Romae, typis M. Herculis, 1670-1671. 482

NOTE.—Collation: v. 1, 2 p. l., [65], 371, [45] pp.; v. 2, 2 p. l., 7 maps on 44 l. Engraved half-titles.
Second latin edition. See title 467 with note.
Though the title-page of v. 1 is dated 1670, the dedication is dated 1671, and at the end of the volume the following is found:
Romae in Ædibus Bvghesianis penes auctorem. 1671.
The following maps relate to America:
v. 2, no. [2] Continendem noviter.
" " [15-18] Mexicvm.
" " [19-22] Perv.

## 1671

**Goos, P.**

Le grand & nouveau miroir ou flambeau, de la mer contenant la defcription de toutes les coftes marines occidentalles & septentrionnalles, defmonstrant en plufieurs cartes tres néceffaire tous les ports, fleuves, bayes rades, profondeurs & bancs chafcun très exactement couché selon leur vraye hauteur pollaire, & pourveu des defcouvrements des terres principales, & à quel cours & diftance elles font fituées les unes des autres. Jamais parcidevant fi clairement mis en lumiere & outre ce augmenté & amandé pour le bien & utilité de tous mariniers & navigateurs. Recueilly des recherches de divers experimantez pilotes & amateurs de la navigation. Avec une tres belle & neceffaire inftruction de l'art de la navigation & auffi pourveu d'almanachs jufques en l'an 1676. Traduict de flaman en françois par Paul Yvounet.   21 p. l., 224 (*i. e.* 124) pp., 33 sheet maps, 2 maps in text.   fol.   A Amsterdam, P. Goos, 1671.   483

> NOTE.—Engraved title. No american maps.
> In four books with continuous pagination.

## 1675?

**Sanson, N.** *d'Abbeville,* **Sanson, G.,** *and* **Sanson, N.,** *fils.*

[Géographie universelle]   2 p. l. (ms.), 76 col. ms. l., 35 eng. l., 44 maps.   fol.   [Paris, 1675?]   484

> NOTE.—No title-page. Cover-title.
> Compiled for "Monseigneur le Dauphin" by "le très humble, très obéissant et très fidèle seruiteur et sujet Fathanaze de Sainct Charles" . . . from "Cartes générales de la géographie ancienne et nouvelle . . . Pars les s<sup>rs</sup> Sanson . . . Paris, 1675," from which all the maps are taken, with the exception of: Mappe monde;—Natvlia quae olim Asia Minor;—Gouvernement général d'Orleans.
> Ms. dedication and tables with colored lettering.
> Maps dated from 1647–1674 (Flanders)
> Original binding bearing the arms of the dauphin of France.
> The following maps relate to America:
> no. [1] Mappe-monde.
> " [43] Amérique Septentrionale.
> " [44] Amérique Méridionale.

## 1675?

**Wit, F. de.**

Atlas. [Zeekaerten]   1 p. l., 27 maps.   fol.   Tot Amsterdam, bij Frederick de Wit in de Calverstraet bij den Dam inde Witte Paskaert [1675?]   485

> NOTE.—Engraved title.
> Index on verso of title-page has heading: Tabulæ maritimæ, ofte zeekaerten.
> Map. no. 1, Orbis maritimus, called for by index, is engraved on the title-page.
> The following maps relate to America.
> nc. 20. Poli Arctici, et circumiacentium terrarum descriptio novissima.
> " 21. Magnum Mare del Zur cum infula California.

no. 22. Septemtrionaliora Americæ à Groenlandia per Freta Davidis et Hudfon, ad Terram Novam.
" 23. Novæ Hispaniæ, Chilie, Peruviæ et Guatimalæ littoræ.
" 24. Pafcaert van Westindien ende Caribise eylanden.
" 25. Terra Nova ac maris tractus circa Novam Franciam, Angliam, Belgium, Venezuelam Novam Andalusiam, Guianam, et Brasiliam.
" 26. Littora Brasiliæ.
" 27. Tractus australior Americæ meridionalis, a Rio de la Plata per Fretum Magellanicum ad Toraltum.

## 1675

**Sanson, N.**, *d'Abbeville*, **Sanson, G.**, *and* **Sanson, N.** *fils*.

Cartes générales de la géographie ancienne et nouvelle, ou les empires monarchies, royaumes, estats, repvbliqves et pevples tant anciens que nouveaux, de toutes les parties du monde, font exactement remarqués & diftingués fuivant leur eftenduë & fubdivisés en leurs régions particulières, ou provinces. 2 v. in 1. fol. Paris, l'auteur et P. Mariette, 1675. 486

Note.—Collation: v. 1; 2 p. l., 34 maps; v. 2: 1 p. l., 130 maps.
Maps have dates 1632, 1641, 1643, 1647, 1648, 1650–1670, 1672, 1674.
v. 1 contains ms. "Liste des cartes," 1 l.
The following maps relate to America:
no. [1] L'hydrographie . . . 1652.
" [2] Harmonie ou correspondance du globe.
" [22] Amérique Septentrionale . . . Par G. Sanson . . . 1669.
" [23] Le Canada, ou Nouvelle France, &c. Par N. Sanson . . . 1656.
" [24] Le Nouveau Méxique, et la Floride . . . Par N. Sanson . . . 1656.
" [25] Méxicque, ou Nouvelle Espagne . . . Par N. Sanson . . . 1656.
" [26] Les îsles Antilles . . . Par N. Sanson . . . 1656.
" [27] Amérique Méridionale. Par N. Sanson . . . 1669.
" [28] Terre Ferme . . . Par N. Sanson . . . 1656.
" [29] Partie de Terre Ferme ou font Gviane et Caribane . . . Par N. Sanson . . . 1656.
" [30] Le Pérou . . . Par N. Sanson. . . . 1656.
" [31] Le Chile . . . Par G. Sanson . . . 1669.
" [32] Le Brésil . . . Par N. Sanson . . . 1656.
" [33] Le Paraguay . . . Par G. Sanson . . . 1668.
" [34] La Terre et îsles Magellaniques . . . 1668.
" [35] Les deux poles . . . Par N. Sanson . . . 1657.

## 1675

**Seller, J.**

Atlas maritimus, or the sea-atlas; being a book of maritime charts. Describing the sea-coasts, capes, headlands, sands, shoals, rocks and dangers . . . in most of the known parts of the world . . . 3 p. l., 12 pp., 1 l., 49 col. charts. fol. London, J. Darby, for the author, 1675. 487

Note.—Engraved title. The leaf mentioned in the collation gives "A catalogue of mathematical instruments, made and sold by John Seller," and "A catalogue of mathematical books, maritime charts, draughts, etc." The engraved title contains portraits of sir Francis Drake and mr. Tho. Candish.

**Seller, J.**—Continued.

The following maps bear dates later than 1675:
no. 3. Schema solis ad ingressum mercurij S$^{tæ}$ Helenæ, anno 1677 octob 28 9$^{h}$ 26. 40″ A. M.
" 9. A mapp of the regions & countreyes vnder and a bout the North Pole . . . 1676.
" 26. A mapp containing the island & kingdome of Sicily . . . London, a? 1676.

Maps engraved by: James Clark; Sa. Moore; Ia. Bennett; Francis Lamb; W. Hollar; Io. Oliver.

Plans of Tangier, Messina, Naples, Tripoli and view of New York city are insets to various charts.

no. [32] A new mapp of the island of Saint Hellena . . .

The following charts relate to America:
no. [1] Novissima totius terrarum orbis tabula.
" [9] A mapp of the regions & countreyes vnder and a bout [!] the North Pole. 1676.
" [37] A chart of the north part of America.
" [38] A general chart of the West India's [!]
" [39] A chart of the Western ocean.
" [40] A chart of the West Indie's [!]
" [41] A chart of the coaſt of America.
" [42] A mapp of New England.
" [43] A chart of the sea coaſts of New England, New-Jarsey, Virginia, Maryland, and Carolina.
" [44] A mapp of New Jarsey.—Inset: [view of New York city]
" [45] A chart of the Caribe islands.
" [46] Noviſſima et accuratiſſima insulæ Jamaicæ descriptio.
" [47] The Windward paſage from Jamaica betwene the eaſt end of Cuba and the weſt end of Hispaniola.
" [48] A chart of the sea coaſt of Brazil.
" [49] A chart of the South-sea.

## 1676

**Speed, J.**

The theatre of the empire of Great Britain, presenting an exact geography of the kingdom of England, Scotland, Ireland, and the isles adjoyning . . . Together with a prospect of the most famous parts of the world, viz: Asia, Africa, Europe, America . . . New ed. . . . 5 pts. in 1 v.; 7 p. l., [219] pp., 4 l., 96 maps. fol. London, for T. Basset & R. Chiswel, 1676. 488

NOTE.—Earlier editions as follows: 1st, 1611; 2d., 1614; 3d., 1627 with title: A prospect of the most famous parts of the world . . . Edition of 1676 has many additions: maps of India, Russia, Palestine and 4 maps of the "king's dominions [American] abroad" with descriptive text. Dedicated to James, king of Great Britain, France and Ireland.

Manuscript annotations, illustrated clippings pasted on maps and hand coloring of many, make this a very unique copy.

Each part has a special title: pt. 1, The theatre of Great Britain . . . pt. 2, . . . containing, the principality of Wales . . . pt. 3, . . . Containing a general view of the kingdom of Scotland . . . pt. 4, Containing, the kingdom of Ireland . . . pt. 5, A prospect of the most famous parts.

Maps are ornamented with the arms of the country and of the nobility, and have border illustrations of figures in national costumes and of views of cities. Many maps have, also, plans of cities, views of castles, cathedrals and other interesting features;—pt. 1, no. 13, Wilshire, with inset showing the druidical monuments at Stonehenge, and inscriptions.
Maps engraved by F. Lamb, A. Goos, D. Grijp, I. Hondius, Corn. Danckertsz and E. Sijmons z. Hamers veldt.
See also title 442.
The following maps relate to America:
pt. 5, no. [1] A new and accvrat map of the world ,. . 1651.
" " " [2] Asia with the iflands adioyning . . . 1626. A. Goos, sculps.
" " " [5] America with thofe known parts in that unknowne worlde both people and manner of buildings . . . 1626. A. Goos, Amstelodaminfis fculpfit.
" " " [19] The kingdome of China . . . 1626 [Part of n. w. coast of America]
" " " [20] A newe mape of Tartary . . . [1626] D. Grijp, sculp. [Part of n. w. coast of America]
" " " [21] A mapp of the Sommer ilands once called the Bermudas . . . Abraham Goos, sculpsit.
" " " [22] A map of Virginia and Maryland. F. Lamb sculp.
" " " [23] A map of New England and New York. F. Lamb sculp.
" " " [24] A map of Jamaica.—Barbados.
" " " [25] A new description of Carolina. Francis Lamb, fculp.
" " " [26] A new map of East India. F. Lamb sculp. [Philippine islands]

**1679**

**Ortelius, A.**

Theatro del mondo. Nel quale fi dà notitia diftinta di tutte le prouincie, regni, & paefi del mondo. Con la defcrittione delle città, territorij, castelli . . . Ridotto à intiera perfettione, & in quefta piciol forma, per maggior commodità de' viaggianti. 1 p. l., 5–255 pp., 4 fold. maps. 24°. Venetia, preffo Stefano Curti, 1679.

489

NOTE.—Collation: A–I, K–Q in eights.
sig. [A1] blank l. sig. [A2] recto: title, verso: blank. sig. A3 recto–verso: Lettore. sig. A4 recto–[P8] recto: Theatro del mondo incl. 4 fold. maps. sig. [P8] verso–[Q8] recto: Tavola delli nomi, et particolarità contenute nella presente opera. sig. [Q8] verso: blank.
The following maps relate to America:
no. [1] Evropa.
" [2] Asia.
" [3] Africa.
" [4] America.

**1679**

**Seller, J.**

Atlas minimus or, a book of geography shewing all the empires, monarchies, kingdomes, regions, dominions, principalities and countries in the whole world . . . 1 p. l., front., [52] l., 53 maps. 32°. [London, J. Seller, 1679] 490

NOTE.—Mentioned in "A catalogue of books. Continued, printed and published at London in easter-term, 1679," numb. 19, column 5; also in "A

**Seller, J.**—Continued.
　catalogue of mathematical books . . . made and sold by John Seller," found in his Atlas maritimus, 1675, probably inserted and of a later date.
　The following maps relate to America:
　no. [1] A mapp of all the world . . .
　" [42] America.
　" [43] The English empire in America.
　" [44] Brazil.
　" [45] Terra Firma.
　" [46] New Mexico.
　" [47] Paragua.
　" [48] The chief islands of y$^e$ Antilles and Lucayes.
　" [49] Canada or New France.
　" [50] Florida.
　" [51] Mexico or new Spain.
　" [52] . . . South America.
　" [53] the [!] artick [!] pole.

## 1682
**Alphen, P. van**
　Nieuwe zee-atlas ofte water-werelt waer in vertoont word alle d . . . zelfs bekende zee-kuſte, gelegt op haer lengte en breete volgens de ronde globe. Zeer dienſtig voor schippers, en stuurluiden, koopluiden, en liefhebbers van de schipvaert, nieuwlÿks uitgegeve.　8 p. l., 14 maps. fol. tot Rotterdam, door Pieter van Alphen, 1682.　491

　NOTE.—This title pasted over the following in the center of the engraved title: De vyerighe colom, waer door de zeen en cuſten van de Noordſche, ooſtersche en weſtersche schipvaert claer verlichtet en de feylen en miſſlagen van't voorgaende licht, of spiegel der zee naecktelÿck verthoont en verbetert werden . . . door Iacob Aertsz. Colom . . . t' Amsterdam, bÿ Iacob Aertsz Colom, 1661.
　The date of the pasted title appears to be 1682 but the 2 has been altered by pen to 1.
　This copy contains only 14 of the 45 maps listed in the table of contents which may possibly belong to "De vyerighe colom . . . 1661". These maps were evidently only collected and published with a new title by Pieter van Alphen in Rotterdam. On each the original imprint has been erased and van Alphen's substituted.
　Map no. 1, "Nova totius terrarum orbis geographica ac hydrographica tabula," is similar to that in Jacob Colom's "Atlas maritimo," Amsterdam 1669, which is the earliest edition of his atlas in this library. It is probable that these maps were published by Colom in an earlier work.

CONTENTS.

　no. [ 1] Nova totius terrarum orbis geographica ac hydrographica tabula. Tot Rotterdam bÿ Pieter van Alphen.
　" [ 2] Paskaart vande zeekuſten van Rvslant, Laplant, Finmarcken, Spitzbergen en Nova Zemla. Nu nieulijcx utgegeven. Tot Rotterdam door Pieter van Alphen.
　" [ 3] Nieuwe waſsende graade paskaert, van'x texel tot yslant en Spitsbergen. Nieuwelÿcks beſchreven. 't Rotterdam, by Pieter van Alphen.

no. [ 4] Paskaart van de Oost-Zee . . . Nu nieuliex uytgegeven. Tot Rotterdam door Pieter van Alphen.
" [ 5] Pascaarte vande Zuijderzee Vlieftroom, Vlie, en Amelandergat. 't Amsterdam, bÿ Jacob Aertfz. Colom op't water.
" [ 6] Paskaart van de Noort-Zee . . . Nu nieuwelicx uytgegeven. Tot Rotterdam door Pieter van Alphen.
" [ 7] Laskaart vant Canaal . . . Nu neuwelicx uytgegeuen. Tot Rotterdam, door Pieter van Alphen.
" [ 8] Nieuwe waffende grade paskaart van't Texel, tot de straat van Gibralter. Nieuwelÿcks befchreven. t' Rotterdam, by Pieter van Alphen.
" [ 9] Middellantfche zee van t' Nauw tot Alexandretta . . . t',Amsterdam Hendrick Doncker . . .
" [10] Nieuwe waffende grade paskaart van Capo S. Vincent, tot Cape Verde. Nieuwelycks befchreven t' Rotterdam, by Pieter van Alphen.
" [11] Nieuwe waffende graade paskaert van Efpanola tot Terranuef. t' Rotterdam by Pieter van Alphen.
" [12] Nieuwe waffende graade paskaert van Efpanola tot straet van Magalaen. t' Rotterdam, door Pieter van Alphen . . .
" [13] Nieuwe waffende grade paskaart van Capo Verde tot Capo de Boâ Efperanca. Nieuwelycks, befchreven. 't Rotterdam, by Pieter Alphen.
" [14] Nieuwe waffende graade paskaert, van C. de Bona Esperanca tot C. Comori. Nieuwelijcks befchreven. 't Rotterdam, by Pieter van Alphen.

## 1683
**Ortelius, A.**

Theatro del mondo. Nel quale fi dà notitia diftinta di tutte le prouincie, regni, & paefi del mondo . . . Ridotto à intiera perfettione, & in quefta picciol forma, per maggior commodità de' viaggianti. Con la tauola delle cose più degne, che nell' opera si contengono.  258 pp., 1 map. 24°. Venetia, presso Steffano Curti, 1683. 492

NOTE.—Collation: A-I, K-Q in eights.
sig. [A1] recto: half-title, Theatro del mondo, verso, blank. sig. [A2] recto: title; verso, blank. sig. A3 recto–verso: Lettore. sig. A4 recto–[P8] verso: Theatro del mondo. sig. Q1 recto–[Q8] recto: Tavola delli nomi, et particolarità contenute nella presente opera; verso, blank.
Map of "Africa" is found between pp. 16 & 17.
Imperfect: wanting maps of Europe, Asia, America.

## 1683
**Robijn, J.**

Zee, zea—atlas—aquatique, del mar. 7 p. l., 41 col. maps. fol. t' Amsterdam, J. Robÿn, 1683. 493

NOTE.—Engraved title, colored. P. Schenk sculp. G. van Houten, fec.
These maps appear to be based upon those of Goos in his Zee-atlas, 1666, but with the exception of the following they are not identical: no. 3. Nieuwe werelt kaert uÿt gegeven tot Amsteldam bÿ Pieter Goos. no. 9. Pascaarte vande Zuyder-zee . . . Bÿ Pieter Goos. no. 31. Noordooft cuft van Asia, van lapan tot Nova Zemla. no. 35. Pas caerte van Nieu Nederlandt en de Englesche Virginies . . . no. 39. Pa kaart van Brasil . . . no. 40. Paskaar-

**Robijn, J.**—Continued.
    te van het zuydelijckſte van America . . . 1666. nos. 31, 35, 39, 40 are not signed but are contained in the zee-atlas. no. 30. "De golf van Bengala" is by Hendrick Doncker.
    The following maps relate to America:
    no. 2. Nieuw aerdsch pleyn.
    " 3. Nieuwe werelt kaert uÿt gegeven tot Amsteldam bÿ Pieter Goos.
    " 23. Paſkaert waer in vertoont, wert de Spaense zee . . .
    " 25. Pascaarte vande zee custen van Guinea; en Brasilia . . .
    " 34. Niewe waſſende graadt kaert van d' noorder zee custen van America . . .
    " 35. Pas caerte van Nieu Nederlandt en de Engelſche Virginies . . .
    " 36. Pascaerte van Westindien . . .
    " 37. Paskaert van de Caribes eylande . . .
    " 38. Pascaerte van Rio Gambia . . .
    " 39. Paskaart van Brasil.
    " 40. Paskaarse van het zuydelijckſte van America . . . 1666.
    " 41. Waſſende graadt kaert, vande groote Zuyd Zee . . .

### 1683

**Sanson, N.,** *d'Abbeville,* and **Sanson, N.,** *fils.*
    L'Europe [l'Asie, l'Afrique, l'Amérique] en plusieurs cartes, et en divers traités de géographie et d'histoire; là où sont decrits succinctement, & avec une belle méthode, & facile. Ses empires, ses peuples, ses colonies, leurs moeurs, langues, religions, richesses, &c. Et ce qu'il y a de plus beau, & de plus rare dans toutes ses parties, & dans ſes iles. 4 pts in 1 v. 8°. Sur la copie imprimée a Paris, chez l'autheur, 1683.      494
    NOTE.—Collation: 3 p. l., 52 pp., [1] l. incl. 11 folded maps; 102 pp., [2] l., 18 folded maps; 98 pp., 18 folded maps; 82 pp., [1] l., 15 folded maps.
    Added, folded title engraved: L'Evrope . . . Par N. Sanson le fils . . . Sur la copie a Paris chez l'autheur, 1683.
    Printed title for entire volume although not so stated. Half titles to pts. [2-4] "L'Asie," "L'Afrique" and "L'Amérique." Each part has separate pagination.
    Maps no. 1, 4, 7, 9, 14, 15, signed: A. d'Winter sculp.
    "L'Europe, l'Asie, l'Afrique & l'Amérique par les sieurs Nicolas Sanson père et fils, in 4. Paris, 1656, 1657, & 1658. 4 volumes qui se relient quelquefois en deux ou en un. L'Europe est de m. Sanson fils: le père a fait les trois autres parties. Les cartes en sont proprement gravées: on l'a contrefait en Hollande; mais la géographie a changé de face depuis que messieurs Sanson ont publié cet ouvrage.—Nicolas Lenglet Dufresnoy. Méthode pour étudier la géographie. v. 1, p. 339.
    There were separate editions of the four parts as follows:
    L'Europe, Paris, 1648, 1651.
    L'Asie, Paris, 1652, 1653, 1658.
    L'Afrique, Paris, 1656, 1660.
    L'Amerique, Paris, 1656, 1657, 1662, [1667?]
    The following maps relate to America:
    no. [1] Américqve Septentrionale . . .
    " [2] Le Canada, ou Nouvelle France, &c. . . .
    " [3] La Floride . . .

no. [4] Audience de México . . .
" [5] Audience de Guadalajara . . .
" [6] Audience de Guatimala . . .
" [7] Les isles Antilles . . .
" [8] Amériqve Méridionale . . .
" [9] Terre Ferme, nouv$^{eau}$ roy$^{me}$ de Grenade . . .
" [10] Guiane . . .
" [11] Le Pérou . . .
" [12] Le Chili . . .
" [13] Le Brésil . . .
" [14] Le Paraguay . . .
" [15] Destroit de Magellan . . .

**1683**

Geographifche en hiftorische beschryvingh der vier bekende werelds-deelen Europa, Asia, Africa en America: of de geheele aerdkloot vertoond en nieuwe feer nette land-kaerten, nevens geographifche en hiftorische berighten aller keyferrijcken, koninghrÿcken, landfchappen, steeden: seeden der volckeren, spraecken, religien, rÿckdommen, &c., door de heer Sanson d'Abbeville, ordinaer geographus der koninghlÿcke majefteyt van Franckrÿck. Vertaeld en doorgaens met historifche byvoeghfelen vermeerdert door S. de Vries. 8 p. l., 688, [4] pp., [46] l., 62 fold. maps. 8°. t' Utrecht, J. Ribbius, 1683. 495

NOTE.—Added engraved title: Geographise en historise werelt beschryving door N. Sanson . . .

pp. 545-688 contain the description of America and the following maps, which are the same as those in the Paris edition, 1683:

no. [1] Américqve Septentrionale . . .
" [2] Le Canada, ou Nouvelle France . . .
" [3] La Floride . .
" [4] Audience de Mexico . . .
" [5] Audience de Guadalajara . . .
" [6] Audience de Guatimala . . .
" [7] Les isles Antilles . . .
" [8] Américqve Méridionale . . .
" [9] Terre Ferme, nouv$^{eau}$ roy$^{me}$ de Grenada . . .
" [10] Guiane . . .
" [11] Le Pérou . . .
" [12] Le Chili . . .
" [13] Le Brésil . . .
" [14] Le Paraguay . . .
" [15] Destroit de Magellan . . .

**1684**

**Ortelius, A.**

Theatro del mondo. Nel quale si dà notitia dìftinta di tutte le prouincie, regni, & paefi del mondo . . . 232, [26] pp., 4 fold. maps. 24°. Venetia, appresso il Brigna, 1684. 496

NOTE.—Collation: A-I, K in twelves, L in ten.

sig. [A] recto: Half title; Theatro del mondo; verso: blank. sig. [A2] recto:

35799—08——16

**Ortelius, A.**—Continued.
   title; verso: blank. sig. A3 recto–verso: Lettore. sig. A4 recto–[K8] verso: Theatro del mondo, incl. 4 fold. maps. sig. [K9] recto–[L9] verso: Tavola delli nomi et particolorità contenute nella presente opera, followed by a blank leaf.

CONTENTS.

no. [1] Evropa.
  " [2] Asia.
  " [3] Africa.
  " [4] America.

**1685?**

**Rossi, G. G. de.**
   Mercvrio geografico overo gvida geografica in tvtte le parti del mondo conforme le tavole geografiche del Sansone, Bavdrand e Cantelli. Data in luce con direttione e cura di Gio. Giacomo de Rossi nella sua stamperia in Roma, alla Pace, all' insegna di Parigi con priu'. del s. pont.   2 p. l., 48 maps, 20 pl. fol. [Roma, G. G. de Rossi, 1685?]   497

   NOTE.—Numerous maps and plates dated 1685. See also titles 515 and 516. Manuscript "Indice."
   Engraved title similar to that in v. 1, editions of 1692–[1694] and 1692–[1743] This edition resembles v. 1 of 1692–[94] edition, exclusive of the maps dated after 1685, and the following plates not found in the later editions:
   no. 48. Vera mostra del ordinanza e marcia dell potentissimo essercito di Mehemet IIII sultan de Tvrchi controli Christiani per l'assedio di Vienna nell anno MDCLXXXIII.
   " 49. Vienna . . . 1683.
   " 50. Vienna in Avstria.—Presbvrg ouero Posonia.—Rab ouero Giavarino.
   " 51. Pianta della Cesarea citta di Vienna . . . 1683.
   " 52. Alba Reale.—Canissa.—Agria Eger, o Erla.—Naihaisel. 1683.
   " 53. Situatione e prospetto della real fortezza di Naihaisel assediata li 14. luglio dall armi di Leopoldo primo imperatore sotto il comando del ser$^{mo}$ sig$^{re}$ duca di Lorena . . . 1685.
   " 54. Gyvla.—Tokay.—1683.
   " 55. Segnalata vittoria ottenvta dalle armi imperiali e Polacche sotto la citta e fortezza di Strigonia con l'acqvisto dell' importante forte di Parkam li IX ottobre . . . 1683.
   " 56. Vacia.—Filek.—Temesvar.—Adrianopoli. 1684.
   " 57. Novigrad.—Sigeth.—Wardein detto Varadino Vicegrad.
   " 58. Cassovia.—Hatwan.—Zolnok.—Belgrado.
   " 59. Pianta et assedio delle citta di Bvda è Pest . . . 1684.
   " 60. Vero-disegno e pianta della citta di Bvda ouero Offen, e Pest.
   " 61. Strigonia liberata dall Assedio con la battaglia data ai Turchi dal ser$^{mo}$ di Lorena . . . 1685.—Esech e suo ponte bruggiato dall' Esercito Cesareo dal marescial Lesle . . . 1685.
   " 62. Disegno del famoso ponte e fortezza di Essech.—Verowitiza.
   " 63. Kamieniec . . . 1684.
   " 64. Constantinopoli . . . 1684.
   " 65. Citta di Coron in Morea . . . 1685.—Citta di Modon in Morea.
   " 66. S. Mavra.—Citta di Scio.
   " 67. Chin ó Sia Clin.—Prevesa con le citta adiacenti.

The following maps relate to America:
no. 1. Mappa mondo overo carta generale del globo terrestre . . . 1674.
" 5. L'America Settentrionale . . . 1677.
" 6. L'America Meridionale . . . 1677.

## 1688

**Morden, R.**
Geography rectified: or, a description of the world, in all its kingdoms, provinces, countries, islands, cities, towns, seas, rivers, bayes, capes, ports; their ancient and present names, inhabitants, situations, histories, customs, governments, &c., as also their commodities, coins, weights, and measures, compared with those at London. Illuftrated with seventy-six maps. 2d ed. enlarged with about thirty sheets more in the description, and about twenty new maps . . .  8 p. l., 596 (*i. e.* 598) pp. incl. 77 maps. sm. 4°. London, for R. Morden & T. Cockerill, 1688. 498

NOTE.—Leaf inserted containing a map of the Bermudas and descriptive text, with the following at end: "Place this between page 544 and 545."
First edition, 1680; second, 1688; third, 1693; fourth, 1700. *cf.* Dictionary of national biography, edited by Sidney Lee. v. 38, pp. 410-411.
The following maps relate to America:
p. l. 7. A new map of ye world . . .
p. 436. The Philipine isles . . .
" 512. America . . .
" 516. Terra Magellanica . . .
" 520. Chili and Paragay . . .
" 523. Brazile . . .
" 526. Castilla del Or, Gviana, Perv. The country of ye Amazones . . .
" 534. A map of the Western islands . . .
" 537. Insulæ Iamaicæ . . .
" 541. The ifland of Barbados . . .
" [544a] Æstivarum insulæ al Barmudas . . .
" 546. Mexico or New Spaine . . .
" 555. New Mexico vel New Granata et Marata et California . . .
" 557. A map of Florida and ye great lakes of Canada . . .
" 559. A new map of Carolina . . .
" 561. A new map of Virginia.
" 567. . . . New Jarsey and Pensilvania . . .
" 576. . . . New England and New York . . .
" 589. The north west part of America . . .

## 1688?

**Wit, F. de**
[Atlas major] 51 maps. fol. [Amsterdam, 1688?] 499

NOTE.—No title-page.
Date on map no. [27], Regni Hungariæ.
Consists of 51 maps, 24 of which are from v. 1 of Wit's Atlas major, and the other 27 from v. 2.
The following map relates to America:
no. [51] Novissima et accuratissima totius Americæ descriptio.

## 1688?

**Wit, F. de**—Continued.

Atlas. 1 p. l., 102 maps. fol. Tot Amsterdam, bij Frederick de Wit in de Calverstraet bij den Dam inde Witte Paskaert [1688?] 500

NOTE.—The engraved title-page represents a globe upon the top of which stands the figure of Atlas supporting the heavens. The engraving is a duplicate of that on the title-page of Justus Danckerts' atlas, 1703?, except it faces the right instead of the left. See also title 540.

At the bottom of the index on the reverse of the title-page is the following, "Amftelodami, apud Fredericum de Wit, in Plateâ Vitulinâ vulgo de Kalverftraat, fub figno de Witte Pafcaart." In addition to those by Wit, the atlas contains maps by the following authors and engravers: Allard, Blaeu, Dauthendeij, Hogeboom, Hondius, Janssen, Labanna, Thuilier, Sweerts, Ten Have, N. Visscher. Map no. 59 is dated 1660; no. 38, 1671; and no. 74, 1688. The following concerning the Wit firm is quoted from Nagler: "Wit, Friedrich de, auch Widt und Witt, kupferstecher und kunsthändler zu Amsterdam, drei künstler dieses namens. Der ältere gründete 1648 eine offizin, und verbreitete besonders landkarten, welche er selbst zeichnete und mit den wappen der länder auf gutes papier abdrucken liess. Diese karten wurden jenen von Danckerts vorgezogen. Im jahre 1698 überliess er die handlung seinem sohne, welcher als gründlicher mathematiker die karten genau revidirte, und einen grossen absatz erzielte. Die zahl der land- und seekarten aus dem verlage der beiden de Wit beliefen sich nach einem cataloge von 1706 über 400 und wurden bis zu dem 1712 erfolgten tod des jüngeren F. de Wit vermehrt. Im dem genannten jahre war sein gleichnamiger sohn bereits theilnahmer des geschäftes, welches dann an C. Mortier und J. Covens überging."

The following maps relate to America:
no. 1. Nova orbis tabvla.
" 2. Noviffima et accuratiffima totius Americæ descriptio.

## 1688-1689

**Du Val, P.**

Cartes de géographie les plus nouvelles et les plus fidèles, auecque leurs diuisions régulières, qui marquent les bornes des éstats felon les dernièrs traités de paix. 1 p. l., [17] pp., 102 maps, 3 pl. fol. Paris, mlle. Du-Val, 1688-[1689] 501

NOTE.—Engraved title.
Dates on maps vary from 1654–1689.
The following maps relate to America:
no. [1] Planisphère, ou carte générale du monde . . . 1684.
" [2] Carte vniverselle de commerce . . . 1686.
" [3] L'Amériqve autrement le novveav monde et Indes Occidentales . . . 1684.
" [7-8] Carte universelle du monde . . . 1684. 2 sheets.—Amérique Septemtrionale [!]—Amérique Méridionale.
" [11-14] L'Amérique . . . 1679. 4 sheets.—Le Nouveau Méxique et la Terre de Iesso . . .—Le Mer de Nort . . .—Le Mer de Sud . . .—Le Pérou, le Chile, la Magellanique, la Plata, et le Brésil . . .
" [15] Le Canada, faict par sr. de Champlain . . . 1677.
" [16] Isles d'Amérique dites Caribes et Antilles et Barlovento. 1677.
" [17] Coste de Gvayane autrement France eqvinoctiale en la Terre Ferme d'Amérique . . . 1677.

## 1689

**Wolfgang, A.**

Atlas minor, noviſſias & maximé neceſſarias orbis terrarum tabulas geographicas complectens.  1 p. l., 1 l., 107 maps. fol. Amstelodami, ex-officinâ Abrahami Wolfgang [1689]  502

NOTE.—Engraved title.  Map no. 78 dated 1688.
Maps by various cartographers, including:  F. Fer, W. Bleau, J. B. Lebanna, I. de Ram, A. Barreo, I. Massa, Ortelius, A. F. de Witt, N. Visscher.
The "Index tabularum" calls for 104 maps.—Map no. 13, Principatus cataloniae is wanting. The four following maps are not included in the index and are probably inserted: "Bvrgvndia dvcatvs" inserted after no. 19;  —"Ducatus Brabantiæ." By H. Jaillot, 1694 and "Estat . . . de l'eves$^{ché}$ de Liège." By Sanson [n. d.] between nos. 38 and 39;—"Status Sabaudiæ." By H. Jaillot, 1694, after no. 74.
This atlas is reviewed in Leclerc's Bibliothèque universelle, 1689 (p. 294): "On met ici ce recueil de cartes parce que sans cela on ne ſauroit bien entendre les voiages.  Il ſeroit même à souhaiter que les voiageurs suſſent en faire, au moins grossièrement . . .  Le s. Wolfgang en a ramaſſé cent & six, qu'il a fait revoir & corriger avec soin, & où l'on trouve les principaux roiaumes de l'univers . . ."
The following maps relate to America:
no.  1. Nova Orbis tabula . . . A. F. de Wit.
"  100. Mar del zur Hispanis mare Pacificum.
"  101. Novissima et aecuratissima totius Americæ descriptio.  F. de Wit.
"  102. Mar del Nort.
"  103. Insulæ Americanæ in oceano septentionali ac regiones adiacentes . . . per Nicolaum Visscher.
"  104. Mar di Æthiopia vulgo oceanus Æthiopicus.

## 1689–1690

**Sanson, N.** *d'Abbeville.*

Atlas nouveav, contenant toutes les parties du monde, où sont exactement remarqués les empires, monarchies, royaumes, estats, républiques & peuples, qui ſi trouuent á prefent.  Présenté à mon seigeur le dauphin, par son très-humble, très obeisant et très fidèle, seruiteur, Hubert Iaillot, géographe du roy.  2 p. l., 19 l., 80 maps. fol. Paris, H. Iaillot, 1689-[1690]  503

NOTE.—Engraved title.  This copy is similar to the edition of 1692 which gives Sanson as the author.  Imperfect.
Map "La Lorraine . . ." dated 1690.
The majority of the maps are by Sanson.
The following maps relate to America:
no [1] Mappe-monde geo-hydrographique . . . 1684.
"  [5] Amérique Septentrionale . . .
"  [6] Amérique Méridionale . . . 1685.

## 1689–1692

**Jacobsz, T., Doncker, H.** *and* **Goos, H.**

The lightning columne, or, sea-mirrour, containing the sea-coaſts of the northern, eaſtern and weſtern navigation: setting forth in divers neceſſaire sea-cards, all the ports, rivers, bayes, roads, depths and sands; very curiouſly placed on ics due polus heigt furniſhed.

**Jacobsz, T., Doncker, H.** *and* **Goos, H.**—Continued.
With the difcoveries of the chief countries, and on what cours and diftance they lay one from another. Never theretofore fo clearly laid open, and here and there very deligently bettered and augmented for the ufe of all seamen. As alsoo the situation of the northernly countries, as iflands, the strate Davids, the ifle of Jan Mayen, Bears ifland, Old Greenland, Spitzbergen and Nova Zembla: adorneth with many sea-cards and difcoveries. Gathered out of the experience and practice of divers pilots and lovers of the famous art of navigation. Where unto is added a brief instruction of the art of navigation, together with new tables of the suns declination, wit [!] an new almanach. 3 parts in 1 v. 2 p. l., 29, [3], 96 pp.; 90 pp.; 1 p. l., [8], 3–104 pp., 84 maps. fol. Amsterdam, C. Loots-Man, 1689–[1692] 504

NOTE.—"With previlege for fiftheen jears." Pt. 3 dated 1692.
On the l. following the engraved title, under the "priviledge" is a description of the book . . . "A sea-book, containing the eaftern, weftern and straits navigation, entitled The mariners sea-mirrour and the new great sea-mirrour, being one book, yet bearing a threefold name and title, with the third part annexed to the end thereof, called The straits book" . . .
"The lighting colom of the Midland-sea," bound at the end, is considered the third part of the work. See also title 510.
The following names appear on the maps:
Theunis Iacobfz; Casparus Loots-Man; Iacob Theunifz, Iacobus en Casparus Loots-man; in pt. 3, map no. 1 is by Theunis Iacobfz; map no. 2 by Anthoni Iacobfz, the others are not credited.

CONTENTS.

A short instruction in the art of navigation. 29, [3] pp.

*Easterne navigation.*

pt. I, book I. The difcription of the North-Sea, the coast of Holland, Freefland, Holfteyn, Jutland, Meklenburgh and Denmark to Valfterboen, in the ifland of Rugen and with all the coast of Norway to Dronten: as alfo de eaft-side of England and Scotland. pp. 1–52, 17 maps.

" " II. The defcription of the sea-coafts of Norway, Finmarck, Lapland and the whole White-Sea. pp. 53–66, 9 maps.

" " III. Easterne and northerne navigation. The defcription of Yceland, Greenland, or the Strait of Davids: likewife the situation of John Mayens ifland and Spitzbergen: alfo situation of Candenoes eaftward, throug Weygats, to the Tartarifh or Yce-sea. pp. 67–76, 3 maps.

" " IV. Easterne navigation. The discription of the whole East-sea. pp. 77–96, 7 maps.

*Wes:erne navigation.*

pt. II, " I. The defcription of the sea-coastf of Holland, Zealand, and Flanders from Teffel to the heads of Dover and Calice. pp. 1–15, 5 maps.

pt. II, book II. The defcription of the sea-coaftf of France, from Blackeneffe to Ushand and the coast of Englant, [!] from Dover west-wards, tho [!] the Lands-end the channel of Briftow, with al [!] the sea-coafts of Ireland. pp. 16–50, 8 maps.
" " III. The defcription of France, Bifcay, Galiffia, Portugall and Algarve, from Heyffant to the straight of Gibralter. pp. 51–80, 11 maps.
" IV. The defcription of the sea-coafts from Barbarie, Gualata, Arguyn, Genehoe and the Flemish and Canary iflands together, from the strait of Gibralter to Cabo Verde. pp. 81–90, 5 maps.
pt. III. Lighting colom of the Midland-sea containing a defcription of all the knowne coasts, iflands, sands, depthes and roads: beginning [!] from the naroweft of the streat [!] unto Alexandrette [!] in the Levant. Amsterdam, printed by C. Loots-Man, 1692. 1 p. l., [8] 3–104 pp., 19 maps.

## 1690?
**Seller, J.**
Hydrographia universalis, or a book of maritime charts, defcribing the sea coafts, iflands and principal harbours, in all the known parts of the world. Usefull for merchants and marriners. By John Seller hydrog[e] to the king, and are sold by him at ye Hermitage in ... Wapping. 2 p. l., 52 maps, 1 pl. 24°. [London, 1690?]
505

NOTE.—Engraved title, colored.
no. [19] "The Prince of Orange at Torbay," bears date "November the 5th 1688."
Maps no. [1, 2, 4, 6, 7, 10, 15, 16, 17, 18, 21, 22, 24, 26, 27, 29, 30, 31, 34, 37, 40, 43, 45, 46, 51] are also in his Atlas terrestris [1700?] See also title 530.

CONTENTS.
no. [1] Pixis nautica ...
" [2] A mapp of the North Pole ...
" [3] A chart of ye Downs ...
" [4] A new map of the world ...
" [5] A chart of the North Sea ...
" [6] A mapp of the sea coaft of England, France & Holland ...
" [7] A chart of the Baltick sea ...
" [8] The ifland of Farne ...
" [9] Noviffima Islandiæ tabula.
" [10] The iflands of Orkney.
" [11] Holy-iland.
" [12] A chart of Spain.
" [13] A draught of ... the coast of England ...
" [14] Milford haven.
" [15] A plat of the channel ...
" [16] A chart of ye Western Ocean ...
" [17] A new chart of the channel ...
" [18] A new chart of the Isle of Wight and Portsmouth.
" [19] The Prince of Orange landing at Torbay november the 5th 1688.
" [20] The coaft of Flanders from Sluys to Calis.
" [21] Virginia and Maryland ...
" [22] New Iarsey ...

**Seller, J.**—Continued.
- no. [23] Insula Matanino vulgo Martanico . . .
- " [24] Carolina, newly difcribed . . .
- " [25] Bermudas . . .
- " [26] New England and New York . . .
- " [27] The ifland of Saint Hellena . . .
- " [28] The north part of America.
- " [29] Mexico or New Spaine . . .
- " [30] Insulæ Iamaicæ . . .
- " [31] The ifland of Barbados . . .
- " [32] The ifland of Tobago . . .
- " [33] A chart of the sea coast of Brazil . . .
- " [34] A chart of the West Indies . . .
- " [35] A chart of Gvinea . . .
- " [36] A chart of y$^e$ eaftermost part of the East Indies . . .
- " [37] A mapp of the South Pole . . .
- " [38] A chart of the weftern part of the East Indies . . .
- " [39] A chart of the sea coaft of Barbary . . .
- " [40] A chart of the Mediterranean sea . . .
- " [41] The town of Malta.
- " [42] A prospect of the Hellespont and propontis.
- " [43] A chart . . . from the Landfend of England to Cape Bona Efperanta . . .
- " [44] The ifland of Garnsey . . .
- " [45] A chart of S$^t$. Malo . . .
- " [46] The river Dee or Chester water . . .
- " [47] The island of man . . .
- " [48] A chart of the sea coafts of France from Callis to Bayon . . .
- " [49] The ifland of Jarsey . . .
- " [50] Brest water . . .
- " [51] New Found Land.
- " [52] A chart of the sea coaft of New England, New Iarfey, Virginia, Maryland & Carolina, from C. Cod to C. Hattaras . . .
- " [53] A chart of the coaft of America from Newfound Land to Cape Cod . . .

**1690?**

**Visscher, N.**

Atlas minor sive geographia compendiosa, qua orbis terrarum, per paucas attamen novissimas tabulas ostenditur.   2 p. l., 130 col. maps. fol. Amstelædami, ex officina N. Visscher [1690?]   506

NOTE.—Engraved title, colored: "Atlas minor sive totius orbis terrarum contracta delinea [ta] ex conatibus Nico. Visscher, Amft: Bat:" signed: Ger: de Lairesfe delin: & sculp:

Maps by various cartographers including: de Witt, Henneberger, Emmius, Carolus, Massa, Schagen, Schotanus à Sterringa, Comenius, Janssen, Laurenberg, Loon, Sanson, Blaeu, Ortelius, Apianus.

The date 1678 is on map no. 44; the maps of the British Isles and of Burgondy are dedicated to William III of England, whose reign began in 1689; the view of Nieuw Amsterdam on map no. 124 has been given the date of 1690 by Asher in "A list of the maps and charts of New Netherland . . . Amsterdam, 1855," p. 14. no. 14, from which the following is quoted: "About

1690 Nicolas Visscher retouched the old plate of N. J. Vifscher. He has added all the emendations of Montanus and Allardt, and also the city of Philadelphia and the name of the state of Pennsylvania. Some names, for instance *Nieu Casteel*, one of the names of Fort Christina, are to be found on no map but his. He had retained the old view of New Amsterdam and has engraved the title upon the shield which forms part of the ornament. This title is as follows: Novi Belgii Novæque Angliæ nec non partis Virginiæ tabula multis in locis emendata *per Nicolaum Visfcher.*—[Nieuw Amsterdam op t eylant Manhattans] The size is of course that of the old plate."

The title of the old plate reads: "Novi Belgii Novæque Angliae nec non partis Virginiæ tabula multis in locis emendata a Nicalao Joannis Visschero.—Size: 1 f. 10 inches by 1 f. 7 inches. This map is very scarce; in fact I know of no copy in the hands of a private individual. There is one in the Royal library at the Hague, and another attached [to a document in the Dutch royal Archives]." *cf.* Asher. op. cit. p. 12. The date of this first map is given as ca. 1656.

Map 37 Dominii ultraiectini tabula . . . has been pasted on a fresh leaf.

Maps 109 & 115 relate to the Philippines.

The following maps relate to America:

no. [1] Orbis terrarum nova et accuratissima tabula: auctore Nicolao Visscher.
" [2] Nova totius terrarum orbis geographica ac hydrographica tabula. Autore N. I. Piscator. 1652.
" [3] Nova et accvrata Poli Arctici descriptio. Apud Ioannem Ianfsonium.
" [4] Typus maritimus Groenlandiæ.
" [5] Europa . . . per Nicolaum Visscher.
" [122] Noviffima et accuratiffima totius Americæ descriptio per Gerardvm a Schagen.
" [123] America Septentrionalis . . . Ioannes Ianfsonius.
" [124] Novi Belgii novæque Angliæ nec non partis Virginiæ tabula multis in locis emendata per Nicolaum Visscher. Inset: Nieuw Amsterdam op t eylant Manhattans.
" [125] Insulæ Americanæ in oceano Septentrionali ac regiones adiacentes.
" [126] Americæ pars Meridionalis . . . Ioannis Ianfony.
" [127] Gviana siue Amazonvm regio. Ioannes Ianfonius.
" [128] Accuratissima Brasiliæ tabula. Ioanness Ianfonius.
" [129] Tabula Magellanica.
" [130] [Terra australis incognita]

## 1690?

—— Same.  2 p. l., 1 l., 127 col. maps.  fol.  Amstelædami, ex officina N. Visscher [1690?]  507

NOTE.—Engraved title, colored.

In this copy several maps have been replaced by others of different cartographers.

A manuscript index on 1 l. has been inserted at the end; according to this index the following maps are wanting: nos. 33, 58, 104, 111.

The following maps relate to America:

no. [1] Novissima totius terrarum orbis tabula, auctore Nicolao Visscher.
" [2] Nova totius terrarum orbis geographica . . . tabula. Auctore N. I. Piscator. 1652.
" [3] Regiones svb polo arctico. Auctore Guiljelmo Blaeu.
" [4] Typus maritimus Groenlandiæ.
" [5] Europa . . . per Nicolaum Visscher.
" [119] Noviffima et accuratiffima totius Americæ descriptio per N. Visscher.

**Visscher, N.**—Continued.
no. [120] America septentrionalis . . . Ioannes Ianſſonius.
" [121] Novi Be.gii novæque Angliæ nec non partis Virginiæ tabula . . .
Inset: Nieuw Amsterdam.
" [122] Insulæ Americanæ in Oceano Septentrionali ac regiones adiacentes . . .
" [123] Americæ pars meridionalis . . . Ioannis Ianſsony.
" [124] Gviana siue Amazonvm regio. Ioannes Ianſsonius.
" [125] Accuratissima Brasiliæ tabula. Ioannes Ianſsonius.
" [126] Tabula Magellanica qua Tierræ del Fuego . . . descriptio exhibetur.
" [127] [Terra Australis incognita]

## 1690?

—— Same. 2 p. l., 115 uncol. maps. fol. Amstelædamı, ex officina N. Visscher [1690?] 508

NOTE.—Engraved title.
Many maps have printed indexes of places on the reverse; these indexes are lacking in the preceding copies.
Excepting two maps by Blaeu, all maps bear Visscher's name.
Several new maps, including Germany, Austria, Danube river, etc., have been incorporated in this copy.
The following maps relate to America:
no. [1] Orbis terrarum nova et accuratissima tabula.
" [2] Europa.
" [110] Noviffima et accuratiffima totius Americæ descriptio per N. Visscher.
" [111] Novi Belgii novæque Angliæ nec non partis Virginiæ tabula . . .
Inset: Nieuw Amsterdam.
" [112] Insulæ Americanæ in oceano Septentrionalis ac regiones adiacentes.
" [113] Jamaica.
" [114] Insula Matanino vulgo Martanico.
" [115] Nova et accurata Brasiliæ . . . tabula, auctore Ioanne Blaev.

## 1692?

**Visscher, N.**
Atlas minor sive geographia compendiosa. 3 p. l., 62 col. maps. fol. Amstelædami, ex officina Nicolai Visscher [1692?] 509

NOTE.—Engraved title, colored.
Map no. 61, Wassende graade Kaart van de Noord ocean, dated 1692.
Title appears on the 2nd p. l.; on the 1st p. l. is the col. eng. title: "Atlas minor sive totius orbis terrarum contracta delinea[ta] ex conatibus Nico. Visscher" . . . signed: "Ger: de Lairesse delin: & sculp:"
A manuscript index on 1 p. has been inserted after the 2nd p. l.
Maps relate mostly to England, Scotland, and Ireland; they are by various cartographers including C. Allard, F. de Witt, J. van Keulen, Voogt, Janssen and Blaeu.
The following maps relate to America:
no. [1] Planisphærium terrestre. Auctore Carolo Allard.
" [2] Poli arctici . . . deſcriptio novissima. Per Fredericum de Wit.
" [3] Wassende graade kaart van . . aardbodem. By Iohannes van Keulen.
" [61] Waſſende graade kaart van de Noord oceaan. By Iohannes van Keulen. 1692.

**1692**

**Jacobsz, T.**, *called* Loots-man.

The lightningh columne, or sea-mirrour, contaigning the sea-coafts of the northern and eaftern navigation : setting forth in divers neceffaire sea-cards, all the ports, rivers, bayes, roads, depths and sands, very curioufly placed on its due polus height furnished. With the difcoveris [!] of the chief countries and on what cours and diftance they lay one from another. Never theretofore fo clearly laid open, and here and there very diligently bettered and augmented for the ufe of all seamen. As alsoo the situation of the northernly countries, as iflands, the Strate Davids, the ifle of Jan Mayen, Bears Ifland, Old Greenland, Spitzbergen and Nova Zembla : adorneth with many sea-cards and difcoveries. Where unto is added a brief inftruction of the art of navigation, together with new tables of the suns declination, with an new almanach. Gathered out of the experience and practice of divers pilots and lovers of the famous art of navigation. 1 p. l., 10, 15–24, 27–29, [3], 96 pp., 35 maps. fol. Amsterdam, C. Loots-Man, 1692. 510

NOTE.—"With privilege for fiftheen jears."
This copy does not contain pts. 2 and 3 found in the 1689 edition. See also title 504.
"The English pilot" published by John Seller, London, 1690, is bound with this.
pp. 11–14 25–26, wanting.
The following names appear on the maps: Theunis Iacobsz; Casparus Lootsman; Iacob Theunisz; Jacobus en Casparus Lootsman.
The family of Jacobsz, map makers and printers of Amsterdam, were called Loots-Man, meaning sea-pilot. Theunis or Anthonie Jacobsz made the maps. Caspar is mentioned as the printer or publisher although his name appears on some of the maps. Jacob Theunis was the son of Theunis Anthonie. The name appears in various forms and spelling.—*cf.* Tiele, P. A. Nederlandsche bibliographie-Amsterdam, 1884.

CONTENTS.

"A short instruction in the art of navigation." 29 pp.
"Almanach" . . . "Table" . . . [3] pp.

*Easterne navigation.*

part I, book  I. "The discription of the North-Sea, the coaft of Holland, Freefland, Holfteyn, Jutland, Meklenburgh and Denemark to Valfterboen in the ifland of Rugen and with all the coaft of Norway to Dronten, as alfo de eaft-fide of England and Scotland." pp. 1–52. 17 maps.

"    "    II. "The defcription of the sea-coafts of Norway, Finmarck, Lapland and the whole White sea." pp. 53–66. 8 maps.

*Eafterne and northerne navigation.*

"    "    III. "The defcription of Yceland, Greenland, or the Strait of Davids: likewise the situation of John Mayens ifland and Spitzbergen: also situation of Candenoes eaftward, throug Weygats to the Tartarifh or Yce-sea." p. 67–76. 3 maps.

"    "    IV. "The discription of the whole East-sea." pp. 77–96. 7 maps.

**Luyts, J.**

**1692**

Joannis Luyts, philoſophiæ profeſſoris, introductio ad geographiam novam et veterem; in qua neceſſaria hujus scientiæ prolegomena, intermixto uſu globi terrestris, nec non oceani & conſtitutio perſpicuo ordine pertractantur. Adÿciuntur suis locis oceani, terræ, & cujuſque regionis tabulæ, item chartæ LXV Sansonis, inter quas quædam hac forma ante ineditæ. 14 p. l., 764, [24] pp., 66 maps. 8°. Trajecti ad Rhenum, ex officina Francisci Hahna, 1692. 511

> NOTE.—The maps are signed variously: le s$^r$. Sanson, le s$^r$. Sanson d'Abbeville, N. Sanson d'Abbeville and N. Sanson le fils. The map of the Netherlands, p. 259, listed in the "Index gallico-latinus LXV chartarum Sansonis . . ." as no. x of the maps of Europe, is unsigned.
> The following maps relate to America:
> p. 524. Les isles Philippines . . .
> " 693. Americqve Septentrionale . . .
> " 694. Le Canada, ou Nouvelle France, &c. . . .
> " 702. La Floride . . .
> " 704. Audience de Guadalajara . . .
> " 710. Audience de Mexico . . .
> " 712. Audience de Guatimala . . .
> " 716. Les isles Antilles . . .
> " 726. Amériqve Méridionale . . .
> " 727. Terre Ferme . . .
> " 730. Guiane . . .
> " 732. Le Brésil . . .
> " 738. Le Paraguay . . .
> " 740. Le Pérou . . .
> " 748. Le Chili . . .
> " 750. Destroit de Magellan . . .

**1692**

**Müller, J. U.**

Kurtz-bündige abbild- und vorſtellung der gantzen welt, worinnen alle in derſelben, ſonderlich aber in Teutschland belegene kőnigreiche, fürſtenthumer provintzen und landſchafften . . . Wie nicht weniger die jetzigen hohen regenten dieſer und jener lånder bemercket werden. 10 p. l., [103] l., 103 pp. incl. 103 maps. 16°. Ulm, G. W. Kühnen, 1692. 512

> NOTE.—Engraved title added "Orbis terræ cum suis partibus Europa, Asia, Africa et America per tabulus præsentatus. Ulmæ, 1692."
> The following maps relate to America:
> no. 1. Vorbild der welt . . .
> " [86] Die arctiſchen lande.
> " [87] Die antarctischen lande.
> " [88] America Septentrionales.
> " [89] Canada.
> " [90] Virginia.
> " [91] Florida.
> " [92] New Mexico.
> " [93] Mexico sive Nova Hispania.
> " [94] Die Americaniſ. inſuln Antilles.

no. [95] Das Mittägige America.
" [96] Caftilla d'Or . . .
" [97] Guajana.
" [98] Peru.
" [99] Chili.
" [100] Brafilia.
" [101] Tucuman.
" [102] La Plata.
" [103] Das Magellanifche land.

## 1692
**Peeters, J.**
L'atlas en abregé, ou nouvelle description du monde, tirée des meilleurs auteurs de ce siècle.   3 p. l., 82, [2] pp., 42 maps, 1 pl. 12°.   Anvers, l'auteur, 1692.   513

NOTE.—Engraved half-title signed: Harréwyn fecit.
At end, "Extrait du privilége du roi . . . à Brusselle, le 12 décembre, 1691."
Descriptive text on pages between maps.   Another copy without text.
The following maps relate to America:
no. [1] [Planisphere]
" [3] Asiæ.
" [5] Americæ.
" [42] Les isles Philippines . . .

## 1692-1696
**Sanson, N.,** *d'Abbeville.*
Atlas nouveav, contenant toutes les parties du monde, où sont exactement remarqués les empires, monarchies, royaumes, estats, républiques & peuples qui sy trouuent à présent.   2 v.   1 p. l., 49 maps, 47 l.; 1 p. l., 60 maps, 58 l.   fol.   Paris, H. Iaillot, 1692-96.   514

NOTE.—Engraved titles.
v. 1, dated 1692; v. 2, 1696.
The following maps, by various cartographers, have been inserted in this atlas: v. 1, no. 7, Le Canada ou partie de la Nouvelle France . . . par . . . Iaillot, Paris, 1696.— no. 20, Plan de la ville, cité . . . de Paris. Dressé sur les lieux et sur les mémoires de mr. Iouvin de Rochefort. Paris, N. de Fer, 1694.— no. 47, Le diocèse de Tournay . . . par H. Iaillot.— no. 48, Les campemens des armées du roy . . . aux Pays Bas. Par le sr. Vaultier. Paris, 1695.— v. 2, no. 58, Les déserts d'Egypte . . . Paris, E. Michalet, 1693.
The text of the "Nouvelle introduction à la géographie" is wanting; but the title page, dated Paris 1692, is on the recto of the third leaf.—On the two leaves preceding the title pages of each volume, are manuscript indexes, supplementing the printed indexes following the title pages.—Special indexes or "Tables géographiques" have been inserted between the maps.—The leaves of both volumes have manuscript numbering.—Maps have ornamental titles.
The following maps relate to America:
v. 1, no. 1. Mappe-monde=géo-hydrographique.
" no. 2. L'Afrique [showing] Amérique Méridionale.
" no. 5. L'Amérique Septentrionale.
" no. 6. L'Amérique Méridionale.
" no. 7. Le Canada.

## 1692-1694
**Rossi, G. G. de.**

Mercvrio geografico overo gvida geografica in tvtte le parti del mondo conforme le tavole geografiche del Sansone, Bavdrand e Cantelli. Data in luce con direttione, e cura di Gio. Giacomo de Rossi nella sua stamperia in Roma, alla Pace, all' insegna di Parigi con Priu' del S. Pont.  2 v.  fol.  [Roma, G. G. de Rossi, 1692-94]  515

> NOTE.—Collation: v. 1, engraved title, 52 maps; v. 2, engraved title, 60 maps. Dates on maps vary from 1669-1694.
> v. 1, not dated; v. 2, dated 1692.
> Title-page of v. 2 reads: Mercvrio geografico ouero guida geografica in tutte le parti del mondo conforme le tauole di Giacomo Cantelli da Vignola . . . intagliate albulino dà Antonio Barbey. Tomo secondo, dato in luce con direttione e cura da Domenico de Rossi erede di Gio. Giacomo de Rossi . . . 1692.
> Maps also by Agostino Lubin, Giacomo Ameti, and Jacobius Cantellius.
> Manuscript index to v. 1, calls for 1 pl. and 66 maps; to v. 2, for 66 maps. See also title 497.
> The following maps are wanting:
> v. 1, no.    [15]  Alta Lombardia.
> "    "    [16]  Bassa Lombardia.
> "    "    [37]  Il regno d Vngaria.
> "    "    [38-39]  Vngaria nuouam$^{te}$ descritta.
> "    "    [40]  Vngaria Occidentale.
> "    "    [41]  "      Orientale.
> "    "    [42]  La Transilvania.
> "    "    [43]  La Moldavia e Vallachia.
> "    "    [44]  Dalmatia, Istria, Bosnia, Servia, Croatia, e parti Schiavonia.
> "    "    [45]  Corso del Danvbio.
> "    "    [46]  La Grecia vniuersale.
> "    "    [47]  Macedonia.
> v. 2, "    [ 3]  Parte settentrionale del regno di Portogallo.
> "    "    [19]  Parte occidentale della Lingvadoca.
> "    "    [27]  Italia ecclesiastica.
> "    "    [28]  Variæ ciuitatum nomenclaturæ ad historiæ ecclesiasticæ intelligentiam.
> "    "    [34]  Il Ducato d'Avosta il Canavese et il Marchesato di Svsa.
> "    "    [64]  Dalmatia maritima orientale.
> The following maps relate to America:
> v. 1, no. [2]  Mappa mondo o vero carta generale del globo terestre . . . da N. d'Abbeuille  [N. Sanson]  1674.
> "    "    [6]  L'America Settentrionale . . . da Gvglielmo Sansone.  1677.
> "    "    [7]  L'America Meridionale . . . da Gvglielmo Sansone.  1677.

## 1692-1714

Mercvrio geografico overo gvida geografica in tvtte le parti del mondo conforme le tavole geografiche del Sansone, Bavdrand e Cantelli. Data in luce con direttione, e cura di Gio. Giacomo de Rossi nella sua stamperia in Roma, alla Pace, all' insegna di

Parigi con Priu' del S. Pont. 2 v. fol. [Roma, G. G. de Rossi, 1692–1714] 516

NOTE.—Collation: v. 1, title, engraved title, 1 l., 95 (*i. e.* 77) maps; v. 2, engraved title, [3] l., 92 (*i. e.* 78) maps.
Dates on maps vary from 1676–1714.
v. 1, not dated; v. 2, dated 1692.
Title-page of v. 2 reads: Mercvrio geografico ouero guida geografica in tutte le parti del mondo conforme le tauole di Giacomo Cantelli da Vignola . . . intagliate albulino dà Antonio Barbey. Tomo secondo, data in luce con direttione e cura da Domenico de Rossi erede di Gio. Giacomo de Rossi . . . 1692.
Maps also by Lubin, Ameti, Campiglia, Domenico de Rossi and Jacobius Cantellius.
The following maps are wanting:
v. 2, no. 153. Illirico occidentale antico del Sansone.
"   "   154. Illirico orientale antico del medefimo.
"   "   177. Il mar Cafpio con tutt le fue adjacenze.
The following maps relate to America:
v. 1, no. 1. Mappa mondo o vero carta generale del globo terestre raprefentato in due planisferi . . . da N. Sanson . . . 1684.
" 2, " 186. L'America Settentrionale . . . da Gvglielmo Sanson . . . 1687.
"   " 187. L'America Meridionale . . . da Gvglielmo Sanson . . . 1687.

### 1693–1700
**Neptune françois, Le.**
De fransche neptunus, of nieuwe atlas van de zeekaarten, opgenomen en gegraveerd door uitdrukkelyke order des konings, tot het gebruik van zyne zeemachten. Waar in men ziet de naauwkeurige beschryving van alle de kuften van den oceaan, en d'Ooft-zee, van Noorwegen af tot aan de straat van Gilbraltar: mitsgaders waar in ook naauwkeuriglijk zyn aangetekend de streeken die men moet houden, de banken, klippen, plaaten, en in 'talgemeen alles 't geen de zeevaart betreft. Altemaal gemaakt op de waarneemingen en d' ondervinding der gaauwfte ingenieurs en stuurlieden. Overgezien en in goede ordre gesteld door de heeren Pene, Cassini, en anderen. 2 v. in 1. fol. Amsterdam, P. Mortier, 1693–1700.
517

NOTE.—Collation: v. 1, 2 p. l., front., 6 pp., 30 maps, 32 pl., diagr.; v. 2, 1 p. l., 6 pp., 33 maps on 55 l.
Engraved, colored frontispiece with the inscription, "Le neptune françois," signed: Jan van Vianen fecit.
v. 1, pp. 1–6, contain remarks, problems and explanatory notes.
v. 2, pp. 1–6, contain a description of the coast of Africa.
Engraved, colored title following p. [7] reads: Plan de plusieurs bâtimens de mer, avec leurs proportions, et les pavillons, et les enseignes, que chaque nation porte à la mer. Amsterdam, P. Mortier.
Maps in v. 1 are similar to those in "Le neptune françois. Paris, imprimerie royale, 1792–1803." Maps have french text.
Following the maps in v. 1 is an engraved colored frontispiece entitled: "Atlas maritime. Tom. 2.", with a poem commencing "Non pius Aeneas, non sic eraffet Ulyfes;" underneath: "Romanus de Hooghe, J. U. D. et com. reg. tab. hanc

**Neptune françois, Le**—Continued.

fuis D. dedit auct. et inv. 1693;" imprint: "A Amsterdam, chez Pierre Mortier." The "Table des cartes" following the title calls this: "Atlas maritime de Romain de Hooge." This "Atlas maritime" is followed by a title in dutch, which reads, "Vervolg van de neptunus, of zee atlas van de nieuwe zee-kaarten; opgenomen door uitdrukkelyke order der koningen van Portugaal, onder wiens regeeringe 't geheel Afrika etc. ontdekt is: En in 't light gebraght door de sorge van wijlen d' heer d'Ablancourt. Waar in men ziet de naauwkeurige beschryving van alle de kusten van de waereld, de naauwte van Gibraltar, de oceaan of Noord zee van Ethiopien, van de Oost en West-Indische zee, &c: Mitsgaders waar in ook naauwkeuriglyk zyn aangeteekend de streeken die men moet houden; de banken, klippen, plaaten, diepten, en in 't algemeen alles wat de zeevaart betreft. Altemaal gemaakt op de waarneemingen en d' ondervinding des gaauwste ingenieurs en stuurlieden. Amsteldam, P. Mortier, 1700." Each map has colored engraved inset views of important cities and harbors. The map entitled "Carte nouvelle de la mer Méditerranée" contains 38 views of cities and ports. The descriptive text is a dutch extract from Nicolas Perrot d'Ablancourt's translation of Luis del Marmol's L'Afrique, 1667. For full description see Hooge's Zee atlas . . . 1694. Title 2835.

The following maps relate to America:

v. 1. no. [ 1] Carte générale de toutes les costes du monde et les pays nouvellement découvert . . .
" 2. " [20] Carte des costes de l'Asie sur l'océan . . . [Philippine islands]
" " [23] Le golfe de Mexique et les isles voisine . . .
" " [24] Océan Atlantique, ou mer du Nord.
" " [25] Carte de la mer Méridional . . .
" " [26] Carte nouvelle de l'Amérique angloise . . . par le sieur S . . . [Sanson] Inset: [Boston harbor]
" " [27] Carte particulière de Virginie, Maryland, Pennsilvanie . . .
" " [28] Carte particulière de Isthmus, ou Darien . . .
" " [29] Carte général de la Caroline . . . par le sieur S . . . [Sanson] Inset: [Charleston harbor]
" " [30] Carte particulière de la Caroline . . . par le sieur S . . . [Sanson]
" " [31] Mer de Sud, ou Pacifique . . .
" " [32] Carte particulière de l'Amérique Septentrionale . . .
" " [33] Le Canada, ou partie de la Nouvelle France . . .

### 1696–1697

**Fer, N. de.**

Les forces de l'Europe, ou description des principales villes, avec leurs fortifications. Dessignées par les meilleurs ingénieurs, particulièrement celles qui sont sous la domination de la France, dont les plans ont esté levez par monsieur de Vauban . . . Le tout recüeilli par les soins du sr. de Fer, geographe du roy. 204 l. incl. 177 maps, 8 pl., 1 tab. obl. 4°. Paris, chez l'auteur, 1696–[1697]

517a

NOTE.—See also title 537. Consists of 8 parts, each having a similar title-page with different dates of publication; pt. 5 dated 1694; pt. 2, 1695; pts. 1, 3, 6–8, 1696; pt. 4, 1697.

pls. I–VIII relate to fortifications and have a special title-page, on the leaf following the general title-page of the atlas, reading, "Introduction à la

fortification, dédiée à monseigneur le duc de Bourgogne par . . . de Fer. A Paris, chez l'auteur . . . 1693." Each plate is accompanied by explanatory text.—On l. 3 is an index to the atlas.—On the leaf following the title-page of pt. 2, is the plate, "Partie des forces de l' Europe, mis au jour par N. de Fer, géographe de monseigneur le dauphin" [1693] signed, "Schoonebeck, del. et fecit."
Maps "Belgrade" and "Veue de Constantinople", [nos. 106 & 107] pt. 6, nos. 6 & 7, are not in their places; in the index they are given in pt. 8, as nos. 20 & 21.—The "Table géographique," and maps nos. 176-177, L'isle de Wight . . . 1692, and Plan de la bataille de Fleurus . . . do not belong to the atlas, as they are not included in the index, and have been inserted at a later date.
The following map relates to America:
pt. 5, no. 23. [Quebec]

## 1695

**Ptolemæus, C.**

Claudii Ptolemaei | Tabulae geographicae | Orbis Terrarum | Veteribus cogniti. | [*Colophon:*] Franequeræ, | Apud Leonardvm Strik, Bibliopolam. | Trajecti ad Rhenum, | Apud Franciscvm Halmam, Acad. Typograph. | M.D.C.XCV. | 518

58 l., comprising: 2 p. l., 28 maps on 56 l. fol.

Collation: engraved title, verso blank; "Index Tabularum," 1 l. ending on verso with colophon; 28 double page maps on 56 l., without text.

"A new edition of Mercator's maps to Ptolemy's geography, apparently from the same copper-plates that were used in the earlier editions, but with the old ornamental map-titles erased and new ones engraved in their places."
*cf.* Eames.

The maps comprise the "Vniversalis Tabvla Ivxta Ptolemæum," five of Africa, twelve of Asia, and ten of Europe. No american maps. See title 575.

Eames mentions a copy in which one of the maps of Africa is on a single leaf.
Title-page engraved by J. V. Vianen.
Modern binding, half morocco.
Eames-Sabin, no. 66498.

## 1695

**Jaillot, C. H. A.**

Atlas françois, contenant les cartes géographiques dans lesquelles sont très exactement remarquez les empires, monarchies, royaumes et estats de l'Europe, de l'Asie, de l'Afrique et de l'Amérique: avec les tables et cartes particulières, de France, de Flandre, d'Allemagne, d'Espagne et d' Italie . . .   2 p. l., 38 l., 84 maps.  fol. Paris, Iaillot, 1695-[1696] 519

NOTE.—Copy no. 1. See title 520. Engraved title, signed, "Dieu inuen. sc."
Wanting: La Lorraine, le duché d'Avost, la haute Alsace, principauté de Catalogne, l' Italie."
Maps by various cartographers including: Sanson, Jaillot, G. de Lambilly, B. Cappelier, H. Sengre, and dated 1692-1696.
Index has imprint: A Rotterdam, chez Reinier Leers, 1695.
Contains plans of the following cities:

**Jaillot, C. H. A.**—Continued.
 no. 75. Plan de la ville et chasteau de Namur.
 " 96. Plan de la ville de Vienne en Austriche et ses environs.
 The following maps relate to America:
 no. [1] Mappe-monde géo-hydrographique . . . 1695.
 " [4] L' Afrique . . . 1695 [showing part of] Amérique Méridionale.
 " [5] Amérique Septentrionale . . . 1695.
 " [6] Partie de la Nouvelle France . . . 1695.
 " [7] Amérique Méridionale . . . 1695.

### 1695

 Atlas françois, contenant les cartes géographiques dans lesquelles sont très exactement remarquez les empires, monarchies, royaumes et estats de l'Europe, de l'Asie, de l'Afrique et de l'Amérique: avec les tables et cartes particulières, de France, de Flandre, d'Allemagne, d'Espagne et d'Italie.   2 p. l., front., [254] l. incl. 94 maps, 19 tab. fol. Paris, Iaillot, 1695.      520

 Note.—Copy no. 2, containing 38 maps not in copy no. 1. See title 519.
 Frontispiece, engraved portrait of author.
 Manuscript "Table des cartes" precedes one in print.
 Imperfect: maps, no. 4, L' Europe . . . no. 26, Le canal de la rivière d' Eure, (en deux feuilles), no. 44, Les mont Pirénées . . . no. 45, Les Alpes . . . no. 118, La mer Méditerranée, are wanting according to the "Catalogue des cartes." Leaves between maps contain "Tables géographiques." Of the 94 maps, 62 are by Sanson. no. [79] Plan de la ville de Vienne . . . 1695.
 Contains the following maps not called for:
 no. [ 5] Partie de la Nouvelle France . . .
  " [20] Le gouvernement général d' Anjou . . . par J. le Loyer . . .
  " [56] Du haut Rhin . . . par Henry Sengre . . .
  " [57] Le duché de Deux Ponts . . .
  " [58] La Basse Alsace . . .
  " [59] La Haute Alsace . . . par Henry Sengre.
 The following maps relate to America:
 no. [1] Mappe-monde géo-hydrographique . . . par le s$^r$. Sanson . . . 1695.
  " [2] L'Asie . . . par le s$^r$. Sanson . . . 1695 [Isles Philippines]
  " [4] Amérique Septentrionale . . . par le s$^r$. Sanson. 1695.
  " [5] Partie de la Nouvelle France . . . H. Iaillot. 1695.
  " [6] Amérique Méridionale . . . par le s$^r$. Sanson . . . 1695.

### 1695–1697

**Coronelli, M. V.**
 Atlante veneto, nel quale si contiene la descrittione geografica, storica, sacra, profana, e politica, degl' imperÿ, regni, provincie, e stati dell' universo . . .   2 v. in 3. fol. Venetia, a' spese dell' autore, 1695–[1697]      521

 Note.—Collation: v. 1, 7 p. l., 154, 26, [14] pp., 28 maps, 32 pl.; v. 2, pt. 1, 6 p. l., 312 (*i. e.* 354), [9] pp. incl. 41 maps, 19 pl.; v. 2, pt. 2, 5 p. l., 166, 467–474 (*i. e.* 320), [4] pp. incl. 66 maps, 8 pl.
 v. 2 in 2 pts. entitled: Isolario descrittione . . . di tutte l' isole . . .

Imprint varies: v. 1: Venetia, 1695; v. 2: Venetia, a' spese dell' autore 1696. Dedication of v. 2 dated 1697.

Difference of opinion in regard to the author's given name—Brunet's Manuel du libraire, and British Museum catalogue use "Vincenzo Maria," and the author's signature to the dedication is the same. Bibliographers seem to have agreed on "Marco Vincenzo," notwithstanding the fact that the author himself is the best authority. It is probable that the error arose from changing the latin Marcus into the italian Marco, instead of Maria.

Woltersdorf's Repertorium der land- und seekarten, Wien 1813, cites an edition in 4 v., published at Venice and Padua, 1690-1696.

Grässe, Trésor de livres rares, cites the "Corso geograf. universale o sia la terra divisa nelle sue parti . . . exposte in tavole geografiche. Ven. 1692," adding in a note that the same maps with an accompanying text were published under the title, "Atlante veneto. Venetia, 1695."

The text, which precedes each map, is devoted to the geography and history of the country delineated, and contains innumerable maps and illustrations not included in the collation; also, a brief bibliography of each country.

Biographical notes of ancient and modern cartographers—v. 1, pp. [7-8]

References to the discoveries of the Zeno brothers: v. 1, p. 20, and maps [3], [9b], [11], [15]; v. 2, pt. 2, p. 165, and maps [22], [41]; no. [22] contains the following note: "Estotiland, ò Tierra de Laborador scoperta da Antonio Zeno N. Veneto nel 1390." Each map has a special dedication. v. 2 contains plans of cities, including the following: pt. 1, no. [1] Città di Venetia . . .—pt. 1, no. [4] Pianta iconografica di Venetia.—pt. 1, no. [30] Pianta della real fortezza e città di Candia.—pt. 1, no. [38] Città e fortezza di Malta.—pt. 2, no. [1] Londra.

The following maps relate to America:

v. 1, no. [2] Planisfero del mondo vecchio . . .
" " [3] Planisfero del mondo nuovo . . .
" " [4] La Lovisiana, parte settetrionalle . . .
" " [7b] Asia . . . [Las Felipinas]
" " [9a-b] America Settentrionale . . . 1688 . . .
" " [10] [America Meridionale]
" " [11-12] Terre Artiche . . .
" " [13] America Meridionale.
" " [14] Mare del Svd . . .
" " [15] Mare del Nord . . .
" " [28] Corso del fiume dell Amazoni . . .
v. 2, pt. 2, no. [22] Mare del Nord . . . [like v. 1, no. 15]
" " " [29] Isole dell' Indie diuise in Filippine, Molucche, e della Sonda . . .
" " " [36] Mare de Svd . . . [like v. 1, no. 14]
" " p. 156. [Mexico and Central America]
" " " 157. Isola e città di Cartagena . . .
" " " 158. Isola di Capo Breton.
" " no. [37] Canada . . .
" " " [38] Isola di Maria Galante . . .
" " " [39] Isole Antili, la Cuba, e la Spagnuola . . .
" " p. 163. La Spagomola . . .
" " no. [40] Isola Cuba . . .
" " " [41] Terre Artiche . . . [like v. 1, no. 11]

## 1695-1756?

**Ottens, R.,** *and* **Ottens, J.**

Atlas minor sive geographia compendiosa in qva orbis terrarvm pavcis attamen novissimis tabvlis ostenditvr.—Atlas nouveau, contenant toutes les parties du monde, où sont exactement remarquées les empires, monarchies, royaumes, états, républiques, &c. &c. &c. Receuillies des meilleurs auteurs. 2 v. 2 p. l., 86 maps, 1 chart, 2 pl., 3 tab.; 1 p. l., 102 maps, 3 pl., 1 tab. fol. Amsterdam, R. & J. Ottens [1695-1756?] 522

NOTE.—Engraved titles. See also title 616. Dates on maps vary from 1695-1734. Map no. 203, "Insulæ Americanæ," has on the margin the title "Stoel des oorlogs in America waar in vertoont werden alle desself voornaamste eylande nieuwelycks uytgegeven door Reinier & Josua Ottens," showing it was issued to illustrate the war between the french and british, beginning in 1756. In addition to those by Ottens, the maps are by: Alberti, Blaeu, Danckerts, Delisle, de Wit, Fricx, Gephart, Halley, Halma, Homann, Jaillot, Jansson, Kæmpfer, Leth, Loon, Moll, Persoy, Placide, Ram, Reland, Sanson, Schenk, Scheuchzer, Specht, Starckenburg, Valk, Visscher, Anse, Hogeboom, Hooghe, Keyser, Ruyter, Schut.

Title-page engraved by "I. van Munnikhause," colored by "L. Webbers."

Inset to map no. 202, "Totius Neobelgii nova et accuratissima tabula," is a view of New Amsterdam entitled, "Nieuw-Amsterdam onlangs Nieuw Jorck genâmt, ende hernomen by de Nederlanders op den 24 aug: 1673. eindelyk aan de engelse weder afgestaan." W. L. Andrews, in his New Amsterdam, New Orange, New York . . . 1897, says that this view was printed from the same plate as the view upon the map of Hugo Allard, 1673. "This engraving is supposed by Asher to have been executed by the celebrated Romeyn de Hooghe." See title 540.

The following is a list of the plates and tables:
v. 1, pl. 3. Sphærarum artificialium typica repræsentatio.
" pl. 5. Véritable représentation des premières matières ou éléments. Par A. de Wit.
" tab. 11. Historische en geographische tafel . . . vande landen en staaten in Europa.
" " 12. Poliometria Evropæ maxime avtem Germaniae ac finitimorvm locorvm.
" " 58. Kort begryp van Duytsland. By C. Specht [Contains a small map of Germany]
v. 2, " 100. Tafel van de xvii Nederlandze provincien. By C. Specht [Contains a small map of the Netherlands]
" pl. 207. Carte qui représente toutes les pièces qui sont comprises dans l'architecture militaire, ou l'art des fortifications.
" " 208. Doorgesneede Hollands admiraals schip, voerende 96 stukkenkanon.
" " 209. Schouw-park aller scheepsvlaggen des geheelen water-waerelds. Door Pieter Schenck. 1711.

The following maps relate to America:
v. 1, no. 6. Nova totius terrarum orbis tabula. Per F. de Witt.
" " 7-9. Nova & accuratissima totius terrarum orbis tabula nautica. Per Edm: Halley.

v. 2, no. 198. Recentissima novi orbis sive Americæ Septentrionalis et Meridionalis tabula. Per Fred. de Witt.
" " 199. Amérique Septentrionale. Per H: Iaillot.
" " 200. L'Amérique Méridionale. Par. H: Iaillot.
" " 201. Le Canada ou partie de la Nouvelle France. Par H: Iaillot.
" " 202. Totius Neobelgii nova et accuratissima tabula.
" " 203. Insulæ Americanæ.
" " 204. Tabula . . . Caraibicarvm insularum sive Cannibalvm.
" " 205. Nova isthmi Americani, qui et Panamiensis item Dariensis tabvla.
" " 206.' Nieuwe kaart van Suriname.

Maps no. 168-178, v. 2, relate to Japan; no. 168 is by Adrianus Reeland and was originally published in Recueil de voyages au Nord. Amst. 1713-1738; nos. 169-178 were originally made for Engelbert Kæmpfer's De beschryving van Japan, 1729.

The following is a list of the maps of Japan:
v. 2, no. 168. Imperivm Japonicvm . . . descriptvm ab Hadriano Relando.
" " 169. La ville de Nagasaki . . .
" " 170. . . . Route depuis Nagasaki jusqu'à Kokura.
" " 171. . . . Route depuis Kokura jusqu'à Khurissima.
" " 172. . . . Route depuis Khurissima jusqu'à Osacca.
" " 173. . . . Route par terre depuis Osacca jusqu'à Miaco, et depuis Miaco, jusqu'à Jokaitz.
" " 174. Plan de Miaco . . .
" " 175. . . . Route par terre depuis Jokaitz jusqu'à Fammamatz.
" " 176. . . . Route par terre depuis Fammamatz jusqu'à Farra.
" " 177. . . . Route par terre depuis Farra jusqu'à Jedo.
" " 178. Plan de Jedo . . .

Zach, in his Correspondance, Gênes, 1824, v. 10, pp. 161-473, article entitled, "Carte des îles du Japon et plan de la ville de Yedo", erroneously states concerning plans of Nagasaki, that, "il y a plus de deux siècles, on n'en ait cependant jamais eu un plan de ce port, jusqu'en 1805 qu'un *suisse* en ait fait un très-bon."

**Allard, C.**
### 1696?

Atlas minor, seu universi terrarum orbis geographicum compendium, recentiffimas, &a. Probandis auctoribus editas tabulas exhibens. 2 p. l., 150 (*i. e.* 142) maps on 296 l. fol. Amstelodami, ex officinâ Caroli Allard [1696?] 523

NOTE.—Date 1696 appears on maps:
no. 20. L'isle de Ré.
" 21. La Bretagne.
" 31. La Provence.

Woltersdorf's Repertorium der land-und seekarten, 1813, gives an "Atlas minor" by Allard, 1682.

Engraved, colored title reads: Atlas minor sive tabulæ geographicæ præcipuorum regnorum regionum, infularum provinciarum etc. Per Carolum Allard. Amstelodami apud Carolum Allard.

Maps by various cartographers including: Visscher, Wit, Lavaña, Jaillot, Templeux, Schenck, Sanson, Penez, Pynacker, Jansson de Waesberg, Ten Have, Sterringa, Valck, Witsen, J. Blaeu, Jansson and Loon.

Map no. 140, Totius Neobelgii nova et accuratissima tabula, has inset a very interesting early view of New Amsterdam entitled, "Nieuw-Amsterdam

**Allard, C.**—Continued.

onlangs Nieuw jorck genâmt, ende hermomen bij de Nederlanders op den 24 aug: 1673. eindelijk aan Engelse weder afgestaan," thought to be by Romain de Hooghe. Muller gives the date about 1674, and states that this Allard map is of greater rarity even than Visscher's map. Same map and view given in Ottens, "Atlas minor". See title 522.

The following maps relate to America:
- no. 1. Planisphærium terrestre.
- " 138. Recentifsima Novi Orbis sive Americæ Septentrionalis et Meridionalis tabula . . .
- " 139. America Septentrionalis. Amstelodami, excudit Iôhannes Ianssonius.
- " 140. Totius Neobelgii nova et accuratissima tabula.
- " 141. Virginiæ partis avftralis, et Floridæ partis orientalis . . .
- " 142. Nova Hispania et Nova Galicia.
- " 143. Insulæ Americanæ in Oceano Septentrionali ac regiones adiacentes . . . Per Nicolaum Visscher . . .
- " 144. Insvla S. Iuan de Puerto Rico Caribes; vel Canibasum infulæ.
- " 145. Americæ pars Meridionalis. Amftelodami sumptibus Ioannis Ianssony.
- " 146. Nova et accurata Brasiliæ totius tabula, auctore Ioanne Blaev . . .
- " 147. Perv. Amstelodami, apud Ioannem Ianfsonium.
- " 148. Chili. Amstelodami, Ioannes Ianfsonius exudit.
- " 149. Paraqvaria vulgo Paragvay cum adjacentibus. Ioannes Blaeu exc. Amstelædami.
- " 150. Tabula Magellanica, qua Tierræ del Fuego . . . Amstelodami apud Joannem Janfsonium.

## 1696

**Sanson, N.,** *d'Abbeville.*

Atlas nouveav, contenant toutes les parties du monde, où sont exactement remarqués les empires, monarchies, royaumes, estats, républiques & peuples qui sy [!] trouuent à present. 4 p. l., 16 pp., 22 l., 112 col. maps. fol. Paris, H. Iaillot, 1696. 524

NOTE.—"Nouvelle introduction à la géographie pour l'usage de monseigneur le dauphin. Par le s.r Sanson. Paris, H. Jaillot, 1696," pp. 1–16.

This has also a second title, with the imprint "Amsterdam, P. Mortier."

Latest date is 1696 which has been changed from an earlier date on many of the maps.

Engraved title, and "Table des cartes etc. du s.r Sanson . . . " colored.

Maps ornamented with views, plans, etc. and some accompanied by "Cartes géographiques . . ."

no. 35, Plan de la ville, cité, université et fauxbourgs de Paris . . . dressé sur les lieux & sur les mémoires de m.r Iouvin de Rochefort . . . 1694.

no. 107. Plan de la ville de Vienne . . .

The following maps relate to America:
- no. 5. Mappe-monde=géo-hydrographique, ou description générale du globe . . . 1696.
- " 13. Amérique Septentrionale . . . 1696.
- " 15. Amérique Méridionale . . .
- " 16. Le Canada ou partie de la Nouvelle France . . . 1696.

### 1697
**Ortelius, A.**
Teatro del mondo . . . nel quale fi dà notizia diftinta di tutte le prouincie, regni e paefi del mondo. Con la defcritione delle città, territorii, caftelli, monti, mari, laghi, e fiumi, le popolationi, i coftumi, le ricchezze, & ogn' altra particolarità. Ridotto à intiera perfettione, & inquesta picciol forma, per maggior commodità de' viaggianti. Con la tauola delle cose più degne, che nell opera fi contengono. 2 p. l., 237 pp. incl. 109 maps. 24°. In Venezia, D. Lovisa, 1697. 525

NOTE.—Collation: 2 l. unsig.—sig. A-I, K-P in eights.
l. [1] recto: title; verso: blank.—l. [2] recto-verso: Al lettore.—sig. [A] recto: blank; verso: "Carta marina."—sig. A2 rect-[O7] recto: Teatro del mundo; incl. 108 maps.—sig. [O7] verso-[P7] recto: Tavola delli nomi e particolarità contenute nella presente opera.—sig. [P7] verso; blank, 1 blank l. maps are on the verso of the leaves; the letterpress on the recto.
The following maps relate to America:
p. [2] Carta marina.
" [6] Typvs orbis terrarvm.
" [14] Americae sive novi orbis nova descriptio.

### 1698
**Ptolemæus, C.**
Claudii Ptolemaei | Tabulae geographicae | Orbis Teriarum | Veteribus cogniti. | [*Colophon:*] Trajecti ad Rhenum, | Apud {Francisvm Halmam}, | {Gviljelmvm vande Water,} | Bibliop. | et Franequeræ, | apud Leonardvm Strick, Bibliop. | MDCXCVIII. | 526

58 l. comprising: 2 p. l., 28 maps on 56 l. fol.
Collation: engraved title, verso blank; "Index Tabularum,", 1 l., ending on verso with colophon; 28 maps on 56 l. without text.
Excepting the colophon, this edition is similar to that of 1695. See title 518.
Woltersdorf's Repertorium der land- und seekarten, 1813, p. 35, gives an edition of 1695 with a colophon similar, excepting the date.

### 1700?
**Lea, P.**
[Hydrographia universalis, or the sea coasts of the known parts of the world. Containing general and particular charts of all the harbours, bayes, islands, &c. upon ye said coasts, according to actual surveys by several hands. To the right honbl. the lords and other of the principal officers of the admiralty. This book is most humbly dedicated by Philip Lea. Sold by Philip Lea at the Atlas and Hercules in Cheapside, near Friday street end] 101 maps, 5 pl. obl. 16°. [London, 1700?] 527

NOTE.—Title page wanting. By comparison with a description furnished by the British Museum, it appears that this is an imperfect copy of the same although there is a difference in size which may be explained by margins or binding.

**Lea, P.**—Continued.

The maps with ms. numbers correspond to the description of those in British Museum copy, numbered in ms. to 137.

The french charts have plate numbers, as used by a publisher to identify his own stock in his own shop, but not necessarily to denote the order of arrangement in an atlas.

Contains views of Messina,—Navarin,—Modon,—Napoli di Romania,—Port and mole of Algier.

no. [ 10] "A new map of the sea-coasts of England, Scotland and Ireland" . . . is indistinctly signed "H. Moll fecit 1699." This date is frequently mistaken for 1690.
" [ 64] "A prospect of White Bay and Conquest Road" . . . notes english and french naval action of may 10, 1694.
" [135] "Isthmus of Darien New Edenburgh & bay of Panama." New Edinburgh was founded in 1699, and surrendered to the spanish in 1700.

The following are wanting:

Colored title, with royal arms of William III. W. R., in two medallions, right and left of title.

no. [ 1] Zones.
" [ 2] Compass.
" [ 3] A ship in full rigging.
" [ 4] Compass.
" [ 5] Compass, dated feb. 1, 1655.
" [ 7] The world in two hemispheres, with two figures of Hercules as Atlas, and the arms of William the third. P. Lea.
" [ 8] The world according to Mercator's projection. P. Lea.
" [ 12] Tyne river.
" [ 13] Humber river.
" [ 14] Harwich.
" [ 15] West part of the river Thames. P. Lea.
" [ 30] Sea coast of England, Scotland, and Ireland . . .
" [ 31] Shetland & Orkney islands. Robert Gordon, with arms of James IV. duke of Hamilton.
" [ 32] Edinbourgh and Dundee.
" [ 33] Londonderry, by captain T. Phillips. P. Lea.
" [ 34] Dublin haven.
" [ 35] Kinsale.
" [ 36] North & Baltic Sea.
" [ 37] Danish islands.
" [ 38] Elbe.
" [ 39] Hamburg with the Four Lands.
" [ 40] Coast of Holland and Zeeland.
" [ 41] Table of high water, Picardy . . .
" [ 42] The Channel.
" [ 43] (1) Nieuport.
" [ 44] Dunkerkee.
" [ 45] (2) Calais . . .
" [ 46] (3) Ambletuse . . .
" [ 47] (4) Monstreiul . . .
" [126] Cariby Islands.
" [**136**] Potozi. P. Lea.

The following maps relate to America:
no. [6] A new mapp of all the earth . . .
" [9] North Pole. South Pole.
" [119] Newfoundland.
" [120] The english empire.
" [121] The harbour of Boston or Metathusets bay.
" [122] Ashley & Cooper river.
" [123] [Staten Island]
" [124] Pennsylvania and West Jersey.
" [125] Virginia & Mary-Land.
" [127] North Caribe islands.
" [128] South Caribe islands.
" [129] [Antegoa and Bermudas]
" [130] The island of Tobago, by P. Lea.
" [131] [Barbadoes]
" [132] Bahama islands, Cuba, Hispaniola, Jamaica. &c. P: Lea.
" [133] Havana in the island of Cuba.
" [134] The island of Jamaica.
" [135] Isthmus of Darien, New Edenburgh & bay of Panama.
" [137] Magellanick Streights & island.

**1700**

**Sanson, N.**, *d'Abbeville, and* **Sanson, N.,** *fils.*
Description de tout l'univers, en plufieurs cartes, & en divers traitez de géographie et d'histoire; où font décrits fuccinctement & avec une méthode belle & facile fes empires, fes peuples, fes colonies, leurs mœurs, langues, religions, richeffes, &c. Et ce qu'il y a de plus beau & de plus rare dans toutes fes parties & dans fes ifles. L'on a ajouté à cette nouvelle édition plufieurs cartes trés-exactes, qui ne fe trouvent point dans les éditions précédentes; comme aussi des tables géographiques pour l'intelligence des cartes; & un traité des globes céleftes & terreftres. Le tout à l'ufage de fon alteffe, monseigneur le prince électoral de Brandebourg. 6 pts. in 2 v. 8°. Amsterdam, F. Halma, 1700. 528

NOTE.—Collation: v. 1, 10 p. l., 30 pp., 1 l.; 102 pp., 1 l.; 98 pp., 1 l.; 82 pp., 1 l., 2 maps; v. 2, 120 pp.; 4 p. l., 144, [2], 145–256 pp., 1 l., 15 pl.
Folded title page in red and black.
Added folded title-page, engraved: Description de l'univers expliquée par m[rs] Sanson et Bion . . .
Each part has separate pagination; pts. 2-5 have half titles, pt. 6 has special title-page.
The following maps are bet. pp. 78–79: Le Paraguay subdivisé en ses principales parties . . . —Destroit de Magellan, terre et isles Magellanicques, &c. . . .

CONTENTS.

[ptie. 1] L'Europe [par N. Sanson le fils]
[ " 2] L'Asie.
[ " 3] L'Afrique.
[ " 4] L'Amérique.
[ " 5] **Tables géographiques** . . . tr. du latin de m[r] **Luyts.**
[ " 6] L'usage des globes célestes et terrestres . . . Recueillis par le sieur Bion. 1700.

## 1700?

**Seller, J.**

Atlas terrestris: or a book of mapps, of all the empires, monarchies, kingdoms, regions, dominions, principalities and countreys in the whole world. Accomodated with a brief description of the nature and quality of each perticular[!] countrey. 2 v.   1 p. l., 60 maps, 3 pl., 2 tab.; 46 maps, 14 pl., tab.   obl. 24°.   London [J. Seller, 1700?] 529

NOTE.—Engraved title.
Accompanying text: A new system of geography.  40 pp.  This was announced in the Term catalogue, february 1685.
The atlas is included in "A catalogue of mathematical books . . . made and sold by John Seller," found inserted in his "Atlas maritimus, 1675" and probably of a later date. Many of these maps were published in his Hydrographia universalis. . . [1690?]  See title 505.
Map no. 2, v. 1, dated 1700; no. 21, "sold by J. Seller, jun°."
British Museum copy dated [1676] may be an earlier edition.
This copy "Varies much from copy in British Museum; those maps with * not being in that copy, while their copy has some not in this."  Henry N. Stevens.
British Museum copy does not contain "A new system of geography."

### CONTENTS.

v. 1, [no.   I] Spheræ materialis.
"     [ "    II] A mapp of the world.
"     [ "    III] A mapp of the five zones.
"     [ "    IV] Pixis nautica.
"     [ "    V] Scales of miles and leagues of diverse nations . . .
"   no.  1.* A new & correct sea chart of the whole world.
"    "    2.* A mapp of the world, shewing what a [!] clock it is (at any time) in any part of the world.
"    "    3.  A mapp of the North Pole.
"    "    4.  A mapp of the South Pole.
"    "    5.  The Planisphere of the antients.
"    "    6.* A new map of the world.
"    "    7.* A mapp shewing how the world was divided among the sons of Noah after the flood.
"    "    8.* A geneological table of the sons of Noah.
"    "    9.  Europe.
"    "    10.* A chart of the sea coast from the Land end of England to Cape Bona Esperanta.
"    "    11.  A new mapp of Great Britain and Ireland.
"    "    12.* A plat of the channel.
"    "    13.* A new chart of the channel.
"    "    14.  A new mapp of England and Wales.
"    "    15.* A new chart of the Isle of Wight and Portſmouth.
"    "    16.* The river Dee.
"    "    17.  The principality of Wales.
"    "    18.  Scotland.
"    "    19.* The iſlands of Orkney.
"    "    20.  Ireland.
"    "    21.* A mapp of the sea coaſt of England, France & Holland.
"    "    22. . France.

**Seller, J.**—Continued.
    v. 1, no. 23.* A chart of S⁺. Malo.
    " " 24. The xvii provinces.
    " " 25. The ten spanish provinces.
    " " 26. A map of the seven provinces.
    " " 27.* Comitatus Holandiæ.
    " " 28.* A mapp of Zeland.
    " " 29.* The province of Zutphen and the river Isell.
    " " 30.* Groenin gæ dominii.
    " " 31.* Comitatus Frisiæ.
    " " 32.* County of Flanders.
    " " 33.* The duchie of Limbourg.
    " " 34.* The duchy of Luxembourg.
    " " 35.* The duchy of Brabant.
    " " 36.* Marquifat of the holy empire.
    " " 37.* The county of Alost.
    " " 38.* The county of Artois.
    " " 39.* The county of Hainault.
    " " 40.* The county of Namur.
    " " 41.* Namur and the adjacent country.
    " " 42.* The seigniory of Malines.
    " " 43.* The duchy of Gueldre.
    " " 44.* Duchy of Cambra.
    " " 45.* The county of Burgundy.
    " " 46.* Germany [B. M. copy without text]
    " " 47. Denmark.
    " " 48.* A chart of the Baltick sea.
    " " 49.* Swedeland and Norway [B. M. copy without text]
    " " 50.* Moscovia or Russia.   "   "   "   "
    " " 51. Poland.
    " " 52.* Lithuania.
    " " 53. Hungaria and Sclavonia.
    " " 54. Turkey in Europe.
    " " 55. The south part of Turky in Europe.
    " " 56. The northern part of Turky in Europe.
    " " 57. Italy.
    " " 58.* A chart of the Mediterranean sea.
    " " 59. Spaine.
    " " 60. Portugal.
    v. 2, no. [i] Hypothefis Ptolomaica.
    " " [ii] Hypothefis Tychonica.
    " " [iii] Hypothefis Copernicana.
    " " [iv] A mapp of yᵉ two hemispheres of yᵉ heavens.
    " " [v] A mapp of the constellations about yᵉ North Pole.
    " " [vi] Schema corporis solaris . . .
    " " [vii] Phasis lunæ naturalis.
    " " [viii] Phasis lunæ artificialis.
    " " [ix] Phafes-Planetarum.
    " " [x*] The syfteme of Jupiter.—The phafis of Venus & Mars.
    " " [xi] Incrementum et decrementum dierum.—Syftema Saturni.
    " " [xii] Æstus maris per motum lunæ r. des cartes.—Illuminatio lunæ per solem.
    " " [xiii*] The eclipse of the moon.—The eclipse of the sun.
    " " [xiv] Scales of miles and leagues, of diverfe nations.

**Seller, J.**—Continued.

v. 2, no. 1. Asia.
" " 2.* China [B. M. copy without text]
" " 3. Empire of Mogol.
" " 4.* India beyond Ganges [B. M. copy without text]
" " 5.* India on this side Ganges [B. M. copy without text]
" " 6.* Persia. " " " "
" " 7.* Turky in Asia. " " " "
" " 8. Lesser Tartaria.
" " 9. Georgia.
" " 10. Arabia.
" " 11.* A map of Canaan as it was divided in Abraham's time . . .
" " 12.* Canaan as it was divided into 31 kingdomes . . .
" " 13.* The journey of the israelites in the defert of Paran.
" " 14.* The land of Canaan.
" " 15.* Canaan as it was divided into the provinces of Jewry, Samaria and Galilee.
" " 16.* A mapp shewing the travels of st. Paul.
" " 17. Africa.
" " 18. Ægypt.
" " 19. A mapp of Biledulgerid, Defart of Saara [!] county of Negros and Guinea.
" " 20. The kingdom and desart of Barca.
" " 21. The kingdomes of Tunis and Tripoli.
" " 22. The kingdom of Alger [!]
" " 23. The kingdom of Tesset, Darha & Segelomess.
" " 24. The kingdom of Moroco in Barbary.
" " 25. The kingdom of Fez.
" " 26. The ifland of Saint Helena.
" " 27. South America.
" " 28.* Brasil [B. M. copy without text]
" " 29. Terra Firma.
" " 30. The Amazones country.
" " 31. Peru.
" " 32. Paraguay.
" " 33. The Magellanick land.
" " 34. Chili.
" " 35. North America.
" " 36.* A chart of y$^e$ Western ocean.
" . " 37.* New Found Land.
" " 38.* A chart of the West Indies.
" " 39. Insulæ Jamaicæ
" " 40. The ifland of Barbados.
" " 41. Mexico or New Spaine.
" " 42. Carolina.
" " 43. Virginia and Maryland.
" " 44. Pensilvania.
" " 45. New England and New York.
" " 46. New Iarsey [!]
" " 47.* A generall description of the several parts of fortification.

**1700?**

**Voogt, C. J.**
La nueva, y grande relumbrante antorcha de la mar, que contiene. Todas las coftas meredionales, y septentrionales, el canal a la parte del poniente d' Ingalatierra, Efcocia, Yrlanda, Francia, Efpaña, Marrocos, Galatia, Genehoa, y Gambia con las islas Terceras, de Canarias, y las de la Sal. Como tambien las coftas del otro lado de Gujana, Cartagena nueva, Cofta Rico, d'Honduras, Yuctan, Mexico, Florida, Carolina, Virginia, Nueva Francia, Tierra nueva, y coftas septentrionales de America; y mas Guinea, Angola, y toda Oftende con la cofta del Brazil hafta el eftrecho de Magallanes, y todo el mar meredional . . . fol. Amsterdam, J. van Keulen [1700?]  530

>NOTE:—Collation: title, eng. title, 1 l.;
>Parte nueva . . . Libro primero. Que contiene, las difcripciones de las coftas maritimas de Holanda, Zelanda, Flandes, y de la ribera de Londres, de Teffel, y Ael-Burg, hafta los Cabos . . . 21 pp., 12 maps, 1 astronomical chart.
>Segunda parte . . . El segundo livro, que contiene, la defcription de las coftas maritimas de Francia, de Cales, hafta Oudejarne, y de las costas meridionales, y occidentales d' Inglaterra como tambien de la costa occidental d' Efcocia de Dowré hafta el cabo de Wrath, y las coftas maritimas de Irlanda. 22–57 pp., 10 maps.
>pp. 29–32 bound in wrongly; pp. 29, 39 & 44 wrongly numbered 31, 55 & 40 respectively.
>Segunda parte . . . El segundo livro, que contiene, la difcripcion de Francia, Biscaya, Galicia, Portugal, Algarve, depuis Oudejarne, hasta el Rache. 58–83 pp., 18 maps.
>Livro quarto; que contiene, las coftas de Berberia y Galata Argun, Geneœ y las islas de Canary y las islas de J. Jago y la Rache al Cabo de Cantin. 84–98 pp., 8 maps.— . . . El primero libro, que contiene, la defcripcion de las coftas maritimas de Guinea y Angola de Caffers desde el Cabo de Verde hafta el Cabo de buena efperança, Indias orientales, y mar meridional, con las iflas que eftan entre efa cofta y la cofta del Brafil. 1 p. l., 20 pp., 11 maps.
>Libro segundo, que contiene, la description delas costas maritimas de Brazil. 20 pp., 9 maps.
>Parte quarta, demueftra las coftas maritimas de Guiana, Venezuela, Cartagena Nueva, Cofta Rica, de Honduras, Jucatan, Mexico, Florida, Carolina, Virginia, Nuevo Pais Baxo, Nueva Inglaterra, Nuevo Francia, Tierra Nueva, y las coftas maritimas septentrionales dela America, con las iflas, que le pertenecen, y eftàn entre ellas . . . Por Nicolas Jansz. Vooght . . . Amsterdam, J. van Keulen, 1698. eng. title, 1 l., 52 pp., 28 maps. p. 4 wrongly numbered 2.
>At the top of page 1 of this part is a title similar to the above, except that it commences with the words "Tercera parte."
>The arrangement of this volume is irregular and inconsistent. Although the text of the atlas is in spanish, the titles of the maps are in dutch. Throughout the text are numerous delineations of the coasts in woodcut.
>The date on the first engraved title-page is "Anno de 170." [!] The "privilegio" on its reverse is dated "23 octubre 1695;" also the two other privileges in the book. The last engraved title-page, "Parte Quarta," is dated "Año de

**Voogt, C. J.**—Continued.

1698," and the dedicatory poem following has the same date. The dates on the maps vary from 1680 to 1695.

The maps, in addition to those by Voogt, bear the names of: Ludovicus Vlasblom, Nikolaas DeVries, Gerrard van Keulen, Ervaren Stuurlieden, I. Stevinkhof, and P. Pickart.

The following maps relate to America:

no. 2. Wafsende graade kaart van alle bekende zeekuften op den geheelen aardbodem . . .
" 3. . . . Noordlyckfte deel van Europa . . .
" 50. . . . Gedeelte van de custen van Africa en America . . .
" 51. . . . Zee custen van Guinea en Brasilia . . .
" 60–69. . . . Zee-kusten van Brazilia . . .
" 70. . . . Zuyd zee en een gedeelte van Brasil . . .
" 71. . . . West Indien . . .
" 72. . . . Zee-kusten van Guiana . . .
" 73. . . . Rivieren Commewini, Suriname en Cupanama . . .
" 74. . . . Kuft van Guiana . . .
" 75. . . . Rio Oronoque, golfo de Paria . . .
" 76. . . . Pas kaart van de Caribes . . .
" 77. . . . T'eyland S. Iuan de Porto Rico, met d'eylanden daar beooften . . .
" 78. . . . Zee kuften van Venecuela . . .
" 79. . . . Zuyd-kuft van Espanjola met de zee kust van Nuevo Reyne de Granada . . .
" 80. . . . Noord kuft van Espaniola . . .
" 81. . . . Zee kusten van Carthagena, Tierra Firma, Costa Rica ende Honduras . . .
" 82. . . . Zuyd kuft van Cuba en van geheel Yamaica . . .
" 83. . . . Golff de Guanaios . . .
" 84. . . . Golff van Mexico . . .
" 85. . . . Boght van Florida . . .
" 86. . . . Noord oost kuft van Cuba en d'ooft kust van Florida . . .
" 87. . . . I. la Barmuda . . .
" 88. . . . Kuft van Carolina . . .
" 89. . . . Kuften van Virginia . . .
" 90. . . . Kuften van Niew Nederland . . .
" 91. . . . Zee kuften inde boght van Niew Engeland . . .
" 92. . . . Zee-kuften van Terra Nova . . . Francia Nova, Canada en Accadie . . .
" 93. . . . Grand Banq by Terra Neuff . . .
" 94. . . . Noorder zee cuften van America . . .
" 97. . . . Noord oost cuft van Asia . . .

### 1700

**Wells, E.**

A new sett of maps both of antient and present geography . . . Together with a geographical treatise particularly adapted to the use and design of these maps. 2 p. l., 41 maps. fol. Oxford, theatre, 1700. 531

NOTE.—"A treatise of antient and present geography" to accompany this atlas, is wanting. See also title 564.

Library of Congress has the 4th edition of the "Treatise of antient and present geography. London, 1726." Atlas wanting.
The following maps relate to America:
no. [ 1] A new map of the . . . globe according to the ancient discoveries . . .
" [ 2] A new map of the globe . . . according to the latest discoveries . . .
" [28] A new map of present Asia . . . [Philippine islands]
" [30] A new map of the East Indies . . . from m. de Fer's map of Asia . . . [Philippine islands]
" [30] A new map of North America . . .
" [39] " " " " South "
" [41] " " " " the plantations of the english in America.

## 1700–1704

**Fer, N. de.**

[L'atlas curieux, ou, le monde représenté dans des cartes générales et particulières du ciel et de la terre divisé tant en ses quatre principales parties que par états et provinces et orné par des plans et descriptions des villes capitales et principales, et des plus superbes édifices qui les embelissent: comme sont les églises, les palais, les maisons de plaisance, les iardins, les fontaines &c. . . .] 1 p. l., [89] l., 121 maps, 27 pl. obl. 4°. Paris, de Fer, 1700–[1704] 532

NOTE.—Issued in five annual parts from 1700-1704; pt. 1, with "Titre général," pt. 2, "Titre en port de mer," pt. 5, "Titre." This copy wants general title but contains in the middle of the volume an engraved "Titre en port de mer" dated 1700. See also title 546.
Probably published in 1704 upon completion of pt. 5 which is here included with the exception of title and (1) "Veuë de Verfailles;" (2) "Ecuries du roy à Verfailles;" (3) "Marquifat du saint empire, & la ville d'Anvers."
According to "Table . . . de cet ouvrage en 1703" including the first four parts, the following are wanting:
no. [ 1] Titre général.
" [ 2] Figures de la sphère & des globes artificiels.
" [ 6] Planisphères terrestres.
" [14] Veuë des Invalides.
" [65] Palais & places de Madrid.
" [75] Détroit de Gibaltar[!]
Description of:
no. [ 3] Différens sistêmes.
" [ 5] Mappemonde quarrée.
" [12] Environs de Paris.
" [54] Bas Cologne.
" [69] Plan de Madrid.
Geographical arrangement of plates without reference to the five parts. One leaf of descriptive text accompanying each plate.
Contains numerous plans of cities and the following folded views of Meudon by Israel Silvestre issued with pt. 5, in 1704:
Veüe de château du Meudon du côté de l'entrée apartenant à monseigneur le marquis de Louvois . . . [n. d.]
Veüe du château de Meudon du côté du jardin . . . 1685.
Veüe du château de Meudon du côté du village de Fleury . . . 1688.
Veüe du jardin et parc du château de Meudon . . . 1686.
Veüe du parterre de la grotte du château de Meudon . . . 1685.

**Fer, N. de**—Continued.
   Veüe de la grotte de Meudon . . . [n. d.]
   The following maps relate to America:
   no. [ 4] Mappe-monde, ou carte universelle . . . 1702.
   " [ 8] L'Amérique, Méridionale et Septentrionale . . . 1700.
   " [138] Les isles Philippines . . . 1702.
   " [139] Le Canada, ou Nouvelle France, la Floride, la Virginie, Penfilvanie, Caroline, Nouvelle Angleterre et Nouvelle Yorck, l'isle de Terre Neuve, la Louifiane . . . 1702.
   " [140] Les costes aux environs de la rivière de Misisipi . . . 1701.
   " [141] . . . Carte de Californie et du Nouveau Mexique . . . 1700.
   " [142] Le vieux Mexique ou Nouvelle Espagne auec les costes de la Floride . . . 1702.
   " [143] Les isles de l'Amérique . . . 1702.
   " [144] La Terre Ferme et le Pérou avec les pays des Amazones et le Brésil . . . 1702.
   " [145] Plan des villes, forts, port, rade et environs de Cartagène . . . 1700.
   " [146] Le Chili et les provinces qui composent celle de Rio de la Plata . . . 1702.
   " [147] Le détroit de Magellan . . . 1700.

### 1700–1712

**Delisle, G.**
   [Atlas de géographie]   59 maps.   fol.   [Paris 1700–1712]   533
   NOTE.—See also titles 535, 580, 581, 594, 596 and 636. Collection of maps dated 1700–1712, relating to Europe, Asia, Africa, America, to the history of the ancients and of the middle ages, by Guillaume Delisle, bound together in an atlas, without title page.
   "Liste des ouvrages géographiques de Guillaume de l'Isle . . . avec le tems auquel ils ont été publiéz" . . . Pasted on the verso of the front cover.
   The following maps relate to America:
   no. [1] Mappe-monde. 1700.
   " [44] L'Amérique Septentrionale. 1700.
   " [45] Carte du Canada. 1703.
   " [46] Carte du Mexique. 1703.
   " [47] L'Amérique Méridionale. 1700.
   " [48] Carte de la Terre Ferme. 1703.
   " [49] Carte du Paraguay . . . 1703.
   " [50] Theatrum historicum ad annum . . . quadringentesimū. 1705.

### 1700—1724

**Jaillot, C. H. A.** *& others.*
   Atlas françois, contenant les cartes géographiques dans lesquelles sont très exactement remarquez les empires, monarchies, royaumes et estats de l'Europe, de l'Asie, de l'Afrique et del'Amérique: avec les tables et cartes particulières, de France, de Flandre, d'Allemagne, d'Espagne et d'Italie.   1 p. l., 57 maps.   fol.   Paris, chez le sr. Jaillot, 1700–[1724]   534
   NOTE.—Engraved title.
   Maps dated 1700–1724.
   Contains a plan of Paris and its environs.

The following maps relate to America:
no. [1] Mappe-monde géo-hydrographique . . . par le sr. Sanson . . . 1719.
" [4] L'Asie . . . [Isles Phillippines] par le sr. Sanson . . . 1719.
" [6] Amérique Septentrionale . . . par le sr. Sanson . . . 1719.
" [7] Amérique Méridionale . . . par le sr. Sanson . . . 1719.

## 1700-1763

**Delisle, G.**
[A collection of maps of the world] 94 maps, 1 plan, 1 pl. fol. [Paris, 1700–1763] 535

NOTE.—No title-page. See also titles 533, 580, 581, 594, 596 and 636. Contains a "Plan de la ville et fauxbourgs de Paris, 1716."
The following maps relate to America:
no. [1] Mappemonde . . . 1754.
" [3] Hémisphère occidental. 1760.
" [4] Hémisphère septentrional. 1714.
" [5] Hémisphère méridional. 1714.
" [62] Carte des Indes et de la Chine. 1705.
" [66] Carte des nouvelles découvertes au nord de la mer du Sud.
" [72] Carte d'Amérique. 1763.
" [73] Carte du Canada ou de la Nouvelle France. 1703.
" [74] Carte de la Louisiane et du cours du Mississipi. 1745.
" [75 a] Carte du Mexique et de la Floride. 1713.
" [77] Carte de l'isle de Saint Domingue. 1725.
" [78] Carte des Antilles françoises et des isles voisines. 1717.
" [79] Carte de l'isle de la Martinique. 1732.
" [80] Carte de la partie de l'océan vers l'équateur entre les côtes d'Afrique et d'Amérique: plan de l'isle de Fernand de Noronha. 1737.
" [81] Carte de la Terre Ferme du Pérou, du Brésil et du pays des Amazones. 1703.
" [82] Carte du Paraguay, du Chili, du détroit de Magellan . . . 1703.

## 1701

**Moll, H.**
A system of geography: or, a new & accurate description of the earth in all its empires, kingdoms and states. Illustrated with history and topography, and maps of every country, fairly engraven on copper, according to the latest discoveries and corrections . . . 3 p. l., 4, [28], 26 pp., 1 l., [2], 444 pp. incl. front., 20 maps; 1 l., 230, [26] pp. incl. 23 maps. fol. London, for T. Childe, 1701. 536

NOTE.—Pagination irregular; 2 pts. in 1 v.
"Some perſons by not looking enough into this Syſtem of geography have concluded it only a new edition of the late Theſaurus geographicus . . . Though part of it, ſo far as to the end of the deſcription of Germany be the fame, the rest is entirely [!] new . . . The rest of the deſcription of Europe was written by mr. Rob. Falconer . . . The other parts are tranſlated from mr. Luyts . . ." cf. Advertisement, p. 4. A copy of "Thesaurus geographicus. London, for A. Swall & T. Child, 1695," in the Library of Congress, with following maps of America: p. 473, America.—p. 480, A map of the english plantations in America.

**Moll, H.**—Continued.
The following maps relate to America:
no. [1] The world in planisphere.
p. 148. America.
" 152. The ifle of California, New Mexico, Louisiane, the river Misisipi and the lakes of Canada . . .
" 161. The english empire in America, Newfound-land, Canada, Hudsons bay &c. in plano . . .
" 178. Mexico, or New Spain . . .
" 199. Terra Firma and the Caribbé iflands &c. . . .
" 203. Brasil, divided into its captainships . . .
" 206. The great province of Rio de la Plata . . .
" 209. Peru and the Amazones country . . .
" 214. Chili, Magellans-land and Terra del Fuego . . .

### 1702?
**Mortier, P.**

Les forces de l'Europe, Asie, Afrique et Amérique ou description des principales villes, avec leurs fortifications. Deffignées par les meilleurs ingénieurs, particulièrement celles qui sont sous la domination de la France, dont les plans ont efté levez par monfieur de Vauban, avec la defcription de tous les inftrumens fervans à la fortification, à l'attaque & deffenfe des places, enfemble ceux qui fervent pour l'artillerie, des magafins; la manière de dresser un camp devant une ville assiégée, &c. Et ornées de plufieurs fuperbes édifices. Ouvrage nécessaire pour toutes sortes de personnes. 2 v. obl. fol. Amsterdam, P. Mortier [1702?] 537

NOTE.—Collation: v. 1, 1 p. l., [2] pp., 6 l., 132 maps, 26 pl.; v. 2, title, 6 l., 124 maps, 23 pl.
Date 1702 on maps no. 34, v. 1, and no. 274, v. 2.
Originally published by Nicolas de Fer at Paris in 1694–1697. See also title 517a. The plates were copied by Pieter Mortier at Amsterdam for the present edition. Mortier's plates were bought by van der Aa, who reissued them with many others in an edition published at Paris and Leide, 1726.
The following maps relate to America:
v. 1, no. 160. Quebec.
" " 161. Bay et chateav de Porto Bello.
" " 162. Baye et ville de Havana ou S. Christoval.
" " 163. Cartagene avec ses ports, et fortresses.

### 1702
**Allard, C.**

Magnum theatrum belli, quousque se hodie in orbe extendit; continens novissimas & perfectissimas, tam particulares quam generales, tabulas geographicas Germaniæ, Belgii, Hungariæ, Italiæ, Galliæ, Hispaniæ, Magnæ Britanniæ, Scandinaviæ, Poloniæ, Moscoviæ, Asiæ, Americæ, et Africæ. Cum speciali indice, quô cujuslibet tabulæ notabilia exhibentur. Het groot tooneel des oorlogs, zo ver

dezelve zich tegenwoordig in de waereld uitstrekt . . . [2] pp.,
54 maps, pl. fol. Amstelo Batavo [C. Allard, 1702] 538

NOTE.—Latin and dutch titles.
Maps generally are not dated. The latest date 1702, occurs in the border text of no. [46], "Vigo, ville, fort et port . . ." and in the index on the verso of the title-page.
An edition of 1700 is described in Tiele's Nederlandsche bibliographie.
no. [18] is dedicated to "D. Ferdinando Iosepho de Croy, duci de Havre . . ." The year of his death, 1694, may be an approximate date of this map.
A collection of maps by various cartographers, including: N. Visscher, F. de Wit, le sr. Sanson and A. Penez.
The following maps relate to America:
no. [51] . . . Asiæ . . . [Philippinæ insulæ]
" [52] . . . Americæ Septentrionalis et Meridionalis . . .
" [53] Insulæ Americanæ in oceano Septentrionali ac regiones adiacentes . . .

## 1702
**Scherer, H.**
Atlas Marianus sive præcipvæ totivs orbis habitati imagines et statuæ magnæ Dei matris beneficiis ac prodigiis inclytæ succincta historia propositæ et mappis geographicis expressæ. 5 p. l., 130, [12] pp., 23 maps. 4°. Monachii, M. M. Rauchin, 1702. 538a

NOTE.—Engraved title. Maps have engraved titles. Text in double columns.
"C'est l'abrégé de l'*Atlas Marianus* [edition of 1682] du p. [Wilhelm] Gumppenberg" *cf.* Backer's Bibliothèque de la compagnie de Jésus, 1890.
This work forms v. 3 of his "Tabellae geographicae . . . Monachi, M. Rauchin, 1703," in 8 v. 4°. *cf.* Sabin's Bibliotheca Americana.
The following maps relate to America:
no. [1] [Map of the world, with corner illustrations representing Europe, Asia, Africa & America]
" [4] Africæ dei mater Alicubi nota & haec ibidem benefica. 1699.
" [5] America borealis . . . 1699.
" [6] America avstralis . . . [n. d.]

## 1702-1750
**Homann, J. B.**
Atlas novus terrarum orbis imperia, regna et status exactis tabulis geographicè demonstrans. 1 p. l., 61 maps, 3 pl., 4 diagr. fol. Noribergæ [1702-1750] 539

NOTE.—Title-page is hand colored and a duplicate of that in his Grosser atlas über die gantze welt . . . Nürnberg, 1737.
Maps, dated 1702-1750, are hand colored and ornamented with many engravings.
Contains maps and plans by various cartographers, including: Tobias Mayer, T. Danckerts, A. F. Zürner, J. M. Hasi, Matthæus Seutter and Homann heirs.
Contains plans of the following cities:
no. 57. Dantzig und ihrem werder . . .
" 58. Magdeburg . . .
" 59. . . . Hamburg . . .

**Homann, J. B.**—Continued.
no. 61. . . . Leipzig . . .
" 62. . . . Florentiæ . . . 1731.
" 63. . . . Breslau . . .
" 64. Berlin . . .
" 65. Mantua . . .
" 66. Mayland . . . 1734.
" 67. Franckfurt am Mayn . . .
The following maps relate to America:
no. 1. Planiglobii terrestris . . .
" 3. Geographische universal zeig und schlag-uhr . . .
" 6. Représentation de l'éclipse partiale de la lune . . . 1748.
" 11. Asiæ . . . [Insulæ Philippinæ]
" 13. Iotius Americae Septentrionalis et Meridionalis . . .

## 1703?
**Danckerts, J.**

Atlas. eng. title, 90 col. maps, 4 pl., 2 tab., 74 maps and views of cities on 4 double pages. fol. Tot Amsterdam, bij Iustus Danckers in de Calverstraet in de Dancbaerheijt [1703?]  540

NOTE.—See also title 541. The engraved title-page represents a globe upon the top of which stands the figure of Atlas supporting the heavens. The maps are variously signed by Justus, Cornelis, Theodorus, Johannes and Justinus Danckerts. The other authors and engravers whose names appear on the maps are "A. van Luchtenburg," " Frederici de Wit," "A. Schut," " I. de Bróen," and "Remmet Teunisse Backer."
nos. 69-70 are parts of a large map of Brabantia, Lotnaringia, etc., which is incomplete, wanting a sheet containing part of the title.
The following maps relate to America:
no. 2. Nieuw aerdsch pleyn.
" 5. Nova totius terrarum orbis tabula.
" 8. Recentissima novi orbis sive Americæ Septentrionalis et Meridionalis tabula.
" 98. Novi Belgii Novæque Angliæ nec non Pennsylvaniæ et partis Virginiæ tabula multis in locis emendata.
This map contains an inset view of New York city entitled, "Nieuw Yorck, eertijs genaemt Nieuw Amsterdam op't eylant Manhattans." The view dates back to 1655 (?) being a copy from the second known view of New York, *i. e.*, that on N. J. Visscher's map of about that date . . . The Danckerts map contains the city of Philadelphia which was founded in 1683. The rest of the map represents a much earlier period, and it has been surmised that " Philadelphia" was added to an old plate without making any other change.
The date 1703 appears on table numbered 10. On this table the king of Spain is given as " Philippus de v of Carolus III," which shows that the table was made during the war of the spanish succession, 1699-1714. The theatre of this war is shown in maps no. 21, "Sedes belli in Dauphinæ et Provincæ;" no. 23, "Le théatre de la guerre dans les Sévennes;" no. 25, "Sedes belli in Italia;" no. 27, "Sedes belli in Italiâ;" no. 28, "Sedes belli in Italia."
no. 3, "Nieuwe hemels spiegel" is dedicated to Frederick III elector of Brandenburg. Frederick III was elector from 1688-1701. He then became king Frederick I of Prussia (1701-1713), and it was forbidden to speak of him as elector. This chart must therefore have been made between 1688-1701.

Larousse states that the publisher of this atlas, Justus Danckerts, whose name appears upon the title page, died between the years 1690–1695. However, if we assume that all the maps in the atlas were published during the life of Justus Danckerts, the date of his death must be as late as 1703. He would then have been 73 years old. On the other hand, the map dated 1703 and the maps of the "seat of war" may have been inserted in the atlas at a later date. It is possible that the sons of Justus after his death continued to use his name as a firm name.

## 1703?

**Danckerts, J.**
Atlas. 1 p. l., 100 col. maps, 1 l. fol. Amsterdam, I. Danckers [1703?] 541

NOTE.—Engraved, colored title. See also title 540. On map no. 94, "Pelonnesus hodie Moreæ Regnum", the date 1687 occurs four times. The date 1703 was supplied from the first copy of Danckerts' Atlas in which it occurs on pl. 10, "Historische en geographische tafel". On this table the king of Spain is given as "Philippus de v of Carolus III", which shows that the table was made during the war of the spanish succession, 1699–1714. Although the table does not appear in this atlas the following map, no. 22, "Le théâtre de la guerre dans les Sévennes avec les plaines des environs de Lanquedoc", is a duplicate of one of the five maps, showing the theatre of the war of the spanish succession, 1699–1714, which appears in title 540.

Most of the maps carry the name of the Danckerts,—Justus, Cornelius, Theodore, or Johann. Other maps are by various cartographers, including Abraham Allard, Frederick de Wit, Carl Allard, P. Du Val, and Nicolas Witsen.

Six of the seven maps bearing the name of Carl Allard are taken from his "Atlas minor", 1696?

The following maps relate to America:

no. 2. Nova totius terrarum orbis tabula . . . per I. Danckerts.
" 3. Recentissima novi orbis, sive Americæ . . . Caroli Allard.
" 4. Insulæ Americanæ . . . par Cornelium Danckerts.
" 5. Novi Belgii Novæque Angliæ nec non Pennsylvaniæ et partis Virginiæ tabula . . . a Iufto Danckers. This map contains an inset view of New York city entitled, "Nieuw Yorck eertijs genaemt Nieuw Amsterdam op't eylant Manhattans". For note on this map, see title 540.

## 1703–1756?

**Ottens, R.,** *and* **Ottens, J.**
Atlas minor sive geographia compendiosa in qva orbis terrarum pavcis attamen novissimis tabvlis ostenditvr.—Atlas nouveau, contenant toutes les parties du monde, où sont exactement remarquées les empires, monarchies, royaumes, etats, repubuliques, &c. &c. &c. receuillies des meilleurs auteurs. 2 p. l., 48 maps, 1 tab., 1 chart. fol. Amsterdam, R. & J. Ottens [1703–1756?] 542

NOTE.—Engraved title.
See also title 522. The title page, uncolored, is engraved by "I. van Munnikhuyse", and drawn by "L. Webbers." In addition to those by

**Ottens, R.,** *and* **Ottens, J.**—Continued.
  Ottens, the atlas contains maps by: Cantelli, Delisle, Halma, Husson, Jaillot, Leth, Sanson, Schenk, Specht, Starckenburg, Visscher.—Anse, Hogeboom, Keyser, Moll. Maps numbered 2, 3, 10, 15, 19, 28, 31, 32, 37, 42, 46, 47, and 48 were published by Schenk, who died in 1715. Map no. 10 dated 1703; maps no. 47 and 48 dated 1708; other maps without dates.
  Table no. 50 is entitled, "Poliometria Evropae maxime avtem Germaniae ac finitimorvm locorvm".
  The following maps relate to America:
  no. 2. Planisphærium terrestre cum utroque coelesti hemisphærio. Opera A. F. Zürneri [1712?]
  "   3. Europæ in tabula geographica delineatio. Opera A. F. Zürneri [1712?]
  "  46. Americæ . . . delineatio. Opera A. F. Zürneri [1712?]
  "  47. L'Amérique Septentrionale. Par G. Del'Isle. 1708.
  "  48. L'Amérique Méridionale. Par G. Del'Isle. 1708.
  "  49. Insulæ Americanæ. On the margin is a title in dutch, "Stoel des oorlogs in America waarin vertoont werden alle desself voornaamste eylande nieuwelycks uytgegeven door Reinier & Josua Ottens", showing that this map was issued to illustrate the war between the french and british, which began in 1756.

### 1703–1807

**Dalrymple, A.,** *& others.*
  [Charts and plans]   3 v.   obl. fol. (v. 3. fol.)   [London, 1703–1807]   543
  NOTE.—Without title page. Dates on maps vary from 1703–1807.
  The following maps are reproductions:—
  v. 2, no. 34. . . . Iaponiæ terræ Esonis . . . 1658.
  "    "   158. Part of a map of America . . . 1574.
  "    "   159. Part of . . . chart of Asia . . . 1646.
  "    "   160. North coast of New Guinea . . . 1649.
  v. 3, "   36. Mer des Indes . . .
  "    "    37. Insvlæ Molvccæ . . . 1598.
  Accompanying this work are 4 v. of descriptive text—an **autograph presentation** copy from the author to rear-admiral sir Francis Beaufort.

CONTENTS.

TEXT.

  v. [1] no. [1] General introduction, to the charts and memoirs. Originally printed in 1772. 2d ed. XXXVI pp. 1786.
  "    "  [2] Essay on nautical surveying. Originally published in 1771. 2d ed. 2 p. l., 20 pp. 1786.
  "    "  [3] A brief statement of the prevailing winds from m. d'Après de Mannevillette. 22 pp. [1782]
  "    "  [4] Madeira. [Signed T. H.] 4 pp. [1762]
  "    "  [5] Memoir of a chart of the Southern ocean. 8 pp. [1769]
  "    "  [6] Memoir of a chart of the Indian ocean. 2 p. l., 48 pp. 1787.
  "    "  [7] An account of a shoal to the eaftward of the cape of Good Hope, taken from the relation of some englifh paffengers and alfo from the journal of the brigantine Telemaque, captain Geraud . . . 1786. Communicated by William Petrie. 20 pp. [1786]

v. [1] no. [8] Collection of papers concerning the navigation, winds, and weather at the french iflands Mauritius and Bourbon. 1 p. l., 30 pp. 1794.

" " [9] A description of the island called St. Paulo, by the dutch, and by the english, Amsterdam . . . by John Henry Cox. Publiſhed, with a plan and views, from his mss. by Dalrymple. 1 p. l., 10 pp. 1790.

" " [10] Memoir concerning the Chagos and adjacent islands.—Memoir of a chart of the iflands and dangers to the n. e. of Madagascar . . . by m. d'Après [de Mannevillette] Translated from the french by Dalrymple. 4, 31 pp. 1786.

" " [11] Remarks and observations in a survey of the Chagos archipelago, by lieut. Archibald Blair, 1786 and 1787. 2 p. l., 32 pp. 1788.

" " [12] Collection of plans of ports in the East-Indies. 1779-1780. 2d ed. 1 p. l., 70 pp. 1787.

" " [13] Explanations to plans of ports, &c. 1781-1782. 2d ed. 1 p. l., 38 pp. 1787.

" " [14] Memoir of a chart of the east coast of Arabia from Dofar to the island Maziera. 1784. From an eye-draught taken by capt. John S. Smith in december 1781. v, 11 pp. 1783.

" " [15] Remarks on the Bloachee, Brodia and arabian coasts. By lieut. John Porter in the Dolphin brigg. 2d ed. 2 p. l., 16 pp. 1787.

" " [16] An account of the navigation between India and the gulph of Persia, at all seaſons . . . by lieut. John McCluer. LVI, VI, 98 pp., 2 l., 5 tab. 1786.

" " [17] Memoir of a chart from St. John's on the coast of India to cape Arubah on the coast of Persia . . . 2d ed. 1 p. l., 10 pp. 1787.

" " [18] Description of the coast of India, by John McCluer, 1787 & 1788. 1 p. l., VI, 64 pp. 1798.

" " [19] Continuation of the description of the coast of Malabar, from Bancoot, downwards by John McCluer, 1798 and 1790. 1 p. l., 38 pp. 1791.

v. [2] no. [1] A collection of plans of ports in the East Indies. 1774-1775. 3d ed. 4 p. l., 40, 172 pp. 1787.

" " [2] Memoir of a chart from cape Mons to Acheen . . . 20 pp. 1785.

" " [3] Memoir of a chart of the bay of Bengal. 1772. 2d ed. 2 p. l., 8 pp. 1787.

" " [4] Collection of nautical papers, concerning the bay of Bengal. 1785. 2d ed. [2] l. 1787.

" " [5] An hydrographical journal of a curſory survey of the coasts and islands in the bay of Bengal, by capt. John Ritchie. 1770 and 1771. 2d ed. vi, 94 pp. 1787.

" " [6] Appendix to capt. [John] Ritchie's survey of the bay of Bengal. 2d ed. 2 p. l., 55 pp. 1787.

" " [7] A survey of the Pulicat shoals, made . . . by John Goldingham. 1792. IV, 20 pp. 1794.

" " [8] A journal of the Esther brig, captain Thomas Forreſt, from Bengal to Quedah. 1783. XI, 32 pp. 1788.

" " [9] Memoir of the chart of the straits of Sunda and Banka—Appendix to memoir of chart. 12, 52, 4 pp. 1786.

**Dalrymple, A.**, & *others*—Continued.
v. [2] no. [10] Account of the passage of ship Atlas, capt. Allen Cooper, to tne eastward of Banka. 1785. 1 p. l., iv, 30 pp. 1789.
" " [11] Remarks on a passage from P? Wawoor, to the strait of Sunda, by the Macklesfeild-strait on the east of Banka, with the journal of the Carnatic, by capt. Lestock Wilson. 1 p. l., vi, 60, xii, 52 pp. 1789.
" " [12] Account of the passage of the ship Warren-Hastings, capt. John Pafcal Larkins, by the Mackelsfeild strait, on the east of Banka. 1788. 1 p. l., 34 pp. 1789.
" " [13] Memoir of a chart of the passages at the southern extremity of Asia. 12 pp. 1805.
" " [14] Memoir of a chart of the China sea. Originally publifhed in 1771. 2d ed. iv, 12, 4 pp. 1786.
" " [15] Memoir of a chart of part of the coast of China, and the adjacent iflands near the entrance of Canton river: containing obfervations in the schooner Cuddalore, 1759 & 1760 and in the ship London, 1764. With feveral views of the lands. Originally publifhed in 1771. 2d ed. 56 pp. 1786.
" " [16] Journal of the schooner Cuddalore, Oct. 1759, on the coast of China. 2d ed. 20 pp. 1786.
" " [17] Journal of the schooner Cuddalore on the coast of Hainan, 1760. 2d ed. 2 p. l., 36 pp. 1786.
" " [18] Mr. [John Paskall] Larkins's obfervations concerning the chart and passage from St. John's to the Ladrone. 4 pp. [n. d.]
v. [3] no. [1] Memoir concerning the passages to and from China. June, 1782. 3d ed. iv, 28 pp. 1787.
" " [2] Memoir concerning the passages, at a late seafon, from India to China. viii, 23 pp. 1788.
" " [3] Strait of Allass by mr. George Robertfon, in the Van Sittart. 4 pp. 1780.
" " [4] Memoir of the chart of the west coast of Palawan or Paragua. Containing the journal of the schooner Cuddalore, dec. 1761. 2d ed. 32 pp. 1786.
" " [5] Journal of ship London, captain Walter Alves, along the north coast of Megindanao, oct. 1764; by Alexander Dalrymple. 1 p. l., 30 pp. 1781.
" " [6] An exact and true description of the coasts, ports, islands, and shoals, with the soundings and marks on the coast of Luzon: from the port or bay of Mariveles, to beyond cape Engano, together with the description of the Babuyanes islands: by don Manuel Correa. Tranflated from the spanifh ms. by the late sir Hyde Parker. iv, 68 pp. 1789.
" " [7] A voyage in the Flying-Eagle from Bantam to Baber and other islands to the eastward of Timor. 1672. Now firft publifhed from the original m. s. s. at the East-India house [First journal by Payne; second journal by Hugh Levelis] 2 p. l., 92 pp. 1781.
" " [8] Journal of the Jane, captain Richard Pinnell, from Banjar to Timor and back again to Banjar. Now firft publifhed from a m. s. at the East-India house. 2 p. l., 84 pp. 1781.
" " [9] Observations on the navigation of the Eastern seas, by mr. James Horfburgh. 2 p. l., 80 pp. 1797.

v. [3] no. [10] Journal of the schooner Cuddalore through the strait of Sapy, and on the south coast of Mang-e-rye [or Flores] in february, march, and april, 1761. IV, 52 pp. 1793.
" " [11] Memoir of a chart from the strait of Allass to the island of Bouro, and defcription of Carimata, Manevafa, Maragolong iflands, and Sciao, by captain George Palmer. 1 p. l., 12 pp., 1 l. 1799.
" " [12] Considerations on m. [Philippe] Buache's memoir concerning New-Britain and the north coaft of New-Guinea, by Dalrymple. 1 p. l., II, 12 pp. 1790.
v. [4] no. [1] Memoir of a chart of the NW. coast of Madagascar, by capt. David Inverarity, 1803; and Comoro islands, by the hon. Thomas Howe. 1766. 1 p. l., 18 pp. 1806.
" " [2] Catalogue of authors who have written on Rio de La Plata, Paraguay and Chaco, collected by Dalrymple. 1 p. l., 22 pp. 1807.
" " [3] Directions for the mouth of Rio de La Plata by the hon. Duncombe Pleydell Bouverie, captain of h. m. ship Medusa . . . 2 p. l., 36 pp. 1808.
" " [4] A voyage from England to the Red-sea, and along the east coast of Arabia to Bombay, by a squadron under the command of commodore (afterwards rear-admiral) John Blankett, by Austin Bissell, r. n. 1798 & 1799 1 p. l., XII, 84 pp., 1 l. 1806.
" " [5] The nature and properties of the winds and moussons in the navigation from England to the East-Indies, and all over the Oriental ocean: collected for the general benefit of our own countrymen, by John Seller, hydrographer to the king, London, printed in 1675: re-printed by Dalrymple, 1807. 2 p. l., 28 pp., 1 fold. tab. 1807.
NOTE.—Taken from Seller's The english pilot. The 3d book. The "Atlas maritimus, or the sea atlas of the world," by John Thornton, 1703, is copied almost verbatum from the above.
" " [6] [A form, by attention to which, the several gentlemen in the service will, in future be enabled to express completely and uniformly the observations which occur in their respective voyages, by Dalrymple] 8 pp. 1779.
" " [7] List of charts, plans of ports, &c. publifhed by Dalrymple, before 1ft of June, 1789. [8] l. 1789.
Another copy of the atlas, v. 3 only, is like the one described, except in addition, it contains a chart of California, by Miguel Costanso, 1770.
The following maps relate to America:—
v. 1, no. 15. St. Ann's bay on the coast of Brazil by capt. Robert Scott, 1763.
" " 16. . . . Coast of Brazil . . . 1785.
" " 17. Rio Janeiro . . . by William Stevens, 1763.
" " 18. Coast views of Brazil . . . 1780.
" " 19. St. Sebastian . . .—Isle Grande . . .—St Francisco . . . pub. 1786.
" " 20. Great & Small bays of le Grande . . .—Plan of isle Grande . . . pub. 1781.
" " 21. Ascension . . .—Trinidad . . .—Ascensao . . .—Trinidada . . . pub. 1781.
v. 2, no. 40. . . . Part of the n. w. coast of America . . .—St. Patrick's bay . . . by James Hanna, 1786.

**Dalrymple, A.**, *& others*—Continued.

v. 2, no. 41. Rose's harbour . . . by James Johnstone, 1787.
" " 42. Sketch of a bay at the southern part of Nova Hibernia . . .—Etches sound . . . by Charles Duncan, 1788.
" " 44. Friendly cove . . .—Raft cove . . . by capt. Robert Funter. pub. 1791.—Scott's bay . . . by David Scott . . .—Friendly bay . . . pub. 1789.
" " 45. Sketch of Ahouset, by Charles Duncan, 1788.—Clioquot, or Port Cox . . . by capt. Robert Funter, 1791.
" " 46. Sketch of the entrance of the strait of Juan de Fuca, by C: Duncan, 1788.
" " 47. Plan of port St Francisco . . . pub. 1789.
" " 48. " " Monterey . . .—Plan of the port of St Diego, by Josef Tobar, 1782-86.
" " 49-51. The Philippine islands, 1759-69.
" " 59-85. " " " 1744-91.
" " 93-98. " " " 1754-98.
" " 111. " " " 1774-75.
" " 158. Part of the map of America . . . by Abraham Ortelius . . . 1574.
" " 159. The Philippine islands, pub. 1791.
" " 201. Chart of the strait on the east of Banka, by capt. Lestock Wilson, 1787.
v. 3, no. 1. The ocean between South America & Africa . . . pub. 1768.
" " [2] The east coast of Brazil, pub. 1779.
" " [22] Part of the Philippine islands, pub. 1771.
" " [26-27] " " " " " 1761-74.
" " [28(b)] " " " " " 1761.
" " [29-33] " " " " " 1761-64.
" " [48] The straits of Sunda & Banka . . . 1786.
" " [49(c)] Part of the New Caroline islands, by James Mortlock, 1795.
" " [49(e-f)] The strait of Banka . . . by Robert Torin, pub. 1797.
" " [49(o)] Part of the Philippine islands, by James Horsburgh, 1792-1801.

MAPS.

v. 1, no. 1. Coast views of Porto Santo & Madeira.
" " 2. South side of the island Madeira & city of Funchal . . . pub. 1787.—Insets: Plan of Funchal road.—Sketch of the south coast of Madeira, by Thomas Howe, 1762.
" " 3. Plan of the channel through the Azores . . . by capt. Charles Chapman. Pub. 1782.—Insets: View of the city of Fayal.—South point of Fayal island, from John Sellar, 1675.
" " 4. Coast of Africa from cape Blanco to cape Verd . . . 1769.
" " 5. Coast of Africa . . . by William Dupond, 1755.
" " 6. Plan of the islas dos Idolos . . . by William Woodville, 1777.
" " 7. Plan of Angra-Pequena on the coast of Angola. 1733. Insets:—Plan of Angra Pequena on the west coast of Africa.—Sketch of Sandwich harbour, 1789.
" " 8. Sketches of the coast of Guinea, island St Thomas & island Annabona, by P. Begbie, 1781.
" " 9. Plan of Spencer's bay on the west coast of Africa. 1796.—Plan of Angra Pequena, pub. 1796.

v. 1, no. 10. Island St Thomas.—Track of soundings in the "Grenville". 1775.
" " 11. Benguela road.—Village bay.—Sketch of Anna de Chaves bay . . . by H. R. Popham, 1784.
" " 12. Plan of port Alexander . . . 1796.
" " Fish bay . . . 1786.
" " 13. Plans of Walwich bay . . . Inset: Plan of Fish bay, 1796.
" " 14. Plan of the island of Fernando Noronha, from a french m. s. by m. Delesquellen, 1735.
" " 15. Plan of St Ann's bay on the coast of Brazil, by capt. Robert Scott, 1763.
" " 16. Coast of Brazil . . . by Simao Antonio de Rosa Pinheiro, 1785.
" " 17. Plan of Rio Janeiro, by William Stevens, 1763.
" " 18. Coast views of Brazil, pub. 1779.
" " 19. Isle Grande & adjacent parts of the coast of Brazil.—Insets: St Sebastian.—Entrance of the river St Francisco on the coast of Brazil, from Bellin's Petit atlas maritime, pub. 1786.
" " 20. Plan of the Great & Small bays of le Grand . . . by William Funnell, 1703.—Plan of isle Grande . . .
" " 21. Plan of Ascension island.—Island of Trinidad.—Ascensao island.—Draught of the island of Trinidada, pub. 1781.
" " 22. Chart of the islands Tristan da Cunha, by le sr. Donat, 1767.
" " 23. St Helena bay . . . from . . . N. Bellin's Hist. des voy.— Insets:—Coast views of Gough's island, or Diego Alvares.
" " 24. Plan of St Helena bay . . . 1796.—Insets: Entrance of St Helena bay.—Land to the eastward of St Helena bay.—St Helena bay.—Cape Deseada, the north point of the bay.
" " 25. Coast views of the south of Africa.
" " 26. Chart of the Worcester's track over the Cape bank, by R. H. Gower, 1791.
" " 27. Table bay of the Cape of Good Hope.—Sketch taken from the heights of Hout bay & Chapman's bay . . . by capt. Edward Riou, 1790.
" " 28. Plan of Simon's bay . . . 1775.
" " 29. Sketch of the south coast of Africa, by Robert Torin, 1785.
" " 30. Flesh bay; or, bay St Bras, from J. van Keulen, pub. 1774.
" " 31. Mossell bay, from van Keulen.—Bay St Sebastian . . . 1705.
" " 33. Plan of Alagoa bay . . . pub. 1785.
" " 34. Bay of Algoa.—Island Chaos . . .
" " 35. Mozambique channel.—St. Augustine's bay.—Madagascar.
" " 36. East coast of Madagascar . . . by m. Mengaud de la Hage, 1775-76.
" " 37. Part of the east coast of Madagascar by m. le chevalier Grenier, 1768.
" " 38-39. East coast of Madagascar . . . from m. d'Aprés [de Mannevillette] pub. 1784.
" " 40. North-west coast of Madagascar . . . by Charles Wilde, 1650.
" " 41. Part of the north-west coast of Madagascar, by capt. Jacob Holst, 1738.—North-west part of Madagascar, pub. 1784.
" " 42-43. Part of the west coast of Madagascar . . .
" " 44. Plan of the bay of fort Dauphin on Madagascar . . . from m. d'Aprés [de Mannevillette] [1784]
" " 45. Plans of fort Dauphin . . . pub. 1784.

**Dalrymple, A.**, & *others*—Continued.

v. 1, no. 46. Plan of fort Dauphin, by m. Le Gentil.—Bay of fort Dauphin, from Bellin's Petit atlas maritime.—Plan of Matatanné . . .—Bay and islots of St Lucé . . . from m. d'Aprés [de Mannevillette] pub. 1782.
" " 47. Bay of Tamatavé . . .—Road of Manourou . . . from m. d'Aprés [de Mannevillette]
" " 48. Foul point . . .—Bay and road of Foul point . . . pub. 1784.
" " 49. Foul point, from m. Le Gentil.—Port of Foul point.—Foul point, from . . . Admiral Kempenfelt, pub. 1784.
" " 50. Bay and road of Foul point.—Road of Foul point . . . by m. le chevalier Grenier, 1768.
" " 51. Long point on Madagascar . . . pub. 1784.
" " 52. Port of Teintingue . . . from m. D'Aprés [de Mannevillette]—Harbour on the island St Mary . . . by capt. Lockhart Russell, 1771.
" " 53. Harbour of St Mary's . . . by John Brohier, 1746.
" " 54. Bay of Veninguebe . . .—Part and bay of cape East . . . by m. d'Aprés [de Mannevillette] pub. 1782.
" " 55. Port Louquez . . . from m. D'Aprés [de Mannevillette]
" " 56. Harbour of Managar . . . by Seth Loftus.—Entrance of the river New Matheleage . . . from van Keulen.—Inset: View of the island Makamby, pub. 1782.
" " 57. Manumbagh . . . from van Keulen.—Shoal of Coffin island . . . 1781.
" " 58. Road and river of Moroundava . . . from m. d'Aprés [de Mannevillette] pub. 1782.
" " 59. Tollear bay, from van Keulen.—Majambo bay . . . by David Inverarity, 1803.
" " 60. Delagoa bay, by David Inverarity.
" " 61. Bay Rio Delagoa; or, Lorenço Marques.—Inset: Plan to show the extent of the rivers, pub. 1786.
" " 62. Delagoa bay, by James Mayo, 1787.
" " 63. Hiarbane.—Quelimanie.—Sofala.—East coast of Africa.—Coast of Angoxa.—Rivers of Cuama. 1787.
" " 64. Bay of Inhamban . . . by David Inverarity, pub. 1806.
" " 65. Mozambique channel . . . by John Thornton, 1703.
" " 66. Coasts of Suffalo and Mozambique, by John van Keulen, pub. 1791.
" " 67. Mozambique channel, with the island Madagascar and the . . . coast of Africa, by m. d'Aprés [de Mannevillette] 1753.
" " 67(a) Mozambique channel and island Madagascar, by N. Bellin, 1767.
" " 67(b) Mozambique channel, with Madagascar and the opposite coast of Africa, by m. d'Aprés [de Mannevillette] 1775.
" " 67(c) Mozambique harbour . . . by David Inverarity, 1802.
" " 68. Mombass.—Part of the east coast of Africa.—Zanzibar . . . by Austin Bissell, 1799.
" " 69. East coast of Africa . . . pub. 1794.
" " 70–71. Parts of the east coast of Africa.
" " 72. Zemzibar, pub. 1796.
" " 73. Querimboo and the adjacent islands.—Bay of Macaloé . . .
" " 74. Riv. Lindy . . . pub. 1789.
" " 75. Bays and islands of Quiloa.—River Mongallou . . . pub. 1789.
" " 76. Quiloa and its environs . . . pub. 1784.
" " 77. Zanzibar . . . pub. 1784.

v. 1, no. 78. Road, or harbour of Zinzinbara, or Zanzibar . . .—Monbaze . . . pub. 1784.
" " 79. Bahia Fermosa on the coast of Melinde.—Zanzibar, by Manoel Pimentel.—Zanzibar road, by Austin Bissell, 1799.
" " 80. Plan of Patta . . . by capt. D. Crichton, 1751.
" " 81. Brava.—West side of Comoro, or, Anga-Zecha . . . by Alexander Sibbald, pub. 1774.
" " 82. Island Anzuani, or, Anjaanna, from Van Keulen.—Part of Johanna, by Alexander Sibbald, pub. 1774.—Bay on the north side of Johanna, by C. Peter Pigou, 1762.
" " 83. Mayotta island, from John van Keulen.—Mayotta road.—N. W. part of island Mayotta, by John Watson, 1754.—Sketch of Mayotta, by capt. George Stainforth, 1768.—West side of Mayotta, by John Barker, 1750.
" " 83(a) N. W. part of the island Mayotta, by John Watson, 1754, with some additions by capt. Peter Pigou, 1762.—Insets: Moelali, or Mohilla, by van Keulen.—West side of Mayotta, by J. Lindley, 1787.—View of Mohilla, by capt. George Richardson.
" " 84. Coast views of Chagos and adjacent islands, 1712–1774.
" " 85. The archipelago to the northward of Mauritius, by m. le vicounte Grenier, 1776.
" " 86. Bourbon.—I. Rodrigues; or, Diego Rais, from m. d'Aprés [de Mannevillette]
" " 87. Isle de France; or, Mauritius, by l'abbé de la Caille, 1753.
" " 88. N. W. coast of Mauritius . . . by John Blake, 1738.
" " 89. Port Louis . . . by m. de Boisquenay, 1775.—Insets: Four plans of the south east harbour of Mauritius.
" " 90. Is. l'Assomption.—Islands Cosmoledo . . . from John van Keulen.—Wood island, by John Ringrove, 1776.—Insets: Isle de Sable; or, Sandy island, from m. d'Aprés [de Mannevillette]—Dangerous shoals of St. Brandon, from Thornton. Pub. 1782.
" " 91. Islands Albadra . . . 1744.—Islands John de Nova, by m. Margaro, 1776.
" " 92. Bank of Cargados Garajos . . . 1742.—Bank of Cargados Garajos and the adjacent islands, by m. Grenier.
" " 93. Eagle island . . . by David Thomas & William Robinson, 1771.—Bird island . . . 1771.—Harbour of Seychelles, by David Thomas, 1771.—The harbour adjacent to Bat river on is. Seychelles . . . 1756.
" " 94. Harbour of Praslin, by David Thomas & William Robinson, 1771.—Insets: African islands, by Charles Shackleton.—African islands . . . by capt. Guieysse, 1771.
" " 95. Islands and dangers situated to the north east of Madagascar . . .
" " 96. Islands discovered by Lazare Picault . . . 1744.
" " 97. Coast views of Great & Little Eagle islands.—Three Brothers.—Pedros Banhos.—Eleven islands.
" " 98. Chagos archipelago, by Archibald Blair, 1787.
" " 99. Peros Banhos.—Eleven islands, by Archibald Blair, 1786.
" " 100. Track near the Chagos archipelago. Track over the Basses de Chagos, by W: Nicholls. Pub. 1784.
" " 101. Part of the island Chagos; or, Diego Garcia, 1774.—The island Diego Garcia; or Chagos, by m. la Fontaine. 1770.
" " 102. Diego Garcia . . . pub. 1786.
" " 103. The Eagle's track, 1772 . . .

**Dalrymple, A.**, *& others*—Continued.

v. 1, no. 104. The Pitts track, 1763, by William Stevens.
" " 105. The track in the Salomon, capt. m. Bourdé. 1776.—The soundings on the Chagos . . . by capt. James Dewar, 1763.—Inset: Eleven islands; or, Salomon islands, by m. Bourdé, 1786.
" " 106. N. E. part of the Bassas de Chagos, 1763. — Islands near the Maldivés, from John van Keulen, pub. 1782.
" " 107. South part of the Maldivés . . . Insets: Aria Attoll on the west side of the Maldivés.—Atoll Maldiva; or, King's island Atol . . . pub. 1782.
" " 108. King's island road . . . by Peter Sandelyn, 1727.
" " 109. Maldivés, from english ms. of 1759.
" " 110. Harbour & road of Suez . . . by George Trotter, 1777.—Harbour & road of Suez . . . by John Mascall, 1777.
" " 110(a) Bay, s. w. of Suez, by J. Ellis.—Insets: Suez road & harbour.—Tor harbour . . . by Austin Bissell, 1801.
" " 110(b) Adaga point & bay, by Austin Bissell, 1801. — Jaffatine islands . . .
" " 111. Suez harbour, surveyed by capt. W. Robinson, 1777.—Harbour of Tor . . . by George Trotter, 1777.
" " 111(a) Cossier . . . by Austin Bissell.—Part of the coast of Egypt. 1806.
" " 112. Torr harbour . . . 1785.—Yambo harbour . . . pub. 1779.
" " 112(a) The shoals at and near Jeddah in the Red sea, by Austin Bissell, 1800.—Bay of Kossier . . . by W. H. Dobbie, 1799.
" " 113. Mursah Gedan . . .—Mursah Sememah . . .—Mursah Koof, from english m. s. pub. 1783.
" " 114. Bahia de Fucha . . .—Arequea . . .—Rio Farat . . .—Porto de Gidid . . .—Porto Quilfit . . .—Porto Xerme Elcoemata . . . from van Keulen, pub. 1784.
" " 115. Moca road . . .—Insets: Suakem.—Port & city of Suakem.—Port Dradart . . . from van Keulen, pub. 1784.
" " 116. Bay of Huddada.—Mocha road.—Messaua.—Harbour of Messaua. Inset: Matzua & Arkiko, from m. d'Anville, pub. 1784.
" " 116(a) Ports in the Red sea, from m. Bruce's m. s., pub. 1784.
" " 117. Moha . . . by m. Hunter.—Bay Denis . . . by m. Trobriand, pub. 1784.
" " 118. Asab . . . by M. Hunter.—Road and bay of Asab . . . pub. 1806.
" " 119. Maculla bay, by Thornton, 1703.—Anchorage in Mocha road . . . by Austin Bissell.—Babel Mandel harbour . . . pub. 1806.
" " 120. Aden . . . from capt. Cornwall. Insets: Plans of the straits of Babelmandell . . . 1703.
" " 120(a) Dhalac and parts adjacent . . .
" " 121. Island Socotora . . .—Road of Tameren (Tamarida) by I. Browne, 1615.—Harbour at the island of Piram.—Harbour Babelmandel., pub. 1802.
" " 122. Morebat bay . . . by capt. John Smith, 1781.—Kisseen bay . . . by C. David Crichton, pub. 1775.
" " 123. Coast views of Arabia and Persia, pub. 1794.
" " 124. Muscat cove & Mutrah harbour, surveyed by John McCluer, 1785.
" " 125. Bushier, in the Persian gulph, by capt. David Simmons, pub. 1774.
" " 126. Island Karak & bay of Bundereek . . . from an english m. s.

v. 1, no. 127. Coast views of Persia & Arabia.
" " 128. Islands Karak & Korgo . . . 1787.
" " 129. Kismis channel . . . from van Keulen.—Road of Jasques . . . by M. Hunter, pub. 1783.
" " 130. Road of Jasques . . . by W. Baffin & R. Sommerson, pub. 1795.
" " 131. Churbar, Goadel & Arrubah bays, on the south coast of Persia.
" " 132. Coast views of Arabia . . . 1781.
" " 132(a) Bate harbour . . . 1803.
" " 133. Crotchey bay . . . by Joseph Mascall, 1774.—Coasts of Cutch & Guzarat, by J. G. Richardson . . . pub. 1803.
" " 134-135. Coast of Scindy, pub. 1784.
" " 136. Coast of Scindy.—Bay of Cutch with part of the coast of Guzurat, pub. 1786.
" " 137. Bay of Coche . . .—River Nagor . . . by Charles Massey.—Coast of Guzarat from a french m. s. 1760.
" " 137(a). Diu in Guzurat . . . Inset: City of Diu, pub. 1802.
" " 138. Views of Diu.—Diu island, by John McCluer, 1788.
" " 139. Scarbett island & Church river . . . by John McCluer, 1788.
" " 140. Jaffrabat . . . by John McCluer, 1788.
" " 141. Rajapora . . . by A. Blair, 1795.—Nowa Bunder, by A. Blair, 1795.
" " 142. Gogo in the gulph of Cambay, by m. Hunter, pub. 1784.
" " 143. Broach bar and river, surveyed by W. A. Skynner, 1773.
" " 144. Coast views to the northward of Bombay, pub. 1779.
" " 145. Coast of India . . . by lieut. John Ringrose, 1782.
" " 146. Nursaree river . . . by J. Ringrose.
" " 146(a) Guordivee river by John Ringrose.
" " 147. Bulsaur river.—Omersary river, by John Ringrose, pub. 1784.
" " 148. Collack river, by John Ringrose.—Demaon, by John McCluer, 1788.—Insets: Views of Demaon.
" " 149. Danno river, by John Ringrose.
" " 150. Vassava, by Edward Harvey, 1777.—Mayham, surveyed in 1777 by Edward Harvey . . .
" " 151. Angassea river, by John Ringrose.—Inset: Island Arnol.
" " 152. Manhora river in the island Salset, by Archibald Blair, 1777.
" " 153. Choul on the Malabar coast.—Surat river—1750, from an english m. s.
" " 154. Malabar coast, by P. Heywood, pub. 1806.
" " 154(a). Coast views of Malabar, pub. 1780.
" " 155. Part of the Malabar coast by John McCluer, 1787.
" " 156. Port of Chaoul on the coast of Concan . . . pub. 1784.
" " 157. Gingerah; or, Donda Rajapore, by A. Werner.—Radjapore river, by John McCluer 1788.—Insets:—Conserah island.—Gingerah fort.
" " 158. Bar and entrance of Bancoot river . . . by John McCluer. pub. 1789.
" " 159. Bancoot river by John McCluer, 1788.
" " 160. Boncout.—Bassalore.—Sinderdroo; or, Melundy . . . by John Watson, 1765.
" " 161. Gariah harbour . . . by William Hewett, 1756.
" " 162. Dewgur harbour . . . by Archibald Blair, pub. 1784.
" " 163. Vingorla . . . — Inset: Rocks of Vingorla by capt. Joseph Huddart.
" " 164. Goa harbour . . . by Reeves Woodson.

**Dalrymple, A.**, *& others*—Continued.
v. 1, no. 165. Entrance of Salt river.—A small bay on the Malabar coast.—
　　　　　Oyster rocks in Carway bay, by Thomas Haswell, 1790. Plan
　　　　　of Merjee . . . by E. Bates, 1725.
" 　" 　165 (a) Merjee river . . . by C. Heywood, 1803.
" 　" 　166. Comptee . . . & Onore . . . by Elias Bates, 1725.
" 　" 　167. Coast views of Malabar. 1773.
" 　" 　168. Malabar coast from Mahé to Mount Dely by capt. James de
　　　　　Funk, 1755.—Insets:—Plan of Tellichery . . . by P. Daser,
　　　　　1780.—Survey of Rhandaterra, by Charles Turner, 1770.
" 　" 　169. Billiapatam river . . . pub. 1792.
" 　" 　170. 　　"　　　　" 　by John D. Spaeth.—Island Durmaptam . . .
" 　" 　171. Coast views of Malabar . . . 1772.
" 　" 　172. Tellicherry road . . . by capt. Thomas Lynn . . . pub. 1784.
" 　" 　173. Ramdilly & its dependencies, from a french m. s. . . . — Plan
　　　　　of Ramdilly . . . pub. 1786.
" 　" 　174. Mud bank of Cranganor . . . — Part of the Malabar coast . . .
　　　　　between Cape Comorin and the point of Veniam . . . pub.
　　　　　1791.
" 　" 　175. Underoot island, by John McCluer, 1790.
" 　" 　176. Seuheli islands and reef . . . by John McCluer, 1790.
" 　" 　177. Island Maliqué; or, Lackardiva, by Archibald Blair, 1787.—
　　　　　Insets: Kalpeni islands.—Courutee island; & Minicoy island,
　　　　　by John McCluer, 1790.
" 　" 　177 (a) Part of the west coast of Ceylan, from a dutch m. s., pub.
　　　　　1799.
" 　" 　178. Coast of Madura from a dutch m. s.
" 　" 　179. Porto Cayl.—Tutucoryn.—Haven of Colombo, on the west coast
　　　　　of Ceylon, from J. van Keulen, pub. 1782.
" 　" 　180. The passage between point Ramen & the island Ramisseram, by
　　　　　William Stevens.—Calpentyn road . . . from John van Keu-
　　　　　len, pub. 1788.
" 　" 　181. West coast of Ceyloan, from Manaar to Calpentyn . . . pub.
　　　　　1782.
" 　" 　181 (a) Ceylon, from Columbo to Tranquebar, by P. Heywood . . .
　　　　　pub. 1806.
" 　" 　182. Shoal & soundings between Ceylan & the Little Basses.—Chart
　　　　　showing the position of the Great & Little Basses, by T. G.
　　　　　Shortland, 1803.—Venloos bay on east coast of Ceylan by P.
　　　　　Heywood, 1802.
" 　" 　182 (a) Two plans of Punta Gaula.—Nyle; or, Nylewelle bay . . .
　　　　　1783.
" 　" 　183. The shoal & soundings between Ceylan & the Little Basses.—
　　　　　Venloos bay . . . — Bay of Aproeretotte . . . pub. 1789.
" 　" 　184. East coast of Ceylon, pub. 1789.
" 　" 　185. Batacaloe . . . 1762.—Road & river of Batacolo, by P. Heywood,
　　　　　1802.
" 　" 　185 (a) Batacalao road . . . 1802.
" 　" 　186. Part of Calymere reef . . . by James Rennell, 1763-64.
" 　" 　186 (a) North end of Ceylan, by P. Heywood, 1802; & Negapatam
　　　　　road, by T. G. Shortland, 1803.
" 　" 　187. River & bay of Nagore, by Thomas Dibdin, 1779.
" 　" 　188. Coast views of Choromandel . . .
" 　" 　189. Plan of a shoal between point Callimere & Negapatnam . . .
　　　　　1781.

v. 1, no. 190. Negapatam road, by George Trotter, 1782.—Inset: Negapatam . . . 1782.
" " 191. Road & reef of Palleacatte, or Pulicat . . .— Tegenepatnam reef on the coast of Choromandel, from van Keulen, pub. 1782.
" " 192. Coast views of Choromandel.
" " 193. Part of the coast of Choromandel, by capt. John Ritchie, 1771.
" " 194. Coast views of Choromandel.—Survey of the Pulicat shoals, by John Goldingham, 1792.
" " 195. Devy point . . . —Kanneka river.—Part of the coast of Orissa, by John Ritchie, pub. 1795.
" " 196. Survey of Narsipore river, by Charles Knapton, 1751.—Plan of Vizagapatnam, by John Seaton, pub. 1783.
" " 197. Kannaka near point Palmiras, by capt. John Sampson . . .— Plan of the island and harbour of Codgone, or Codjon . . . by William Helman, 1742.
" " 198. Bomeeny harbour, 1770.
" " 199. Coast of Bengal, from Putnay to Ramnabad, pub. 1785.
" " 200. Mouth of the Megna river in Bengal . . . pub. 1785.
" " 201. Coast of Chittigan, by Barth. Plaisted, 1761.
" " 202. Islamabad: or, Chittagong river by Barth. Plaisted, 1764.
" " 203. Khaut Colley, by B. Plaisted.—River of Chittegan, by capt. Herbert Sutherland.—Chittegan river, from english m. s., 1764.
" " 204. Coast of Arrackan & Chettigon by Jon: Ransom, 1739.—Two charts of the coast of Chittagong.—Coast of Arracan, 1759.
" " 205. Coast of Chittigong, by John Ritchie, pub. 1785.
" " 206. Coast of Arrackan, by capt. Richard Peirce, 1759.—Coast of Chittegonge by Jeremiah Lawrance, 1740.—Inset: Coast of Chittagong with part of Arakan coast . . . pub. 1784.
" " 207. Two charts of the coast to the northward of Arackan river, 1762-63.
" " 207 (a) Mouth of the Aracan river, by William North, pub. 1802.
" " 208. Coast of Aracan and Ava . . . by Philip Parsons, 1743-44.— Inset: The coast of Aracon from Negrais to the Sambelong islands, by Alexander Wood, 1740.
" " 209. Coasts of Aracan & Ava, by John Ritchie, 1770-71.
" " 210. Arackan river from an english m. s.
" " 211. Entrance of Arrackan river, by Jeremiah Lawrence, 1740.— Channel within the island Cheduba, by capt. Walter Alves. pub. 1782.—Inset: Plan of Arackan river, from m. d'Anville.
" " 212. Negrais & the adjacent parts, by capt. J. G. Wragg.—Track of the Nassau thro' the Cocos islands, by William Green, 1779.— Part of the coast of Ava, by capt. Charles Newland, pub. 1784.
" " 213. West coast of Ava, by capt. George Hayter, 1757-58.
" " 214. Coast of Ava, by Alexander Sibbald, 175(?)—Coast of Ava . . . from Pagoda point to Church rock, 1765.
" " 215. Negrais harbour, by Thomas Taylor, 1753.—Plan of the entrance of Persaim river by capt. George Baker, pub. 1774.
" " 216. The passage between Negrais and the Andaman, by Alexander Sibbald . . .— Chart of the Neptune's track off Diamond island.
" " 217. River of Persaim, by capt. George Baker, 1754.
" " 218. Siriam . . . river in Pegu, pub. 1775.

**Dalrymple, A.**, *& others*—Continued.

v. 1, no. 219. Martavan river, from an english m. s.
" " 220. Tavay river, by capt. Palairet, 1753.
" " 221. Negrais to the island Carnicobar, by John Ritchie, 1771.
" " 222. Andaman islands, by capt. John Ritchie, 1771.
" " 223. West coast of Andaman, by capt. J. G. Wragg, 1771.—Great Andaman . . . by Alex. McCleod, 1764.
" " 224. Andaman islands . . .—Track of the Stretham, by capt. H. Gough, 1708.
" " 225. Track . . . thro' the Andamans, 1775 . . .
" " 226. North part of the Andaman islands . . .—Little Andaman island, by Robert Moorsom, 1790.
" " 227. Carnicobar island from an english m. s.
" " " by P. Hunt, 1769.
" " 228. Bay on the east side of Island Camorta, by James Rennell, 1762.—Nicobar island, by John Ritchie, 1771.
" " 229. Nicobar islands, by capt. John Ritchie, 1771.
" " 230. Nicobar islands, by capt. Robert Lindsay, 1758.
" " 231. Noncowrey harbour, between three of the Nicobar islands, by capt. Robert Lindsay, 1758.—Noncowrey harbour, by John Ritchie, pub. 1782.
" " 232. Harbour of Nancowry . . . by capt. Alexander Kyd, 1790.
" " 233. Chain of Angles from Po. Pinang to the westernmost Torres, by David Inverarity, pub. 1804.
" " 233 (a) Islands & straits situated to the south of Mergui archipelago, by capt. Thomas Forrest, 1783.—Aladin islands and adjacent coast, by capt. Thomas Forrest, 1783.
" " 234. Island St. Mathew & adjacent islands by capt. T. Forrest, 1783.
" " 235. Strait of Mallacca, by capt. Richard Peirce, pub. 1779.
" " 236. Jan Sylan to Queda, by T: Forrest.
" " 237. Coast of Malaya . . . by Martin Lindsey.—Inset: Sketch from Salang to Po. Pinang, by Archibald Blair, pub. 1794.
" " 238. Bass harbour in the strait of Malacca, by capt. Thomas Forrest, pub. 1786.
" " 239. Quedah road, by capt. John Athbridge.—Po. Pinang . . . by capt. Walter Alves, 1763.
" " 240. Strait of Mallacca, by capt. Richard Peirce, pub. 1779.
" " 241. South part of Po. Pinam . . .—Sambeelan islands . . . by James Rennell, 1763.
" " 242. Prince of Wales island; or, Poolo Peenang, by Archibald Blair, 1787.—East side of Prince of Wales island, by A. Blair, 1787.
" " 242 (a) The strait within Poolo Pinang . . . by capt. James Scott. pub. 1786.
" " 243. Strait of Mallacca, by capt. Richard Peirce, pub. 1779.
" " 243 (a) Malacca road & the Water islands from an english m. s.— Inset: Malacca, 1750.
" " 244. Pera river, Po. Dingding & the Sambelong islands, by Thomas Forrest.
" " 244 (a) Passage from Tree island to St. John's island, by George Thomas, pub. 1805.
" " 245. Part of the islands Cardiman . . . & Sabon at the entrance of the strait of Malacca.—Island Barella; or, Farella off Jambey river . . .—Siacca river . . . from capt. F: Taylor, pub. 1805.
" " 245 (a) Strait of Dryon . . . pub. 1805.

v. 1, no. 245 (b) Straits of Dryon . . . pub. 1805.
" " 246. Strait of Mallacca, by capt. Richard Peirce, pub. 1779.
" " 246 (a) Track of the Nonsuch, by capt. William Richardson, 1783.
" " 247. Strait between point Romania & the islands, by capt. Walter Alves, 1763.
" " 247 (a) Straits of Sinquapore and Dryon . . . 1689.
" " 248. Strait of Sincapore . . . pub. 1780.
" " 248 (a) Coast to the westward of Point Romania, by George Thomas, pub. 1786.
" " 249. Harbour on the south-part of the Great Rydangh island, 1764.
" " 249 (a) West part of the strait of Sincapore.—Strait of Sincapore, by capt. George Thomas.—Inset: Entrance of strait Sincapore . . . pub. 1805.
" " 250. Blair's harbour . . . pub. 1793.
" " 251. Straits of Sincapore by Thomas Howe, 1759.
" " 252. Straits & islands at the southern part of Asia . . .—Strait of Sincapore, by Duncan Weir, 1805.
" " 253. Straits of Sincapore, by Thomas Evans.
" " 254. " " Sinkapoura . . . pub. 1805.
" " 255. Point Romania to the Anambas islands, by James Downie, 1805.
" " 256. Entrance of the Strait of Malacca & port of Rio, by George Bass, pub. 1805.—Plan of Riho, by capt. Hugh Mackay.
" " 257. South side of the Island Byntang, 1762.—Insets: Plan of Rheho . . . by Alexander Scott, 1750.—Port of Rio . . . by m. d'Aprés [de Mannevillette] 1753.
" " 258. Passage of the Royal George, capt. Nicholas Skottowe, 1762.
" " 259. Passage to southward of Po. Bintang & Po. Gallatt . . . by David Inverarity.
" " 250. Chain of Angles and track of soundings from Haycock is to Rehio road.—Chain of Angles and track of soundings from Lingen road to Haycock island, by David Inverarity, pub. 1804.
" " 261. Coast of Sumatra . . .—North end of Banka from an english m. s.
" " 262. Strait of Banka to Po. Panjang, pub. 1805.
v. 2, no. 1. South coast of Cochin-China . . . 1804.
" " 1 (a) Cancao and part of the coast of Cambodia . . . pub. 1792.
" " 2-3. Camboja river . . . pub. 1791.
" " 4. Poolo Condor . . .—Varella harbour, 1760.—Coast of Cochin-China . . . pub. 1802.
" " 5. Po. Condor, by m. Dedier.—Po. Condor, from a Swedish m. s. 1759.—Inset: Po. Condor port, by William Bligh, 1780.
" " 6. Binkank, Nha Trang, Cuá Be & Camranh bay on Cochin-China . . . pub. 1802.
" " 6 (a) South coast of Camboja . . . 1793.
" " 7-7 (a) Bay and port of Quinhou . . . by I. M. & F. Dayot, 1793.
" " 8. Padaran bay on the coast of Tsiompa, from van Keulen.—Harbour on the coast of Cochin-China, pub. 1780.
" " 9. Part of the coast of Cochin-China.—The river of the Court in Cochin-China. Pub. 1791.
" " 10. Turon harbour . . . by capts. Arthur Gore & Philip Bromfield, 1764.
" " 11. Tonqueen bar, by John Walsh, 1719.—Tonquin river . . . pub. 1791.
" " 12. Coast views of Hainan . . . 1760.

**Dalrymple, A.**, *& others*—Continued.
- v. 2, no. 13. Tien-pe-Hien . . . by capt. George Stainforth.—Galloon; or, Gelang bay, by capt. James Haldane.—Yu-Lin-Kan bay . . . by m. Omerat, 1760.
- " " 14. South coast of Hainan.—South coast of Hainan . . . by capt. Haldane.
- " " 15. S. E. coast of Hainan . . . by capt. C. G. Elkberg, 1760.—Shitoe bay . . . by J. P. Larkins, pub. 1786.
- " " 16. Coast views of China . . . pub. 1788.
- " " 17. Harbour of Olinchy . . .—Coast view of Koan.—Inset: Twin Point from Outer-twin hill . . . 1804.
- " " 17 (a) Southern coasts of the islands between St. John's & the Ladrone . . . by J. P. Larkins, pub. 1786.
- " " 18. The Typa . . . by capt. George Baker, 1759.
- " " 18 (a) City of Macao . . . 1792.
- " " 19. Coast views of China, pub. 1780.
- " " 20. Islands to the Se of Lantao . . . 1764.—Coast of China adjacent to Honghai island . . . 1759.
- " " 21. Coast views of China, pub. 1783.
- " " 22. Pescadore islands in the straits of Formosa, from capt. Robert Duffin, 1792.
- " " 23. Part of the coast of China, by Felis Mendoça, 1760. Inset: C. Alves's sketch of his passage. 1765.
- " " 24. Coast views of China, pub. 1780.
- " " 25. Mirs bay.—Lamock, Lamon and part of Nangoa islands . . .—Ping Hai bay, by Edward Murphy, 1793.
- " " 26. Pehoe; or, Ponghou islands . . . 1714.
- " " 27. Bay Hocsieu & the mouths of the river Chang . . .—Entrance of Aimoey harbour of Chinchew river, from J: van Keulen, pub. 1784.
- " " 28. Harbour of Chusan in China, by capt. John Clements, 1756.—S. W. part of Japan, pub. 1792.
- " " 29. Coast of China, from Kittow point to Limpo river, by Ferd. Wallis, 1755.
- " " 30. Limpo; or, Ning-Po . . . by capt. John Clements, 1756.—Entrance of Limpo river, pub. 1784.
- " " 31. Harbour of Nangasaky in Japan . . . by Alexander Hume, pub. 1788.
- " " 32-33. Nanga Sacqui . . . or, Nangasacky.
- " " 34. Part of a map entitled Nova et accurata Iaponiæ terræ Esonis . . . 1658.
- " " 35. Port Etches, by James Johnstone, 1787.—The strait between the Islands Oonalaska & Sedaghur, by J. H. Cox, 1789.
- " " 36. Port Stephens, by Charles Duncan, 1788.—Snug-corner cove in Prince William sound, pub. 1789.
- " " 37. Inlet of Bucareli . . . 1779.
- " " 38. Calamity harbour . . . by John Johnstone, 1787.
- " " 39. Milbank's sound . . .—Port Safety on the east side of Calvert's island, by Charles Duncan, 1788.
- " " 40. N. W. coast of America.—St. Patrick's bay, by James Hanna, 1786.—Track of the Snow Experiment . . . by S. Wedgbrough, pub. 1789.
- " " 41. Rose's harbour, by James Johnstone, 1787.
- " " 42. Sketch of a bay at the southern part of Nova Hibernia.—Etches-sound, by Charles Duncan, 1788.

v. 2, no. 43. Port Brooks, by James Johnstone, 1787.
" " 44. Clioquot, or Port Cox, by capt. Barkley, 1787.—Raft-cove in Queen Charlotte sound, by capt. Robert Funter.—Scott's bay on the n. w. coast of America . . . pub. 1789.—Friendly bay in Nootka sound . . .
" " 45. Ahouset, by Charles Duncan, 1788.—Clioquot or Port Cox . . . by capt. Robert Funter, pub. 1791.
" " 46. Entrance of the strait of Juan de Fuca, by Charles Duncan, 1788.
" " 47. Port St Francisco . . . pub. 1789.
" " 48. Monterey.—San Diego.—Inset: Road del Principe, in the channel of St. Barbara, by J. Tobar. 1786.
" " 49. Coast views of Formosa & Bashee islands, pub. 1781.
" " 50. Channel between the islands Monmouth & Bashee . . . pub. 1784.
" " 51. Musa bay, by capt. George Baker, 1759.
" " 52. The Caroline islands.—Insets: Garbanzos islands.—Track for the discovery of the Palaos islands.
" " 52 (a) Earl Spencer's keys . . . pub. 1803.
" " 53. Part of the New Caroline islands . . .—Inset: Philip island, by capt. John Hunter.—Peeloo islands . . . 1791.
" " 54. Puerto de Apra on the island Guahan vulgo Guam, by Antonio Rodrigues, 1733.—Inset: Tinian bay, surveyed in 1767.
" " 55. Peeloo archipelago, by John McCluer, 1794.
" " 56. Southern range of Pelew islands . . .—Amallakell harbour . . . by John McCluer, 1791.
" " 57. The harbour at the east & southeast side of Corror . . .—Inset: North part of the Peeloo islands, by John McCluer, 1794.—Marianes islands, Guahan & Rota . . . pub. 1796.
" " 58. Coast views of island Guam—Umatac bay on island Guam, pub. 1796.
" " 59. Bay of Ivanna on the island Batanes, by capt. George Baker, 1759.—Islands Tinian & Saypan, by John Townshend, 1765.
" " 60. Plans of islands Tinian & Saypan, from spanish m. s., 1758-82.
" " 61. Philipine islands, by f. Pedro M. Velarde, 1744.
" " 62. Port on Camiguing one of the Babuyanes islands . . .—Bay of St Vincente or Palaniguin . . .—Port San Pio Quinto . . . by Jonn McCluer, 1791.
" " 63. Chief ports on the coast of Ylocos in Luzon . . .—Mariveles bay on Luzon, by John Watson.—Inset: Port of Salomague, by don Manuel Galves, pub. 1781.
" " 64. West coast of Luzon . . . pub. 1788.
" " 65. Port of Subec near Manila . . . 1766.
" " 66. Palaon bay on Mindora, by Thomé Gaspar de Leon.—Bay on west coast of Mindora . . . 1799.—Insets: Port St. Andrés on the Island Marinduque . . . —Port Mangarin . . .—Sketch of islands . . . supposed to be Cawely & the Cagayanes . . . 1764.
" " 67. Calapan . . .—Capa-Luan . . . on Luzon, by don Manuel Galves.—Batangas bay . . . by capt. W: Brereton, 1763.
" " 68. Cuyos & part of Panay, pub. 1775.
" " 69. East coast of Panay . . . 1761.
" " 70. St. Jacinto on Ticao . . . 1763.
" " 71. Sorsogon harbour . . .—Shoals . . . south west of Mindora . . . pub. 1800.

**Dalrymple, A.**, *& others*—Continued.

v. 2, no. 72. Bay of S. Miguel de Naga on Luzon.—Inset: Port Seeseeran ... by don Manuel Galves, pub. 1774.
" " 73. Lampon bay ...—Port of Palapa ... by don Manuel Galves, pub. 1774.
" " 74-75. Part of the Philipinas ... pub. 1788.
" " 76. Embocadero.—Island Leyté ...
" " 77. Coast views of Palawan. 1761.
" " 78. Bay called by the natives Dalawan on s. e. part of island Balabac, by don Thomas de Castro, 1753.—Insets: Island & shoals in the China sea.—Plans of shoals ... pub. 1785.
" " 79. Balabac and part of the east coast of Palawan or Paragua, by don Antonio F. Quesdal, 1753.
" " 80. Bay and rivers of Ypoloté on Palawan ... by don Thomas de Castro, 1753.
" " 81. Island Balambangan ... pub. 1794.
" " 82. North harbour of Balambangan ...
" " 83. " " " " —Malloodoo bay at the north end of Borneo, by John Roberts.—Inset: Plan of the settlement at Balambangan.
" " 84. Part of Balambangan ... 1764.
" " 85. Southern harbour, or Looc See Kooamboo & Looc Seempool on Balambangan ... 1764.
" " 86. Habour of Sandakan on n. e. part of Borneo.—Inset: Strait between Tambeesan & Oonsang, 1764.
" " 87. Abai harbour on the n. w. coast of Borneo, by James Rennell, 1762.
" " 88. N. W. coast of Borneo ...—Plan of Mantannané ... by Dato Saraphodin ... 1763.—Island Mangalloom ... 1763.
" " 89. Port & river of Borneo.—Northern part of the Natunas islands, by capt. John Clements, 1773.
" " 90. The river of Borneo-proper ... by William Kirton, pub. 1787.
" " 91. East & south coast of the Natunas islands ... pub. 1781.
" " 92. Coast views seen from the Flying Eagle, 1672.
" " 93. Surigao bay at the north point of Mageendanao island, by William Greer, 1762.—Cagayan river ...
" " 94. Part of the island Magindanao.—Bongo bay on Mageendanao, or Mindanao ... pub. 1774.
" " 95. Bay of Panguyl on Mindanao ... 1754.
" " 95 (a) Pollock bay ... by P. Heywood, 1798.
" " 96. The Couts's track from Mageendanao thro' the islands to the west & south-west of Baseelan, by capt. Robert Torin, pub. 1802.
" " 96 (a) Bunwood island.—Kamaladan harbour on Magindanao.—Inset: Plan of Leno harbour on Magindanao, by capt. Thomas Forrest, pub. 1781.
" " 97. Track of the Fox to the attack of Samboangan on the island Mageendanao, by P. Heywood, pub. 1804.
" " 97 (a) Maloza bay on Basseelan, by capt. Walter Alves, 1764.
" " 98. Port of St. Maria ...—Part of the south coast of Mageendanao ...—Town & fort on the bay of Pachira in the island Dumaran by don Pedro Gastambide, 1762.
" " 99. Coast views of Borneo, pub. 1796.
" " 100. Track of the ship Union, capt. Robert Lindsay, 1771.

v. 2, no. 101. Coast of Borneo . . . by Stephen MacDonald, 1788.
" " 102. Coast views of Borneo & strait of Macassar . . . 1788.
" " 103. Part of the coast of Borneo, by William Bampton, 1788.
" " 104. South east coast of Borneo . . . pub. 1788.
" " 105. Coast views of Borneo & the strait of Macassar, by Stephen MacDonald, 1788.
" " 106. Kanneeoongan on the east coast of Borneo, by William McNamara, 1787.
" " 107. Nine islands called Po. Balabalakan by Malays . . . by Thomas Forrest.—Coast view of Borneo.—Paternosters, by John Watson, 1764.—Survey of the south end of Sanguey . . . by P. Heywood, pub. 1804.
" " 108. Coast views of Gilolo . . . & Mortay, by Stephen MacDonald 1788-89.
" " 109. Sangir island.—Talautse islands.
" " 110. Coast views in the strait of Macassar & along the north coast of Celébes . . .
" " 111. The track of the Tartar galley, 1774-75, by Thomas Forrest.—Part of Mindanao . . . pub. 1789.
" " 111 (a) East side of Gillolo & adjacent islands . . . 1807.
" " 111 (b) North end of Celébes . . .—Taloutse islands . . . Inset: Siao & adjacent islands by capt. George Millet, 1799.
" " 112. Coast views of Siao . . . & Celébes.
" " 113. Sketch of the anchorage off Hummock island . . . by capt. John Hunter, 1791.
" " 114. Coast views of New Holland . . . 1747.
" " 115. Bally High hill lying in Carang-Assem road, by capt. Thos. Forrest.
" " 116. Coast views of Java, Sumbava, Lomboc & adjacent islands, pub. 1780.
" " 117. West coast of Lombock . . .—Strait of Allass . . . by George Robertson, 1781.
" " 118. Sumbawa road . . .—Strait of Sapy . . . 1761.
" " 118 (a) Sapy strait with the northern entrance of Mangaryn, by capt. William Layman.—Straits of Sapy, by Robert Torin, 1797.
" " 119. Sapy bay on the island Sumbawa, by Thomas Welladvice, 1780.—Insets: Part of Sumbawa, by Charles Christie, 1780.—Water bay on Sumbawa. 1780.
" " 120. Coast views of Shalombo, Olombo, Vogels, Lety, Rote, Timor & Anamaboa islands, pub. 1782.
" " 121. South coast of Mangarye . . . by capt. William Bligh, pub. 1792.
" " 121 (a) Part of the coast of Mangerye . . . 1761.
" " 122. Dellie harbour on the island of Timor.—Inset: Delhi harbour on the island Timor . . . pub. 1802.
" " 123. Baring's bay on Sandal-wood island . . . 1790.—West end of the island Timor . . . pub. 1786.
" " 123 (a) Coupang road on the island of Timor . . . pub 1805.
" " 124. Copang bay . . . 1791.
" " 125. Coast views of Hummock, Mangery, Saddle, Tower, Camara, Flat & Sintodo islands. 1761.
" " 126. Aligator bay on the island Floris . . . 1761.—Inset: Coast of Floris, or Mangerye . . . pub. 1780.
" " 127. Mangrove harbour on Floris . . .

**Dalrymple, A.**, & *others*—Continued.

v. 2, no. 128. Mangaray & Sumba with Timor & adjacent islands, pub. 1786.
" " 129. Coast views of Celébes & adjacent islands, pub. 1780.
" " 130. South part of Celébes . . . pub. 1787.
" " 131. Bay of Bony on south part of Celébes . . . pub. 1786.
" " 131 (a) Kalan-soe-soe harbour . . . pub. 1805.
" " 132. South coast of Celébes, pub. 1786.
" " 132 (a) West " " " " "
" " 133. Macassar road . . . pub. 1804.
" " 134. S. W. coast of Celébes, pub. 1787.
" " 135. Islands & shoals to the westward of Celébes . . . pub. 1786.
" " 136. Turatte bay . . . 1761.—Bonthain bay.—Straits of Salayn, by capt. John Watson, 1764.
" " 137. Gorontalo river . . . on Celébes, by V. V. Ballard . . .—Inset: Gorantallo river, by Robert Pavin, 1798.
" " 137 (a) Coast views of Celébes & adjacent islands. 1768.
" " 138. East coast of Celébes . . .—Islands between Banda & Papua . . . 1727.—Inset: Castricom's bay . . . pub. 1781.
" " 139. Coast views of Celébes & adjacent islands, by com. John Watson, 1763-64.
" " 140. Islands seen in the Warwick, capt. James Dewar, 1761.
" " 141. Coast views of Celébes . . . 1761.
" " 142. Track of the Princess Augusta, capt. Thomas Baddison, 1761.
" " 143. Island Amboina . . . Inset: Plan of Castle Victoria . . . pub. 1782.
" " 144. Coast views of the lands around the Pitts-strait . . . 1780.
" " 145. Track of East India company's cruizers . . . John McCluer 1792.
" " 146. Island Boero . . .—Inset: Lake a-top of the mountain of Boero . . . pub. 1793.
" " 147. Islands of Banda . . . pub. 1788.
" " 148. Islands to eastward & southward of Banda with part of adjacent coasts of New Guinea & New Holland, pub. 1788.
" " 149. Lands around Dampier's strait . . . 1781.
" " 150. New Guinea, pub. 1780.
" " 151. East end of the island Baber, by Hugh Levelis, 1672.—Selang harbour, by capt. Thomas Forrest.
" " 152. Kanary islands.—Island Geby, by John McCluer, 1794.
" " [152a] Islands adjacent to Mysol, by Robert Scott . . . pub. 1802.
" " 153. Port of Geby in the Maluco islands.—Inset: Port of I. Faux . . . pub. 1779.
" " 154. Island of Aiou or Yowl.—Part of Efbe island . . .—Harbour of Offak on Waygiou.—Harbour of Piapis . . . by capt. Thomas Forrest . . . pub. 1781.
" " 155. Coast views of lands around Dampier's strait, by capt. William Fraser. 1781.
" " 156. Rawak harbour on the north side of Waygiou.—Dory harbour, by capt. Thomas Forrest, 1775.
" " 157. Part of Papua & New Britain, or the Salomon islands.—Copy of part of Dampier's chart from Cape of Good Hope to New Britain.—Inset: De Bry, 1596.
" " 158. Nova Guinea.—South sea, by Abraham Ortelius, 1589.—Nova Guinea . . . 1600.—Inset: Part of a map of the Arcano del mare, by Dudley . . . 1661.

v. 2, no. 159. Copy of . . . charts of the Arcano del mare, by Dudley . . . 1661.—Copy of part of the chart of Asia in the Arcano del mare . . . 1646.
" " 160. North coast of New Guinea, by Joao Teixeira . . . 1649.
" " 161. New Guinea . . . by Guillaum Sanson, 1719.—New Guinea by Robert de Vaugondy, 1756-74.—Part of New Guinea . . . 1643-44.—North coast of New Guinea, by W: C. Schouten, 1617.
" " 162. Track of the Princesa . . . 1781.—Track of the Swallow . . . 1767.
" " 163. Part of m. Bougainville's track thro' Bougainvilles strait.— Inset: South coast of New Guinea, called . . . Louisiade. pub. 1790.
" " 164. Mackrel bay & Water bay.—Port Montague.—Bay Choiseuil.— Carteret's harbour in St. Georges sound, New Britain, 1767.
" " 165. English cove & Gower's harbour . . . 1767.—Plan of port Hunter . . . pub. 1794.
" " 166. Port Praslin . . . — Byrons bay on St. Cruz island 1767.— Swallow or Water bay . . . 1767.
" " 167. Lord Howe's group of islands . . .—Inset: Sketch of Stewart's islands, by John Hunter, 1791.
" " 168. Islands in the South sea . . . capt. Maitland, 1799.—Track of the Princesa . . . 1781.
" " 169. Bay of Lauriston on New-Zeland . . . pub. 1781.
" " 170. Oyster bay and part of Maria's island.
" " by capt. J: H: Cox, 1789.
" " 171. Edels land . . . pub. 1779.
" " 172. West court of New Holland . . . pub. 1779.
" " 173. Houtman's Abrolhos near the w. coast of New Holland . . .— Dangerous rocks off the coast of New Holland . . . 1681.— Tryall rocks . . .
" " 174. Island Rottenest, ie Rat's nest . . .—Part of New Holland, by John Thornton & Joel Gascoyn, pub. 1790.
" " 175. Comparative plan of Tryal rocks & adjacent island . . . —Coast views of the island called Amsterdam, 1763.
" " 176. Vlamings road on east side of Amsterdam, by J: H: Cox, 1789.— Jervis bay . . . by Mathew Weatherhead . . .
" " 177. Coast views of islands west of Sumatra, pub. 1782.
" " 178. Achen road . . . pub. 1785.
" " 178 (a) " " & the Swrat & Sedre passages, by James Downie . . . pub. 1806.
" " 179. Coast of Sumatra . . . by capt G: Baker.
" " 179. Inset: Coast of Sumatra from point Pedro to Passeir, by capt. G: French, 1784-85.
" " 180. Palumbang river.—Lands on east side of Banka . . . 1773.
" " 181. Mintow road, pub. 1789.
" " 182. North end of Banka, by capt. Lestock Wilson, pub. 1791.
" " 183. Plan of the Warren Hastings' track to the east of Banka, by J: P. Larkins, 1788.—Strait of Chinabata . . . now called Banka, pub. 1786.
" " 184. The Carnatick's track from North Watcher to North island . . .—Inset: Bay, adjacent to North island, by capt. Lestock Wilson 1787.

**Dalrymple, A.**, & *others*—continued.

v. 2, no. 185. Mouths of the straits of Malacca & Banka to the coast of Borneo, from m. d'Aprés [de Mannevillette] pub. 1786.
" " 186. Lingen to Borneo . . . pub. 1786.
" " 187. Chart of capt. Gaspar's track, from m. d'Aprés [de Mannevillette]—Track of the Mascarin . . . pub. 1786.
" " 188. Clements strait to the west of Billiton . . . by George Robertson, pub. 1786.
" " 189. Track of the Atlas thro' the islands to the east of Banka, by capt. Allen Cooper, 1785.
" " 190. Tracks of the Elephant & Camel.—Plans of the Osterly's tracks . . . pub. 1786.
" " 191. Track of the Hector, capt. John Williams, 1759.—Track of the Glatton . . . by Thomas Welladvice, 1779.
" " 192. South coast of Borneo . . . by George Baker . . . pub. 1786.
" " 193. Carimon Java . . .— Part of the island Lubeck; or, Babean, pub. 1780.
" " 194. Turtle bay . . .— Vleer Muys bay . . .—Inset: Patsietam bay on south coast of Java. pub. 1780.
" " 195. Ballambouang bay in the strait of Bally, by capt. Nicholas Skottowe, 1766.—Turtle bay . . .—Patietan bay.—Flittermous bay, on south coast of Java . . . pub. 1782.
" " 196. Vinkops; or Wine-coopers point & bay . . .—Dirck Vries & Maurice bays . . . by capt. C: G. Ekeberg.—Mew bay in the strait of Sunda, by John Watson, 1762.
" " 197. Po. Pontangh; or, Princes island & adjacent coast of Java . . . pub. 1888.
" " 198. Part of the strait of Sunda . . . by William Bampton . . . pub. 1787.
" " 198(a) North coast of Java, pub. 1804.
" " 199. Batavia road . . . pub. 1786.
" " 200. Road of Batavia . . . Plan of the city of Batavia . . . 1763.
" " 201. Strait on the east coast of Banka, by capt. Lestock Wilson, 1787 . . .
" " 202. Zutphen; or, Hounds islands . . .—Lampoon bay on the south part of Sumatra . . . 1764.
" " 203. Coast viéws of Sumatra, pub. 1774.
" " 204. Passage between P. Krokatoa & Po. Slebeze, by Robert Torin.—Keyser's bay . . . by Thomas Forrest, pub. 1774.
" " 205. Billimbing bay . . .—Bencoonat bay on west coast of Sumatra, by C: G. Wahlfeldt, pub. 1774.
" " 206. Croee, on the west coast of Sumatra, by John Watson, 1762.—Insets: Harbour at Po. Pisang . . .—Po. Pisang, on the west coast of Sumatra . . . capt. Tyson, 1763.
" " 207. Cawoor; or Sambat . . . by C: G. Wahlfeldt, 1771.—Poolo bay, near Bencoolen, by William Tolley.
" " 208. Coast views of No. Nassau; or Poggy island, pub. 1774.
" " 209. West coast of Sumatra . . . by William Kirton, 1781.—Indparour on the west coast of Sumatra . . . pub. 1774.
" " 210. Padang . . .—Batang-Capay bay, on the west coast of Sumatra, by capt. John McDonald, pub. 1788.
" " 211. Coast & islands adjacent to Padang . . . pub. 1774.
" " 212. Padang the chief settlement of the dutch company . . . pub. 1782.

v. 2, no. 213. Part of the west coast of Sumatra by John McDonald . . . pub. 1788.
" " 214. From Padang to Boongas bay . . . 1784.
" " 215. Po. Marra & adjacent islands, by John McDonald . . . pub. 1788.
" " 216. Pooloo Saytan island . . . pub. 1788.
" " 217. Polo Babee bay, on the west coast of Sumatra, by John McDonald, pub. 1788.
" " 218. Po. Chenco, with the adjacent bays on the west coast of Sumatra, by capt. John McDonald, pub. 1788.
" " 219. Priaman & the Ticoo islands . . . by com. John Watson, 1762.—Tappean-oely, or, Tappanooly . . . pub. 1774.
" " 219 (a) Track of the Ariel . . . between Hog island & Tapanooly.—Inset: Sketch of Hog island . . . pub. 1805.
" " 220. Tapanooley bay . . . by capt. Robt. Moorsom, 1790.—Ayer-Bongy . . . pub. 1774.
" " 221. North part of Pooloo Batoo.—Trieste island . . . by John Hunter, 1802.
" " 221 (a) Passage between Po. Banjac & the west coast of Sumatra.—Bay on the north part of Po. Banjack, pub. 1791.
" " 222. S. Leaga bay . . . by Stephen H. Bunyan.—Passage between the islands of Great Fortune lying off the west coast of Sumatra . . . pub. 1786.
" " 223. Po. Nayas . . . pub. 1780.
" " 224. North part of Pooloo Nayas . . . pub. 1774.
" " 225. Coast views of Sumatra . . . 1794.
" " 226. Passage between Po. Bato & Se Beeroo, called Natian & Good Fortune, by capt. George Hayter, 1755.
" " 227. The Pigot's track from Se Beeroo to the North Poggy, by Robert Torin, 1794.
" " 228. Strait of Secockup between the No. & So. Poggy islands . . . by capt. John Whiteway, 1750. Strait of Secockup . . .—Mazular island, by Thomas Forrest, pub. 1782.
" " 229. Harbour of Mansillar near Sumatra, surveyed by John Macdonald, 1789.
" " 230. Hurlock's bay on the island Good Fortune, or Poorah . . . by capt. John Whiteway, 1750.
" " 231. Harbour of Se Laubo Laubo, on the west side of the No. Poggy island . . . by capt. John Whiteway, 1750.—Three bays on the island Good-Fortune . . . 1750.
" " 232. Part of the islands of Pora, or Good Fortune; & Poggys, or Nassau . . .—Harbour on the east side of So. Poggy island . . . by capt. John Whiteway, 1750.
" " 233. Island Engano . . .—They bay on the south east coast of island Engano; by Charles Gustavus Wahlfeldt, 1771.
" " 234. Track of the Houghton passing the Cocos, or Keeling islands, by capt. James Munro, 1788.—Keeling, or Cocos Islands, from John Van Keulen.—Inset: The Cocos islands . . . by capt. don Alexandro Malaspina, 1788.
" " 235. Pescadore islands in the straits of Formosa, from . . . capt. Robert Duffin, 1792.—Port Alexander on the west coast of Africa . . . 1796.
" " 236. Spencer's bay . . .—Walwich bay . . .—Fish bay on the west coast of Africa . . . 1796.

**Dalrymple, A.**, & *others*—Continued.
- v. 2, no. 237. Angra Pequena . . .—St Helena bay on the west coast of Africa . . . 1796.
- v. 3, no. 1. Santa Cruz on the island Tenerife, by capt. Henry Roberts . . . —Plan of the fortifications next the sea . . .—Elizabeth bay & Possession island, 1793.
- " " 2. Walvisch bay . . .—St Helena's bay . . .—Inset: Plan of the Beschermer's harbour in bay Rhenius & Daniels (Angra Pequena) laid down by chevalier Duminy, 1793.
- v. 3, no. 3. N. W. coast of Madagascar . . . pub. 1798.
- " " [1 (a)] Ocean between South America and Africa . . . 1700-38.
- " " [2 (a)] East coast of Brazil . . . pub. 1779.
- " " [3 (a)] " " " " pub. 1779.
- " " [4 (a)] " " " Africa . . . 1787.
- " " 5. Harbour at the island Chagos, or Diego Garcia . . . pub. 1787.
- " " 6. An eye draught from Dofar to Shoal Cliff on the coast of Arabia . . . by capt. John S. Smith . . . pub. 1783.
- " " 7. Coast of Persia with the various branches of Bussora river.—Inset: Catif bay . . . in gulph of Persia . . . pub. 1780.
- " " 8. Head of the gulph of Persia, by lieut. John McCluer . . . pub. 1788.
- " " 9. The Persian gulph from Muscat to Bushere, by John McCluer, 1785.
- " " 9 (a) The Red sea, by Robert White, 1795.
- " " " (b) Part of the Red sea . . .—Harbour of Dareedy . . . by George Trotter, 1776.
- " " " (c) Mocha road, by G. G. Richardson, 1795.
- " " " John McCluer, pub. 1798.
- " " " (d) Track of ship Pearl near same dangerous shoals in the gulph of Persia, by Thomas D. Lippiatt . . . pub. 1797.
- " " 9 (e) Bussora river . . . by John McCluer.
- " " " " by capt. William Layman.
- " " " (f) False bay . . . 1775.
- " " " (g) Coast of Arabia from Aden to Bab-el-Mandeb . . .—South coast of Arabia from Aden to cape St Anthony . . . pub. 1801.
- " " " (h) Ports in the Red sea . . . pub. 1800.
- " " " (i) Island Cabrity . . . 1795. Inset: Plan of the island Underoo . . . 1795.—Muscat cove, by W. Layman, pub. 1797.
- " " 10. Coast from cape Arubah to the entrance of the gulph of Persia . . . 1774.
- " " 11. Coast from Scindy to cape Gaudell . . .—Coasts of Guazarat & Scindy . . . 1783.
- " " 12. Coasts of India & Guzarat . . . by John McCluer, 1788.
- " " 12 (a) Fort Marlbro & its environs, by capt. John Macdonald, 1793.—Plan of Bencoolen road . . . pub. 1797.
- " " 13. Belapore river, by J. Lendrum, 1793.
- " " 14. Charts of the Malabar coast . . . from Mangalore to Bombay . . .—Inset: Angrias lands, by Nicholas Struyck, 1757.
- " " 15. Part of the Malabar coast . . . by John McCluer, 1789-90.
- " " 16. Part of the Malabar coast & part of the Laccadivés . . . by John McCluer, 1790.
- " " 16 (a) The Laccadivés in the province of Malabar, surveyed by lieut. John Wedgebrough, 1795.

v. 3, no. 16 (b) Island Kalpeni & its dependencies . . .—Inset: Islands Seuhelipar . . . by Robert Bentley, 1795.
" " " (c) Island Minicoy . . . by R. Bentley, 1795.
" " " (d) " Aucutta with its dependencies . . . —Inset: Islands Tingaro & Bingaro surveyed by R. Bentley, 1795.
" " 16 (e) Coast views of Laccadivés, by lieut. John McCluer, pub. 1791.
" " " (f) Coast views in the gulph of Manar, by Samuel Snook, 1795.
" " " (g) Northern part of the gulph of Manaar, by John Wedgbrough . . . 1795-96.
" " " (h) Coast views of Tutacarine, by Samuel Snook, 1795.
" " " (i) Plan of Tutacorin, by John Wedgbrough, 1796.
" " 16 (j) Kalirrewoe, or river Serto, on the n. e. side of Ceylan . . .— Plan to show the position of the Fairlie rock . . .
" " " (k) Part of the coast of Madura, from Manapar to Baypar, by John Wedgbrough, 1796.
" " 17. Coasts of Galconda & Orixa, by John Thornton, 1703.—Coasts of Choromandel & Orixa . . .—Coast of Coremandell, from fort St. George to Visiagapatam . . .—Insets: Plans of Coringo & Vizagapatam road, by John Ritchie, 1771.—The Armegon shoals, by A. Fisherman, 1762.
" " 18. Bay of Coringa, by Michael Topping, 1789.
" " 19. Northern part of the bay of Bengal . . .
" " 20. Nancowry harbour . . . 1790.
" " 21. Strait of Papra . . . by A. Blair, 1788.
" " 22. China sea . . . pub. 1771.
" " " (a) Poolo bay, by capt. John Macdonald, 1793.—Soosoo, on the west coast of Sumatra . . . pub. 1797.
" " " (b) Bason at Rat island near Bencoolen . . .—Plan of Rat island . . . 1789.—Sketch of the environs of Rat island . . . by capt. Henry Burges . . . 1789.
" " " (c) Strait of Malacca, by Archibald Blair, pub. 1805.
" " " (d) River Saigon, from the city to the mouth of the river. Port of Candiu . . . pub. 1802.
" " " (e) Part of the west coast of Ceylan, by John Wedgbrough, 1795-96.
" " 23. Chart showing all the passages & channels into the harbour of Chusan on the coast of China, by John Thornton . . . 1703.
" " " (a) Andaman islands . . . by A. Blair . . . 1793.
" " 24. Island Pakan, or Formosa . . . pub. 1792.
" " " (a) Andaman islands, by Archibald Blair.
" " 25. Part of the coast of China & the adjacent islands . . . 1764.
" " " (a) Andaman islands, by A. Blair.
" " 26. West coast of Palawan . . . 1761.
" " " (a) Part of the coast of Great Andaman & adjacent islands, by lieut. Archibald Blair, 1789.
" " 27. Island Palawan, by James Barton, pub. 1781.
" " 28. Part of the Philippine islands, pub. 1781.
" " " (a) Part of the coast of Borneo, by capt. Adies, 1789.
" " " (b) Coast of Luzon . . . 1761.
" " " (c) Five plans of the Menam river.—Insets: Plans of city of Siam, or Juthia; and Louvo, pub. 1797.
" " " (d-f) Coast views along the Red sea, pub. 1799.
" " 29-30. Part of the Philipinas . . . pub. 1799.

**Dalrymple, A.**, *& others*—Continued.

v. 3, no. 31. Part of Borneo & the Sooloo archipelago . . . 1761-64.
" " 32. Felicia . . .—Island Balambangan . . .
" " 33. Sooloo archipelago . . . 1761-64.—Insets: Toolyan bay, by James Rennel.—Sooloo road. 1761-64.
" " 34. Track of the ship Glatton, from Sanguin island to Tolour islands.
" " " (a) Part of the coast of Ceylan . . . pub. 1800.
" " " (b) River Cey, or Say Gon . . .—Bay St. James . . . pub. 1800.
" " " (c) Punta Gala on Ceylan, by George Robertson, 1797.—Inset: Plan of point de Gale . . . pub. 1801.
" " " (d) Part of the Malabar coast from Barcelor peak to St Mary's rocks.—Inset: Plan of Cundapore . . . pub. 1801.
" " " (e) Ports of Xum Day, Vung Lain & Vung on the coast of Cochin-China.
" " 35. Tracks along the coast of Borneo, pub. 1795.
" " 36. Mer des Indes; copy of an ancient map.
" " 37. Insulae Moloccae . . . imprinted at London by John Wolfe, graven by Robert Becket, 1598.
" " 38–40 East coast of New Holland, by James Cook, 1770.
" " 40 (a) Track thro' the strait between New Guinea & New Holland, by W. Bampton, 1793.
" " " (b) Passage . . . thro' Torres strait, 1793.
" " 40 (c) Maragalong islands . . .—Manevasa & the adjacent small islands . . .—Cajeli bay on the island of Bouro, by capt. George Palmer, 1797.
" " " (d) Cajelie bay . . . pub. 1805.
" " " (e) Track from strait of Allas to the island Bouro, by capt. George Palmer, 1797.
" " " (f) Part of the island Honimoa.—Plan of Saparooa bay . . . & of Noessa Laut, by John Wales . . . pub. 1801.
" " 40 (g) Bay of Amahoy on Ceram, by lieut. John Wales, pub. 1801.
" " " (h) Tong-Hou cove, by capt. George Palmer, 1797.
" " 41. Papua, or New Guinea. 1790-91.
" " 42. West part of " " & the adjacent straits . . . 1705.
" " 43. Great bay on the north side of New Guinea . . . pub. 1781.
" " 44. Strait of Galowa, called Revenges strait, by com. John Watson, 1764.
" " 45-46. Straits of Solor . . . 1781.
" " 47. Timoor & adjacent islands . . . pub. 1792.
" " 48. Straits of Sunda & Banka . . . 1786.
" " 49. Passage to the east of Banka, by capt. Lestock Wilson, 1789.
" " " (a) Strait of Allass, 1796.—Part of Lombock.—Strait of Alass, by William Palmer, 1792.
" " " (b) Straits of Allass, by James Murray, 1797.
" " " (c) Part of the New Caroline Islands . . .—Passage between Augusta & Pidgeon islands in Dampier's strait, by H. Moor. pub. 1798.
" " " (d) Passage between Lusipara & Sumatra . . . by Robert Torin . . . pub. 1797.
" " " (e) Strait of Banka, by Robert Torin . . . pub. 1797.
" " " (f-g) " " " " " " .—Islands in the Pacifick ocean . . . pub. 1802 laid down by G. Bass & R. Simpson.
" " " (h) Bishop's Junction islands & Bass's Reef-tied islands . . . 1799.

v. 3, no. 49 (i) Port of Coumong . . . on the coast of Cochin-China . . . pub. 1800.
" " " (j) Bay of Selema & harbour of Saway on the west side of Ceram, by lieut. Thomas Hayward, pub. 1800.
" " " (k) Tracks . . . thro' the Eastern islands, by Edward Studd, 1797.
" " " (l) Straits of Aluer, by John Wales . . .—Track thro' the Philipinas islands, by William Layman, pub. 1799.
" " " (m) Coast views of Mangerye, or Floris & Timor islands, pub. 1799.
" " " (n) Dampier's straits, by James Murray, pub. 1799.
" " " (o) Part of the coast of Madura, by capt. James Horsburgh, 1801.—Tracks . . . between Sooloo & Mindoro . . . 1793.
" " " (p) Track from New Guinea to Salombo, by James Horsburgh 1793.
" " " (q) Tracks thro' the strait of Maccassar, by James Horsburgh . . .—Insets: Boddan's track thro' the strait of Macassar, by George Palmer, 1794.—Two shoals off the coast of Borneo . . . pub. 1800.
" " " (r) The Indian ocean with coasts, islands, rocks & shoals from Madagascar to India, Sumatra & Java . . . 1787.
" " " (s) Strait of Limbe . . . by John Wales, 1798.
" " " (t) Coast of Cochin-China . . . 1773.
" " " (u) The sea, from Timor to Ceram, by Thomas Hayward, pub. 1801.
" " " (v) Mysory & adjacent islands . . .—Two charts of Scouten's island . . . pub. 1799.
" " " (w) South coast of China, from Macao to the Brothers, by capt. David Inverarity, 1793.
" " " (x) N. W. coast of Madagascar, by capt. David Inverarity . . . pub. 1806.—Inset: Plan of north part of Madagascar . . .
" " " (y) Bembatooka bay . . . on Madagascar, by David Inverarity, 1802.
" " " (z) Passandava . . . with the bays of Marbacool & Chimpaykee . . . by David Inverarity, 1803.
" " " (a') Narreenda bay & Luza river, on the n. w. coast of Madagascar, by D. Inverarity, 1803.
" " " (b') Harbour of point de Galle . . . by capt. David Inverarity . . . pub. 1801.
" " " (c') Part of the west coast of Borneo & track of soundings to Lingen and Malaya, by capt. David Inverarity, pub. 1807.
" " " (d') Linear tables, pub, 1783.

**1703-1807**

——Same.  5 v. obl. fol. (v. 4–5: fol.)  London, 1703–1807.  544

NOTE.—This copy is like the one described in detail, except that on verso of maps nos. 54, 60–65, 67, & 69, of v. 5, are the following manuscripts, by sir Francis Beaufort:
no. [1] City and harbour of Rhodes, 1811.
" [2] Sketch of Monte Video.
" [3] " " the harbour of Monte Video & the adjacent coasts, from pt. Braba to pt. Yeguas, with the intermediate soundings.

**Dalrymple, A.**, & *others*—Continued.

    no. [4] Soundings and bearings taken on the 8th of august, 1807, at pt. Espinilla.
    " [5] Sketch of the islands Flores, taken in the Protector, august 1807.
    " [6] Sketch of part of that extensive shoal, called the English bank.
    " [7] Sketch of Archimedes bank.
    " [8] Soundings from pt. Braba to St Lucia river.
    " [9] Sketch of Syracuse bay. 1808.

### 1704?
**Bodenehr, G.**

    Atlas curieux, oder neuer und compendieuser atlas, in welchem aufser den general land charten von America, Africa, Asia und Europa, und der in letzterem gelegenen reichen und ländern, fehr viele speciale von besondern provincien und territorien fonderlich deren, die in letzteren kriegen renomiert worden, enthalten sind. 3 p. l., 99 maps, 3 tab. 8°. Augspurg, G. Bodenehr [1704?]   545

    NOTE.—Text of map no. 11 dated 1704.
    Map no. 102, "Russlands oder Moskoviens, nord-west theil" . . . is not referred to in the table of contents.
    Maps signed "G. Bodenehr exc." or, "Georg Christoph Kilian excudit."
    The following maps relate to America:
    no. 1. Der gantze welt Kreis.
    " 2. Der neven welt begriff . . . Nord America und Sud America . . .
    " 4. Carta hydrographica oder algemeine welt und commercien carte . . .
    " 6. Europæ [showing part of North America]

### 1705
**Fer, N. de.**

    L'atlas curieux ou le monde représenté dans des cartes générales et particulières du ciel et de la terre divisé tant en ses quatre principales parties que par états et provinces et orné par des plans et descriptions des villes capitales et principales et des plus superbes édifices qui les embelissent. Comme sont les églises, les palais, les maisons de plaisance, les jardins, les fontaines &c. 1 p. l., [110] l., [155] maps, [33] pl. obl. fol. Paris, chez l'auteur, 1705.   546

    NOTE.—See also title 532. Issued in five annual parts from 1700–1704. In 1703 an edition appeared containing almost all the maps, plates and descriptions in the first four parts. The edition of 1705 contains almost all designs and explanations in the five parts, together with forty others.
    A number of the dates on the maps have been changed by pen.
    The general title page is bound in the center of the atlas, and the "Title en port de mer," which is the title-page of the 2nd part, appears in place of the general title.
    See "Table de ce qui est contenu dans chacune des parties de l'atlas curieux, & les années que ces parties ont été mises au jour. Par N. de Fer . . . Avec privilège du roy, 1703," in edition of 1700–[1704]
    A water color sketch of the Rialto is inserted at end.
    The following maps relate to America:
    no. [ 96] Les isles Philippines . . . 1700.
    " [103] Le Canada . . . 1702.

no. [104] Le costes aux environs de la rivière de Misisipi . . . 1701.
" [105] . . . Carte de Californie et du Nouveau Mexique . . . 1700.
" [106] Le vieux Mexique ou Nouvelle Espagne. 1705.
" [108] Isle de la Martinique. 1704.
" [109] Plans des villes, forts, port, rade et environ de Cartagène . . . 1700.
" [110] La Terre Ferme et le Pérou avec le pays des Amazones et le Brésil . . . 1705.
" [111] Le Chili et les provinces qui composent celle de rio de la Plata avec les Terres Magellanique. 1705.
" [112] Le detroit de Magellan. 1700.
" [116] Mappe-monde ou carte générale de la terre . . . 1705.
" [117] Mappe-monde ou carte universel$^{le}$. 1762.
" [121] L'Amérique, Méridionale et Septentrionale. 1700.

### 1705

—— Petit et nouveau atlas.  1 p. l., [19] 1., 18 maps, 1 pl.  obl. 4°.
Paris, de Fer, 1705. 547
> NOTE: –Engraved title.
> Text by Pierre Du Val.
> The following maps relate to America:
> [no. 5] L'Amérique Septentrionale.
> [no. 6] L'Amérique Méridionale.

### 1705-1720

**Châtelain, H. A.**

Atlas historique, ou, nouvelle introduction à l'histoire, à la chronologie & à la géographie ancienne & moderne . . . par mr. C. * * * [anon.] Avec des dissertations sur l'histoire de chaque état, par m. [Nicolas] Gueudeville. 7 v. fol. Amsterdam, F. l'Honoré & Châtelain, 1705-20. 548
> NOTE.—Edition varies: v. 1, 1705; v. 2-3, 1708; v. 4, 1714; v. 5-6, 1719; v. 7, 1720. See also title 579.
> v. 3 published as tome 2, seconde partie.
> Engraved frontispiece.
> Title of v. 7: Suplément à l'Atlas historique . . .
> The following maps relate to America:
> v. 1, no. 2. Mappe monde . . .
> "   "   4. Plan . . . ou l'on voit les quatre monarchies du monde . . .
> "   "   34. [Les Antilles et Philippines]
> "   "   35. . . . l'Amérique Septentrionale et Méridionale.
> "   "   43. Mappe monde.
> " 2, "  43. Inset: . . . l'Amérique.
> " 5, "  45. [Isles Philippines]
> " 6, "  20. . . . Canada . . .
> "   "   21. . . . Fleuve Saint Louis . . .
> "   "   23. La Nouvelle France . . .
> "   "   26. Insets: Île des Barbades.—Nouvelle Angleterre et Nouvel York.—Les Barmudes.—Partie de la mer de Sud.—La Jamaique.—La Caroline.—Pensylvanie.—Maryland.—Virginie.—et Nouvelle Jarsey.—Partie de l'Amérique Septentrionale.

**Châtelain, H. A.**—Continued.

v. 6, no. 27. . . . Mexique.—Environs du lac de Mexique.
" " 30. . . . L'Amérique Septentrionale et Méridionale.—Les Antilles, les isles Philippines.
" " 31. . . . Pérou, Brésil, et les pays des Amazones . . .
" " 32. Carte particulière du Pérou et plan de la ville de Lima . . .
" " 33. . . . Le Paraguai, le Chili . . .
" " 35. . . . Les Antilles françoises et les isles voisines.

CONTENTS.

v. 1. Qui comprend la Grèce, l'Italie, la France, l'Espagne, et des Païs bas.
" 2. Qui comprend l'Allemagne, la Pruſſe, la Hongrie, & la Bohême.
" 3. Qui comprend la Grand Bretagne, l'Irlande, la Suisse, la Savoye, la Lorraine et la république de Veniſe.
" 4. Qui comprend le Dannemarck, la Suède, la Pologne, la Moſcovie, la Turquie, &c.
" 5. Qui comprend l'Asie en général et, en particulier, l'Aſſyrie, l'Arménie, la Géorgie, la Turquie aſiatique, la Terre Sainte, l'Arabie, la Perſe, la Tartarie, les états du Grand Mogol, les Indes Orientales, la Chine, le Japon et le roïaume de Siam.
" 6. Qui comprend l'Afrique, & l'Amérique Septentrionale & Méridionale tant en général qu'en particulier, l'Egypte, la Barbarie, la Nigritie, la Guinée, l'Éthiopie, le Congo, la Cafrérie, et le Cap de Bonne Eſpérance; la Canada; ou, la Nouvelle France, la Louïſiane; ou, le Mississipi, la Virginie, la Floride, le Mexique, le Pérou, le Chili & le Brésil; avec les îles de Madagaſcar, les Philippines, les Moluques, les Antilles & l'île de Ceylan.
" 7. Contenant diverses piéces de chronologie, de généalogie, d'histoire, et d'autres sciences qui avoient été omiſes dans les précédens volumes.

## 1706?

**Wit, F. de**

Atlas maior. 2 v. fol. Amstelodami, ex officina F. de Wit [1706?] 549

NOTE.—Collation: v. 1, 1 p. l., 77 maps, 1 pl.; v. 2, 82 maps, 2 pl.
Maps dated 1651-1705. v. 2, no. [40] . . . Turin, contains the historical date 1706.
Title headed, "Londini apud Chriſtophorum Browne." Additional imprint, "Sold by Chriſtopher Browne at the weſt end of Saint Paull's church."
Numerous maps bear imprint of Christopher Browne.
Engraved title signed, "Lauwerens Scherm. delin. et sculp."
Maps by various cartographers, including: Allard, Browne, Norden, Jaillot, Jansson, Loon, Moll, Valk, Visscher, Danckerts.
Contains the following plans of cities:
v. 1, no. [29] Lutetiæ Parisiorum universæ Galliæ metropolis . . . per Jacobum de la Feuille.
" " [48] Vienna Avstriæ . . .
" " [60] Inset: Emporium Hamburgum.
" " [69] D'Fortresse der tien Spaansche provintien of Belgii regii . . .
" " [75] Exactissima Amstelodami veteris et novissimi delineatio per F. de Wit.
v. 2, " [19] D'Voormaamste fortressen van Hungaria . . .

v. 2, no. [24] D'voornaamste fortressen van Moræa . . .
" " [29] Messina.—Milazzo.—Palermo.—Catania.—Trapano. [Insets in] Insula five regnum Siciliæ . . .
" " [31] D'voornaamste fortresse van ţ koningryck Napels en Sisielie in Italie . . .
" " [33] A new map of Rome . . . by Christopher Browne . . .
" " [38] D'kracht van Italien of de fortresse van Lombardye . . .
" " [40] Plan de la ville et citadelle de Turin . . . deliverez par le duc de Savoye et le prince Eugène de Savoye le 7. septemb. l'an 1706.

The following maps relate to America:
v. 1, no. [1] Planisphærium terrestre five terrarum orbis . . . Carolo Allard . . .
" " [2] Nieuw aerdsch pleyn. Cornelius Danckerts del.
" " [6] Recentifsima novi orbis sive Americæ Septentrionalis et Meridionalis tabula . . . Caroli Allard.
" 2, no. [55] Indiæ Orientalis . . . per Nicolaum Visfcher . . .
" " [70] Nova Canadæ sive Novæ Franciæ in America Septentrionali . . . 1696.
" " [71] A new map of the english empire in America . . . by Rob: Morden. Inset: A general map of the coafts & isles of Europe, Africa and America . . .
" " [72] A new map of Virginia, Mary-land and the improved parts of Penn-sylvania & New-Jersey . . .
" " [73] Insulæ Americanæ . . . per Nicolaum Visscher . . .
" " [74] The principall islands in America belonging to the english empire . . .
" " [75] Mappa Æstivarum . . . A mapp of the Sommer iflands . . .
" " [76] Nova Hispania et Nova Galicia.
" " [77] Terra Firma et novum regnum Granatense et Popayan . . . Joannes Janfsonius excudit.
" " [78] Venezuela cum parte auftrali Novæ Andalusiæ . . . Ioannes Janssoniue excudit.
" " [79] Gviana fiue Amazonvm regio . . . Ionannes Ianfsonius excudit.
" " [80] Nova et accurata Brasiliæ totius tabula, auctore Ioanne Blaev . . .
" " [81] Paraqvaria vulgo Paragvay . . .
" " [82] Perv . . . apud Ioannem Ianffonnium.
" " [83] Chili . . . Giuljelmus Blaeuw excudit.

## 1708–1725
**Senex, J.**

Modern geography: or all the known countries in the world. Laid down from the latest observations and discoveries, communicated to the Royal society of London and Academy of sciences at Paris. To which is added the geography of the antient world, showing in six maps the grecian and roman empires . . . and in another map those parts of Africa which ferve to illustrate ecclesiastic history.  cover-title, 34 fold. maps. fol. [London] for T. Bowles & T. Bowles & son [1708–1725] 550

NOTE.—A collection of Senex's sheets maps bound together with cover-title as above. Some with dates from 1708 to 1725 and others without dates. The

**Senex, J.**—Continued.

map of North America is dated 1710. South America without date. The world, 1725. The seven last maps are copied from Delisle's ancient geography.

CONTENTS.

no. 1. Whiston's solar system.
" 2. The world.
" 3. Europe.
" 4. Asia.
" 5. Africa.
" 6. North America.
" 7. South America.
" 8. Great Britain.
" 9. Ireland.
" 10. The vii United provinces.
" 11. The x spanifh provinces.
" 12. County of Flanders.
" 13. The provinces of Hainault, Namur, and Cambry.
" 14. Artoïs.
" 15. France.
" 16. The provostship and vifcounty of Paris.
" 17. Spain and Portugal.
" 18. Old and New Caftile.
" 19. Italy.
" 20. Germany.
" 21. Denmark.
" 22. Sweden and Norway.
" 23. Mufcovy.
" 24. Poland.
" 25. Hungary.
" 26. Turkey in Europe.
" 27. Turkey, Arabia and Perfia.
" 28. Tabula Italiæ antiquæ.
" 29. Regionum Italiæ mediarum, &c.
" 30. Theatrum historicum ad annum Chrifti quodringenteffimum, &c. Pars orientalis.
" 31. . . . Pars occidentalis.
" 32. Greciæ antiquæ tabula nova, pars meridionalis.
" 33. . . . Pars septentrionalis.
" 34. In notitiam ecclefiafticam Africæ tabula geographica.

**1709?**

**Schenk, P.**

Atlas contractus five mapparum geographicarum Sansoniarum auctarum et correctarum nova congeries. 2 p. l., 47 col. maps, 3 pl., 3 tab. fol. Amstelædami, P. Schenck [1709?] 551

NOTE.—First engraved title-page, colored. Second title-page uncolored, reads, "Nova totius geographica telluris projectio. Edita per Gerardum Valk; Amstelodami." Maps by various authors including: Schenk, Valk, Zürner, Jaillot, Ottens, Jean de Lat, Visscher, Sanson and Sprecht.
Dates on maps vary from 1703–1709.

The following maps relate to America:
no. [1] Planishphærium terrestre cum utroque coelesti hemisphærio . . . Opera et studio A. F. Zurneri.
" [5] Americæ tam septentrionalis quam meridionalis in mappa geographica delineatio . . . Opera A. F. Zurneri.

### 1709?
**Visscher, N.**
Variæ tabulæ geographicæ in quibus loca in orbe bells flagrantia conspiciuntur . . .    2 p. l., 36 maps, 1 pl. fol. Amstelodami, â Nicolas Visscher [1709?]    552

NOTE.—Title of map no. 16, "Carte géographique qui contient le théâtre de la guerre en Artois . . . mise au jour chez la veve de Nicolaus Visscher," shows that the atlas was published after Visscher's death.
Titles in latin, french and dutch.
Engraved title reads, "Atlas minor sive totius orbis terrarum contracta delinea[ta] ex conatibus Nico. Visscher . . ." signed, "Ger: de Lairesse delin: & sculp:" Maps relate chiefly to the countries in which were fought the wars between 1667 and 1697, and the war of the spanish succession beginning in 1701. Several maps have indexes on the reverse.
The following map relates to America:
no. [1] Orbis terrarum nova et accuratissima tabula.

### 1709
**Moll, H.**
Atlas manuale: or, a new sett of maps of all the parts of the earth, as well Asia, Africa and America, as Europe. Wherein geography is rectify'd, by reforming the old maps according to the modern obfervations. And the coasts of all countries are laid down, agreeable to mr. Edmund Halley's own map. Which is not done in any before extant. This being the firft whole sett of maps that agrees with the obfervations and corrections that have been made by the astronomers and travellers of this age. The maps are fairly engraven on copper; and the scale is large enough to fhew, not only the provinces, but alfo all confiderable cities, and the towns too of chiefeft note. Mostly perform'd by Herman Moll.    1 p. l., v, [3] pp., 43 maps.    12°.    London, for A. & J. Church, 1709.    553

NOTE.—A reprint "for F. Fayran" noted in the Monthly catalogue, february, 1723-24. v. 1, no. 11, p. 5.
The following maps relate to America:
no. [ 1] The world in planisphere.
" [35] America.
" [36] The ifle of California, New Mexico, Louisiane, the river Misisipi and the lakes of Canada . . .
" [37] The english empire in America, New-foundland, Canada, Hudsons bay, &c . . .
" [38] Mexico, or New Spain . . .
" [39] Terra Firma and the Caribbe iflands &c . . .

**Moll, H.**—Continued.
  no. [40] Peru and the Amazones country . . .
  " [41] Brasil, divided into its captainships . . .
  " [42] The great province of Rio de la Plata . . .
  " [43] Chili, Magellans-land and Terra del Fuego &c . . .

### 1709–1720

——The world defcribed; or, a new and correct sett of maps: shewing the feveral empires, kingdoms, republics . . . in all the known parts of the earth . . . Each map is engraved on copper by Herman Moll, and printed on two sheets of elephant paper . . . 1 p. l., 30 fol. maps.  fol.  [London] J. Bowles [1709–1720]  554

   NOTE.—A collection of Moll's maps, some published with dates and others without. The earliest, that of Rome, was published in 1709; the latest, "A new map of the north parts of America claimed by France . . . 1720."
   The following maps relate to America:
   no. 1. A new and correct map of the world.
   "  2. A new and correct map of the whole world. 1719.
   "  7. . . . Map of North America.—Insets: S$^t$. John's harbour.—Bofton harbour.—[New York]—Afhley & Cooper river.—Port Royal harbour.—The bay & city of $\hat{y}$ Havana.—The bay of P$^{to}$ Bello.—La Vera Cruz.—Cartagena harbour and forts.—The port of Acapulco.
   "  8. A new and exact map of the dominions of the king of Great Britain on $\hat{y}$ continent of North America.—Insets: A map of . . . Carolina.—The gulf of Mexico.—Charles-Town.—A map of . . . North America.
   "  9. A new map of the north parts of America claimed by France . . . 1720.—Insets: The harbour of Annapolis Royal.—A map of $\hat{y}$ mouth of Mississipi and Mobile rivers, &c.—The Indian fort Sasquesahanok.
   " 10. A map of the West-Indies.—Insets: A draught of S$^t$. Augustin.—La Vera Cruz.—A draught of $\hat{y}$ bay & citty [!] of Havana.—The bay of Porto Bella [!]—A draught of $\hat{y}$ citty of Cartagena.
   " 11. . . . Map of South America.—Inset: Potosi.
   " 12. A new & exact map of the coaft, countries, and iflands, within $\hat{y}$ limits of $\hat{y}$ South Sea Company.—Insets: A map of . . . Baldivia.—The bay of Guiaquil.—A map of the ifle Chiloe.—A chart from England to the river Aronoca, &c.—Peypses or Pepys I.—A map of $\hat{y}$ straits of Magellan, &c.—The port of Acapulco.—The gulf of Omapalla or Fonesca.—The gulf of Nicoya.—The Gallapagos iflands.—The ifland of Juan Ferdinando.—A map of the isthmus of Darien, the bay of Panama, &c.

### 1710

**Bæck, E.**

   Atlas geographicus, oder accurate vorstellung der gantzen welt bestehend in denen vornehmsten und nothwendigsten universal und particular land-karten nach dem berühmten französischen geographo Hubert Iaillot und anderer vornehmer männer . . .—Atlas géographique, ou représentation juste de tout le monde . . .

2 p. l., front., 26 maps, 4 diagr.   obl. 8°.   Sachs-Weimar, E. Bæck
[1710]   555

> NOTE.—Engraved frontispiece signed: Elias Bæck à H. sculps. et exc. Aug.
> Vind.
> German and french titles.
> Engraved dedication in german, signed: Elias Bæck à H.
> Several maps are handcolored.
> Border illustrations of maps are the coats of arms of the kingdoms and provinces of Augsburg.
> Maps have french and german titles, but lettering on maps is in french.
> The following maps relate to America:
> no. 7. L'Asie [Isles Philippines]
> "   9. L'Amérique Méridionale.
> "  10.   "    Septentrionale.

## 1710-1731

**Homann, J. B.**
Neuer atlas beftehend in einig curieufen aftronomifchen mappen und vielen auserlefenen allerneueften land-charten über die gantze welt, erftlich vorgeftellt nach Copernicanifchen grund-satz der bewegung des himmels in dem systemate solari, und ephemeridibus motuum cælestium geometricis, des hochgelehrten herrn Johann Gabriel Doppelmayrs . . . Dann auch nach der natürlichen befchaffenheit und geographitchen, eintheilung der mit waffer umgebenen allgemeinen erd-kugel, in ihre befondere monarchien, königreiche, staaten und låndersc. Mit anmerckung der ordentlichen winde und gegen-winde; der berühmteften schiffarchen um die gantze welt, auch aller bifsher an denen euffersten welt-enden gefchehenen neuen land-entdeckungen aus denen vortrefflichften geographis und auctoribus diefes seculi zusammen getragen und ausgefertiget.   2 p. l., 40 col. maps, 2 pl. fol.   Nûrnberg, in verlegung des auctoris, 1710-[1731]   556

> NOTE.—Maps not arranged according to index. "Tabula poliometrica Germaniae ac praecipuorum quorundam locorum Europae," at end, dated 1731, probably inserted.
> The following maps relate to America:
> no. [2] Planiglobii terrestris cum utroq hemisphærio cælesti generalis exhibitio.
> "  [8] Totius Americae.

## 1711-1717

**Atlas geographus**: or, a compleat syftem of geography, ancient and modern. Containing what is of moft ufe in Bleau, Varenius, Cellarius, Cluverius, Baudrand, Brietius, Sanfon, &c. with the difcoveries and improvements of the beft modern authors to this time.

**Atlas geographus**—Continued.
Illuftrated with about 100 new maps . . . by Herman Moll . . . 5 v. 8°. [London] J. Nutt [etc.] 1711–1717. 557

    Note.—The following maps relate to America:
- v. 1, p. [74a] A view of ye general & coafting trade-winds, monfoons . . .
- " " 110 A new map of the world . . .
- v. 3, p. [1] Asia antiqua et nova [showing] Americæ pars.
- " " [792a] The principal islands of the East Indies . . . [Philippine islands]
- v. 5, front. New Guinea, New Britain, and New Holland &c. . . .
- " p. [22a] A map of America. According to ye newest and most exact observations . . .
- " " [58a] A chart of the streights of Magellan.
- " " [76a] A map of South America . . .
- " " [108a] A chart of the South-sea coast from the steight's [!] of Magellan to Arica.
- " " [148a] A map of Chili, Patagonia part of La Plata &c. . . .
- " " [164a] A map of Peru and the west part of the country of the Amazones . . .
- " " [206a] A chart of the coafts of Peru, Quito, Popayan and the ifthmus of Darien.
- " " [254a] A map of Brasil and part of La Plata &c. . . .
- " " [388a] The great river Marañon or of the Amazons geographically describ'd by Samuel Fritz . . .
- " " [396a] A map of Terra Firma, Guiana and the Antilles islands . . .
- " " [452a] A new map of North America . . .
- " " [462a] A new map of the ifland of Barbadoes . . .
- " " [500a] The ifland of St. Christophers . . .
- " " [556a] A new map of the island of Jamaica . . .
- " " [676a] A map of New France containing Canada, Louisiana &c. in N$^{th}$ America. According to the patent granted by the king of France to monsieur Crozat, dated the 14th of sep. 1712 n. s. and registred in the parliament of Paris the 24th of the same month . . .
- " " [694a] Carolina . . .—. . . Bermudos . . .
- " " [700a] A new map of Virginia and Maryland . . .
- " " [732a] New England, New York, New Jersey, and Pennsilvania &c. . . .
- " " [774a] A new map of Newfoundland, New Scotland, the isles of Breton, Anticofte, S! Johns &c. . . .
- " " [796a] A map of Mexico or New Spain, Florida now called Louisiana and part of California &c. . . .

    CONTENTS.
- v. 1–2. Europe.
- " 3. Asia.
- " 4. Africa.
- " 5. America . . . "To which is added, a catalogue of the maps, cuts, and Sanson's tables in all the five volumes and a description of Bofnia, by omiffion left out in Europe."

## 1713

**Gueudeville, N.**

Le nouveau théâtre du monde, ou la géographie royale, composée de nouvelles cartes trés-exactes, dreffées fur les obfervations de meffieurs de l'Académie royale des sciences à Paris, fur celles des plus célèbres géographes, fur de nouveaux mémoires, & rectifiées sur les relations les plus récentes des plus fidèles voyageurs. Avec une description géographique et historique des quatre parties de l'univers, defquelles l'Europe en detail eft écrite par mr. Gueudeville, & les trois autres parties par mr. Ferrarius. Ouvrage qui donne une idée claire & facile de la terre, & de ce qu'elle comprend de plus considérable. 8 p. l., 66, 76 pp., 94 maps. fol. Leide, P. vander Aa, 1713. 558

NOTE.—Engraved title.
Map entitled "Mappe-monde," wanting. A colored copy of this map is in the L. C. collection as a "separate."
Map no. [1], Planisphère terrestre, by Cassini; no. [14], Nouvelle carte de de l'Italie, by Vignola.
This work contains an extensive list of 42 pages, printed in three columns, giving the latitude and longitude of places, islands, etc.
At the end a sheet has been added containing plans of Embrun, Montauban, Masdazil, St. Tropez, Realmont, Tovlon, Pezenas, Roqvecovre, Vzez, Blaye, Navarrins, Narbonne, Nismes, Bergerac, Libovrne, and Bayonne.
The parts relating to Asia, Africa and America have been taken from Philippi Ferrari's work entitled "Lexicon geographicum," published at Milan in 1627, and reprinted at Paris in 1670.
Six of the maps are on sheets, the remainder, two on a leaf.
The following maps relate to America:
no. [1] Planisphère terrestre.
" [48] L'Amérique.
" [49] Canada.
" [49] La Floride.
" [50] Mexique.
" [50] Le Brésil.

## 1715

**Renard, L.**

Atlas de la navigation, et du commerce qui se fait dans toutes les parties du monde. Expliquant par des cartes & par des defcriptions particulières de toutes les côtes & ports de mer de l'univers, la nature, les productions, & les ouvrages ou manufactures de chaque païs en particulier: la religion, le gouvernement, & les maniéres de vivre des peuples; les marchandifes que l'on porte d'un païs à un autre; & celles que l'on rapporte de chaque païs, & qui fe debitent dans toutes les parties du monde pour l'utilité, la magnificence, la curiofité, & la nourriture des hommes, &c. On a marqué très-exactement les routes, les ifles, les bancs de sable, les profondeurs des ports, & généralement tout ce qui regarde la navigation. Les cartes & les defcriptions fe

**Renard, L.**—Continued.

fuccédent très-ponctuellement les unes aux autres, & accompliffent le tour du monde, commençant toutes par les côtes où chaque carte précèdente a fini. Le tout dreffé sur les mémoires les plus récens; revû & corrigé fur les nouvelles obfervations. 2 p. l., 96, [2] pp., 28 maps, 6 pl. fol. A Amsterdam, L. Renard, 1715. 559

> NOTE.—Plate following title represents "Atlas" carrying map entitled "Planisphère repréfentant toute l'étendue du monde, dans l'ordre qu'on a suivi dans ce livre," which serves as an index to the maps contained in the atlas.
> Portrait of "George premier, roy de la Grande Bretagne, de France et d'Irlande," engraved by B. Picart.
> Four plates at the end of the atlas, contain drawings and plans of fortifications, with explanations and instructions. See also title 592 and 601.
> The following maps relate to America:
> no. 1. Nova totius terrarum orbis tabula . . .
> " 3. Poli Arctici et circimiacentium terrarum descriptio novissima. Per F. de Wit.
> " 22. Magnum Mare del Zur cum infula California . . .
> " 23. Novæ Hispaniæ, Chili, Peruviæ, et Guatimalæ littoræ . . .
> " 24. Tractus australior Americæ Meridionalis a Rio de la Plata per fretum Magellanicum ad Toraltum . . .
> " 25. Littora Brasiliæ . . .
> " 26. Terra Nova ac maris tractus circa Novam Franciam, Angliam, Belgium, Venezuelam, Novam Andalusiam, Guianam, et Brasiliam . . .
> " 27. Indiarum Occidentalium . . .
> " 28. Septemtrionaliora [!] Americæ à Groenlandia, per freta Davidis et Hudfon, ad Terram Novam . . .

### 1717?

**Le Masson du Parc,** —

[Collection of maps] 2 v. 11 p. l., 38 l. incl. 17 maps, 1 pl.; 1 p. l., 86 l. incl. 42 maps. fol. [n. p., 1717?] 560

> NOTE.—Collection of miscellaneous maps, dated 1637–1717, by various authors including de Fer, Nolin, Duval, Coronelli, Sanson, Delisle, Vaultier, P. A. Déchaussé, brought together by Le Masson du Parc.
> The first 8 p. l. of v. 1 contain two manuscript indexes, "Table des cartes contenües dans ce préfent livre," and "Autre table des provinces particulières contenües dans les diverses cartes de ce préfent livre."
> Preliminary leaves 9–10 contain, "Table des sciences dont la géographie tire plusieurs principes," and "Description générale du globe terrestre," in manuscript, within colored engraved ornamental borders. "De la géographie en général et, en particulièr," in manuscript, p. l. 11.
> The following maps relate to America:
> v. 1, no. 7. L'Amérique Méridionale . . . par le p. Coronelli. 1689.
> " " 8. La mer de Sud . . . par Du-val. 1679.
> " " 14. Theatrum historicum. Auctore Guillelmo Del'Isle. 1705.

## 1717-1740

**Fer, N. de**
    Introduction à la géographie avec une description historique sur toutes les parties de la terre. 2. éd.    1 p. l., 197 pp. [4] l., 6 maps. 12°.   Paris, Danet, 1717–[1740?]                       561

    NOTE.—Maps, entitled, "Mappe-monde ou carte générale de la terre" and "L'Amérique Méridionale et Septentrionale," dated 1740.
    The last two pages contain a "Catalogue des ouvrages de géographie que l'auteur a mis au jour jusques en l'année 1716."
    Probably the same as his "Méthode pour apprendre facilement la géographie". La Haye, 1706.  Editions published also in 1708 and 1719.

## 1720?

**Valck, G.**
    Nova totius geographica telluris projectio.   1 p. l., 26 col. maps, 1 l.  fol.  Amstelodami, G. Valk [1720?]                       562

    NOTE —The colored, engraved title-page is identical with the second title-page of Schenk's "Atlas contractus" [1709?] title 551; but the maps in the two atlases are not the same.
    The following is quoted from Nagler's Neues allgemeines künstler-lexicon, v. 19, p. 304:
    "Valck, Gerard, maler und kupferstecher, wurde um 1626 zu Amsterdam geboren, und von A. Blooteling in den anfangsgründen der kunst unterrichtet. Dieser meister nahm den knaben als diener in sein haus, bildete aber dann sein talent heran, um einen gehülfen an ihm zu haben. Im jahre 1672 nahm er den Valck mit sich nach London, und gab ihm zuletzt seine schwester zu ehe. Nach seiner 1673 erfolgten rückkehr verband er sich mit Peter Schenk zur herausgabe eines grossen atlasses, welcher 1683 erschien. Schenk brachte die kunsthandlung des J. Janssen an sich, an welcher auch G. Valk theil nahm. Mit ihm arbeitete ein Leonhard Valk, dessen namen man auf karten findet. Auch mehrere blätter unsers künstlers erschienen in diesem verlage, worauf die adresse: G. Valck exc., deutet. Verlagswerke sind auch die ansichten von Loo, Honslardyk, Soesdyck u. s. w., dann jene der stadt Cleve. Beide folgen bestehen in 64 blättern. Amsterdam, 1695. qu. fol. Später trennte sich Valck von Schenk, und arbeitete auf eigene rechnung. Er starb zu Amsterdam gegen 1720."
    Maps by G. Sanson, P. Schenck, M. Seutter and G. Valck.
    The following maps relate to America:
    no. [1] Mappe-monde géo-hydrographique, ou, description générale du globe terrestre et aquatique en deux-plans-hémisphères . . . par G. Valck.
    " [2] L'Amérique Septentrionale & Méridionale divisée en ses principales parties . . . par G. Valck.
    " [4] L'Asie . . . par G. Valck [Isles Philippines]

## 1721

**Senex, J.**
    A new general atlas, containing a geographical and hiftorical account of all the empires, kingdoms, and other dominions of the world: with the natural history and trade of each country. Taken from the best authors, particularly Cluverius, Brietus, Cellarius, Bleau, Baudrand, Hoffman, Moreri, the two Sansons, Luyts, the

**Senex, J.**—Continued.

Atlas hiſtorique, sir John Chardin, Le Brun, Tournefort, &c. To which is prefixed, an introduction to geography . . . Together with a copious alphabetical index. The maps . . . are all engraven or revised by mr. Senex . . .    4 p. l., 272, 141-261, [11] pp., 34 maps, 14 pl.   fol.   London, for D. Brown [etc., etc.] 1721.   563

    Note.—Map no. [33], A map of Louisiana and of the river Mississipi . . . is dedicated to William Law.
    The following maps relate to America and the Philippines:
    no. [1] A new map of the world.
    " [27] A new map of the english empire in the ocean of America or West Indies . . .
    " [29] A new map of America.
    " [30] A new map of the english empire in America . . . 1719.—Inset: The harbour of Boston.
    " [31] A new map of Virginia, Mary-land and the improved parts of Pennsylvania & New-Jersey . . . 1719.
    " [32] A new map of India and China.
    " [33] A map of Louisiana and of the river Mississipi.
    " [34] A draft of the Golden & adjacent islands . . . by cap$^t$ Ienefer . . .— A new map of ỹ isthmus of Darien in America . . .

### 1722

**Wells, E.**

A new sett of maps both of antient and present geography . . . Together with a geographical treatise particularly adapted to the use and design of these maps . . .   2 p. l., 41 maps.   fol.   London, for R. Bonwicke, J. Walthoe [etc.] 1722.   564

    Note.—This is like the edition of 1700 excepting a difference of lettering on maps nos. [10], [13], [15], [26] and [37]  See also title 531.
    "A treatise of antient and present geography" to accompany this atlas is wanting.
    Library of Congress has the 4th edition of the "Treatise of antient and present geography.  London, 1726."  Atlas wanting.
    The following maps relate to America:
    no. [1] A new map of the . . . globe according to the ancient discoveries . . .
    " [2] A new map of the . . . globe according to the latest discoveries . . .
    " [28] A new map of present Asia . . . [The Philippine islands]
    " [30] A new map of the East Indies . . . from m. de Fer's map of Asia . . . [The Philippine islands]
    " [39] A new map of North America . . .
    " [40] A new map of South America . . .
    " [41]  "   "   "   "  the plantations of the english in America . . .

### 1722-1774

**Delisle, G.**

[Collection of maps]    34 col. maps on 80 l.   fol.   [Amsterdam, J. Cóvens & C. Mortier, 1722-1774]   565

    Note.—No title page.
    Dates on maps vary from 1722-1774.
    Maps nos. [12-13] wanting.
    Maps nos. [3-8, 10-11, 15, 17-20, 24-25, 31-35, 37-40] are exact duplicates of corresponding maps in: Delisle, Guillaume, Atlas nouveau, contenant toutes les

parties du monde . . . Amsterdam, J. Cóvens & C. Mortier, 1733. See title 580.
Maps nos. [2, 9, 14, 16, 30] are the same as the maps in the "Atlas nouveau" with slight changes.
Map no. [1] is an exact duplicate of corresponding map in Cóvens, Johannes, *and* Mortier, Cornelis, Nieuwe atlas, inhoudende de vier gedeeltens de waereld . . . Amsterdam, J. Cóvens & C. Mortier [1740-1817] See title 595.
Maps nos. [21-22] carry Delisle's name as author, but are not in either the "Atlas nouveau", or the "Nieuwe atlas."
Map no. [23] is the same as corresponding map in "Nieuwe atlas," with slight changes.
Maps nos. [26-29] are duplicates of maps in "Nieuwe atlas," but do not carry Delisle's name.
Map no. [36] Carte de la Louisiane, Maryland, Virginie, Caroline, Georgie, avec une partie de la Floride, is found in neither "Atlas nouveau," nor "Nieuwe atlas."
All maps except no. [29] carry Cóvens & Mortier as publishers.

CONTENTS.

no. [1] Mappemonde.
" [2] Carte d'Europe. 1739.
" [3] Les isles Britanniques.
" [4-5] Carte des Courones du Nord. 2 sheets.
" [6] Carte du royaume de Danemarc.
" [7-8] Carte de Moscovie. 2 sheets.
" [9] Carte de France.
" [10] Carte des Pays bas Catholiques.
" [11] Carte des Provinces unies des Pays bas.
" [14] L'Allemagne.
" [15] Nova Helvetiæ.
" [16] La Pologne.
" [17] L'Espagne.
" [18] L'Italie.
" [19] Le royaume de Hongrie.
" [20] Carte de la Grece.
" [21-22] Græciæ antiquæ tabula nova. 2 sheets.
" [23] Carte d'Asia.
" [24] Carte de la Turquie de l'Arabie et de la Perse.
" [25] Carte de Perse.
" [26] Carte d'une partie des Indes Orientales . . .
" [27] Carte d'une partie de la Chine, les isles Philippines . . .
" [28-29] Carte générale de l'empire de Russie. 2 sheets.
" [30] Carte d'Africa.
" [31] Carte de la Barbarie de la Nigritie et de la Guinée.
" [32] Carte de l'Egypt de la Nubie de l'Abissinie.
" [33] Carte du Congo et du Pays de Cafres.
" [34] Carte d'Amerique . . . par G. Delisle . . . Rectifiée après les nouvelles reservations du sr. d'Anville. 1774.
" [35] L'Amérique Septentrionale. 1757.
" [36] Carte de la Louisiane, Maryland, Virginie, Caroline, Georgie, avec une partie de la Floride. 1758.
" [37] Carte du Mexique et de la Floride. 1722.
" [38] L'Amérique Méridionale. 1757.
" [39] Carte de la Terre Ferme du Pérou, du Brésil et du Pas des Amazones.
" [40] Carte du Paraguay, du Chili, du detroit de Magellan &c.

## 1723

**Compleat geographer, The:** or, the chorography and topography of all the known parts of the earth. To which is premis'd an introduction to geography, and a natural history of the earth and the elements . . . To which are added maps of every country, fairly engraved on copper . . . most engrav'd by Herman Moll. 4th ed. [anon.] 2 pts. in 1 v. fol. London, for J. Knopton [etc.] 1723.

566

NOTE.—Collation: pt. 1, 11 p. l., front., li, [5], 402 pp. incl. 23 maps (1 not in pp.); pt. 2, 288, xx pp. incl. 22 maps.

pt. 2 entitled: Thefaurus geographicus; or, the compleat geographer . . . 4th ed. much amended. London, 1722. See title 536 (note) for edition 1695.

Map facing page 1, of pt. 1, is not in the table of contents and is probably inserted.

The following maps relate to America:

pt. 1, p.   1. [Map illustrating the variable winds]
"   "   "  [1iii] The world in planisphere.
" 2,  "    3. Asia  [Philippine islands]
"   "   "  106. The principal islands of the East Indies.
"   "   "  189. America.
"   "   "  194. The ifle of California, New Mexico, Louisiana, the river Misisipi and the lakes of Canada . . .
"   "   "  195. The english empire in America, Newfoundland, Canada, Hudfon bay, &c.
"   "   "  214. Mexico or New Spain. . . .
"   "   "  237. Terra Firma and the Caribbé iflands, &c. . . .
"   "   "  244. Peru and the Amazones country.
"   "   "  258. Brasil divided into its captainships . . .
"   "   "  265. The great province of Rio de la Plata . . .
"   "   "  272. Chili, Magellans-land and Terra del Fuego, &c.

## 1724?

**Köhler, J. D.**

Io. Davıdis Koeleri hift. et polit. pp. Altdorfini atlas manvalis scholasticvs et itinerarivs complectens novae geographiae tabvlas XLII . . . 1 p. l., 42 col. maps. fol. Norimbergenfi, a C. Weigelio [1724?]

567

NOTE.—The following maps relate to America:

no. 1. Planigiobium terrestre minus . . . à Johanne Bapt. Homanno.
"  42. Novi orbis sive totius Americæ.

## 1724?

Io. Davidis Koeleri hist. et polit. pp. Altdorfini atlas manvalis scholasticvs et itinerarivs complectens novae geographiae tabvlas L cvm gratia et pprivilegio [!] sacrae Cæsareae maiestatis.   1 p. l., 51 col. maps.   obl. fol.   Norimbergenfi, a C. Weigelio [1724?]   568

NOTE.—Contains maps drawn by J. B. Homann, Herman Moll, and Abraham Goos. Maps are illustrated with coats of arms and landscapes. There is evidence that this atlas was published not earlier than 1720, and not later than 1725, in which year Weigel died. It is supposed that a book of instructions

was published at the same time. Meusel, in his Lexikon, gives the following in a list of works by Köhler, "Anleitung zu der verbesserten neuen geographie, vornemlich zum gebrauch der Weigelischen landcharten. Nürnb. 1724."
The following maps relate to America:
no. 1. Plani globium terrestre minus in hanc formam reductam à Johanne Bapt. Homanno geogr . . .
" 50. Novi orbis sive totius Americæ cum adiacentibus insulis . . .

### 1724?

Io. Davidis Koeleri hift. et polit. pp. Altdorfini atlas manvalis scholasticvs et itinerarivs complectens novae geographiae tabvlas LI. cvm gratia et pprivilegio [!] sacrae Cæsareae maiestatis . . . 1 p. l., 51 col. maps. sm. fol. Norimbergenfi, a C. Weigelio [1724?] 569

Map no. 14, Germania in circulos divifa, differs from corresponding map in other edition.
Map no. 48, Terra Sancta, wanting.
The following maps relate to America:
no. 1. Planiglobium terrestre minus in hanc formam reductam à Iohanne Bapt. Homanno . . .
" 50. Novi orbis sive totius Americæ cum adiacentibus insulis . . .

### 1726

T'Sersteuens,—

Cartes descriptions générales et particulières pour l'intelligence des affaires du temps au sujet de la succession de couronne d'Espagne en Europe, en Asie, Afrique, et Amérique. Dédiées à monsieur de Verbōm brigadier des armées du roy et son ingénieur directeur. Par son très humble et très obéisant seruiteur T'Sersteuens. Dans les cartes on a peint en rouge ce que posse de le roy d'Espagne. 3 p. l., 15 col. maps. obl. 4º. [1726] 570

Note.—In manuscript. Title-page ornamented with the coat of arms of Spain.

CONTENTS.

no. [1] Le royaume de Naples. Colacioné sur celle de m$^r$ de Fer. 1726.
" [2] Espagne et Portugal. Divifés en fes principales parties ou royaumes. Colacioné sur celle de m$^r$ de Fer. 1726.
" [3] L'Italie. Colacioné sur celle de m$^r$ de Fer. 1726.
" [4] Isle et royaume de Sicile. Colacioné sur celle de m$^r$ de Fer. 1726.
" [5] Partie occidentale d'Afrique . . .
" [6] Les isles Philippines et celles Deslarrons ou de Marianes, les isles Moluques et de la Sonde avec la Presquisle de l'Inde de la Gange ou orientale.
" [7] Le vieux Mexique ou Nouvelle Espagne auec les costes de la Floride faisant partie de l'Amérique Septentrionale. Colacioné sur celle de m$^r$ de Fer. 1726.
" [8] Le Détroit de Magellan . . . Colacioné sur celle de m$^r$ de Fer. 1726.
" [9] Le Chili et les provinces qui composent celles de Rio de la Plata avec les Terres Magellanique. Colacioné sur celle de m$^r$ de Fer. 1726.

**T'Serteuens,**—Continued.
- no. [10] La Terre Ferme et le Pérou avec le pays des Amazones et le Brésil dans l'Amérique Méridionale.
- " [11] Les isles de l'Amérique connue sous le nom d'Antilles . . . 1726.
- " [12] Cette carte de Californie et du Nouveau Mexique est tirée de celle qui a esté envoyée par un grand d'Espagne pour être communiquée a mʳ de l'Académie Royale.
- " [13] Les estats du duché de Milan.
- " [14] Les duchez de Mantoue et de la Mirandole. Avec la plus grande partie des territoire de Verone Brescia et de Cremone.
- " [15] Frontières du Milanez du Cremonese et du Lodesan au roy d'Efpagne le Bergamas le Bressan et le Cremas à la republique de Venise ou sont remarqué les endroits ou les armées des alliez et des impériaux ont campez en 1701.

## 1727–1780

**Anville, J. B. B. d'**

[Atlas general]  1 p. l., 47 maps on 51 sheets. fol. [Paris, 1727–1780]  571

NOTE.—A collection of d'Anville maps without a general title-page. See also title 599.

Preliminary leaf comprises "Cartes géographiques de m. d'Anville . . ." and "Ouvrages par écrit, et qui ont été imprimés."

### CONTENTS.

- no. [1] Hémisphère occidental ou du nouveau monde. 1761.
- " 1. Hémisphère oriental ou de l'ancien monde. 1761.
- " 2. Première partie de la carte d'Europe. 1754.
- " 3. Seconde partie de la carte d'Europe. 1758.
- " 4. Troisième partie de la carte d'Europe. 1760.
- " 5. Première partie de la carte d'Asie. 1751.
- " 6. Seconde partie de la carte d'Asie. 1752.
- " 7. Troisième partie de la carte d'Asie. 1753.
- " 8– 9. Afrique. 1749.
- " 10–11. Amérique Septentrionale. 1746.
- " 12–13. Amérique Méridionale. 1748.
- " 14. La France. 1780.
- " 15. L'Italie. 1743.
- " 16. Les côtes de la Grèce et l'Archipel. 1756.
- " 17. Détroit des Dardanelles. 1756.
- " 18. L'Euphrate et le Tigre. 1779.
- " 19–20. Carte de l'Inde. 1752.
- " 21. Coromandel. 1753.
- " 22. Essai d'un nouvelle carte de la mer Caspienne. 1754
- " 23. Golfe Persique. 1776.
- " 24. Golfe Arabique ou mer Rouge. 1765.
- " 25. Egypte. 1765.
- " 26. L'Ethiopie occidentale. 1732.
- " 27. Carte de l'Ethiopie orientale. 1727.
- " 28. Carte particulière de la côte occidentale de l'Afrique. 1751.
- " 29. Carte particulière des royaumes d'Angola, de Matamba et de Benguela. 1731.
- " 30. Carte particulière du royaume de Congo. 1731.
- " 31. Guinée. 1775.
- " 32–33. Canade, Louisiane et terre angloises, 1755.

no. 34. Le fleuve Saint Laurent. [n. d.]
" 35. Carte de la Louisiane. Dressée en mai 1732. Publié en 1752.
" 36. Carte des isles de l'Amérique. 1731.
" 37. Orbis veteribus notus. 1763.
" 38. Orbis Romani pars occidentalis. 1763.
" 39. Orbis Romani pars orientalis. 1764.
" 40. Gallia antiqua. 1760.
" 41. Tabula Italiæ antiqua geographica. 1764.
" 42. Græciæ antiquæ specimen geographicum. 1762.
" 43. Asiæ et Syriæ 1764.
" 44. La Palestine. 1767.
" 45. Aegyptus antiqua. 1765.
" 46. Ad antiquam Indiæ geographiam tabula. 1765.
" 47. Patriarchatus Constantinopolitani tabula. 1741.
" 48. Patriarchatus Antiochenus. 1732.
" 49. Patriarchatus Hierosolymitanus. 1732.
" 50. Patriarchatus Alexandrinus. 1731.
" 51. Germanie, France, Italie, Espagne, Isles Britanniques. 1771.

**1727–1786**
**Anville, J. B. B. d'.**
[Atlas général]   1 p. l., 44 maps on 60 sheets.   fol.   [Paris, 1727–1786]   572

NOTE.—See also 571 and 599. Manuscript "Table des cartes."
No title-page; following maps wanting: Carte du diocèse de Lisieux. 2 sheets.—Carte du Roussillon.

CONTENTS.

no. [1] Hémisphère oriental, ou de l'ancien monde . . . Revu et augm. . . .
    en 1786 par m. Barbié du Bocage.
" [2] Hémisphère occidental, ou du nouveau monde . . . 1786.
" [3] Première partie de la carte d'Europe . . . 1754. 2 sheets.
" [4] Seconde partie de la carte d'Europe . . . 1758. 2 sheets.
" [5] Troisième partie de la carte d'Europe . . . 1760. 2 sheets.
" [6] Première partie de la carte d'Asie . . . 1751. 2 sheets.
" [7] Seconde partie de la carte d'Asie . . . 1752. 2 sheets.
" [8] Troisième partie de la carte d'Asie . . . 1753. 2 sheets.
" [9] Afrique . . . 1749. 2 sheets.
" [10] Carte de l'Ethiopie orientale . . . 1727.
" [11] L'Ethiopie occidentale . . . 1732.
" [12] Carte particulière du royaume de Congo . . . 1731.
" [13] Amérique Septentrionale . . . 1746. 2 sheets.
" [14] Amérique Méridionale . . . 1748. 3 sheets.
" [15] Carte de la Guïane françoise . . . [1729]
" [16] Carte de l'isle de Caïnne . . . [1729]
" [17] La France divisée en provinces . . . 1780.
" [18] La France divisée en provinces et en généralités . . . 1780.
" [19] L'Italie . . . 1743. 2 sheets.
" [20] Les côtes de la Grèce et l'archipel . . . 1756.
" [21] Carte de la Phœnicie et des environs de Damas . . . 1780.
" [22] L'Euphrate et le Tigre . . . 1779.
" [23] Carte de l'Inde . . . 1752. 2 sheets.

**Anville, J. B. B. d'**—Continued.
- no. [24] Coromandel . . . 1753. 2 sheets.
- " [25] Essai d'une nouvelle carte de la mer Caspienne . . . 1754.
- " [26] Golfe persique . . . 1776.
- " [27] Golfe arabique ou mer Rouge . . . 1765.
- " [28] Egypte . . . 1765.
- " [29] Carte particulière de la côte occidentale de l'Afrique . . . 1751. 2 sheets.
- " [30] Guinée . . . 1775.
- " [31] Le fleuve Saint-Laurent . . . [1755?]
- " [32] Canada, Louisiane et terres angloises . . . 1755. 3 sheets.
- " [33] Carte de la Louisiane . . . 1752.
- " [34] Orbis veteribus notus . . . 1763.
- " [35] Orbis Romani, pars occidentalis . . . 1763.
- " [36] Orbis Romani, pars orientalis . . . 1764.
- " [37] Gallia antiqua . . . 1760.
- " [38] Tabula Italiæ antiquæ geographica . . . 1764.
- " [39] Græciæ antiquæ . . . 1762.
- " [40] Asiæ . . . Minor . . . et Syriæ . . . 1764.
- " [41] La Palestine . . . 1767.
- " [42] Ægyptus antiqua . . . 1765.
- " [43] Ad antiquam Indiæ geographiam tabula . . . 1765.
- " [44] Germanie, France, Italie, Espagne, Isles Britanniques . . . 1771.

**1729**
**Cluver, P.**

Philippi Cluveri introductionis in universam geographiam, tam veterem quam novam libri vi. Cum integris Johannis Bunonis, Joh. Frid. Hekelii, & Joh. Reiskii, & felectis Londinensibus notis. Textum ad optimas editiones recognovit; pauca Cluverii, multa interpretum fphalmata obeló. notavit; Bunonianis tabulis geographicis paffim emendatis novas accuratiores addidit; præfationemque de Cluverii fatis & scriptis historico-criticam; cum præcognitis geographicis, præfixit Augustinus Bruzen la Martinière, sapientiffimi Hifpaniarum Indiarum que regis Philippi v, geographus. Editio omnivm locvpletissima. 21 p. l., front., 688, [60] pp., 47 maps, 6 pl. 4°. Amstelaedami, apud Joannem Pauli, 1729. 573

NOTE.—The following maps relate to America:
p. 50. Typus orbis terrarum.
p. 666. America.

**1729**
**Moll, H.**

Atlas minor: or, a set of sixty-two new and correct maps of all the parts of the world. 2 p. l., 62 maps. obl. 8°. London, H. Moll, 1729. 574
[*With* Templeman, Thomas. A new survey of the globe . . . London, engrav'd by I. Cole [1729]]

NOTE.—First edition. See also titles 578, 585, 602 and 635.
The basis of this atlas was the set of thirty-two maps of the principal parts of Europe and the world published by Moll about 1727. This set was enlarged

and entirely new maps added. "The curious will find several valuable pieces, particularly in America, new and never engraven before, taken from original draughts, communicated to me by perfons of note. Fundy bay and Annapolis, I take after an original draught . . . the ifland Antegoa, Port Royal, &c. And for as much as fome of them differ from the reft in size, it cou'd not poffibly be avoided, without cramping the defign. The first meridian in all thefe maps is taken from London, which was never done before in any famll set." Templeman made the geographical tables as nearly as possible the same size as these maps so that the two might be bound together. *cf.* Preface. Map no. 46, is the earliest known map relating to post routes in the United States.

In this copy the tables face the maps to which they refer.

The following maps relate to America:

no. [1] A new map of the whole world with the trade winds . . .
" [2] A map of the North Pole . . . 1728.
" [39] The principal iflands of the East-Indies . . . 1729 [Shows] Philippine islands.
" [40] Africa . . . 1727 [Shows] C. S[t]. Augustin [Brazil]
" [45] America . . . 1726.
" [46] New England, New York, New Jersey and Pensilvania . . . 1729. [Contains descriptive legend entitled, "An account of ye post of ye continent of N[th] America as they were regulated by ye postmasters gen[l]. of ye post house." This is the map reproduced by the U. S. post office department]
" [47] Virginia and Maryland . . . 1729.
" [48] A plan of Port Royal harbour in Carolina . . .
" [49] A new map of ye north parts of America claimed by France under ye names of Louisiana, Mississippi, Canada & New France with the adjeyning [!] territories of England & Spain . . . 1729.
" [50] Florida calle'd [!] by ye french Louisiana &c. . . . 1728.
" [51] Carolina . . . 1729. Spain . . . 1727.
" [53] The Scots settlements in America calle'd [!] New Caledonia . . . 1729.
" [54] A description of the bay of Fundy . . .—The harbour of Annapolis Royal by Nathaniel Blackmore esq[r]. . . . 1729.
" [55] A map of Terra Firma, Peru, Amazone land, Brazil & and the north p. of La Plata . . . 1729.
" [56] A map of Chili, Patagonia, La Plata and ye south part of Brazil . . . 1729.
" [57] New Found Land S[t]. Laurens bay, the fishing banks, Acadia, and part of New Scotland . . . 1729.
" [58] The island of Jamaica . . . 1728.
" [59] The island of Bermudos . . . 1729.
" [60] The island of Barbadoes . . . 1728.
" [61] The island of Antego . . . 1729.
" [62] The island of S[t]. Christophers, alias S[t]. Kitts . . . 172⟨⟩.

### 1730

**Ptolemæus, C.**

Orbis antiqvi Tabvlae Geographicae secundum C[.]. Ptolemaevm, cum Indice Philologico absolutiffimo omnium locorum, montium, fluminum, &c. in Tabulis occurrentium, situm, nomina recentiora, & alia eò pertinentia, lineis per ipfas ductis, accuratiffime indicante;

**Ptolemæus, C.**—Continued.

in vsvm geographiae veteris stvdiosorvm. [*Vignette*] Amstelaedami, Apud R. & J. Wetstenios & Guil. Smith. MDCCXXX. 575
>100 l., comprising: 6 p. l., 28 maps on 56 l., [38] l. fol.
>(sig. 4 l. unsigned; * * in one; 1 l. unsigned; A-T in twos)
>Collation: half-title, verso blank; eng. title, verso blank; title, verso blank; dedication, with engraving, 1 l.; "Ad lectorem praefatio," 1 l., (sig. * *); "Index tabularum," 1 l., 28 double page maps on 56 l.; "Index," [38] l. verso l. [38] blank, (sig. A-T)
>A reprint of the maps of Mercator, without text. They comprise the "Vniversalis Tabvla Ivxta Ptolemaeum," five of Africa, twelve of Asia, and ten of Europe. They are identical with those in the edition of 1695, except that "Tab. VII Europæ" is less fully engraved. See title 518. No maps of America. Title-page engraved by "J. V. Vianen." The engraving preceding the dedication is inscribed "G. F. L. Debrie inv." and "K. De Putter fecit 1729."

### 1730-1739

**Cóvens, J.** *and* **Mortier, C.**

Nieuwe atlas inhoudende de vier gedeeltens der waereld, waar in duydelyk aangeweefen worden de monarchien, keysserryken, koningryken, staten republyken, &c. Versameldt van de beste autheuren. 1 p. l., 62 col. maps, 1 pl. fol. Te Amsterdam, J. Cóvens & C. Mortier, 1730-[1739] 576
>NOTE.—Vignette on title dated 1730. Date 1739 on map no [2] entitled: Carte d' Europe. See also title 595.
>A collection of maps by various cartographers including: Delisle, de Wit, Allard, Halma, van Keulen and vander Aa.
>The following maps relate to America:
>no. [1] Mappe-monde . . . Par m. de L'isle.
>" [53] Carte d'une partie de la Chine les isles Philippines.
>" [59] Carte d' Amérique . . . Par Guillaume Delisle . . .
>" [60] L'Amérique Septentrionale . . . Par G. de L'isle . . .
>" [61] L'Amérique Méridionale . . . Par G. de L'isle . . .
>" [62] Iles del'Amérique . . . Par Pierre vander Aa . . .

### 1732?

**Homann, J. B.**

Kleiner atlas scholasticus von achtzehen charten . . . und mit einer accuraten illumination zu seinen geographifchen fragen accommodiret durch Johann Hübnern . . . 3 p. l., 32 col. maps, 1 pl. fol. Nûrnberg, den dem autore; Hamburg, den Johann Hûbnern [etc., etc., 1732?] 577
>NOTE.—Date 1732 on map no. [12] entitled: Potentissimæ Helvetiorem . . . Also [no. 14] Imperium Romano Germanicum . . .
>Engraved title reads: Atlas novus, terrarum orbis imperia, regna et status exactis tabulis geographice demonitrans, opera Iohannis Baptistæ Homanni . . . Noribergæ.
>Imperfect: map no. 18, Von Moscau, wanting.
>The following maps relate to America:
>no. 1. Planiglobii terrestris cum utroq hemisphærio cælesti generalis exhibitio.
>" 5. Totius Americae . . .

## 1732?

**Moll, H.**

Atlas minor: or a set of sixty-two new and correct maps, of all the parts of the world. 2d ed. 1 p. l., 62 maps. obl. 8°. London, printed for T. Bowles and J. Bowles [1732?] 578

 NOTE.—First edition published 1729. See titles 574, 585, 602 and 635.
 In this edition dates have been erased from the plates and many maps changed and supplemented.
 Map no. 32, "Great Tartary," dated 1732, substituted for "Great or Asiatick Tartary," undated, in 1st ed.
 Map no. 41, "The west part of Barbary," date changed from 1729 to 1732.
 Changes noted in American maps nos. 1, 2, 47, 48, 56, 57, 58, 59.
 The following maps relate to America:

no. 1. A new map of the whole world with the trade winds . . . Printed for Thos. Bowles . . . and John Bowles . . . London. [Imprint first appears in this ed.]
"  2. A map of the North Pole . . . Printed for Tho. Bowles . . . & John Bowles . . .
" 40. Africa . . . [Shows] C. S.t Augustine [Brazil]
" 45. America . . .
" 46. A new map of y.e north parts of America claimed by France under y.e names of Louisiana, Mississipi, Canada & New France, with the adjoyning territories of England & Spain . . .
" 47. New Found Land S.t Laurence bay, the fishing banks, Acadia and part of New Scotland . . . [Differs from 1st ed. "Point Raye" omitted, "C. Ray" and "C. Sud" added]
" 48. A description of the bay of Fundy . . .—The harbour of Annapolis Royal by Nathaniel Blackmore esq.r Printed and sold by Tho: Bowles . . . & In.o Bowles . . .
" 49. New England, New York, New Jersey and Pensilvania . . .
" 50. Virginia and Maryland . . .
" 51. Carolina.
" 52. A plan of Port Royal harbour in Carolina . . .
" 53. The island of Bermudos . . .
" 54. Florida called by y.e french Louisiana &c . . .
" 55. A map of the West-Indies &c. Mexico or New Spain . . .
" 56. The island of Jamaica . . . [Legend added]
" 57. The island of S.t Christophers alias S.t Kitts . . . [Legend added]
" 58. The island of Antego . . . Sold by T. Bowles . . . and I. Bowles.
" 59. The island of Barbadoes . . . Printed and sold by Tho: Bowles . . . & I. Bowles . . . [Legend added and notes changed]
" 60. The Scots settlement in America calle'd [!] New Caledonia . . .
" 61. A map of Terra Firma Peru, Amazone-land, Brasil & the north p. of La Plata . . .
" 62. A map of Chili, Patagonia, La Plata and y.e south part of Brasil . . .

## 1732–1739

**Châtelain, H. A.**

Atlas historique; ou, nouvelle introduction à l'histoire, à la chronologie & à la géographie ancienne & moderne . . . par m. C. * * * [anon.] Avec des dissertations fur l'histoire de chaque état, par m.

**Châtelain, H. A.**—Continued.

[Nicolas] Gueudeville. Dernière éd. cor. & aug. 7 v. fol. Amsterdam, Z. Châtelain, 1732–39. 579

    Note.—An earlier edition published 1705–20. See title 548. Edition varies: v. 1, Dernière éd., cor. & aug. 1739; v. 2–3, Nouvelle éd., revûë, cor. & considerablement aug., 1737; v. 4, Nouvelle éd., revûë, cor. & considerablement aug., 1735; v. 5–6, Seconde éd., cor. et aug., 1732. Engraved title. The title of v. 7 reads: Suplément à l'Atlas historique . . .

The following maps relate to America:

v. 1, no.  1. Nouveaux mappe monde . . .
"   "  3. Nouvelle carte de l'Asie . . . [Philippine islands]
"   "  5. Nouvelle carte de géographie de la partie méridionale de l'Amérique . . .
"   "  6. Nouvelle carte de l'Amérique Septentrionale . . .
"   "  8. Nouvelle carte pour conduire à l'astronomie et à la géographie et pour faire conoitre les differens sistèmes du monde . . .
"   " 10. Mappe monde, ou description générale du globe terrestre.
"   " 12. Plan de l'histoire universelle, où l'on voit les quatre monarchies du monde . . .
"   " 38. Carte d'Espagne et des principaux états appartenans à cette monarchie dans les quatre parties du monde [Isles Antilles; Nouveau Mexique; Nouvelle Espagne, Terre Ferme, Le Pérou, Chili, Rio de la Plata, ou Paraguay, Isles Philipines]
"   " 39. Carte de l'Amérique.
"   " 45. Mappe-monde . . .
" 3, " 43. Mappe-monde ou partie du globe pour faire connoitre les états de l'Angleterre dans l'Amérique.
" 5, " 45. Carte des Indes, de la Chine et des îles de Sumatra, Java etc. [Philippine islands]
"   " 57. Le royaume de Siam avec les royaumes qui sont tributaires et les isles de Sumatra, Andemaon etc. [Part of the Philippine islands]
" 6, " 20. Carte du Canada ou de la Nouvelle France . . .
"   " 21. Carte particulière du fleuve Saint Louis . . .
"   " 23. Carte de la Nouvelle France où se voit des grande rivières de S. Laurens & de Mississipi . . .
"   " 26. Carte qui contient une description des îles & terres que les Anglois possèdent dans l'Amérique Septentrionale, et en particulier de la Jamaique . . .
"   " 27. Carte contenant le royaume du Mexique et la Floride . . .
"   " 28. Carte du Mexique.—Environs du lac de Mexique.
"   " 29. Carte de l'Isthme de Darien et du golfe de Panama.
"   " 30. Carte . . . de la mer du Sud . . . [contenant l'Amérique Septentrionale et Méridionale, les isles Philippines et les isles Antilles]
"   " 31. Carte de la Terre Ferme, du Pérou, du Brésil, et du pays des Amazones . . .
"   " 32. Carte particulière du Pérou . . .
"   " 33. Carte du Paraguai, du Chili, du détroit de Magellan . . .
"   " 35. Carte des Antilles françoises et des isles voisines . . .

CONTENTS.

v. 1. Contenant la Grèce, l'histoire romaine, Rome moderne, Naples, la France, l'Efpagne et les provinces Unis.
" 2. Qui comprend l'Allemagne, la Pruffe, la Hongrie & la Bohême.
" 3. Qui comprend la Grande Bretagne, l'Irlande, la Suiffe, la Savoye, la Lorraine & la république de Venife.
" 4. Qui comprend le Dannemarck, la Suède, la Pologne, la Mofcovie, la Turquie, &c.
" 5. Qui comprend l'Asie en général & en particulièr, l'Affyrie, l'Arménie, la Géorgie, la Turque afiatique, la Terre fainte, l'Arabie, la Perfe, la Tartarie, les états du Grand-Mogol, les Indes orientales, la Chine, le Japon, et le royaume de Siam.
" 6. Qui comprend l'Afrique & l'Amérique Septentionale & Méridionale, tant en général qu'en particulièr; l'Égypte, la Barbarie, la Nigritie, la Guinée, l'Éthiopie, le Congo, la Cafrerie, & le Cap de Bonne Espérance; le Canada, ou la Nouvelle France, la Louisiane, ou le Mississipi, la Virginie, la Floride, le Mexique, le Pérou, le Chili & le Brésil; avec les îles de Madagascar, les Philippines, les Moluques, les Antilles et l'île de Ceylan.
" 7. Contenant diverses pièces de chronologie, de généalogie, d'histoire et d'autres sciences, qui avoient été omises dans les précédens volumes . . .

**1733**

**Delisle, G.**

Atlas nouveau, contenant toutes les parties du monde, où sont exactment remarquées les empires, monarchies, royaumes, états, républiques &c. 4 p.l., 31, [1] pp., 66 col. maps. fol. Amsterdam, J. Cóvens & C. Mortier, 1733. 580

NOTE.—Copy no. 1. See also titles 533, 535, 581, 594, 596 and 636. Title in red and black.
Primary title-page, engraved by R. de Hooghe, reads: Atlas novus ad usum serenissimi Burgundiæ ducis.—Atlas françois à l'usage de monseigneur le duc de Bourgogne . . .
Text preceding maps, has a special title-page: Introduction à la géographie, où sont la géographie astronomique . . . le géographie naturelle . . . la géographie historique . . . par le sieur Sanson d'Abbeville . . . Amsterdam, J. Cóvens & C. Mortier.
A collection of maps representing Delisle's work from 1700–1726, brought together by the publishers in 1733.
no. [13], Le plan de Paris, ses faubourgs et ses environs.
The following maps relate to America:
no. [ 1] Mappe-monde . . .
" [ 2] Hémisphère Septentrional . . .
" [ 3] Hémisphère Méridional . . .
" [42] L'Asie . . . [Isles Philippines]
" [46] Carte des Indes et de la Chine [Philippines]
" [56] L'Amérique Septentrionale . . .
" [57] L'Amérique Méridionale . . .
" [58] Carte du Canada ou de la Nouvelle France . . .
" [59] Carte de la Louisane et du cours du Mississippi . . .
" [60] Carte du Mexique et de la Floride des Terres angloises et des isles Antilles . . .
" [61] Carte de l'isle de Saint Domingue, dressée en 1722 . . .

**Delisle, G.**—Continued.

no. [62] Carte des Antilles françoises et des isles voisines . . .
" [63] Carte de la Terre Ferme, du Pérou, du Brésil et du pays des Amazons dressée sur les descriptions de Herrera, de Laet, et des p. p. d'Acuña, et m. Rodriguez . . .
" [64] Carte du Paraguay, du Chili, du Détroit de Magellan &c. . . .
" [65] Supplementum Theatro historico [South America and part of North America outlined]

### 1733

Atlas nouveau, contenant toutes les parties du monde, où font exactement remarquées les empires, monarchies, royaumes, états, républiques &c.   4 p. l., 31, [1] pp., 72 col. maps on 152 l.   fol. Amsterdam, J. Cóvens & C. Mortier, 1733.   581

NOTE.—Map no. [39e], Le cours du Po . . . par le p. Placide . . . dated 1735. See also titles 533, 535, 580, 594, 596 and 636.

Copy no. 2, with the following additional maps not found in copy no. 1:—no. [14], Carte particulière d'Anjou et de Touraine ou de la partie méridionale de la généralité de Tours . . .—no. [33], Landcharte des churfurstenthums Brandenburg.—Nova electoratus Brandenburgici tabula, edita per I. P. Fr. von Gundling.—no. [39, a-e], Le cours du Po . . . par le p. Placide . . . 1735.—no. [41], Insula Corsica . . .—no. [44], Théâtre de la guerre dans la Petite Tartarie, la Crimée, la mer Noire . . .—no. [45], Séconde partie de la Crimée, la mer Noire &c. . . .—no. [68], Carte de l'isle de la Martinique . . . dressée sur les plans manuscrits entr' autres sur celui de m. Houel . . . et conciliés avec des mémoires de feu m. Guill. Delisle . . . Par . . . Philippe Buache.

### 1734?

**Köhler, J. D.**

Johann David Köhlers . . . bequemer schul- und reisen-atlas aller zu erlernung der alten, weittlern und neuen geographie dienlichen universal- und particular-charten, welche alle auf eine folche neue und befondere art illuminirt, daſs man nicht nur alleine nach denen verfchiedentlich aufgetragenen farbenderen abtheilung und gräntzen alfobald genau unterfcheiden, fondern auch noch über diefes daben gleich bey den erften augenblick erkennen kan wen erftlich jegliches land in denen welt-theilen zugehöre, und dann auch was folches für einer religion zugethan, nebft einer im druck beygefügten kurtzen geographifchen anleitung und etlichen heraldifchen charten, welche die wappen aller königreiche und länder, davon die charten in diefen atlante befindlich, und die fonften gewöhnlicher maſſen denenfelben pflegen zur vierde beygeftochen zu werden, zu beſſern gebrauch befonders, und auf das alleraccuratefte vorftellen. 1 p. l., 279 l. incl. 95 col. maps, 38 pl.   fol.   Nürnberg, C. Weigeln [1734?]   582

NOTE.—Date on map no. 49, "Eigentlischer plan des feldlagers der kayserlichen und reichs-armee unter dem cőmando des printzens Evgnii vom 1ſten bis 22 julii aº. 1734 bey der von der frantzöſichen armee hart belagerten festung Philipsbvrg nebſt dem accuraten plan des frantzöſichens retrenchments.

Maps by various cartographers including: Homann, Moll, Goos, Valvasor, Kauffer, Muller, Falda, Reland, Delisle and Weigel.

Engraved title-page reads: Atlas scholasticus et itinerarius cura Io. Davidis Koeleri hist. et polit. pp. Altdorfini, a Christophoro Weigelio, Norimbergensi excusus.

See titles 567, 568 and 569.

The following maps relate to America:

no. 5. Plani globium terrestre minus in hanc formam reductam à Iohanne Bapt. Homanno . . .
" 6. Facies Poli Arctici . . . delineate cura Christophori Weigelii . . .
" 7. Facies Poli Antarctici . . . descripta a Christophoro Weigelio.
" 11. Novi orbis sive totius Americæ cum adiacentibus insulis . . .
" 97. America Septentrionalis studio Guilielmi de l'Isle . . .
" 98. Novissima tabula regionis Lvdovicianæ Gallice dictæ la Lovisiane tam olim quidem sub Canadæ et Floridæ nomine in America Septentrionali . . . delineata . . . a Chr: Weigelio . . .
" 99. America Meridionalis studio Guilielmi de l'Isle . . .

**Seutter, M.**

**1734?**

Groffer atlas, worinnen enthalten alle die jenige geographifche univerfal-special-und particular-mappen, mit über die mehreften gedrukten alphabetifchen regiftern | auch unterfchiedlicher vornehmften ståden profpect, und grund-riffe | wie nicht weniger einige genealogifche båume | und chronologifche tabellen, welche da durch befonderen fleiff | und rûhe in kupfer gebracht | und ausgefertiget seynd. 4 p. l., [7] l., 131 col. maps, 63 pl. fol. Augspurg, zu finden in Augspurg in verlegung des autoris, und zu Wien in der Straubischen buch-handlung [1734?] 583

NOTE.—Engraved title-page reads: Atlas novus sive tabulæ geographicæ totius orbis faciem, partes, imperia, regna et provincias exhibitentes exactissima cura iutxa recentissimas observation. Æri incisæ et venum expositæ à Matthæo Seütter, s. c. m. g. Augustæ Vindelicorum.

Engraved title-page, plates and maps hand colored.

Date 1734 occurs on the following plates:

no. 189. Genealogischer stamm baum aller marggraf u. churfürsten zu Brandenburg . . .
" 191. Dem durchlauchtigsten fürsten und herrn, herrn Eberhard Ludwig, herzogen zu Würtenberg und Teck . . .

A double paged plate contains dedication in verse to Charles VI.

Contains plans of the following cities: Madrid.—Paris.—London.—Ostend.—Amsterdam.—Luxemburg.—Milan.—Mantua.—Venice.—Naples.—Rome.—Vienna.—Cologne.—Munich.—Ratisbon.—Leipsic.—Gotha.—Nuremberg.—Augsburg.—Strasburg.—Freiburg.—Landau.—Manheim.—Frankfort.—Magdeburg.—Hamburg.—Prag.—Breslau.—Dantzic.—Copenhagen.—Stockholm.—St. Petersburg.—Constantinople.—Jerusalem.

The following maps relate to America:

no. 3. Diversi globi terr-aqvei.
" 8. Novus orbis sive America Meridionalis et Septentrionalis.
" 160. Accurata delineatio celeberrimæ regionis Ludovicianæ vel Gallice Louisane ot Canadæ et Floridæ adpellatione in Septemtrionali America.
" 161. Recens edita totius Novi Belgii in America Septentrionalem.

## 1734
**Keulen, J. van.**
[De groote nieuwe vermeerderde zee-atlas]  front., 38 maps.
fol. [Amsterdam, I. van Keulen] 1734.  584

NOTE.—Engraved frontispiece, "Gedrukt tot Amſterdam bij Ioannes van Keulen boeck zee kaardt ver-kooper en graad boogh maker aande ooſt zijde vande Nieuwebrug inde gekroonde Lootſman. Met previlegie . . . 1734," signed, "Ian. Luyken, invenit; Aernout Naghtegael, sc."
Title supplied from Muller, Catalogue of books . . . on America. 1872. p. 139. no. 1953.
Maps by Gerard and Joannes van Keulen.
English, dutch and french titles on some maps.
The following maps relate to America:
no. [1] . . . Aard booden of werelt door Gerard van Keulen . . .
" [9] . . . Noord occiaen van Hitland tot inde Straet Davids . . . door Gerard van Keulen.
" [10] . . . De Straat Davids . . . Ioannes van Keulen.
" [11] . . . Noorder deel van Europa . . . Groenland . . . [Ysland] door Gerard van Keulen.
" [25] . . . Spaanse zee vant kanaal tot 't eyland Cuba . . .
" [26] . . . Geheel-Westindien . . .
" [27] . . . Rivieren Commewini Suriname Suramaca, Cupanama en Courantin . . . Gerard van Keulen
" [28] . . . West Indien . . . van rio Oronoque tot . . . Cartagena met . . . Caribische eylanden . . . Porto Rico . . .
" [29] . . . Hispaniola of St Domingo . . .
" [30] . . . Kust van Guinea en Brasilia . . .
" [32] Pacific ocean showing part of North and South America.

## 1734–1738
**Du Sauzet, H.**
Atlas de poche, à l'usage des voyageurs et des officiers. Avec un traité de la sphère, de la géographie, & de l'hydrographie. 34 pp., 38 maps, 2 (*i. e.* 3) pl. nar. 8°. Amsterdam, H. du Sauzet, 1734–[1738]  584a

NOTE.—Maps by N. Sanson, and son, engraved by A. de Winter and G. Drogenham. Map no. 19, "Théâtre de la guerre en Allemagne," dated 1735.
Map no. 26, "Carte des Espagnes" with inset entitled, "Vue de Gibraltar," dated 1738.
Bound with this atlas is the following work, "Profils ou vues des principales villes de l'Europe, &c. Amsterdam, H. du Sauzet, 1739." For contents see title 592a.
The following maps relate to America:
no. 3. Mappe-monde ou carte générale du globe terrestre . . . par le S.$^r$ Sanson.
" 7. Américqve Septentrionale par N. Sanſon.
" 8. Américqve Méridionale par N. Sanſon.

## 1736?
**Moll, H.**
Atlas minor: or a new and curious set of sixty two maps, in which are shewn all the empires, kingdoms, countries, states, in all the known parts of the earth; with their bounds, divisions, chief

cities & towns, the whole composed & laid down agreable to modern history. 2 p. l., 62 fold. maps. 8°. London, for T. Bowles & J. Bowles [1736?] ˙585

NOTE.—New illus. title, engraved. See also titles 574, 578 and 635.
Map no. 13, "Germany", carries added legend, "Lorrain was ceded to France a. d. 1736 . . .."
Maps same as those in 2d ed. [1732?] except nos. 46, 49, 51, 54, 55 which contain added place names.
The following maps relate to America:

no. 1. A new map of the whole world with the trade winds . . . Printed for Thos. Bowles . . . and John Bowles . . . London.
" 2. A map of the North Pole . . . Printed for Tho. Bowles . . . & Iohn Bowles . . .
" 40. Africa . . . [Shows] C. S$^t$. Augustin [Brazil]
" 45. America . . .
" 46. A new map of y$^e$ north parts of America claimed by France under y$^e$ names of Louisiana, Mississipi, Canada & New France, with the adjoyning territories of England & Spain . . .
" 47. New Found Land S$^t$. Laurence bay, the fishing banks, Acadia, and part of New Scotland . . .
" 48. A description of the bay of Fundy . . .—The harbour of Annapolis Royal by Nathaniel Blackmore esq$^r$. Printed and sold by Tho. Bowles . . . & In°. Bowles . . .
" 49. New England, New York, New Jersey and Pensilvania . . .
" 50. Virginia and Maryland . . .
" 51. Carolina.
" 52. A plan of Port Royal harbour in Carolina . . .
" 53. The island of Bermudós . . .
" 54. Florida called by y$^e$ French Louisiana &c. . . .
" 55. A map of the West-Indies &c. Mexico or New Spain . . .
" 56. The island of Jamaica . . .
" 57. The island of S$^t$. Christophers, alias S$^t$. Kitts . . .
" 58. The island of Antego . . . Sold by T. Bowles . . . and I. Bowles . . .
" 59. The island of Barbadoes . . . Printed and sold by Tho: Bowles . . . & I Bowles . . .
" 60. The Scots settlement in America calle'd [!] New Caledonia . . .
" 61. A map of Terra Firma Peru Amazoneland, Brasil & the north p. of La Plata . . .
" 62. A map of Chili, Patagonia, La Plata and y$^e$ south part of Brasil . . .

## 1737

**Homann, J. B.**

Groffer atlas über die gantze welt wie diefe fowol, nach Göttlicher allweisen schöpffung aus den heutigen grundsätzen der berühmteften astronomorum Nicolai Copernici und Tychonis de Brahe, in der bewegung und unermesslichen weite des himmels/ als auch in dem umfang unserer mit waffer umgebenen allgemeinen erdkugel/ zu betrachten/ samt einer kurtzen einleitung zur geographie worinnen die erde 1. Mathematice: Nemlich was fie mit der himmlifchen sphæra für eine übereinftimmung habe. 2. Phyfice: wie fie in ihren natürlichen stücken durch waffer und land unterschieden. 3.

**Homann, J. B.**—Continued.

Hiftorice: wie fie in ihre darauf befindliche monarchien, königreiche, staaten und herrschafften, auch nach ausbreitung verfchiedener religionen eingetheilet, deutlich befchrieben durch herrn Johann Gabriel Doppermahr . . . und mit mehr als zwei hundert auferlesenen/ theils aftronomifchen meiftentheils aber geographifchen charten, in welchen alle bifzher zu waffer und land gefchehene land-entdeckungen aus denen berühmteften autoribus diefes jahrhunderts anbemercket worden. 2 p. l., 148 col. maps, 3 pl. fol. Nürnberg, verlegung der Homannischen erben, gedruckt bey J. H. G. Vieling, 1737. 586

NOTE.—First edition published in 1716; another edition in 1731.
Dates on maps vary from 1710–1775.

Engraved title-page, hand colored, reads: Atlas novus terrarum orbis imperia, regna et status exactis tabulis geographicè demonstrans, opera Johannis Baptistæ Homanni . . . Noribergae . . .

Maps, hand colored and ornamented with many engravings, by various cartographers including: Lowitz, Hasius, Petit, Maier, Schaz, Coronelli, Carl, Nell, Visscher, Lauterbach, Zollmann, Paderborn, Vierenklee, Hübner, Barnikel, Müller, Harenberg, Lucas, Delisle, and Boehmius.

The following maps relate to America:
no. [3] Planiglobii terrestris . . . 1746.
" [146] Americæ. 1746.
" [147] Regni Mexicani . . .
" [148] Domina Anglorum in America Septentrionali.
" [149] Tabula Americanæ specialis geographica regni Peru, Brasiliæ, Terre Firme, & reg: Amazonum.
" [150] Typhus geographicus Chili Paraguay Freti Magellanici &c. 1733.

## 1737–1772

**Bellin, J. N.**

L'hydrographie françoise, recueil des cartes générales et particulières qui ont été faites pour le service des vaisseaux du roy, par ordre des ministres de la marine, depuis 1737, jusqu'en 1765, par le s. Bellin, ingénieur de la marine et du dépost des cartes, plans et journaux de la marine, censeur royal, de l'académie de marine, et de la société royale de Londres . . . 2 v. fol. Paris, chez m. Bellin [1737–1772] 587

NOTE.—Engraved title-page states: Arrivet delineavit & sculpeit 1765.
Collation:—v. 1, 2 p. l., [3], 47 maps on 86 l.; v. 2, 2 p. l., [4], 39 maps on 76 l.
Maps dated 1737–1772.

v. 1, nos. 1, 3, 29–31, wanting; no. 1, Tableau des pavillons arborés à la mer, and no. 29, Carte réduite des côtes d'Espagne et de Portugal, are in 1737–91 & 1737–94 ed.; no. 3, Carte des variations de la boussole, and no. 31, Plan du port et de la ville de Lisbonne, are in 1737–91, 1737–94 & 1737–1807 ed.; no. 30, Le Portugal et ses frontières, is in 1737–1807 ed.

This copy is like the 1737-1807 ed., see title 589, with the following exceptions:
v. 1, no. 1. Carte réduite des parties connues du globe terrestre . . . 1755.
" " 7. Carte réduite de l'océan occidental contenant partie des costes d'Europe et d'Afrique . . . 4 éd. . . . 1766.
" " 14. Carte réduite des isles Britanniques . . . contenant l'Irlande.
" " 18. Carte réduite de la rade des Dunes . . . 1757 . . .
" " 23. Carte réduite de la Manche . . . 1763.
" " 25. Carte réduite du golphe de Gascogne . . . 2 éd. de 1757.
" " 32. Carte hydrographique de la baye de Cadix . . . 1762.
" " 33. Carte du détroit de Gibraltar . . . 1761.
" " 36. Carte de la baye de Gibraltar. 1762.
" " 48. Théâtre de la guerre dans l'Inde sur la coste de Caromandel . . . 1770.
" " 49. Plan de la ville du Cap de Bonne-Espérance et environs . . . 1770.—Insets: Ville et partie de Ste Hélène . . . 1770.—Partie de l'isle de l'Ascension . . .—Baye de la Pray dans l'isle de St Yago . . .
v. 2, no. 1. Carte réduite des isles Açores . . . 1755.
" " 3. Carte réduite des costes occidentales d'Afrique . . . contenant les costes de Barbarie depuis le détroit de Gibraltar jusqu'au cap Bojador et les isles Canaries . . . 1753.
" " 13. Carte réduite des mers comprises entre l'Asie et l'Amérique apelées . . . mer du Sud, ou mer Pacifique . . . 1742.
" " 17. Carte réduite du golphe de St Laurent contenant l'isle de Terreneuve et partie de la coste des Esquimaux, l'isle Royale, l'isle St Jean, et d'Anticosti . . . 1754.
" " 20. Carte réduite du Grand banc et d'une partie de l'isle de Terre neuve . . 1764.
" " 21. Carte réduite de la partie septentrionale de l'isle de Terre neuve . . . 1764.
" " 22. Suite de la carte réduite du golphe de St Laurent, contenant les costes de Labrador depuis Mecatina . . . jusqu'à la baye des Esquimaux . . . 1753.
" " 28. Carte réduite des isles Antilles . . . 1758.
" " 29. Carte réduite de l'isle de Saint Domingue et de ses débouquemens . . . 1750.
" " 30. Carte de l'isle de Saint Domingue . . . 1764.
" " 31. Carte réduite des débouquemens de St Domingue . . . 1768.
" " 35. Carte particulière de l'isle de la Jamaique . . . 1758.
Explanatory notes, by m. Bellin, precede the following maps:
v. 1, no. 1. Carte réduite des parties connues du globe terrestre . . .
" " 19-22. Cartes des isles de Jersey, Grenesey et d'Aurigny.
" " 23. Carte réduite de la Manche.
v. 2, " 1. " " des isles Açores.
" " 2. " " de l'océan Méridionale . . .
" " 3-4. Cartes . . . des costes occidentales d'Afrique . . .
" " 5. Carte générale de la coste de Guinée . . .

## 1737-1791

**Bellin, J. N.**, *& others.*

Hydrographie françoise. Recueil des cartes marines, général et particulières dressées au dépôt des cartes, plans et journaux, par ordre des ministres de la marine, depuis 1737 jusques en 1772, par feu

**Bellin, J. N.**, *& others*—Continued.

m. Bellin, ingénieur-hydrographe du dépôt, et autres. 2 v. fol. [Paris, dépôt général de la marine, 1737-1791]     588

   Note.—Title-page of v. 1, wanting.
   Engraved title-page of v. 2 signed: Arrivet delineavit & sculpsit 1765.
   Collation: v. 1, 1 p. l., 59 maps on 110 l., 2 pl.; v. 2, 2 p. l., 55 maps on 99 l.
   Dates on maps vary from 1737-91.
   This copy is like the 1737-1807 ed., see title 590, with the following exceptions:

   v. 1, no. 16. Carte réduite des isles Britanniques . . . contenant l'Irlande.
   "    "    18. Carte réduite de la rade des Dunes avec une partie des entrées de la Tamise . . . 1757.
   "    "    21. Carte réduite de la Manche . . . 1763.
   "    "    28. Carte réduite du golphe de Gascogne. Seconde édition of 1757 . . .
   "    "    32. Carte réduite des costes d'Espagne et de Portugal . . . 1751.
   "    "    34. Carte hydrographique de la baye de Cadix, 1762.
   "    "    35. Carte du détroit de Gibraltar . . . 1761.
   "    "    36. Carte de la baye de Gibraltar . . . 1762.
   "    "    52 (a) Carte réduite des costes occidentales d'Afrique . . . contenant les costes de Barbarie depuis le détroit de Gibraltar jusqu'au cap Bojador, 1753.
   v. 2, no. 67. Carte réduite du golphe du Mexique et des isles de l'Amérique . . . Second édition année 17[!] . . .
   "    "    69. Carte hydrographique de la bay de la Havane avec le plan de la ville . . . 1762.
   "    "    71. Carte particulière de l'isle de la Jamaique . . . 1758.
   "    "    72. Carte réduite des débouquements de St Domingue . . . 1787.
   "    "    75. Carte réduite des isles Antilles . . . 1758.
   "    "    87. Carte hydrographique de la rivière de la Plata . . . 1770.
   "    "    100. Carte réduite des mers comprises entre l'Asie et l'Amérique apelées . . . mer du Sud, ou mer Pacifique, 1742 . . . cor. en 1756.

**1737-1794**

Hydrographie françoise. Recueil des cartes marines, générales et particulières, dressées au dépôt des cartes, plans et journaux, par ordre des ministres de la marine, depuis 1737 jusques en 1772, par feu m. Bellin, ingénieur-hydrographe du dépôt, et autres. 2 v. fol. [Paris, dépôt général de la marine, 1737-94]     589

   Note.—Engraved title-page signed: Arrivet delineavit & sculpsit, 1765.
   Collation:—v. 1, 2 p. l., front., 60 maps on 112 l., 2 pl.; v. 2, 1 p. l., front., 53 maps on 99 l.
   Dates on maps vary from 1737-94.
   This copy is like the 1737-1807 ed., see title 590, with the following exceptions:

   v. 1, no. 16. Carte réduite des isles Britanniques . . . contenant l'Irlande.
   "    "    18. Carte réduite de la rade des Dunes avec une partie des entrées de la Tamise . . . 1757.
   "    "    21. Carte réduite de la Manche . . . 1763.
   "    "    32. Carte réduite des costes d'Espagne et de Portugal . . . 1751.
   "    "    34. Carte hydrographique de la baye de Cadix, 1762.
   "    "    35. Carte du détroit de Gibraltar . . . 1761.

v. 1, no. 36. Carte de la baye de Gibraltar . . . 1762.
" " 52. Carte réduite des costes occidentales d'Afrique . . . contenant les costes de Barbarie depuis le détroit de Gibraltar jusqu'au cap Bojador, 1753.
v. 2, " 59. Carte de l'ile de Fogo à la côte orientale de Terre-Neuve . . . par le lieutenant Michael Lane en 1785 . . .
" " 65. Carte réduite des costes orientales de l'Amérique Septentrionale . . . contenant l'isle Royale, l'Acadie, la baye Françoise, la Nouvelle Yorc . . .
" " 67. Carte réduite de golphe du Mexique et des isles de l'Amerique . . .
" " 69. Carte hydrographique de la baye de la Havane, avec le plan de la ville . . . 1762.
" " 70. Carte particulière de l'isle de la Jamaique . . . 1758.
" " 74. Carte réduite des débouquemens de St Domingue . . . 1768.
" " 75. Carte réduite des isles Antilles . . . 1758.
" " 87. Carte hydrographique de la rivière de la Plata . . . 1770.
" " 100. Carte réduite des mers comprises entre l'Asie et l'Amérique apelées . . . mer du Sud, ou mer Pacifique . . . 1742 . . . cor. en 1756.

## 1737–1807

Hydrographie françoise. Recueil des cartes marines, générales et particulières dressées au dépôt des cartes, plans et journaux, par ordre des ministres de la marine, depuis 1737, jusques en 1772, par feu m. Bellin, ingénieur-hydrographe du dépôt, et autres. 2 v. fol. [Paris, dépôt général de la marine, 1737–1807]    590

NOTE.—Engraved title-page signed: Arrivet delineavit & sculpsit, 1765.
Collation:—v. 1, 2 p. l., 73 maps on 136 l., 2 pl.; v. 2, 1 p. l., 66 maps on 122 l. Maps dated 1737–1807.
Three other copies have dates as follows:— copy 2, 1737–94; copy 3, 1737–91; copy 4, 1737–72.
v. 1, no. 18, Carte de la rade des Dunes, wanting; no. [57] substituted for this, is unlike no. 18 in copies 2, 3 & 4.
The following maps relate to America:

v. 1, no. 1. Carte réduite des parties connues du globe terrestre . . . 1784.
" " 2. Carte des variations de la boussole et des vents généraux . . . 1765.
" " 3. Carte réduite des mers du Nord . . . 1751.
" " 20. Carte générale de l'océan Atlantique . . . cor. en 1792.
" " 20 [a] Carte réduite d'une partie de l'océan Atlantique . . . par m. de Verdun de la Crenne, 1775.
v. 2, no. 4. Carte réduite des parties connues du globe terrestre . . . 1784.
" " 5. Carte des variations de la boussole et des vents généraux . . . 1765.
" " 56. Carte de l'Amérique Septentrionale . . . 1755.
" " 56 [a] Carte réduite des côtes de l'Acadie, de l'isle Royale, et de partie de l'isle de Terre-neuve, par m. le marquis de Chabeat . . . 1751.
" " 57. Carte réduite des bancs et de l'ile de Terre-neuve avec les côtés du golfe de St Laurent et de l'Acadie. 1784.
" " 58. Carte réduite de l'isle de Terre-neuve . . . 1784.

**Bellin, J. N.**, *& others*—Continued.

v. 2, no. 59. Carte des isles de Saint Pierre et Miquelon . . . 1763.
" " 60. Plan de l'île de Saint Pierre . . . par le sr. Fortin . . . 1763.
" " 61. Cartes réduite des côtes orientales de l'Amérique Septentrionale, contenant celles des provinces de New York et de la Nouvelle Angleterre, celles de l'Acadie . . . de l'île Royale, de l'île St Jean . . . 1780.
" " 62. Carte réduite des côtes orientales de l'Amérique Septentrionale, contenant partie du Nouveau Jersey, la Pen-sylvanie, le Maryland, la Virginie, la Caroline Septentrionale, la Caroline Méridionale et la Georgie . . . 1778.
" " 63-64. Carte du cours du fleuve de St Laurent . . . 1761.
" " 65. Carte réduite de l'Acadie . . . comprenant une partie de l'île Royale, de l'île St. Jean et du Canada, 1779.
" " 66. Carte réduite des costes de la Louisiane et de la Floride . . . 1764.
" " 67. Carte générale du golfe du Mexique et de l'archipel des Antilles . . . 1807.
" " [67a] Carte des côtes du golfe du Mexique . . . [1800]
" " [67b] Port de la Vera Cruz à la côte occidentale du golfe du Mexique . . . [1802]
" " [67c] Carte de la partie occidentale des îles Antilles, comprenant St Domingue, la Jamaique, Cuba, et les îles et bancs de Bahama . . . [1801]
" " 68. Carte réduite de l'isle de Cube . . . 1762.
" " [68a] Carte réduite d'une partie du vieux canal de Bahama et des bancs adjacents . . . [1792]
" " 69. Plan du port et de la ville de la Havanne, levé en 1798, par D. José del Rio . . .
" " [69a] Plan du principal port de l'ile de Porto Rico, levé en 1794, par D. Cosme de Churruca . . .
" " 70. Carte réduite de l'isle de la Jamaique . . . 1753.
" " [70a] Carte de l'île de la Jamaique . . . 1786.
" " 71. Carte réduite de l'isle de St Domingue . . . par m. le cte. de Chastenet-Puisegur . . . 1787.
" " 72. Carte réduite des désbouquements de St Domingue . . . 1787.
" " 73-74. [Plans] des environs de l'isle de Saint Domingue.
" " [74a] Carte de la Gonave . . . 1788, par m. de Lieudé.
" " 75. Carte générale des îles Antilles . . . 1806.
" " [75a] Carte réduite des îles Antilles. 1775.—Carte réduite des désbouquements de Saint Domingue, par m. de Verdun de la Crenne . . . 1775.
" " 76. Carte réduite de l'isle de Saint Christophe . . . 1758.
" " 77. Carte réduite de l'isle d'Antigue . . . 1758.
" " 78. Carte réduite des isles de la Guadeloupe . . . 1759.
" " 79. Carte réduite de l'isle de la Martinique . . . 1758.
" " 80. Carte de l'isle de Saint Lucie . . . 1763.
" " 81. Carte de l'isle de la Barbade . . . 1758.
" " 82. Carte de l'isle de la Grenade . . . 1760.
" " 83. Carte réduite des costes de la Guyane . . . 1760.
" " 84. Carte de la Guyane françoise et l'isle de Cayenne . . . 1763.
" " [84a] Plan de la côté de la Guyane . . . comprenant la rade de Cayenne . . . par m. Dessigny . . . 1765.

v. 2, no. [84b] Carte de l'île de la Trinité . . . [1804]—Plan de la presqu'île et du port de Chaguaramas . . . [1804]
" " 85. Carte réduite pour la navigation de Cayenne à la Martinique . . . 1764.
" " 86. Carte réduite de l'océan Méridional . . . 1753.
" " 87. Carte de la rivière de la Plata . . . 1794.
" " [87a] Carte des côtes de l'Amérique Méridionale . . . 1790.
" " 88. Carte réduite . . . des isles de Falkland . . . 1771.
" " 91. Carte réduite de l'océan Oriental, ou mer des Indes . . . 2 éd. 1757.
" " 98. Carte réduite des isles Philippines . . . 1752.
" " 99. Carte réduite de l'océan Septentrional compris entre l'Asie, et l'Amérique . . . 1766.
" " 100. Carte réduite de Grand océan compris entre l'Asie et l'Amérique . . . [1797]

**1738–1774**

**La Harpe, J. F. D. de.**
[Abrégé de l'histoire générale des voyages . . . Nouvelle éd., rev. et cor. . . . Atlas]    74 maps.  4°. [Paris, E. Ledoux, 1820]    591

NOTE.—Without title. Maps are like those of 1780 edition which are bound with the text.
Atlas accompanying this work contains maps by lieut. J. Cook, Laurent and Bellin, dated 1738–1774.
The following maps are reproductions from works of d'Anville, Delisle and others:
no. [12] Le pays des Hottentots . . .
" [13] Empire du Monomotapa . . .
" [24] Carte de la Tartarie orientale.
" [25] " " " " occidentale.
" [38] Suite du Brésil . . .
" [42] Carte de la Guyane . . .
" [43] " du Brésil . . .
" [47] " de la Caroline et Georgie.
" [53] Suite du Brésil . . .
" [63] Carte particulière de l'isle de Juan Fernandes . . .
The following maps relate to America:
no. [1] Essay d'une carte réduite . . . du globe terrestre . . . 1748.
" [17] Carte des isles Philippines . . . 1752.
" [21] " " " " 1752.
" [29] " de l'empire du Mexique . . . 1754.
" [31] " du cours du Maragnon ou de la grande rivière des Amazones . . .
" [32] Carte du Pérou . . .
" [35] " " golphe du Mexique et des isles de l'Amérique . . . 1754.
" [36] " " lac de Mexico . . .
" [37] " de l'Amérique Méridionale . . .
" [38] Suite du Brésil . . .
" [40] Carte de la rivière de la Plata.
" [41] " du Paraguay . . . 1756.
" [42] " de la Guyane . . . 1757.

**La Harpe, J. P. D. de**—Continued.
- no. [43] Carte du Brésil . . .
- " [44] " de la Floride, de la Louisiane et pays voisins . . .
- " [45] " " " Virginie, de la baye Chesapeack, et pays voisins.
- " [46] " " " Nouvelle Angleterre, Nouvelle Yorck, et Pensilvanie . . . 1757.
- " [47] Carte de la Caroline et Georgie . . . 1757.
- " [48] " " " " baye de Hudson . . .
- " [49] " " l'Acadie, isle Royale, et païs voisins . . . 1757.
- " [50] " du cours du fleuve de St Laurent . . . 1757.
- " [51] Suite du cours du fleuve de St Laurent . . . 1757.
- " [52] Carte du golphe de St Laurent et pays voisins.
- " [53] Suite du Brésil . . .
- " [54] Carte de l'isle de la Grenade . . . 1758.
- " [55] " " " " Saint Domingue . . .
- " [56] " " " " la Martinique . . . 1758.
- " [57] " " " " " Guadeloupe . . . 1758.
- " [58] " " " " Sainte Lucie . . . 1758.
- " [59] " " " St Christophe . . .
- " [60] " " " de la Jamaique . . . 1758.
- " [61] Carte réduite du détroit de Magellan . . . 1753.
- " [62] Carte du détroit de la Maire . . . 1753.
- " [63] " particulière de l'isle de Juan Fernandes . . .
- " [74] Carte de l'Hémisphere Austral . . .

## 1739
**Renard, L.**

Atlas de la navigation, et du commerce qui se fait dans toutes les parties du monde. Expliquant par des cartes & par des defcriptions particulières de toutes les côtes & ports de mer de l'univers, la nature, les productions, & les ouvrages ou manufactures de chaque païs en particulier: la religion, le gouvernement, & les manières de vivre des peuples; les marchandises que l'on porte d'un païs à un autre; & celles que l'on rapporte de chaque païs, & qui fe débitent dans toutes les parties du monde pour l'utilité, la magnificence, la curiofité, & la nourriture des hommes, &c. . . . Le tout dreffé sur les mémoires les plus récens; revû & corrigé sur les nouvelles obfervations.   2 p. l., 96 pp., front., 28 maps, 2 fold. pls., por. fol.   Amsterdam, R. & J. Ottens, 1739.   592

NOTE.—Frontispiece representing "Atlas" carrying a "Planisphère représentant toute l'étendue du monde, dans l'ordre qu'on a suivi dans ce livre," serves as an index.

Engraved portrait of "George premier, roy de la Grande Bretagne, de France et d'Irlande," by B. Picart.

The two plates at the end of the atlas contain drawings and plans of fortifications, with explanations. See also titles 559 and 601.

The following maps relate to America:
- no. 1. Nova totius terrarum orbis tabula . . .
- " 3. Poli Arctici et circimiacentium terrarum descriptio novissima. Per F. de Wit.

no. 22. Magnum mare del Zur cum insula California . . .
" 23. Novæ Hispaniæ, Chili, Peruviæ, et Guatimalæ littoræ.
" 24. Tractus australior Americæ Meridionalis a Rio de la Plata per fretum Magellanicum ad Toraltum . . .
" 25. Littora Brasiliæ.
" 26. Terra Nova, ac maris tractus circa Nova Franciam, Angliam, Belgium, Venezuelam Novam, Andalusiam, Guianam et Brasiliam.
" 27. Indiarum Occidentalium, tractus littorales cum insulis Caribicis.
" 28. Septemtrionaliora Americæ à Groenlandia, per freta Davidis et Hudson, ad Terram Novam.

## 1739

**Du Sauzet, H.**
Profils ou vues des principales villes de l' Europe, &c. 2 p. l., 33 pl. nar. 8°. Amsterdam, H. du Sauzet, 1739. 592a

NOTE.—Bound with his "Atlas de poche, à l'usage des voyageurs et des officiers." 8°. Amsterdam, 1734. See title 584a.
The following map relates to America: no. 30. [City of] Mexico.

CONTENTS.

no. 1. Paris.
" 2. Londres.
" 3. Anvers.
" 4. Amsterdam.
" 5. La maison de ville d' Amsterdam.
" 6. Batavia.
" 7. Genève.
" 8. Basle.
" 9. Straetsbourg.
" 10. Heydelberg ou le Mont Payen.
" 11. Trèves.
" 12. Maience.
" 13. Cologne.
" 14. Münster.
" 15. Francfort sur le Main.
" 16. Nurenberg.
" 17. Augsbourg.
" 18. Dresde.
" 19. Berlin.
" 2<). Koningsberg.
" 21. Dantzig.
" 22. Koppenhague.
" 23. Stockholme.
" 24. Vienne.
" 25. Prague.
" 26. Constantinople.
" 27. Alger.
" 28. Madrid.
" 29. L' Escurial.
" 30. Mexico.
" 31. Vue de Lisbonne du côté du Tage. W. Jongman sculp.
" 32. Rome.
" 33. Venise.

## 1740

**Seutter, M.**

Atlas novus sive tabulæ geographicæ totius orbis faciem, partes, imperia, regna et provincias exhibentes exactissima cura iuxta recentissimas observation . . . 1 p. l., 49 col. maps. fol. Augustæ Vindelicorum [Augsburg, 1740?] 593

> NOTE.—Engraved title-page, colored. The "Index atlantis" is a manuscript page subscribed "Abbatiæ Gradicensis anno 1762." This index was probably made at the abbey of Gray, France, in 1762. Map no. 15, "Dominium Venetum," dated 1729.
> The following maps relate to America:
> no. 2. Diversi globi terr-aqvei statione variante et visu intercedente.
> " 6. Novus orbis sive America Meridionalis et Septentrionalis.
> " 7. Inset: Brasiliæ regnum in America Meridio.

## 1740–1750

**Delisle, G.**

Atlante novissimo che contiene tutte le parti del mondo, nel quale sono esattamente descritti gl' imperj, le monarchie, stati, repubbliche, ec. . . . Al quale fi premette la prima parte della introduzione alla geografia. Del sig. Sanson di Abbeville ove fi fpiegano i suoi principj, le varie maniere onde viene rapprefentata, i fuoi termini, e l' ufo che fi deve far delle carte . . . 2 v. in 1. fol. Venezia, G. Albrizzi Q. Girol. 1740–1750. 594

> NOTE.—Collation: v. 1, 8 p. l., 59 pp., 34 maps; v. 2, 5 p. l., 79 pp., 44 maps. Engraved half titles. See also titles 533, 535, 580, 581 and 596.
> Half titles read, Atlante novissimo. Del sig$^r$. Guglielmo de l' Isle; v. 1, dated 1740; v. 2, 1750.
> Edition varies: v. 2, "Ed ultimo."
> Dedication differs: v. 1, to "Il sig. cavaliere Pier Andrea Capello"; v. 2, to "La signora Eleonora Co. Collalto K$^a$. Capello."
> Six maps carry the name of Isaac Tirion.
> The following maps relate to America:
> v. 1, no. 1. Mappamondo.
> " " " 21. Nuova carta del Polo Artico.
> " 2, " 39. Carta geografica dell' America Settentrionale.
> " " " 40. Carta geografica del Canada nell' America Settentrionale.
> " " " 41. Carta geografica della Florida nell' America Settentrionale.
> " " " 42. Ca..a geografica del Messico o sia della Nuova Spagna.
> " " " 43. Carta geografica della America Méridionale.
> " " " 44. Carta geografica del Brésil.

## 1740–1817

**Cóvens, J.** *and* **Mortier, C.**

Nieuwe atlas, inhoudende de vier gedeeltens der waereld, waar in duydelyk aangeweefen worden de monarchien, keysserryken, koningryken, staaten republieken, &c. Verfameldt van de befte autheuren. 1 p. l., 43 col. maps on 88 l. fol. Te Amsterdam, J. Cóvens & C. Mortier [1740–1817] 595

> NOTE.—Dates on maps vary from 1740 to 1817. See also title 576.
> Maps by Delisle, Visscher, Jaillot and de Wit.

Map no. 20, Nieuwe kaart van het koningrijk der Nederlanden . . . 1816, probably inserted.
The following maps relate to America:
no. 1. Mappe monde, à l'usage du roy. Par Guillaume Delisle . . .
" 2. L'hémisphère septentrional . . . 1740.
" 3. L'hémisphère méridional . . . [After 1739]
" 5. Hémisphère occidental . . .
" 40. Carte d'Amérique . . .
" 41. L'Amérique Septentrionale . . . 1757.
" 42. Carte générale des treize États Unis de l'Amérique Septentrionale . . . Title in french and dutch "à Amfterdam, chez C. Mortier & J. Cóvens & fils."
" 43. L'Amérique Méridionale . . . 1757.

## 1741?
**Delisle, G.**

Atlas nouveau, contenant toutes les parties du monde, ou font exactement remarquées les empires, monarchies, royaumes, états, républiques, &c. 2 v. Amsterdam, J. Cóvens & C. Mortier [1741?] 596

NOTE.—See also titles 533, 535, 580, 581, 594 and 636. Contains a french titled edition of Henry Popple's A map of the british empire in North America, London, 1733, in seven sheets. Maps dated 1741, are the following: v. 1, no. [52] Sup$^s$. et inferioris ducatus Silesiæ . . .—v. 2, no. [31], Plan du port de la ville et des forteresses de Carthagene . . . par . . . Guillaume Laws. Title and text in french and dutch.
Collation: v. 1, 4 p. l., 31, [1] pp., 57 col. maps; v. 2, 50 col. maps on 118 l., [2] l.
Title in red and black.
Primary title-page, engraved by R. de Hooghe, reads: Atlas novus ad usum serenissimi Burgundiæ ducis.—Atlas françois à l'usage de monseigneur le duc de Bourgogne . . .
The text of v. 1, which precedes the maps has a special title-page:—Introduction à la géographie où font la géographie astronomique . . . la géographie naturelle . . . la géographie historique . . . par le sieur Sanson d'Abbeville . . .
v. 2, without title-page.
The text of v. 2, "Remarques sur le théâtre historique pour l'an 400 de l'ère chértienne," follows map no. [38]
A collection of maps brought together by the publishers, representing chiefly Delisle's work, but also containing maps by H. Popple, le p. Placide, H. Jaillot, Sanson, and G. Laws.
v. 1, no. [15], Le plan de Paris, ses faubourgs et ses environs . . . [Title in french and dutch]
The following maps relate to America:
v. 1, no. [1] Mappemonde . . .
" " [2] L'hémisphère Septentrional . . . 1740.
" " [3] L'hémisphère Méridional . . . [After 1739]
" " [4] Hémisphère Oriental . . . [Isles Philippines]
" " [5] Hémisphère Occidental . . .
v. 2, " [11] Carte d'Asie . . . [Isles Philippines]
" " [15] Carte des Indes et de la Chine. [Isles Philippines]
" " [24] Carte d'Amérique . . . 1739.

**Delisle, G.**—Continued.

   v. 2, no. [25] L'Amérique Septentrionale . . .
   "   " [26] Carte du Canada ou de la Nouvelle France . . .
   "   " [27] A map of the british empire in America with the french, spanish and hollandish settlements adjacent thereto by Henry Popple. 7 sheets [incl. views of Mexico, Niagara falls, New York city, Quebec, and principal fortresses]
   "   " [28] Carte de la Louisiane et du cours du Mississipi . . .—Inset: Carte particulière des embouchures de la rivière S. Louis et de la Mobile.
   "   " [29] Carte du Mexique et de la Floride . . . 1722.
   "   " [30] Plan du port de la ville . . . de Carthagène. 1741.
   "   " [31] Carte de l'isle de Saint Domingue . . . 1722.
   "   " [32] Carte des Antilles françoises et des isles voisines . . .
   "   " [33] Carte de l'isle de la Martinique . . .
   "   " [34] L'Amérique Méridionale . . .
   "   " [35] Carte de la Terre Ferme, du Pérou, du Brésil et du pays des Amazones . . .
   "   " [36] Carte du Paraguay, du Chili, du détroit de Magellan &c. . . .
   "   " [38] Inset: Supplementum theatro historico [South America and part of North America outlined]

### 1742?

**Rousset de Missy, J.**

   Nouvel atlas géographique & historique, pour l'étude facile de la géographie, et pour l'intelligence des nouvelles publiques, tant dans la guerre que dans la paix. Revu & augmenté . . .—Nieuwe geographische en historische atlas tot de gemakkelyke oefeninge der geographie en tot het begrip der openbaare tydingen, zo in den oorlog als in den vrede. [152] pp., 26 fold. maps, 4 pl., 3 tab. nar. 12°. Amsterdam, H. de Leth [1742?]    597

   Note.—Engraved title. With text.
   Latest date in text is 1737.
   The following maps relate to America:
   no. [ 5] Le globe terrestre représenté en deux plans-hémisphères.
   " [ 9] L'Amérique Septentrionale qui fait partie des Indes occidentales dressée selon les dernières relations des voiageurs . . .
   " [10] Carte de l'Amérique Méridionale . . .

### 1742?

   Nouvel atlas géographique & historique, pour l'étude facile de la géographie, et pour l'intelligence des nouvelles publiques tant dans la guerre que dans la paix. Revu & augmenté . . .—Nieuwe geographische en historische atlas tot de gemakkelyke oefeninge der geographie, en tot het begrip der openbaare tydingen, zo in den oorlog als in den vrede. 1 p. l., 32 maps, 4 pl., 3 tab. obl. 12°. Amsterdam, H. de Leth [&] S. J. Baalde [1742?]    598

   Note.—No text.
   The following maps relate to America:
   no. [1] Le globe terrestre représenté en deux plans-hémisphères.
   " [5] L'Amérique Septentrionale qui fait partie des Indes occidentales . . .
   " [6] Carte de l'Amérique Méridionale . . .

## 1743-1780

**Anville, J. B. B. d'.**
[Atlas général]  1 p. l., 30 maps on 101 l. fol. [Paris, 1743-1780]  599

NOTE.—A collection of maps without title-page. See titles 571 and 572.
Manuscript table of contents.
Maps dated 1743-1780.

CONTENTS.

no. [1] Orbis veteribus notus . . . 1763.
" [2] Orbis Romani, pars occidentalis . . . 1763.
" [3] Orbis Romani, pars orientalis . . . 1764.
" [4] Græciæ antiquæ . . . 1762.
" [5] Asiæ . . . Minor . . . et Syriæ . . . 1764.
" [6] La Palestine . . . 1767.
" [7] Ægyptus antiqua . . . 1765.
" [8] Tabula Italiæ antiquæ . . . 1764.
" [9] Gallia antiqua . . . 1760.
" [10] Ad antiquam Indiæ . . . 1765.
" [11] Germanie, France, Italie, Espagne, Isles Britanniques dans un âge intermédiaire . . . 1771.
" [12] Hémisphère Oriental, ou de l'ancien monde . . . 1761.
" [13] Hémisphère Occidental . . . 1761.
" [14] Première partie de la carte d'Europe . . . 1754. 2 sheets.
" [15] Seconde partie de la carte d'Europe . . . 1758. 2 sheets.
" [16] Troisième partie de la carte d'Europe . . . 1760. 2 sheets.
" [17a-b] La France divisée en provinces et en généralités . . . 1780. 2 sheets.
" [18] L'Italie . . . 1743. 2 sheets.
" [19] Les côtes de la Grèce et l'archipel . . . 1756.
" [20] Première partie de la carte d'Asie . . . 1751. 2 sheets.
" [21] Seconde partie de la carte d'Asie . . . 1752.
" [22] Troisième partie de la carte d'Asie . . . 1753. 2 sheets.
" [23] Essai d'une nouvelle carte de la Mer Caspienne . . . 1754.
" [24] Carte de l' Inde . . . 1752. 2 sheets.
" [25] Coromandel . . . 1753. 2 sheets.
" [26] Afrique . . . 1749. 2 sheets.
" [27] Guinée . . . 1775.
" [28] Carte particulière de la côte occidentale de l'Afrique . . . 1751. 2 sheets.
" [29] Golfe Arabique ou Mer Rouge . . . 1765.
" [30] Carte de la Phœnicie et des environs de Damas . . . 1780.
" [31] L'Euphrate et le Tigre . . . 1779.
" [32] Egypte . . . 1765.
" [33] Amérique Septentrionale . . . 1746. 2 sheets.
" [34] Canada, Louisiane et terres angloises . . . 1755.
" [35] Le fleuve Saint Laurent . . . [1755?]
" [36] Carte de la Louisiane . . . 1752.
" [37] Amérique Méridionale . . . 1748. 3 sheets.

## 1744-1769
**Tirion, I.**

Nieuwe en beknopte hand-atlas. Bestaande in eene verzameling van eenige der algemeenste en nodigste handkaarten; alle in der Nederduitsche taal en na de alderlaatste ontdekkingen van de L'Isle en anderen opgesteld, en in een voegzaame grootte uitgegeven; om op eene gemaklyke wyze by het leezen der nieuws-tydingen en historien te konnen worden gebruikt.  2 p. l., 111 col. maps.  fol. te Amsterdam, I. Tirion, 1744–[1769]  600

NOTE.—Collation: [226] l. incl. title, 1 l.; register, 1 l.; 2 blank l.; 111 col. maps. Most of the american maps and plans are also in Thomas Salmon's Hedendaagsche historie, of tegenwoordige staat von America . . . 3 v. 8°. te Amsterdam, I. Tirion, 1766–69.

In the "Register" three maps, nos. 56–57, 58–59, 95–96 are each given two numbers making the total 114, the number usually credited to this atlas.

Dates on maps vary from 1730 to 1769 which appears on map no. 113.

Contains the following plans:

no. [15] Kaart van Londen . . . 1754.
" [26] Nieuwe kaart van de heerlykheid Creveld . . . 1758.
" [63] Kaart van de stad Utrecht . . . 1757.
" [71] Nieuwe kaart van Parys en Versailles . . . 1756.
" [72] Nieuwe kaart der platte grond van de stad Parys . . . 1756.
" [107] Platte grond van de stad en 't kasteel van Cayenne [Inset]

The following maps relate to America:

no. [1] Wereld kaart . . . 1744.
" [2] Nieuwe kaart van het oostelykste deel der weereld . . . 1753.
" [3] Nieuwe kaart van het westelykste deel der weereld . . . 1754.
" [4] Nieuwe wereld kaart, waar in de reizen van den h$^r$ Anson rondsom de wereld . . .
" [12] Nieuwe kaart van de Noord Pool . . . 1735.
" [92] Nieuwe kaart van de Filippynsche, Ladrones, Moluccos of Specery eilanden als mede Celebes etc. . . .
" [94] Nieuwe kaart van Africa . . . Dese kaart is gemaakt na het orgeneel van de L'Isle [Shows] Brasilien.
" [100] Nieuwe kaart van America . . .
" [101] Kaart van de onderkonigschappen van Mexico en Nieuw Granada in de Spaansche West-Indien . . . 1765.
" [102] Kaart van het westelyk gedeelte van Nieuw Mexico en van Californa . . . 1765.
" [103] Kaart van de langengte van Panama . . .
" [104] Nieuwe kaart van de Grootbrittannische volkplantingen in Noord America . . . 1755.
" [105] Kaart van het onderkonigschap van Peru . . . Chili . . . Paraguay . . . Brazil . . . in Zuid Amerika . . . 1765.
" [106] Kaart van de Aller-Heiligen baay waar aan de hoofstad legt van Brazil . . .
" [107] Land-kaart van het eiland en de volkplanting van Cayenne . . .
" [108] Landkaart van de volkplantingen Suriname en Berbice. Inset: Plan van de stad Paramaribo.
" [109] Kaart van geheel Guajana of de wildenkust, on de der Spaansche Westindiën . . .

no. [110] Algemeene kaart van de Westindische eilanden . . .
" [111] Het Westindisch eiland Martenique . . .
" [112] Grondvlakte van Nieuw Orleans de hoofstad van Louisiana . . .
" [113] Nieuw kaart van Kanada . . . 1769.
" [114] Quebek, de hoofdstad van Kanada . . .1759.

**1745**

**Renard, L.**

Atlas van zeevaert en koophandel door de geheele weereldt. Vertoonende in bizondere op elkander volgende kaerten, alle deffelfs zeekuften en haevens; met befchryvingen van de natuur, voortbrengfels, hardwerkfels, godsdienften, beftier en koophandel van alle geweften, &c. Voorheen in de franfche taele uytgegeven door den heer Louis Renard . . . En nu alle de kaerten op't naeukeurigfte met hulpe van voornaeme kundigen naer de laetfte ontdekkingen vernieuwt; en een groot getal plaetfen neevens verfcheide nieuwe kaerten daer ingebragt. Door Reinier en Iosua Ottens. De befchryvingen met veele vereifchte zaeken vermeerdert, en naer den tegenwoordigen tydt gefchikt. By de nieuwe kaerten, befchryvingen gevoegt; en met natuurkundige aenmerkingen over de 'sterreen aerdtrykskunde, zeën en winden &c. verrykt. Door Ian van den Bosch Melchiorsz. 5 p. l., 152 pp., 32 col. maps. fol. Amsterdam, R. & I. Ottens, 1745.

601

NOTE.—French edition has title: Atlas de la navigation, et du commerce qui se fait dans toutes les parties du monde . . . 1715. See also titles 559 and 592. Title in red and black.

Full page engraving precedes title page: in the background, a ship in full sail; in the foreground, navigators in colloquy; at the right, on a dais, "Atlas" bearing a globe.

Dedication, to the East India company.

Contains maps by G. Delisle, E. Halley, Jan Bruyst, and N. Witsen.

Latin and dutch titles on many maps.

The following maps relate to America:—

no. [1] Nieuwe en allernaeukeurigfte weereldt-kaert . . .
" [2] Hémisphère Septentrional . . . par G. Delisle.
" [3] Hémisphère Méridional . . . par G. Delisle.
" [4] Nova & accuratissima totius terrarum orbis tabula nautica . . . par Edm: Halley.
" [25] Pafcaert van t'oofter gedeelte van Oost Indien van C. Comorin tot Iapan . . . [Isles de Philepines]
" [26] De groote Zuyd-zee en't eylandt California.
" [27] Novæ Hispaniæ, Chili, Peruviæ et Guatimalæ littoræ . . .
" [28] . . . Americæ Méridionalis . . .
" [29] Littora Brasiliæ . . .
" [30] Terra Neuf, en de cuften van Nieu Vranckryck, Nieu Engeland, Nieu Nederland, Nieu Andalusia, Guiana en Venezuela . . .
" [31] . . . West Indien ende Caribise eylanden.
" [32] De noordelyckfte zee kuften van America . . .

## 1745?

**Moll, H.**

Atlas minor: or, a new and curious set of sixty two maps, in which are shewn all the empires, kingdoms, countries, states, in all the known parts of the earth; with their bounds, divisions, chief cities & towns, the whole composed & laid down agreable to modern history . . . 1 p. l., 60 maps. obl. 8°. London, for T. Bowles & J. Bowles [1745?]    602
[ *With* Templeman, T. A new survey of the globe. obl. 8°. London, for J. Bowles, 1732?]

NOTE.—See also titles 574, 578, 585, and 635. The date 1736 is found on map no. 13, Germany, but owing to the short legend on map no. 47, this edition has been given the date [1745?] as the english held Cape Breton from 1745 to 1748. This map contains additions not found on the 1729, [1732?] and [1736?] editions. The other maps are the same as those in the [1736?] edition.

Templeman's geographical tables were designed to accompany Moll's Atlas minor and were published simultaneously with the 1st ed. in 1729. It was sold either separately or bound with the atlas. This edition with the Bowles imprint is not earlier than 1732.

Imperfect: maps no. 3, 21 wanting:

The following maps relate to America:

no. 1. A new map of the whole world with the trade winds . . . Printed for Thos. Bowles . . . and John Bowles . . . London.
" 2. A map of the North Pole . . . Printed for Tho: Bowles . . . & Iohn Bowles . . .
" 40. Africa . . . [Shows] C. S! Augustin [Brazil]
" 45. America . . .
" 46. A new map of ye north parts of America claimed by France under ye names of Louisiana, Mississippi, Canada & New France, with the adjoyning territories.
" 47. New Found Land, S! Lawrence bay, the fishing banks, Acadia and part of New Scotland . . .
" 48. A description of the bay of Fundy . . . —The harbour of Annapolis Royal by Nathaniel Blackmore esq! Printed and sold by Tho. Bowles . . . & Jn° Bowles . . .
" 49. New England, New York, New Jersey and Pensilvania . . .
" 50. Virginia and Maryland . . .
" 51. Carolina.
" 52. A plan of Port Royal harbour in Carolina . . .
" 53. The island of Bermudo's . . .
" 54. Florida called by ye French Louisiana &c . . .
" 55. A map of the West-Indies &c. Mexico or New Spain . . .
" 56. The Island of Jamaica . . .
" 57. The island of S! Christophers, alias S! Kitts . . .
" 58. [The island of Antego]
" 59. The island of Barbadoes . . . Printed and sold by Tho: Bowles . . . & I. Bowles . . .
" 60. The Scots settlement in America calle'd New Caledonia . . .
" 61. A map of Terra Firma, Peru, Amazoneland, Brasil & the north p. of La Plata . . .
" 62. A map of Chili, Patagonia, La Plata and ye south part of Brasil . . .

## 1747

**Complete, A,** system of geography. Being a description of all the countries, iſland, cities, chief towns, harbours, lakes, and rivers, mountains, mines, &c. of the known world . . . The whole illustrated with seventy maps, by Emanuel Bowen . . . making, of themselves, a complete atlas . . . This work, extracted from ſeveral hundred books of travels and history, is brought down to the preſent time; preſerving all that is useful in the fourth and last edition of The complete geographer, publish'd under the name of Herman Moll, &c. 2 v. fol. London, W. Innys [etc. etc.] 1747.

603

Note.—Collation: v. 1, 1 p. l., iv, xxviii, 1013, [3] pp., 27 maps, 2 pl; v. 2, xi, [1] 804, [24] pp., 41 maps. See title 566, "The compleat geographer . . . 1723."

The following maps relate to America:
v. 1, no. [1] A new & accurate map of all the known world.
v. 2, " 51. A new general map of America.
" " 52. A new & accurate map of Brasil.
" " 53. A new and accurate map of Paraguay, Rio de la Plata, Tucumania Guaria &c.
" " 54. A new and accurate map of Chili, Terra Magellanica, Terra del Fuego &c.
" " 55. A new and accurate map of Peru, and the country of the Amazones.
" " 56. A new and accurate map of Terra Firma and the Caribbe islands.
" " 57. A new & accurate map of Mexico or New Spain together with California New Mexico &c.
" " 58. A new and accurate map of Louisiana, with part of Florida and Canada.
" " 59. A new & accurate map of the provinces of North and South Carolina Georgia &c.
" " 60. A new and accurate map of Virginia & Maryland.
" " 61. A new and accurate map of New Jersey, Pensylvania, New York and New England.
" " 62. A new & accurate map of the islands of Newfoundland, Cape Breton, S$^t$. John and Anticosta.
" " 63. Particular draughts and plans of some of the principal towns and harbours belonging to the english, french, and spaniards in America and West Indies.
" " 64. A new & accurate map of Bermudas or Sommer's islands.—An accurate map of the island of S$^t$. Christopher.
" " 65. A new & accurate map of the island of Cuba.—A new & accurate map of the islands of Hispaniola.
" " 66. A new & accurate map of the island of Jamaica.
" " 67. A new & accurate map of the island of Antigua.
" " 68. An accurate map of the West Indies.
" " 69. An accurate map of the island of Barbadoes.
" " 70. A new & accurate map of the North Pole.
" " 71. A map of old Greenland.

**1747-1757**

**Homann** heirs.

Homannifcher atlas von hundert landkarten darinne die erdkugel mit allen ihren theilen geographisch vorgeftellet und nach dem unterfchied der reiche und staaten deutlich illuminiret warden. Nebft einer einleitung in die mathematifche, natûrliche und hiftorische geographie. 2 p. l., 40 pp., 95 col. maps, 3 tab. fol. Nûrnberg, in verlag der Homannifchen erben, 1747-[1757] 604

NOTE.—Map no. 75, Carte des états de la covronne de Pologne . . . par Tob. Mayer, dated 1757.

Imperfect: no. 2, Systema Copernicanum, and no. 31, Saxon. Super. p. boreal, wanting.

Maps by various cartographers including: Lowitz, Hasius, Vissher Delisle, Valk, Nolin, S. Tillemon, Mayer, d'Anville.

no. 79, Ingermanlandiæ seu Ingriæ . . . contains an inset view of St. Petersburg.

no. 91, Statuum Marocca Norum . . . contains inset views of Morocco and Mequinez.

The following maps relate to America:
no. 3. Mappe-monde . . . 1746.
" 93. Americae mappa generalis . . . 1746.
" 94. Regni Mexicani . . .
" 95. Dominia Anglorum in America Septentrionali.
" 96. Tabula Americæ specialis geographica regni Peru, Brasiliæ, Terræ Firmæ & reg: Amazonum.
" 97. Typus geographicus Chili Paraguay Freti Magellanici &c. 1733. Inset: Plan de la ville de Santiago . . .

**1748?**

**Valck, G.**

Nova totius geographica telluris projectio. 1 p. l., 141 maps, 4 pl. fol. Amstelodami [1748?] 605

NOTE.—Engraved title-page, colored. Thirty-two maps are pasted four on a page.

Date on map no [62], Belli ab obitu Caroli VI. Imperatoris usqve ad pacem Dresdæ d. 25 dec. 1745. Facem tam in Germania quam Belgio ob succefsionem Avstriacam gefti theatrvm geographice delineatum a L. I. Krausio . . . 1748.

Maps by various cartographers including: Homann, Visscher, de Wit, Schenk, Schuchart, Leonard Valk, Casimirus, Flandro, Cóvens, Mortier, Nolin, Abraham and Carlo Allard, Delisle, Joan Blaeu, Sanson, Fer, Petty, Jaillot, Coronelli, Gerard van Keulen, Müller, and Kraus.

The following maps relate to America:
no. [5] Planisphærum terrestre . . . auctore Carolo Allard.
" [127] Recentissima Novi orbis sive Americæ Septentrionalis et Meridionalis tabula. Per Caroli Allard.
" [129] L'Amérique Méridionale . . . Par G. De Lisle.
" [132] Carte de la Terre Ferme du Pérou du Brésil et du pays des Amazones . . . Par Guillaume Del 'Isle.
" [133] Carte du Paraguay, du Chili, du détroit de Magellan . . . Par Guillaume De l'Isle.
" [134] Nova et accurata Brasiliæ totius tabula. Auctore Ioanne Blaev.
" [135] Insulæ Americanæ in Oceano Septentrionali ac regiones adiacentes. Per Nicolaum Visscher.

## 1748

**English pilot, The.** The third book. Describing the sea-coafts, capes, headlands, straights, soundings, sands, shoals, rocks and dangers. The iflands, bays, roads, harbours and ports in the oriental navigation; shewing the property and nature of the winds and monfoons in thofe seas; with the courfes and diftances from one place to another: The setting of the tides and currents; the ebbing and flowing of the sea. Also, a new table of variations; and a correct table of longitudes and latitudes. With many other things neceffary to be known. Being furnished with new and exact large draughts of ports, iflands, and defcriptions; gathered from the practice and experience of divers able and expert navigators of our englifh nation. Divided into three parts. The first part, shewing the nature and properties of the winds and monsoons in the navigation from England to the East Indies, and all over the oriental ocean; and thereby how to fhape a courfe from one port to another, according to the time of the year in thofe seas. The second part, containing neceffary instructions for sailing between England and the East Indies in the spring and fall. The third part, defcribing the seacoafts, capes, headlands, straights, soundings, sands, shoals, rocks and dangers. The iflands, bays, roads, harbours and ports, from cape Bona-Esperance, all over the oriental ocean, being very much corrected and augmented with several additions, not heretofore publifh'd. Collected for the general benefit of our own countrymen. 70 pp., 41 maps. fol. London, for W. & J. Mount & T. Page, 1748.

606

NOTE.—Map no. 1, A new map of the world . . . H. Moll, fecit.
  no. 7. A correct chart of the coast of Portugal & Barbaria. By C. Price.
  " 21. A new map of the island of Bambay and Sallset. By Sam$^l$. Thornton.
  " 29. A new and correct chart . . . from p. Palmiras to Calcutta . . . By Tho. Greg. Warren surv$^r$. William Wood, pilot.
  " 30. A mapp of the great river Ganges as it emptieth itself into the bay of Bengalia [By Sam$^l$. Thornton]
  " 38. A large draught of the north part of China . . . By Sam$^l$. Thornton.
  " 41. A draught of the coast of New Holland. By Sam$^l$. Thornton.

## 1748

**Le Rouge, G. L.**

Atlas nouveau portalif . . . à l'usage des militaires et du voyageur contenant 91 cartes dressées sur les nouvelles observations. Dédié à monseigneur le comte de Maurepas . . . 2 p. l., vi, [2], 36, [2] pp., 87 maps. 8°. Paris, Le Rouge [1748]

607

NOTE.—Engraved title.
A new edition was published in 1756. See also title 618.
Title-page preceding text reads: Introduction à la géographie, par le sieur Le Rouge . . . Paris . . . 1748.

**Le Rouge, G. L.**—Continued.

The date 1748, on several of the maps, appears to have been changed from 1740.

Contains the following plan:

no. 49. Plan de Paris et de ses faubourgs dedié à m. de Bernage . . . 1748.

The following maps relate to America:

no. 4. Mappe monde. 1748.
" 8. L'Amérique Septentrionale.
" 9. Amérique Méridionale.
" 83. Isles Philippines.
" 84. Isle de S$^t$. Dominque.
" 85. Isle de la Martinique.
" 86. Antigue, une des Antilles.
" 87. La Jamaique.—La Bermude.
" 88. Isle S$^t$. Christophle.—La Barbade.

## 1748–1749

**Robert de Vaugondy, G.**

Atlas portatif, universel et militaire, composé d'après les meilleurs cartes, tant gravées que manuscrites, des plus célèbres géographes et ingénieurs. 3 p. l., 209 maps. obl. 8°. Paris, l'auteur; Durand; Pissot fils, 1748–[1749]     608

NOTE.—Engraved title. Many maps are by Robert de Vaugondy the son, and dated 1749.

The following maps relate to America:

no. [2] Mappe monde . . . 1748.
" 184. Amérique Septentrionale . . . 1748.
" 185. Partie du Mexique . . . Par le s$^r$. Robert de Vaugondy fils . . . 1749.
" 186. Partie du Mexique . . . Par le s$^r$. Robert de Vaugondy fils . . . 1749.
" 187. Partie du Mexique . . . Par le s$^r$. Robert de Vaugondy fils . . . 1749.
" 188. Cours du Mississipi et la Louisiane. Par le s$^r$. Robert de Vaugondy fils . . . 1749.
" 189. La Floride divisée en Floride et Caroline. Par le s$^r$. Robert de Vaugondy fils . . . 1749.
" 190. Les Isles Antilles. Par le s$^r$. Robert de Vaugondy fils . . . 1749.
" 191. L'isle S$^t$. Domingue. Par le s$^r$. Robert de Vaugondy fils. 1749.
" 192. L'isle de la Martinique. Par le s$^r$. Robert de Vaugondy fils . . . 1749.
" 193. Les lacs du Canada et Nouvelle Angleterre. Par le s$^r$. Robert de Vaugondy fils . . . 1749.
" 194. Nouvelle Angleterre, N$^{lle}$. York, N$^{lle}$. Jersey Pensilvanie, Mariland et Virginie. Par le s$^r$. Robert de Vaugondy fils . . . 1749.
" 195. Partie du Canada . . . Par le s$^r$. Robert de Vaugondy fils . . . 1749.
" 196. L'Arcadie. Par le s$^r$. Robert de Vaugondy fils . . . 1749.
" 197. Golfe de S$^t$. Laurent, Isle et bancs de Terre Neuve. Par le s$^r$. Robert de Vaugondy fills . . . 1749.
" 198. Isle Royale. Par le s$^r$. Robert de Vaugondy fills . . . 1749.
" 199. Isle de Terre-Neuve. Par le s$^r$. Robert de Vaugondy fils . . . 1749.

no. 200. Bayes d'Hudson et de Baffins, et Terre de Labrador. Par le sr. Robert de Vaugondy fils . . . 1749.
" 201. Amérique Méridionale . . . 1748.
" 202. Partie occidentale de la Terre Ferme. Par le sr. Robert de Vaugondy fils . . . 1749.
" 203. Partie orientale de la Terre Firme . . . Par le sr. Robert de Vaugondy fils . . . 1749.
" 204. Partie septentrionale du Pérou . . . Par le sr. Robert de Vaugondy fils . . . 1749.
" 205. Partie méridionale du Pérou . . . Par le sr. Robert de Vaugondy fils. 1749.
" 206. Le Chili. Par le sr. Robert de Vaugondy fils . . . 1749.
" 207. Les Terres Magellaniques. Par le sr. Robert de Vaugondy fils . . . 1749.
" 208. Le Paraguay. Par le sr. Robert de Vaugondy fils . . . 1749.
" 209. Terre de Sainte Croix nommée à présent Brésil. Par le sr. Robert de Vaugondy fils . . . 1749.

### 1749?

**Schreiber, J. G.**

Atlas selectus von allen königreichen und ländern der welt, zum beqvemen gebrauch in schulen, auf reifen und beij dem lefen der zeitungen verfertiget.   2 p. l., 126 (*i. e.* 127) col. maps, 1 tab. obl. 8°.   Leipzig [1749?] 609

NOTE.—Engraved title-page, colored.
Date 1749 on map no. 125, Gantz Grichenland.
A number of the maps were published by the Schreiber heirs.
Maps not arranged according to index.
Contains the following maps not included in index:
Ober-Hessen, Hessen-Darmstadt und Hessen Rheinfels . . .
Die Aemter Freyberg und Frauenstein . . .
Die Neue-Marck und die Ucker-Marck in der Marck Brandenburg.
The following maps relate to America:
no. 3. Globus terrestris.
" 7. America.
" 8. Chart von dem engellændischen u. franzoesischen besitzungen in Nord America.

### 1749?

Atlas selectus von allen königreichen und ländern der welt, zum beqvemen gebrauch in schulen auf reifen und beij dem lefen der zeitungen verfertiget und in kupffer geftochen.   2 p. l., 44 (*i. e.* 42) col. maps.   8°.   Leipzig [1749?] 610

NOTE.—Engraved title-page, colored.
Title-page and maps all appear in fuller edition of 1749?, see title 609, the date of which is on map no. 125, Gantz Grichenland.
Map no. 32, Eertz-gebûrgifcher creyss, wanting.
The following maps relate to America:
no. 3. Globus terrestris.
" 7. America.

## 1749 ?

Atlas selectus von allen königreicben und ländern der welt, zum beqvemen gebrauch in schulen auf reifen und beij dem lefen der zeitungen verfertiget. 2 p. l., 39 (*i. e.* 38) col. maps. 12°. Leipzig, J. G. Schreibern [1749?]    611

NOTE.—Engraved title-page, colored.
All maps in this edition appear in the fuller edition of 1749?, the date of which is on map no. 125, Gantz Grichenland; also in the edition of 44 maps, to which the date 1749? has been given.
At the foot of the title-page the words, "C. G. Foerster, 1778," are printed in red. This is probably the name of an owner of the atlas.
The following maps relate to America:
no. 3. Globus terrestris.
" 7. America.

## 1749

**Brouckner, I.**

Nouvel atlas de marine composé d'une carte générale, et de cartes particulières qui représentent le globe terrestre jusqu'au 82° degré du côté du nord, et jusqu'au 60° du côté du sud. Le tout dressé sur les observations les plus nouvelles et les plus approuvées . . . 12 maps. fol. Berlin, 1749.    612

NOTE.—Title of atlas on map no. [4], Carte marine de la mer glaciale . . . "Avertiffement fur l'atlas de marine", 3 l., map, pl. 12°. inserted before map no. [1]
no. [1] Carte générale du globe terrestre. Publish'd according to act of parliament by John Rocque.
The following maps relate to America:
no. [5] Carte marine de la b. de Baffin et une partie d'Hudson, d'Island et Groenland. 1749.
no. [7] Carte marine entre Californie et une partie de l'Asie la plus orientale. 1749.
no. [8] Carte marine de l'Amérique Septentrionale et une partie de la b° d'Hudson. 1749.
no. [12] Carte marine de l'Amérique Méridionale. 1749.

## 1751

**Bellin, J. N.**

Atlas maritime ou recueil des cartes réduites dressées au dépost des cartes et plans de la marine, pour le service des vaisseaux du roi. Par ordre du ministère . . . 1751. 1 p. l., 22 maps. fol. [Paris] 1751.    613

NOTE.—Engraved title-page. F. Boucher, invenit. F. A. Aveline, sculpsit. Beneath title: Quos ego. Sed motos præstat componere fluctus: Eneid. Virg. lib. 1.

CONTENTS.

no. [1] Les parties connuees du globe terrestre. 1748.
" 2. Carte réduite des mers du nord. 1751.
" 3. Carte réduite de l'ocean occidental. 1742.
" 4. Carte réduite de l'ocean-méridional. 1739.

no. 5. Carte réduite de l'océan-oriental. 1740.
" 6. Carte réduite des mers comprises entre l'Asie et l'Amérique. 1742.
" 7. Nouvelle carte réduite de la Manche. 1749.
" 8. Carte réduite du golphe de Gascogne. 1750.
" 9. Carte réduite des costes d'Espagne et de Portugal. 1751.
" 10. Carte générale de la coste de Guinée. 1750.
" 11. Carte particulière de la coste d'Or. 1750.
" 12. Carte réduite du golphe du Mexique. 1749.
" 13. Carte réduite de l'isle de Saint Domingue. 1750.
" 14. Carte réduite de la mer Méditerranée. 1737.
"15-16. Noms de quelques isles comprises entre le méridien de Gênes et celuy de Candie.
" 17. Carte réduite de l'Archipel. 1738.
" 18. Carte des isles de Maiorque, Minorque et Yvice. 1740.
" 19. Nouvelle carte de l'isle de Corse. 1749.
" 20. Partie orientale de la Nouvelle France. 1745.
" 21. Partie occidentale de la Nouvelle France. 1745.
" 22. Carte de la Louisiane. 1750.

## 1752

**Bowen, E.**

A complete atlas or distinct view of the known world; exhibited in sixty-eight maps ... in which the latitude and longitude of the principal places ... are laid down ... 4 pp., 69 maps. fol. London, for W. Innys [etc.] 1752. 614

CONTENTS.

no. 1. ... Chart of the world ... 1744 ...
" 2. ... A new and accurate map of all the known world ...
" 3. ... Europe ...
" 4. ... Great Brit. and Ireland ...
" 5. ... England and Wales ...
" 6. ... Scotland ...
" 7. ... Ireland ...
" 8. ... France ... Inset: The harbour of Brest. ... Toulon ...
" 9. ... Spain and Portugal ... Inset: The harbour of Port Mahon.
" 10. ... Portugal ...
" 11. ... Netherlands, or Low Countries ...
" 12. ... Seven United Provinces ...
" 13. ... Germany divided into its circles ...
" 14. ... South west part of Germany ... Inset: ... Plans of old and new Brisach.
" 15. ... South east part of Germany ...
" 16. ... North east part of Germany ... Inset: A plan of the city of Breslaw.
" 17. ... North west part of Germany ...
" 18. ... Switzerland ... Inset: A new plan of the city of Geneva.
" 19. ... Savoy and Piedmont ... Inset: A plan of Coni.
" 20. ... Italy ... Inset: A draught of the eruption of Mt. Ætna in 1669 &c.—Mt. Vesuvius ...
" 21. ... Northern parts of Italy ... —A draught of the road of Leghorn.
" 22. ... Naples and Sicily ...

**Bowen, E.**—Continued.
- no. 23. . . . Scandinavia . . .
- " 24. . . . Denmark . . .
- " 25. . . . Sweden . . .
- " 26. . . . Moscovy . . .
- " 27. . . . Poland, Lithuania. &c. . . .
- " 28. . . . Hungary and . . . Transilvania . . .
- " 29. . . . Turkey in Europe . . .
- " 30. . . . Islands of the Archipelago together with the Morea, and the neighbouring counties in Greece . . .
- " 31. . . . Asia . . .
- " 32. . . . Turkey in Asia, Arabia &c.
- " 33. . . . Anatolia . . . with Syria and such other provinces of the Turkish Empire as border thereon . . .
- " 34. . . . Asia Minor . . .
- " 35. . . . The Holy Land . . .
- " 36. . . . Caspian sea . . .
- " 37. . . . Persia . . .
- " 38. . . . Russian empire . . .
- " 39. . . . China . . .
- " 40. . . . Japan . . .
- " 41. . . . Empire of the Great Mogul . . .
- " 42. . . . East India islands . . .
- " 43. . . . Africa . . .
- " 44. . . . Nubia & Abissinia.
- " 45. . . . Barbary . . .
- " 46. . . . Negroland and . . . upper Guinea . . .
- " 47. . . . Southern parts of Africa . . .
- " 48. . . . African islands . . .
- " 49. . . . America . . .
- " 50. . . . Brasil . . .
- " 51. . . . Paraguay, Rio de la Plata, Tucumania Guaria &c. . . .
- " 52. . . . Chili, Terre Magellanica, Terra del Fuego &c. . . .
- " 53. . . . Peru and the country of the Amazones.
- " 54. . . . Terra Firma and the Caribbe islands . . .
- " 55. . . . West Indies . . .
- " 56. . . . Mexico, or New Spain, together with California, New Mexico &c. . . .
- " 57. . . . Louisiana, with part of Florida, and Canada . . .
- " 58. . . . North and South Carolina, Georgia &c. . . .
- " 59. . . . Virginia & Maryland . . .
- " 60. . . . New Jersey, Pensilvania, New York and New England . . .
- " 61. . . . Newfoundland, Cape Briton [!] St. John and Anticosta . . . Nova Scotia, Canada &c. . . .
- " 62. . . . Bermudas . . . St. Christopher . . .
- " 63. . . . Cuba . . . Hispaniola . . .
- " 64. . . . Jamaica . . .—. . . Harbour of Port Antonio & St. Francis . . . —Port Royal or Kingston harbour.
- " 65. . . . Maps of . . . Antigua . . .
- " 66. . . . Towns and harbours . . . in America and West Indies . . .
- " 67. . . . Barbadoes . . .
- " 68. . . . North Pole . . .
- " 69. . . . Greenland . . .

## 1754

**Homann** heirs.
Beqvemer hand atlas avs sechs vnd zwanzig Homannischen landkarten nach der vorfchrifft des Hübnerifchen musei geographici no. 2 zum gebrauch der Hübnerifchen geographifchen fragen alfo eingerichet a. 1754 . . . 2 p. l., 26 col. maps, 1 pl. fol. [Nuremberg, Homann heirs] 1754.  615

> Note.—Maps, dated 1736–1799, are from various authors including J. B. Homann, Lowitz, Hasius, Güssefeld, Lopez, T. Mayer and Rizzi-Zannoni.
>
> Engraved, colored title reads: Atlas novus terrarum orbis imperia regna et status exactis tabulis geographicè demonstrans opera Iohannis Baptistæ Homanni . . . Noribergæ.
>
> The following maps relate to America:
> no. [1] Planiglobii terrestris mappa universalis . . . a G. M. Lowizio. 1746.
> " [5] Charte von America . . . von Güssefeld. 1796.

## 1756?

**Ottens, R.,** *and* **Ottens, J.**
Atlas minor sive geographia compendiosa in qva orbis terrarum pavcis attamen novissimis tabvlis ostenditvr.—Atlas nouveau, contenant toutes les parties du monde, où font exactement remarquées les empires, monarchies, royaumes, états, républiques, &c, &c, &c. Receuillies des meilleurs auteurs. 2 p. l., 42 maps, 7 pl. fol. Amsterdam [1756?]  616

> Note.—See also title 522. The first title-page is the much used copper plate of "Atlas" mounted on the globe supporting the heavens, and carries the word "Atlas" at the top. The second title is the Ottens' title-page with their name and the date omitted, and without the small engraving by F. Ottens at the foot of the page, which appears on other copies of this title-page.
>
> Maps by various cartographers, including: Theodore, Justus and Cornelius Danckerts, de Wit, Placide, Delisle, Jaillot, Feuille Joachim Ottens and Sanson.
>
> Maps by the Danckerts are evidently of an earlier date than the others.
>
> Maps by Delisle are preceded by a plate carrying the following title: Grand thèatre de la guerre sur les frontières de France & d'Allemagne ou carte nouvelle du cours du Rhin . . . This plate contains plans of the fortifications of eight towns on the Rhine, and an engraving of the siege of Philipsbourg which occurred in 1734.
>
> Two maps entitled, "Theatrum belli á 1737 a milite Augustæ Russorum imperatricis adversus Turcas Tattarosque gesti ex autographis in Acad. scient: Petropol" . . . and " Verus Chersonesi Tauricæ seu Crimea conspectus adjacentium item regionum itineris q, ab exercitu Rutheno á 1736 et 1737 aduersus Tattaros susceptis editus ex autographis Carolia Frauendorff centurionis in Acad. sc. Petropolit . . ."
>
> Map no. [47], Insulæ Americanæ . . . has on the margin the title, "Stoel des oorlogs in America waar in vertoont werden alle desself voornaamste eylande nieuwelycks uytgegeven door Reinier & Josua Ottens," which shows that this map was issued to illustrate the war between the french and british which began in 1756.

**Ottens, R., *and* Ottens, J.**—Continued.

The following maps relate to America:

    no. [ 2] Nova terrarum orbis tabula. a. T. Danckerts.
    " [46] Recentissima novi orbis sive Americæ Septentrionalis et Meridionalis tabula per I. Danckerts.
    " [47] Insulæ Americanæ . . .
    " [48] Nova Isthmi Americani . . .

### 1756?

Atlas sive geographia compendiosa in qva orbis terrarum pavcis attamen novissimis tabvlis ostenditvr.—Atlas nouveau, contenant toutes les parties du monde, où sont exactement remarquées les empires, monarchies, royaumes, états, républiques, &c., &c. &c. Receuillies des meilleurs auteurs. En deux tomes. Tome premier. 2 p. l., 1 l., 114 maps, 1 pl., 3 tab. fol. Amstelædami, R. & J. Ottens [1756?] 617

    NOTE.—Map no. 4, Halley's map of the world, is accompanied by one leaf of explanatory text in dutch, signed by the author; no. 5 has upon the margin a copy of a letter written by Swartz, printed in both french and dutch, and dated "St. Petersburg den $\frac{13}{24}$ january, 1740." On the margin of map no. 116, "Insulæ Americanæ," is the title "Stoel des oorlogs in America waarin vertoont werden alle desself voornaamste eylande nieuwelycks uytgegeven door Reinier & Josua Ottens," which shows that this map was issued to illustrate the war between the french and british which began in 1756.
Map no. 95, "Imperivm Japonicvm . . . descriptvm ab Hadriano Relando," was originally published in "Recueil de voyages au Nord." Amst. 1713-1738.
Map no. 96, "Het koninkryk Japan . . . door Joh: Casp: Scheuchzer," is based upon the maps of Engelbert Kæmpfer, originally published in his "De beschryving van Japan, 1729."
Map no. 93 dated 1739.
Many of the maps are ornamented with coats-of-arms, views, etc.
Title-page engraved by "I. van Munnikhuyse," and colored by "L. Webbers."
Tab. 8, "L'Europe représentée par la géographie naturelle et historiqve et par le blazon des monarques, des princes, des républiques, &c." Contains a small map of Europe. Tab. 35, "Kort begryp van Duytsland . . ." by C. Specht. Contains a small map of Germany. Tab. 52 is a "Description historiqve et géographiqve (très redvite) fur les xvii provinces des Pais-Bas. Par Henry de Sagvliers." Pl. 118 is a "Nieuwe tafel van alle de scheeps vlaggen des gehelē water-waerelds," by I. Hasebroek. Title in dutch, english and french.
In addition to those by Ottens, the atlas contains maps by the following authors and engravers: Covens, de Leth, Delisle, de Wit, Fricx, Haas, Halley, Halma, Homan, Iaillot, Loon, Mortier, Pynacker, Reland, Sanson, Schenk, Specht, Starkenburg, Valk, van Keulen, Visscher, Voogt, Zürner, Anse, Broeck, Broen, Goerê, Gouwen, Hogeboom, Keyser, Moll and Ruyter.
The following maps relate to America:

    no. 3. Planisphærium terrestre. Opera A. F. Zürneri ex officine Petri Schenkii in Platea vulgo.
    " 4. Nova & accuratissima totius terrarum orbis tabula nautica. Per Edm. Halley [1739]
    " 5. Hémisphère Septentrional. Par G. Delisle [1740]

no. 6. Hémisphère Méridional. Par G. Delisle [1739]
" 113. Americæ . . . delineatio. Opera A. F. Zürneri.
" 114. Amérique Septentrionale. Par H. Iaillot.
" 115. L' Amérique Méridionale. Par H. Iaillot.
" 116. Insulæ Americanæ [1756?]
" 117. Carte nouvelle de la Mer du Sud. Par And. & Henry de Leth [1730?]

### 1756–1759

**Le Rouge, G. L.**
Atlas nouveau portatif à l'usage des militaires collèges et du voyageur . . .   2 v.   8°.   Paris, Le Rouge [1756]–1759.   618

NOTE.—Collation: v. 1, vi, [1], 36 pp., 90 maps on 180 l., 2 pl.; v. 2, viii, 20 pp., 100 maps on 202 l. See title 607.
Engraved title.
Printed title of v. 1 reads: Introduction à la géographie.  Preface of v. 2, states that v. 1 is an introduction to geography in general.
Title of v. 2 reads: Atlas portatif des militaires et des voyageurs.   1759.
The following maps relate to America:
v. 1, no. 4. Mappe-monde . . .
"   "   8. Amérique Septrionale.
"   "   9. Amérique Méridionale.
"   "   83. Isles Philippines.
"   "   84. Isle de Saint Domingue.
"   "   85. Isle de la Martinique.
"   "   86. Antique, une des Antilles.
"   "   87. La Jamaique . . .
"   "   88. Isle Saint Christophle, une des Antilles.

### 1757

**Robert de Vaugondy, G.,** *and* **Robert de Vaugondy, D.**
Atlas universal, par m. Robert, géographe ordinaire du roy et par m. Robert de Vaugondy son fils, géographe ord. du roy et de s. m. polonoise duc de Lorraine et de Bar, et associé de l'académie royale des sciences et belles lettres de Nancy.   Avec privilège du roy. 1757.   2 p. l., 40 pp., 108 maps.   fol.   Paris, chez les auteurs; Boudet, 1757–[1758]   619

NOTE.—Engraved title. See also title 678.
Map no. 104, "Carte du royaume de France où sont tracées exactement les routes des postes," dated 1758. An earlier edition of this atlas was published in 1752.
The following maps relate to America:
no. 1. Orbis vetus . . .
" 97. Amérique Septentrionale . . . 1750.
" 98. Partie de l'Amérique Septent? qui comprend la Nouvelle France . . . 1755.
" 99. Partie de l'Amérique Septentrionale qui comprend le cours de l'Ohio . . . 1755.
" 100. Carte de la Virginie et du Maryland . . . 1755.
" 101. Amérique Méridionale . . . 1750.
" 102. Partie de la mer du nord où fe trovent les grandes et petites isles Antilles . . . 1750.
" 103. Isles de Saint Domingue . . . 1750.

## 1757-1758

**Robert de Vaugondy, G.**, *and* **Robert de Vaugondy, D.**—Continued.
—Same.   2 p. l., 34 pp., 108 maps.   fol.   Paris, chez les auteurs; Boudet, 1757–[1758]   620

> NOTE.—Map no 92, "Carte de l'Asie," dated 1751.
> Same map in copy no. 1, dated 1750.
> pp. 34–40 wanting.

## 1758

**Gibson, J.**

Atlas minimus, or a new set of pocket maps of the several empires, kingdoms and states of the known world, with historical extracts relative to each.   Drawn and engrav'd by J. Gibson, from the best authorities, revis'd, corrected and improv'd by Eman: Bowen, geographer to his majesty.   3 p. l., front., 52 maps, [1] l.   sm. 32°.   London, J. Newberry, 1758.   621

> NOTE.—Engraved frontispiece. See also titles 676 and 691.
> The following maps relate to America:
> no. 5. North America.
> " 6. South America.
> " 39. Nova Scotia.
> " 40. New England.
> " 41. New York and Pensilvania.
> " 42. Pensilvania, Maryland and Virginia.
> " 43. The english and french settlements in N$^{th}$ America.
> " 44. Carolina and Georgia.
> " 45. Newfoundland.
> " 46. Island of Cape Breton.
> " 47. West Indies.
> " 48. Canada or New France.
> " 49. Mexico or New Spain.
> " 50. Brasil.
> " 51. Paraguay and Tucuman.
> " 52. Peru.

## 1759-1781

**Homann** heirs.

Atlas geographicvs maior exhibens tellurem seu globum terraqueum in mappis generalibus & specialibus per Iohannem Baptistam Homannvm ejusque heredes editis.   Praemiſsa introductione geographica mathematico-phyſico-historico . . .   2 v.   fol.   Norimbergae, curantibus Homannianis heredibus, 1759–[1781]   622

> NOTE.—Copy no. 1. Collation: v. 1, 3 p. l., 38 pp., 150 (*i. e.* 139) col. maps on [292] l., 1 tab.; v. 2, 4 p. l., 20 pp., [2] l., 125 (*i.e.* 123) col. maps on [282] l., 1 tab. Dates on maps vary from 1696–1781.
> First engraved title-pages read: Atlas Homannianvs mathematico-historice delineatus. I. Iust. Preisler del. 1762.
> Title varies, v. 2 reads: Atlas Germaniae specialis . . . Opus inceptum a Ioh. Bapt. Homanno, et ad hunc usque diem ab Homannianis heredibus studiose continuatum.   Appellatum alias, tomvs secvndvs Atlantis maioris. Norimbergae, prostat in officina Homanniana, 1753.
> In v. 1, maps nos. 46–47, Historia belli in Italia, 1746, have border text.

Maps are by various cartographers including: Hasius, Nolin, Petit, Beaurain, Rizzi-Zannoni, Ruperto Carl, Delisle, Majer, Pejer, Walser, Boehmius, Barnikel, Harenbergh, Velarde, Lowitz, Bellin, Schatz, Wheler, Müller, Zollman, Cnopf, Falkenstein, Blaettner, Pronner, Gigas and Visscher.

Wanting:
v. 1, no. 2. Planiglob. fec. relig.
" " 4. Europa " "
" " 7. Hispania Benedict.
" " 48. Sabaudia f. Lombardiae.
" " 137. America fec. relig.
v. 2, " d. Matricula imperii.
" " 2. Germania fecundum provincias. 2 sheets.
" " 4. Germania fecundum religiones. 1 sheet.
" " 7. Germania hydrographia.
" " 55. Wimarienfis Ducatus. 1 sheet.
" " 125. Expeditiones bellicae in Germania post annum 1741. 2 sheets.

Contained in atlas but not called for by index:
v. 1. Potentissimæ Helvetiorum reipublicæ cantones tredecim cum foederatis et subjectis provinciis exhibiti a Joh. Baptista Homanno. Noribergæ.— Tabula ad Geographiam Hübnerianam recentisfime recognita nec minus passim anota et religionum simul diftinctione illustrata per Homannianos heredes. Anno 1732.
" 2. Circvlvs Bvrgvndicvs . . . editus à Homannianis heredib. A°. 1747.

The following maps relate to America:
v. 1, no. 1. Planiglobii terrestris . . . defignata a G. M. Lowizio . . . 1746.
" " 129–130. Carte hydrographique & chorographique des Isles Philippines . . . Dreffée par le r. père Pierre Murillo Velarde . . . à Manille 1734 . . . Tirée de l'original, et réduite George Maurice Lowitz . . . Nuremberg l'an 1750. Publiée par les héritiers de Homann l'an 1760.
" " 136. Americae mappa generalis . . . delineata ab Aug. Gottl. Boehmio . . . 1746.
" " 138. America Septentrionalis a domino d'Anville . . . 1777.
" " 139. Ampliffimæ regionis Mississipi . . . edita a Io. Bapt. Homanno . . .
" " 140. Nova Anglia . . . à Ioh. Baptista Homann . . .
" " 141. Dominia Anglorum in America Septentrionali specialibus mappis Londini primum a Mollio edita, nunc recufa ab Homannianis hered.
" " 142. Dominia Angloriun in præcipuis infulis Americæ . . .
" " 143. Virginia, Marylandia et Carolina in America Septentrionali . . . à Ioh. Bapt. Homann . . .
" " 144. . . . Indiae occidentalis . . .
" " 145. Partie orientale de la Nouvelle France ou du Canada. Par m.̣ Bellin . . . 1755.
" " 146. Partie occidentale de la Nouvelle France ou du Canada. Par m.̣ Bellin . . . 1755.
" " 147. Regni Mexicani . . . exhibita a Ioh. Baptista Homanno . .
" " 148. Tabula Americæ specialis geographica regni Peru, Brasiliæ, Terræ Firmæ & reg: Amazonum . . .
" " 149. Typus geographicus Chili Paraguay Freti Magellanici &c. . . . à Guiliel. de l'Islio defcripta . . . 1733.
" " 150. Carte de l'isle de la Martinique dressée par m.̣ Bellin . . . 1762.

## 1759-1784

**Homann** heirs—Continued.

Atlas geographicvs maior exhibens tellurem seu globum terraqueum in mappis generalibus & specialibus per Iohannem Baptistam Homannvm ejusque heredes editis. Praemifsa introductione geographica mathematico-phyfico-historica . . . 2 v. in 4. fol. Norimbergae, curantibus Homannianis heredibus, 1759-[1784] 623

NOTE.—Copy no. 2. Dates on maps vary from 1728-1784.

v. 1. Contains title and engraved title as in copy no. 1, together with an engraved portrait of Johann Baptist Homann, not in copy no. 1. The "Einleitung zur geographie" in 38 pp., and the index are wanting.

"Atlas novus reipublicae Helveticae . . . 1769," consisting of title and 20 maps, forms part of v. 1, and includes maps nos. 67-69 called for by index of copy 1.

v. 2. Contains title and "Allegemeine einleitung zu dem special-atlas von Deutfchland . . . 1777" title and 20 pages, as in copy no. 1, but lacks engraved title and index.

"Atlas regni Bohemiae . . . 1776" consisting of title and 15 maps, forms part of v. 2, and includes maps nos. 10-12.

Wanting:

v. 1, no. 4. Europa sec. relig.
" " 86. Scandinavia.
" " 100. Borufsia.
" " 107. Rufsia imperium.
" " 111. Tartaria minor.
" " 132. Africa sec. relig.
" " 137. America " "
v. 2, " 2. Germania fecundum provincias. 2 sheets.
" " 4. Germania fecundum religiones. 1 sheet.

Copy no. 2 contains the following wanting in copy no. 1:

v. 1, no. 7. Hispania Benedict.
" " 48. Sabaudia f. Lombardiae.
v. 2, " 6. Germania hydrographica.
" " 60. Brandenburg: Marchion.
" " 95. Expeditio belli Rhenani ad Philippb.
" " 119. Meklenburg: Duc.
" " 125. Expeditiones bellicae in Germania post annum, 1741.

Maps no. 28, "Magna Brittannia," no. 84, "Morea," no. 137, "America Septentrionalis, 1756," in v. 1, and no. 45, "Circuli super. Saxoniae pars meridionalis," in v. 2, show alterations.

In addition to maps relating to America in copy no. 1, this copy contains: v. 1, "Neue weltkarte . . . 1784;" and v. 2, "Nouvelle carte des découvertes faites par des vaisseaux russiens aux côtes inconnues de l'Amérique Septentrionale avec les pais adiacents . . . À S$^t$. Pétersbourg, à l'académie impériale des sciences, 1758."

Following is a list of maps and plates appearing in copy no. 2, not called for by index of copy no. 1, many of which are undoubtedly inserted:

In v. 1, pt. 1:

no. [3] Sphærarvm artificialivm typica repræsentatio . . .
" [4] Schematismvs geographiae mathematicae . . . 1753.

Nouvelle méthode de géographie ou voiage du monde par les villes les plus confidérables de la terre ou par un jeu . . . Paris, Crépy, 1718.

no. [ 5] Neue welt-karte . . . Nürnberg, Homannifchen erben, 1784.
" [11] Regnorum Hispaniæ et Portvgalliæ . . . per d. T. Lopez in nonnullis emendavit F. L. Güffefeld. Edentibus Homannianis hæredibus, 1782.
" [13] Sevilla regnum in fuos archiepiscopatos episcopatus et praefecturas divisum per Franciscum Ellobet et Thom. Lopez delineatum aliisque subfidiis emendatum a F. L. Güffefeld. Denuo per Homañianos heredes editium, 1781.
" [14] Castiliæ Novæ pars occidentalis . . . Ex dom. T. Lopez mappis colligavit F. L. Güsfefeld. Norimbergæ apud Homannianos heredes, 1781.
" [15] Castiliæ Novæ pars orientalis . . . ex dom. T. Lopez mappis colligavit F. L. Güffefeld. Norimbergæ, apud Homannianos heredes, 1781.
" [16] Granadæ, Cordovæ et Gienensis regna ex Thomæ Lopezii mappis collegavit F. L. Guffefeld. Norimbergæ, apud Homannianos heredes, 1782.
" [21] Regni Galliæ . . . Per Hermannianos heredes 1741.
" [41] Delineatio ac finitima regio Magnæ Brittaniæ metropoleos Londini . . . à T. Conr. Lotter.
" [52] Brabantiæ Batavæ pars orientalis . . . accuratiffime divisum per Nicolaum Visscher Amst: Bat: . . . Nunc apud Petrum Schenk iunior.
" [53] Brabantiæ Batavæ pars occidentalis . . . per Nicolaum Visscher Amft: Bat: . . . Nunc apud Petrum Schenk iunior.
" [54] Lovaniensis Tetrarchia una cum Arscotano Ducatu . . . per Nic: Visscher Amst: Bat: . . . Nunc apud Petrum Schenk iunior.
" [55] Bruxellensis Tetrarchia . . . per Nicolaum Visscher Amst: Bat: . . . Nunc apud Petr. Schenk iun.
" [56] Tetrarchiæ Antverpiensis pars meridionalis . . . per Nicolaum Visscher Amft: Bat: . . . Nunc apud Petr: Schenk iunior.
" [57] Mechlinia Dominium et Aerschot Ducatus. Auctore Nicolao Visscher. Nunc apud Pet. Schenk iun.
" [58] Tractus inter Sabim et Mosam . . . per Nicolaum Visscher Amft: Bat: . . . Nunc apud Petrum Schenk iunior.
" [59] Leodiensis episcopatus pars septentrionalis . . . per Nicolaum Visscher Amft: Bat: . . . Nunc apud Petrum Schenk iunior.
" [60] Leodiensis episcopatus pars media . . . per Nicolaum Visscher Amft: Bat: . . . Nunc apud Petrum Schenk iunior.
" [63] Kennemaria et Westfrisia vulgo et vernaculé Noord-Holland . . . per Nicolaum Visscher Amft: Bat: . . . Nunc apud Petrum Schenk iunior.
" [64] Hollandiæ pars meridionalior, vulgo Zuyd-Holland. Auctore Nic: Visscher . . . Nunc apud P. Schenk jun.
" [65] Nova totius provinciæ Groningo-Omlandiæ in Belgio tabula. Norimbergæ, edentibus Homannianis heredibus, 1784.
In v. 1, pt. 2:
no. [ 8] Imperii Tvrcici Evropaei terra, in primis Graecia . . . adornavit Ioannes Chriftoph Harenberg . . . Curantibus Homannianis heredibus, 1741.
" [ 9] Mappa geographica Græciæ Septentrionalis hodiernæ . . . Norimbergæ, cura Homannianorum heredum, 1770.
" [10] Græcia Nova et Mare Ægeum f. Archipelagus . . . distinctæ exhibentur, opera et fumtibus Tobiæ Conradi Lotteri geographi Augustæ Vindel.

**Homann** heirs—Continued.
- no. [14] Scandinavia . . . ex tabulis Ioh. Bapt. Homanni Norimbergæ.
- " [27] Tabula Regni Borussiæ, Borussiam orientalem exhibens 1775, F. L. Güffefeld.
- " [28] Borussiæ occidentalis tabula. Impenfis hæredum Homannianorum, 1775.
- " [29] Mappa geographica trivm insularvm in Prvssia, qvae Poloniarvm regi serenissimo paret . . . Iohannes Fridericvs Endersch . . . 1753.
- " [30] Mappa geographica Borvssiam orientalem æque occidentalem . . . a Ioh: Frideric Endersch . . . Elbingæ, 1758.
- " [31] Tabvla geographica episcopatvm Warmiensem in Prvssia . . . Elbingæ, 1755.
- " [32] Prussia accurate descripta a Gafparo Henneberg Erlichenfi.
- " [36] Polonia propria tanquam Regni Polonici . . . per Homannianos heredes, 1772.
- " [37] Tabula geographica continens Despotatus Wallachiæ atque Moldaviæ, Provinciam Bessarabiæ fub clientela Turcica itemque provinciam Polonicam Podoliæ . . . ex Hasianis . . . edita ab Homannianis heredibus, 1769.
- " [38] Lubomeriæ et Galliciæ regni. Tabula geographica impenfis Homannianorum hæredum, 1775.
- " [40] Charte von Russisch Litauen . . . Nürnberg, Homännifchen erben, 1775.
- " [43–45] Totius Imperii Russici . . . per magnam cl. dn. dr. Ant. Frid. Büfching . . . Berol. 1769. 3 sheets.
- " [46] Nouvelle carte des découvertes faites par des vaisseaux russiens aux côtes inconnues de l'Amérique Septentrionale avec les pais adiacents . . . À S! Petersbourg, à l'académie impériale des sciences, 1758.
- " [50] Nova et accurata Tartariæ Europææ seu Minoris . . . manu et fumtibus Matthæi Seutteri . . . Augustæ Vindelicor.
- " [51] Provinciarum Turcico Tartaricarum inter Tanaim Boryfthenem et Bogum fitarum quas duobus añis viz. 1736 et 1737.
- " [52] Carte de la Crimée levée pendant la derniere guerre de 1772 . . . 1776.
- " [55–57] Carte géographique repréfentant la mer Mediterranée . . . Par Tobie Conrad Lotter . . . à Augsbourg, 1770. 3 sheets.
- " [60] Turcia Asiatica . . . Impensis Homannianorum heredum, Norimbergæ, 1771.
- " [64] Terræ Yemen maxima pars . . . Auctore C. Niebuhr. 1771.
- " [76] Le cours entier du grand et fameux Nil . . . par où il passe gravé Tobie Conrad Lotter . . . à Ausbourg.

In v. 2, pt. 1:
- no. [42] Lusatiae inferioris . . . delineata et edita curis Homannianorum heredum. Norimbergæ, anno 1768.
- " [72] Comitatvs Hohnstein . . . Homannianorum heredum a. 1761.
- " [78] Sectio Svperior Thvringiae orientalis . . . Iohannes Wilhelmus Zollmann. Curantibus Homannianis heredibus, a. 1747.
- " [83] Geographische abbildung des gantzen umfangs der marggrafschaft Meissen . . .
- " [84] Comitatvs Schoenburgensis . . . edentibus Homannianis heredibus Norimbergae a. 1760.

pt. 2, no. [ 2] Electoratus Moguntinus . . . Conante Ioh. Bapt. Homanno.
- " " [ 6] Principatus Brandenbvrgico-Cvlmbacensis . . . delineata a Matthaeo Ferdinand: Cnopf et edita cura Homannianorum heredum. a? 1763.

no. [ 8] Mappa geographica exhibens principatvm Brandenbvrgico Onolsbacensem . . . delineata a Matthæo Ferdinand Cnopf et edita cura Homañianorum heredum. 1763.
" [14] Tabula geographica novissima principalis episcopatûs Bambergensis . . . à Matthæo Seuttero . . . Aug. Vind.
" [15] Nova et accuratior repræsentio geographica Sacr. Rom. Imperii episcopatus Würceburgensis . . . impenſis Matthæi Seutteri . . . Augustæ Vind. 1741.
" [16] Episcopatus Aichstettensis . . . à Matthæo Seuttero . . . Aug. Vind.
" [17] Tabulæ geographicæ principatus Brandenburg: Culmb: sive Baruthini pars inferior . . . à Matth. Seutter . . . Aug. Vindel.
" [18] Tabulæ pr:ncipatus Brandenburgico = Culmbacensis sive Baruthini pars superior . . . exhibita à I. A. Riediger . . . sculpta à Matth. Seutter . . . Aug. Vindel.
" [19] Territorii S. Rom. Imp. lib. civitatis Norimbergensis . . . edita ab Alberto Carolo Seuttero . . . Aug. Vind.
" [20] Marchionatus Onoldini . . . nova delineatio geographica ſtudio et opera T. C. Loṭter . . . Aug. Vind.
" [30] Ducatus Wurtenbergici . . . per m. Iohannem Majer . . . opera Ioh. Baptistæ Homanni Noribergæ.
" [60] S. R. I. Principatus Fuldensis in Buchonia . . . à Ioh. Baptista Homanno . . . Noribergæ.
" [67] Charte vom herzogthum Cleve . . . Nürnberg bey denen Homaenniſchen erben, 1777.
" [72] Territorium seculare episcopatvs Monasterii . . . per Homanianos heredes, 1757.
" [73] Episcopatvs Paderborn . . . quem Ioh. Gigas de Paderborn . . . Curantibus Homannianis heredibus. a. 1757.
" [76] Das herzogthum Magdeburg . . . Entworfen von F. L. Güſſefeld und herausgegeben durch die Homænniſchen erben zu Nürnberg. aº 1784.
" [79] Comitatvvm Oldenbvrg et Delmenhorst . . . edita impenſis Homannianorum heredum. a. 1761.
" [83] Ducatus Meklenburgici . . . excudente Io. Baptista Homanno Noribergæ.

**1759-1784**

Atlas geographicvs maior exhibens tellurem seu globum terraqueum in mappis generalibus & specialibus per Iohannem Baptistam Homannvm ejusque heredes editis. Præmiſsa introductione geographica mathematico-phyſico-historico . . .   3 v. fol. Norimbergae, curantibus Homannianis heredibus, 1759-[1784]   624

NOTE.—Copy no. 3. Dates on maps vary from 1729-1784.
This copy is not arranged like either of the other two, but contains with many additions, all maps called for by index, except no. 58, Patrimonium Petri.
Seven maps of v. 2, copy no. 1, also appear:
no. 1. Germania ſecundum circulos.
" 10. Bohemiae regnum.
" 11. Pragenſis circulos.

**Homann** heirs—Continued.

  no. 12. Egranus districtus.
  "  60. Brandenburg: marchion:
  " 115. Brunsvicenf: ducat:
  " 118. Luneburg: ducat:

Several maps are duplicated; and the two maps of Asia nos. 112-113 and one of Africa no. 132, differ from those in copy no. 1.

v. 1. Contains the title and engraved title as in copy no. 1, together with an engraved portrait of J. B. Homann not in copy no. 1, the index, and the "Einleitung zur geographie" in 38 pp.

In addition to pl. e, "Tabula defcript. orbis," called for by index, are found "Orbis in tabula pars secunda," 1 sheet, and "Orbis in tabula," 4 sheets.

v. 2. Contains "Atlas novus reipublicae Heletvicae . . . 1769" consisting of title and 20 maps, no. 67-69 called for by index; and "Atlas regni Bohemiae," consisting of title and 15 maps, which include maps nos. 10-12 of v. 2 in copy no. 1

v. 3. Twelve pages of text have been inserted, entitled: "Tabula synoptica pro mappa Russiæ atque Tartariæ . . . auctore Joh. Matth. Hasio . . . Sumptibus Homanniorum heredum, Noribergæ, 1752;" and 6 pages of text entitled: Africae tabula synoptica . . . auctore Joh. Matth. Hasio . . . Sumptibus Homannianorum, 1737.

In addition to maps relating to America in copies no. 1-2, this copy contains:
v. 3, no. [65] Charte über die xiii Vereinigte Staaten von Nord-America, entworfen durch F. L. Güffefeld und herausgegeben von den Homænhischen erben . . . A? 1784.

  no. [66] Mappa geographica provinciæ Novæ Eboraci ab Anglis New York dictae ex ampliori delineatione ad exactas dimenfiones concinnata in arctius fpatium redacta cura Claudii Josephi Sauthier cui accedit Nova Jersey . . . Norimbergæ sumtibus Homannianor. heredum 1778. 2 sheets.

Twenty-three of the additional maps mentioned in copy no. 2, are found in this copy, together with the following:

  v. 1, no. [21] Mare Mediterranevm . . . projectionis delineatum et editum ab Homannianis heredibvs . . . 1770.
      " [46] Circvlvs Bvrgvndicvs . . . editus à Homannianis heredib9 a? 1747.
" 2, " [71] Gli stati del sommo pontifice chiamati, il Patrimonio di S$^{to}$ Pietro, con insieme il Latio Vecchio et Campagna di Sabina . . . delineata da Matteo Seuttero . . . in Augufta.
      " [ 2] Mappa chorographica omnivm episcopatvvm Germaniae ab ac md ad MDCCLX existentium . . . a Iosepho Harzheim, s. i. excusa studio Homannianorum heredum. Norimbergae a. 1762.
      " [19] Potentissimæ' Helvetiorum reipublicæ cantones tredecim cum foederatis et subjectis provinciis exhibiti a Ioh. Batista Homanno Noribergæ. Tabula ad geographiam Hübnerianam recentisfime recognita nec minus pasfim auota et religionum fimul diftinctione illustrata per Homannianos heredes. Anno 1732.
      " [39] Der fraenkische kreis von F. L. Güffefeld Nürnberg bey denen Homaennischen erben 1782.
      " [42] Grund-rifs der hoch-fürstlichen residentzstat Ansbach oder Onoltzbach.
      " [43] Windsheim . . . herausgegeben von Homaeñifchĕ erben Nürnberg a? 1760.

v. 2, no. [44] Tabula geographica fiftens territorivm liberae Sacri Romani Imperii civitatis Svevo-Hallensis . . . delineata a Mattheo Ferdinand Cnopf et edita cura Homannianorvm heredvm a? 1762.
" [46] Landgraviatus Alsatiae . . . editore Ioh: Baptista Homanno Noribergæ.
" [47] Theatrum belli Saxionia inferiori . . .
" [50] Prospect und grundriss der stadt und universitæt Iena . . . Nürnberg, bey denen Homænn erben, 1766.
" [55] Tractvs Eichsfeldiae . . . Homañianorum heredum a. 1759.
" [56] Der Rhein die Maafs und Mofel . . . durch F. L. Güfsefeld Nürnberg bey denen Homænischen erben, 1783.
" [57] Ducatvs Westphaliae . . . quem aº. zittart, S. I. olim designavit, ftatui recentifsimo correctior reddita, ftudio Homannianorum heredum, 1757.
" 3, " [16] Borussiæ occidentalis tabula a Franc. Ludov. Güffefeld editio emendatior impenfis heredum Homannianorum, 1780.
" [29] Tartariæ maioris . . . exacta opera Ioh. Matthiæ Hasii m. p. p. Impenfis Homannianorum heredum. Norib. a. 1730.
" [35] Asia fecundum legitimas projectionis stereographicæ . . . a Ioh. Matth. Hasio . . . nunc ex beate defuncti fubsidiis et m. s. c. tis defignata a m. Aug. Gottlob Boehmio. Impenfis Homannianorum heredum. A. 1744.
" [38] Accurate vorftellung der orientalifch-kayserliehen haupt-und residenz-stadt Constantinopel . . . herausgegeben von Iohann Baptist Homann . . . Nürnberg.
" [65] Charte über die xiii Vereinigte Staaten von Nord-America, entworfen durch F. L. Güffefeld und herausgegeben von den Homænnischen erben . . . Aº. 1784.
" [66] Mappa geographica provinciæ Novæ Eboraci ab Anglis New-York dictae ex ampliori delineatione ad exactas dimenfiones concinnata in arctius fpatium redacta cura Claudii Josephi Sauthier cui accedit Nova Jersey . . . Norimbergæ sumtibus Homannianor. heredum 1778. 2 sheets.

**1760**

**Euler, L.**

Geographifcher atlas beftehend in 44 land-charten, worauf alle theile des erd-creyses vorgeftellet werden . . .—Atlas geographicus omnes orbis terrarum regiones in xliv tabulis exhibens . . .— Atlas géographique représentant en xliv cartes toutes les régions de la terre . . .    12 pp., 38 col. maps. fol. Berolini, ex officina Michaelis, 1760.    625

NOTE.—Text in german, french and latin.
The following maps relate to America:
no.   1. Mappa geographica utriusque, terræ hemisphærii.
"     2. Tabula geographica utriusque hemisphærii terrestris exhibens declinationem acus magneticæ . . . 1744.
"     3. Tabula geographica hemisphærii borealis.
"     4. "     "     "     australis.
"     5. Mappa-mundi generalis.
"    39. Tab: geogr: Americæ.
"  40–43. Mappa geographica Americæ septentrionalis.
"    44. Tabula geographica partis septentrionalis maris Pacifici.

## 1760-1761

**Du Caille, L. A.**

Étrennes géographiques. 2 v. in 1.   2 p. l., 26 maps; 2 p. l., 31 maps, 1 l.   obl. 32°.   Paris, Ballard, 1760-1761.   626

> NOTE.—Title page of v. 2 reads: Étrennes géographiques, année 1761. Royaume de France, divisé par généralités, subdivisé par élections, diocèses, bailliages &c? Par L. A. Du Caille. Gravé par Lattré. A Paris, chez Ballard . . . All the maps are reduced reproductions of works of the best cartographers. The last page contains the "Privilége du roy" authorizing the printing and publication of this atlas.
> The following maps relate to America:
> v. 1, no. 6. Amérique Septentrionale.
> "    " 7. Amérique Méridionale.

## 1761

**Dury, A.**

A new general and universal atlas, containing forty-five maps . . . engraved by mr. Kitchin & others.   2 p. l., 7 pp., 1 l., 38 maps on 39 l.   obl. 24°.   [London] printed for & sold by A. Dury & R. Sayer, 1761.   627

> NOTE.—See also title 634. Engraved title and dedication.
> The following maps relate to America:
> no. 1. World.
> "   8. North America.
> "   9. South America.
> "  10. Canada.
> "  12. West Indies.

## 1761-1762

**Buy de Mornas, C.**

Atlas méthodique et élémentaire de géographie et d'histoire. 4 v.   fol.   Paris, l'auteur, 1761-62.   628

> NOTE.—Titles vary; v. 2-4 are entitled, "Atlas historique et géographique . . . Paris, l'auteur, 1762. See also title 656.
> The engravings on the title-pages of v. 2-4 are the same, and differ from that of v. 1.
> Maps have ornamental borders.
> Brunet says: Cet ouvrage commencé sur un plan trop vaste n'a pas été terminé, on y trouve quelquefois joint un 5e volume qui n'est autre chose que le mauvais atlas universel publié par Desnos.
> The following maps relate to America:
> v. 1, no. 28. Carte réduite de l'Océan occidental. 1761.
> "    " 38. Amérique. 1761.

## 1762

**Atlas moderne** ou collection de cartes sur toutes les parties du globe terrestre. Par plusieurs auteurs . . .   3 p. l., [1] l., 35 maps, 1 pl.   fol.   Paris, Lattré; J. T. Herissant [1762]   629

> NOTE.—Later editions are dated [1771-1783] and 1787-[1791] See also titles 646 and 664.
> Engraved title.

Maps by Bonne, Janvier and Rizzi-Zannoni.

The "Avertissement" states that the abbé Nicolle de La Croix, before his death, wished to prepare an atlas to accompany his Géographie moderne, and that it was partly to carry out his views that this work was undertaken. Though the maps are arranged according to the articles of this book, many details have been added to render the atlas more generally useful.

Maps are not correctly numbered but all maps called for by index appear in atlas.

The following maps relate to America:

no. 1. Mappe-monde . . . Par le s.[r] Janvier . . . 1762.
" 32. L'Amérique divisée par grands états. Par le s.[r] Janvier . . . 1762.
" 33. L'Amérique Septentrionale divisée en ses principaux états. Par le s.[r] Janvier . . . 1762.
" 34. L'Amérique Méridionale divisée en ses principaux états par le s.[r] Janvier. 1762.
" 34 bis. Carte géo-hydrographique du golfe du Mexique et de ses isles . . Par m. Rizzi Zannoni.

## 1762?

**Lobeck, T.**

Kurzgefasste geographie, in sich haltend einen aneinander hangenden entwurf aller theile des bevvohnten erdbodens, nebst compendieusen landcharten, welche einen kleinen sackatlas ausmachen.   72 pp., 1 l., front., 29 col. maps.  obl. 32°.  Augspurg, A. Brinhauser [1762?]   630

NOTE.—Copy no. 1.  Engraved frontispiece signed: Gottfr. Eichler jun., inv. et delin.—Tobias Lobeck sculpsit et excudit Aug: Vind:

Maps preceded by engraved title-page: Atlas geographicus portatilis, XXIX mappis orbis habitabilis regna exhibens.  Cælo accurate expressit Tobias Conradus Lotterus, delineavit et excudit Tobias Lobeck, chalcograph . . .

Atlas published also without text.

Maps not dated.  Copy no. 3 of the "Atlas geographicus" . . . contains maps nos. [25] and [32], not in the "index mapparum," but dated 1762, which has been assigned to this copy.

British Museum catalogue has a copy under the date 1720 (?), but no other authority for this date is found.

The following maps relate to America:

no [1] Planisphærium globi terrestris.
" [4] Asia [Insulæ Philippinæ]
" [6] America.

## 1762?

Atlas geographicus portatilis, XXIX, mappis orbis habitabilis regna exhibens.  Cælo accurate expressit Tobias Conradus Lotterus, delineavit et excudit Tobias Lobeck, chalcograph . . .   2 p. l., [2] l., front., 37 col. maps.  32°.  [Augsburg, 1762?]   631

NOTE.—Copy no. 2.  Engraved frontispiece and title-page, signed: G. Eichler, jun. inv. et delin.—Tobias Lobeck, sculps. et excud. Aug. Vind.

Maps are generally signed Tobias Lobeck del. et excud.—Tob. Conr. Lotter sculpsit.

Maps not dated. Copy no. 3 contains maps nos. [25] and [32], not in the "index mapparum," but dated 1762, which has been assigned to this copy.

British Museum catalogue has a copy under date 1720 (?), but no other authority for this date is found.

The following maps are not in the table of contents and are probably inserted: no. [22] Ducatus Silesiæ inferioris tabula.—no. [23] Ducatus Silesiæ' superioris.—no. [24] . . . Saxoniæ pars meridionalis . . .—no. [25] Pars meridionalis circuli Saxoniæ superioris.—no. [26] Tabula circulus Saxoniæ inferioris . . .—no [27] Circulus Westphalicus. I. pars.—no. [28] Circuli Thuringiæ. I pars-no. [29] Circuli Saxoniæ inferioris . . . II pars.

The following maps relate to America:
no. [1] Planisphærium globi terrestris.
" [4] Asia [Insulæ Philippinæ]
" [6] America.

## 1762 ?

Atlas geographicus portatilis [!] xxix mappis orbis habitabilis regna exhibens. Cælo accurate exprefsit Tobias Conradus Lotterus, delineavit et excudit Tobias Lobeck, chalcograph: Auguftan Vendit: in ejus ædib. in fuburb; Jacobæo in reg. paradifi.  3 p. l., 49 col. maps.  obl. 32°.  [Augsburg, 1762?]  632

NOTE.—Copy no. 3. Engraved title and plate signed: G. Eichler jun: inv: et delin. Tobias Lobeck, sculps et exc. A. V.

"Index mapparum" to 29 maps evidently belonged to an earlier edition, as this contains 20 additional maps two of which, no. 25, "Schwaben land" and no. 32, "Bayer land" are dated 1762.

The following maps relate to America:
no. 1. Planisphærium globi terrestris.
" 5. America.

## 1762

**Zannoni, G. A. Rizzi-**

Atlas géographique contenant la mappemonde et les quatre parties, avec les différents états d'Europe . . .  1 p. l., [2], 55, [2] pp., front., 22 maps on 60 l., 1 diagr.  24°.  Paris, Lattré, 1762.  633

NOTE.—Engraved frontispiece, title-page and maps.
no. [8] "Golfe du Mexique avec ses isles" is not referred to in the "Table des cartes."

The following maps relate to America:
no. 2. Mappe-monde, hémisphère occidental
" 4. L'Asie . . . [Isles Philippines]
" 6. Amérique Septentrionale . . .
" 7. Amérique Méridionale . . .
" [8] Golfe du Mexique avec ses isles.

## 1763?
**Dury, A.**

A new general and universal atlas containing forty five maps. Engraved by mr. Kitchin, & others.   3 p. l., 45 (*i. e.* 39) maps obl. 32°.   London, printed for & sold by A. Dury, R. Sayer & C. Bowles [1763?]   634

 NOTE.—See also 627. Maps nos. 8, 10-12 show the results of the treaty of Paris, 1763.
 nos. 10-11 gives additional place names.
 Majority of maps have an added title above the upper margin.
 List of subscribers' names omitted.
 The following maps relate to America:
 no. 1-2. World.
 "  8. North America.
 "  9. South America.
 " 10-11. Canada.
 "  12. A map of the West India islands.

## 1763?
**Moll, H.**

Atlas minor: or a new and curious set of sixty two maps, in which are fhewn all the empires, kingdoms, countries, states, in all the known parts of the earth; with their bounds, divisions, chief cities & towns, the whole compofed & laid down agreable to modern hiftory . . .   1 p. l., 64 maps. obl. 8°.   [London, for J. & C. Bowles, 1763?]   635

 NOTE.—Engraved title. See also titles 574, 578, 585 and 602.
 A new edition with the american maps showing additions, changes in boundaries, additional inscriptions and the date 1763 in the title of no. 46 and the legend of no. 47. The old world maps are the same as those in the [1745?] edition excepting the imprints. See title 602.
 no. [45½] "The theatre of war in North America, with the roads and a table of the distances . . . 1776," inserted.
 " 49½. [Long Island] Imperfect. From "Geographische belustigungen zur erläuterung der nevsten weltgeschichte . . . Leipzig, 1776,' inserted.
 The following maps relate to America:
 no. 1. A new map of the whole world with the trade winds . . . for John Bowles . . . and Carington Bowles . . . London.
 " 2. A map of the North Pole . . . London, for John Bowles . . . & Carington Bowles . . .
 " 40. Africa . . . [Shows] C. S! Augustin [Brazil]
 " 45. America . . .
 " 46. A new map of y$^e$ north parts of America according to the divisions thereof by the articles of peace in 1763 . . .  [Very different, although same base map as in [1745?] edition. Lettering entirely changed, both as to type and location. "Nova Scotia" replaces New Scotland; New England first appears; Virginia is in larger type, over a more extended area; Carolina is divided into north and south; Georgia first appears; New France changed to Louisiana, west of and along the Mississippi]

**Moll, H.**—Continued.
> no. 47. New Found land, S! Laurence bay, the fishing banks, Acadia, and part of New Scotland . . . [Same base map with many changes. The last lines of the legend in the lower right hand corner of the other editions, reading "and ye Gulph of ye same name are given to the French," are here changed to one line in very small letters, "& ye gulf of ye same name were given to the French." The scale is replaced by a long legend, "By the Articles of Peace in 1763 . . . by the treaty of Utrecht"]
> " 48. A description of the bay of Fundy . . .—The harbour of Annapolis Royal by Nathaniel Blackmore esq! [Numerous changes and additions]
> " 49. New England, New York, New Jersey and Pensilvania . . . [Many changes and additions]
> " 49½. [Long island]
> " 50. Virginia and Maryland . . . [Additions]
> " 51. Carolina . . . [Additions]
> " 52. A plan of Port Royal harbour in Carolina . . .
> " 53. The island of Bermudo's . . .
> " 54. Florida called by yᵉ French Louisiana &c . . . [Additions]
> " 55. A map of the West-Indies &c. Mexico or New Spain . . . [Additions]
> " 56. The island of Jamaica . . .
> " 57. The ifland of S! Christophers, alias S! Kitts . . .
> " 58. The island of Antego . . .
> " 59. The island of Barbadoes . . .
> " 60. The scots settlement in America called New Caledonia . . .
> " 61. A Map of Terra Firma, Peru, Amazoneland, Brasil & the north p. of La Plata . . .
> " 62. A map of Chili, Patagonia, La Plata and ye south part of Brasil . . .

## 1763

**Delisle, G.**
[A collection of maps of the world]    97 maps on 203 l.  fol.
[Paris, 1763]                                              636
> NOTE.—Without title-page. See also titles 533, 535, 580, 581, 594 and 596.
> Maps dated 1700–1763; no. [72] Carte d'Amérique . . . augm. en 1763 . . .
> Compiled by P. Buache, by whom most of the maps were revised.
> no. [19] Plan de la ville et faubourgs de Paris . . . 1716.—no. [46] Inset: Plan de la ville de Genève . . .—no. [92] Inset: Veterum Syracusarum typus.
> Border text on nos. [44], [45], [76], [80].
> The following maps relate to America:
> no. [1]  Mappemonde . . . 1720, augmentée en 1755.
> " [3]  Hémisphère Occidental . . . 1720 . . . Revu et augmentée . . . en . . . 1760.
> " [4]  Hémisphère Septentrional . . . 1714.
> " [5]  Hémisphère Méridional . . . 1714.
> " [56] Carte d'Asie. Publiée en 1723 . . . [augm.] 1762.
> " [62] Carte des Indes et de la Chine . . . 1745. [Philippine islands]
> " [66] Carte des nouvelles découvertes au nord de la mer du Sud, tant à l'est de la Siberie et du Kamtchatka, qu'à l'ouest de la Nouvelle France. Dressée sur les mémoires de mr. De l'Isle . . . Par Philippe Buache . . . 1750.

no. [67] Carte d'Afrique . . . 1722 . . . 1745 [Shows Brazil]
" [72] Carte d'Amérique . . . augmentée . . . en 1763 . . .
" [73] Carte du Canada ou de la Nouvelle France . . . 1703 . . .
" [74] Carte de la Louisiane et du cours du Mississipi . . . 1718 . . . 1745.—Inset: Carte particulière des embouchures de la rivie. S. Louis et de la Mobile.
" [75a-b] Carte du Mexique et de la Floride des Terres angloises et des isles Antilles du cours et des environs de la rivière de Misfisfipi . . . 1703 . . . 1745. 2 sheets.
" [76] Carte d'une partie de l'Amérique pour la navigation des isles et du golfe du Mexique avec l'intérieur des terres depuis la Bermude jusqu'à Cayenne—partie méridionale, réduite de la carte angloise en 20 feuilles par mr. Popple . . . cor. et aug. par Phil. Buache en 1740.
" [77] Carte de l'isle de Saint Domingue . . . Dressée en 1722 . . . 1745.
" [78] Carte des Antilles françoises et des isles voisines . . . 1717 . . . 1745.
" [79] Carte de l'isle de la Martinique . . . 1745.
" [80] Carte de la partie de l'océan vers l'equateur entre les cotes d'Afrique et d'Amérique . . . 1737.
" [81] Carte de la Terre Ferme, du Pérou, du Brésil et du pays des Amazones . . . 1703 . . . 1745.
" [82] Carte du Paraguay, du Chili, du détroit de Magellan &c . . . 1703 . . . 1745.
" [85] Inset: Supplementum Theatro historico [1705]

**1763**

**Gourné, P. M.**

Atlas abrégé et portatif. Contenant la mappemonde, les 4 parties du monde, et des tables sur lefquelles on voit le nom françois et latin des continents, des ifles, des différentes capitales des empires, des royaumes, des républiques, celui des fleuves qui les arrofent et le souverain à qui elles appartiennent; avec la fituation aftronomique de tous ces lieux. Ouvrage généralement utile à l'instruction de la jeunesse, et à ceux qui veulent avoir une connoissance méthodique de l'univers. Revû, corrigé et augmenté sur les nouvelles observationes astronomiques faites en 1741. Par m. m. Tchirikcow et De l'Isle. 2 p. l., 5 col. maps, 10 tab. fol. Paris, L. C. Desnos, 1763. 637

NOTE.—Engraved title-page.
Maps by Beaurain, Brion and Janvier.
The following maps relate to America:
no. [1] Mappe-monde . . . Par le ch! de Beaurain. 1763.
" [5] L'Amérique . . . Par le s! Janvier en 1753. Revue corrigée et augmentée par Desnos en 1763.

## 1764
**Bellin, J. N.**
Le petit atlas maritime recueil de cartes et plans des quatre parties du monde . . .   5 v.   fol.   [Paris] 1764.   638

CONTENTS.

v. 1. Amérique Septentrionale et Isles Antilles.
" 2. Amérique Méridionale, Mexique, Terre-Ferme, Brésil, Pérou, Chily.
" 3. Asie et Àfrique.
" 4–5. Europe et les états qu'elle contient.

## 1766
**Universal, An, history.**
The maps and charts to the modern part of the Universal history. 2 p. l., 39 maps.   fol.   London, for T. Osborne [etc.] 1766.   639

NOTE.—To accompany: An universal history from the earliest account of time. 65 v.   London, 1747–1768.
The following maps relate to America:
no. [1] A new & accurate map of the world.   By Eman. Bowen.
" [2] A new & accurate chart of the world.   By Eman. Bowen.
" [38] A new general map of America.   By Eman. Bowen.
" [39] A new and accurate map of the british dominions in America, according to the treaty of 1763. By Tho? Kitchin. Constructed on a scale equally adapted to both the octavo and folio editions of the history.

## 1767
**Brion de la Tour, L.**
Atlas général, civil et ecclésiastique, méthodique et élémentaire pour l'étude de la géographie et de l'histoire. Ouvrage destiné spécialement à l'inftruction de la jeune noblefe de l'école royale militaire.  Adapté aux livres de géographie les plus fuivis, entr'autres à ceux de mm. l'abbé Langlet du Fre[s]noy . . . dédié a mademelle Crozat, et de l'abbé Nicole de la Croix. Dressé d'après les nouvelles observations astronomique, faites par mm. Thirikcow et de L'Isle, par m. Brion, ingénieur-géographe du roy.  Dirigé par le sr. Desnos . . .   2 p. l., 10 pp., 50 (*i. e.* 51) l., 46 maps, 7 pl. 4°.  Paris, 1767.   640

NOTE.—Another edition of this atlas was published with 15 "Cartes pour le détail de France" which were also published separately. This copy contains the "Avertissement de l'éditeur" and "Catalogue" of the above edition which is probably that of Paris, 1766.
The following maps are not included in the index:
no. [13] Carte itinéraire du royaume de France . . .
" 44. Carte des pays et principaux lieux connus dans les premiers âges du monde . . . 1766.
" 45. La Judée, ou Palestine . . .

The following maps relate to America:
no. 3. Mappe-monde . . . 1766.
" 4. Hémisphère occidental.
" 36. Chine, et Indes avec les Isles [Philippines] . . . 1766.
" 40. L'Amérique . . . 1764.
" 41. Chili, Paraguay, Brésil, Amazones, et Pérou . . . 1766.
" 42. Guayane, Terre Ferme, Isles Antilles, et N.$_e$ Espagne . . . 1766.
" 43. Nouveau Mexique, Louisiane, Canada, et N$^{lle}$ Angleterre . . . 1766.

## 1768
**Julien, R. J.**
Le théatre du monde contenant les cartes générales et particulières des empires, royaumes et états qui le composent. 2 v. fol. Paris, le s$^r$ Julien, 1768. 641

NOTE.—Collation: v. 1, 1 p. l., 80 maps on 208 l.; v. 2, 1 p. l., 95 maps on 200 l., 1 pl., 1 tab.

Engraved title-pages.

A collection of maps by various cartographers including: Boullanger, Bailleul, Delisle, Nolin, Cantel, Tillemont, Beaurain, Robert de Vaugondy, Anville, Homann, Robert, Jaillot, S. Angelo, Le Rouge, Caille, Delamarche, Sanson, Palairet, Mitchel, Coronelli, Buache, Jefferys, Caylus, Halley, Rizzi-Zannoni, Scheuchzer, de Vezon, Lamare, Lagrive, Dheulland, Visscher, de Wit, Cóvens and Mortier.

Dates on maps vary from 1665 to 1814. Maps dated after 1768 were evidently inserted.

vol. 2 contains a fine set of Nicolas de Lamare's eight maps of Paris, signed "M. L. C. D. L. M," made to accompany his "Traité de la police . . . avec une description historique et topographique de Paris, et 8 plans représentant son ancien état et ses divers acroissements, plus un recueil des statuts et des règlements des six corps de marchands et des autres communautés des arts et métiers. [t. 4. Continuation . . . by Le Cler du Brillet] 4 v. 1705-1735," and entitled:

v. 2, no. [9 ] Lutèce ou premier plan de la ville de Paris, tiré de César, de Strabon . . .
" " [9a] Lutèce conquise par les françois sur les romains, ou second plan de la ville de Paris.
" " [9b] Troisième plan de la ville de Paris . . . Sous le règne de Loüis le Ieune VII$^e$ du nom.
" " [9c] Quatrième plan de la ville de Paris . . . sous le règne de Philippe Auguste.
" " [9d] Cinquième plan de la ville de Paris . . . sous Charles V l'an 1367 et . . . sous Charles VI l'an 1383.
" " [9e] Sixième plan de la ville de Paris . . . du règne de Charles VII . . . jusqu'à la fin du règne d'Henri III l'an 1589.
" " [9f] Septième plan de la ville de Paris . . . sous Henry IIII et Louis XIII depuis 1589 jusqu'en 1643.
" " [9g] Huitième plan de Paris devisé en ses vingts [!] quartiers, par N. de Fer, pour servir au Traité de la police.

Also includes l'abbé Delagrive's "Neuvième plan de Paris, ses accroiffemens fous le règne de Louis XV pour fervir au IV$^e$ tome du traité de la police par M. L. C. D. L. C. D. B. 1735"—Dheulland's "Ville cité et université de Paris;" and Robert de Vaugondy's "Plan de la ville et des faubourgs de Paris. 1766."

**Julien, R. J.**—Continued.

The following maps relate to America:

v. 1, no. 1. Nouvelle mappe monde. Dressée par mʳ Boullanger. 1760.
" " 43. Carte générale des découvertes de l'admiral de Fonte et autres navigateurs espagnols, anglois et russes, pour la recherche du passage à la Mer du Sud. Par mʳ Del'Isle 1752.
" " [53a] Carte générale de l'Amérique . . . Par Fˣ Delamarche fils. 1814.
" " 54. L'Amérique Septentrionale et Méridionale . . . par le sʳ Robert. 1767.
" " 55. Carte des possessions angloises & françoises du continent de l'Amérique Septentrionale. Par I. Palairet. 1759.
" " 56–56a. Amérique Septentrionale . . . Par le sʳ d'Anville. 1746. 2 sheets.
" " 57–57g. Amérique Septentrionale . . . Par le docteur [John] Mitchel. Traduit de l'anglois . . . par le Rouge . . . 1756. 8 sheets.
" " 58. Carte du Mexique et de la Floride des terres angloises et des isles Antilles du cours et des environs de la rivière de Misfisfipi . . . Par Guillaume Del'Isle. 1703.
" " 59. Archipelague du Mexique . . . Par le p. Coronelli . . . Corrigée et augmentée par le sʳ Tillemon. 1742.
" " 60. Partie de la Mer du Nord . . . Par le sʳ Robert. 1750.
" " 61. Carte des Antilles françoises et des isles voisines . . . 1717. Cette carte a été rectifiée en 1760 par Phil. Buache.
" " 62. Carte de l'isle de la Martinique . Par . . . Philippe Buache. 1745.
" " 63. Carte de l'isle de Saint-Domingue dressée d'après la carte originale de mʳ Frezier par le sʳ Robert. 1749.
" " 64. An authentic plan of the town and harbour of Cap-François in the isle of Sᵗ Domingo. By Thomas Jefferys.
" " 65. Plan of the town and citadel of Fort Royal the capital of Martinico with the bay of Cul de Sac Royal. By mʳ de Caylus.
" " 66. La Guadeloupe . . . Par . . . Le Rouge . . . 1753.
" " 67–67b. Amérique Méridionale . . . Par le sʳ d'Anville. 1748. 3 sheets.
" " 68. Carte de la Terre Ferme, du Pérou, du Brésil, et du pays des Amazones . . . Par Guillaume Del'Ifle . . . 1703.
" " 69. Carte du Paraguay du Chili du détroit de Magellan &c . . . Par Guillaume De l'Isle . . . 1703.
" " 70. Carte de l'Isle de Caïenne et des rivières voisines . . . Par le sʳ d'Anville . . . 1729.
" " 71. Carte de la partie de l'océan vers l'équateur entre les côtes d'Afrique et Amérique . . . Dressée par Philippe Buache. 1737.
" " 72. Nova & accuratissima totius terrarum orbis tabula nautica . . . per Edm. Halley. 1700.
" " [79] Carte générale de l'empire de Russie. 1812.
v. 2. " [2] Mappe-monde géo sphérique . . . Par . . . Louis Claude de Vezou.
" " 3. Mappe-monde . . . Par le sʳ Robert de Vaugondy . . . 1812.

## 1769-1772

**Hawkesworth, J.**

An account of the voyages undertaken by the order of his present majesty for making discoveries in the southern hemisphere, and successively performed by commodore Byron, captain Wallis, captain Carteret and captain Cook . . . Atlas. 26 maps, 26 pl. fol. [London, for W. Strahan & T. Cadell, 1773]  642

NOTE.—First edition.
Atlas without title page.
Maps dated 1769–1772.
The following maps relate to America:

no. [1] Chart of part of the South sea, shewing the tracts & discoveries made by his majesty's ships Dolphin . . . 1765, & Tamer . . . 1765, Dolphin . . . & Swallow . . . 1767, and Endeavour . . . 1769.
" [2] A chart of the straights of Magellan.
" [22] A chart of the s. e. part of Terra del Fuego including strait Le Maire and part of Staten-land. 1769.

CONTENTS.

MAPS

no. [1] Chart of part of the South sea shewing the tracts & discoveries made by his majesty's ships . . .
" [2] A chart of the straights of Magellan.
" [3] Port Famine.—Woods bay.—Port Gallant and Fortescue bay.—Cordes bay and harbour.
" [4] Cape Providence with the bay and anchoring places . . .
" [5] From York bay to Three island bay and harbour.
" [7] A chart of Hawkins's Maidenland discovered . . . in 1574 and Falkland sound . . . 1689.
" [11] [Cocos island.—Traitors island]
" [12] [Wallis's islands]
" [14] A chart and views of Pitcairns island. 1773.
" [15] Queen Charlotte's islands. 1773.
" [16] [Swallow's bay.—Byron's harbour. 1772]
" [17] Nova Hibernia.
" [18] A chart of capt? Carteret's discoveries at New Britain . . .
" [20] The south end of Mindanao.
" [21] A draught of Bonthain bay. 1772.
" [22] A chart of the s. e. part of Terra del Fuego including strait le Maire and part of Staten-land. 1769.—A plan of Success bay in strait Le Maire.
" [24] Chart of the island Otaheite by lieut. J. Cook, 1769.
" [33] Chart of the Society isles discovered by lieut. J. Cook, 1769.
" [34] Matavia bay in Otaheite.—Owharre harbour in Huaheine.—Ohamaneno harbour in Ulietea.—Oopoa harbour in Ulietea.
" [35] A chart of the islands discovered in the neighbourhood of Otaheite . . . in the years 1765, 1767, 1769.
" [39] Chart of New-Zealand explored in 1769 and 1770 by lieut. I. Cook, 1772.
" [41] River Thames and Mercury bay in New Zealand.—Bay of islands in New Zealand.—Tolaga bay in New Zealand.
" [43] Chart of Cooks strait in New Zealand.

**Hawkesworth, J.**—Continued.
>  no. [48] A chart of New South Wales or the eaſt coast of New-Holland discover'd . . . in the year 1770.
> " [49] Entrance of Endeavour river.—Botany bay.
> " [52] Chart of part of the coast of New South Wales . . . by lieut. J. Cook, 1770.

### 1770?

**Kitchin, T.**, & *others*.

A general atlas: or, description at large of the whole universe. Being a collection of the moſt approved and correcteſt maps hitherto publiſhed. The whole engraved on forty-four large copper plates. 1 p. l., 11 fold. maps on 22 sheets. fol. London, for R. Sayer & T. Jeffrys [1770?] 643

>  NOTE.—The edition of 1773, "A general atlas defcribing the whole univerſe . . . by Thomas Kitchen," is mentioned in the Universal catalogue, 1773, v. 2, title 113, "As far as we can gather this is the best collection of maps extant. It is called Dunn's atlas from some delineations given by mr. Dunn to the map of the world."
>  This earlier and smaller edition was published between 1768, the date on map no. 4, "The East Indies, with the roads, by Thomas Jefferys," and 1771, the year of the death of Thomas Jefferys, one of the publishers of this atlas. See also titles 653, 668, 682, 685, 687, 699 and 709.
>  The following maps relate to America:
>  no. [1] Scientia terrarum et coelorum . . . By S. Dunn. 2 sheets.
>  " [6] A new and compleat map of all America . . . By John Gibson. 2 sheets.
>  " [7] An accurate map of North America . . . By Eman. Bowen and John Gibson. 2 sheets.

### 1770

**Desnos, L. C.**

Almanach géographique ou, petit atlas élémentaire, compoſé de cartes générales et particulières des différens empires, royaumes et républiques de l'Europe et des autres parties de la terre. Suivi de descriptions sous le titre d'idée générale de la géographie et de l'histoire moderne. 3 p. l., front., port., 32 maps, 2 l. 32°. Paris, Desnos, 1770. 644

>  NOTE.—Engraved title, frontispiece and portrait of Christian VII king of Denmark and Norway, to whom the work is dedicated.
>  The following maps relate to America:
>  no. 2. Hémisphère occidentale.
>  " 6. Amérique Septentrionale.
>  " 7. Amérique Méridionale.

### 1770

**Maclot, J. C.**

Atlas général méthodique et élémentaire, pour l'étude de la géographie et de l'histoire moderne dressé d'après les meilleurs cartes françoises et étrangères, aſſujetti aux obſervations aſtronomiques de m. m. de l'ac. roy. des sc. et des s$^{rs}$ Tchirikow et Delisle par une société d'ingénieurs géographes du roi. Adopté fpécialem! pour l'inftruction de la jeune nobleffe de l'école royale militaire en vertu d'une délibération du confeil de cette école, avec des descriptions historiques et géographiques, imprimées sur les marges de chaque carte, pour en faciliter l'étude. Mis au jour et executé par le s$^r$ Desnos. 2 p. l., 136 l. incl. 59 col. maps, 7 col. pl. fol. Paris, Desnos, 1770. 645

NOTE.—Engraved title. First edition 1768; other editions 1776 and 1786. See also title 658.

The following maps relate to America:
- no. 8. Mappe-monde . . . par m. Brion. 1766.
- " 9. Hémi-sphère occidental.
- " 47. L'Amérique . . . par m. Brion. 1764.
- " 48. Chili, Paraguay, Brésil, Amazones, et Pérou. Par m. Brion. 1766.
- " 49. Guayane. Terre Ferme, Iles Antilles, et N$^{lle}$ Espagne. Par m. Brion. 1766.
- " 50. Nouveau Mexique, Louisiane, Canada, et N$^{lle}$ Angleterre. Par m. Brion. 1766.

### 1771-1783

**Atlas moderne** ou collection de cartes sur toutes les parties du globe terreftre par plusieurs auteurs . . . 3 p. l., 36 maps, 1 pl. fol. Paris, Lattré; & Delalain [1771–1783] 646

NOTE.—First published in 1762. See title 630. A later edition published in 1787–[1791] See title 664.

Map no. 31, L'Amérique . . . dated 1783.

Engraved title.

Map entitled, "La France divisée en 83 départemens . . ." is not called for by the index. All maps are by Bonne, Janvier and Rizzi-Zannoni. The "Avertissement" states that the abbé Nicolle de La Croix, before his death, wished to prepare an atlas to accompany his Géographie moderne, and that it was partly to carry out his views that this work was undertaken. Though the maps are arranged according to the articles of this book, many details have been added to render the atlas more generally useful.

A note following the "Avertissement," speaks of this atlas as prepared by m! Bonne.

The following maps relate to America:
- no. 1. Mappe-monde . . . Par. le s$^r$ Janvier . . . 1782.
- " 31. L'Amérique divisée par grands états. Par le s$^r$ Janvier . . . 1783.
- " 32. L'Amérique Septentrionale divisée en ses principaux états par le s$^r$ Janvier . . . 1782.
- " 33. L'Amérique Méridionale divisée en ses principaux états par le s$^r$ Janvier . . . 1782.
- " 34. Carte géo-hydrographique du golfe Mexique et de ses isles . . . Par m. Rizzi-Zannoni . . .

### 1776–1784
**Santini, P.**

Atlas universel dressé sur les meilleures cartes modernes. 2 v. 2 p. l., 68 maps; 1 p. l., 68 maps. fol. Venise, Remondini, 1776–[1784]    647

NOTE.—Dates on maps vary from 1776 to 1784.
Binder's title: Remondini Atlas Universel.
A collection of maps by various cartographers, including: d'Anville, Janvier, Robert de Vaugondy, and others.
The following maps relate to America:
v. 1, no. 1. Mappemonde, par le sr. Janvier.
"    "    2. Nouvelle mappemonde.
v. 2, no. 43. L'Amérique, par le sr. Janvier.
"    "    44. Carte des nouvelles descouvertes au Nord de la Mer du Sud.
"    "    45. Carte générale du Canada, de la Louisiane, de la Florida, de la Caroline, de la Virginie, de la Nouvelle Angleterre, par le sr. d'Anville.
"    "    46. Partie occidentale du Canada et septentrionale de la Louisiane avec une partie de la Pensilvanie, par le sr. d'Anville.
"    "    47. Partie orientale du Canada avec la Nouvelle Angleterre, l'Acadie et la terre neuve, par le sr. d'Anville.
"    "    48. Partie méridionale de la Louisiane avec la Floride, la Caroline e la Virginie, par le sr. d'Anville.
"    "    49. Carte du Mexique et de la Nouvelle Espagne, par mr. d'Anville.
"    "    50. Les grande et petites isles Antilles et les isles Lucayes avec une partie de la Mer du Nord le sr. Robert.
"    "    51. Carte du Pérou et Brésil sepl de Tierre-Firme, de Guayana, et de la rivière des Amazones, par le sr. d'Anville.
"    "    52. Carte qui représente la partie méridionale du Brésil et du Pérou, le Chili septentrional, et le Paraguay, par le sr. d'Anville.
"    "    53. Carte du Chili méridionale, du Rio de la Plata des Patagons, et du détroit de Magellan, par le sr. d'Anville.

### 1776–1799
**Cook, J.**

Reizen rondom de waereld door James Cook, vertaald door J. D. Pasteur . . . Atlas. 1 p. l., 51 maps, 131 pl., 2 diagr. obl. fol. Leyden, Amsterdam en s'Haage, Honkoop, Allart & van Cleef, 1797–1809.    648

NOTE.—A collection of maps and plates without title to accompany "Reizen rondom de waereld."
Size of maps and plates varies.
Maps dated 1776–1799.
Map no. 31, "Algemeene kaart," shows tracks of Cook's three voyages 1768–1780.
Map no. 11, "Kaart van het eiland Otahiti door . . . J. Cook. 1769. Sculpt. apud T. S. Klauber . . . 1794."
The atlas to accompany the english edition of 1784 contains two maps; no. 1: A general chart exhibiting the discoveries made by capt.[n] James Cook in this and his two preceeding voyages; with the tracks of the ships under his command. W. Palmer fculp.—no. 36: Chart of the n. w. coast of America and n. e. coast of Asia explored in the years 1778 & 1779. Writing engrav'd by T. Harmar.

The following maps relate to America:
no. 1. Kaart van de Good Success baai in de straat van le Maire.—Kaart van het z. o. gedeelte van het Vuurland de straat le Maire en een gedeelte van Staatenland . . . 1769. 1794.
" [15] Kaart van het Zuider halfrond . . .
" 23. Kersmis kanaal aan de z. w. kust van het voorland.
" [25] Kaart van het zuidlyk eind van Amerika. 1775.
" [31] Algemeene kaart van de ontdekkingen van kapt Cook . . .
" 37. Gezigten der west-kust van Amerika.
" [38] Plan der haven van Samganoodha, in het eiland van Oonalaska.
" 40. Kaart van Cook's rivier in het n. o. gedeelte van Amerika.
" [42] Gezigt der Sandwich's eilanden.
" [43] Gezigten der landen van de west kust van Amerika, ten westen van Cook's rivier.
" [44] Kaart van den mond van Norton, en van de engte van Bhering, toonende . . . den westlijken uithoek van Amerika.
" [45] Kaart van de noord-weft kust van Amerika . . . 1778-1779.
" [47] Kaart van de Sandwich eilanden.

## 1778
**Robert de Vaugondy, D.**
Nouvel atlas portatif destiné principalement pour l'instruction de la jeunesse, d'après la géographie moderne de feu l'abbé Delacroix . . . 9 pp., 52 maps. 4°. Paris, Fortin, 1778. 649
NOTE.—Engraved title. Maps engraved by E. Dussy.
Map no. 1, Mappemonde . . . wanting.
The following maps relate to America:
no. 2-4. Mappemonde . . . 1778.
" 42. L'Amérique . . .
" 43. Canada, Louisiane, possessions Angl ? . . . 1778.
" 44. Nouvelle Espagne, Nouveau Mexique, isles Antilles . . .
" 45. Terre-Ferme, Pérou, Brésil, Pays de l'Amazone . . .
" 46. Paraguay, Chili, Terre Magellan ? . . .

## 1779-1788
**Zatta, A.**
Atlante novissimo. 4 v. fol. Venezia, A. Zatta, 1779-1788 [1788] 650
NOTE.—Engraved title to each volume. Dates vary: v. 1, 1779; v. 2, 1782; v. 3, 1784; v. 4. 1785. See also title 695.
Title-page of volumes 2-4 read: Atlante novissimo, illustrato ed accresciuto sulle osservazioni e scoperte fatti dai più celebri e più recenti geografi.
Dates on maps vary from 1774-1788.
The following maps are wanting:
v. 1, no. 28, Li contorni de Parige. This map appears in copy no. 1, title 651.
v. 2, P. v. I Principati di Moldavia, e Vallachia.
Map entitled, "Teatro della guerra presente tra la Russia e la Porto Ottomana, 1788," inserted in v. 2.
Map no. [4], Regno di Boemia, wanting in copy no. 1, title 651, appears in v. 2, of this copy.
In v. 4, map no. [22], L'America divisa né suoi principali stati . . . is a duplicate of no. 14 in v. 1.

**Zatta, A.**—Continued.

The following maps relate to America:

v. 1, no. 6. Il mappamondo, o sia descrizione generale del globo ridotto in quadro. 1774.
" " 7. Il mappamondo o sia descrizione generale del globo. 1774.
" " 8. Emisfero terrestre meridionale. 1779.
" " 9. Emisfero terrestre settentrionale. 1779.
" " 14. L' America divisa ne' suoi principali stati. 1776.
" " 15. Nuove scoperte de' Russi al nord del mare del Sud sí nell' Asia, che nell' America. 1776.
" " 53. Il Canadá, le colonie Inglesi con la Luigiana, e Florida . . . 1778.
" " 54. La Baja d' Hudson, Terra di Labrador e Groenlandia con le isole adiacenti . . . 1778.
" " 55. Le Isole de Terra Nuova e Capo Breton . . . 1778.
" " 56. L Isole Bermude.
" " 57–68. Le Colonie Unite dell' America Settentr$^{le}$ . . . [in fogli xii] 1778.
v. 4, no. [22] L' America divisa né suoi principali stati. . . . 1776.
" " [23] America Settentrionale divisa ne' fuoi principali stati.
" " [24] America Meridionale divisa ne' fuoi principali stati.
" " [25] Messico . . . 1785.
" " [26] La Terra Ferma la Gujana, Spagnola, Olandese, Francese, e Portughese e la parte settentr$^{le}$ del Bresil. 1785.
" " [27] Il Paraguai . . . 1785.
" " [28] Il Perù ove si trovano le Udienze di Quito, Lima, e Plata. 1785.
" " [29] Stabilimenti de francesi, inglesi e spagnuoli nelle isole Antille. 1785.
" " [30] Chili la terra Magellanica coll' isola della Terra del Fuoco. 1785.

### 1779–1799
**Zatta, A.**

Atlante novissimo. 4 v. fol. Venezia, A. Zatta, 1779–1785 [1799] 651

NOTE.—Engraved title-pages. Dates vary: v. 1, 1779; v. 2, 1785; v. 3, 1785; v. v, 1785. See also title 695.
Maps dated 1775–1799.
Imperfect: v. 2, no. [4], Regno di Boemia; v. 4, no. [58], Gallia antiqua, wanting. Both in copy 2, title 650.

#### CONTENTS.

v. 1, no. [1] Mappa dell' universo . . . 1779.
" " [2] Tavola sferica . . . 1777.
" " [3] Posizione diversa degli abitanti della terra . . . 1779.
" " [4] Planisferio celeste settentrionale . . . 1777.
" " [5] Planisferio celeste meridionale . . . 1777.
" " [6] Il mappamondo . . . ridotto in Quadro . . . 1795.
" " [7] Il mappamondo . . . 1774.
" " [8] Emisfero terrestre meridionale . . . 1779.
" " [9] Emisfero terrestre settentrionale . . . 1779.
" " [10] L' Europa . . . 1798.

v. 1, no. [11 ] Regno di Portogallo. 1775.
" " [12 ] L' Estremadura di Portogallo Alentejo, ed Algarve. 1775.
" " [13 ] Il Portogallo cioè le provincie di Entre Douro, e Minho, Trazos-Montes, e Beira . . . 1776.
" " [14 ] Li regni di Spagna e Portogallo . . . 1796.
" " [15 ] Li regni di Galizia, Asturies, Leon, Castiglia Vecchia . . . 1776.
" " [16 ] I dipartimenti de' Pirenei e dell' Alta Garonna . . . 1793.
" " [17 ] L' Estremadura e la Castiglia Nuova . . . 1776.
" " [18 ] Li regni di Valenza, e Murcia . . . 1775.
" " [19 ] Isole di Majorca, d' Ivica, e di Formentera . . . 1778.
" " [20 ] Andalusia e Granada . . . 1776.
" " [21 ] Regno di Francia . . . 1776.
" " [22 ] Li Contorni di Parigi . . . 1789.
" " [23 ] Li governi dell' isola di Francia, ed Orleanois . . . 1776.
" " [24 ] Li governi del Limosin, Quercy, e Perigord . . . 1776.
" " [25 ] Li governi di Guyenna Guascogna . . . 1776.
" " [26 ] Li governi della Fiandra Francese d' Artois di Picardia e del Boulonois . . . 1794.
" " [27 ] Li governi del Berri, del Nivernois, della Marche, del Bourbonnois . . . 1776.
" " [28 ] Li governi d' Angió del Saumurois, della Touraine e Poitou, d' Aunis e Saintonge, . . . 1777.
" " [29 ] Li governi di Normandia del Maine e Perche . . . 1777.
" " [30 ] Li governi di Sciampagna e Brie . . . 1777.
" " [31 ] Il governi di Bretagna . . . 1777.
" " [32 ] Li governi di Borgogna della Franca Contea e del Lyonois . . . 1777.
" " [33 ] Li governi del Delfinato e di Provenza . . . 1777.
" " [34 ] Li governi di Lorena, Barr, ed Alsazia . . .
" " [35 ] Li governi di Linguadoca, di Foix, e di Rossiglione . . . 1777.
" " [36 ] Li regni d' Inghilterra e d' Irlanda . . . 1796.
" " [37 ] Parte meridionale dell' Inghilterra, e del principato dl Gailes . . . 1798.
" " [38 ] Parte settentrionale dell' Inghilterra, e del principato di Galles . . . 1778.
" " [39 ] Provincia di Surrey . . . 1779.
" " [39a] Provincia di Kent . . . 1779.
" " [40 ] Provincia di Essex . . . 1779.
" " [40a] Provincia di Middlesex . . . 1779.
" " [41 ] Isola di Minorca . . . 1796.
" " [42a] Parte del regno d' Irlanda, cioè le provincie d'Ulster, e Leinster . . . 1794.
" " [42a] Parte del regno d' Irlanda, cioè le provincie di Connaught e Munster . . . 1796.
" " [43 ] Il regno di Scozia . . . 1796.
" " [44 ] La Scozia Meridionale . . . 1779.
" " [45 ] La Scozia Settentrionale . . . 1795.
v. 2, no. 1. La Germania . . . 1776.
" " 2. Li Circoli d' Austria, e Baviera . . . 1796.
" " 3. Elettorato della Baviera . . . 1796.
" " 4. Regno di Boemia [Wanting]
" " 5-[5a] Parte orientale del regno di Boemia . . . 1796.
" " 6. Parte occidentale del regno di Boemia . . . 1794.

**Zatta, A.**—Continued.

v. 2, no. 7. La Slesia super$^e$ . . . 1779.
" " 8. La Slesia infer$^e$ . . . 1779.
" " 9. La Moravia . . . 1794.
" " 10. La Lusazia . . . 1780.
" " 11. Parte meridionale . . . dell' Alta Sassonia. 1780.
" " 12. Parte settentrionale . . . dell' Alta Sassonia. 1780.
" " 13. Li Circoli dell' Alto, e Basso Reno . . . 1793.
" " 14. Il Circolo di Franconia . . . 1798.
" " 15. Circolo di Westfalia . . . 1780.
" " 16. Il Circolo della Bassa Sassonia . . . 1780.
" " 17. Le Flandre Olande-si ed Austriache . . . 1784.
" " 18. Circolo di Svevia . . . 1798.
" " 19. I Vescovati di Munster . . . 1781.
" " [20] I margraviati di Anspach . . . 1779.
" " [21] Il regno di Ungheria . . . 1790.
" " [22] La repubblica d' Ollanda . . . 1795.
" " [23] Le provincie di Frisia . . . 1778.
" " [24] Le provincie di Zelanda . . . 1794.
" " [25] Li regni di Svezia, Danimarca, e Norvegia . . .
" " [26] La Svezia . . . 1792.
" " [27] Il regno di Danimarca . . . 1781.
" " [28] L' isola d' Islanda . . . 1781.
" " [29] La Norvegia . . . 1791.
" " [30] La Russia Europea . . . 1781.
" " [31] Ducati di Livonia . . . 1792.
" " [32] Governo di Arcangelo . . . 1782.
" " [33] Governi di Moscovia . . . 1782.
" " [34] La piccola Tartaria colla Crimea . . . 1788.
" " [35] La Lapponia Russa . . . 1792.
" " [36] La Polonia . . . 1799.
" " [37] Li palatinati di Mazovia . . . 1781.
" " [38] Li palatinati di Posnania . . . 1791.
" " [39] Li palatinati della Russia Rossa . . . 1781.
" " [40] Li palatinati di Nowogrodek . . . 1791.
" " [41] Li palatinati di Cracowia . . . 1791.
" " [42] Li palatinati di Minsk . . . 1781.
" " [43] Li palatinati di Braclaw . . . 1781.
" " [44] Li palatinati di Wilna . . . 1791.
" " [45] Il regno di Prussia . . . 1799.
" " [46] Turchia d'Europa . . . 1799
" " [47] Le provincie di Bulgaria, e Rumelia. 1791.
" " [48] La Grecia . . . 1781.
" " [49] La Croazia, Bosnia . . . 1782.
" " [50] Moldavia, e Vallachia. 1798.
" " [51] L'Elvezia . . . 1798.
" " [52] Parte orientale dell' Elvezia . . . 1798.
" " [53] Parte occidentale dell' Elvezia . . . 1798.
v. 3, " [ 1] L'Italia . . . 1798.
" " [ 2] Lo stato Veneto da Terra . . . 1795.
" " [ 3] I Contorni di Venezia . . . 1794.
" " [ 4] Il Cremasco . . . 1792.
" " [ 5] Polesine di Rovigo . . . 1795.
" " [ 6] Il Vicentino . . . 1793.

v. 3, no. [ 7] Il Feltrino . . . 1793.
" " [ 8] Il Friuli . . . 1793.
" " [ 9] La provincia di Brescia . . . 1792.
" " [10] Il Bergamasco . . . 1782.
" " 11. Il Trevisano . . . 1793.
" " 12. Il Bellunese . . . 1793.
" " 13. Il Veronese . . , 1793.
" " 14. Il Padovano . . . 1794.
" " 15. Parte settentrionale dell' Istria . . . 1794.
" " [16] Parte meridionale dell' Istria . . . 1794.
" " [17] La Dalmazia Veneta . . . 1794.
" " [18] Lo stato della chiesa . . . 1786.
" " [19] Legazioni di Bologna, e Ferrara . . . 1797.
" " [20] Legazione della Romagna . . . 1783.
" " [21] Legazione d'Urbino . . . 1783.
" " [22] La marca di Ancona . . . 1783.
" " [23] L'Umbria ed i territorj di Perugia . . . 1783.
" " [24] Il patrimonio di S. Pietro . . . 1783.
" " [25] Campagna di Roma . . . 1783.
" " [26] Li ducati di Parma, Piacenza e Guastalla . . . 1782.
" " [27] Gli stati del duca di Modena . . . 1797.
" " [28] Parte del Modenese . . . 1783.
" " [29] La repubblica di Lucca . . . 1781.
" " [30] Il ducato proprio di Milano . . . 1794.
" " [31] Li territorii di Lodi . . . 1794.
" " [32] Il ducato di Mantova . . . 1796.
" " [33] Il Piemonte . . . 1792.
" " [34] Ducati di Chablais, e Genevois . . . 1792.
" " [35] Ducato di Aosta . . . 1792.
" " [36] Distretto di Torino, il contado d'Asti . . . 1792.
" " [37] Pante del Piemonte . . . 1792.
" " [38] L'isola di Sardegna . . . 1792.
" " [39] Repubblica di Genova . . . 1794.
" " [40] Il gran ducato di Toscana . . . 1781.
" " [41] Il Fiorentino . . . 1793.
" " [42] Il Senese . . . 1793.
" " [43] Il Pisano . . . 1793.
" " [44] Il regno di Napoli . . . 1782.
" " [45] Abruzzo ulteriore, e citeriore . . . 1783.
" " [46] Terra di Lavoro . . . 1793.
" " [47] La Capitanata . . . 1783.
" " [48] Li principati ulteriore, e citeriore . . . 1783.
" " [49] Terra d' Otranto . . . 1793.
" " [50] Terra di Bari, e Basilicata . . . 1783.
" " [51] Calabria ulteriore . . . 1793.
" " [52] Calabria citeriore . . . 1793.
" " [53] L'isola di Sicilia . . . 1792.
" " [54] L'isola di Corsica . . . 1794.
v. 4, no. [ 1] L'Asia . . . 1777.
" " [ 2] La Turchia d'Asia . . . 1784.
" " [ 3] L'Arabia . . . 1795.
" " [ 4] L'impero della Persia . . . 1796.
" " [ 5] Le Indie orientali . . . 1799.
" " [ 6] Indie foglio primo.

**Zatta, A.**—Continued.

v. 4, no. [7] Indie foglio secondo.
" " [8] Indie orientali . . . Indie foglio terzo.
" " [9] Indie foglio quarto.
" " [10] Stato del Mogol . . . 1791.
" " [11] Regni d'Aracan, del Pegu . . . 1795.
" " [12] L'impero del Giapon . . . 1785.
" " [13] Impero della China . . . 1795.
" " [14] La Tartaria Chinese. 1794.
" " [15] La Tartaria indipendente . . . 1784.
" " [16] Russia Asiatica . . .
" " [17] Isole Filippine. 1795.
" " [18] L'Africa . . . 1796.
" " [19] L'Egitto . . . 1784.
" " [20] La Nubia, ed Abissinia. 1784.
" " [21] Le coste di Barbaria . . . 1784.
" " [22] La Guinea Occidentale . . . 1794.
" " [23] La Guinea Orientale . . . 1784.
" " [24] Parte della costa orientale dell'Africa . . . 1794.
" " [25] L'America . . . 1796.
" " [26] America Settentrionale . . .
" " [27-38] Le colonie unite dell America Settentr. le . . . 1791.
" " [39] Il Canadà . . . 1778.
" " [40] La baja d'Hudson . . . 1778.
" " [41] L'isole di Terra nouva . . . 1778.
" " [42] Nouve scoperte de' Russi . . . 1776.
" " [43] Messico . . . 1785.
" " [44] America Meridionale . . .
" " [45] La Terra Ferma . . . 1785.
" " [46] Il Paraguai . . . 1785.
" " [47] Il Perù [!] . . . 1785.
" " [48] Stabilimenti de francesi . . . nelle isole Antille . . . 1795.
" " [49] Il Chili . . . 1794.
" " [50] Nouve scoperte . . . nel mar del Sud. 1776.
" " [51] La Nouva Zelanda . . . 1794 . . . [Carte geografische antiche].
" " [52] Orbis veteribus notus . . . 1795.
" " [53] Romanum imperium . . . 1795.
" " [54] Terra di Canaan . . . 1785.
" " [55] Britannicæ Insulæ . . . 1795.
" " [56] Hispania antiqua . . . 1785.
" " [57] Germania antiqua . . . 1785.
" " [58] Italia antiqua . . . 1785.
" " [59] Græcia antiqua . . . 1795.
" " [60] Asia minor . . . 1785.
" " [61] Imperium Alexandri magni . . . 1785.
" " [62] Imperium Caroli magni . . . 1795.

## 1780

**Bonne, R.**

Atlas de toutes les parties connues du globe terrestre, dressé pour l'Histoire philosophique & politique des établiffemens & du commerce des européens dans les deux Indes . . . [Par Guillaume Thomas

François Raynal]     2 p. l., 28 pp., 50 maps, 23 tab. 4°.
[Genève, J. L. Pellet, 1780]     652

NOTE.—The following maps relate to America:
no. 1. L'ancien monde & le nouveau.
" 2. Planisphère, suivant la projection de Mercator.
" 25. L'Amérique Septentrionale.
" 26. Les isles Antilles & le golfe du Mexique.
" 27. Partie méridionale de l'ancien Mexique ou de la Nouvelle Espagne.
" 28. Le Nouveau-Mexique, avec la partie septentrionale de l'ancien, &c.
" 29. L'Amérique Méridionale.
" 30. Le Pérou, &c.
" 31. Le nouveau royaume de Grenade, la Nouvelle Andalousie & la Guyane, &c.
" 32. La Guayne Françoise, avec partie de la Guayane Hollandoise.
" 33. Le Chile, depuis le sud du Pérou jusqu'au Cap Horn, &c.
" 34. Partie méridionale du Brésil.
" 35. Partie septentrionale du Brésil.
" 36. Les isles Antilles &c.
" 37. L'isle de Saint-Domingue.
" 38. L'isle de la Jamaique.
" 39. L'isle de Cuba.
" 40. Les isles de la Guadeloupe, de Marie-Galante, de la Désirade & celle des Saintes.
" 41. L'isle de la Martinique.
" 44. L'isle de Terre-Neuve, l'Acadie ou la Nouvelle-Ecosse, l'isle Saint-Jean, & la partie orientale du Canade.
" 45. Partie occidentale du Canade, contenant les cinq grands lacs du Canada, &c.
" 46. La Louysiane & la Floride.
" 47. La partie nord des États-Unis.
" 48. La partie sud des État-Unis.
" 49. Supplément pour les isles Antilles.

## 1780

**Kitchin, T.,** *sr.*, *& others.*

A general atlas, describing the whole universe. Being a complete and new collection of the most approved maps extant; corrected with the utmost care, and augmented from the latest discoveries, down to 1780. The whole being an improvement of the maps of d'Anville and Robert [de Vaugondy]   1 p. l., 23 maps on 70 l. fol. London, R. Sayer & J. Bennett, 1780.     653

NOTE.—See titles 643, 668, 682, 685, 687, 699 and 709. Known as Dunn's atlas, from some delineations given by mr. Dunn to the map of the world. See Universal catalogue for 1773, title 113. Text on nos. 1-4, 11, 26-32, 35.

CONTENTS.

no. 1-2. Scientia terrarum et coelorum; or, the heavens and earth astronomically and geographically delineated and display'd . . . by S. Dunn. 1780. 2 sheets.

**Kitchin, T.,** *sr.*, *& others*—Continued.

no. 3–4. . . . Europe divided into its empires, kingdoms, states and republics, &c. drawn by . . . Robert de Vaugondy . . . with many additions and improvements by Thoᵒ Kitchin . . . 1772. 2 sheets.
" 5. A complete map of the British Isles, or Great Britain and Ireland . . . 1772.
" 6–7. England and Wales . . . corrected & improv'd by John Rocque. 2 sheets.
" 8–9. . . . Scotland, and islands thereto belonging . . . [Improved from the large map of mr. Dorret] 2 sheets.
" 10–11. . . . The kingdom of Ireland . . . by J. Rocque . . .
" 12. The Catholic Netherlands, divided into their several provinces with the roads . . . 1772.
" 13. The seven United Provinces with their roads and divisions . . . 1772.
" 14. The post roads of France, from the map of Jaillot . . . 1772.
" 15. . . . Spain and Portugal, divided into their great provinces . . . 1772.
" 16. Italy, divided into its several dominions, and the islands of Sicily, Sardinia and Corsica, from mr. d'Anville, by the late Thomas Jefferys . . . 1776.
" 17–18. . . . Empire of Germany . . . with the kingdom of Prussia, &c. by L. Delarochette . . . 2 sheets.
" 19. The northern states, containing the kingdoms of Sweden, Denmark, and Norway, divided into provinces and governments . . . 1772.
" 20. The kingdom of Poland, with the grand dutchy of Lithuania . . . 1772.
" 21. The whole russian empire . . . from d'Anville's maps. 1772.
" 22–23. Asia according to . . . d'Anville divided into its empires, kingdoms & states, shewing the european settlements in the East Indies . . . 1772. 2 sheets.
" 24–25. The East Indies, with the roads. By Thomas Jefferys . . . 1768. 2d. ed. . . .
" 26–27. Africa, according to mʳ d'Anville . . . with a particular chart of the Gold Coast . . . 1772. 2 sheets.
" 28–29. . . . The whole continent of America, divided into North and South and West Indies . . . Compiled from mʳ d'Anville's maps . . . 1777. 2 sheets.
" 30–31. . . . North America with the West India islands . . . corrected from the original materials, of goverʳ Pownall . . . 1777. 2 sheets.
" 32. An exact chart of the River St. Lawrence, from fort Frontenac to the island of Anticofti . . . by . . . Thoᵒ Jefferys. 1775.
" 33. Course of the river Mississippi, from the Balise to fort Chartres; taken on an expedition to the Illinois, in . . . 1765. By lieut. Rofs . . . Improved from the surveys . . . by the french. 1775.
" 34–35. A map of South America . . . from mʳ d'Anville with several improvements and additions, and the newest discoveries. 1775. 2 sheets.—Inset: A chart of Falkland's islands . . . discovered by Hawkins . . . 1593.

## 1781

**Laporte, J.**

Atlas moderne portatif, composé de vingt-huit cartes sur toutes les parties du globe terrestre; à l'usage des colléges, des pensions, des maisons religieuses, & de toutes les personnes qui étudient ou enseignent la géographie . . . Nouvelle éd., augmentée de trois nouvelles cartes astronomiques, & d'une introduction à la connoissance de la geographie. 16 pp., 27 maps, 7 diagr. 12°. Paris, Laporte, 1781.     654

NOTE.—"Avertissement" refers to "1r.e éd." Maps are like those of the "Atlas, ou collection de cartes géographiques," which accompanies his "Voyageur françois . . . Paris, 1787." See also title 662.

The following maps relate to America:
no. 2. Mappe-monde . . .
" 16. Carte d'Asie . . .
" 19. Les Indes orientales et leur archipel . . .
" 23. L'Amérique Septentrionale.
" 24. L'Amérique Méridionale.
" 25. Golfe du Mexique . . .
" 26. Carte de la Nouvelle Angleterre.
" 27. Nouvelle York, Nouvelle Jersey et Pensilvanie.
" 28. Carte de la Virginie et du Mariland.
" 29. Isle de la Jamaique.

## 1781-1784

**Delisle, G.** *and* **Buache, P.**

Atlas géographique et universel . . . 2 v. fol. Paris, Dezauche, 1781-[1784]     655

NOTE.—Collation: v. 1, 2 p. l., 86 (*i. e.* 84) maps; v. 2, 2 p. l., 89-156 maps. See also title 671.

Engraved title-pages.
Several maps dated 1784.
Maps revised and augmented.
Maps by various cartographers including: Jaillot, Le Rouge, Sanson, Placide and Robert de Vaugondy.
Contains, "Catalogue des cartes & ouvrages géographiques de mm. De l'Isle et Buache . . . De celles de m. Jaillot . . . Qui compofent le fonds géographique du sieur Dezauche, succeffeur des sieurs De l'Isle & Buache", on 2 pp. at end of v. 2. "Suplément au catalogue", printed on fly of the leaf.
Contains following plan:
v. 1, no. 10. Nouveau plan routier de la ville et fauxbourgs de Paris. Chez Esnauts & Rapilly. 1784.
The following maps relate to America:
v. 1, no. 3. Mappemonde . . . 1784.
" " 5. Hémisphère occidental . . . 1782.
" " 6. Hémisphère septentrional . . . 1782.
" " 7. Hémisphère méridional . . . 1782.
v. 2, no. 115. Carte des nouvelles découvertes au nord de la Mer du Sud, tant à l'est de la Sibérie et du Kamtchatka, qu'à l'ouest de la Nouvelle France. 1750.

**Delisle, G.,** *and* **Buache, P.**—Continued.
v. 2, no. 120. Carte des Indes et de la Chine. 1781.
" " 128. Carte d'Amérique. 1780.
" " 129. Carte du Canada qui comprend la partie Septentrionale des États Unis d'Amérique. 1783.
" " 130. Carte du Mexique et des États Unis d'Amérique. 1783.
" " 131. Carte de la Louisiane et du cours du Mississipi avec les colonie anglaises. 1782.
" " 132. Carte du golphe du Mexique et des isles Antilles. 1780.
" " 133. Carte de l'isle de Saint Domingue. 1780.
" " 134. Carte des Antilles françoises et des isles voisines. 1769.
" " 135. Carte de l'isle de la Martinique . . .
" " 136. Carte de la Dominique . . . 1778.
" " 137. Carte de la Terre Ferme du Pérou, du Brésil et du pays des Amazones. 1782.
" " 138. Carte du Paraguay du Chili du détroit de Magellan &c. 1780.

**1783**

**Buy de Mornas, C.**

Atlas méthodique et élémentaire de géographie et d'histoire, par une société de gens de lettres . . .   4 v.  fol.  [Paris, Desnos, 1783] 656

NOTE.—Title varies, v. 2, 4, Atlas historique et géographique . . . Paris, Desnos, 1783. See also titles 628.
v. 3, wanting.
First published 1761-1762.
The following printed at foot of title-page: Cet atlas aura 5 vol. in folio composés de trois cent trente deux cartes, un de cosmographie complète, de 57 cartes . . . trois de géographie ancienne, de 209 cartes . . . le dernier de géographie moderne, de 66 cartes . . .
The plates and text are the same as in earlier edition, without the ornamental border, with the exception of pl. no. 30 in v. 2. In v. 1, the engraved title, page differs from the earlier title; in v. 2, 4, the title-page is of similar design to earlier edition, but from a different plate.
The following maps relate to America:
v. 1, no. 23. Diversité des ombres et diverse situation des habitans de la terre.
" " 28. Carte réduite de l'océan occidental.
" " 30. De la géologie.
" " 38. Amérique.
" " 39. Histoire de la découverte des mondes nouveau et inconnu.
" " 44. Pour les vents.

**1785**

**Bachiene, W. A.**

Atlas, tot opheldering der hedendaagsche historie beschreeven door een gezelschap van geleerde mannen in Engeland; overgezien en verbeterd door W. A. Bachiene, in leven hoogleeraar in de sterre en aardrykskunde en predikant te maastricht, lid van verscheiden geleerde genootschappen; en gegraveerd door J. van Jagen.—Aanhangzel tot den atlas, tot opheldering der hedendaagsche historie.

2 v. in 1.    2 p. l., 37 maps; 1 p. l., 23 maps.    fol.    te Amsterdam,
M. Schalekamp, 1785.                                                         657

NOTE.—Each map in v. 1 has the date of engraving, varying from 1769 to 1785. Maps in the supplement have neither date nor engraver's name. Title-page for the supplement has been placed, in re-binding, after the "Lyst der kaarten."

The following maps relate to America:

v. 1, no. 37. . . . America . . .
no. [1] supp. Kaart van Zuid Amerika.
" [2] " Kaart van het zuidelyk gedeelte van oud Mexiko of Nieuw Spanje.
" [3] " Kaart van Nieuw Mexiko . . .
" [4] " Kaart van Peru . . .
" [5] " Kaart van Chili . . .
" [6] " Kaart van het noordiyk gedeelte van Bresil.
" [7] " Kaart van het zuidelyk gedeelte van Bresil . . .
" [8] " Kaart van het nieuw koningrijk Grenada, Nieuw Andalusie en Guyane . . .
" [9] " Kaart van Fransch Guijane . . .
" [10] " Kaart van Noord Amerika.
" [11] " Kaart van het noordlyk gedeelte der Verëenigde Staaten van Nord Amerika.
" [12] " Kaart van het zuidelyk gedeelte der Vereenigde Staaten van Nord Amerika.
" [13] " Kaart van het eiland Terre-Neuve . . .
" [14] " Kaart van ' et westelyk gedeelte van Kanada . . .
" [15] " Kaart van Louisiana en Florida.
" [16] " De Antilles eilanden en de Golf van Mexiko.
" [17] " Kaart van de Antilles . . .
" [18] " Kaart van het eiland Cuba.
" [19] " Kaart van het eiland St Domingo.
" [20] " Kaart van het eiland Jamaika.
" [21] " Kaart van het eiland Martinique.
" [22] " Kaart van de eilanden Guadeloupe, Maria Galante, Désirade en de Saintes.
" [23] " Aanhangsel tot de Antilles eilanden . . .

**1786**

**Maclot, J. C.**

Atlas général méthodique et élémentaire, pour l'étude de la géographie et de l'histoire moderne adapté à toutes les géographies; mais particulièrement è celle de l'abbé Nicole de la Croix: dressé d'après les meilleures cartes françoises et étrangeres, affujetti aux obfervations, aftronomiques de m.m. l'ac. roy. des sc. et des s[rs] Tchirikow et Delisle, par une société d'ingénieurs géographes du roi. Adopté fpécialem[t] pour l'inftruction de la jeune nobleffe de l'école royale militaire en vertu d'une délibération du confeil de cette école, avec des descriptions historiques et géographiques, imprimées sur les marges de chaque carte, pour en faciliter l'étude. Par m.

**Maclot, J. C.**—Continued.

Maclot . . . Mis au jour et éxecuté par le s ̣Desnos. 2 p. l., 137 l. incl. 60 col. maps, 7 col. pl. fol. Paris, Desnos, 1786. 658

   Note.—Engraved title.
   First edition 1768, other editions 1770 (see title 645) and 1776.
   The following maps relate to America:
   no. 8. Mappe-monde . . . par m. Brion. 1786.
   " 10. Hémisphère occidental.
   " 48. L'Amérique . . . par m. Brion. 1786.
   " 49. Chili, Paraguay, Brésil, Amazones, et Péru. Par m. Brion. 1786.
   " 50. Guayane, Terre Ferme, Isles Antilles, et N$^{lle}$ Espagne. Par m. Brion. 1786.
   " 51. Nouveau Mexique, Louisiane, Canada, et N$^{lle}$ Angleterre. Par m. Brion. 1786.
   " [66] Mappe-monde géo-hydrographique, par le s ̣Jaillot . . . augmentée . . . par m. Brion. 1786.

## 1786–1789

**Dunn, S.**

A new atlas of the mundane system; or, of geography and cosmography: describing the heavens and the earth, the distances, motions and magnitudes of the celestial bodies. . . 3d ed. with additions, corrections, and very great improvements. 2 p. l., 20, 4 pp., 44 maps, 6 pl. fol. London, Laurie & Whittle [1786–1789] 659

   Note.—See also title 684.

      CONTENTS.

   pl. A. Cosmography epitomized. 1786.
   " B. The principal elements of the solar system. 1786.
   " C. The magnitude of the sun, the primary and secondary planets . . .
   " D. The principal fixed stars of the northern hemisphere. Delineated on the plane of the equator . . . 1774.
   " E. The principal fixed stars of the southern hemisphere. Delineated on the plane of the equator . . . 1774.
   " F. An analemma . . . 1786.
   " G. A map of the world on a new projection with a delineation of the various parts . . . of the solar system . . . By Benj. Martin . . .
   " H. A map exhibiting the dark shadow of the moon over England and other parts of Europe, in the five great solar eclipses, of the years 1715, 1724, 1737, 1748 and 1764 . . . 1787.
   no. 1. A new map of the world. 1789.
   " 2. A new chart of the world on Mercator's projection with the tracks & difcoveries of the lateft circumnavigators &c. 1789.
   " 3. Europe divided into its principal states. 1787.
   " 4. The British Isles. 1786.
   " 5. A new and compendious map of England and Wales. 1788.
   " 6. Scotland and its islands. 1786.
   " 7. Ireland . . . 1786.
   " 8. The catholic Netherlands. 1787.
   " 9. The seven United Provinces. 1787.

no. 10. The northern states comprehending the kingdoms of **Denmark**, Norway and Sweden. 1789.
" 11. Russia, divided into its governments. 1789.
" 12. A new map of the kingdom of Poland. 1789.
" 13. Hungary, and Transylvania. 1789.
" 14. The empire of Germany. 1786.
" 15. Switzerland. Divided into thirteen cantons. 1786.
" 16. France, divided into military governments. 1786.
" 17. Spain and Portugal. 1786.
" 18. Italy, divided into its states. 1786.
" 19. The north part of Italy. 1786.
" 20. First part of Turkey in Europe. 1788.
" 21. Second part of Turkey in Europe. 1786.
" 22. Asia. Divided into its principal states and regions. 1794.
" 23. A map of Turkey in Asia. 1788.
" 24. Arabia, according to its modern divisions. 1786.
" 25. Persia, divided into its great provinces. 1786.
" 26. A map of independent Tartary. 1786.
" 27. A compleat map of the East Indies. 1786.
" 28. The East India islands. 1789.
" 29. China . . . and the isles of Japan. 1786.
" 30. A map of Chinese Tartary, with Corea. 1786.
" 31-32. A compleat map of the Holy Land; adapted to the Old and New testament. 1786. 2 sheets.
" 33. A map of the countries and places, mentioned in the New **testament**. 1786.
" 34. Africa and its several regions. 1787.
" 35. Antient and modern Egypt. 1786.
" 36. A map of Abyssinia and Nubia. 1786.
" 37. A map of Barbary. 1786.
" 38. America, North and South and the West Indies. 1786.
" 39. North America with the West Indies. 1789.
" 40. A new map of the United States of North America with the british dominions. 1786.
" 41. A compleat map of the West Indies, containing the coasts of Florida, Louisiana, New Spain, with all the islands. 1786.
" 42. South America. 1787.

### 1787?
**Brandis, G. B. a'**

Nieuwe natuur-geschieden handelkundige zak-en reis-atlas . . . Met 50 geographifche kaarten en onderricht om dezelve wel te gebruiken. 4 p. l., 236, [4] pp., 46 maps, 1 pl., 2 tab. 8°. Amsteldam, N. T. Gravius [1787?] 660

NOTE.—Maps nos. 7-8 in "Lijst der kaarten" comprise one map.
Maps by various cartographers including: Guileaume Delisle, Jacob Keizer and Jan de Lat.
The following maps relate to America:
no. 1. Kaart van de twee platte warelds bollen . . .
" 2. De Noord Pool . . .
" 3. De Zuid Pool . . .
" 4. De nieuwe en ouden oppervlakke en doorzigtkundige aardryks bollen . . .

**Brandis, G. B. a'**—Continued.
   no. 5. Schuine ronde aard-klooten . . .
   " 6. Schuine ronde aard-bolle . . .
   " 7-8. De wareld in een ronde gedaante van de Noord Pool . . .—De wareld verbeeld in de gedaante van een hard . . .
   " 9. Kaart van de geheele wereld . . .
   " 13. Kaartje van het noorder-deel van America . . .
   " 14. Kaartje van het zuider-deel van America . . .

### 1787
**Clouet, J. B. L.**
   Géographie moderne avec une introduction ouvrage utile à tous ceux qui veulent se perfectionner dans cette science on y trouve jusqu'aux notions les plus simples dont on a facilité l'intelligence par des figures pour le mettre à la portée de tout le monde, chaque carte a sur les marges l'explication de ce qu'elle renferme, la méthode qu'on y suit a pour objet de développer les connoissances qui tiennent à l'histoire, ce qui rend cette géographic tres intéressante; dédiée à messieurs de l'académie royale des sciences et belles-lettres de Rouen. Par mr. l'abbé Clouet de la même académie avec approbation et p. du r. [!] Corrigée et augmentée des nouvelles découvertes du célèbre captaine Cook et des changements arrivés dans l'Amérique Septentrional. 2 p. l., [137] l. incl. 61 maps, 7 pl. fol. Paris, Mondhare & Jean, 1787.     661

   Note.—Maps and plates have border text. See title 673 for 1791 edition. The following maps relate to America:
   no. 4. Des zones.
   " 8. De la terre en général.
   " 9. Des mers.
   " 11. [Le monde]
   " 15. Lacs, fleuves, rivières, et principals montagnes de l'Amérique.
   " 19. Isles, caps et ports de mer de l'Amérique.
   " 20. Mappe-monde. 1786.
   " 65. Des possessions françoises aujourd'hui sous la domination angloises.
   " 66. Du Mexique.
   " 67. Du Pérou.
   " 68. De l'Amérique en général.

### 1787
**Laporte, J. de.**
   Atlas ou collection de cartes géographiques pour l'intelligence du Voyageur françois; ou la connoissance de l'ancien et du nouveau monde. 3 p. l., 26 maps. 12°. Paris, Moutard, 1787.     662

   Note.—To accompany his: Le voyageur françois ou connoissance de l'ancien et du nouveau monde. 42 v. 12°. Paris, L. Cellot. 1768–1795.
   Maps are like those of "Atlas moderne portatif" . . . Paris, 1781. See title 654.

The following maps relate to America:
no. [ 1] Mappe-monde ou description du glôbe.
" [12] L'Amérique Septentrionale.
" [13] Carte de la Virginie et du Mariland.
" [14] Carte de la Nouvelle Angleterre . . .
" [15] Isle de la Jamaique.
" [16] Golfe du Mexique.
" [17] L'Amérique Méridionale.

## 1787

**Philippe de Prétot, E. A.**, *& others.*
Atlas universal pour l'étude de la géographie et de l'histoire ancienne et moderne. Par m.<sup>r</sup> Philippe et autres auteurs. 4 p. l., 124 maps, 2 pl. 4°. Paris, Nyon l'ainé, 1787. 663

NOTE.—Engraved title.
Contains the following plates and plans:
no. 36. Les environs de Paris . . .
" 52. Rome ancienne du temps des roys . . . 1779.
" [91] La grande mosquée à Medina.
" [92] La grande mosquée à la Mekke.
The following maps relate to America:
no. 5. Carte de l'ancien et du nouveau monde . . .
" 6. Indication nautique des principaux espaces de l'océan . . .
" 6 bis. Tabula totius orbis terrarum exhibens declinationes magneticas, ad annum 1700 composita ab Edmundo Halleys . . .
" 7. Le globe terrestre . . .
" [96] Nouvelle carte des parties orientales du monde . . . [shows] Nouveau Groenland.
" [97] Carte dans laquelle on voit la route que le centurion à tenu dans le voiage au tour du monde.
" 98. Dévelopement de la route faite autour du monde par les vaisseaux du roy la Boudeuse et l'Étoile.
" 102. Carte du canal des isles Philippines . . .
" 103. Plan de la baye de Manille.
" 109. Carte nouvelle d'Afrique . . . [shows] partie de l'Amérique.
" 112. Carte nouvelle d'Amérique . . .
" [113] Nouvelle carte des parties occidentales du monde . . .
" 114. Chorographie du Péru . . .
" 115. Carte de la Mer du Sud ou mer Pacifique . . .
" 116. Carte de la partie méridionale de la Mer du Sud . . .
" 117. Carte de la partie méridionale de l'Amérique Méridionale . . .
" [118] Copie d'une partie de la carte de Dampier depuis le Cap de Bonne Espérance jusqu'à la Nouvelle Bretagne.
" [119] [Rivière de la Plata]
" [120] Carte des isles Malouines.
" 121. Carte du detroit de Magellan avec les routes de la Boudeuse et de l'Étoile.
" 122. Plan géométrique de plusieurs bayes situées au detroit de Magellan, entre les Caps Rond et Forward.
" 123. Plan de plusieurs bayes découvertes aux Terres de Feu au-de-là du Cap Rond, dans le détroit de Magellan.

## 1787–1791

**Atlas moderne** ou collection de cartes sur toutes les parties du globe terrestre. Par plusieurs auteurs . . . 3 p. l., [3] l., 48, 20 pp., 96 (*i. e.* 93) maps, 2 pl. fol. Paris, Delamarche, 1787-[1791]   664

> Note.—First published in 1762. Another edition dated [1771–1783] See titles 629 and 646.
> Map no. 16, Carte du gouvernement de Normandie . . . dated 1791.
> Engraved title.
> In earlier editions all maps are by Bonne, Janvier, and Rizzi-Zannoni; in present edition there are also maps by Delamarche, Robert de Vaugondy, Bauche and Delisle.
> The "Avertissement" states that the abbé Nicolle de la Croix, before his death, wished to prepare an atlas to accompany his Géographie moderne, and that it was partly to carry out his views that this work was undertaken. Though the maps are arranged according to the contents of this book, many details have been added to render the atlas more generally useful.
> A note following the "Avertissement," speaks of the atlas as prepared by m$^r$ Bonne.
> The following maps relate to America:
> no. 3. Mappe-monde . . . Par le s$^r$ Janvier . . . 1782.
> " 64. L'Amérique divisée par grands états par le s$^r$ Janvier . . . 1783.
> " 65. L'Amérique Septentrionale divisée en ses principaux états. Par le s$^r$ Janvier . . . 1782.
> " 65². Partie de l'Amérique Septentrionale . . . 1783.
> " 66. États Unis de l'Amérique.
> " 67. Carte du Mexique . . . Par m. Bonne . . . 1771.
> " 68. Carte géo-hydrographique du golfe du Mexique et de ses isles . . . Par m. Rizzi-Zannone . . .
> " 69. L'Amérique Méridionale divisée en ses principaux états par le s$^r$ Janvier . . . 1782.
> " 70. Carte de la Terre Ferme, de la Guyane et du pays des Amazones . . . par m. Bonne . . . 1785.
> " 71. Carte du Pérou . . . par m. Bonne . . .
> " 72. Carte du Paraguay . . . par m. Bonne . . . 1782.

## 1787–1810?

**Bankes, T., Blake, E. W.** *and* **Cook, A.**

A new royal authentic and complete system of universal geography, antient and modern: including all the late important discoveries made by the english and other celebrated navigators . . . history and description of the whole world . . . Likewise the essence of the voyages of the most enterprifing navigators . . . from . . . Columbus . . . to . . . captain Cook . . . Together with a concife history of every empire, kingdom and state . . . To which is added a complete guide to geography, astronomy, the use of the globes, maps &c. With an account of the rise, progress and present state of navigation . . . 2 v. fol. London, for J. Cook [1787–1810?]   665

> Note.—Collation: v. 1, iv, ii, [5]—460 pp., front., 18 maps, 49 pl.; v. 2, 1 p. l., [461]–990, [6] pp., front., port., 15 maps, 39 pl. Royal license for publication

issued 1787. v. 1, published by John Cook: v. 2, by his son Charles Cook who succeeded his father in 1810. *cf.* Dictionary of national biography.
Title of v. 2 further states, "Published by the royal licence and authority of his britannic majesty king George III and containing every important, interefting, valuable and entertaining discovery throughout the whole of captain Cook's voyages round the world. Together with thofe of all other . . . circumnavigators round the globe, particularly thofe of Byron, Mulgrave, King, Clerke, Gore, Carteret, Wallis, Bougainville, &c. . . ."
The following maps relate to America :
v. 1, no. [1] A new & accurate chart of the difcoveries made by the late capt. Js. Cook, and other distinguished modern navigators . . . Exhibiting Botany bay, with the whole coast of New South Wales in New Holland; also New Zealand, Norfolk and the various other islands situated in the great Pacific ocean . . .
" " [3] A new and complete chart of the world; displaying the tracks of capt? Cook, and other modern navigators.
" " [4] The world including the late discoveries, by capt? Cook and other circumnavigators. Carefully laid down to the present time by Tho! Bowen.
v. 2, " [1] A new & accurate map of North America; with the new difcovered islands on the north east coast of Asia.
" " [2] A new & accurate chart of the Western or Atlantic Ocean. Drawn from the most approved modern maps &c. By Tho! Bowen. 1788.
" " [3] A correct map of the United States of North America. Including the british and spanish territories, carefully laid down agreeable to the Treaty of 1784. By T. Bowen, geog!
" " [4] The West Indies. Exhibiting the englifh french spanifh dutch & danifh settlements with the adjacent parts of North & South America . . .
" " [5] An accurate map of South America . . . By Tho! Bowen, geog!

## 1787-1788

**Bonne, R.** *and* **Desmarest, N.**
Atlas encyclopédique, contenant la géographie ancienne, et quelque cartes sur la géographie du moyen age, la géographie moderne, et les cartes relatives à la géographie physique . . . 2 v. 4°. Paris, hôtel de Thou, 1787-1788. 666

NOTE.—Copy no. 1. Collation: v. 1, 1 p. l., 65 pp., front., 77 maps; v. 2, 110 pp., 1 l., 63 maps.
Atlas to accompany "Géographie ancienne" and "Géographie moderne," v. 92-97, of "Encyclopédie méthodique" . . . Published separately until the complete set of "Encyclopédie méthodique" appeared.
Text of atlas contains "Analyse des cartes."
v. 2, no. 121 [Plan des] environs de Paris. . . .
The following maps relate to America:
v. 1, no. 20. Mappe-monde sur le plan d'un méridien. Hemisphère oriental.
" " 21. . . . Hémisphère occidental . . .
" " 22. . . . Hémisphère septentrional . . .
" " 23. . . . Hémisphère méridional . . .
" " 24. . . . Hémisphère oriental . . .
" " 25. . . . Hémisphère occidental . . .

**Bonne, R.** *and* **Desmarest, N.**—Continued.

v. 1, no. 26. Carte générale de toutes les parties connues de la surface de la terre . . .
"  "  28. Asie [Isles Philippines]
"  "  30. Amérique Méridionale . . .
"  "  31. Amérique Septentrionale . .
v. 2, "  104. Le Chili avec les contrées voisines et le pays des Patagons . . .
"  "  105. Pérou et pays circonvoisins . . .
"  "  106–107. Brésil et pays des Amazons . . . 2 sheets.
"  "  108. Nouveau royaume de Grenade, Nouvelle Andalousie, et Guyane.
"  "  109. Les Petites Antilles ou les isles de Vent, . . .
"  "  110. Isle de la Martinique.—Isles de la Guadeloupe, de Marie Galante, de la Désirade, et celles des Saintes.
"  "  111. L'isle de St Domingue, et celle de Porto-Rico.
"  "  112. Isles de Cuba et de la Jamaïque.
"  "  114. Cartes de supplément pour les isles Antilles.
"  "  115. L'Ancien et le Nouveau Mexique avec la Floride et la basse Louisiane. Partie orientale.
"  "  116. [Same] Partie occidentale.
"  "  117. Les États-Unis de l'Amérique Septentrionale. Partie orientale.
"  "  118. Les États-Unis . . . Partie occidentale.
"  "  119. Isle et banc de Terre-Neuve, isle Royale et isle St. Jean; avec l'Acadie ou la Nouvelle Ecosse.
"  "  120. Canada.
"  "  123. Extrémité méridionale de l'Amérique.
"  "  124. Détroit de Magellan. . . .
"  "  126. Carte de la rivière de Cook, dans la partie n. o. de l'Amérique.
"  "  130. Carte de l'entrée de Norton et du détroit de Bhering ou l'on voit . . . la pointe la plus occidentale de l'Amérique.
"  "  131. Carte de la côte n. o. de l'Amérique.

### 1787–1788

Atlas encyclopédique, contenant la géographie ancienne, et quelque cartes sur la géographie du moyen âge la géographie moderne et les cartes relatives à la géographie physique. 2 v. 4°. Paris, hôtel de Thou, 1787–1788. 667

NOTE.—Copy no. 2.

Collation: v. 1, 1 p. l., 65 pp., front., 77 maps; v. 2, 110 pp., 1 l., front., 73 maps.

### 1788

**Kitchin, T.** *& others.*

A general atlas, describing the whole universe: being a complete collection of the most approved maps extant; corrected with the greatest care, and augmented from the latest discoveries. The whole being an improvement of the maps of d'Anville and Robert [de Vaugondy] . . . 1 p. l., 23 maps on 35 sheets. fol. London, for R. Sayer [1768–1788] 668

NOTE.—Map no. 25, dated 1768; nos. 5, 12–13, dated 1788. See titles 643, 653, 682, 685, 687, 699 and 709.

Descriptive text on nos. 1–4, 11, 26–27, 30, 32 and 35.

The following maps relate to America:
no. 1- 2. A general map of the world or terraqueous globe . . . by Sam! Dunn . . . 1787.
" 23. Asia [continued—showing Philippine islands] 1787.
" 28-29. . . . The whole continent of America divided into North and South and West Indies . . . Compiled from mr. d'Anville's maps . . . & corrected in the several parts belonging to Great Britain, from the original materials of governor Pownall. 1786.
" 30-31. . . . North America; with the West India islands. Divided according to the . . . peace signed at Versailles, 20, jan. 1783. Wherein are particularly distinguished the United States . . . 1783. 1786.
" 32. . . . Chart of the river St. Lawrence, from fort Frontenac to the island of Anticosti . . . By . . . Thoᵉ. Jefferys. 1775.
" 33. Course of the river Mississipi, from the Balise to fort Chartres; taken on an expedition to the Illinois, in . . . 1765. By lieut. Rofs . . . improved from the surveys of that river made by the french. 1775.
" 34-35. . . . South America . . . from mr. d'Anville with . . . additions . . . 1787.

## 1788-1800

[**Atlante geografico**] 102 maps, 2 diagr. obl. 4°. [Siena, P. Carli, 1788-1800]     669

NOTE.—Title-page wanting.
Maps dated 1788-1800.
A collection of maps by various engravers including: Ago Costi, Filippo Conti, Gio. V. Pasquali, Gio. Silvestrini, Gio. Garti d'Alibrandi, G. Bonatti, Abbate Borghi.
Maps are hand colored.
Imprint of map no. [52] differs: Nuova carta della Germania . . . Amsterdam, da Isac Tirion.
The following maps relate to America:
no. [2] Mappa-mondo . . . emisfero occidentale.
" [92] L'Asia [Isole Filippine] 1790.
" [100] L'America divisa nelle sue principali parti.
" [101] Parte meridionale dell' Exalbia o sia de Stati Uniti d' America . . . 1800.
" [102] Le Piccole Antille . . . 1794.

## 1788-1801

**Cassini, G. M.**

Nuovo atlante geografico universale delineato sulle ultime osservazioni. [anon.] 3 v. fol. Roma, calcografia camerale, 1792-1801.     670

NOTE.—Illustrations on engraved title-pages vary; signed as follows: v. 1, Stefo Tofanelli inv. e dis. Ales Mochetti inc.; v. 2-3, Demetrio Dragon, inv: del: inci.
Imprints vary: v. 1, 1792; v. 2, 1797; v. 3, 1801. Maps dated 1788-1801.
"Atlante geografico universale," attributed to Cassini in Woltersdorf's Repertorium, with dates as follows: v. 1, 1780; v. 2, 1797; v. 3, 1802.
Maps signed: Gio. Mᵃ Cassini somᶜᵒ incise.

**Cassini, G. M.**—Continued.

Text accompanying v. 1 entitled: Introduzione generale allo studio della geografia contenente una compendiosa notizia 1. Della sfera, e de' due globi celeste, e terrestre. 2. De' termini generali della geografia. 3. Dell' origine, progressi e stato attuale della medesima. 4. Dell metodo tenuto per il presente atlante. 5. Delle navigazioni degli antichi fino a noi, e delle scoperte, onde per loro mezzo si è arricchita la geografia.

The following maps relate to America:

| | | |
|---|---|---|
| v. 1, no. | [2] Mappa mondo . . . 1788. | |
| " " | [5] Emisfero terrestre settentrionale . . . 1789. | |
| " " | [6] Emisfero terrestre meridionale . . . 1789. | |
| " " | [8] [Isole Filippine] | |
| " " | [10] Globo terrestre . . . 1790. | |
| " " | [20] L' Asia . . . [isole Filippine] 1788. | |
| " " | [22] L' America . . . 1788. | |
| v. 3, no. | [7] Le isole della Sonda, Molucche, e Filippine. 1797. | |
| " " | [12] Le coste nord-ovest dell' America . . . 1798. | |
| " " | [21] Parte occidentale dell' antico, e del nuovo Messico, con la Florida e la bassa Luigiana. 1798. | |
| " " | [22] Parte orientale dell' antico, e del nuovo Messico. 1798. | |
| " " | [23] Gli Stati Uniti dell' America, il Canada e la Florida . . . 1798. | |
| " " [24-29] | Gli Stati Uniti dell' America in 6 fogli . . . 1797. | |
| " " | [30] Le isole Antille. 1798. | |
| " " | [31] La Terra ferma, e la Guiana . . . 1798. | |
| " " | [32] Il Brasile . . . 1798. | |
| " " | [33] Il Perú . . . 1798. | |
| " " | [34] Il Chili . . . | |
| " " | [42] Mappa mondo antico . . . 1801. | |

CONTENTS.

| | | |
|---|---|---|
| v. 1, no. | 1 Tavola sferica. | |
| " " | [2] Mappa mondo. | |
| " " | [3] Planisfero celeste settentrionale. | |
| " " | [4] " " meridionale. | |
| " " | [5] Emisfero terrestre settentrionale. | |
| " " | [6] " " meridionale. | |
| " " | [7-10] Quattro tavole di fusi da univsi per formare il globo terrestre. | |
| " " | [11-14] Altre quattro tavole simili per formare il globo celeste. | |
| " " | [15-18] Altre quattro tavole per gli orizonti, e i meridiani per detti globi. | |
| " " | [19] L' Europa secondo . . . 1788. | |
| " " | [20] L' Asia " . . . 1788. | |
| " " | [21] L' Africa . . . 1788. | |
| " " | [22] L' America . . . 1788. | |
| " " | [23] L' Italia . . . 1790. | |
| " " | [24] Li regni di Napoli, e di Sicilia. 1790. | |
| " " | [25] La terra di Lavoro, ed i principati citeriore, ed ulteriore. 1790. | |
| " " | [26] L' Abruzzo ulteriore e citeriore e la contea di Molise. 1790. | |
| " " | [27] La Capitanata, e la terra di Bari. 1790. | |
| " " | [28] La Basilicata, e la terra d' Otranto. 1790. | |
| " " | [29] La Calabria citeriore. 1790. | |
| " " | [30] " " ulteriore. 1790. | |
| " " | [31] L' isola di Sicilia. 1790. | |
| " " | [32] Lo stato ecclesiastico. . . 1791. | |

v. 1, no. [33] La campagna di Roma, il Patrimonio, e la Sabina. 1790.
" " [34] La legazione d'Urbino, la Marca, l'Umbria, lo stato di Camerino . . . 1791.
" " [35] Le legazioni di Bologna, di Ferrara, e della Romagna. 1791.
" " [36-37] Il gran ducato di Toscana . . .
" " [38-41] Lo stato Veneto di terra in quatro tavole . . . 1791.
" " [42] La Dalmazia Veneta, Austriaca Turca. 1792.
" " [43-46] La Lombardia in quatro tavole . . . 1791.
" " [47-48] Le isole di Corsica, e di Sardegna in due tavole . . .
" " [49] L' Ungheria, e la Turchia Europea. 1788.
" " [50-55] L' Ungheria, e la Turchia Europea in 6 tavole . . . 1788.
v. 2, no. [1-2] Tavole per formare la sfera armilare. 1795.
" " [3] Li regni di Spagna, e Portogallo . . . 1794.
" " [4-5] Il regno di Portogallo, la parte meridionale, e la settentrionale. 1794.
" " [6] La Castiglia nuova, e la Estremadura. 1794.
" " [7] L' Andalusia, la Granata e la Murcia.
" " [8] Il regno di Valenza, colle isole di Majorica, Minorica, e Ivica.
" " [9] L'Aragona e la Catalogna.
" " [10] La Biscaglia, la Castiglia Vecchia, e la Navarra.
" " [11] La Galizia, l'Asturia, e il Leon.
" " [12-13] Il regno di Francia nell' antico sistema . . .
" " [14-15] Il medesimo secondo l' odierno sistema . . .
" " [16-21] Il regno di Francia . . .
" " [22-23] Li cantoni Svizzeri, la parte orientale e la occidentale. 1796.
" " [24-29] . . . Li paési bassi . . . 1795.
" " [30] L'impero di Germania . . .
" " [31] Il circolo di Suevia. 1797.
" " [32] L' elettorato di Baviera.
" " [33-34] L' Austria, la parte meridionale, e la settentrionale.
" " [35] La Moravia . . . 1796.
" " [36-37] Il regno di Boemia, la parte orientale, e la occidentale. 1796.
" " [38-39] La Slesia, la parte super., e l' inferiore. 1797.
" " [40] La Lusasia. 1796.
" " [41] Il circolo di Franconia.
" " [42] Li circoli dell' alto, e basso Reno. 1797.
" " [43-44] L' alta Sassonia, la parte meridionale e la settentrionale. 1796.
" " [45] La bassa Sassonia. 1796.
" " [46] Il circolo di Westfalia. 1795.
" " [47] Il regno di Prussia. 1797.
" " [48] Le isole Britanniche. 1796.
" " [49-50] Il regno d'Inghilterra, la parte meridionale, e la settentrionale. 1795.
" " [51-52] Il regno di Scozia, la parte meridionale e la settentrionale. 1795.
" " [53-54] Il regno d' Irlanda, la parte orientale, e la occidentale. 1795.
" " [55] Li regni di Suezia, Danimarca, e Norvegia . . . 1796.
" " [56] Il regno di Suezia . . . 1796.
" " [57] " " " Danimarca.
" " [58] La Norvegia. 1796.
" " [59] L' isola d' Islanda. 1796.
" " [60] L' impero della Russia in Europa . . . 1795.
" " [61] I governi di Olonechoi, Carelia, Bielozero, ed **Ingria**.
" " [62] I governi di Novogorod, Bielogorod, e **Kiovia**. 1796.

**Cassini, G. M.**—Continued.

| | | |
|---|---|---|
| v. 2, no. | [63] | Il governo di Arcangelo. |
| " " | [64] | I governi di Moscovia, e di Woronez. 1796. |
| " " | [65–66] | La Russia Asiatica, la parte occidentale, e la orientale. 1796. |
| " " | [67–70] | La Polonia . . . 1797. |
| v. 3, no. | [1] | La Turchia Asiatica. 1797. |
| " " | [2] | La Persia . . . 1797. |
| " " | [3] | L' Arabia . . . 1797. |
| " " | [4] | Le Indie orientali. 1797. |
| " " | [5] | Gli stati del Mogol, e la penisola delle Indie di gua dal Gange. 1797. |
| " " | [6] | La penisola delle Indie di la' dal Gange, con parte delle isole della Sonda. 1797. |
| " " | [7] | Le isole della Sonda, Molucche, e Filippine. 1797. |
| " " | [8] | La Cina . . . 1798. |
| " " | [9] | La Tartaria Cinese . . . 1798. |
| " " | [10] | Le isole del Giappone, e la Corea . . . 1797. |
| " " | [11] | La Tartaria indipendente. 1789. |
| " " | [12] | Le coste nord-ovest dell' America, e nord-est dell' Asia. 1798. |
| " " | [13] | L' Egitto antico e moderno. |
| " " | [14] | Le coste di Barberia, o siano i regni di Morocco, di Fez, di Algeri, di Tunisi, e di Tripoli . . . 1799. |
| " " | [15] | Parte dell' Africa, che comprende l' alta Guinea, con la Nigrizia. 1797. |
| " " | [16] | Parte meridionale dell' Africa, che comprende la bassa Guinea, e la Cafreria, con l' isola di Madagascar. 1797. |
| " " | [17] | La Nubia, e l' Abissinia. 1798. |
| " " | [18] | Le isole Canarie . . . 1798. |
| " " | [19] | " "  Azoridi . . . 1798. |
| " " | [20] | " " di capo Verde. 1798. |
| " " | [21] | Parte occidentale dell' antico, e del nuovo Messico, con la Florida e la bassa Luigiana. 1798. |
| " " | [22] | Parte orientale dell' antico e nuovo Messico. 1798. |
| " " | [23] | Gli stati uniti dell' America, con il Canada, e la Florida, carta generale . . . 1798. |
| " " | [24–29] | Gli stati uniti dell' America in 6 fogli . . . 1797. |
| " " | [30] | Le isole Antille. 1798. |
| " " | [31] | La Terra ferma, e la Gujana co' suoi dipartimenti. 1798. |
| " " | [32] | Il Brasile, ed il paése delle Amazoni, con il Paraguai. |
| " " | [33] | Il Perú, con i paési circonvicini . . . 1798. |
| " " | [34] | Il Chili, con le contrade vicine, ed il paése de' Patagoni . . . |
| " " | [35] | La nuova Zelanda. 1798. |
| " " | [36] | " "    Olanda, e la nuova Guinea. 1798. |
| " " | [37] | Le isole della societa, e di Noel. 1798. |
| " " | [38] | Le isole degli Amici. 1798. |
| " " | [39] | L' isola O-Taiti . . . 1798. |
| " " | [40] | Le nuove Ebridi e la nuova Caledonia . . . 1798. |
| " " | [41] | Le isole di Sandwich. 1798. |
| " " | [42] | Mappa mondo antico . . . 1801. |
| " " | [43] | Il mondo noto agli antichi. |
| " " | [44] | La Giudea ovvero Terra Santa . . . 1800. |
| " " | [45] | Gil imperi antichi, parte orientale. 1800. |
| " " | [46] | I medesimi, parte occidentale. |

v. 3, no. [47] L' impero Romano, occidentale ed orientale diviso nelle sue Provincie. 1799.
" " [48] L' Egitto antico. 1800.
" " [49] La Grecia antica . . . 1799.
" " [50] L' Italia antica . . . 1800.
" " [51] I contorni di Roma. 1801.
" " [52] . . . La Gallia . . . 1799.
" " [53] La Germania antica. 1799.
" " [54] L' antica Ispania . . . 1799.
" " [55] Le isole Britanniche . . . 1799.
" " [56] L' Asia Minore . . . 1799.
" " [57] La Pannonia, Dacia, l Illirico, e la Mesia. 1801.

## 1789?

**Delisle, G.**, *and* **Buache, P.**

Atlas géographique des quatre parties du monde . . . Faits [!] pour les Géographies élémentaires de m.rs Buache et de l'abbé Nicolle de la Croix. Revu et augmenté par Dezauche. 1 p. l., 37 maps on 80 l. fol. Paris, Dezauche [1789?] 671

NOTE.—Maps, dated 1716–1789, by the following cartographers: Moullet-Sanson, Robert de Vaugondy, Jaillot, Denis. See also title 655.
The following maps relate to America:
no. 1. Mappemonde à l'usage du roi. 1785.
" 2. Hémisphère septentrional. 1782.
" 3. Hémisphère méridional. 1782.
" 40. Carte d'Amérique. 1785.

## 1790

**Stackhouse, T.**

An universal atlas; consisting of a complete set of maps, peculiarly adapted to illustrate and explain ancient and modern geography: in which the ancient and prefent divifions, as alfo the subdivifions, of countries and names of places are at one view prefented to the eye, in a diftinct and correct manner, on oppofite pages; the different parts of the earth as originally peopled by the defcendents of Noah, pointed out; and the geography of the Old and New testaments included. The whole calculated to facilitate the study of geography; to make that science more extenfively known; and thereby to render history both ancient and modern, more intelligible and ufeful. 4th ed. rev. and cor. 9 p. l., 35 col. maps. fol. London, for the proprietor mrs. Stackhouse, 1790. 672

NOTE.—First edition published 1783; 5th edition, 1798.
Map no. 6, Ancient Asia, wanting.
The following maps relate to America:
no. 2. Western hemisphere. 1785.
" 10. North America in its present divisions agreeable to the peace. 1783.
" 11. South America. 1783.

## 1791

**Clouet, J. B. L.**

Géographie moderne avec une introduction. Ouvrage utile à tous ceux qui veulent se perfectionner dans cette science, on y trouve jusqu'aux notions les plus simples dont on a facilité l'intelligence par des figures pour le mettre à la portée de tout le monde, chaque carte a sur les marges l'explication de ce qu'elle renferme, la méthode qu'on y suit a pour objet de développer les connoissances qui tiennent à l'histoire, ce qui rend cette géographie très intéressante où se trouvent la France. Divisée en ses quatre vingt trois départements. Corrigée et augmentée des nouvelles découvertes du célèbre capitaine Cook et des changements arrivés dans l'Amérique Septentrional. 1791. 2 p. l., [129] l. incl. 57 col. maps, 7 col. pl. fol. [Paris] 1791. 673

NOTE.—Title engraved by Berthaule. Maps and plates have border text. See title 661 for 1787 edition.
The following maps relate to America:
no. 4. Des zônes . . .
" 8. De la terre en général.
" 9. Des mers.
" 11. [Le monde]
" 15. Lacs, fleuves, rivières, et principals montagnes de l'Amérique.
" 19. Isles, caps et ports de mer de l'Amérique.
" 20. Mappe-monde. 1786.
" 61. Des possessions françois[es] aujourd'hui sous la domination angloifes.
" 62. Du Mexique.
" 63. Du Pérou.
" 64. De l'Amérique en général.

## 1792

**Elwe, J. B.**

Atlas. 1 p. l., 22 pp., 79 l. incl. 36 maps, 3 tab., 1 chart. fol. Amstelædami, I. B. Elwe [1792] 674

NOTE.—Copy no. 1. Title of text: Beknopte beschrijving van de geheele wereld. Title-page represents allegorical figures, in color. L. Webbers, pinxit. I. van Munnikhuyse, sculp.
no. [2] [Astronomical chart]
" [5–6] Historical and geographical tables, duplicates, one colored, Amsterdam, Elwe & Langeveld, 1787.
" [26] Estats del'empire du grand seigneur des Turcs. Amsterdam, Ian. B[t]. Elwe, 1792.
Six maps undated.
The following maps relate to America:
no. [3] Mappe-monde.
" [37] Amérique Septentrionale. 1792.
" [38] L'Amérique Méridionale. 1792.
" [39] De golf van Mexico de eilanden en het omleggende land. 1792.
" [30] . . . Les isles Philippines. 1792.
" [40] [Table of distances]

Maps no. 4, 11, 15, 18, 22, 23, 35, 36 by Guillaume de L'Isle.
no. [7] Les royaumes d'Espagne et de Portugal. Amsterdam, Ian B⁺. Elwe, 1792.
" [10] Le royaume de Naples . . . par Sanson. Corrigée après les nouvelles observations du sr. d'Anville et autres géographes. Amsterdam, I. B. Elwe, 1792.
" [24] Nouvelle carte de la petite Tartarie . . . 1787.

### 1792

Atlas.    1 p. l., 75 l. incl. 35 maps, 2 tab., 1 chart.    fol.
Amstelædami, I. B. Elwe [1792]    675

NOTE.—Copy no. 2. Text and map of North America wanting.
Title-page in color, represents allegorical figures. L. Webbers, pinxit. I. van Munnikhuyse, sculp.
no. [2] [Astronomical chart]
" [5] [Historical and geographical tables]
" [38] [Table of distances]
" [6] . . . Spanje en Portugaal door Abraham Allard. No date. Same map, no. [7], in copy no. 1, has title in french, dated 1792.
Maps no. 4, 9, 14, 17, 21, 22, 34, 35 by Guillaume de L'Isle.
no. [10] Le royaume de Naples . . . par Sanson. Corrigée après les nouvelles observations du sr. d'Anville et autres géographes. Amsterdam, I. B. Elwe, 1792.
" [23] Nouvelle carte de la petite Tartarie. Amsterdam, Ian B⁺. Elwe, 1792. Same map no. [24] in copy no. 1, published by Elwe & Langeveld, 1787.
" [25] Estats del'empire du grand seigneur des Turcs. Amsterdam, Elwe & Langeveld. Same map no. [26] in copy no. 1, published by Ian B⁺. Elwe, 1792.
Six maps undated.
The following maps relate to America:
no. [3] Mappe-monde.
" [36] L'Amérique Méridionale. 1792.
" [37] De golf van Mexico, de eilanden en het omleggende land. 1792.
" [29] . . . Les isles Philippines. 1792.

### 1792

**Gibson, J.**

Atlas minimus, or a new set of pocket maps of the several empires, kingdoms and states of the known world, with hiftorical extracts relative to each. Drawn and engrav'd by J. Gibson from the best authorities, revis'd, corrected and improv'd, by Eman. Bowen. A new edition,—corrected.   2 p. l., [1] l., 52 maps.  32°.  London, 1792.    676

NOTE.—See also titles 621 and 691.
The following maps relate to America:
no. 1. The world.
" 5. North America.
" 6. South America.
" 39. Nova Scotia.

**Gibson, J.**—Continued.
no. 40. New England.
" 41. New York and Pensilvania.
" 42. Pensilvania, Maryland and Virginia.
" 43. The United States of America.
" 44. Carolina and Georgia.
" 45. Newfoundland.
" 46. Island of Cape Breton.
" 47. West Indies.
" 48. Canada or New France.
" 49. Mexico or New Spain.
" 50. Brasil.
" 51. Paraguay and Tucuman.
" 52. Peru.

### 1792

**Lopez, T.**, *i. e.* **T. L. de V. M.**
Atlas elemental, moderno ó coleccion de mapas, para enseñar á los niños geografía; con una idea de la esfera. 1 p. l., 24 pp., 27 maps. sm. 4°. Madrid, 1792. 677

NOTE.--The following maps relate to America:
no. 3. Mapa mundi.
" 22. América Septentrional . . .
" 23. Estados unidos . . .
" 24. Golfo de Mexico y las iflas Anullas.
" 25. América Meridional.

### 1793?

**Robert de Vaugondy, G.**, *and* **Robert de Vaugondy, D.**
Atlas universel . . . Corrigé et augmenté de la carte de la république française divisée en départemens par C. F. Delamarche . . . 2 p. l., 34 pp., [8] l., 112 maps. fol. Paris, Delamarche [1793?] 678

NOTE.—See title 619. Date on map no. [25ª], La république française divisée en 89 départemens. 1793.
Map no. [112], Plan géométral de Paris et de ses faubourgs . . . 1797, is not called for by the index. Probably inserted.
Various maps are prepared from those of Sanson, Delisle, Buache, Dezauche, Fry and Jefferson.
Contains a noted map, no. [111], "États-Unis de l'Amérique Septentrionale avec les Isles Royale, de Terre Neuve, de Sᵗ. Jean, l'Acadie &c. 1785. Paris, chez Delamarche," which gives list of the thirteen original states, with Vermont, and the proposed names of the ten new states, provided for in the Jeffersonian ordinance of 1784, and entitled, Sylvania, Michigania, Chersonesus, Assenisipia, Metropotamia, Illenoia, Saratoga, Washington, Polypotamia, Pelisipia.
The following maps relate to America:
no. 1. Orbis Vetus.
" 13. Mappe-monde . . .
" 102. Amérique Septentrionale . . . 1783 . . .
" 103. Partie de l'Amérique Septent. qui comprend la Nouvelle France ou le Canada . . .

no. 104. Partie de l'Amérique Septentrionale, qui comprend le cours de l'Ohio, la N$^{lle}$ Angleterre, la N$^{lle}$ York, le New Jersey, la Pensylvanie, le Maryland, la Virginie, la Caroline . . .
" 105. Carte de la Virginie, et du Maryland . . .
" 106. Amérique Méridionale . . .
" 107. Partie de la Mer du Nord, où fe trouvent les Grandes et Petites Isles Antilles et les isles Lucayes . . .
" 108. Isles de Saint Domingue ou Hispaniola, et de la Martinique . . .
" [111] États-Unis de l'Amérique Septentrionale avec les Isles Royale, de Terre Neuve, de S$^t$. Jean, l'Acadie &c. 1785 . . .

### 1793

Новый атласъ или собраніе картъ всѣхъ частей земнаго шара почерпнутый изъ разныхъ сочинителей и напечатанный въ санктпетербургѣ для употребленія юношества въ 1793 году при горномъ училищѣ. [New atlas or collection of maps of all parts of the globe, compiled from various authors for the use of students. anon.] 2 p. l., 57 maps, 1 pl. fol. [St. Petersburg, school of mines, 1793]   679
 Note.—Engraved title.
 The following maps relate to America:
 no. 2. Карта шара земнаго . . . 1791. [Map of the world]
 " 28. Восточная часть россійскаго государства. [Eastern part of the Russian empire]
 " 48. Америка раздѣленная на главныя области. [America divided into main parts]
 " 49. Америка сѣверная раздѣленная на знажнѣйшія земли. [North America divided into main parts]
 " 50. Часть сѣверной Америки . . . [Part of North America]
 " 51. Американскія соединныя Области. [United States of America]
 " 52. Карта мексики или новой испаніи . . . Map of Mexico or New Spain]
 " 53. Америка южная . . . [South America]
 " 54. Карта земноводная залива мексиканскаго съ островами его. [Map of the gulf of Mexico, and islands]
 " 55. Карта представляющая терру фирму гвіану и землю Амазонокъ. [Map representing Guiana and the country of the Amazones]
 " 56. Карта королевства Перу . . . [Map of the kingdom of Peru]
 " 57. Карта представляющая парагвай . . . [Map representing the Paraguay]

### 1794

**Grenet,** *L'abbé—*
 Compendio di geografia antica e moderna. Formatio sulle carte più esatte opera utilissima per apprendere l'una e l'altra geografia parte tradotta dal celebre sig. abate Grenet e nella parte dell' Italia tratta dai più diligenti geografi moderni; con un breve trattato della sfera del medesimo autore . . . 91, [1] pp., [4] l., 61 maps. 4°. Venezia, A. Santini, 1794.   680
 Note.—Translated from the french.
 Engraved title-page to maps reads: Atlas portatif à l'usage des colleges, pour servir a l'intelligence des auteurs classiques. Par l'abbé Grenet . . .

**Grenet,** *L'abbé*—Continued.
> First french edition of the atlas published in 1781; republished with new maps, and the above title in 1784, followed by many editions. *cf.* Biographie universelle, ancienne et moderne. Sup. v. 66, p. 89, for life and bibliographical notice. See also title 288.
> Maps are by Rigobert Bonne.
> Two maps wanting:
> no. 15. État de l'église et duché de Toscane.
> " 61. Mappa Ægypti antiquæ.
> The following maps relate to America:
> no. 1. Mappemonde en deux hémisphères. 1788.
> " 2. Carte réduite des terres et des mers du globe terrestre. 1789.
> " 3. Carte de la direction des vents generaux et des moussons.
> " 41. Les États Unis de l'Amérique Septentrionale.
> " 42. Carte générale de l'Amérique Septentrionale. 1790.
> " 43. Carte générale de l'Amérique Méridionale. 1789.
> " 44. Carte des isles de Cuba et de la Jamaïque.
> " 45. Carte des isles de S<sup>t</sup>. Domingue et de Porto-rico. 1790.
> " 46. Isles Antilles ou du Vent, avec les isles sous le Vent. 1790.

### 1794-1798
**Palairet, J.,** *& others.*
Bowles's universal atlas: being a complete collection of new and accurate maps, of all the known countries in the world; displaying the whole surface of the terraqueous globe. Laid down from correct surveys, new discoveries, and authentic documents . . . 1 p. l., 37 col. maps. fol. London, for Bowles & Carver [1794–1798]  681
> NOTE.—A collection of maps representing the work of the following geographers and surveyors: Delarochette, Dorret, Evans, Hubner, Mayer, Patterson, Rouvier, and Sheffield.
> Table of contents on title-page.
> Maps nos. 8, 10, 17, 21 and 31 are dated.
> no. 26. Inset: The forty years sojourning of the children of Israel through the wilderness to the land of Canaan.
> no. 29. . . . Map of the coast of Africa. [With explanatory notes in border text]
> " 32. Inset: . . . An accurate plan of the town, harbour and environs of Boston.
> " 34. Inset: A general plan of Port Royal . . .
> The following maps relate to America:
> no. 1. . . . The world . . .
> " 3. . . . Asia. . . . [Philippine islands]
> " 5. . . . America . . .
> " 25. . . . Map of the discoveries made by the russians on the north west coast of America.
> " 30. . . . North America . . .
> " 31. . . . United States of America . . .
> " 32. . . . New England . . .—Inset: Plan of Boston with its harbour and environs.
> " 33. . . . Map of the independent states of Virginia, Maryland, Delaware, Pensylvania, New Jersey, New York, Connecticut, Rhode Island &c. . . . by Lewis Evans.

no. 34. . . . Jamaica . . .—Inset: A general plan of Port Royal . . .
" 35. . . . The Atlantic or Western ocean.
" 36. . . . South America . . . by L. Delarochette.
" 37. . . . Falkland islands . . .

### 1795

**Kitchin, T.,** *& others.*

A new universal atlas, exhibiting all the empires, kingdoms, states, republics, &c., &c., in the whole world. Being a complete collection of the most approved maps extant. Corrected with the greatest care, and augmented from the last edition of d'Anville and Robert [de Vaugondy] With many improvements by major James Rennell and other eminent geographers; including all the tracks and new discoveries of the british circumnavigators Biron, Wallis, Carteret, captain James Cook, &c., &c. Engraved on one hundred plates comprising sixty-six maps . . . 2 p. l., 52 maps on 66 sheets. fol. London, R. Laurie & J. Whittle, 1795. 682

NOTE.—See also titles 643, 653, 668, 685, 687, 699 and 709.
The following maps relate to America:
no. 1. A new chart of the world . . . 1794.
" 2-3. A general map of the world . . . 1794.
" 56-57. A new map of the whole continent of America . . . 1794.
" 58-59. A new map of North America, with the West India islands. 1794.
" 60. A new and complete map of the West Indies. 1794.
" 61. Jamaica, 1794.
" 62. A new and correct map of the british colonies in North America . . . 1794.
" 63. A new and general map of the middle dominions belonging to the United States of America . . . 1794.
" 64. A new and general map of the southern dominions belonging to the United States of America . . . 1794.
" 65-66. A map of South America . . . 1794.

### 1796

**Carey, M.**

Carey's general atlas . . . 1 p. l., 45 maps. fol. Philadelphia, M. Carey, 1796. 683

NOTE.—See also titles 721, 722 and 732.

CONTENTS.

no. 1. A map of the world . . .
" 2. A chart of the world . . .
" 3. An accurate map of Europe . . .
" 4. Sweden, Denmark, Norway, Finland . . .
" 5. The russian empire, in Europe and Asia.
" 6. Scotland . . .
" 7. An accurate map of England and Wales . . .
" 8. A map of Ireland . . .
" 9. The seven United Provinces . . .
" 10. The austrian, french and dutch Netherlands . . .
" 11. The empire of Germany with the 13 cantons of Switzerland . . .

**Carey, M.**—Continued.
- no. 12. France divided into circles and departments.
- " 13. A map of the seat of war in France . . .
- " 14. Turkey, in Europe and Hungary . . .
- " 15. Spain and Portugal . . .
- " 16. Italy and Sardinia . . .
- " 17. Switzerland . . .
- " 18. Poland . . .
- " 19. Asia . . .
- " 20. China, divided into its great provinces . . .
- " 21. An accurate map of Hindostan . . .
- " 22. Africa . . .
- " 23. The british possessions in North America . . . by Samuel Lewis. 1794.
- " 24. A map of the United States . . . by Sam[l] Lewis. 1795.
- " 25. Vermont . . . Delineated & engraved by Amos Doolittle . . .
- " 26. The state of New Hampshire. Compiled . . . by Samuel Lewis, 1794.
- " 27. The province of Maine . . . by Samuel Lewis, 1794.
- " 28. The state of Massachusetts. Compiled . . . by Samuel Lewis.
- " 29. The state of Rhode Island; compiled, from the surveys . . . of Caleb Harris. By Harding Harris.
- " 30. Connecticut . . . Delineated & engraved by A. Doolittle . . .
- " 31. The state of New York, compiled . . . by Samuel Lewis. 1795.
- " 32. The state of New Jersey . . .
- " 33. The state of Pennsylvania, reduced . . . from Reading Howell's map by Samuel Lewis.
- " 34. Delaware . . .
- " 35. The state of Maryland . . . by Samuel Lewis.
- " 36. The state of Virginia . . . by Samuel Lewis. 1794.
- " 37. The state of North Carolina . . . by Samuel Lewis.
- " 38. The state of South Carolina . . . by Samuel Lewis. 1795.
- " 39. Georgia . . .
- " 40. Kentucky, reduced from Elihu Barker's large map.
- " 41. A map of the Tennasee state . . . taken chiefly from surveys by gen[l] D. Smith. & others.
- " 42. A map of South America . . .
- " 43. A chart of the West Indies . . .
- " 44. A map of the countries situated about the North pole.
- " 45. A map of the discoveries made by capt[s] Cook & Clerke in . . . 1778 & 1779 between the eastern coast of Asia and the western coast of North America . . . Also m[r] Hearn's discoveries to the north westward of Hudson's bay, in 1772.

### 1796

**Dunn, S.**

A new atlas of the mundane system; or of geography and cosmography: describing the heavens and the earth, the distances, motions, and magnitudes of the celestial bodies . . . 4th ed. with additions, corrections, and very great improvements. 2 p. l., 20, 4 pp., 44 maps, 6 pl. fol. London, R. Laurie & J. Whittle, 1796.

684

NOTE.—See also title 659.

## CONTENTS.

- no. A. Cosmography epitomised.
- " B. Principal elements of the solar system.
- " C. The magnitude of the sun, the primary and secondary planets . . .
- " D. The principal fixed stars of the north hemisphere. Delineated on the plane of the equator . . . 1774.
- " E. The principal fixed stars of the south hemisphere. Delineated on the plane of the equator . . . 1774.
- " F. An analemma.
- " G. A map of the world on a new projection with delineation of the various parts . . . of the solar system . . . By Benj. Martin . . .
- " H. A map exhibiting the dark shadow of the moon over England and other parts of Europe, in the five great solar eclipses, of the years 1715, 1724, 1737, 1748 and 1764 . . . 1787.
- " 1. A new map of the world. 1794.
- " 2. A new chart of the world on Mercator's projection with the tracks & difcoveries of the lateft circumnavigators &c. 1794.
- " 3. Europe divided into its principal states. 1794.
- " 4. The British Isles. 1794.
- " 5. A new and compendious map of England and Wales. 1794.
- " 6. Scotland and its islands. 1786.
- " 7. Ireland . . . 1786.
- " 8. The Catholic Netherlands. 1794.
- " 9. The seven United Provinces. 1794.
- " 10. The northern states, comprehending the kingdoms of Denmark, Norway and Sweden. 1789.
- " 11. Russia, divided into its governments. 1794.
- " 12. A new map of the kingdom of Poland. 1794.
- " 13. Hungary and Transylvania. 1794.
- " 14. The empire of Germany. 1794.
- " 15. Switzerland. Divided into thirteen cantons. 1794.
- " 16. France, divided into military governments. 1794.
- " 17. Spain and Portugal. 1794.
- " 18. Italy, divided into its states. 1794.
- " 19. The north part of Italy. 1794.
- " 20. First part of Turkey in Europe. 1794.
- " 21. Second part of Turkey in Europe. 1794.
- " 22. Asia. Divided into its principal states and regions. 1794.
- " 23. A map of Turkey in Asia. 1794.
- " 24. Arabia, according to its modern divisions. 1794.
- " 25. Persia, divided into its great provinces. 1794.
- " 26. A map of independent Tartary. 1794.
- " 27. A compleat map of the East Indies. 1794.
- " 28. The East India islands. 1794.
- " 29. China . . . and the isles of Japan. 1794.
- " 30. A map of Chinese Tartary, with Corea. 1794.
- " 31-32. A compleat map of the Holy Land; adapted to the Old and New testament. 1794. 2 sheets.
- " 33. A map of the countries and places mentioned in the New testament. 1794.
- " 34. Africa and it's several regions. 1794.
- " 35. Antient and modern Egypt. 1794.
- " 36. A map of Abyssinia and Nubia. 1794.

**Dunn, S.**—Continued.
  no. 37. A map of Barbary. 1794.
  " 38. America North and South and the West Indies. 1794.
  " 39. North America with the West Indies. 1794.
  " 40. A new map of the United States of North America with the british dominions. 1794.
  " 41. A compleat map of the West Indies containing the coasts of Florida, Louisiana, New Spain, and Terra Firma, with all the islands. 1794.
  " 42. South America. 1794.

## 1796

**Kitchin, T.** & *others.*
  A new universal atlas, exhibiting all the empires, kingdoms, states, republics, etc., etc., in the whole world. Being a complete collection of the most improved maps extant; corrected with the greatest care and augmented from the last edition of d'Anville and Robert. With many improvements by major James Rennell . . . including all the tracks and new discoveries of the british circumnavigators—Biron, Wallis, Carteret, captain James Cook . . . 2 p. l., 66 maps. fol. London, R. Laurie & J. Whittle [1789]-1796. 685

  NOTE.—Maps variously dated. See also titles 643, 653, 668, 682, 687, 699, and 709.
  The following maps relate to America:
  no. 1. A new chart of the world . . .
  " 2–3. The world according to Mercator's projection.
  " 56–57. . . . America divided into North & South, & West Indies . . . compiled from m. d'Anville's maps . . . and corrected . . . from the original materials of governor Pownall.
  " 58. North America with the West India Islands . . .
  " 59–60. West Indies comprehending all the coasts and islands known by that name, by m. d'Anville . . .
  " 61. Jamaica . . . improved and engraved by Thomas Jefferys.
  " 62. The british colonies in North America . . .
  " 63. The middle dominions belonging to the United States . . .
  " 64. The southern dominions belonging to the United States . . .

## 1796

**Reilly, F. J. J. von.**
  Grosser deutscher atlas. 2 p. l., 27 maps, 1 pl. obl. fol. [Wien, F. J. J. von Reilly, 1796] 686

  NOTE.—Engraved title and index sheet.
  Two manuscript leaves inserted.

### CONTENTS.

  no. 1. Karte von de erde. Nach d'Anville.
  " 2. " " Europa. " " " und Has.
  " 3. Grœssen und bevœlkerungs karte von Europa . . . nach Crome . . .
  " 4. " " Asien. Nach d'Anville.
  " 5. " " Afrika. Nach [Robert de] Vaugondy.
  " 6. " " Amerika. Nach d'Anville und Pownall. Inset: [United States]
  " 7. " " de inselwelt Polynesien. Nach Djurberg und Roberts.
  " 8. " " dem königreiche Portugal. Nach Lopez.
  " 9. " " " " Spanien. " "

no. 10. Karte von Grossbritannien und Ireland. Nach Kitchin, Dorret und Jefferys.
" 11. Das königreich England. Nach Kitchin.
" 12. Karte von Scotland. Nach Dorret.
" 13. " " Ireland. " Jefferys.
" 14. " " der republik der vereinigten Niederlande.
" 15. " " Frankreich. Nach Cassini und Julien.
" 16. " " Italien. Nach d'Anville.
" 17. " " der Schweiz. Nach Faden.
" 18. " " Deutschland. Nach Sotzmann.
" 19. " " dem königreiche Böheim. Nach Müller.
" 20. " " " erzherzogthum Oesterreich.
" 21. " " " königreiche Ungarn.
" 22. " " " Oschmanischen reiche in Europa. Nach d'Anville, Schmidt und Santini.
" 23. Karte von dem russischen reiche in Europa. Nach der karte der gesellschaft der künste und wissenschaften in Petersburg.
" 24. Karte von Polen. Nach Sotzmann.
" 25. " " dem kœnigreiche Preussen. Nach Suchodolez und Endersch.
" 26. Karte von dem kœnigreiche Schweden.
" 27. " " " " Dænemark.
" 28. " " " " Norwegen. Nach O. A. Wangensteen und I. N. Wilse.

## 1797

**Kitchin, T.**
Kitchin's general atlas, describing the whole universe; being a complete collection of the most approved maps extant; corrected with the greatest care, and augmented from the last edition of d'Anville and Robert [de Vaugondy] with many improvements by other eminent geographers ... 1 p. l., 37 maps. fol. London, R. Laurie & J. Whittle, 1797. 687

NOTE.—See also titles 643, 653, 668, 682, 685, 699 and 709.
The following maps relate to America:
no. 1-2. The world according to Mercator's projection.
" 32-33. ... America, divided into North & South, and West Indies ... compiled from m. d'Anville's maps ... and corrected ... from the original materials of governor Pownall.
" 34-35. North America with the West Indies ... corrected from the original materials of governor Pownall.
" 36-37. South America ... from m. d'Anville ...

## 1797

**Lapérouse, J. F. de G.**
Voyage de La Pérouse autour du monde, publié conformément au décret du 22 avril 1791, et rédigé par m. L. A. Milet-Mureau ... Atlas. 1 p. l., 32 maps, 37 pl. fol. Paris, l'imprimerie de la république, an v. (1797) 688

NOTE.—Atlas accompanying this work has engraved title: Atlas du voyage de La Pérouse. Gravé par Ph. Triere.
Published also in english. See title 693.

**Lapérouse, J. F. de G.**—Continued.

The following maps relate to America:
- no. 1. Mappemonde ou carte réduite des parties connues du globe. . . .
- " [2] Carte du grand océan ou Mer du Sud . . .
- " [3] Plan de la baie de la Conception située dans le Chili . . .
- " [7] Carte des côtes de l'Amérique et de l'Asie depuis la Californie jusqu'à Macao . . .
- " [8] Carte générale d'une partie de la côte du nord-ouest de l'Amérique . . .
- " [9] Carte particulière de la côte du nord-ouest de l'Amérique . . . 1ᵉ feuille.
- " [10] Plan du port des Français sur la côte du n. o. de l'Amérique . . .
- " [11] Plan de l'entrée du port de Bucarelli sur la côte nord-ouest de l'Amérique . . .
- " [12]-[13] Carte particulière de la côte du nord-ouest de l'Amérique . . .
- " [14] Plan du port de St. François situé sur la côte de la Californie Septentrionale . . .
- " [15] Plan de la baie de Monterey . . .
- " [16] Plan du port de St. Diego . . . & Plan du port et du département de St. Blas . . .
- " [18] Carte générale des découvertes faites en 1787 dans les mers de Chine et de Tartarie ou depuis Manille jusqu'à Avatscha . . .
- " [19] Carte des découvertes faites en 1787 . . . 1ᵉʳᵉ feuille [Îles Philippines]
- " [30] Partie de la mer du Sud comprise entre les Philippines et la Californie d'après la carte espagnole trouvée sur le galion pris par l'amiral Anson en 1743, qui représente l'état des connaissances à cette époque, et les routes que suivaient ordinairement les galions dans leur traversée de Manille à Acapulco.—Partie de la mer du Sud comprise entre les Philippines et la Californie d'après une autre carte espagnole communiquée à La Pérouse dans sa relache à Monterey, sur laquelle il avait tracé sa route ainsi que les îles qu'il avait reconnues avec des notes sur celles qu'il n'avait pas retrouvée.

### 1797

**Walker, J.**

An atlas to Walker's geography and gazetteer. 1 p. l., 25 maps, 5 pl., 1 diagr. 8°. Dublin, T. M. Bates, 1797.   689

NOTE.—Maps and plates are like those in Walker's "Universal gazetteer" and "Elements of geography."

The following maps relate to America:
- no. 1. World.
- " 7. General chart on Mercator's projection.
- " 8. United States of America agreeable to the peace of 1783.
- " 25. Asia [Philippine islands]
- " 28. West Indies.
- " 29. North America.
- " 30. South America.

## 1798

**Faden, W.**

Atlas minimus universalis, or a geographical abridgement ancient and modern of the several parts of the earth, in fifty-five maps composed principally for the use of schools &c.   3 p. l., 55 col. maps. obl. 24°.   [London] W. Faden, 1798.   690

NOTE.—Maps dated 1798, except no. 20, "France divided into one hundred and four departm$^{ts}$", dated 1804; the index calls for, "France divided into 83 departments."
The following maps relate to America:
13. The new world or the western hemisphere.
14. Chart of the world on Mercator's projection with the most recent discoveries.
15. Northern hemisphere.
16. Southern hemisphere.
50. North America, including the West Indies.
51. British possessions in North America and United States with Vermont, Kentucky and Tennassee.
52. Western coast of North America with Behring's straits.
53. West India islands.
54. South America from the latest spanish and portuguefe surveys.

## 1798

**Gibson, J.**

Atlas minimus: or, a new set of pocket maps, of various empires, kingdoms and states, with geographical extracts relative to each. New ed. rev.   2 p. l., 41, [2] l., 41 maps.  24°.  Philadelphia, for M. Carey, 1798.   691

NOTE.—See also titles 621 and 670.
The following maps relate to America:
no. 5. North America.
"   6. South America.

## 1799

**Cruttwell, C.**

Atlas to Cruttwell's gazetteer.   1 p. l., 26 maps.  fol.  London, for G. G. & J. Robinson [1799]   692

NOTE.—To accompany his "The new universal gazetteer." 1798.
The following maps relate to America:
no. [1] The world. 1799.
"  [2] A general chart of the world on Mercator's projection. 1799.
"  [6] British America, comprehending Canada, Labrador, New-Foundland, Nova Scotia &c.  1799.
"  [7] United States of America.  1799.
"  [8] South America. 1799.
"  [9] A map of the countries thirty degrees round the North Pole. 1799.
"  [24] The West Indies. 1799.

## 1799

**Lapérouse, J. F. de G.**

A voyage round the world, performed in the years 1785, 1786, 1787, and 1788, by the Boussole and Astrolabe, under the command of J. F. G. de La Pérouse: published by order of the national assembly under the superintendence of L. A. Milet-Mureau . . . Atlas. 1 p. l., [2] pp., 31 maps, 38 pl. fol. London, for G. G. & J. Robinson, J. Edwards & T. Payne, 1799. **693**

> NOTE.—Atlas accompanying this work has engraved title: Charts and plates to La Pérouse's voyage . . .
> Translated from the french. See title 688.
> Like the "Voyage de La Pérouse autour du monde. Paris, an V (1797)" except, map no. 19, "Carte des découvertes faites en 1787 dans les mers de Chine et de Tartarie" . . . which is not in this atlas.
> The following maps relate to America:
> no. 1. Map of the world . . .
> " [2] Chart of the Pacific ocean or South sea . . .
> " [3] Plan of the bay of Conception in Chili . . .
> " [7] Chart of the coasts of America and Asia from California to Macao . . .
> " [8] Chart of part of the north west coast of America . . .
> " [9] Chart of the north west coast of America . . .
> " [10] Plan of port "des Français" on the north west coast of America . . .
> " [11] Plan of the entrance of the port of Bucarelli on the north west coast of America . . .
> " [12-13] Chart of the northwest coast of America . . .
> " [14] Plan of port St. Francisco . . .
> " [15] " " the bay of Monterey . . .
> " [16] " " " port of S. Diego . . . and Plan of the port and departement of S. Blas . . . 1777.
> " [18] Chart of discoveries made in 1787 in the seas of China and Tartary . . .
> " [29] Part of the Pacific ocean between California and the Philippine islands. From the spanish chart found on board the galleon taken by admiral Anson, in 1743, which exhibits the state of geographical knowledge at that period, & the tracks usually followed by the Galleons, in their voyage between Manilla and Acapulco.—Part of the Pacific ocean between California and the Philippine islands, from the spanish chart shewn to La Perouse at Monterey, on which he had marked his course & the islands he had seen, with notes on those which he could not find.

## 1800

**Schræmbl, F. A.**

Allgemeiner grosser atlass . . . 6 p. l., 55 maps on 134 l. fol. Wien, P. J. Schalbacher [1786]-1800. **694**

> NOTE.—Engraved title-page.
> Added title: Allgemeiner grosser Schrämblischer atlass.
> Imprint date 1800; maps dated 1786-1797.
> A collection of maps by various cartographers including: Anville, Blanco, Bonne, Bowles, Cassini, Crome, Dorret, Djurberg, Endersch, Faden, Kitchin, Lopez, Niebuhr, Pownall, Rizzi-Zannoni, Robert de Vaugondy, Roberts, Santini, Schmid, Schimek, Wenzeley, Wussin.

Each map contains the following, "herausgegeben von F. A. Schræmbl."
The following maps relate to America:

no. [2-3] Oestliche und Westliche halb kugel verfasst von d'Anville . . . 1786.
" [32 a-b] Zweiter theil der karte von Asien welcher . . . die inseln . . . Philippinen . . . enthælt. Verfasst von herrn d'Anville . . . 1786. 2 sheets.
" [36 a-d] General karte von Nord America samt den West Indischen inseln verfasst von herrn Pownall . . . 1788. 4 sheets.
" [37 a-c] Karte von Süd America verfasst von herrn d'Anville . . . 1786. 3 sheets.
" [39] Polynesien (Inselwelt) oder der fünfte welttheil verfasst von herrn D. Djurberg . . . 1789 [Die Philippinischen]
" [40] Karte des Atlantischen oceans . . . 1788.
" [46] Karte der Magellanischen strasse von herrn don Iuan de la Cruz Cano y Olmedillo . . . 1787.
" [50] Karte von den n. w. Amerikanischen und n. oe. Asiatischen küsten, nach den untersuchungen des kapit: Cook in den jah: 1778 und 1779; entworfen von Heinrich Roberts, lieut: . . . 1788.
" [55 a-b] General karte sæmmtlicher entdeckungen auf den drei grossen weltreisen des kapit. Jakob Cook. Verfasst von herrn Heinrich Roberts, lieut. . . . 1789. 2 sheets.

CONTENTS.

" [1] Stereographischer entwurf des gestirnten himmels . . . von I. Bode . . . 1787.
" [2] Oestliche halb-kugel verfasst von d'Anville . . . 1786.
" [3] Westliche halb kugel verfasst von d'Anville . . . 1786.
" [4 a-b] Erster theil der karte von Europa . . . Verfasst von d'Anville 1790. 2 sheets.
" [5 a-b] Zweiter theil der karte von Europa welcher Dænemark und Norwegen, Schweden, und Russland enthælt. Verfasst von d'Anville 1787. 2 sheets.
" [6 a-b] Dritter theil der karte von Europa welcher das südliche Russland, Polen und Ungarn die europæische und beinahe die ganze asiatische Turkei enthælt. Verfasst von d'Anville . . . 1788. 2 sheets.
" [7] Neue karte von Europa . . . Verfasst von A. F. W. Crome . . . 1787.
" [8 a-x] Neueste general kart von Deutschland in xxiv blättern. Nach Büschings erdbeschreibung nach Chauchards und anderen neuesten karten . . . 1797.
" [9 a-d] General karte von Ungarn . . . nach den . . . karten . . . Hell, Liesganig, Mikowiny, Islenief & entworfen und angefangen von I. Wussin . . . vollendet von A. von Wenzely . . . 1790. 4 sheets.
" [10 a-b] General karte von Siebenbürgen . . . von A. von Wenzely 1789.
" [11] Westlicher theil von Delmatien von P. Santini . . . 1789.
" [12] Oestlicher theil von Delmatien von P. Santini . . . 1789.—Inset: Buchten von Cattaro.
" [13 a-d] Neueste general karte von den sæmtlichen oestreichischen Niederlanden . . . nach den karten von Ferraris, A. F. W. Crome, J. B. de Bouge . . . entworfen von A. von Wenzely . . . 1790.
" [14 a-d] General karte von Polen, Litauen, und den angrænzenden lændern nach Zannoni, Folin, Uz, Peau, &c. . . . 1788. 4 sheets.

**Schræmbl, F. A.**—Continued.

no. [15 a–b] Neueste general karte von Tyrol nach den vortreflichen karten P. Anichs und B. Huebers . . . verfast von A. von Wenzely. . . . 1790. 2 sheets.
" [16 a–b] Karte von Italien verfasst von d'Anville . . . 1787. 2 sheets.
" [17 a–c] General karte des russischen reichs mit der eintheilung in die neu errichteten stattshalterschaften und kreise nach der zu Petersburg 1787 verfertigten karte und des von Lesseps reise durch Kamtschatka und Sibirien . . .
" [18] Karte Tauriens oder der halbinsel Krim und der westlichen Nogayischen Tatarei, verfasst von I. F. Schmid . . . 1787.
" [19 a–f] Neueste general karte von Frankreich . . . verfasst von Cassini de Thury . . . 1790. 6 sheets.
" [20 a–d] Karte von England und Wallis . . . von T. Kitchin . . . 1787. 4 sheets.
" [21] Karte von Scotland verfasst von J. Dorret . . . 1787.
" [22] Karte von Ireland versasst von Thomas Kitchin . . . 1787.
" [23 a–f] Neueste general karte von Portugal und Spanien nach den astronomischen beobachtungen und karten des Thomas Lopez . . . verfasst von Michael Votesky . . . 1790. 6 sheets.
" [24 a–f] Karte von Danzig, Elbing, und Marienburg oder erstes blat von west Preussen verfasst von I. F. Endersch . . . 1789.
" [25] Karte von Ermeland oder zweites blat von west Preussen verfasst von I. F. Endersch . . . 1789.
" [26 a–d] General karte von dem koenigreiche Neapel oder Napoli verfasst von Rizzi-Zannoni . . . 1789. 4 sheets.
" [27 a–b] Neue karte von der Schweiz oder Helvetien . . . nach den zuverlæssigsten nachrichten und neuesten astronomischen beobachtungen London 1778 bei W. Faden . . . 1789.
" [28 a–b] Das kœnigreich Bosnien, und die Herzegovina (Rama) . . . nach den militærischen handkarten des prinzen Eugen . . . und nach den . . . nachrichten und reisebeschreibungen berichtiget im jahre 1788 von Max-Schimek . . .
" [29] Karte von der Walachei, Moldau und Bessarabien . . . verfasst von I. F. Schmid . . . 1788.
" [30] Karte von Griechenland nach . . . d'Anville, Choiseul-Gouffier etc. . . . 1791.
" [31 a–b] Erster theil der karte von Asien welche die Türkei, Arabien, Persien Indien . . . und einem theil der Tatarei enthält. Verfasst von d'Anville. 1786. 2 sheets.
" [32 a–b] Zweiter theil der karte von Asien, welcher China, einem theil der Tatarei, Indien jenseits des Ganges, die inseln Sumatra, Java, Borneo, Moluken, Philippinen und Japon enthælt. Verfasst von d'Anville . . . 1786. 2 sheets.
" [33 a–b] Dritter theil der karte von Asien welcher Sibirien und einige andere theile der Tartarei enthælt. Verfasst von d'Anville . . . 1787. 2 sheets.
" [34 a–d] Karte von Africa. Verfasst von Robert Vaugondy . . . 1787. 4 sheets.
" [35] General karte der koenigreiche Marokko, Fez, Algier, und Tunis . . . Verfasst von don Lopez y Vargas &c. . . . 1789.
" [36 a–d] General karte von Nord America samt den West indischen inseln. Verfasst von . . . Pownall . . . 1788. 4 sheets.

no. [37 a-c] Karte von Süd-America verfasst von d'Anville . . . 1786. 3 sheets.
" [38] Karte des Mittellændischen meers . . . Verfesst von Bonne . . . 1787.
" [39] Polynesien (Inselwelt) oder der fü· 'te welttheil. Verfasst von Daniel Djurberg . . . 1789.
" [40] Karte des Atlantischen oceans . . . 1788.
" [41] Karte von Phoenicien und Damask verfasst von d'Anville . . . 1788.
" [42] Karte von dem Caspischen meer nach pr. Güldenstædts entwurf gezeichnet von J. Wussin . . . 1787.
" [43] Karte des Arabischen meerbusens oder des Rothen meeres nach d'Anville, Niebuhr und Irwin entworfen von I. Wussin . . . 1787.—Inset: Bahr el Kolsum oder der nordwestliche arm des Rothen meeres nach de la Rochette's karte vom j. 1785.
" [44] Karte von dem groessten theil des landes Jemen, Imame, Kaukeban &c. . . . verfasst von C. Niebuhr . . . 1789.
" [45] Egypten oder Misir verfasst von d'Anville . . . 1787.
" [46] Karte der Magellanischen strasse von don Iuan de la Cruz Cano y Olmedillo . . . 1787.
" [47] Euphrat und Tigris verfasst von d'Anville . . . 1786.
" [48] Übersicht der Europæischen seeküsten verfasst von Carington Bowles . . . 1791.
" [49 a-b] Koromandel verfasst von d'Anville . . . 2 sheets.
" [50] Karte von den n. w. Amerikanischen und n. oe. Asiatischen küsten . . . entworfen von Heinrich Roberts, lieut. . . . 1788.
" [51] Guinea zwischen Sierra-Leona und dem Aequator verfasst von d'Anville . . . 1786.
" [52 a-b] Special karte der west-küste von Africa von Cabo Blanco bis cabo Verga . . . von d'Anville . . . 1786. 2 sheets.
" [53] Das vorgebir der Guten Hofnung verfasst von L. S. de la Rochette, 1789.
" [54 a-d] Neueste karte von Hindostan, Bengalen etc . . . verfasst von Jakob Rennell . . . 1788. 4 sheets.
" [55 a-b] General karte sæmmtlicher entdeckungen auf den drei grossen weltreisen des capt Jakob Cook. Verfasst von Roberts, lieut. . . . 1789. 2 sheets.

## 1800

**Zatta, A.,** *and* **Zatta, G.**
Nuovo atlante . . . 3. ed.   1 p. l., 24 maps.   12°.   Venezia, A. Zatta qu: Giacomo, 1800.   695

NOTE.—See also titles 650 and 651.
Three maps wanting:
no. [6] La Spagna, e il Portogallo.
" [22] La Turchia d' Europa.
" [24] La Grecia.
The following maps relate to America:
no. [1] Il mappamondo.
" [5] L' America.

## 1800-1802

**Wilkinson, R.**

A general atlas, being a collection of maps of the world and quarters of the principal empires, kingdoms &c. with their several provinces, & other subdivisions, correctly delineated. 2 p. l., 48 col. maps. fol. London, R. Wilkinson, 1800-[1802]  696

NOTE.—Table of contents dated 1801; maps dated 1794-1802. See also title 701.
The following maps relate to America:
no. [1] The world . . . 1800.
" [2] A new Mercator's chart . . . 1800.
" [36] Asia . . . [Philippine islands] 1800.
" [42] . . . Map of the islands and channels between China and New Holland . . . 1794.
" [45] . . . North America . . . 1794.
" [46] . . . United States . . . 1794.
" [47] . . . West Indies . . . 1794.
" [48] . . . South America . . . 1794.

## 1801

**Bellin, J. N.**

Atlas maritime. 2 p. l., 23 maps on 68 l. fol. Gênes, Y. Gravier [1801]  697

NOTE.—Engraved title, "Gravé Antoine Fiori."
Excepting the "Carte de la mer Méditerranée en douze feuilles . . . par . . . Joseph Roux" all the maps of this atlas are by Bellin.
Imperfect: according to the "Table des cartes" on the 2nd. p. l., the "Tableau de tous les pavillons que l'on arbore sur les vaisseaux dans les quatre parties du monde. 1798," is wanting.
Maps dated 1751-1799.
Contains plans of the following cities: Plan de Gibraltar; Plan du port de Lisbonne et des costes voisines; Idée de la ville de Lisbonne; Plan du havre de Baston. Inset to no. 31-32.
The following maps relate to America:
no. [1] Carte des variations de la boussole et des vents généraux . . . dans les mers plus fréquentées. 1765.
" [23] Carte réduite des mers du Nord . . . 1751.
" [25] Carte réduite de l'Océan Occidental . . . 4ᵉ ed. 1766.
" [26] Mapa y planta del Rio de la Plata . . . 1770.
" [27] Carte réduite du Golphe du Mexique et des isles de l'Amérique . . . 1774.
" [30] Carte réduite des mers comprises entre l'Asie at l'Amérique . . . 1776.
" [31-32] Carte réduite des costes orientales de l'Amérique septentrionale . . . 1755-99. 2 sheets.
" [33] Carte réduite des îles Antilles . . . 1755.
" [34] Carte réduite de l'Océan Méridional . . . 1753.

## 1802

**Guthrie, W.**

Atlas universel pour la géographie de Guthrie. Nouvelle édition revue, corrigée, avec les nouvelles divisions, d'après les derniers traités de paix . . .   2 p. 1., 25 col. maps, 1 pl.  fol.  Paris, H. Langlois, 1802.   698

> NOTE.—See also title 738, english edition.
> To accompany the translation of Guthrie's Geographical, historical and commercial grammar. This work, often reprinted, was first published in 1770. *cf.* Dictionary of national biography.
> Maps nos. 15-16, 29-30, 33-40 wanting.
> The following maps relate to America:
> no. 2-3. Mappe-monde ou carte générale de la terre.
> " 24. Amérique Septentrionale.
> " 25. États Unis de l'Amérique.
> " 26. Indes occidentales.
> " 27. Amérique Méridionale.
> " 28. Mappe-monde réduite.

## 1802

**Kitchin, T.,** *& others.*

A new universal atlas; exhibiting all the empires, kingdoms, states, republics, &c. &c. in the whole world: being a complete collection of the most approved maps extant; corrected with the greatest care, and augmented from the last edition of d'Anville and Robert: [de Vaugondy] with many improvements by major James Rennel, and other eminent geographers, including all the tracks and new discoveries of the british circumnavigators, Biron, Wallis, Carteret, captain James Cook, Vancouver, Perouse, &c. &c.  6th ed. . . .   2 p. l., 60 maps on 76 sheets.  fol.  London, R. Laurie & J. Whittle, 1802.   699

> NOTE.—Text on maps no. 2-5, 61-63 and 76. See also titles 643, 653, 668, 682, 687 and 709.
> The following maps relate to America:
> no.   1. . . . Chart of the world on Wright's or Mercator's projection . . . 1800.
> "   2-3. A general map of the world, or terraqueous globe . . . By Saml Dunn . . . 1799.
> "  45-46. Asia . . . [no. 45, showing part of America; no. 46, the Philippine islands] 1799.
> "  65-66. A new map of the whole continent of America, divided into North and South and West Indies . . . Compiled from mr. d'Anville's maps . . . with the addition of the spanish discoveries in 1775 to the north of California . . . 1794.
> "  67-68. . . . North America; with the West India islands. Divided according to the preliminary articles of peace signed at Versailles, 20, jan. 1783 . . . 1794.
> "   69. . . . Map of the West Indies . . . By monsr d'Anville . . . 1794.
> "   70. Jamaica from the latest surveys . . . by Thomas Jefferys . . . 1794.
> "   71. Plan of the isle of Trinidad . . . 1800.

**Kitchin, T.,** & *others.*

no. 72. A new and correct map of the british colonies in North America . . . 1794.
" 73. A new and general map of the middle dominions belonging to the United States of America . . . 1794.
" 74. A new and general map of the southern dominions belonging to the United States of America . . . 1794.
" 75-76. . . . Map of South America . . . from m! d'Anville . . . 1794.

### 1803

**Laurie, R.,** *and* **Whittle, J.**

The complete East-India pilot; or, oriental navigator: being an extensive collection of charts, both general and particular; with plans of bays, roads and harbours, appearances of land, &c. &c., for the navigation not only of the Indian and China seas, with those of New Holland, but also of the seas between the British Isles and the Cape of Good Hope. Chiefly composed from actual surveys and draughts communicated by experienced officers of the honorable East-India company, and from the french Neptune Oriental, by m. d'Après de Mannevillette. A new edition in two large volumes, corrected to the present year. Neatly engraved on one hundred and forty-seven plates, comprising one hundred and twenty-six charts. 2 v. 3 p. l., 60 maps; 2 p. l., 65 maps. fol. London, R. Laurie & J. Whittle, 1803. 700

NOTE.—The maps are numbered continuously; nos. 23, 24 comprise one map in two sheets.

Maps by or after d'Après de Mannevillette, d'Anville, Bordee, Butler, Collins, de Fleurieu, Gerard de Ruyter, Grenier, Haldane, Hayes, Huddart, Jefferys, Lacam, Lempriere, Lesley, Lewis, Lindsay, Magin, Maxwell, Moffat, Murillo, Nichelson, Owen, Price, Popham, Stephenson, van Keulen, Woodville and others. Nearly all the maps are dated, the dates varying from 1793 to 1803. The following maps relate to America:

v. 1, no. 1. A new chart of the world on Wright's or Mercator's projection, in which are exhibited all the parts hitherto explored or discovered . . . 1800.
" " 2. A correct chart of the terraqueous globe . . . 1794.
" " 23. A new and correct chart . . . exhibiting the whole of the Atlantic or Western ocean, and the greatest part of the Ethiopic or Southern ocean; wherein the respective coasts of . . . America North and South . . . are carefully described. 1802.
" " 32. A new chart of the coast of Brazil from the banks of St. Roque, to the island of St. Sebastian . . . 1794.
" " 33. Plan of the island of Fernand de Noronha . . . 1794.
" " 34. Plan of the bay and harbour of Rio-Janeiro on the coast of Brazil . . . 1794.
" " 38. Laurie and Whittle's new chart of the Indian and Pacific oceans . . . comprehending . . . the Pelew, New Caroline, Ladrone and Philippine islands . . . 1800.
v. 2, " 69. A new chart of the oriental seas and islands with the coasts of the continent from the isle of Ceylon to Amoye in China . . . 1794.

v. 2, no. 107. A chart of the passages between the Philippine and the isles of Borneo and Mindanao; with those to the southward of the Sooloo archipelago and the isle of Mindanao . . . 1794.
" " 109. A new chart of the China sea with its several entrances . . . 1802.
" " 118. A chart of the China sea and Philippine islands, with the archipelagos of Felicia and Soloo . . . 1794.
" " 120. Plan of the port of Subec, in the isle of Luconia . . . 1766.
" " 121. Plan of the bay of Manilla in the isle of Luconia . . . 1798.
" " 122. Plan of Solsogon harbour on the south coast of Luconia . . .—Chart of the eastern coast of Bongo bay in the island of Mindanao . . . 1794.

## 1803

**Wilkinson, R.**

A general atlas, being a collection of maps of the world and quarters, the principal empires, kingdoms &c., with their several provinces & other subdivisions, correctly delineated.   2 p. l., 48 maps. fol.   London, R. Wilkinson, 1800-[1803]   701

NOTE.—1800 on title page, 1803 at end of contents. See also title 696.
The following maps relate to America:
no. 45. North America.
" 46. United States.
" 47. West Indies.
" 48. South America.

## 1804

**Arrowsmith, A.** *and* **Lewis, S.**

A new and elegant general atlas, comprising all the new discoveries, to the present time; containing sixty three maps . . .   2 p. l., 63 maps.  4°.  Philadelphia, J. Conrad & co. 1804.   702

NOTE.—See also titles 708, 718, 730 and 734.
The following maps relate to America:
no. 1. The world.
" 2. The world on Mercators's projection.
" 33. Pacific ocean.
" 34. North America.
" 35. United States.
" 36. New Hampshire.
" 37. Massachusetts.
" 38. Maine.
" 39. Vermont.
" 40. Rhode Island
" 41. Connecticut.
" 42. New York.
" 43. New Jersey.
" 44. Pennsylvania.
" 45. Delaware.
" 46. Maryland.
" 47. Virginia.
" 48. North Carolina.
" 49. South Carolina.

**Arrowsmith, A.** *and* **Lewis, S.**—Continued.
" 50. Georgia.
" 51. Kentucky.
" 52. Tennessee.
" 53. Ohio.
" 54. Mississippi territory.
" 55. Louisiana.
" 56. British possessions in America.
" 57. Spanish dominions in North America.
" 58. West Indies.
" 59. South America.

### 1804

**Atlante tascabile** o sia serie di num. xvi cartine geografiche nelle quali si rappresenta in ristretto lo stato attuale di tutte le parti del globo terraqueo. [anon.] 1 p. l., 16 col. maps, 1 pl. 8°. Roma, si vende presso eo stampator Desidery. ai Portoghesi baj. miniato, 1804. 703

> NOTE.—Title-page contains a "Mappa-mondo sul piano dell' equatore."
> The following maps relate to America:
> no. [ 1] Mappamondo.
> " [12] L' Asia [Filippine]
> " [14] L' America Settentrionale.
> " [15]           Meridionale.

### 1804

**Heather, W.**
The marine atlas or seaman's complete pilot for all the principal places in the known world, comprising a new and elegant collection of charts, accurately drawn and engraved from the most approved surveys and publications, exhibiting, on a large scale, the discoveries and improvements of celebrated navigators. 2 p. l., 49 fold. maps. fol. London, W. Heather [1804] 704

> NOTE.—Maps dated 1795–1804. See also titles 713 and 2852 for American contents.

### 1804

**Mentelle, E.** *and* **Malte-Brun, C.**
Géographie mathématique, physique et politique de toutes les parties du monde . . . Atlas composé de 45 cartes, gravées par J. B. P. Tardieu aîné, sur les dessins de J. B. Poirson . . . revues et corrigées d'après les meilleures autorités par Edme Mentelle; avec une notice critique des ouvrages et cartes géographiques les plus remarquables, publiés en langues modernes, par Malte-Brun. 2 p. l., iii, [1] pp, [1] l., 28 pp., 45 (*i. e.* 42) maps, 3 pl. fol. Paris, H. Tardieu; Laporte, 1804. 705

> NOTE.—To accompany: Géographie mathématique, physique et politique de toutes les parties du monde, par Mentelle, Herbin et Malte-Brun. 16 v. fol. Paris, 1803–07

The following maps relate to America:
no. 6. Mappe-monde.
" 25. Carte réduite du grand océan. Partie méridionale. 1802.
" 26. Partie septentrionale de l'océan Pacifique.
" 29. Amérique Septentrionale. 1803.
" 30. Amérique Méridionale. 1803.
" 31. États-Unis de l' Amérique. 1803.
" 32. Carte de la partie de la côte nord-ouest de l' Amérique. Redigée par le lieutenant Edward Roberts . . .
" 33. Indes Occidentales. 1803.
" 34. Carte de S! Domingue. 1803.
" 35. Cartes des îles Antilles. 1802.
" 36. Carte de la Guyane française et hollandaise. 1802.

## 1804-1805

**Mentelle, E.**
Atlas de tableaux et de cartes gravé par P. F. Tardieu [*i. e.* A. F. Tardieu] pour le cours complet de cosmographie, de géographie, de chronologie et d'histoire ancienne et moderne. 2. éd.  2 p. l., 20 maps, 6 tab.  4°.  Paris, Bernard, 1804-[1805]  706

NOTE.—Map of France dated 1805.
Correct name of engraver is Antoine François Tardieu. "Comme par erreur on l'appelait Pierre, dans sa jeunesse, il signa long-temps ses ouvrages, P. F. Tardieu." Annuaire nécrologique. 1822.
The following maps relate to America:
no. 1. Mappe-monde en deux hemisphères
" 18. Amérique Méridionale.
" 19. Amérique Septentrionale.

## 1804-1806

**Patteson, E.**
A general and classical atlas: accompanied with a concise treatise on the principles of geography; and with a few practical remarks on the application of maps to the purpose of instruction. 2 v. fol. Richmond [Surrey, Eng.] for the author by G. A. Wall, 1804-[1806]  707

NOTE.—Collation: v. 1, 2 p. l., vii, 42 pp., 34 col. maps; v. 2, 32 col. maps, [1] l. First part published in 1804. Second part without title contains maps dated as late as 1806.
The following maps relate to America:
v. 1, no. 3. The world. 1804.
"    "    7. North America. 1804.
"    "    8. South America. 1804.
"    "   30. United States. 1804.
v. 2,  "  31. The West Indies. 1805.

## 1805

**Arrowsmith, A.** *and* **Lewis, S.**
A new and elegant general atlas. Comprising all the new discoveries, to the present time; containing sixty-three maps . . . Intended to accompany the new improved edition of Morse's geog-

**Arrowsmith, A.** *and* **Lewis, S.**—Continued.
    raphy . . .    2 p. l., 63 maps.  4°.  Boston, Thomas & Andrews, 1805.    **708**

    NOTE.—See also titles 702, 718, 730 and 734.
    The following maps relate to America:
    no.  1. The world.
    "   2. The world on Mercator's projection.
    "  33. Pacific Ocean.
    "  34. North America.
    "  35. United States.
    "  36. New Hampshire.
    "  37. Massachusetts.
    "  38. Maine.
    "  39. Vermont.
    "  40. Rhode Island.
    "  41. Connecticut.
    "  42. New York.
    "  43. New Jersey.
    "  44. Pennsylvania.
    "  45. Delaware.
    "  46. Maryland.
    "  47. Virginia.
    "  48. North Carolina.
    "  49. South Carolina.
    "  50. Georgia.
    "  51. Kentucky.
    "  52. Tennessee.
    "  53. Ohio.
    "  54. Mississippi territory.
    "  55. Louisiana.
    "  56. British possessions in America.
    "  57. Spanish dominions in North America.
    "  58. West Indies.
    "  59. South America.

## 1805

**Kitchin, T.** *& others.*

    A new universal atlas; exhibiting all the empires, kingdoms, states, republics, &c. &c. in the whole world: being a complete collection of the most approved maps extant; corrected with the greatest care, and augmented from the last edition of d'Anville and Robert; with many improvements, by major James Rennel, and other eminent geographers; including all the tracks and new discoveries of the british circumnavigators, Biron, Wallis, Carteret, capt. James Cook, Vancouver, Perouse, &c. &c. 7th ed. . . . 2 p. l., 60 maps on 76 sheets. fol. London, R. Laurie & J. Whittle, 1805.    **709**

    NOTE.—See also titles 643, 653, 668, 682, 685, 687 and 699.
    The following maps relate to America:
    no.  [1] The world on Wright's or Mercator's projection.
    "   [2–3] A general map of the world or terraqueous globe . . . by Sam! Dunn. 1799.
    "   [46] [Asia—showing the Philippine islands] 1799.

no. [65-66] . . . Whole continent of America divided into North & South, and the West Indies . . . compiled from m. d'Anville's maps . . . and corrected . . . from the original materials of governor Pownall.
" [67-68] . . . North America, with the West India islands . . .
" [69] . . . The West Indies . . . by m. d'Anville . . . 1794.
" [70] Jamaica, from the latest surveys; improved and engraved by Thomas Jefferys. 1794.
" [71] Plan of the isle of Trinidad . . . 1800.
" [72] . . . British colonies in North America . . .
" [73] A new and general map of the middle dominions belonging to the United States . . . 1794.
" [74] . . . Map of the southern dominions belonging to the United States . . . 1794.
" [75-76] . . . South America . . . from m. d'Anville . . . 1794.

## 1806

**Boiste, P. C. V.**
Dictionnaire de géographie universelle, ancienne, du moyen âge et moderne, comparées . . . Atlas. 2 p. l., 45 maps. obl. 12°. Paris, Desray, 1806. 710

NOTE.—Atlas accompanying this work entitled: Atlas du Dictionnaire de géographie universelle, ancienne, du moyen age et moderne, comparées . . . par Hérisson . . . et gravée . . . par Glot.
Half-title: Atlas du Dictionnaire de géographie universelle.
Maps are hand colored.
The following maps relate to America:
no. 1. La mappemonde.
" 34. L'Asie [Isles Philippines]
" 38. La Chine [Luzon]
" 39. Australasie et Polynesie.
" 43-44. L'Amérique Septentrionale et Méridionale.
" 45. Les États Unis d'Amérique.

## 1806

**Cyclopædia, The**; or, universal dictionary of arts, sciences and literature. By Abraham Rees . . . with the assistance of eminent professional gentlemen . . . First american edition, revised, corrected, enlarged and adapted to this country by several literary and scientific characters. Ancient and modern atlas. 2 p. l., 61 maps. 4°. Philadelphia, S. F. Bradford; Murray, Fairman & co. [1806] 711

The following maps relate to America:
no. [23] The world.
" [24] The world on Mercator's projection.
" [53] Chart of the East India islands.
" [54] Chart of the Pacific ocean.
" [58] North America.
" [59] South America.
" [60] British possessions in North America.
" [61] West Indies.

## 1807?

**Mentelle, E.** *and* **Chanlaire P. G.**

[Atlas universel de géographie physique et politique, ancienne et moderne] 2 v. obl. fol. [Paris, E. Mentelle; P. G. Chanlaire, 1807?] 712

    Note.—v. 1, 57 maps on 76 l.; v. 2, 57 maps on 74 l.
    Title page wanting.
    Pagination irregular.
    Maps dated from 1797–1807.
    The following maps relate to America:
      v. 1, no. [1] Mappemonde physique d'après les vues du prof! Pallas. Rédigées par André Mongez . . . 1779.
      " " [4] Mappemonde en deux hemisphères. An vi [1797]
      " " [5] Mappemonde suivant la projection des cartes réduites . . . An vi [1797]
      " " [6] Planisphère en quatre feuilles . . .
      v. 2, " [43] Carte générale des États-Unis. 1806.
      " " [44] Carte de la partie septentrionale des États-Unis comprenant le Canada . . .
      " " [45] Carte de la Caroline Méridionale et Septentrionale et de la Virginie.
      " " [46] Carte de la Floride et de la Géorgie.
      " " [47] Carte du Golfe du Mexique et des isles Antilles.
      " " [53] Carte général et politique de l'Amérique.
      " " [54] Carte de l'isle de Cuba et des isles Lucayes.
      " " [55] Carte des isles de la Jamaïque et de S! Domingue.
      " " [56] Carte des Antilles.
      " " [57] Carte des colonies française et hollandaise de la Guyane.

## 1808?

**Heather, W.**

The marine atlas, or seaman's complete pilot for all the principal places in the known world, comprising a new and elegant collection of charts, accurately drawn and engraved from the most approved surveys and publications. Exhibiting, on a large scale, all the discoveries and improvements of the most celebrated navigators, both english and foreign, ancient and modern, particularly those of Cook, d'Après [de Mannevillette] Byron, King, Vancouver, Phipps, Mackenzie, Clerke, Carteret, Dalrymple, Furneaux, Bligh, Wallis, Bougainville, Forrest, Dampier, Portlock, Shortland, Dixon, Anson, Maurelle, Wilson, Marchand, Perouse, &c. &c. With many additions and improvements. Now first made public, under the patronage of several able and distinguished officers in the navy and East-India company's service; the whole forming a valuable and extensive selection, methodized, arranged, and published for the use of the mariners of Great-Britain. 2 p. l., 28 maps on 36 sheets. fol. London, W. Heather [1808?] 713

    Note.—Map no. 9 dated 1808. See also titles 704 and 2852.
    Imperfect: contains only 24 of 49 maps and 1 pl. noted in the table of contents.

The following maps relate to America:
no 1. A new chart of the world . . . 1803.
" 2. The Atlantic or Western ocean. 2d. ed. 1807.
" 3. The Southern ocean. 1799.
" 4. . . . Survey of the river Plate . . . by . . . Juan de Saugara. 1806.

### 1808

**Cary, J.**
Cary's new universal atlas containing distinct maps of all the principal states and kingdoms throughout the world. 5 p. l., 56 maps on 60 sheets. fcl. London, for J. Cary, 1808.     714
    NOTE.—See also titles 736 and 745.

#### CONTENTS.

no. 1-2. Eastern and western hemispheres.
"   3. World (Mercator's projection)
"   4. Europe.
"   5. British Isles.
"   6. England.
" 7-8. Scotland, southern part.
" 9-10.   " northern part.
" 11. Ireland.
" 12. France in departments.
" 13.   " in provinces.
" 14. Netherlands.
" 15. Holland.
" 16. Swisserland [!]
" 17. Piedmont and Savoy.
" 18. Italy.
" 19. Spain.
" 20. Portugal.
" 21. Germany.
" 22. Westphalia.
" 23. Upper Saxony.
" 24. Lower Saxony.
" 25. Bohemia.
" 26. Franconia.
" 27. Upper and Lower Rhine.
" 28. Swabia.
" 29. Bavaria.
" 30. Austria.
" 31. Tyrol and republic of Venice.
" 32. Hungary.
" 33. Sweden, Denmark, and Norway.
" 34. Denmark.
" 35. Poland.
" 36. Prussia.
" 37-38. Russian empire.
" 39. Turkey in Europe.
" 40. Asia.
" 41. Turkey in Asia.
" 42. Persia.
" 43. Hindoostan.
" 44. East India Isles.

**Cary, J.**—Continued.
    no. 45. Arabia.
    " 46. China.
    " 47. Tartary.
    " 48. Africa.
    " 49. Egypt.
    " 50. America (General)
    " 51. North America.
    " 52. Nova Scotia and Newfoundland.
    " 53. Canada.
    " 54. United States of America.
    " 55. " " New Hampshire, &c.
    " 56. " " Western Territory, &c.
    " 57. " " Floridas, &c.
    " 58. West Indies.
    " 59–60. South America.

## 1808
**Cruttwell, C.**

Atlas to Cruttwell's gazetteer . . .    1 p. l., 28 maps. fol. London, for Longman, Hurst, Rees, & Orme [1808]    715

    NOTE.—To accompany his: The new universal gazetteer. 1808.
    The following maps relate to America:
    no. [1] The world.
    " [2] A general chart of the world on Mercator's projection. 1808.
    " [6] British America, comprehending Canada, Labrador, Newfoundland, Novo Scotia, &c. 1808.
    " [7] United States of America. 1808.
    " [8] South America. 1808.
    " [9] A map of the countries thirty degrees round the North Pole. 1808.
    " [24] The West Indies. 1808.

## 1808
**Laurie, R.,** *and* **Whittle, J.**

A new and elegant, imperial, sheet atlas: comprehending general and particular maps of every part of the world. Principally compiled from the great french atlas, and others of the most distinguished geographers in Europe; forming the completest collection of single sheet maps hitherto published, and rendered particularly convenient by opening without folds. A new edition, comprising fifty-six maps, beautifully coloured.    2 p. l., 56 maps. fol. London, R. Laurie & J. Whittle, 1808.    716

    NOTE.—Maps by Samuel Dunn, J. Enouy, J. Lodge, John Armstrong, Francis De Caroly, Robert Mylne, Thomas Jefferys, John Roberts, John Stephenson, James Rennel, d'Anville. See also title 720.
    The following maps relate to America:
    no. 1. A new map of the world, with capt. Cook's tracks . . .
    " 2. A new chart of the world . . . 1794 . . .
    " 48. . . . New general map of America . . . 1805 . . .
    " 49. The United States of America . . . 1794 . . .
    " 50. A new and correct map of the british colonies in North America . . . 1794.

no. 51. A new and general map of the middle dominions belonging to the United States of America . . . 1794.
" 52. A new and general map of the southern dominions belonging to the United States of America . . . 1794.
" 53. A new and complete map of the West Indies . . . by mons. d'Anville with . . . improvements . . . 1794.
" 54. Jamaica . . . by Thomas Jefferys . . . 1794.
" 55. Plan of the isle of Trinidad, from actual surveys made in the year 1797. . . . 1800.
" 56. South America . . . by Thomas Kitchin . . . 1794.

## 1810

**Evans,** *Rev.* **J.**
A new royal atlas, illustrative of the various divisions which comprise the surface of the globe; intended also as an interesting companion to Bigland's View of the world, and the New geographical grammar.   2 p. l., 20 col. maps.   8°.   London, for J. Cundee [1810]   717

## 1812

**Arrowsmith, A.,** *and* **Lewis, S.**
A new and elegant general atlas. Comprising all the new discoveries, to the present time. Containing sixty three maps, drawn by Arrowsmith and Lewis. Intended to accompany the new improved edition of Morse's geography . . .   2 p. l., 63 maps.   4°.   Boston, Thomas & Andrews, 1812.   718

NOTE.—See also titles 702, 708, 730 and 734.
The following maps relate to America:
no. 1. The world.
" 2. The world on Mercator's projection.
' 29. North America.
" 30. United States.
" 31. New Hampshire.
" 32. Massachusetts.
" 33. Maine.
" 34. Vermont.
" 35. Rhode Island.
" 36. Connecticut.
" 37. New York.
" 38. New Jersey.
" 39. Pennsylvania.
" 40. Delaware.
" 41. Maryland.
" 42. Virginia.
" 43. North Carolina.
" 44. South Carolina.
" 45. Georgia.
" 46. Kentucky.
" 47. Tennessee.
" 48. Ohio.
" 49. Mississippi territory.

**Arrowsmith, A.,** *and* **Lewis, S.**—Continued.
   no. 50. Louisiana.
   "  51. British possessions in America.
   "  52. Spanish dominions in North America.
   "  53. Viceroyalty of New Grenada.
   "  54. Government of Caracas with Guiana.
   "  55. Viceroyalty of Peru.
   "  56. Chili.
   "  57. Viceroyalty of La Plata.
   "  58. West Indies.
   "  59. South America.

## 1812-1814

**Darton, W.**

Union atlas, containing new and improved maps of all the empires, kingdoms & states in the known world, designed as a companion to the various gazetteers & books of geography now in use. The whole clearly engraved by artists of eminence and carefully coloured. Including maps of the roman empire and ancient Greece.   1 p. l., 36 maps.   fol.   London, W. Darton, 1812-[1814]
719

   NOTE.—Several maps are dated 1814.
   The following maps relate to America:
   no. 1. The western hemisphere or new world.
   " 29. North America.
   " 30. The United States of America.
   " 31. The West India islands.
   " 32. South America.

## 1813-1814

**Whittle, J.** *and* **Laurie, R. H.**

A new and elegant imperial sheet atlas: comprehending general and particular maps of every part of the world. Principally compiled from the great french atlas, and others of the most distinguished geographers in Europe; forming the completest collection of single sheet maps hitherto published . . . New ed.   2 p. l., 55 col. maps.   fol.   London, J. Whittle & R. H. Laurie, 1813-[1814]
720

   NOTE.—See also title 716.
   The following maps relate to America:
   no. 1. A new map of the world . . . 1812.
   "  2. A new map of the world on Mercator's projection . . . By Samuel Dunn.
   " 47. . . . New general map of America . . . 1813.
   " 48. The United States of America . . . 1794.
   " 49. A new and correct map of the british colonies in North America . . . 1794.
   " 50. A new and general map of the middle dominions belonging to the United States of America . . . 1794.
   " 51. A new and general map of the southern dominions belonging to the United States of America . . . 1794.

no. 52. A new and complete map of the West Indies . . . By monsʳ d'Anville. 1794.
" 53. Jamaica . . . By Thomas Jefferys. 1810.
" 54. Plan of the isle of Trinidad . . . 1797.
" 55. South America with its several divisions. By Thomas Kitchin . . . 1794.

## 1814?

**Carey, M.**

[Carey's general atlas, improved and enlarged: being a collection of maps of the world and quarters, their principal empires, kingdoms, &c. . . . ] 2 p. l., 58 maps. fol. [Philadelphia, M. Carey, 1814?] 721

NOTE.—Title-page wanting. See also titles 722 and 732.
This copy corresponds with the 1814 edition except in map no. 39, Russian empire, and in the preface signed M. Carey, march 17, 1814.
For list of maps of America, see title 722.

## 1814

Carey's general atlas, improved and enlarged: being a collection of maps of the world and quarters, their principal empires, kingdoms, &c. . . . 3 p. l., 58 maps. fol. Philadelphia, M. Carey, 1814. 722

NOTE.—The following maps relate to America:
no. 1. A map of the world . . .
" 2. A chart of the world . . .
" 3. A new and accurate map of North America . . .
" 4. The british possessions in North America . . . 1814.
" 5. A map of the United States of America.
" 6. Vermont . . . Delineated & engraved by Amos Doolittle . . .
" 7. The state of New Hampshire. Compiled . . . by Samuel Lewis, 1813.
" 8. The district of Maine.
" 9. The state of Massachusetts.
" 10. The state of Rhode Island; compiled, from the surveys . . . of Caleb Harris. By Harding Harris.
" 11. Connecticut . . . Delineated & engraved by A. Doolittle . . .
" 12. The state of New York. S. Lewis del.
" 13. The state of New Jersey . . .
" 14. Pennsylvania.
" 15. Delaware . . .
" 16. Maryland.
" 17. A correct map of Virginia.
" 18. North Carolina. S. Lewis del.
" 19. The state of South Carolina . . . by Samuel Lewis.
" 20. The state of Georgia.
" 21. Kentucky.
" 22. The state of Tennessee.
" 23. Mississippi territory.
" 24. The state of Ohio with part of upper Canada, &c.
" 25. The upper territories of the United States.
" 26. Louisiana.

**Carey, M.**—Continued.
  no. 27. Missouri territory . . .
  " 28. Plat of the Seven Ranges of townships
  " 29. Mexico . . .
  " 30. A chart of the West Indies . . .
  " 31. Carte de la partie françoise de S! Domingue. Faite par Bellin . . .
  " 32. A new map of South America . . .
  " 33. A map of the Caracas.
  " 34. Peru.
  " 35. Chili and part of the viceroyalty of La Plata.
  " 36. A map of Brazil . . .
  " 57. A map of the countries situated about the North pole.
  " 58. A map of the discoveries made by capts. Cook & Clerke in the years 1778 & 1779 between the eastern coast of Asia and the western coast of North America . . . Also mʳ Hearn's discoveries to the north westward of Hudson's bay, in 1772.

## 1814
**Playfair, J.**
  A new general atlas, ancient and modern; accurately constructed by principal Playfair, St. Andrews, and elegantly engraved by the most eminent artists in London.  2 p. l., 46 maps. fol. London, for the author, 1814. 722

  NOTE.—Three historical maps of the world not noted in contents.
  The following maps relate to America:
  no. [11] [Western hemisphere]
  " [16] North America . . .
  " [17] South America . . .
  "   42  Asiatic islands.
  " [43] West Indies.

## 1815
**Pinkerton, J.**
  A modern atlas, from the latest and best authorities, exhibiting the various divisions of the world, with its chief empires, kingdoms, and states, in sixty maps, carefully reduced from the largest and most authentic sources.  1 p. l., VII pp., 61 maps. fol. London, for T. Cadell & W. Davies; & Longman, Hurst, Orme & Brown, 1815. 724

  NOTE.—First edition. See also title 733.
  The following maps relate to America:
  no. [1] Western hemisphere.
  " [3] Northern hemisphere.
  " [4] Southern hemisphere.
  " [40] North America . . . 1812.
  " [41] United States . . . 1810.
  " [42] United States . . . southern part . . . 1809.
  " [43] Spanish dominions in North America. Northern part . . . 1811.
  " [44] Spanish dominions in North America. Middle part . . . 1811.
  " [45] Spanish dominions in North America. Southern part . . . 1811.
  " [46] British possessions in North America . . . 1814.
  " [47] West Indies . . . 1809.

no. [48] South America . . . 1811.
" [49] La Plata . . . 1812.
" [50] Peru . . . 1810.
" [51] New Granada . . . 1811.
" [52] Chili . . . 1809.
" [53] The Caracas . . . 1810.

## 1815-1816
**Luffman, J.**

Luffman's geographical & topographical atlas, consisting of maps of countries, plans of cities and forts, ports and harbours, battles &c. 2 v. in 1. 3 p. l., 5 l., 171 maps, 2 pl. 4°. London, I. Luffman, 1815-1816. 725

NOTE.—Title-page for v. 2 follows that for v. 1. Imprint date varies: v. 1, 1816; v. 2, 1815.
Maps are dated 1802-1816.
Plans of many cities including: Dresden, Leipzig, Madrid, Moscow, Paris and vicinity, Rome and environs of Vienna.
The following maps relate to America:

no. [3] The world on Mercator's projection . . . 1809.
" [4] The world on a spheric projection . . . 1809.
" [5] The world in three sections. 1812.
" [6] Asia [Philippine islands]
" [10] East Indian archipelago . . . 1812.
" [72] Iceland 1813.
" [151] North America.
" [152] South America.
" [153] The british colonies, North America.
" [154] The West Indies.
" [155] A chart of the Windward and Leeward islands . . . 1813.
" [156] A map of the american lakes and adjoining country, the present seat of war between Great Britain & the United States . . . from a sketch of the late major general sr. Isaac Brock.
" [157] A map of the Caribbee islands in the West Indies, and parts adjacent.
" [158] The coast of America, from Sandy-hook, s. s. west, to the capes of Virginia, including the Delaware & Chesapeak bays.
" [159] Antigua. 1810.
" [160] Barbadoes.
" [161] Brazil.
" [162] St Christopher and Nevis.
" [163] Carthagena.
" [164] A map of the "captain generalship of Carracas comprehending the provinces of Venezuela, Maracaybo, Varinas, Cumana, Guiana & the island of St. Marguerite.
" [165] [Plan of] Carracas . . .
" [166] The island of St. Domingo. 1802.
" [167] Hallifax. 1812.
" [168] Jamaica.
" [169] Paraguay.
" [170] The Isthmus of Panama. 1816.
" [171] Rio de la Plata.

## 1816

**Brué, A. H.**

Grand atlas universel, ou collection de cartes encyprotypes, générales et détaillées des cinq parties du monde . . . 3 p. l., 17 maps on 82 l. fol. Paris, Desray, 1816. 726

Note.—See also title 758.
The following maps relate to America:
no. [A] Mappe-monde en deux hémisphères . . . 1816.
" 1. Mappe-monde sur la projection de Mercator . . . 1816.
" 2. Mappe-monde " " " " " 1816. 4 sheets.
" 11. Carte encyprotype de l'Amérique Septentrionale . . . 1815.
" 12. Carte encyprotype de l'Amérique Septentrionale . . . 1815. 4 sheets.
" 13. Carte encyprotype de l'Amérique Méridionale . . . 1816.
" 14. Carte encyprotype de l'Amérique Meridionale . . . 1816. 4 sheets.
" 15. Océanie . . . 1814.
" 16. " " 4 sheets.

## 1816

**Delamarche, C. F.**

Atlas élémentaire, composé de xxxiii cartes, revues, corrigées et augmentées, tant des nouvelles découvertes faites en Asie, en Afrique et en Amérique, que des nouveaux changemens politiques survenus en Europe; lequel comprend aussi la carte générale de la France ancienne et de la nouvelle, celle-ci accompagnée de cartes particulières, pour le detail du royaume; précédé 1º. Des institutions géographiques et historiques . . . 2º. De la nomenclature comparative des départemens avec les anciennes provinces, etc. etc. 4. éd. xii, 128 pp., 33 maps. 8°. Paris, F. Delamarche & C. Dien, 1816. 727

Note.—The following maps relate to America:
no. 1. Mappe-monde . . .
" 29. Amérique Septentrionale . . .
" 30. Amérique Méridionale.
" 31. États-Unis de l'Amérique . . .

## 1816

**Maverick, P.**

[General atlas] 5 maps. obl. 24°. [New York, P. Maverick, Durand & co. 1816] 728

Note.—No title page. Publishers name on cover. Date on map of the world.
Contains also maps of North America and South America.

## 1816

**Smith, C.**

Smith's new general atlas containing distinct maps of all the principal empires, kingdoms, & states throughout the world, arranged according to the general treaty signed in congress at Vienna.

June, 1815.   2 p. l., 48 l. incl. 46 col. maps.   fol.   London, for C.
Smith, 1816. 729
NOTE.—An edition published in 1808. Forty maps in this edition dated 1808.
The following maps relate to America:—
no. 1. Western hemisphere. 1808.
" 3. The world on Mercator's projection. 1808.
" 44. America. 1808.
" 45. North America. 1808.
" 46. United States. 1808.
" 47. West Indies. 1808.
" 48. South America. 1808.

**1817**
**Arrowsmith, A.**
A new general atlas, constructed from the latest authorities . . . Exhibiting the boundaries and divisions, also the chains of mountains and other geographical features of all the known countries in the world.   Comprehended in fifty-three maps from original drawings. 2 p. l., 53 maps, 1 l. at end.   4°.   Edinburgh, London, A. Constable & co. 1817. 730
NOTE.—See also titles 702, 708, 718 and 734.
The following maps relate to America:—
no. 1. The world.
" 2. The world on Mercator's projection.
" 48. North America.
" 49. Canada.
" 50. United States.
" 51. Mexico.
" 52. West Indies.
" 53. South America.

**1817**
**Thomson, J.**
A new general atlas, consisting of a series of geographical designs, on various projections, exhibiting the form and component parts of the globe; and a collection of maps and charts, delineating the natural and political divisions of the empires, kingdoms, and states in the world.   Constructed from the best systematic works, and the most authentic voyages and travels.   With a memoir of the progress of geography, a summary of physical geography, and a consulting index to facilitate the finding out of places.   2 p. l., xxiii, [1], 22 pp., front., 74 (*i. e.* 80) col. maps.   fol.   Edinburgh, for J. Thomson & co. 1817. 731
NOTE:—See also title 750.
Map of Europe on 4 sheets.
The following maps relate to America:
no. 1. Hydrographical chart of the world. 1814.
" 2. Northern hemisphere. 1814.
" 3. Southern hemisphere. 1814.
" 5. Western hemisphere. 1815.

**Thomson, J.**—Continued.
 no. 6. Northern hemisphere. 1816.
 " 7. Southern hemisphere. 1816.
 " 51. Chart of north Atlantic ocean. 1815.
 " 52. America. 1813.
 " 53. North America. 1814.
 " 54. Canada and Nova Scotia. 1814.
 " 55. United States of America.
 " 56. Northern provinces of the United States. 1817.
 " 57. Southern provinces of the United States. 1817.
 " 58. Spanish North America. 1814.
 " 59. Spanish North America. Southern part. 1816.
 " 60. West Indies. 1814.
 " 61. Island of Cuba.
 " 62. Jamaica.
 " 63. Haiti . . . Porto Rico and Virgin isles. 1815.
 " 64. West India islands.
 " 65. West India islands. 1814.
 " 66. West India islands.
 " 67. West India islands. 1814.
 " 68. West India islands. 1816.
 " 69. South America. 1814.
 " 70. Caraccas and Guiana.
 " 71. Peru, Chili and La Plata.
 " 72. Map of the islands in the Pacific ocean. 1817.
 " 74. Chart of the northern passage between Asia & America.

## 1818

**Carey, M.**
  Carey's general atlas, improved and enlarged; being a collection of maps of the world and quarters; their principal empires, kingdoms, &c. . . . 3 p. l., 58 maps. fol. Philadelphia, M. Carey & son, 1818. 732

 NOTE.—See also titles 721, 722.
 The following maps relate to America:
 no. [1] A map of the world . . .
 " [2] A chart of the world . . .
 " 3. A new and accurate map of North America . . .
 " 4. The british possessions in North America . . . 1814.
 " 5. Map of the United States of America.
 " 6. Vermont . . . Delineated and engraved by Amos Doolittle . . .
 " 7. The state of New Hampshire. Compiled . . . by Samuel Lewis. 1813.
 " 8. The district of Maine.
 " 9. The state of Massachusetts.
 " 10. The state of Rhode Island; compiled from the surveys . . . of Caleb Harris. By Harding Harris.
 " 11. Connecticut . . . Delineated & engraved by A. Doolittle . . .
 " 12. The state of New York. S. Lewis del.
 " 13. The state of New Jersey . . .
 " 14. Pennsylvania.
 " 15. Delaware.

no. 16. Maryland.
" 17. A correct map of Virginia.
" 18. North Carolina . . . by Samuel Lewis.
" 19. The state of South Carolina . by Samuel Lewis.
" 20. The state of Georgia.
" 21. Kentucky.
" 22. The state of Tennessee.
" 23. The state of Mississippi and Alabama territory.
" 24. The state of Ohio with part of upper Canada, &c.
" [25] The upper territories of the United States.
" 26. Louisiana.
" 27. Missouri territory . . .
" 28. Plat of the Seven Ranges of townships . . .
" 29. Mexico . . .
" [30] West Indies.
" 31. Carte de la partie françoise de S$^t$. Dominque. Faite par Bellin . . .
" 32. A new map of South America . . .
" 33. A map of the Caracas.
" 34. Peru.
" 35. Chili and part of the viceroyalty of La Plata.
" 36. A map of Brazil . . .
" 57. A map of the countries situated about the North pole.
" 58. A map of the discoveries made by capt$^s$ Cook & Clerke in the years 1778 & 1779 between the eastern coast of Asia and the western coast of North America . . . Also m$^r$ Hearn's discoveries to the north westward of Hudson's bay, in 1772.

## 1818

**Pinkerton, J.**

A modern atlas, from the latest and best authorities, exhibiting the various divisions of the world, with its chief empires, kingdoms and states; in sixty maps carefully reduced from the largest and most authentic sources. 1 p. l., 7, [1] pp. 61 maps. fol. Philadelphia, T. Dobson & son, 1818. 733

NOTE:—First edition published in 1815. See also title 724.
The "Introduction" contains a brief history of map making.
The following maps relate to America:
no. 1. Western hemisphere.
" 3. Northern hemisphere.
" 4. Southern hemisphere.
" 40. North America.
" 41–42. United States.
" 43–45. Spanish dominions.
" 46. British possessions.
" 47. West-Indies.
" 48. South America.
" 49. La Plata.
" 50. Peru.
" 51. New Grenada.
" 52. Caracas.
" 53. Chili.
" 60–61. World on Mercator's projection.

## 1819

**Arrowsmith, A.** *and* **Lewis, S.**

A new and elegant general atlas. Comprising all the new discoveries, to the present time . . . Intended to accompany the new improved edition of Morse's geography . . .   2 p. l., 63 maps. 4°.  Boston, Thomas & Andrews, 1819.   734

NOTE.—See also titles 702, 708 and 718.
The following maps relate to America:
no.  1. The world.
"    2. The world on Mercator's projection.
"   29. North America.
"   30. United States.
"   31. New Hampshire.
"   32. Massachusetts.
"   33. Maine.
"   34. Vermont.
"   35. Rhode Island.
"   36. Connecticut.
"   37. New York.
"   38. New Jersey.
"   39. Pennsylvania.
"   40. Delaware.
"   41. Maryland.
"   42. Virginia.
"   43. North Carolina.
"   44. South Carolina.
"   45. Georgia.
"   46. Kentucky.
"   47. Tennessee.
"   48. Ohio.
"   49. Mississippi territory.
"   50. Louisiana.
"   51. British possessions in America.
"   52. Spanish dominions in North America.
"   53. Viceroyalty of New Granada.
"   54. Government of Caracas, with Guiana.
"   55. Viceroyalty of Peru.
"   56. Chili.
"   57. Viceroyalty of La Plata.
"   58. West Indies.
"   59. South America.

## 1819

**Borghi, B.**

Atlante generale . . . Corredato di prospetti istorici-politici-civili-naturali di ciascheduno stato. Pubblicato a spese di Rosa Parigi, e del c$^{re}$ Giulio Cesare Bertolini fotto la ditta Aristide Parigi e comp?. e dai medesimi dedicato alla loro patria.   1 p. l., [158] l. incl. 119 maps, 1 por., 2 pl.  obl. fol.  Firenze [nella stamperia granducale] 1819.   735

NOTE.—The following maps relate to America:
no.  [2] Mappa mondo, emisfero nuovo.  1819.

no. [100] America Settentrionale. 1819.
" [101] I Stati Uniti nell' America Settentrionale. 1818.
" [102] Possessioni spagnole nell' America Settentrionale. 1818.
" [103] Le Grandi Antille e l'isole Lucaje. 1817.
" [104] Le Piccole Antille dette anche l' isole del Vento. 1817.
" [105] America Meridionale. 1819.
" [106] Possessioni spagnole nell'America Meridionale parte al nord. 1818.
" [107] Parte media delle possessioni spagnoli nell'America Meridionale. 1818.
" [108] Possessioni spagnole nell'America Méridionale parte del Sud. 1818.
" [109] Parte orientale dell America Meridionale o sia il Brasile. 1818.

## 1819

Cary, J.
Cary's new universal atlas, containing distinct maps of all the principal states and kingdoms throughout the world. From the latest . . . authorities extant and shewing the whole of the new divisions according to the congress of Vienna. 2 p. l., 61 maps. fol. London, J. Cary, 1819. 736

NOTE.—See also titles 714 and 745. Like the edition of 1808 with the following exceptions: no. 5, A map of the central states of Europe . . . and no. 18, A new map of the kingdom of Sardinia . . . 1819, are not in the earlier edition; the following maps are different:—
no. 19. A new map of Italy . . .
" 23. A new map of the circle of Westphalia . . .
" 24. . . . Upper Saxony; with the duchy of Silesia and Lusatia . . .
" 25. . . . Lower Saxony . . .
" 27. . . . Franconia . . .
" 28. . . . Circles of the Upper and Lower Rhine . . .
" 29. . . . Circle of Swabia . . .
" 30. . . . Circle of Bavaria . . .
" 31. . . . Circle of Austria . . .
" 32. . . . The kingdom of Lombardo Venetian, and the county of Tyrol . . .
" 36. . . . Poland and the grand duchy of Luthuania . . .
" 43. . . . Persia . . .
" 44. Hindoostan . . .
" 51. . . . America . . .
" 52. . . . North America . . .
" 55. . . . United States . . .
" 57–58. . . . Part of the United States . . .
" 60. . . . South America . . .
" [17] A new map of Piedmont, the duchies of Savoy and Milan . . . of the edition of 1808, is not found in the present edition.
The following maps relate to America:
no. 1. The western and eastern hemispheres.
" 2. A new chart of the world on Mercator's projection . . .
" 41. A new map of Asia . . . [Philippine islands]
" 48. A new map of Chinese & independent Tartary . . . [Philippine islands]
" 51. A new map of America . . .
" 52. . . . North America . . .
" 53. . . . Nova Scotia, Newfoundland &c.
" 54. . . . Upper & Lower Canada . . .

**Cary, J.**—Continued.
    no.  55. . . . United States . . .
    "   56–58. . . . Part of the United States . . .
    "   59. . . . West India isles . . .
    "   60. . . . South America . . .

### 1819-1820

**Robert de Vaugondy, D.**
    Novissimo atlante geografico in tavole XXII per la studiosa gioventù di C. F. Delamarche successore di Robert de Vaugondy. 1 p. l., 23 maps, pl. 8°. Milano, P. & G. Vallardi, 1819–[1820]    737

    NOTE.—Translated from Robert de Vaugondy's "Atlas pour l'instruction de la jeunesse. Paris, 1783."
    Imprint date 1819. Map no. [5], "Carta della monarchia Austriaca," dated 1820.
    The following maps relate to America:
    no. [1] Mappa mondo . . .
    "  [3] L'Asia [Philippine islands]
    "  [4] America Settentrionale . . .
    "  [9]   "    Meridionale.
    "  [22] Le isole della Sonda, Molucche, Filippine, Caroline e Marianne.

### 1820

**Guthrie, W.**
    General atlas for Guthrie's geography . . .    1 p. l., 22 maps. 8°. Philadelphia, B. Warner, 1820.    738

    NOTE.—To accompany Guthrie's "A universal geography . . . 3d am. ed. Philadelphia, 1820." See also title 698, french edition.
    The following maps relate to America:
    no.  1. United States of America.
    "   2. The world. From Arrowsmith's map.
    "   3. Chart of the world on Mercator's projection.
    "  20. North America.
    "  21. West Indies.
    "  22. South America.

### 1820-1821

**Rossi, L.**
    Nuovo atlante di geografia universale in 52 carte compilazione ridotta ad uso degl' Italiani, riveduta ed ampliata . . .    xx, 150 pp., 48 maps, 4 pl. fol. Milano, Batelli & Fanfani, 1820–[1821]    739

    NOTE.—Maps no. 34–35, 41–43 dated 1821.
    The following maps relate to America:
    no.  3. Mappa-mondo . . .
    "   4. Regioni polari . . .
    "   5. Observazioni recentissime, fatte nell' America Meridionale da m$^r$. Humboldt . . .
    "   6. Mappa-mondo . . .
    "   7. Mappamondo ridotto.
    "  34. L'America Settentrionale.  1821.
    "  35. L'America Meridionale.  1821.

no. 36. Stati Uniti di America.
" 37. Possessioni della spagna nell' America Settentrionale. Carta generale del Messico.
" 38. Dominj inglesi in America.
" 39. Carta della parte della costa nord-ovest dell' America . . .
" 40. Indie Occidentali.
" 41. Carta di S. Domingo, giusta quella di Poirson. 1821.
" 42. Carta delle isole Antille. 1821.
" 43. Carta della Gujana Francese ed Olandese. 1821.

### 1821?
**Cummings, J. A.**
School atlas to Cummings' ancient and modern geography. 8th ed. cover-title, 8 maps. 8°. Boston, Cummings & Hilliard [1821?]     740

NOTE.—See also titles 274, 275, and 276. Maps engraved by H. Morse.
The following maps relate to America:
no. [1] The world . . .
" [2] North America . . .
" [3] The United States . . .
" [4] South America . . .

### 1821?
**Lattré, J.**
Petit atlas moderne ou collection de cartes élémentaires dedié à la jeunesse. 2 p. l., 34 pp., 30 (*i. e.* 26) maps, 2 pl. 8°. Paris, Delamarche [1821?]     741

NOTE.—First published 1763.
Accompanied by Idée de la sphère, by C. F. Delamarche.
New edition revised and corrected.
The following maps relate to America:
no. [1] Mappe-monde . . . 1811.
" 25 [*i. e.* 21] Amérique Septentrion$^{le}$. . . . 1783.
" 26 [*i. e.* 22] États-Unis de l'Amérique Sep$^{le}$.
" 27 [*i. e.* 23] Golfe du Mexique . . . 1783.
" 28 [*i. e.* 24] Amérique Méridionale.

### 1823
**Lucas, F.**
A general atlas containing distinct maps of all the known countries in the world . . . 3 p. l., 100 col. maps. fol. Baltimore, F. Lucas, jun. [1823]     742

NOTE.—Engraved title. Copyright june 3, 1823.
Map no. 60, Maryland, has an inset plan of the city of Baltimore.
The following maps relate to America:
no. 14. Western hemisphere.
" 16. World, Mercator's projection.
" 47. North America.
" 48. Canada.
" 49. United States.
" 50. Maine.
" 51. New Hampshire.

**Lucas, F.**—Continued.
- no. 52. Massachusetts.
- " 53. Vermont.
- " 54. Rhode Island.
- " 55. Connecticut.
- " 56. New York.
- " 57. New Jersey.
- " 58. Pennsylvania.
- " 59. Delaware.
- " 60. Maryland.
- " 61. Virginia.
- " 62. North Carolina.
- " 63. South Carolina.
- " 64. Georgia.
- " 65. Ohio.
- " 66. Kentucky.
- " 67. Tennessee.
- " 68. Mississippi.
- " 69. Alabama.
- " 70. Louisiana.
- " 71. Indiana.
- " 72. Illinois.
- " 73. Missouri.
- " 74. Arkansas.
- " 75. Michigan.
- " 76. Florida.
- " 77. Mexico.
- " 78. West Indies.
- " 79. Bermudas.
- " 80. Bahamas.
- " 81. Cuba.
- " 82. Jamaica.
- " 83. St. Domingo.
- " 84. Porto Rico.
- " 85. Virgin islands.
- " 86. St. Christophers.
- " 87. Nevis.
- " 88. Antigua.
- " 89. Guadaloupe.
- " 90. Dominica.
- " 91. Martinico.
- " 92. St. Lucia.
- " 93. St. Vincent.
- " 94. Barbadoes.
- " 95. Grenada.
- " 96. Tobago.
- " 97. Trinidad.
- " 98. Curaçoa.
- " 99. South America.
- " 100. Colombia.
- " 101. Brazil.
- " 102. Peru.
- " 103. United provinces, S. A.
- " 104. Chili.

## 1824

**Bossi, L.**

Nuovo atlante universale della antica e moderna geografia dei signori Arrowsmith, Poirson, Sotzmann, Lapie, d'Albe, Malte-Brun ed altri più accreditati autori e per la parte antica dei signori d'Anville e Bonne. Nuovamente tradotto, inciso e ricorretto a norma dei viaggi più accreditati e delle più recenti scoperte, degli ultimi trattati di pace e delle nuove divisioni politiche ad uso delle scuole d' Italia con una introduzione alle geografia generale riformata sopra quella di G. Goldsmith dal cav. Luigi Bossi.   39, [1] pp., 37 maps, 1 pl. fol.   Milano, P. & G. Vallardi, 1824. 743

NOTE.—The following maps relate to America:
- no. 1. Mappamondo.
- " 2. Planisfero . . . Ridotto secondo la projectione di Mercatore di Arrowsmith.
- " 31. America Settentrionale di Arrowsmith.
- " 32. Stati Uniti di Arrowsmith.
- " 33. Messico o Nuova Spagna e Nuovo Messico ora in parte America indipendente. da Arrowsmith.
- " 34. Golfo del Messico ed arcipelago delle Antille di P. Lapie.
- " 35. America Meridionale da Arrowsmith.

## 1824

**Lapie, P.**

Atlas clafsique et universel de géographie ancienne et moderne, dressé pour l'instruction de la jeunesse, et servant à l'intelligence tant de l'histoire que des voyages dans les differentes parties du monde.   3. 6d.   4 p. l., 42 (*i. e.* 41) maps, 1 pl.   fol.   Paris, Anselin & Pochard; & Picquet, 1824. 744

NOTE.—The following maps relate to America:
- no. 13. Mappe-monde.
- " 14. Mappemonde physique sur la projection de Mercator.
- " 39. Amérique Septentrionale ou Colombie.
- " 40. États-Unis de l'Amérique Septentrionale.
- " 41. Golfe du Mexique et archipel des Antilles.
- " 42. Amérique Méridionale.

## 1824-1825

**Cary, J.**

Cary's new universal atlas, containing distinct maps of all the principal states and kingdoms throughout the world. From the latest and best authorities extant and shewing the whole of the new divisions according to the congress of Vienna.   2 p. l., 57 col. maps on [114] l.   fol.   London, for J. Cary, 1824–[1825] 745

NOTE.—See also titles 714 and 736.
The following maps relate to America:
- no. 1-2. The western hemisphere.—The eastern hemisphere . . . 1824.
- " 3. A new chart of the world . . . 1824.
- " 51. A new map of America . . . 1825.

**Cary, J.**—Continued.
 no. 52. A new map of North America . . . 1824.
  " 53. A new map of Nova Scotia . . . 1824.
  " 54. A new map of Upper & Lower Canada . . . 1824.
  " 55. A new map of the United States of America . . . 1824.
  " 56 . . . Part of the United States of North America containing those of New York, Vermont, New Hampshire, Massachusetts, Connecticut, Rhode Island, Pennsylvania, New Jersey, Delaware. Maryland and Virginia . . . 1825.
  " 57 . . . Part of the United States, exhibiting the northwest, Michigan, Indiana and Illinois territory, the states of Kentucky, Ohio. Virginia, Maryland and Pennsylvania . . . 1825.
  " 58 . . . Part of the United States of North America, containing the Carolinas and Georgia, also the Floridas and part of the Bahama islands &c. . . . 1825.
  " 59. A new map of the West India isles . . . 1821.
  " 60–61. A new map of South America . . . 1824. 2 sheets.

## 1825

**Morse, S. E.**

A new universal atlas of the world, on an improved plan; consisting of thirty maps carefully prepared from the latest authorities, with complete alphabetical indexes. iv pp., [27] l., 30 maps. 4°. New Haven, N. & S. S. Jocelyn, 1825. 746

NOTE.—The following maps relate to America:
 no. [1] The world. 1825.
  " [2] North America.
  " [3] Canada.
  " [4] United States.
  " [5] Maine, New Hampshire and Vermont.
  " [6] Massachusetts, Rhode Island and Connecticut.
  " [7] New York.
  " [8] North Carolina, South Carolina and Georgia.
  " [9] Virginia, Maryland and Delaware.
  " [10] Pennsylvania and New Jersey.
  " [11] Alabama, Mississippi and Louisiana.
  " [12] Kentucky and Tennessee.
  " [13] Ohio and Indiana.
  " [14] Illinois and Missouri.
  " [15] West Indies.
  " [16] South America.
  " [27] Asia [Philippine islands]
  " [30] Pacific ocean.

## 1826

**Blake, J. L.**

A geographical, chronological, and historical atlas, on a new and improved plan; or, a view of the present state of all the empires, kingdoms, states, and colonies in the known world. ix, [2], 10–196 pp., [34] l., 1 map, 3 pl. 8°. New York, Cooke & co. 1826. 747

NOTE.—The following map relates to America:
 no. [1] The world.

## 1826

**Stucchi, S.**
Grande atlante universale di geografia moderna secondo i principj di Malte-Brun . . . 1 p. l., 8 col. maps on 26 l., 1 pl.  fol.  Milano, trovasi venibile presso l' autore, 1826.  748
> NOTE.—The following maps relate to America:
> no. 1. Nuovo mappa-mondo fisico sulla projezione di Mercatore, 1822.
> " 5. America Settentrionale o Colombia. 1825.
> " 6. America Meridionale. 1825.
> " 7. Oceanica o quinta parte del mondo.

## 1827

**Vandermaelen, P. M. G.**
Atlas universel de géographie, physique, politique, statistique et minéralogique, sur l'échelle de $\frac{1}{1641}$ 1836 ou d'une ligne par 1900 toises . . . lithographié par H. Ode . . . 6 v. fol. Bruxelles, 1827.  749

### CONTENTS.

> v. 1. Europe. 2 p. l., 27 col. maps on 30 sheets, 1 tab.
> " 2. Asie. 2 p. l., 111 col. maps on 112 sheets.
> " 3. Afrique. 2 p. l., 58 col. maps on 61 sheets.
> " 4. Amérique Septentrionale. 2 p. l., 77 col. maps on 78 sheets.
> " 5. Amérique Méridionale. 2 p. l., 45 col. maps on 47 sheets.
> " 6. Océanique. 2 p. l., 61 col. maps.

## 1827

**Thomson, J.**
A new general atlas, consisting of a series of geographical designs, on various projections, exhibiting the form and component parts of the globe and a collection of maps and charts, delineating the natural and political divisions of the empires, kingdoms, and states, in the world. Constructed from the best systematic works, and the most authentic voyages and travels. 2 p. l., xxiii, [1], 22 pp., front., 76 (*i. e.* 83) col. maps, 1 pl. fol. Edinburgh, for J. Thomson & co. 1827.  750
> NOTE.—See also title 731. The following maps relate to America:
> no. 1. Chart of the world on Mercator's projection.
> " 2. Southern hemisphere.
> " 3. Northern hemisphere.
> " 5. Western hemisphere.
> " 6. Northern hemisphere.
> " 7. Southern hemisphere.
> " 51. Atlantic ocean.
> " 52. America.
> " 53. North America.
> " 54. Canada.

**Thomson, J.**—Continued.
  no. 55. United States.
  " 56. " "
  " 57. Mexico.
  " 58. "
  " 59. Central America.
  " 60. West Indies.
  " 61. " " (Cuba, etc.)
  " 62. Jamaica.
  " 63. West Indies.
  " 64. " "
  " 65. " "
  " 66. " "
  " 67. " "
  " 68. " "
  " 69. South America.
  " 70. Caraccas and Guiana.
  " 71. Peru, Chili and La Plata.
  " 74. Chart of the northern passage between Asia and America.
  " 76. A chart of the discoveries of captains Ross . . . etc.

## 1828

**Malte-Brun, C.**

Universal geography, or a description of all the parts of the world, on a new plan, according to the great natural divisions of the globe . . . Atlas. 2 p. l., 40 maps. 4°. Philadelphia, A. Finley, 1827–1829.     751

    NOTE.—See also titles 763 and 775. Atlas has title: A new general atlas, exhibiting the five great divisions of the globe . . . Drawn and engraved, particularly to illustrate the Universal geography by m. Malte-Brun. Philadelphia, J. Grigg, 1828.
    Text, a translation of the author's, Précis de la géographie universelle," Paris, 1810–29.
    The following maps relate to America:
  no. 1. Western hemisphere.
  " 2. Eastern hemisphere [Philippine islands]
  " 14. Asia [Philippine islands]
  " 20. Chin India & n. w. Oceanica, Philippine is.
  " 22. Eastern Oceanica.
  " 27. North America.
  " 28. British America.
  " 29. United States.
  " 30. New England states.
  " 31. The middle states—Maryland & Virginia.
  " 32. N. & S. Carolina, Georgia & Florida.
  " 33. Alabama, Mississippi, Louisiana & Arkansas ter.
  " 34. Western states & territories.
  " 35. Mexico and Guatimala.
  " 36. West Indies.
  " 37. South America.
  " 38. Colombia and Guiana.
  " 39. Brazil, Bolivia & Peru.
  " 40. United provinces—Chili & Patagonia.

## 1829

**Finley, A.**
A new general atlas, comprising a complete set of maps representing the grand divisions of the globe, together with the several empires, kingdoms and states in the world; compiled from the best authorities and corrected by the most recent discoveries. 3 p. l., 58 col. maps, 2 tab. fol. Philadelphia, A. Finley, 1829. 752

NOTE.—See also titles 755 and 760.
The following maps relate to America:
- no. 1. Western hemisphere.
- " 2. Eastern "
- " 3. World.
- " 4. North America.
- " 5. Canada.
- " 6. United States.
- " 7. Maine.
- " 8. New Hampshire.
- " 9. Vermont.
- " 10. Massachusetts.
- " 11. Rhode Island.
- " 12. Connecticut.
- " 13. New York.
- " 14. New Jersey.
- " 15. Pennsylvania.
- " 16. Delaware.
- " 17. Maryland.
- " 18. Virginia.
- " 19. North Carolina.
- " 20. South "
- " 21. Georgia.
- " 22. Alabama.
- " 23. Ohio.
- " 24. Kentucky.
- " 25. Tennessee.
- " 26. Indiana.
- " 27. Illinois.
- " 28. Mississippi.
- " 29. Louisiana.
- " 30. Missouri.
- " 31. Mexico.
- " 32. West Indies.
- " 33. South America.

## 1829-1835

**Society, The,** for the diffusion of useful knowledge. A series of maps, modern and ancient under the superintendence of The society for the diffusion of useful knowledge. 54 pts. incl. 108 maps. fol. London, Baldwin & Cradock [1829-35] 753

NOTE.—Cover of pt. 54 used as title page for the series. See also titles 794 and 811.

**Society, The**—Continued.

The following maps relate to America:
no. 21. North America. Sheet  ii. Lower Canada.
"  26.      "        "      "    iii. Upper    "
"  27.      "        "      "    vi. New York ...
"  29.      "        "      "    iv. Lake Superior.
"  33.      "        "      "    i. Nova Scotia.
"  35.      "        "      "    v. The Northwest.
"  36.      "        "      "    viii. Ohio.
"  39.      "        "      "    xi. North & South Carolina.
"  40.      "        "      "    xiii. Louisiana ...
"  41.      "        "      "    vii. Pennsylvania.
"  42.      "        "      "    ix. Missouri.
"  47.      "        "      "    xii. Georgia.
"  48.      "        "      "    x. Missouri.
"  53.      "        "      "    xiv. Florida.
"  70.      "        "      "    Index map.
"  72. British North America.
"  73. The Antilles or West India islands.
"  74. The british islands in the West Indies.

## 1829-1833

**Lapie, P.** *and* **Lapie, A. E.**, *fils.*

Atlas universal de géographie ancienne et moderne, précédé d'un abrégé de géographie physique et historique. 4 p. l., 100 pp., 50 maps. fol. Paris, Eymery, Fruger & cie. 1829-[1833]    754

NOTE.—First edition published in 1828. Quérard states that Lapie, in colaboration with his son, published this edition in 1842. See also title 123, 123a, 765 and 787.

The date 1833 is the latest in this atlas and appears on 4 maps.

## 1830

**Finley, A.**

A new general atlas, comprising a complete set of maps, representing the grand divisions of the globe, together with the several empires, kingdoms and states in the world; compiled from the best authorities, and corrected by the most recent discoveries. 3 p. l., 58 col. maps, 2 pl. fol. Philadelphia, A. Finley, 1830.    755

NOTE.—See also titles 752 and 760.

The following maps relate to America:
no. 1. Western hemisphere.
"   3. The world on Mercator's projection.
"   4. North America.
"   5. Canada.
"   6. United States.
"   7. Maine.
"   8. New Hampshire.
"   9. Vermont.
"  10. Massachusetts.

no. 11. Rhode Island.
" 12. Connecticut.
" 13. New York.
" 14. New Jersey.
" 15. Pennsylvania.
" 16. Delaware.
" 17. Maryland.
" 18. Virginia.
" 19. North Carolina.
" 20. South Carolina.
" 21. Georgia.
" 22. Alabama.
" 23. Ohio.
" 24. Kentucky.
" 25. Tennessee.
" 26. Indiana.
" 27. Illinois.
" 28. Mississippi.
" 29. Louisiana.
" 30. Missouri.
" 31. Mexico.
" 32. West Indies.
" 33. South America.

**1830**

**Hall, S.**
A new general atlas, with the divisions and boundaries carefully colored; constructed entirely from new drawings . . . 2 p. l., 53 maps. fol. London, for Longman, Rees, Orme, Brown & Green, 1830. 756

NOTE.—See also titles 777, 779, 793 and 821.
The following maps relate to America:
no. 2. Western hemisphere . . . 1829.
" 3. The world . . . 1829.
" 43. North America . . . 1829.
" 44. United States . . . 1828.
" 45. British North America . . . 1829.
" 46. Mexico and Guatimala . . . 1828.
" 47. West Indies . . . 1827.
" 48. Canada, New Brunswick and Nova Scotia . . . 1830.
" 49. South America . . . 1829.
" 50. Colombia . . . 1828.
" 51. Brazil and Paraguay . . . 1828.
" 52. Peru . . . 1828.
" 53. Chili, La Plata and Bolivia or upper Peru . . . 1829.

## 1830

**Hart, J. C.**

A modern atlas, of fourteen maps. Drawn and engraved to illustrate Hart's geographical exercises . . . 7th ed. rev. and cor. 1 p. l., 14 col. maps. fol. New York. R. Lockwood; Philadelphia, A. Finley [etc.] 1830.

757

NOTE.—The following maps relate to America:
- no. 1. The world on Mercator's projection.
- " 2. Map of North America.
- " 3. Map of the United States.
- " 4. Map of the state of New York.
- " 5. The West Indies.
- " 6. Map of South America.
- " 12. The Pacific ocean.

## 1830–1834

**Brué, A. H.**

Atlas universel de géographie physique, politique, ancienne & moderne, contenant les cartes générales et particulières de toutes les parties du monde; rédigé conformément aux progrès de la science pour servir à l'intelligence de l'histoire, de la géographie et des voyages . . . 2. éd. 4 p. l., 65 col. maps. Paris, l'auteur, 1830–[1834]

758

NOTE.—See also title 726.

The following maps relate to America:
- no. 15. Mappemonde sur la projection de Mercator. 1830.
- " 16. Mappemonde en deux hémisphères. 1830.
- " 17. Mappemonde. 1828.
- " 57. Carte générale de l'Amérique Septentrionale et des îsles qui en dépendent. 1828.
- " 58. Carte générale des États-Unis, du Haute et Bas-Canada de la Nouv$^{le}$. Ecosse du Nouv$^{au}$ Brunswick de Terre Neuve &$^a$ 1832.
- " 59. Carte générale des états-unis Mexicains et des provinces-unies de l'Amérique Centrale. 1825.
- " 60. Carte des Îles Antilles, des états-unis de l'Amérique-Centrale, et de la mer du Mexique. 1832.
- " 61. Carte particulière des Îles Antilles. 1828.
- " 62. Carte générale de l'Amérique Méridionale et des îles qui en dépendent. 1826.
- " 63. Carte générale de Colombie, de la Guyane Française, Hollandaise et Anglaise. 1826.
- " 64. Carte générale du Pérou, du Haut-Pérou, du Chili et de La Plata. 1826.
- " 65. Carte du Brésil et d'une partie des pays adjacents. 1826.

## 1831?

**Delisle, G.**, *and* **Buache, P.**

Atlas géographique des quatre parties du monde . . . fait pour les géographies élémentaires de mr. Buache et de l'abbé Nicolle de la Croix. Revu et augmenté par Dezauche. 2 p. l., 35 maps. fol. Paris, Dezauche [1831?]

759

NOTE.—Imperfect; maps no. [8], Plan de Paris, and no. [9], Prevôté, vicomté et environs de Paris, wanting.

"Nouveau plan de la ville de Paris, ou guide exacte de cette capitale" 1833, is an inserted map, substituted for no. [8]
no. [3], Carte de l'Europe . . . and no. [10], Carte des royaumes de Belgique et de Hollande . . . dated 1831.
Explanatory text on nos. [2] and [4]
The following maps relate to America:
no. [1] Mappemonde . . . 1828.
" [2] Planisphère physique . . .
" [24] Carte de l'Asie . . . 1830.
" [26] Carte des Indes et de la Chine . . . 1781 [Philippine islands]
" [27] Carte de l'Afrique . . . 1830. [Part of South America]
" [28] Carte de l'Amérique . . . 1830.
" [29] Carte du Canada qui comprend la partie septentrionale des États-Unis . . . 1783.
" [30] Inset: Supplementum Theatro historico. [South America and part of North America outlined]
" [32] Inset: "Carte des anciens empires et grandes monarchies." . . . 1828.

## 1831

**Finley, A.**

A new general atlas, comprising a complete set of maps, representing the grand divisions of the globe, together with the several empires, kingdoms and states in the world; compiled from the best authorities and corrected by the most recent discoveries.  3 p. l., 60 col. maps, 2 tab.  fol.  Philadelphia, A. Finley, 1831.  760

NOTE.—See also titles 752 and 755.
The following maps relate to America:
no. 1. Western hemisphere.
" 4. North America.
" 5. Canada.
" 6. United States.
" 7. Maine.
" 8. New Hampshire.
" 9. Vermont.
" 10. Massachusetts.
" 11. Rhode Island.
" 12. Connecticut.
" 13. New York.
" 14. New Jersey.
" 15. Pennsylvania.
" 16. Delaware.
" 17. Maryland.
" 18. Virginia.
" 19. North Carolina.
" 20. South Carolina.
" 21. Georgia.
" 22. Alabama.
" 23. Ohio.
" 24. Kentucky.
" 25. Tennessee.
" 26. Indiana.
" 27. Illinois.
" 28. Mississippi.

**Finley, A.**—Continued.
　no. 29. Louisiana.
　" 30. Missouri.
　" 31. Florida.
　" 31. Mexico.
　" 32. West Indies.
　" 33. South America.

### 1831?
**Lizars, D.**

The Edinburgh geographical and historical atlas, comprehending a sketch of the history of geography; a view of the principles of mathematical, physical, civil, and political geography; an account of the geography, statistics, and history of each continent, state, and kingdom, delineated. And a tabular view of the principal mountain chains in the world . . .　6 p. l., 16, 288; 4 pp., 116 l. incl. 51 maps. fol. Edinburgh, J. Hamilton, successor to D. Lizars [1831?]　761

　NOTE.—See also title 782.
　The following maps relate to America:
　no. 1. Western hemisphere.
　" 4. Chart of the world on Mercator's projection.
　" 58. America.
　" 60. South America.
　" 62. North America.
　" 63. United States.
　" 64. West India islands.
　" 65. Chart of the Atlantic ocean.
　" 66. Mexico & Guatimala.
　" 67. Colombia & Guayana.
　" 68. Lower Peru, Brazil & Paraguay.
　" 69. Bolivia or upper Peru; Chili and the United Provinces of South America, or La Plata.

### 1832
**Carey, H. C.,** *and* **Lea, I.**

Family cabinet atlas. 1st american ed., rev., cor. and enl.　2 p. l., 44 l., 48 maps, 4 pl. 12°. Philadelphia, Carey & Lea, 1832.　762

　NOTE.—See also title 767.
　The following maps relate to America:
　no. 8. The world.
　" 9–10. The world. 2 maps.
　" 78. North America.
　" 79. British possessions in North America.
　" 82. Canada with New Brunswick, Nova Scotia & Newfoundland.
　" 83. United States.
　" 86. United States, northern section.
　" 87. United States, southern section.
　" 90. Mexico and Guatimala.
　" 91. West Indies.

no. 94. South America.
" 95. Colombia.
" 98. La Plata, Chili and the Banda orientale.
" 99. Brazil, with Guiana & Paraguay.

## 1832
**Malte-Brun, C.**
Universal geography, or a description of all the parts of the world, on a new plan, according to the great natural divisions of the globe . . . 5 v. Atlas. 2 p. l., 40 maps. 4°. Philadelphia, J. Laval, 1832. 763

NOTE.—Atlas has title: A new general atlas, exhibiting the five great divisions of the globe . . . Drawn and engraved, particularly to illustrate the Universal geography by m. Malte-Brun. Philadelphia, Grigg & Elliot, 1832. Text, a translation of the author's "Précis de la géographie universelle," Paris, 1810-29. See also titles 751 and 775.

The following maps relate to America:
no. 1. Western hemisphere.
" 2. Eastern hemisphere [Philippine islands]
" [14] Asia [Philippine islands]
" 20. Chin India & n. w. Oceanica.
" 22. Eastern Oceanica.
" [27] North America.
" [28] British America.
" [29] United States.
" [30] New England states.
" [31] The Middle states—Maryland & Virginia.
" [32] N. & S. Carolina, Georgia & Florida.
" 33. Alabama, Mississippi, Louisiana & Arkansas ter.
" [34] Western states & territories.
" [35] Mexico and Guatimala.
" [36] West Indies.
" [37] South America.
" [38] Colombia and Guiana.
" [39] Brazil, Bolivia & Peru.
" [40] United provinces—Chili & Patagonia.

## 1832-1846
**Arrowsmith, J.**
London atlas. 4 v. [Consisting of folded maps in 4 cases] 8°. [London, J. Arrowsmith, 1832-1846] 764

NOTE.—First edition published in 1834. Reviewed in the Royal geographical society. London. Journal, 1834, v. 4, p. 320; also in Kritischer wegweiser, feb. 28, 1835. v. 7, pp. 92-96. See also titles 789 and 790.
"The atlas consists of fifty sheets."

CONTENTS.
vol. 1. Europe.
no. 1. Orbis veteribus notus. 1834.
" 2.
" 3. Europe. 1834.
" 4.
" 5. . . . England and Wales . . . [Geological] 1834.

**Arrowsmith, J.**—Continued.
   vol. 1. Europe—Continued.
      no. 6. Scotland. 1834.
      " 7. Ireland. 1834.
      " 8. Sweden & Norway. 1834.
      " 9. Denmark. 1834.
      " 10. Holland & Belgium . . . 1834.
      " 11.
      " 12.
      " 13. Prussia & Poland. 1834.
      " 14. Russia & Poland. 1834.
      " 15. Austrian empire. 1834.
      " 16. Switzerland &c. . . . 1834.
      " 17. North Italy &c. . . . 1834.
   vol. 2. Part of Europe & Africa.
      no. 18. South Italy. 1834.
      " 18a. . . . Ionian islands and Malta . . . 1842.
      " 19. Turkey in Europe. 1834.
      " 20. Greece and the Ionian islands. 1834.
      " 21. Spain & Portugal. 1834.
      " 22. Africa. 1834.
      " 23. Northwestern Africa. 1834.
      " 23a. West coast of Africa . . . 1842.
      " 24. Cape of Good Hope. 1834.
      " 24.
      " 25. Nubia and Abyssinia. 1832.
      " 26. Egypt. 1834.
   vol. 3. Asia.
      no. 27. Asia. 1834.
      " 28. Turkey in Asia. 1834.
      " 28a. . . . Asia Minor . . . 1842.
      " 29. Central Asia . . . 1834.
      " 30. India. 1834.
      " 31. Burmah, Siam, and Cochin China. 1834.
      " [32] . . . Punjab and the Sikh territory . . . 1846.
      " 33. Northern Asia [1834?]
      " 34. Asiatic Archipelago. 1834.
      " [35] The Caspian sea, Khivah and the surrounding country . . . 1841.
      " 36. . . . Western Australia . . . 1833.
      " 37. Van Diemens land. 1832.
      " 38. Pacific ocean. 1832.
   vol. 4. America.
      no. 39. America. 1834.
      " 40. British North America. 1834.
      " 41. Upper Canada &c. 1834.
      " 42. Lower Canada . . . 1834.
      " 43. United States. 1834.
      " [43a] . . . Texas . . . 1841.
      " 44. Mexico. 1834.
      " 45. West Indies. 1834.
      " 46. South America. 1834.
      " 47. Colombia. 1834.
      " 48. Peru & Bolivia. 1834.
      " 49. Brazil. 1832.
      " 50. . . . La Plata, Banda Oriental, & Chile . . . 1834.

## 1833

**Lapie, P.** *and* **Lapie, A. E.** *fils.*
Atlas universel de géographie ancienne et moderne, précédé d'un abrégé de géographie physique et historique. Dédié au roi. 4 p. l., 100 pp., 50 maps, 1 pl.   fol.   Paris, Eymery, Fruger & cie. 1829–[1833]

NOTE.—See also titles 123, 123a, 754 and 787. The following maps dated 1833:
no. 12 . . . Syrie et de l'Egypte . —no. 13. . . . Palestine.—no. 20 . . . l'Europe.—no. 27 . . . Royaumes de Belgique et Hollande.
Half-title:—Atlas universel de géographie ancienne et moderne.
Map no [27 bis], "Plan de la ville . . . d'Anvers 1832," not in the "Liste des cartes," is probably inserted.
The following maps relate to America:
no. 16. Mappe-monde sur la projection de Mercator . . . 1832.
" 17. Mappe-monde en deux hémisphères . . . 1831.
" 33. Carte de l'Asie . . . 1832 . . . [Îles Philippines]
" 36. Carte de l'empire Chinois et du Japon . . . 1832 . . . [Îles Philippines]
" 37. Carte de la Sibérie ou Russie d'Asie . . . 1832 . . . [Amérique Russe]
" 38. Carte de l'Océanie . . . 1829 . . .
" 42. Carte de l'Amérique Septentrionale . . . 1830 . . .
" 43. Carte des États-Unis d'Amérique . . . 1832 . . .
" 44. Carte des États-Unis du Mexique . . . 1829 . . . Inset: . . . Guatemala . . .
" 45. Carte des Antilles, du golfe du Mexique et d'une partie des états voisins. 1829.
" 46. Carte générale de l'Amérique Méridionale . . . 1829.
" 47. Carte de Colombie et des Guyanes . . . 1828.
" 48. Carte du Brésil . . 1829.
" 49. Carte du Pérou et du Haut Pérou . . . 1829.
" 50. Carte de la Plata du Chili et de la Patagonie . . . 1828.

## 1833–1834

**Stein, C. G. D.**
Neuer atlas der ganzen erde nach den neuesten bestimmungen für zeitlungsleser, kauf- und geschäftsleute jeder art, gymnasien und schulen, mit besonderer rücksicht auf die geographischen werke von dr C. G. D. Stein . . . In 24 charten, grösstentheils neu entworfen und gezeichnet von d. F. W. Streit . . . und gestochen von H. Leutemann, nebst sieben historischen, geographischen und statistischen tabellen und uebersichten. 12. verm. und verb. aufl. 2 p. l., [6] l., 24 col. maps.   fol.   Leipzig, J. C. Hinrichs, 1833–[1834]

NOTE.—The following maps relate to America:
no. [1] Oestliche und westliche halbkugel der erde. Neu entworfen und gezeichnet von M. Riedig. 1834.
" [5] Nord Amerika und West Indien . . . Entworfen und gezeichnet von dr. F. W. Streit. 1834.
" [6] Sud America entworfen und gezeichnet von F. W. Streit.
" [24] Charte von dem Nordamericanischen Staatenbunde . . . entworfen und gezeichnet von F. W. Streit.

### 1834
**Carey, H. C.** *and* **Lea, I.**
Family cabinet atlas. 2d american ed., rev., cor. and impr. 2 p. l., 46 l., 48 maps, 4 pl. 12°. Philadelphia, Carey, Lea & Blanchard, 1834. 767

NOTE.—See also title 762. Title headed: The geographical annual, for 1834. The following maps relate to America:
no. 8. The world.
" 9. The world.—Western hemisphere.—Eastern hemisphere.
" 10. The world.—Polar regions, north.—Polar regions, south.
" 78. North America.
" 79. British possessions in North America.
" 82. Canada with New Brunswick, Nova Scotia & Newfoundland.
" 83. United States.
" 86. United States, northern section.
" 87. United States, soutnern section.
" 90. Mexico and Guatimala.
" 91. West Indies.
" 94. South America.
" 95. Colombia.
" 98. La Plata, Chili and the Banda orientale.
" 99. Brazil, with Guiana & Paraguay.

### 1834
**Vivien de Saint-Martin, L.**
Atlas universel pour servir à l'étude de la géographie et de l'histoire anciennes et modernes. Dressé par L. Vivien. 2 p. l., 48 maps. fol. Paris, Desenne; Menard, 1834. 767a

NOTE.—First published 1825.
The following maps relate to America:
no. 1. Mappe-monde en deux hémisphères . . .
" 31. Carte de l'Amérique Septentrionale avec les régions polaires . . .
" 32. Carte de la partie septentrionale du Nouveau Monde où sont comprises les possessions anglaises de l'Amérique du Nord, l'Amérique rufse et les régions polaires arctiques . . .
" 33. Carte générale des États Unis de l'Amérique Septentrionale . . .
" 34. Carte générale du Mexique et des provinces-unies de l'Amérique Centrale . . .
" 35. Carte particulière des Antilles et du golfe du Mexique avec l'isthme de Panamá . . .
" 36. Carte de l'Amérique Méridionale . . .
" 37. Carte de la république de Colombie . . .
" 38. Carte générale d'une partie de l'Amérique du Sud où sont comprises les nouvelles républiques du Pérou, du Haut Pérou, et de Buenos-Ayres . . .
" 39. Carte générale de l'empire du Brésil . . .

## 1835

[**Atlas** aī mejmuā khartat resm al-arz.—Atlas, that is, a collection of maps of geography] cover-title, 11 maps. obl. fol. [Malta, 1835] 768

>NOTE.—Arabic atlas of the world.
>No author given.
>Transliterated from the arabic.
>
>CONTENTS.
>
>no. 1. Eastern hemisphere.
>" 2. Western "
>" 3. Europe.
>" 4. Asia.
>" 5. Africa.
>" 6. America.
>" 7. Australia.
>" 8. North Africa.
>" 9. Egypt and Palestine.
>" 10. East India.
>" 11. Turkey in Europe and Greece.

## 1835

**Bradford, T. G.**

Atlas designed to illustrate the abridgment of universal geography, modern & ancient. Chiefly compiled from the Abrégé de géographie of Adrian Balbi. cover-title, 4 p. l., 32 maps. 4°. Boston, W. D. Ticknor; New York, F. Hunt & co. [etc.] 1835. 769

>The following maps relate to America:
>no. [1] Maine.
>" [2] New Hampshire & Vermont.
>" [3] Massachusetts.
>" [4] Connecticut and Rhode Island.
>" [5] New York.
>" [6] Pennsylvania and New Jersey.
>" [7] Virginia, Maryland and Delaware.
>" [8] North Carolina, South Carolina and Georgia.
>" [9] Mississippi & Alabama.
>" [10] Louisiana and part of Arkansas.
>" [11] Tennessee & Kentucky.
>" [12] Illinois & Missouri.
>" [13] Indiana & Ohio.
>" [14] Michigan and the great lakes.
>" [15] United States.
>" [16] Mexico, Guatemala and the West Indies.
>" [17] North America.
>" [18] South America.
>" [19] Atlantic ocean.

**Bradford, T. G.**—Continued.
A comprehensive atlas geographical, historical & commercial. 3 p. l., 100 pp., front., 66 maps, 7 pl., 3 diagr. 4°. Boston, W. D. Ticknor; New York, Wiley & Long [etc.] °1835.  770

NOTE.—Another copy of this atlas, with same date published by American stationers' company. Illustrations: The five varieties of the human race.—Comparative chart of the continents, oceans, islands &c.—Comparative heights of mountains.—Distribution of vegetables and snow line.—Comparative size of animals.—Modes of travelling.—Dwellings of different countries.—Comparative heights of monuments.—Comparative chart of different countries.—Distance and direction of various places from New York.
Small plans of: London.—Edinburgh.—Paris.—Madrid.—Brussels.—Vienna, Portland & vicinity.—Boston & vicinity.—Providence & vicinity.—New York & vicinity.—Albany & vicinity.—Baltimore & vicinity.—Philadelphia & vicinity.—Charleston & vicinity.—Savannah & vicinity.—New Orleans & vicinity.—St. Louis & vicinity.—Louisville & vicinity.—City of Nashville.—Niagara Falls & vicinity.—Cincinnati & vicinity.
The following maps relate to America:
no. [1] Maine.
" [2] New Hampshire & Vermont.
" [3] Massachusetts.
" [4] Connecticut and Rhode Island.
" [5] New York.
" [6] Pennsylvania.
" [7] Virginia, Maryland and Delaware.
" [8] District of Columbia.
" [9] North Carolina, South Carolina and Georgia.
" [10] Florida.
" [11] Mississippi & Alabama.
" [12] Louisiana and part of Arkansas.
" [13] Tennessee & Kentucky.
" [14] Illinois & Missouri.
" [15] Indiana & Ohio.
" [16] Michigan and the great lakes.
" [17] Cities
" [18] United States exhibiting the railroads and canals.
" [19] United States.
" [20] Upper & Lower Canada.
" [21] British America.
" [22] Mexico, Guatemala, and the West Indies.
" [23] West Indies.
" [24] North America.
" [25] Colombia & Guiana.
" [26] Brazil, Bolivia & Peru.
" [27] United Provinces, Chili & Patagonia.
" [28] South America.
" [29] Atlantic ocean.

## 1835?

**Burr, D. H.**

A new universal atlas; comprising separate maps of all the principal empires, kingdoms & states throughout the world: and forming a distinct atlas of the United States. Carefully compiled from the best authorities extant. 2 p. l., 63 maps. fol. New York, D. S. Stone [1835?] 771

NOTE.—Several maps are dated 1835.
The following maps relate to America:
no. [2] Western Hemisphere.
" [30] Lower Canada. 1834.
" [31] Upper Canada. 1833.
" 32. Newfoundland, Nova Scotia and New Brunswick. 1833.
" 33. United States. 1833.
" 34. Maine. 1835.
" 35. Vermont and New Hampshire. 1835.
" 36. New York. 1832.
" 37. New York city. 1831.
" 38. Massachusetts Rhode Island and Connecticut. 1835.
" 39. Pennsylvania. 1834.
" 40. New Jersey. 1835.
" [41] Delaware and Maryland. 1833.
" 42. Virginia. 1834.
" 43. Ohio. 1831.
" 44. Michican. 1831.
" 45. Indiana. 1833.
" 46. Illinois. 1834.
" 47. Missouri. 1834.
" 48. Oregon territory. 1833.
" 49. Kentucky and Tennessee. 1834.
" 50. Arkansas. 1835.
" [51] North and South Carolina. 1834.
" 52. Georgia. 1834.
" 53. Alabama. 1834.
" 54. Mississippi. 1835.
" 55. Louisiana. 1834.
" 56. . . . Florida. 1834.
" 57. Mexico. 1832.
" 58. West Indies. 1834.
" 59. South America. : '33.
" 60. Colombia. 1834.
" [61] Peru and Bolivia. 1833.
" 62. Brazil with Guiana & Paraguay. 1834.
" 63. United provinces, Chili & Patagonia. 1833.

## 1835

**Dower, J.**

A new general atlas of the world, compiled from the latest authorities both english & foreign, containing separate maps of its various countries & states, and exhibiting their boundaries & divisions also the chains of mountains, rivers, lakes and other geograph-

**Dower, J.**—Continued.

ical features, comprehended in forty six maps, including ancient maps of Greece, the roman and persian empires & Palestime from drawings made exprefsly for this work.   2 p. l., 45 fold. maps, 1 pl.   fol.   London, H. Teesdale & co. 1835.   772
[ *With* Teesdale, H. & co.   Improved edition of the new british atlas.   fol.   London, H. Teesdale & co. [1835] ]

> NOTE:—Known as "Teesdale's general atlas of the world."  See also titles 796 and 812.
> The following maps relate to America:
> no. 35. America.
> " 36. Canada.
> " 37. United States.
> " 38. Mexico and Guatemala.
> " 39. West Indies.
> " 40. Columbia.
> " 41. Peru and Bolivia.
> " 42. Brazil.

### 1835

**Lütke, F. P.**

Путешествіе вокругъ свѣта, совершенное по повелѣнію императора Николая I, на военномъ шлюпѣ сенявинѣ, въ 1826, 1827, 1828 и 1829 годахъ, флота капитаномъ Ѳедоромъ Литке.  Атласъ.   6 p. l., 29 maps, 4 pl.   fol. Санктпетербургъ, Х. Гиппе, 1835.   773

> NOTE.—Atlas accompanying this work has title: Атласъ къ путешествію вокругъ свѣта шлюпа сенявина . . .
> French title follows pl. 1: Atlas du voyage autour du monde de la corvette Seniavine fait en 1826, 1827, 1828 et 1829 sous les ordres de Frédéric Lutké . . .
> Maps dated 1827-28.
> Titles, and lettering on maps in french and russian.
> The following maps relate to America:
> no.  1. Генеральная карта берингова моря.—Carte générale de la mer de Behring.
> "  2. Карта западнаго берега Берингова пролива.—Carte de la côte occidentale du détroit de Behring.
> " 10. Планъ губы Св. Лаврентія.—Plan de la baie St Laurent.
> " 13. Карта острова Беринга.—Carte de l'île Behring.—Карта острововъ Прибылова.—Carte des îles Pribyloff.—Планъ губы на осстровѣ Беринга.—Plan d'une baie dans l'ile Behring.
> " 14. Карта полуострова Аляски.—Carte de la presqu'île Alaska.
> " 15. Виды разныхъ пунктовъ Америки и острововъ въ Беринговомъ морѣ.—Vues des différents points de l'Amérique et des îles de la mer de Behring.

### 1836

**Tanner, H. S.**

A new universal atlas containing maps of the various empires, kingdoms, states and republics of the world . . .   4 p. l., 68 col. maps, 1 pl.   fol.   Philadelphia, published by the author, 1836.

774

> NOTE.—See also title 788.

The following maps relate to America:
no. 1. A new map of the world. 1833.
" 2. North America.
" 3. Lower Canada.
" 3½. Upper Canada.
" 4. United States.
" 5. A new map of Maine.
" 6. New Hampshire & Vermont.
" 7. Massachusetts and Rhode Island. Inset view of Boston.
" 8. Connecticut.
" 9. A new map of New York.
" . 10. New Jersey, reduced from T. Gordon's map.
" 11. A new map of Pennsylvania.
" 12. A new map of Maryland. Inset plan of Baltimore.
" 13. A new map of Virginia.
" 14. A new map of North Carolina.
" 15. A new map of South Carolina. Inset plan of Charleston.
" 16. A new map of Georgia.
" 17. Florida. Inset plan of Pensacola. Tallahassee and harbour of St. Augustine.
" 18. A new map of Alabama.
" 19. A new map of Mississippi.
" 20. A new map of Louisiana. Inset plan of New Orleans.
" 21. A new map of Arkansas.
" 22. A new map of Tennessee.
" 23. A new map of Kentucky.
" 24. A new map of Ohio. Inset plan of Cincinnati.
" 25. A new map of Michigan.
" 26. A new map of Indiana.
" 27. A new map of Illinois.
" 28. A new map of Missouri.
" 29. West Indies.
" 30. Mexico & Guatemala.
" 31. South America.
" 32. Venezuela, New Grenada & Equador.
" 33. Brazil.
" 34. Peru and Bolivia.
" 35. Chile, La Plata and Montevideo.
" 63. Oceana or Pacific ocean.
" 64. City of New York.
" 65. Philadelphia.
" 66. City of Washington.

## 1837

**Malte-Brun, C.**

A new general atlas exhibiting the five great divisions of the globe, Europe, Asia, Africa, America & Oceanica . . . Drawn and engraved, particularly to illustrate the universal geography by m. Malte Brun. 2 p. l., 40 col. maps. 4°. Philadelphia, Grigg & Elliot, 1837. 775

NOTE.—See also titles 751 and 763.

**Malte-Brun, C.**—Continued.
The following maps relate to America:
no. 1. Western hemisphere.
" 2. Eastern hemisphere.
" 27. North America.
" 28. British America.
" 29. United States.
" 30. New England states.
" 31. The middle states, Maryland & Virginia.
" 32. N. & S. Carolina, Georgia & Florida.
" 33. Alabama, Mississippi, Louisiana, & Arkansas ter.
' 34. Western states & territories.
" 35. Mexico and Guatimala.
" 36. West Indies.
" 37. South America.
" 38. Colombia and Guiana.
" 39. Brazil, Bolivia & Peru.
" 40. United provinces, Chili & Patagonia.

### 1838–1845
**Ptolemæus, C.**

Claudius Ptolemæi geographiæ libri octo. Græce et latine ad codicum manu scriptorum fidem edidit dr. Frid. Guil. Wilberg . . . vi, 440 (*i. e.* 456) pp., 1 pl., 2 facs. fol. Essendiæ, sumptibus et typis G. D. Bædeker, 1838–45. 776

NOTE.—Without maps. Issued in six parts with separate title-pages, one book to each part. Brunet states that the publication began in 1832, and ended with part VI in 1843. The translation was never finished.
On title-pages of pts. 2–6: socio adiuncto Car. Henr. Frid. Grashofio.

### 1840
**Hall, S.**

Black's general atlas: a series of fifty-four maps from the latest and most authentic sources . . . 1 p. l., 12, 40 pp., 46 maps on 55 l. fol. Edinburgh, A. & C. Black; London, Longman & co. [etc.] 1840. 777

NOTE.—See also titles 756, 779, 793, 821, 826, 829, and 849.
The following maps relate to America:
l. 1. The world.
" 2. The world on Mercator's projection.
" 3. A chart of magnetic curves of equal variation. By Peter Barlow.
" 5. Humboldt's distribution of plants in equinoctial America according to elevation above the level of the sea.
" 45. North America.
" 46. Canada, New Brunswick &c.
" 47–48. United States.
" 49. Mexico.
" 50. West Indies.
" 51. South America.
" 52. Colombia, Peru &c.
" 53. Chili, La Plata and part of Bolivia.
" 54. Brazil.

## 1840

**He mau** palapala aina a me na niele e pili ana.  Hookahi ke pai ana.
1 p. l., [3]–14 pp., 9 maps, 1 pl.   fol.   Lahainaluna, 1840.   778

   Note.—See also title 830.   Letterpress follows the maps.
   The following maps relate to America:
   no. [1] Na palapala honua ho ka poepoe, 1839.
     " [3] Aina moana.
     " [4] Amerika akau.
     " [5] Amerika hema.
     " [6] Amerika huipuia.

## 1841

**Hall, S.**
   Black's general atlas: a series of fifty-four maps from the latest and most authentic sources . . . 1 p. l. 12, 40 pp., 54 maps on 55 l. fol.   Edinburgh, A. & C. Black; London, Longman & co. 1841.
779

   Note.—See also titles 756, 777, 793, 821, and 826.
   The following maps relate to America:
   l.   1. The world.
   "   2. The world on Mercator's projection.
   "   3. A chart of magnetic curves of equal variation.  By Peter Barlow.
   "   5. Humboldt's distribution of plants in equinoctial America according to elevation above the level of the sea.
   "  45. North America.
   "  46. Canada, New Brunswick &c.
   " 47–48. United States.
   "  49. Mexico.
   "  50. West Indies.
   "  51. South America.
   "  52. Colombia, Peru &c.
   "  53. Chili, La Plata and part of Bolivia.
   "  54. Brazil.

## 1841?

**Mudie, R.**
   Gilbert's modern atlas of the earth, with an introduction to physical and historical geography, and an alphabetical index of the latitudes of 60,000 places.  4 p. l., xx, 228, 53, [2] pp., front., incl. 52 maps, pl.   fol.   London, H. G. Collins [1841?]   780

   Note.—Pagination irregular.
   The following maps relate to America:
   no. [1] The world.
   "  43. North America.
   "  44. British and Russian America.
   "  45. Canada, New Brunswick, Nova Scotia, etc.
   "  46. United States.
   "  47. Mexico & Texas.
   "  48. West Indies, Guatimala, etc.
   "  49. South America.
   "  50. South America.  no. 1.  [Northwest coast]

**Mudie, R.**—Continued.
  no. 51. South America. [Brazil]
  " 52. South America. no. 3. [Chili, Patagonia, La Plata]
  " 53. South America. no. 4.
  " 56. The world on Mercator's projection.

## 1841

**Radefeld,** ———  *and* **Renner,** ———.
  Atlas zum handgebrauche für die gesammte erdbeschreibung. In 116 karten gezeichnet vom hauptmann Radefeld und prem. lieut. Renner. 2 p. l., 115 maps. obl. 32°. [Hildburghausen] bibliographischen instituts [1841]     781
  NOTE.—Contains plans of the following cities:
  no. [104] Stockholm.—Lissabon. 1838.
  " [105] Oporto.—Carlsruhe. "
  " [106] Mayland.—Verona. "
  " [107] Venedig.—Mantua. 1838.
  " [108] Dresden.—Bremen.
  " [109] Breslau.—Liegnitz.
  " [110] Halle.—Erfurt.
  " [111] Strasburg.—Basel.
  " [112] Baden-Baden.—Heidelberg.
  " [113] Würzburg.—Ulm.
  " [114] Marienbad.—Teplitz.
  " [115] Darmstadt.—Frankfurt.
  The following maps relate to America:
  no. [3] Oestliche und westliche halbkugel der erde. 1835.
  " [4] Die erde in der polar-projection.
  " [5] Welt-charte in Merkators projection. 1836.
  " [11] Süd-America.
  " [91] Verein-Staaten von Nord-America.
  " [92] Canada, New Brunswick, Nova Scotia und Newfoundland. 1837.
  " [93] Mexico und Guatimala.
  " [94] West Indien.
  " [95] Brasilien Guyana Paraguay u. Montevideo.
  " [96] Columbia. 1839.
  " [97] La Plata, Chile und Cisplatina.

## 1842?

**Lizars, W. H.**
  Lizars' Edinburgh geographical atlas: containing maps of every empire, state and kingdom; with a tabular view of the heights of the great mountain chains, and a very copious and comprehensive consulting index. Compiled, drawn and engraved from the latest and most authentic sources. The maps of the new british colonies upon an extra large scale; and the whole engraved upon sixty-nine plates. 2 p. l., 29 pp., 68 maps, on 69 sheets. fol. Edinburgh, W. H. Lizars [1842?]     782
  NOTE.—See also title 761.

The following maps relate to America:
no. 1. Western hemisphere.
" 3. Chart of the world on Mercator's projection.
" 42–45. Asia. 4 sheets.
" 51. East India islands. [Philippine islands]
" 58–61. America. 4 sheets.
" 62. North America. British possessions.
" 63. United States & Texas.
" 64. West India islands.
" 65. Chart of the Atlantic ocean.
" 66. Mexico & Guatimala with the republic of Texas.
" 67. Colombia & Guayana.
" 68. Lower Peru, Brazil & Paraguay.
" 69. Bolivia or Upper Peru and the united provinces of South America or La Plata.

## 1842

**Bradford, T. G.** *and* **Goodrich, S. G.**
A universal, illustrated atlas, exhibiting a geographical, statistical and historical view of the world. 3 p. l., IV, 218 pp., front., 49 maps. fol. Boston, C. D. Strong, 1842. 783

CONTENTS.

no. 1. Western hemisphere. 1841.
" 2. Eastern " 1841.
" 3. North America. 1838.
" 4. Upper Canada. 1838.
" 5. Lower Canada. 1838.
" 6. United States. 1838.
" 7. Plan of Washington.—New Orleans.—Louisville and Jeffersonville.—Cincinnati. 1838.
" 8. Maine. 1838.
" 9. New Hampshire. 1838.
" 10. Vermont. 1838.
" 11. Massachusetts. 1838.
" 12. [Plan of] Boston.
" 13. Rhode Island. 1838.
" 14. Connecticut. 1838.
" 15. New York. 1838.
" 16. [Plan of] New York.
" 17. New Jersey. 1838.
" 18. Pennsylvania. 1838.
" 19. [Plan of] Philadelphia. 1838.
" 20. Ohio. 1838.
" 21. Indiana. 1838.
" 22. Illinois. 1838.
" 23. Michigan. 1838.
" 24. Delaware. 1838.
" 25. Maryland. 1838.
" 26. [Plan of] Baltimore. 1838.
" 27. Virginia. 1838.

**Bradford, T. G.** *and* **Goodrich, S. G.**—Continued.
   no. 28. Kentucky. 1838.
   " 29. North Carolina. 1838.
   " 30. Tennessee. 1838.
   " 31. South Carolina. 1838.
   " 32. Georgia. 1838.
   " 33. Florida. 1838.
   " 34. Alabama. 1838.
   " 35. Mississippi. 1838.
   " 36. Louisiana. 1838.
   " 37. Arkansas. 1838.
   " 38. Missouri. 1838.
   " 39. Wisconsin and Iowa. 1838.
   " 40. Texas. 1838.
   " 41. West Indies. 1838.
   " 42. South America. 1841.
   " 43. Atlantic ocean. 1841.
   " 44. Europe. 1841.
   " 45. Western Europe. 1841.
   " 46. Southern and middle Europe. 1841.
   " 47. Africa. 1841.
   " 48. Asia. 1841.
   " 49. Pacific ocean. 1841.

## 1842

**Greenleaf, J.**

A new universal atlas; comprising separate maps of all the principal empires, kingdoms & states throughout the world: and forming a distinct atlas of the United States. Carefully compiled from the best authorities extant. New ed. rev. 2 p. l., 11 pp., 65 col. maps. fol. Brattleboro, Vt., G. R. French, 1842.    784

   Note.—The following maps relate to America:
   no. 2. Western hemisphere.
   " 3. Northern hemisphere.
   " 4. Southern hemisphere.
   " 29. North America.
   " 30. East part of Canada.
   " 31. West part of Canada.
   " 32. Newfoundland, Nova Scotia, and New Brunswick.
   " 33. United States.
   " 34. Maine.
   " 35. Vermont and New Hampshire.
   " 36. New York.
   " 37. Map of the country twenty five miles round the city of New York.
   " 38. Massachusetts, Rhode Island, and Connecticut.
   " 39. Pennsylvania.
   " 40. New-Jersey.
   " 41. Delaware and Maryland.
   " 42. Virginia.
   " 43. Ohio.
   " 44. Michigan.

no. 45. Indiana.
" 46. Illinois.
" 47. Missouri.
" 48. Oregon territory.
" 49. Kentucky and Tennessee.
" 50. Arkansas.
" 51. North and South Carolina.
" 52. Georgia.
" 53. Map of the state of Alabama.
" 54. Mississippi.
" 55. Louisiana.
" 56. Map of the territory of Florida.
" 57. The United States of Mexico.
" 58. West Indies.
" 59. South America.
" 60. New Grenada, Venezuela, & Ecuador.
" 61. Peru and Bolivia.
" 62. Brazil with Guiana & Paraguay.
" 63. Buenos Ayres, Chili & Patagonia.
" 64. Texas . . .
" 65. Wisconsin and Iowa.

**1842**

**Tardieu, A.**

Atlas universel de géographie, ancienne et moderne, dressé par Ambroise Tardieu pour l'intelligence de la Géographie universelle par Malte-Brun. 2 p. l., 27 maps. fol. Paris, Furne & cie. 1842. 785

NOTE.—Copy no. 1. The following maps relate to America:
no. 23. Amérique Septentrionale.
" 24. " Méridionale.

**1842**

[Atlas universel de géographie, ancienne et moderne, dressé par Ambroise Tardieu pour l'intelligence de la Géographie universelle par Malte-Brun] 30 maps. fol. [Paris, Furne & cie, 1842?]
786

NOTE.—Copy no. 2. Title-page wanting. Cover-title, "Malte-Brun atlas."
The following maps in copy no. 2, do not appear in copy no. 1:
no. 22. Presqu'ile de l'Inde.
" 25. États-Unis & Mexique. Dressés . . . par J. T. Thunot-Duvotenay.
" 28. Algérie. Dressée . . . J. Th. Thunot-Duvotenay.
" 30. Plan de Paris.
Map no. 26, Algérie, in copy no. 1, not in copy no. 2.
The following maps relate to America:
no. 8. Mappe-monde.
" 24. Amérique Septentrionale.
" 25. États-Unis & Mexique. Dressés . . . J. Th. Thunot-Duvotenay.
" 26. Amérique Méridionale.

## 1841-1842

**Lapie, P.** *and* **Lapie, A. É.** *fils.*
Atlas universel de géographie ancienne et moderne, précédé d'un abrégé de géographie physique et historique. 2 p. l., 98 pp., 49 maps, 1 pl. fol. Paris, P. C. Lehuby, 1841-[1842] 787
NOTE.—See also titles 123, 123a, 754 and 765.
The following maps relate to America:
no. 17. Mappe-monde en deux hémisphères. 1842.
" 42. Carte de l'Amérique Septentrionale. 1842.
" 43. Carte des États-Unis d'Amérique, du Canada, du Nouveau Brunswick et d'une partie de la Nouvelle France. 1842.
" 44. Carte des États Unis du Mexique. Inset: Carte du Guatémala. 1842.
" 45. Carte des Antilles, du golfe du Mexique et d'une partie des états voisins. 1842.
" 46. Carte générale de l'Amérique Méridionale. 1842.
" 47. Carte de Colombie. 1842.
" 48. Carte du Brésil. 1842.
" 49. Carte du Pérou et du haut Pérou. 1842.
" 50. Carte de La Plata, du Chili et de la Patagonie. 1842.

## 1842-1843

**Tanner, H. S.**
A new universal atlas, containing maps of the various empires, kingdoms and republics of the world, with a special map of each of the United States, plans of cities &c. 4 p. l., 68 (*i. e.* 70) maps. fol. Philadelphia, Carey & Hart, 1842-[1843] 788
NOTE.—Preface dated 1843. See also title 774.
Contains plans of the following cities:
no. 64. . . . New York. 1835.
" 65. Philadelphia. 1836.
" 66. Washington. 1836.
The following maps relate to America:
no. 1. A new map of the world . . . 1843.
" 2. North America. 1836.
" 3. Lower Canada.
" 3½. Upper "
" 4. United States. 1839.
" 5. . . . Maine. 1840.
" 6. New Hampshire & Vermont . . . 1840.
" 7. Massachusetts and Rhode Island . . . 1841.
" 8. Connecticut . . . 1839.
" 9. . . . New York . . . 1840.
" 10. New Jersey . . . 1841.
" 11. . . . Pennsylvania . . . 1840.
" 12. . . . Maryland and Delaware . . .
" 13. . . . Virginia . . .
" 14. . . . Nth. Carolina . . . 1841.
" 15. . . . South Carolina . . . 1841.
" 16. . . . Georgia . . . 1839.
" 17. Florida. 1839.
" 18. . . . Alabama . . . 1841.
" 19. . . . Mississippi . . . 1836.

no. 20. . . . Louisiana . . . 1833.
" 21. . . . Arkansas . . . 1841.
" 22. . . . Tennessee . . . 1841.
" 23. . . . Kentucky . . . 1839.
" 24. . . . Ohio . . . 1841.
" 25. . . . Michigan . . . 1841.
" 25½. Wisconsin.
" 26. . . . Indiana . . . 1841.
" 27. Illinois . . . 1841.
" 27½. Iowa . . .
" 28. . . . Missouri . . . 1841.
" 29. West Indies. 1834.
" 30. Mexico & Guatemala . . . 1834.
" 30ª. Texas. 1833.
" 31. South America. 1836.
" 32. Venezuela, New Grenada & Equador.
" 33. Brazil.
" 34. Peru and Bolivia.
" 35. Chile, La Plata and Montevideo.

## 1842-1850

**Arrowsmith, J.**

The London atlas of universal geography, exhibiting the physical & political divisions of the various countries of the world, constructed from original materials . . . 2 p. l., 67 col. maps. fol. London, J. Arrowsmith, 1842-[1850]  789

NOTE.—See also titles 764 and 790.
The following maps are dated 1850:
no. 22. Africa.
" 40. British North America.
" [59] Australia.
" [60] Eastern Australia . . .
" [62] New Zealand.
First edition, published in 1834, contained 50 maps; later editions of 1842 and 1847, contain 67 maps. See English catalogue of 1837-55, and Quaritch, General catalogue . . . v. 5, no. 28263.
The last 17 maps of the present copy are not referred to in the table of contents.

CONTENTS.

no. 1. Orbis veteribus notus. 1842.
" 2. The world on Mercator's projection. 1844.
" 3. Europe. 1842.
" 4. England. 1842.
" 5. . . . England & Wales. 1842.
" 6. Scotland. 1846.
" 7. Ireland. 1842.
" 8. Sweden & Norway. 1842.
" 9. Denmark, Inset:—Iceland. 1842.
" 10. Holland & Belgium. 1842.
" 11. France. 1842.
" 12. Western Germany. 1842.
" 13. Prussia & Poland. 1842.
" 14. Russia & Poland. 1842.

**Arrowsmith, J.**—Continued.
- no. 15. Austrian Empire. 1842.
- " 16. Switzerland &c. . . . 1842.
- " 17. North Italy &c. . . . 1842.
- " 18. South Italy. 1842.
- " 19. Turkey in Europe. 1842.
- " 20. Greece & the Ionian islands. 1842.
- " 21. Spain & Portugal. 1842.
- " 22. Africa. 1850.
- " 23. North-western Africa. 1842.
- " 24. Cape of Good Hope. 1842.
- " 25. Nubia & Abyssinia. 1842.
- " 26. Egypt. 1842.
- " 27. Asia. 1842.
- " 28. Turkey in Asia. 1842.
- " 29. . . . Persia, Cabul, Beloochistan. 1842.
- " 30. India. 1842.
- " 31. Burmah, Siam & Cochin China. 1842.
- " 32. China. 1843.
- " 33. Northern Asia . . . 1842.
- " 34. Asiatic Archipelago—1848.
- " 35. Southeastern portion of Australia. 1848.
- " 36. . . . Western Australia. 1843.
- " 37. Van Diemen's Land. 1842.
- " 38. Pacific ocean. 1842.
- " 39. America. 1844.
- " 40. British North America. 1850.
- " 41. Upper Canada &c. 1846.
- " 42. Lower Canada . . . 1846.
- " 43. United States. 1842.
- " 44. Mexico. 1842.
- " 45. West Indies. 1847.
- " 46. South America . . . 1842.
- " 47. Colombia. 1842.
- " 48. Peru & Bolivia. 1842.
- " 49. Brazil. 1842.
- " 50. La Plata . . . & Chile. 1842.
- " [51] . . . Acquisitions of Russia. 1842.
- " [52] . . . Ionian is. & Malta. 1844.
- " [53] . . . West coast of Africa . . . 1843.
- " [54] The river Niger . . . 1843.
- " [55] Eastern frontier . . . of C. of Good Hope . . . 1848.
- " [56] . . . Asia Minor . . . 1842.
- " [57] The Caspian sea, Khivah . . . 1841.
- " [58] . . . Punjab, Kashmir . . . 1849.
- " [59] Australia . . . 1850.
- " [60] Eastern portion of Australia. 1850.
- " [61] . . . South Australia. 1840.
- " [62] . . . New Zealand. 1850.
- " [63] . . . Texas. 1843.
- " [64] . . . Jamaica . . . 1848.
- " [65] . . . Leeward islands . . . 1842.
- " [66] . . . Windward islands . . . 1842.
- " [67] . . . British Guiana . . . 1842.

## 1842-1853

The London atlas of universal geography, exhibiting the physical & political divisions of the various countries of the world, constructed from original materials. . . . 2 p. l., 67 col. maps. fol. London, J. Arrowsmith, 1842–[1853] 790

NOTE.—See titles 764 and 789. Like the edition of 1842, having maps dated 1850, with the following exceptions:
no. [55] Eastern frontier of the colony of the Cape of Good Hope . . . 1853.
" [61] The maritime portion of South Australia . . . 1840.
" [62] . . . New Zealand . . . 1853.

## 1843

**Perrot, A. M.** *and* **Aragon, A. A.**
Atlas de 59 cartes coloriées ou noires du Dictionnaire universel de géographie moderne. 4. éd. 1 p. l., 59 maps. 4°. Paris, E. & A. Picard, 1843. 790a.
[ *With their*, Dictionnaire universel de géographie moderne . . . 4. éd. Rev. et corrigée. 4°. Paris, 1843]

## 1843-1844

**Andriveau-Goujon, J.**
Atlas classique et universel de géographie ancienne et moderne contenant les découvertes et les divisions les plus nouvelles dans les cinq parties du monde pour servir à la lecture des voyages, des ouvrages historiques et des meilleurs traités de géographie. Publié par J. Andriveau-Goujon. Adopté par le ministre de la guerre pour les bibliothèques régimentaires. Nouvelle éd. 2 p. l., 88 l. incl. 36 maps, 8 pl. fol. Paris, 1843–[1844] 791

NOTE.—Catalogue of Bibliothèque du dépôt de la guerre, gives the 1869 edition under E. Andriveau-Goujon. Lorenz gives 1865 edition under Gabriel-Gustave Andriveau-Goujon, 1808.—La Grande encyclopédia also gives an edition under Gabriel-Gustave.
"Un ancien éditeur de Paris, des plus honorablement connus, m. Gilbert-Gabriel Benjamin Andriveau, vient de mourir, en sa maison de campagne de Palaiseau, à l'âge de soixante dix-neuf ans. Etabli libraire dès l'âge de vingt ans, m. Andriveau avait épousé la fille de m. Goujon, éditeur-géographe, et lui avait succédé dans sa maison de la rue du Bac. La science géographique lui doit de nombreuses et excellentes publications, éditées avec un soin tout particulier. Son établissement jouissait depuis longtemps déjà d'une bonne renommée, et son nom de l'estime de tous, lorsqu'en 1858 il céda la place à son fils, m. Eugène Andriveau, aujourd'hui membre du cercle de la librairie."
*cf.* Journal général de l'imprimerie et de la librairie. 2e partie. Chronique. Paris, 1884. no. 43, p. 196.
The following maps relate to America:
no. 13. Terre suivant la projection de Mercator, et conforme à l'état actuel des connaissances géographiques. 1843.
" 14. Mappemonde en deux hémisphères. 1843.
" 40. Carte de l'Amérique du Nord. 1841.

**Andriveau-Goujon, J.**—Continued.

   no. 41. Carte des États-Unis d'Amérique comprenant une partie des districts de l'ouest et de la Nouvelle Bretagne. 1841.
   " 42. Carte de l'Amérique du Sud. 1841.

### 1844

**Butler, S.**

An atlas of modern geography. A new edition reengraved with corrections from the government surveys and most recent sources of information. Edited by the author's son [Thomas Butler] 2 p. l., 1 l., 38 pp., 23 maps. 8°. London, Longman, Brown, Green & Longmans, 1844.    792

   NOTE.—See also title 861.
   The following maps relate to America:
   no. 19. North America.
   " 20. United States.
   " 21. South America.
   " 22. West Indies.

### 1844

**Hall, S., Hughes, W.,** & *others*.

Black's general atlas: comprehending sixty-one maps from the latest and most authentic sources . . . With geographical descriptions, and an index of 56,000 names. 2 p. l., 12, 57 pp., 53 maps on 68 l. fol. Edinburgh, A. & C. Black; London, Longmans & co. [etc.] 1844.    793

   NOTE.—See also titles 756, 777, 779, 821, 826, 829, and 849.
   The following maps relate to America:
   l.   1. The world.
   "   2. The world on Mercator's projection.
   "   3–1. A chart of magnetic curves of equal variation. By Peter Barlow.
   "   3–2. Chart of isothermal lines . . .
   "   5. Humboldts distribution of plants in equinoctial America according to elevation above the level of the sea.
   "   45. North America.
   "   46. Canada, New Brunswick, &c.
   " 47–48. United States.
   "   49. Mexico.
   "   50. West Indies.
   "   51. South America.
   "   52. Colombia, Peru, &c.
   "   53. Chili, La Plata and part of Bolivia.
   "   54. Brazil.
   "   55. China.

### 1844

**Society, The,** for the diffusion of useful knowledge. Maps of the Society for the diffusion of useful knowledge. 2 v. in 1. 1 p. l., 107 maps; 1 p. l., 39 pp., 99 maps. fol. London, Chapman & Hall, 1844.    794

   NOTE.—See also titles 753 and 811. At end is an "Index to the principal places in the world," by the rev. James Mickleburgh. The title page of this atlas gives date of publication 1844, but each map has separate date of publication from 1830 to 1844.

Contains plans of the following cities: Amsterdam, Antwerp, Athens, Berlin, Birmingham, Bordeaux, Boston, Brussels, Calcutta, Constantinople, Copenhagen, Dresden, Dublin, environs of Dublin, Edinburgh, environs of Edinburgh, Florence, Frankfort, Geneva, Genoa, Hamburg, Lisbon, Liverpool, London, London 1843, environs of London, Madrid, Marseille, Milan, Moscow, Munich, Naples, New York, Oporto, eastern division of Paris, western division of Paris, environs of Paris, Parma, St. Petersburg, Philadelphia, Pompeii, plan of ancient Rome, by W. B. Clarke, plan of modern Rome, by W. B. Clarke, Stockholm, Syracuse, Toulon, Turin, Venice, Vienna, Warsaw.

The following maps relate to America:

v. 1, no. 1. Western hemisphere. no. 3. The world on Mercator's projection.
" 2, no. 127. North America.—no. 128. British North America.—no. 129-143. North America. Index map to Canada and the United States, Sheets 1—xiv.—no. 146-147. Central America. Including Texas, California and the northern states of Mexico . . . Sheets i-ii.—no. 144. The Antilles or West India islands.—no. 145. The British Isles in the West Indies.—no. 149-153. South America Sheets 1—V.—no. 155. Pacific ocean.

## 1844

**Mickleburgh,** *Rev. J., of Ashill.*

Index to the principal places in the world (modern), with reference to the maps of the Society for the diffusion of useful knowledge. 1 p. l., 183 pp. 8°. London, C. Knight & co. 1844.    794a

## 1844-1851

**Robiquet,** ———

[Atlas hydrographique ]    34 maps. fol. [Paris, Robiquet, 1844-1851]    795

NOTE.—See also title 909. A collection of maps edited by Robiquet, without title-page, of different dates, and by various hydrographers, many of them officers of the english or french navy, including: Dumoulin, Beechey, Denham, Gauttier, Berard, W. H. Smyth, Copeland, Graves, Vidal, Boteler, Arlett, Roussin, Tofino, Mudge, Bedford, Lavaud, Bullock, Bayfield, Hurd, Barnett, Owen, T. Smyth, Fitzroy and Tardy de Montravel.

Contains map by capitaine Th. Hurd, entitled "Plan des Iles Bermudes . . . publié en 1827. Havre, Tehenne, 1844."

Edition of 1882 contains the following maps not found in this atlas:

no. [5] Carte . . . de l'Europe.
" [6] " des bancs situés au s. o. des îles Feroë et au n. o. des îles Shetland.
" [7] Carte de la mer Baltique . . .
" [10] " " " côte orientale d'Angleterre.
" [14] Carte générale des côtes de France, de Portugal, & d'Espagne.
" [17-21] Carte de côtes de France . . .
" [22] France. Embouchure de la Loire.
" [27] Méditerranée partie orientale . . .
" [28] Carte des côtes d'Espagne . . .
" [30] " " îles Baléares . . .
   [32] " de la côte d'Italie . . .

**Robiquet,** —— Continued.
no. [33] Carte de l'ile de Sardaigne.
" [34] "  " l'Archipel . . .
" [35] "  " mer de Marmara.
" [36] "  générale de la mer Noire.
" [37] "  de la mer d'Azov.
" [42] "  "  " côte s. o. d'Afrique . . .
" [44] "  des îles Canaries . . .
" [47] "  particulière des bancs de Terre-Neuve.
" [48] "  de la côte des États-Unis.
" [51] "  réduite de la Guadaloupe . . .
" [63]-[64] "  de la côte orientale d'Afrique . . .
" [65] "  des côtes de Perse et d'Arabie.
" [66] "  du golf du Bengale . . .
" [67] "  générale des îles de la Sonde comprenant Sumatra, Java, Borneo, Celebes . . .
" [68] Mer de Chine et îles Philippines.
" [69] Carte des mer du Japon et de la Corée.
" [70] "  " détroits de Malacca et Singapour . . .
" [71] "  de l'Australie ou Nouvelle Hollande.

The following maps differ from edition of 1882:
no. [9] . . . La Manche . . .
" [10] . . . golfe de Gascogne . . .
" [11] . . . La Gironde . . .
" [12] Carte générale des côtes Portugal.
" [13] "  de la Mediterranée.
" [14] . . . Mediterranée, partie occidentale.
" [17] Carte des côtes de France.
" [20] "  de la côte d'Afrique . . .
" [21] "  des îles Açores.
" [22] . . . îles du cap Verd.
" [23] Carte de la côte d'Afrique . . .
" [33] "  des côtes de l'Amérique du Sud.

The following maps relate to America:
no. [1] Carte générale de l'océan Atlantique septentrionale.
" [2] Océan Atlantique méridionale.
" [4] Carte générale de l'océan Pacifique . . . 1851.
" [24] "  générale de l'île et des bancs de Terre-Neuve et du golfe St Laurent . . . 1847.
" [25] Plan des îles Bermudes par cap. Th. Hurd . . . publié en 1827.  1844.
" [26] Carte des îles et bancs de Bahama, par mm. E. Barnett, R. Owen, T. Smyth.  1850.
" [27] Carte des côtes de la Patagonie et des mers du cap Horn, dressée d'après . . . R. Fitz Roy, 1849.
" [30] Carte générale des îles Antilles et du golfe du Mexique.  1851.
" [31] "  de la côte des Guyanes et la partie n. e. du Brésil, dressée d'après . . . mm. Rousin, Tardy de Montravel & ra.  1851.
" [32] Carte de la côte du Brésil.  1851.
" [33] "  des côtes de l'Amérique du Sud . . . 1851.

## 1848

**Teesdale, H. & co.**

A new general atlas of the world, compiled and constructed with the greatest care from the latest government and other approved modern surveys and authorities . . .  4 p. l., 45 col. maps, 1 pl. fol. London, H. Teesdale & co. 1848. 796

NOTE.—See also titles 772 and 812.
The following maps relate to America:
no. [2] Western hemisphere.
" 3. The world.
" 32. Chart of the Pacific ocean.
" 35. America.
" 36. Canada.
" 37. United States.
" 38. Mexico and Guatimala.
" 39. West Indies.
" 40. Columbia.
" 41. Peru and Bolivia.
" 42. Brazil.

## 1849

**Mitchell, S. A.**

A new universal atlas containing maps of the various empires, kingdoms, states and republics of the world, with a special map of each of the United States, plans of cities, &c., comprehended in seventy sheets and forming a series of one hundred and seventeen maps, plans and sections. 2 p. l., front., 72 maps. fol. Philadelphia, S. A. Mitchell, 1849. 797

NOTE.—Plate 73 used as frontispiece. Atlas copyrighted 1846. See also titles 800, 805, 807, 809, 813, 814, 823, 831, 846, 847, 848, 850, 859, 869, 879, 890, 892, 895, 906, and 920.
Plans of the following cities: New York, Philadelphia, Washington.
The following maps relate to America:
no. 1. A new map of the world . . .
" 2. North America.
" 3–4. Canada . . .
" 5. United States.
" 6. . . . Maine.
" 7. New Hampshire & Vermont.
" 8. Massachusetts and Rhode Island. Inset: Plan of Boston.
" 9. Connecticut.
" 10. . . . New York . . .
" 11. City of New York.
" 12. New Jersey . . .
" 13. . . . Pennsylvania . . .
" 14. Philadelphia . . .
" 15. . . . Maryland and Delaware.
" 16. City of Washington.
" 17. . . . Virginia . . .

**Mitchell, S. A.**—Continued.
- no. 18. . . . Nth. Carolina . . .
- " 19. . . . South Carolina . . .
- " 20. . . . Georgia . . .
- " 21. Florida.
- " 22. . . . Alabama . . .
- " 23. . . . Mississippi . . .
- " 24. . . . Louisiana . . .
- " 25. . . . Arkansas . . .
- " 26. . . . Tennessee . . .
- " 27. . . . Kentucky . . .
- " 28. . . . Ohio . . .
- " 29. . . . Michigan . . .
- " 30. . . . Indiana . . .
- " 31. . . . Illinois . . .
- " 32. . . . Missouri . . . 1847.
- " 33. Wisconsin.
- " 34. Iowa.
- " 35. . . . Texas . . . 1845.
- " 36. Oregon, Upper California, & New Mexico . . . 1845.
- " 37. Mexico & Guatemala.
- " 38. West Indies.
- " 39. South America.
- " 40. Venezuela, New Granada & Equador.
- " 41. Brazil.
- " 42. Peru and Bolivia.
- " 43. Chili, La Plata and Uruguay.
- " 63. Asia [Philippine islands]
- " 71. Oceana or Pacific ocean.

**1850**

**Findlay, A. G.**

A modern atlas; forming a complete compendium of geography, exhibiting in thirty maps, the extent, divisions, physical and political arrangements of every country in the known world . . . 4th ed. 2 p. l., xii, 51 pp., 30 maps, 1 diagr. 8°. London, W. Tegg & co. 1850.           798

**1850**

**Johnston, A. K.**

The national atlas of historical, commercial and political geography, constructed from the most recent and authentic sources, by Alexander Keith Johnston . . . Accompanied by maps and illustrations of the physical geography of the globe, by dr. Heinrich Berghaus . . . and an ethnographic map of Europe by dr. Gustaf Kombst . . . 4 p. l., 11 pp., 56 maps. fol. Edinburgh and London, W. Blackwood & sons, 1850.           799

## 1850

**Mitchell, S. A.**

A new universal atlas containing maps of the various empires, kingdoms, states and republics of the world, with a special map of each of the United States, plans of cities &c . . .   2 p. l., front., 72 maps. fol. Philadelphia. Thomas, Cowperthwait & co. 1850.
800

NOTE.—See title 797 for the various editions. Plate 73 used as frontispiece. Like the edition of 1849 with the following maps revised : no. 5. . . . United States.—no. 28. . . . Ohio.—no. 32. . . . Missouri.—no. 33. . . . Wisconsin.—no. 34. . . . Iowa.

## 1850

**Modern, A**, and ancient geography, comprising descriptions of the world in its present state and as it was known to the writers of the ancient classics and sacred scriptures. Accompanied by a new and valuable atlas . . . By a teacher. [anon.] 1 p. l., 78 pp. fol. New York, * * * * * 1850.
801

NOTE.—Atlas wanting.
Copyrighted by "F. H. Brooks" as proprietor.

## 1850

**Potel, F.**

Atlante universale di geografia antica e moderna dedicato alla gioventù pubblicato . . .   1 p. l., 50 pp., 49 maps, 1 pl. obl. 4°. Napoli, F. Potel, 1850.
802

NOTE.—The following maps relate to America:
no. 2. Mappa-mondo.
" [3] Planisferio.
" 18. Asia [Isole Filippine]
" 29. America del nord.
" 30. Stati-Uniti.
" 31. Messico.
" 32. Guatemala, Antille e golfo del Messico.
" 33. America del sud.
" 34. Brasile e Uruguay.
" 35. Peru e Bolivia.
" 36. Plata, Chili, Paraguay Patagonia.
" 37. Colombia e Guyane.
" 38. Oceania.

## 1850

**Sharpe, J.**

Sharpe's student's atlas, comprising twenty-six maps, constructed upon a system of scale and proportion, from the most recent authorities. Engraved on steel by Joseph Wilson Lowry. With a copi-

**Sharpe, J.**—Continued.
ous consulting index. 2 p. l., 34 pp., 24 maps. fol. London, Chapman & Hall, 1850. 803

NOTE.—These maps are a selection of the general maps from the fifty-four contained in "Sharpe's corresponding atlas," 1849 and the numbers appended to each are the same as those which appear on the larger atlas.
The following relate to America:
no. 1–3. The world.
" 43. British North America.
" 44. Central America and the West Indies.
" 51. South America.

### 1851

**Martin, R. M.**, *editor*.
Tallis's illustrated atlas, and modern history of the world, geographical, political, commercial and statistical. 3 p. l., iv, [156] pp., front., 81 maps, 2 pl. fol. London & New York, Tallis & co. 1851. 804

NOTE.—Primary title-page engraved.
Maps drawn and engraved by J. Rapkin.
Each map followed by descriptive text.
The following maps relate to America:
no. [1] World on Mercator's projection.
" [2] The world on Mercator's projection showing the voyages of cap. Cook . . .
" [3] Eastern hemisphere.
" [4] Western hemisphere.
" [27] Islands in the Atlantic.
" [30] Asia.
" [45] Russia in Asia.
" [47] Malay archipelago or East India islands.
" [57] Polynesia or islands of the Pacific ocean.
" [64] North America.
" [65] South America.
" [66] British America.
" [67] West Canada.
" [68] East Canada and New Brunswick.
" [69] Nova Scotia and Newfoundland.
" [70] United States.
" [71] Mexico, California and Texas.
" [72] Central America.
" [73] Isthmus of Panama.
" [74] Venezuela, New Granada, Equador and the Guayanas.
" [75] Peru and Bolivia.
" [76] Chili and La Plata.
" [77] Falkland islands and Patagonia.
" [78] Brazil.
" [79] British Guyana.
" [80] West India islands.
" [81] Jamaica.

## 1851

**Mitchell, S. A.**

A new universal atlas containing maps of the various empires, kingdoms, states and republics of the world, with a special map of each of the United States, plans of cities, &c., comprehended in seventy five sheets and forming a series of one hundred and twenty two maps, plans and sections. 2 p. l., front., 73 maps. fol. Philadelphia, Thomas, Cowperthwait & co. 1851. 805

NOTE.—Plate 74 used as front. Atlas copyrighted 1850. See title 797 for the various editions.
Like the edition of 1850 with the following exceptions: no. 36, Map of Minnesota territory, and no. 37, Map of the state of California . . . are added. "Oregon, Upper California & New Mexico," is omitted.

## 1852

**Lowry, J. W.**

Lowry's table atlas constructed and engraved from the most recent authorities. 2 p. l., 27 pp., 66 maps. 4°. London, Chapman & Hall [1852] 806

NOTE.—Issued in numbers under the title of "Penny maps." Titles 1–4, 83–100 relate to America.

## 1852

**Mitchell, S. A.**

A new universal atlas containing maps of the various empires, kingdoms, states and republics of the world, with a special map of each of the United States, plans of cities, &c. . . . 2 p. l., front., 73 maps. fol. Philadelphia, Thomas, Cowperthwait & co. 1852.

807

NOTE.—Plate 74 used as frontispiece. Atlas copyrighted 1850. See title 797 for the various editions.
Like the edition of 1851 with the following maps revised: nos. 3–4, Canada . . .—no. 25 . . . Texas.—no. 37 . . . California . . .—no. 38, Mexico & Guatemala. — no. 71 . . . Africa. — no. 73, The Pacific ocean including Oceanica . . .

## 1852

**Vincendon-Dumoulin, C. A.**

Portulan général contenant les plans des ports, rades, baies, etc., du globe . . . Océan Atlantique. 2 p. l., 37 l. incl. 24 maps. fol. Paris, dépôt général de la marine, 1852. 807a

NOTE.—The following map relates to America:
no. [1] Ile de Sable d'après la carte no. 267 de l'amiraute anglaise. 1852.
" [10] Iles Bermudas. 1852.—Entrée du Mouillage de Murray.
" [19] Ile Fernando—Noronha (Croquis fait en 1760) 1852.
" [22] Ile de la Trinidad d'après un vieux manuscrit espagnol.—Ile de la Trinidad, ilots de Martin—Vaz. 1852.

## 1852

**Wyld, J.**

A new general atlas of modern geography, consisting of a complete collection of maps of the four quarters of the globe; delineating their physical features and colored to show the limits of their respective states; including also the latest geographical and nautical discoveries. 2 p. l., 120 l. incl. 57 col. maps, 1 pl., 3 tab. fol. London, J. Wyld [1852] 808

NOTE.—Maps dated 1843–1852.
Contains maps from various sources: no. 6. Orbis veteribus notus auctor d'Anville. 1843.—no. 20. The french empire . . . from Lapie's map of 1811. . . . Published 1844.—no. 28. The prussian government of Stralsund . . . from the original map by F. W. C. baron Schmettau.—no. 31 . . . Dutchy of Holstein . . . laid down from Fisher's map and corrected by B.—no. 34. The russian dominions in Europe . . . revised and corrected . . . from the russian atlas of 1806; by Iasper Nantiat.

The following maps relate to America:

no. 7. The world on Mercator's projection. . . . 1852.
" 8. Eastern hemisphere [Philippine islands]
" 9. Western hemisphere.
" 10. Northern hemisphere.
" 11. Southern hemisphere.
" 38. . . . Asia [Philippine islands]
" 57. . . . America.
" 58. . . . North America, exhibiting the recent discoveries. Geographical & nautical.
" 59. . . . Province of Upper Canada . . .
" 60. . . . Province of Lower Canada . . .
" 61. The United States . . .
" 62. Mexico and Guatemala shewing the position of the mines.
" 62a. . . . Central America . . . 1852.
" 63. . . . West India & Bahama islands with the adjacent coasts of Yucatan, Honduras, Caracas &c. 1851.
" 64–65. Colombia prima, or South America drawn from the large map in eight sheets by Louis Stanislas d'Arcy Delarochette.
" 65. The basin of the Pacific.

## 1853

**Mitchell, S. A.**

A new universal atlas containing maps of the various empires, kingdoms, states and republics of the world, with a special map of each of the United States, plans of cities, &c., comprehended in seventy five sheets and forming a series of one hundred and twenty two maps, plans and sections. 2 p. l., 73 maps, 1 pl. fol. Philadelphia, Thomas, Cowperthwait & co. 1853. 809

NOTE.—Plate 74 bound before map no. 1. Atlas copyrighted 1850. See title 797, for the various editions.
Like the edition of 1852 except plate 74 is not a frontispiece.

## 1853

**Philip, G., & son.**
Philips' series of penny maps, forming a comprehensive atlas of modern and ancient geography. 1 p. l., 47 maps, 2 diagr. fol. Liverpool, G. Philip & son, 1853. 810

NOTE.—The following maps relate to America:
no. 1-2. The world.
" 3. The world on Mercator's projection.
" 4. Polar regions shewing the recent discoveries.
" 37. America.
" 38. North America.
" 39. United States.
" 40. British possessions in North America.
" 41. Central America.
" 42. West Indies.
" 43. South America.

## 1853

**Society,** The, for the diffusion of useful knowledge. General atlas published under the superintendence of the Society for the diffusion of useful knowledge. Compiled from the latest and most authentic sources, including all the recent geographical discoveries with plans of the principal cities of the world. 2 v. 3 p. l., 112 maps; 2 p. l., 97 maps. fol. London, G. Cox [1853] 811

NOTE.—See also titles 753 and 794. At the end of v. 2, is "The stars, in six maps, on the gnomonic projection. Originally designed by sir John Lubbock."
"Index to the principal places in the world." By the rev. James Mickleburgh.
The following maps relate to America:
v. 1, no. 1. Western hemisphere.—no. 3. The world on Mercator's projection.—no. 7. World on gnomonic projection.
" 2, no. 127. North America.—no. 128. British North America.—no. 128. North America, Canada and the United States.—no. 129-144. North America, Sheets i-xv.—no. 145. North America, including Yucatan, Belize, Guatemala, Salvador . . . no. 146. The Antilles or West-India islands.—no. 147. The British islands in the West-Indies.—no. 148-154. South America. Sheets i-vi.
This volume also contains plans of the following cities: Amsterdam, Antwerp, Athens, Berlin, Birmingham, Bordeaux, Boston, Brussels, Calcutta, Canton and its approaches, Constantinople, Copenhagen, Dresden, Dublin, environs of Dublin, Edinburgh, environs of Edinburgh, Florence, Frankfort, Geneva, Genoa, Hamburg, Lisbon, Liverpool, London, environs of London, Madrid, Marseille, Milan, Moscow, Munich, Naples, New York, Oporto, western division of Paris, eastern division of Paris, environs of Paris, Parma, St. Petersburg, Philadelphia, Pompeii, plan of ancient Rome, by W. B. Clarke, plan of modern Rome, by W. B. Clarke, Stockholm, Syracuse, Toulon, Turin, Venice, Vienna, Warsaw.

**Dower, J.**

**1854**

A new general atlas of the world, compiled from the latest authorities both english & foreign, containing separate maps of its various countries & states . . . Corrected to 1854. 2 p. l., 46 col. maps, 1 pl. fol. London, H. Teesdale & co. [1854] 812

> NOTE.—Known as Teesdale's general atlas of the world. See also title 772 and 796.

**1854**

**Mitchell, S. A.**

A new universal atlas containing maps of the various empires, kingdoms, states and republics of the world, with a special map of each of the United States, plans of cities, &c., comprehended in seventy five sheets, and forming a series of one hundred and twenty nine maps, plans and sections. 2 p. l., front., 71 maps. fol. Philadelphia, Cowperthwait, Desilver & Butler, 1854. 813

> NOTE.—Plate 75 used as frontispiece. Atlas copyrighted 1850. See title 797, for the various editions. Like the edition of 1853 with the following exceptions: Plans of cities of New York and Philadelphia are omitted.—no. 11, New York (state) and no. 45, Europe, are double sheet maps instead of single.—no. 7, Maine, and no. 17, Virginia, are revised.

**1854**

A new universal atlas containing maps of the various empires, kingdoms, states and republics of the world . . . 2 p. l., front., 74 l. incl. 72 maps. fol. Philadelphia. Cowperthwait, De Silver & Butler, 1854. 814

> NOTE.—Cover-title "Mitchells universal atlas." See title 797, for the various editions.

**1855**

**Kiepert, H.,** *i. e.* **J. S. H.**

Compendiöser allgemeiner atlas der erde und des himmels . . . 11th verb. und verm. aufl. 6 p. l., 35 maps. 8°. Weimar, geographisches institut, 1855. 815

> NOTE.—The following maps relate to America:
> no. 1. Erdkarte in Mercatorscher projection . . .
> " 2. . . . Amerika.
> " 6. Westlicher halbkugeln der erde . . .
> " 30. Süd America.
> " 31. Nord Amerika und West-indien.
> " 32. Die Vereinigten Staaten . . .

## 1856

**Colton, G. W.**
Colton's atlas of the world, illustrating physical and political geography. Accompanied by descriptions geographical, statistical, and historical, by Richard Swainson Fisher. 2 v. fol. New York, J. H. Colton & co. 1856. 816

NOTE.—See also titles 827, 856, 866, 878, 885, and 911.
Collation: v. 1, 3 p. l., [70] l., 58 maps, 1 pl.; v. 2, 2 p. l., [67] l., front., 34 maps, 2 pl.

CONTENTS.

v. 1. North and South America, etc.
" 2. Europe, Asia, Africa, Oceanica, etc.

## 1856

**Morse, C. W.**
Morse's general atlas of the world. Containing seventy maps, drawn and engraved from the latest and best authorities. With descriptions and statistics of all nations to the year 1856, by Charles Colby . . . 3 p. l., [33] l., 66 maps. fol. New York, D. Appleton & co. 1856. 817

NOTE.—The following maps relate to America:
no. [2] Western hemisphere.
" [3] The world . . .
" [4] Chart showing the recent search for a north-west passage . . .
" [5] North America.
" [6] Nova-Scotia, New Brunswick &c.
" [7] Canada east.
" [8] Canada west.
" [9] United States.
" [10] Maine.
" [11] Vermont and New Hampshire.
" [12] Massachusetts and Rhode Island.
" [13] Connecticut.
" [14] New York.
" [15] New Jersey.
" [16] Pennsylvania.
" [17] Maryland and Delaware.
" [18] Virginia.
" [19] North Carolina.
" [20] South Carolina.
" [21] Georgia.
" [22] Alabama.
" [23] Mississippi.
" [24] Florida.
" [25] Louisiana.
" [26] Texas.
" [27] Arkansas.
" [28] Kentucky and Tennessee.

**Morse, C. W.**—Continued.
　no. [29] Ohio.
　" [30] Indiana.
　" [31] Michigan.
　" [32] Wisconsin.
　" [33] Illinois.
　" [34] Iowa.
　" [35] Missouri.
　" [36] Territories of the United States.
　" [37] California.
　" [38] Mexico.
　" [39] West India islands.
　" [40] South America.
　" [41] Equador, New Grenada, Venezuela, English, French, Dutch and Brazilian Guiana.
　" [42] Brazil, Peru, Chile, Bolivia, La Plata, Paraguay and Uruguay.

### 1856
**Perthes, J.**
　Taschen-atlas über alle theile der erde nach dem neuesten zuftande in 24 illuminirten karten in kupferstich. Nach Stieler's hand-atlas verkleinert. 7. aufl. 1 p. l., 24 maps. obl. 24°. Gotha, J. Perthes, 1856. 818
　　Note.—The following maps relate to America:
　　no. 2. Westliche halbkugel.
　　" 6. Nord-America und West-Indien.
　　" 7. Süd-America.

### 1856
**Stieler, A.**
　Hand-atlas über alle theile der erde nach dem neuesten zustande und über das weltgebäude. Herausgegeben von Adolf Stieler, bearbeitet von demselben so wie von F. v. Stülpnagel, Heinr. Berghaus, Herm. Berghaus u. Aug. Petermann. [Vollständige ausg. 6. aufl.] cover-title, 1 p. l., 52 maps on 84 sheets. fol. Gotha, J. Perthes [1856] 819
　　Note.—See title 910.
　　Plan of "Gotha und umgebung," on title page. Accompanied by a text in 30 pp., 2 l., entitled "Bericht zu Stieler's hand-atlas nebst ausführlichen erläuterungen einzelner karten. Des berichts sechste auflage."

### 1857
**Colby, C. G.**
　The world in miniature, with descriptions of every nation and country. Together with a treatise on physical geography. The western hemisphere. 239 pp., 55 maps, 1 pl. sq. 12°. New Orleans, A. B. Griswold, 1857. 820
　　Note.—See titles 824 and 1181.

### 1857

**Hall, S.**
A new general atlas . . . constructed entirely from new drawings . . . New ed. rev.   2 p. l., 59 pp., 53 col. maps.   fol.   London, Longman, Brown, Green & Longmans [1857]   821

> NOTE.—See also titles 756, 777, 779, and 793.
> The following maps relate to America:
> no. 2. Western hemisphere.
> " 3. The world on Mercator's projection.
> " 33. East India islands [Philippine islands]
> " 34. Pacific Ocean.
> " 43. North America.
> " 44. United States.
> " 45. British North America.
> " 46. Mexico and Central states.
> " 47. West Indies.
> " 48. Canada, New Brunswick and Nova Scotia.
> " 49. South America.
> " 50. Venezuela, New Granada & Ecuador.
> " 51. Brazil and Paraguay.
> " 52. Peru.
> " 53. Chili, La Plata, Uruguay & upper Peru.

### 1857

**Martin, R.**
The illustrated atlas and modern history of the world, geographical, political, commercial & statistical . . .   1 p. l., iv, [168] pp., 81 maps, 2 pl.   fol.   London & New York, J. & F. Tallis [1857]   822

> NOTE.—Engraved title.
> Illustrated maps.

### 1857

**Mitchell, S. A.**
A new universal atlas containing maps of the various empires, kingdoms, states and republics of the world, with a special map of each of the United States, plans of cities, &c., comprehended in eighty one sheets and forming a series of one hundred and forty five maps, plans and sections.   2 p. l., front., 75 maps.   fol.   Philadelphia, C. Desilver, 1857.   823

> NOTE.—Plate 77 used as frontispiece.
> Maps revised to 1856, date of copyright. See title 797 for the various editions. Contains the following maps not found in earlier editions: no. 38, Nebraska, Kansas, New Mexico and Indian territories.—no. 40, Central America.—no. [58½] A complete map of the Crimea.—no. [59½] Chart of the Baltic.

### 1857

**Morse, C. W.**
The diamond atlas. With descriptions of all countries, exhibiting their actual and comparative extent, and their present political divisions, founded on the most recent discoveries and rectifica-

**Morse, C. W.**—Continued.

tions . . . The Eastern hemisphere. 2 p. l., viii-239 pp., 31 maps. sq. 12? New York, S. N. Gaston, 1857.    824

   Note.—See Colby's The diamond atlas . . . western hemisphere . . . New York, 1857. Titles 820, 1180, and 1181.

### 1857
**Ward & co.**

A miniature atlas of the earth, with short descriptive letter-press to each map. [43] l. incl. 20 maps. 32°. London, Ward & co. 1857.    825

   Note.—The following maps relate to America:
   no. 1. The world.
   " 17. North America.
   " 18. United States.
   " 19. South America.

### 1858
**Bartholomew, J.**

Supplement to Black's general atlas of the world. A series of six new maps suitable for being incorporated with recent editions. 1 p. l., 7 maps. fol. Edinburgh, A. & C. Black, 1858.    826

   Note.—See also titles 777, 779 and 793.
   The following is a list of the principal maps added to the more recent editions:
   The world on Mercator's projection.
   Canada, in two sheets.
   General map of the United States.
   Australia.
   The Arctic regions and British America.

            CONTENTS.
   I. North America, with an enlargement of British Columbia and Vancouver's island.
   II. South America.
   III. Sweden and Norway-Baltic sea, etc.
   IV. East Indian archipelago and Further India-Burmah-Siam, etc.
   V. Oceania and Pacific ocean, including all the South sea islands.
   VI. Chart of the Atlantic ocean, showing the various routes between Europe, North America and the Pacific, and the line of the Atlantic telegraph. To which is added a supplementary map, shewing dr. Livingstone's route across the interior of Africa.

### 1858
**Colton, G. W.**

Colton's general atlas, containing one hundred and seventy steel plate maps and plans, on one hundred imperial folio sheets, by G. Woolworth Colton. Accompanied by descriptions, geographical, statistical, and historical, by Richard S. Fisher . . . 3 p. l., [256] pp. incl. 96 maps, 1 pl. fol. New York, J. H. Colton & co. 1858.    827

   Note.—Pagination irregular. See also titles 816, 856, 866, 878, 885, and 911.

## 1858

**Marmocchi, F. C.**

Il globo atlante di carte geografiche compilate . . . per servire di corredo al suo corso di geografia commerciale.  1 p. l., 50 maps. obl. fol.  Genova, Paolo Rivara fu Giacomo, 1858.  828

NOTE.—Wanting map no. 48. Le vie ferrate e postali dell' Italia in relazione con le vie ferrate e postali della Francia, della Svizzera e della Germania.

The following maps relate to America:

no. 1. Mappamondo. Distribuzione delle colonie Europee nelle diverse parti del mondo. 1855.
" 22. Nuovo mondo parte settentrionale.
" 23. Nuovo mondo parte meridionale.
" 24. Le Indie Occidentali . . . L' America Centrale, l'istmo di Panama, la Nuova Granata e la Venezuela.
" 25. Peru e Bolivia.
" 26. Impero del Brasile parte nord.
" 27. Brasile parte sud Argentina, Chili, Uruguay e Paraguay.
" 28. Le Terre Magellaniche e le Antartiche.
" 29. Confederazione Messicana.
" 30. Stati orientali della Unione Americana.
" 31. Stati e territorii occidentali della Unione Americana.
" 32. Mari e arcipelaghi polari artici dalla baia d' Hudson all' America Russa.
" 33. Islanda Groenlandia e Mediterraneo Artico.
" 34. America Russa.
" 35. Oceania.
" 50. Distribuzione geografica delle piante coltivate . . .

## 1860

**Bartholomew, J.**

Black's general atlas of the world. A series of fifty-six maps. New edition, with numerous additions and improvements . . . Accompanied by an index of 65,000 names.  26, 63 pp., 52 maps on 85 l., 2 pl. fol.  Edinburgh, A. & C. Black, 1860.  829

NOTE.—See also titles 777, 779, 793, 826, and 849.

CONTENTS.

no. 1. The world.
" 2. The world on Mercator's projection . . .
" 3. Chart of the world exhibiting its chief physical features.—Ethnographical chart of the world.
" 4. Zoological chart of the world.—Chart of the world shewing the distribution of the principal plants . . .
" 5. Chart of isothermal lines.
" 6. Northern celestial hemisphere.—Southern celestial hemisphere.
" 7. Solar system.—Theory of the seasons.
" 8. Europe.
" 9-10. England and Wales.
" 11-12. Scotland.
" 13. Ireland.
" 14. France.
" 15. Switzerland.

**Bartholomew, J.**—Continued.
- no. 16. Holland & Belgium.
- " 17. Map of central Europe . . . showing the roads, canals, and railways. By W. Hughes.
- " 18. Germany.
- " 19. Austrian dominions.
- " 20. Prussia.
- " 21. Denmark.
- " 22. Sweden & Norway, Baltic sea &c.
- " 23. Russia in Europe.
- " 24. Spain & Portugal.
- " 25. Italy, North part.
- " 26. " South part.
- " 27. Turkey in Europe.
- " 28. Hellas or Greece. And Ionian islands.
- " 29. Asia.
- " 30. Turkey in Asia.
- " 31. Palestine.
- " 32. Persia and Afghanistan.
- " 33. India.
- " 34. China. By W. Hughes.
- " 35. Indian archipelago, and Further India, including Burmah, Siam, Anam &c.
- " 36. Africa.
- " 37. Egypt and Arabia Petræa.
- " 38. South Africa.
- " 39. North America.
- " 40. British America, containing all the discoveries in the Arctic seas up to 1860.
- " 41. Canada, New Brunswick, Nova Scotia, &c. East sheet.
- " 42. Canada. West sheet.
- " 43. Central maps of the United States.
- " 44. Eastern. United States.
- " 45. United States. Western states.
- " 46. Central America, Mexico & West Indies.
- " 47. West Indies.
- " 48. South America.
- " 49. Venezuela, New Granada, Equador, Peru, &c.
- " 50. Chili, La Plata or the Argentine republic & Bolivia.
- " 51. Brazil, Uruguay, Paraguay, & Guayana.
- " 52. Australia.
- " 53. New Zealand. By W. Hughes.
- " 54. Oceania and Pacific ocean.
- " 55. The world as known to the ancients.
- " 56. Map of the principal countries of the ancient world.

## 1860

[**He** ninau no ka palapala honua]    12 pp., 13 maps.   fol.   [1860?]

830

NOTE.—See also title 778. Title page wanting. Chadenat's catalogue no. 33, 1904, gives date 1860

Title heads list of questions on the maps.

The following maps relate to America:
no. [2] Poepoe Hikina.
" [4] Amerika Akau.
" [5] Amerika Huipui.
" [6] Mesiko, Guatimala, ame Inia Komohana.
" [7] Amerika Hema.

**1860**

**Mitchell, S. A.**
Mitchell's new general atlas, containing maps of the various countries of the world, plans of cities, etc., embraced in forty-seven quarto maps, forming a series of seventy-six maps and plans, together with valuable statistical tables. 2 p. l., 26 pp., 43 maps on 47 l. fol. Philadelphia, S. A. Mitchell, jr. 1860. 831

NOTE.—See title 797, for the various editions. Maps drawn and engraved by W. Williams.
Plans of the following cities: New York, Boston, Philadelphia, Baltimore and Cincinnati.
The following maps relate to America:
no. 1. . . . World on the globular projection.
" 2. . . . World on Mercator's projection.
" 3. . . . North America.
" 4. . . . Nova Scotia, New Brunswick, Cape Breton i$^d$. and Pr. Edward's i$^d$.
" [5-6] . . . Canada.
" [7] . . . United States.
" 11. . . . Maine.
" 13. . . . New York, New Hampshire, Vermont, Massachusetts, Rhode I$^d$. and Connecticut.
" 16. Plan of New York &c.
" 17. Plan of Boston.
" 18. . . . Pennsylvania, New Jersey, Maryland and Delaware.
" 21. Plan of Philadelphia.
" 21 [*] Plan of Baltimore.
" 23. . . . Virginia and North Carolina.
" 24. . . . Kentucky and Tennessee.
" 25. . . . Georgia and Alabama.
" 25 [*] . . . Florida.
" 28. . . . Louisiana, Mississippi and Arkansas.
" 29. . . /. Texas.
" 31. . . . Ohio and Indiana.
" 32. Plan of Cincinnati.
" 33. Illinois, Missouri, Iowa, Nebraska and Kansas.
" 34. . . . Michigan and Wisconsin.
" 35. Minnesota and Dacotah.
" 36. . . . Oregon, Washington and part of British Columbia.
" 37. . . . California.
" 40. . . . Mexico, Central America and the West Indies.
" 45. . . . South America.
" 47. New Grenada, Venezuela and Guiana . . .—Peru and Equador.—Argentine Confederation.
" 50. . . . Brazil, Bolivia, Paraguay and Uruguay.— . . . Chili.
" 69. . . . Asia.
" 75. . . . Oceanica.

## 1860

**Swanston, G. H.**

The companion atlas to the gazetteer of the world, comprehending forty-three beautifully coloured maps; engraved in the first style of art according to the latest and most authentic information. 4, [2] pp., 48 col. maps. fol. Edinburgh, A. Fullarton & co. [1860] 832

NOTE.—Published in 18 parts, beginning in 1852. To accompany: A gazetteer of the world. 7 v. 8°. London, A. Fullarton & co. [1850]-1856; a copy of which is in the Library of Congress.
The following maps relate to America:
no. 1. The world in hemispheres.
" 2. The world on Mercator's projection.
" 13. British empire throughout the world.
" 18. Newfoundland, New Brunswick . . .
" 19. Canada with part of United States.
" 30. North America.
" 31. United States . . .
" 32. United States . . . The north eastern states.
" 33. United States . . . The north central section.
" 34. United States . . . The south eastern states.
" 35. United States . . . The south central section.
" 36. The West Indies.
" 37. Central America.
" 38. South America.
" 39. East coast of South America.
" 41. South American states. New Granada & Venezuela.
" 42. West coast of South America.

## 1860-1861

**Dufour, A. H.**

Atlas universel physique, historique et politique de géographie ancienne et moderne. Gravé sur acier par Ch. Dyonnet . . . 2 p. l., 40 maps. fol. Paris, Paulin & Le Chevalier, 1860-[1861] 833

NOTE.—See titles 852 and 894. Maps no. 4, "Europe," no. 8, "Europe en 1789," no. 25, "Suisse," dated 1861.
nos. 12-15, "Carte administrative et physique de la France," one map in four sheets.
The following maps relate to America:
no. 10. Mappe-monde . . .
" 37. Amérique du Nord . . . 1857.
" 38. Amérique du Sud . . . 1857.
" 39. Mexique . . . 1858.
" 40. Océanie . . . 1857.

## 1861

**Babinet, J.**

Atlas universel de géographie, physique, politique et historique à l'usage des lycées, colléges et autres établissements d'instruction publique. Projection de m. Babinet . . . Dressé par

A. Vuillemin ... 2 p. l., 58 maps, 2 pl. fol. Paris, E. Bourdin [1861] 834

> NOTE.—Nouvelles annales des voyages, août 1857, 6$^{mo}$ série, pp. 129-141, contains an article by V. A. Malte-Brun, entitled, "Du nouveau système de projection homolographique de m. Babinet, et de son application à la construction des cartes géographiques."

## 1861

**Johnston, A. K.**
The royal atlas of modern geography, exhibiting, in a series of entirely original and authentic maps, the present condition of geographical discovery and research in the several countries, empires and states of the world. With a special index to each map. viii, [1] pp., 48 maps. fol. Edinburgh & London, W. Blackwood & sons, 1861. 835

> NOTE.—See also titles 867 and 905. Several maps have insets showing plans of cities and environs. For "Index geographicus," see title 842.

The following maps relate to America:
no. 1. The world.
" 2. The world on Mercator's projection.
" 4. Basin of the North Atlantic ocean.
" 41. North America.
" 42. Province of Canada (western)
" 43. ... Canada, New Brunswick, Nova Scotia.
" 44. United States ... (Western states)
" 45. "    "   ... (Eastern   " )
" 46. West India islands & Central America.
" 47-48. South America.

## 1862

**Garnier, F. A.**
Atlas sphéroïdal et universel de géographie dressé à l'aide des documents officiels, récemment publiés en France et à l'étranger ... 5 p. l., [19] pp., 59 maps, 4 pl. fol. Paris, veuve J. Renouard, 1862. 836

> NOTE.—All maps dated 1860. Two maps of special interest are, no. 3, "Tableau des principales projections usitées pour la construction des cartes géographique," including the projections of Lahire, Babinet, Flamsteed, Flamsteed modified by Bonne, and Mercator; and no. 4, "Tableau synoptique de géographie de l'antiquité."

The following maps relate to America:
no. 5. Tableau comparatif de l'état des connaissances géographiques.
" 6. Tableau du monde actuel ou planisphère terrestre.
" 7. Tableau général des courants atmosphériques et océaniques.
" 8. Tableau général de navigation.
" 9. Tableau général de thermométrie dans le divers contrées du globe.
" 10. Tableau synoptique et abrégé du système magnétique terrestre, 1860.
" 12. Tableau des régions circumpolaires.
" 13. Tableau sphéroïdal de la terre. 1860.

**Garnier, F. A.**—Continued.
   no. 14. Tableau synoptique de la sphéricité de la terre.
   " 15. Europe sphéroïdale.
   " 16. Asia "
   " 17. Afrique "
   " 18. Amérique du Nord sphéroïdale.
   " 19. " " Sud "
   " 20. Océanie sphéroïdale.
   " 35. Asie.
   " 36. Asie boréale.
   " 41. Afrique.
   " 47. Amérique.
   " 48. Amérique russe, et partie des regions polaires boréales.
   " 49. Amérique boréale.
   " 50. États-Unis . . . limites en 1835.
   " 50$^{bis}$. " " " 1860.
   " 51. Mexique.
   " 52. Ancienne Colombie, N$^{le}_{r}$ Grenada, Vénézuéla, Équateur, Guyanes.
   " 53. Brésil.
   " 54. Péru et Bolivie.
   " 55. Republique Argentine.
   " 56. Patagonie.
   " 57. Océanie.

**1862.**

**Johnson, A. J.**

Johnson's new illustrated . . . family atlas, with descriptions, geographical, statistical, and historical. Compiled, drawn and engraved under the supervision of J. H. Colton and A. J. Johnson. 4 p. l., 97, 67–99 pp. incl. 59 col. maps, 1 pl., 1 diagr. fol. New York, Johnson & Ward, 1862. 837

   NOTE.—Engraved title.
   Imperfect: Maps no. 23–24 and 36–37, wanting.
   no. 30, A map of New York and adjacent cities.—no. 34, Georgetown and the city of Washington. Maps generally have insets which are views or plans of cities, harbors, islands, etc.
   Other editions published 1863, 1864, 1870 and 1883. See titles 840, 843, 858, and 914.
   The following maps relate to America:
   no. 2–3. [A plate showing] mountains and rivers.
   " 4–5. Western and Eastern hemispheres.
   " 6–7. . . . the world on Mercator's projection.
   " 9. The world, showing the geographical distribution . . . of the animal kingdom.
   " 10. The world, illustrating the productive industry of various countries.
   " 11. The world, illustrating the principal features of the land . . .
   " 12. The world, showing the principal ocean currents . . .
   " 13. The world, illustrating the principal features of meteorology . . .
   " 14. The world, showing the distribution . . . of the principal plants . . .
   " 15–16. . . . North America.
   " 17–18. Lower and Upper Canada.
   " 19. New Brunswick, Nova Scotia, Newfoundland and Prince Edward i$^d$.
   " 20–21. Military map of the United States . . .
   " 22. . . . Maine.

no. 23-24. . . . **New Hampshire** and Vermont (wanting)
" 25-26. . . . Massachusetts, Connecticut and Rhode Island.
" 27-28. . . . New York . . . Insets: plans of Albany, Troy, New York, Syracuse, Buffalo, Rochester and Oswego.
" 29-30. New York and the adjacent cities.
" 31. . . . New Jersey.
" 32-33. . . . Pennsylvania, Virginia, Delaware and Maryland.
" 34. Georgetown and the city of Washington.
" 35. Delaware and Maryland. Inset: District of Columbia.
" 36-37. North and South Carolina. Inset: Plan of Charleston vicinity and harbor (wanting)
" 38-39. . . . Georgia and Alabama.
" 40. . . . Florida.
" 41-42. . . . Arkansas, Mississippi and Louisiana.
" 43-44. . . . Texas. Insets: Plan of Galveston bay.—Plan of the northern part of Texas.—Plan of Sabine lake.
" 45-46. . . . Kentucky and Tennessee.
" 47-48. . . . Ohio and Indiana.
" 49-50. . . . Michigan and Wisconsin.
" 51. . . . Illinois.
" 52-53. . . . Missouri and Kansas.
" 54. . . . Iowa and Nebraska.
" 55. . . . Nebraska, Dakota, Colorado and Kansas.
" 57. . . . Washington and Oregon.
" 58-59. California, territories of New Mexico and Utah.
" 60. . . . Mexico. Inset: Territory and isthmus of Tehuantepec.
" 61. . . . Central America. Insets: Isthmus of Panama.—Nicaragua route.—Harbor of San Juan . . .
" 62. Cuba, Jamaica and Porto Rico. Insets: Porto Rico . . . Havanna.
" 63-64. . . . South America.
" 65. Venezuela, New Granada, Ecuador, Peru, Bolivia, Chile & Guiana.
" 66. . . . Brazil, Argentine Republic, Paraguay, Uruguay.
" 87. . . . Asia. [Philippine islands]

## 1862

**Royal, The,** illustrated atlas, of modern geography. With an introductory notice by dr. N. Shaw, secretary to the Royal geographical society &c. eng. title, 3, 84, 4 pp., 1 l., 75 col. maps, [102] pp. fol. London and Edinburgh, A. Fullarton & co. [1862] 838

NOTE.—This atlas was published in 27 parts from 1854 to 1862. The original covers to these various parts are bound in at the end of this copy. The date 1862, is found in "Special directions to binder at end." Maps by G. H. Swanston, A. Petermann, John Bartholomew, T. Hugh Johnson and John Macnab. Following the "Geographical notice to the Royal illustrated atlas, by dr. Norton Shaw," are extensive bibliographies as follows:
  I. Collections and histories of voyages and travels.
  II. General atlases.
  III. Voyages and travels round the world. Maps of the world.
  IV. Voyages and travels towards the North Pole.
  V. Voyages and travels in the South Atlantic and Pacific, and towards the South Pole.
  VI. Voyages and travels in Europe and Asia.

**Royal, The**—Continued.
    vii. Voyages and travels in Europe and Africa.
    viii. Voyages and travels in Europe, Asia and Africa.
    ix. Voyages and travels in Europe, Asia, Africa, America or Australia, etc.
    x. Voyages and travels in Asia and Africa.
    xi. Voyages and travels in Asia and America.
    xii. Voyages and travels in Asia, Africa, America, or Australia.
    xiii. Voyages and travels in Africa and America—
    xiv. Voyages and travels in different quarters without names in titles—
    xv. Voyages and travels in Europe.
    xvi. Maps of Europe—
    xvii. Voyages and travels in Africa.
    xviii. North Africa.
    xix. Voyages and travels &c., in East Africa to Delagoa bay, with islands.
    xx. Voyages and travels, &c., in South Africa to Angola from Delagoa bay.
    xxi. Western Africa, Angola to Morocco and its islands.
    xxii. Central Africa.
    xxiii. Voyages and travels in Asia.
    xxiv. Voyages and travels, &c. in India.
    Various maps have inset plans and views of cities. At the end is an "Index, in four parts. Compiled by John Bartholomew.
    The following maps relate to America:
    no.   1. The world in hemispheres.
    "   2. The world on Mercator's projection.
    "   3. The Arctic region.
    "   6. Russian empire [showing Russian Alaska]
    "   21. Dutch possessions in South America and the West Indies.
    "   23. British empire throughout the world.
    "   36-38. British North America.
    "   39. British West Indian possessions, northern.
    "   40. British possessions on the north west coast of South America.
    "   54. North America.
    "   55-59. United States.
    "   60. Northern ports & harbours in the United States.
    "   60a. Southern ports & harbours in the United States.
    "   61. The West Indies.
    "   62. Central America.
    "   63. South America.
    "   64. South American states, New Grenada & Venezuela.
    "   65. East coast of South America. Brazil, middle provinces.
    "   66. West coast of South America including Chile & part of Bolivia & Peru.
    "   71. Oceania, or islands of the Pacific ocean, on Mercators projection.

## 1863

**Dispatch**, The, atlas.   3 p. l., 204 maps on 294 l. fol. London, "Weekly Dispatch" office, 1863.     839
    Note.—Contains plans of the following cities:
    London in the reign of queen Elizabeth.—London, (in 9 sheets).—Suburbs of London (6 sheets).—The landmarks of London.—Birmingham.—Leeds.—Liverpool.—Manchester and Salford.—Cambridge.—Oxford.—Edinburgh.—Glasgow.—Plan of Paris, & the surrounding communes.—Environs of Paris.—Berlin and environs.—Venice.—Rome.

The following maps relate to America:
no.     [1] The world on Mercators projection.
"     [134] Greenland.
"     [200] North America.
"     [201] Upper Canada.
"     [202] Lower Canada.
"     [203] British Columbia.—Vancouver island.
"     [204] United States of North America.
"   [205-209] United States of North America.
"     [210] California, Utah, L: California and New Mexico.
"     [211] Map of the Great Salt Lake.—The Great Salt Lake city.
"     [212] The arctic regions of North America.
"     [213] Central America (Northern part)
"     [214]    "      " (Southern " )
"     [215] Jamaica.—Hayti.
"     [216] Cuba and Jamaica.
"     [217] The Leeward & Windward islands.
"     [218] South America.
"     [219] Guiana.
"     [220] Brazil, Bolivia, Peru & Ecuador.
"     [221] Southern states of South America.
"     [222] Seat of war in Virginia and Maryland. Sheet 1.
"     [223] Seat of war in Virginia, &c. Sheet 2.
"     [224]  "  "  "  "    "    "    " 3.
"     [233] The Pacific ocean.

## 1863

**Johnson, A. J.**

Johnson's new illustrated . . . family atlas, with descriptions, geographical, statistical, and historical. Compiled, drawn and engraved under the supervision of J. H. Colton and A. J. Johnson. 4 p. l., 5-99 pp., 64 col. maps, 1 pl., 1 diagr. fol. New York, Johnson & Ward, 1863.     840

Note.—Engraved title.
Like the edition of 1862 except a difference of lettering on nos. 50 and 86. See titles 837, 843, 858 and 914.
no. 30, A map of New York and adjacent cities.—no. 34, Georgetown and the city of Washington. Maps generally have insets which are views or plans of cities, harbors, islands, etc.
The following maps relate to America:
no.   2-3. [A plate showing] mountains and rivers.
"   4-5. Western and Eastern hemispheres.
"   6-7. . . . the world on Mercator's projection.
"     9. The world, showing the geographical distribution . . . of the animal kingdom.
"   10. The world, illustrating the productive industry of various countries.
"   11. The world, illustrating the principal features of the land . . .
"   12. The world, showing the principal ocean currents . . .
"   13. The world, illustrating the principal features of meteorology . . .
"   14. The world, showing the distribution . . . of the principal plants
"  15-16. . . . North America.
"  17-18. Lower and Upper Canada.

**Johnson, A. J.**—Continued.
no. 19. New Brunswick, Nova Scotia, Newfoundland and Prince Edward Id
" 20-21. Military map of the United States . . .
" 22. . . . Maine.
" 23-24. . . . New Hampshire and Vermont.
" 25-26. . . . Massachusetts, Connecticut and Rhode Island.
" 27-28. . . . New York . . .
" 29-30. New York and the adjacent cities.
" 31. . . . New Jersey.
" 32-33. . . . Pennsylvania, Virginia, Delaware and Maryland.
" 34. Georgetown and the city of Washington.
" 35. Delaware and Maryland.
" 36-37. North and South Carolina.
" 38-39. . . . Georgia and Alabama.
" 40. . . . Florida.
" 41-42. . . . Arkansas, Mississippi and Louisiana.
" 43-44. . . . Texas.
" 45-46. . . . Kentucky and Tennessee.
" 47-48. . . . Ohio and Indiana.
" 49-50. . . . Michigan and Wisconsin . . .
" 51. . . . Illinois.
" 52-53. . . . Missouri and Kansas.
" 54. . . . Iowa and Nebraska.
" 55. . . . Nebraska, Dakota, Colorado and Kansas.
" 57. . . . Washington and Oregon.
" 58-59. . . . California, territories of New Mexico and Utah.
" 60. . . . Mexico.
" 61. . . . Central America.
" 62. Cuba, Jamaica and Porto Rico.
" 63-64. . . . South America.
" 65. Venezuela, New Granada, Ecuador, Peru, Bolivia, Chile and Guiana.
" 66. . . . Brazil, Argentine Republic, Paraguay, Uruguay.
" 87. . . . Asia [Philippine islands]

**1863**

**Leutemann, H.**
Illustrirter handatlas für freunde der erdkunde und zum gebrauch beim unterricht. Im verein mit Heinrich Leutemann herausgegeben von Ehrenfried Leeder und Theodor Schade. Zweiundzwanzig blätter . . . mit erläuterndem texte.   3 p. l., [82] pp., 22 col. maps.  fol. Leipzig, F. A. Brockhaus, 1863.    841

NOTE.—Maps have border illustrations.
Explanatory and descriptive text, 3-4 pp., precedes each map.
The following maps relate to America:
no. 1. Planigloben . . . Westliche erdhälfte.—. . . die ganze erdoberfläche.
" 2. Luft und meeresströmungen.
" 4. Asien [Philippine islands]
" 8. Nordamerika.
" 9. Südamerika.

**1864**

**Johnston, A. K.**
Index geographicus; being a list, alphabetically arranged, of the principal places on the globe . . . and their latitudes and longitudes; compiled specially with reference to Keith Johnston's Royal atlas . . . 2 p. l., 676 pp. 4°. Edinburgh & London, W. Blackwood & sons [1864] 842

NOTE.—See title 835 for atlas.

**1864**

**Johnson, A. J.**
Johnson's new illustrated . . . family atlas, with physical geography, and with descriptions, geographical, statistical, and historical, including the latest federal census, a geographical index, and a chronological history of the civil war in America, by Richard Swainson Fisher. Maps compiled, drawn, & engraved under the supervision of J. H. Colton & A. J. Johnson . . . 3 p. l., 5–123 pp., incl. 62 col. maps, 2 pl., 1 diagr. fol. New York, Johnson & Ward, 1864. 843

NOTE.—Engraved title. See also titles 837, 840, 858, and 913.
The following maps relate to America:
- no. 8. North and South America: (a) showing the geographical distribution . . . of the animal kingdom. (b) illustrating productive industry and exhibiting the principal features of commerce & navigation. (c) showing the principal ocean currents and boundaries of river systems.
- " 9. North and South America (a) illustrating the principal features of meteorology. (b) illustrating the principal features of the land . . . (c) showing the distribution . . . of the principal plants . . .
- " 11. Western hemisphere.
- " 13–14. The world on Mercator's projection.
- " 15–16. North America.
- " 17–18. Canada.
- " 19. New Brunswick, Nova Scotia, Newfoundland & Prince Edward Is.
- " 20–21. United States showing the forts, military posts etc, with enlarged plans of southern harbors . . .
- " 22. Maine.
- " 23–24. Vermont, New Hampshire, Massachusetts, Rhode Island and Connecticut.
- " 25–26. Massachusetts, Connecticut and Rhode Island.
- " 28. New York.
- " 29–30. New York and the adjacent cities.
- " 31–32. Pennsylvania and New Jersey.
- " 33–34. Virginia, Delaware and Maryland.
- " 35–36. Vicinity of Richmond, and peninsular campaign in Virginia . . .
- " 37. Georgetown and the city of Washington.
- " 38. Delaware and Maryland.
- " 39–40. North & South Carolina.
- " 41–42. Georgia and Alabama.
- " 43. Florida.

**Johnson, A. J.**—Continued.
no. 44. West Indies.
" 45–46. Arkansas, Mississippi & Louisiana.
" 47–48. Texas.
" 49–50. Kentucky & Tennessee.
" 51–52. Ohio.
" 53–54. Indiana.
" 55–56. Illinois.
" 57–58. Michigan & Wisconsin.
" 59–60. Missouri & Kansas.
" 61–62. Iowa & Nebraska.
" 63. Nebraska, Dakota, Colorado, Idaho & Kansas.
" 64. Minnesota & Dakota.
" 65. Washington, Oregon & Idaho.
" 66–67. California, with Territories of Utah, Nevada, Colorado, New Mexico & Arizona.
" 68. Mexico.
" 69. Central America.
" 70–71. South America.

### 1864

**Kuyper, J.**
Nieuwe atlas der wereld naar de laatste ontdekkingen, verslagen, mededeelingen, reisbeschrijvingen, enz; . . . herzien door W. B. J. F. Terlaak. 15. geheel bijgewerkte en vermeerderde druk. 2 p. l., 35 maps. fol. Amsterdam, L. J. Veen [1864] 844

NOTE.—The following maps relate to America:
no. 1. Wereldrond.
" 2. Wereldkaart (Mercator's projectie)
" 3. Wereldkaart.
" 28. Noord-Amerika.
" 29. Vereenigde Staten van Noord- Amerika.
" 30. West Indië.
" 31. Zuid-Amerika.

### 1865

**Colton, J. H.**
Colton's quarto atlas of the world: containing fifty copperplate maps, with valuable tables of population statistics. 15 pp., 47 maps, 1 pl. 4°. New York, J. H. Colton, 1865. 845

### 1865

**Mitchell, S. A.**
Mitchell's new general atlas, containing maps of the various countries of the world, plans of cities, etc. embraced in fifty-three quarto maps, forming a series of eighty-four maps and plans, together with valuable statistical tables. 2 p. l., 31 pp., 51 maps, 1 pl. fol. Philadelphia, S. A. Mitchell, jr. 1865. 846

NOTE.—Copyrighted 1860. See title 797 for the various editions.
Resembles the edition of 1860 but the following maps are different: no. 1. World.—no. [6] Canada . . .—no. [14] Pennsylvania . . .—no. [19] Vir-

ginia . . .—no. [22] North Carolina . . .—no. [26] Ohio and Indiana—no [30] Michigan and Wisconsin.—no. [32] Kansas, Nebraska and Colorado.— no. [33] Oregon, Washington . . .—no. [67] France, Spain and Portugal. Maps added are the following: no. [9] New Hampshire . . .—no. [10] Massachusetts . . .—no. [16] New Jersey.—Maryland and Delaware.—no [18] Plan of . . . Washington . . .—no. [24] Plan of New Orleans.—no. [28] . . . Illinois.—no. [31] . . . Minnesota.—no. [48] A new map of Palestine or the Holy Land . . .

The following maps relate to America:
no. 1. The world in hemispheres . . . 1860.
" 2. The world on Mercator's projection . . . 1860.
" 3. . . . North America . . . 1860.
" 4. . . . Nova Scotia, New Brunswick . . . 1860.
" 6. . . . Canada east . . . 1860.
" 8. . . . Canada west . . . 1860.
" 9. . . . United States . . . 1860.
" 12. . . . Maine. 1860.
" 14. New Hampshire and Vermont. 1862.
" 15. . . . Massachusetts, Connecticut and Rhode Island. 1862.
" 16. . . . New York, New Hampshire, Vermont, Massachusetts, Rhode Id. and Connecticut . . . 1860.
" 19. Plan of New York &c. 1860.
" 20. Plan of Boston. 1860.
" 21. . . . Pennsylvania, New Jersey, Maryland and Delaware. 1860.
" 24. Plan of Philadelphia. 1860.
" [24a] . . . New Jersey.—Maryland and Delaware. 1864.
" 25. Plan of Baltimore. 1860.
" 26. Plan of the city of Washington . . . 1861.
" 27. . . . Virginia and West Virginia. 1863.
" 28. . . . Kentucky and Tennessee. 1860.
" 29. . . . Georgia and Alabama. 1860.
" 30. . . . North Carolina.—. . . South Carolina.—. . . Florida. 1860.
" 32. . . . Louisiana, Mississippi and Arkansas. 1860.
" 33. Plan of New Orleans. 1860.
" 34. . . . Texas. 1860.
" 36. . . . Ohio and Indiana. 1863.
" 37. Plan of Cincinnati . . . 1860.
" 38. . . . Illinois. 1861.
" 40. . . . Iowa and Missouri. 1861.
" 41. . . . Michigan and Wisconsin. 1863.
" 42. . . . Minnesota. 1862.
" 43. . . . Kansas, Nebraska and Colorado . . . 1861.
" 44. . . . Oregon, Washington, Idaho and part of Montana. 1860.
" 45. . . . California . . . Great Salt Lake . . . 1860.
" 48. . . . Mexico, Central America and the West Indies. 1860.
" 53. . . . South America . . . 1860.
" 55. . . . New Grenada, Venezuela and Guiana.—. . . Peru and Equador.—. . . Argentine Confederation. 1860.
" 58. . . . Brazil, Bolivia, Paraguay and Uruguay. 1860.
" 77. . . . Asia . . . 1860.
" 81. . . . Oceanica . . . 1860.

## 1865

**Mitchell, S. A.**—Continued.

Mitchell's new reference atlas for the use of colleges, libraries, families, and counting houses in a series of fifty-six copper plate maps, exhibiting the several countries, empires, kingdoms, and states in the modern and ancient world. Compiled from the latest authorities. 2 p. l., 7 pp., 56 maps on 40 l. fol. Philadelphia, E. H. Butler & co. 1865. 847

NOTE.—The following maps relate to America:
no. 1. The western hemisphere . . .
" 3. . . . North America.
" 4–6. Canada and New Brunswick.
" 7. . . . United States.
" 8. Maine, New Hampshire and Vermont.
" 9. Massachusetts, Rhode Island and Connecticut.
" 10. New York, New Jersey, Pennsylvania and Delaware.
" 11. Maryland, Virginia, West Virginia and North Carolina.
" 12. South Carolina, Georgia, Florida, Alabama, Mississippi, Louisiana, Tennessee and Arkansas.
" 13. Texas.
" 14. Ohio, Kentucky, Indiana, Illinois, Iowa, and Missouri.
" 15. Michigan and Wisconsin.
" 16–17. Minnesota and Dakota.—Nebraska.
" 18. Kansas, Colorado, New Mexico & Indian Territory.
" 19. California, Oregon, Idaho, Utah, Nevada, Arizona and Washington.
" 20. Mexico and Central America.
" 20–23. . . . Cuba . . . Hayti . . . West Indies.
" 24. South America.
" 25–26. Venezuela, United States of Colombia and Ecuador.—Isthmus of Panama.
" 27. Peru and Bolivia.
" 28. Chili, Paraguay, the Argentine confederation and Uruguay

## 1866

**Mitchell, S. A.**

Mitchell's new general atlas, containing maps of the various countries of the world, plans of cities, etc., embraced in fifty-five quarto maps, forming a series of eighty-seven maps and plans, together with valuable statistical tables. 2 p. l., 31 pp., 52 maps, 1 pl. fol. Philadelphia, S. A. Mitchell, jr., 1866. 848

NOTE.—Copyrighted 1865. See title 797 for the various editions. Like the edition of 1865 with one additional map: no. [33] . . . Utah and Nevada. 1865.

## 1867

**Bartholomew, J.**

Black's general atlas of the world . . . New edition. 33, 70 pp., 56 (*i. e.* 66 maps, 3 pl.) fol. Edinburgh, A. & C. Black, 1867. 849

NOTE.—Frontispiece, The flags of all nations, pl. no. 1. See also titles 777, 779, 793, 821 and 826. In front of map no. 39, a list of the maps of America printed on a slip of paper has been inserted. It

is entitled: Black's general atlas, extra edition. The table of contents of the atlas gives only the thirteen maps of America which appear in an earlier edition. The titles of the new maps are given on the extra list.
The following maps relate to America:
no. 2. The world.
" 3. The world on Mercator's projection.
" 4. Chart of the world exhibiting its chief physical features.—Ethnographical chart of the world.
" 5. Zoological chart of the world.—Chart of the world shewing the distribution of the principal plants.
" 39. North America. Inset: British Columbia and Vancouver island.
" 40. Atlantic ocean . . .
" 41. General map of the United States.
" 41 supp. United States after cession of Russian-America, april 1867.
" 42. United States north eastern section and Canada.
" 42^A. Maine.
" 42^B. New York, Vermont, New Hampshire, Rhode Island, Massachusetts & Connecticut. Inset: City of New York.
" 42^C. Pennsylvania and New Jersey.
" 43. United States southern section.
" 43^A. Virginia, Maryland & Delaware.
" 43^B. North and South Carolina.
" 43^C. Georgia & Florida. Inset: Continuation of Florida.
" 43^D. Alabama.
" 43^E. Mississippi & Louisiana.
" 43^F. Texas, part of New Mexico &c.
" 43^G. Missouri and Arkansas.
" 43^H. Kentucky and Tennessee.
" 44. Western states. Michigan, Wisconsin, Minnesota, Iowa, with portions of Illinois & Indiana.
" 44^A. Ohio, Indiana & Illinois.
" 45. United States. Pacific states.
" 46. Central America, Mexico & West Indies. Inset: Panama railway.
" 47. West Indies. Inset: Panama railway.—Jamaica.
" 48. South America.
" 49. Venezuela, New Granada, Equador, Peru &c.
" 50. Chili, La Plata or the Argentine republic & Bolivia.
" 51. Brazil, Uruguay, Paraguay & Guayana.
" 54. Oceania and Pacific ocean.

## 1867

**Mitchell, S. A.**

Mitchell's new general atlas, containing maps of the various countries of the world, plans of cities, etc., . . . together with valuable statistical tables. 2 p. l., 31 pp., 53 maps, 1 pl. fol. Philadelphia, S. A. Mitchell, jr., 1867. 850

NOTE.—See title 797 for the various editions. Like the edition of 1866 with the following additional maps: no. [12] . . . New York.—no. [23] . . . Arkansas, Mississippi and Louisiana.—no. [29] Chicago.

## 1867

**Naymiller, F.** *and* **Allodi, P.**

Atlante di geografia universale cronologico, storico, statistico e letterario ... 1 p. l., [128] pp., 55 maps, 8 pl. obl. fol. Milano, F. Pagnoni; Napoli, G. Marghieri [1867] 851

NOTE.—The following maps relate to America:
no. [2] Mappamondo ...
" [3] Planisfero.
" [46] Asia [Isole Filippine]
" [47] Impero Russo d'Asia e d'America.
" [49] Impero Cinese ... [I. Luzon]
" [51] America Settentrionale.
" [52] America Meridionale.
" [53] Impero del Messico.
" [54] Impero del Brasile.
" [55] Oceania.

## 1868

**Dufour, A. H.**

Atlas universel physique, historique et politique de géographie ancienne et moderne. Gravé sur acier par Ch. Dyonnet ... 2 p. l., 40 col. maps. fol. Paris, A. Le Chevalier [1868] 852

NOTE.—"L'introduction dans les établissements d'instruction publique, des cartes composant cet atlas, a été autorisée par décision du ministre de l'instruction publique, en date du 8 décembre 1863." To accompany this atlas is a volume of descriptive text entitled "Cahier des notices des quarante cartes."
Maps no. 20, 22, show "États conquis par la Prusse en 1866."
The maps in this atlas are not dated as are those in the edition of 1860. See titles 833 and 894.
"Carte administrative et physique de la France," 4 sheets, no. 12–15.
The following maps relate to America:
no. 10. Mappe-monde.
" 37. L'Amérique du Nord.
" 38. Amérique du Sud.
" 39. Mexique, Antilles, États-Unis.
" 40. Océanie.

## 1868

**Johnston, A. K.**

Handy royal atlas of modern geography exhibiting the present condition of geographical discovery and research in the several countries, empires, and states of the world. 4 p. l., 98 pp., 45 maps. fol. Edinburgh & London, W. Blackwood & sons, 1868.

853

NOTE.—The following maps relate to America:
no. 1. The world.
" 2. The world on Mercator's projection.
" 38. North America.
" 39–40. Canada.
" 41–42. United States.
" 43. West India Islands.
" 44–45. South America.

### 1869?
**Steinwehr, A. W. A. F. von.**
[Atlas]   19 maps.   fol.   [Washington, H. Lindenkohl 1869?]
NOTE.—Title-page wanting.   854

### 187—
**Vandermaelen, P. M. G.**
Atlas universel de géographie moderne, composé de 20 belles cartes ornées des armoiries et pavillons des principales nations . . . 1 p. l., 20 col. maps. fol. Bruxelles, l'établissement géographique de P. Vander Maelen [187—]   855

### 1870
**Colton, G. W.**
Colton's general atlas, containing one hundred and eighty steel plate maps and plans, on one hundred and nineteen imperial folio sheets. Letter-press descriptions, geographical, statistical,and historical by Richard Swainson Fisher. 2 p. l., front., [313] pp. incl. 101 col. maps, 3 pl. fol. New York, G. W. & C. B. Colton & co. 1870.   856
NOTE.—Pagination irregular.   See also title 827, 866, 879, 886, and 911.

### 1870
**Huberts, W. J. A.**
Nieuwe geographische atlas der geheele aarde, geschikt voor alle inrichtingen van onderwijs. Naar de nieuwste bronnen bewerkt onder toezicht . . .   1 p. l., 30 col. maps.   4°.   Groningen, P. Noordhoff; Arnhem, J. Voltelen [1870]   857
NOTE.—The following maps relate to America:
no. 1. Wereld Kaart.
" 27. Noord Amerika.
" 28. De Vereenigde Staten van Noord-Amerika.
" 29. Zuid-Amerika.

### 1870
**Johnson, A. J.**
Johnson's new illustrated family atlas of the world . . . with a treatise on physical geography, by A. Guyot . . . with descriptions, geographical, statistical and historical. Also including a dictionary of religious denominations, sects, parties, and associations, compiled by professor Roswell D. Hitchcock . . . 3 p. l., 2–126 pp., incl. front., 68 maps, 5 pl., diagr. fol. New York, A. J. Johnson, 1870.   858
NOTE.—See also titles 837, 840, 843, and 913. Containing plans of the following cities:
no. 36–37. Boston.
" 40–41. New York.
" 48. Washington.

## 1870

**Mitchell, S. A.**

Mitchell's new general atlas, containing maps of the various countries of the world, plans of cities, etc. . . . together with valuable statistical tables.   2 p. l., 31 pp., 57 maps, 1 pl.   fol.   Philadelphia, S. A. Mitchell, jr., 1870.   859

> NOTE.—See title 797 for the various editions.   Like the edition of 1867 with the following maps revised:
> no. [2] . . . World.
> " [3] North America.
> " [13] New York and Brooklyn.
> " [22] North and South Carolina.
> " [23] Florida.
> " [37] Arizona and New Mexico.
> " [39] California.
> The following additional maps:
> no. [5] Quebec.
> " [6] Ontario.
> " [32] St. Louis.
> " [40] North western America showing the territory ceded by Russia to the United States.

## 1871

**Bartholomew, J.**

Zell's descriptive hand atlas of the world.   By J. Bartholomew . . . pt. 1; cover-title, 4, 4 pp., 2 maps, 1 pl.   fol.   Philadelphia, T. E. Zell, ᶜ1871.   860

> NOTE.—See also title 865.

## 1871

**Butler, S.**

An atlas of modern geography.   New edition, with additional maps, and with corrections from the government surveys and the most recent sources of information.   Edited by the author's son the rev. T. Butler . . .   4 p. l., 60 pp., 32 maps.   8°.   London, Longmans, Green & co. 1871.   861

> NOTE.—See also title 792.
> The following maps relate to America:
> no. 1. The world.
> " 2. Map of the world . . .
> " 24. North America.
> " 25. British "
> " 26. United States.
> " 27. Canada, New Brunswick . . .
> " 28. West Indies.
> " 29. South America.

## 1872

**Appleton, D., & co.**

Appleton's general atlas of the world, containing maps of various countries, and particularly of the United States . . .   1 p. l., 99 pp., 33 maps.   4°.   New York, D. Appleton & co. 1872.   862

## 1872

**Cleveland, J. F.,** *and* **Schem, A. J.**
Contents of new letter-press descriptions of Johnson's new illustrated family atlas of the world. Compiled from the latest official sources . . .   29, [1] pp.   fol.   [New York, A. J. Johnson, 1872]
863

## 1872

**Lloyd, H. H., & co.**
Lloyd's handy atlas, containing maps of the world, and its grand divisions, the United States, and the different states and territories of the Union, etc. etc. Letter-press matter embracing the census of 1870, and a list of all the post offices in the United States.   91 pp. incl. 25 col. maps, 1 col. pl.   fol.   Concord, N. H. and Boston, D. L. Guernsey, 1872.
864

## 1873

**Bartholomew, J.**
Zell's descriptive hand atlas of the world.   By John Bartholomew . . .   1 p. l., xii, [175], 102 pp., front., 35 col. maps, 3 pl.   fol.   Philadelphia, T. E. Zell, 1873.
865

NOTE.—Engraved title. See title 860.

## 1873

**Colton, G. W.**
Colton's general atlas, containing one hundred and eighty steel plate maps and plans, on one hundred and nineteen imperial folio sheets. Letter-press descriptions, geographical, statistical and historical by Richard Swainson Fisher.   2 p. l., front., [302] pp. incl. 104 maps, 3 pl.   fol.   New York, G. W. & C. B. Colton & co. 1873.
866

NOTE.—See also titles 816, 827, 856, 879, 886, and 911.

## 1873 ?

**Hubault, G.**
Atlas de géographie et d'histoire à l'usage des candidats à l'école militaire de Saint-Cyr . . .   1 p. l., 35 maps.   sm. fol.   Paris, E. Belin [1873?]
867

NOTE.—"Cet atlas renferme en outre un choix de cartes tirées de l'atlas de mm. Drioux et Leroy."

## 1873

**Johnston, A. K.**
The royal atlas of modern geography exhibiting, in a series of entirely original and authentic maps, the present condition of geographical discovery and research in the several countries, empires and states of the world. With a special index to each map. New

**Johnston, A. K.**—Continued.
ed. viii, [1] pp., front, 48 maps. fol. Edinburgh & London,
W. Blackwood & sons, 1873. 868
> NOTE.—See also title 835 and 905. Several maps have insets showing plans of cities and environs.
> Accompanying the edition of 1864, is the Index geographicus, being a list . . . of the principal places on the globe . . . and their latitudes and longitudes; compiled specially with reference to the Royal atlas. See title 842.

## 1873
**Jones, C. H. *and* Hamilton, T. F.**
The peoples' pictorial atlas. Being a complete and popular account of all the countries of the world, in their geographical, statistical, topographical and commercial aspects. With 52 maps, constructed by A. Keith Johnston . . . H. D. Rogers . . . Edward Weller . . . and other eminent geographers. Compiled and edited by Charles H. Jones, assisted by Theodore F. Hamilton. 2 p. l., 87, [1] pp., 42 col. maps, 2 pl. fol. New York, J. D. Williams, 1873. 869

## 1873
**Mitchell, S. A.**
Mitchell's new general atlas, containing maps of the various countries of the world, plans of cities, etc. . . . together with valuable statistical tables. Also, a list of post-offices of the United States and territories, and census of 1860 and 1870. 2 p. l., 31 pp., 58 maps, 1 pl. fol. Philadelphia, S. A. Mitchell, 1873. 870
> NOTE.—Copyrighted 1870; maps copyrighted 1872. See title 797 for the various editions.
> Like the edition of 1870 with the following exceptions: no. [11] Plan of Boston.—no. [21] Georgia and Alabama.—no. [33] Michigan and Wisconsin have been revised and enlarged; no. [42] Cuba, is added.

## 1874?
**Kiepert, H., Gräf, C., Gräf, A., *and* Bruhns, K. C.**
Hand-atlas der erde und des himmels. In funfzig blättern. 42. aufl. 2 p. l., 49 maps, 1 pl. fol. Weimar, geographisches institut [1874?] 871
> NOTE.—The maps, variously dated from 1856 to 1874, are irregularly numbered. The following maps relate to America:
> no. [2] Planiglob der erde.
> " [3] Erdkarte in Mercators projection.
> " 4 Isothermen der erde.
> " " [b] Verbreitung der vulcane.
> " 50. Asien [Philippine islands]
> " 59. America.
> " 60. Nordamerica mit Westindien.

no. 62. Die Vereinigten Staaten von Nord Amerika . . . (östlicher theil)
Inset: New York city.
" 63. Mexico und die republiken von Central-America.
" 65. Süd-America.

### 1874
**Taintor bros. & Merrill.**
The american household and commercial atlas of the world. Carefully prepared and drawn from the coast survey reports, and other official surveys and authorities of the United States and other governments.  2 p. l., 38 col. maps on 54 l, 55-60 pp. fol. New York, Taintor bros. & Merrill, 1874. 872

### 1875
**Gray, O. W. & son.**
The national atlas. Containing elaborate topographical maps of the United States and the Dominion of Canada, with plans of cities and general maps of the world. Also, descriptions and tables, historical and statistical . . . Accompanied by maps, plans, and descriptions of local interest.  179 pp., incl. 72 col. maps. fol. Philadelphia, O. W. Gray & son, 1875. 873

NOTE.—Contains special maps of Allegany co., Maryland, and its principal towns.

### 1875
**Guigoni, M.**
Atlante geografico universale antico e moderno composto di 56 carte disegnata e compilate sulle più recenti Francesi dei signori J. G. Barbie du Bocage, A. Vuillemin, J. B. Charle, V. Levasseur, T. Duvotenay, H. Dufour. Casa editrice italiana. 2 p. l., 50 maps, 6 pl. fol. Milano, 1875. 874

NOTE.—The following maps relate to America:
no. 6. Mappamondo in due emisferi.
" 38. Carta dell'America Settentrionale e Terre Colombiane.
" 39. Stati-Uniti, per T. Duvotenay.
" 40. Messico, per T. Duvotenay.
" 41. Antille . . . per . . . T. Duvotenay.
" 42. Carta dell'America Meridionale.
" 43. Columbia e Guiana, per . . . Th. Duvotenay.
" 44. Impero del Brasile, del . . . Th. Duvotenay.

### 1876
**Gray, O. W. & Son.**
Atlas of the world. Supplement. 3 p. l., 9-37 pp. incl. 13 col. maps.
[*In their* New illustrated atlas of Dutchess county, N. Y. fol. Reading, Pa., Reading publishing house, 1876] 875

NOTE.—Map no. 32-33 entitled: Gray's geological map of the United States by Charles H. Hitchcock. Map no. 36-37 entitled: New York by Frank A. Gray.

**1876**
**Gray, O. W. & Son.**
Atlas of the world. Supplement. 1 p. l., 5-37 pp. incl. 13 col. maps. [*In their* New topographical atlas of Essex county, N. Y. fol. Philadelphia, O. W. Gray & son, 1876] 876

NOTE.—Same maps as in title 875.

**1876**
**Gray, O. W.**
Gray's atlas of the United States with general maps of the world Accompanied by descriptions geographical, historical, scientific, and statistical. 2 p. l., 7-204 pp., 70 maps. fol. Philadelphia, J. W. Lyon & co. 1876. 877

NOTE.—Contains plans of the principal cities in the United States.

**1876**
**Gray, O. W., & son.**
The national atlas. Containing elaborate topographical maps of the United States and the dominion of Canada, with plans of cities and general maps of the world. Also, descriptions and tables, historical and statistical . . . Accompanied by special, railway, and scientific maps and articles. 2 p. l., 7-204, [4] pp. incl. 70 col. maps, 3, [3] l. fol. Philadelphia, O. W. Gray & son, 1876. 878

**1876**
**Colton, G. W.**
Colton's general atlas of the world . . . accompanied by descriptive, statistical and historical letter-press descriptions. 2 p. l., front. [282] pp. incl. [106] col. maps, 3 pl. fol. New York, G. W. & C. B. Colton & co. 1876. 879

NOTE.—See also titles 816, 827, 856, 866, 886, and 911.

**1876**
**Mitchell, S. A.**
Mitchell's new general atlas, containing maps of the various countries of the world, plans of cities, etc. . . . Together with valuable statistical tables. Also, a list of post-offices of the United States and territories, and census of 1860 and 1870. 2 p. l., 37 pp., 63 maps, 1 pl. fol. Philadelphia, S. A. Mitchell, 1876. 880

NOTE.—See title 797 for the various editions. Like the edition of 1873 with the following exceptions: nos. [1-2] western and eastern hemispheres.—no. [11] New Hampshire and Vermont.—no. [12] Massachusetts, Connecticut and Rhode Island.—no. [16] Pennsylvania.—no. [17] Plan of . . . Philadelphia.—no. [22] Kentucky and Tennessee.—no. [27] Texas.—no. [34] Iowa and Missouri.—no. [39] Kansas and Nebraska, have been revised and enlarged. The following maps are added: no. [8] Map of the original thirteen colonies.—no. [35] Plan of Milwaukee.—no. [37] Plan of Detroit.—no. [40] Colorado, Wyoming, Dakota, Montana.

## 1876
**Stieler, A.**
Hand atlas über alle theile der erde und über das weltgebäude. [Neue auf.] 4 p. l., 11 pp., 90 maps. fol. Gotha, J. Perthes [1876] 881

## 1877
**Bouillet, M. N.**
Atlas universel d'histoire et de géographie . . . 3. éd. 2 p. l., ii, 1101 pp., 12 col. pl., 88 maps. 8°. Paris, Hachette & cie. 1877. 882

NOTE.—First edition published posthumously in 1865, edited by Ph. Bouillet.

CONTENTS.
1. Chronologie [avec la collaboration de M. Caillet]
2. Généalogie [ "   "    "    " " Garnier]
3. Géographie [ "   "    "    " " Desjardins]

## 1877
**Chambers, W.** *and* **Chambers, R.**
Handy atlas. A series of forty maps for the use of the general reader. (Being the maps that accompany the subscription edition of Chambers's Encyclopædia) 2 p. l., 40 maps. 8°. Philadelphia, J. B. Lippincott & co. 1877. 883

## 1877
**Fayard de la Brugère, J. A.** *and* **Baralle, A.**
Atlas universel contenant la géographie physique, politique, historique, théorique, militaire, industrielle, agricole & commerciale du monde avec la statistique la plus récente et la plus complète, précédé d'une astronomie et d'un planisphère céleste. Le texte par F. de la Brugère . . . et Alphonse Baralle . . . Contenant 84 cartes géographiques dressées par Vuillemin, Charles Lacoste, Monin et Clerot, gravées sur acier par Lacouchy, Lorsignol et Haussermann, en plus 64 plans des principales villes du monde, imprimés en plusieurs couleurs (chromo) gravés par Haussermann . . . 2 p. l., 408, [4], 409-410 pp., front., 94 col. maps, 7 pl. fol. Paris, A. Fayard, 1877. 884

NOTE.—pp. 245-248 wanting.

## 1877
**Gray, O. W. & son.**
The national atlas containing elaborate topographical maps of the United States and the dominion of Canada, with plans of cities and general maps of the world . . . 2 p. l., 7-204 pp. incl. 75 col. maps. fol. Philadelphia, O. W. Gray & son, 1877. 885

NOTE.—The following maps are inserted: pl. 69a, Richmond.—pl. 88a, Nashville.—pl. 88b, Kentucky (railroad)—pl. 88c, Indianapolis.—pl. 88d, Indiana (railroad)

## 1878

**Colton, G. W.**
Colton's general atlas of the world . . . Drawn by G. Woolworth Colton. Accompanied by geographical, statistical, and historical letter-press descriptions. 2 p. l., front., 282 pp. incl. [106] col. maps, 3 pl. fol. New York, G. W. & C. B. Colton & co. 1878. 886

## 1878

**Marmocchi, F. C.**
Nuovo atlante cosmografico, fisico, storico e politico-statistico in lxxxiv carte. Diligentemente riveduto e corretto . . . per cura del cavaliere Celestino Peroglio . . . 3 p. l., [2] pp., 83 maps, 1 pl. fol. Torino, Roux & Favale, 1878. 887

NOTE.—The following maps relate to America:
no. 70. Carta dell' America settentrionale. 1877.
" 71. Stati Uniti dell' America settentrionale
" 72. Repubblica del Messico.
" 73. America Centrale ed Indie Occidentali od Antille.
" 74. Carta dell' America meridionale.
" 75. Guiana e repubbliche di Venezuela, Granata ed Equatore.
" 76. Le repubbliche del Perù e di Bolivia.
" 77. Impero del Brasile.
" 78. La confederazione Argentina [etc.]

## 1878

**Mitchell, S. A.**
Mitchell's new general atlas, containing maps of the various countries of the world, plans of cities, etc. . . . Together with valuable statistical tables. Also, a list of post-offices of the United States and territories, and census of 1860 and 1870. 2 p. l., 37, [1] pp., 67 maps, 1 pl. fol. Philadelphia, S. A. Mitchell, 1878. 888

NOTE.—See title 797 for the various editions.
"Map of Turkey and Greece," inserted before no. 115.
Like the edition of 1876 with the following maps revised: no. [22] Kentucky and Tennessee.—no. [29] Ohio and Indiana.—no. [31] Illinois.—no. [41] Colorado, is added.

## 1879

**Drioux, C. J. *and* Leroy, C.**
Atlas universel et classique de géographie ancienne romaine, du moyen-âge, moderne et contemporaine, à l'usage des établissements d'instruction publique, par mm. Drioux et Ch. Leroy. Nouvelle éd. contenant quatre-vingt-huit cartes et cartons . . . vii, [1] pp., 55 maps on 97 l., 2 pl. fol. Paris, E. Belin, 1879. 889

## 1879

**Mitchell, S. A.**
Mitchell's new general atlas, containing maps of the various countries of the world, plans of cities, etc. . . . Together with valuable statistical tables. Also, a list of post-offices of the United States and territories, and census of 1860 and 1870.   2 p. l., 37, [1] pp., 72 maps, 1 pl. fol. Philadelphia, S. A. Mitchell, 1879.
890

NOTE.—See title 797, for the various editions. Like the edition of 1878 with the following additional maps:
no. [39] Territory of Montana.
" [41] Territory of Wyoming.
" [42] Territory of Dakota.
" [44] Indian Territory.
" [48] Territory of Idaho. Also, 2 inserted maps.
" [63] Map of Turkey in Europe.
" [70] Africa.
" [32] [Plan of] Chicago, enlarged.

## 1880?

**Bryce, J., Collier, W. F. and Schmitz, L.**
The international atlas and geography: modern, historical, classical, and physical, containing one hundred and thirty maps. The descriptive letter press by James Bryce . . . William F. Collier . . . and Leonhard Schmitz . . .   156, 38 pp., 122 (*i. e.* 124) col. maps, 6 pl. fol. London and Glasgow, W. Collins, sons, & co. [1880?]
891

## 1880

**Mitchell, S. A.**
Mitchell's new general atlas, containing maps of the various countries of the world, plans of cities, etc. Together with valuable statistical tables. Also, a list of post-offices of the United States and territories, and census of 1860 and 1870.   2 p. l., 45 pp., 73 maps, 1 pl. fol. Philadelphia, Bradley & co. 1880.
892

NOTE.—See title 797 for the various editions. Like the edition of 1879 with the following exceptions : no. [23] Kentucky and Tennessee.—no. [46] Utah and Nevada.—no. [47] Arizona and New Mexico.—no. [48] Oregon and Washington, are revised and enlarged.—no. [10] Railroad map of the United States, is inserted.

## 1881

**American express co.**
Tourists' pocket atlas. [6] l. 12 maps. 32°. New York, American express company, 1881.
893

## 1881

**Dufour, A. H.**

Grand atlas universel, physique, historique et politique de géographie ancienne et moderne. Gravé sur acier par Ch. Dyonnet, graveur du dépôt de la marine. Complété et tenu constamment au courant des nouvelles découvertes d'après les données officielles des ministères de la guerre et de la marine . . . 2 p. l., 40 col. maps. fol. Paris, Le Vasseu [1881] 894

NOTE.—See also titles 833 and 852. nos. 12-15 comprise one map.
The following maps relate to America :
no. 10. Mappe-monde.
" 37. Amérique du Nord
" 38. Amérique du Sud.
" 39. Mexique, Antilles, États-Unis.
" 40. Océanie.

## 1881

**Mitchell, S. A.**

Mitchell's new general atlas, containing maps of the various countries of the world, plans of cities, etc. . . . Together with valuable statistical tables. Also, a list of post-offices of the United States and territories, and the census 1860 and 1870. 2 p. l., 45 pp., 73 maps, 1 pl. fol. Philadelphia, Bradley & co. 1881. 895

Copyright 1880. See title 797 for the various editions.
NOTE.—Pagination irregular.
Map no. 10 not included in the table of contents.
Like edition of 1880.

## 1881

**Rand, McNally & co.**

Rand, McNally & co.'s improved indexed business atlas and shippers' guide . . . 8th ed. 427 pp. incl. 54 maps. fol. Chicago, Rand, McNally & co. 1881. 896

## 1881

Rand, McNally & co.'s improved indexed business atlas and shippers' guide . . . 9th ed. 429 pp. incl. 54 maps. fol. Chicago, Rand, McNally & co. 1881. 897

## 1881

Rand, McNally & co.'s indexed atlas of the world, containing large scale maps of every country and civil division upon the face of the globe . . . 2 p. l., 852 pp., 6 fold. maps. fol. Chicago, Rand, McNally & co. 1881. 898

## 1881

**Vivien de Saint-Martin, L.**
Atlas universel.   cover-title, 19 maps, 1 pl.   fol.   [Paris, Hachette & cie. 1881]   899
 NOTE.—Maps dated 1876–1881.
 The following maps relate to America:
 no. [5] Région Arctique. 1880.
 " [8-9] [Map of Mexico and Central America showing physical features only, without title, imprint, or text]

## 1881-1883

**Letts, son & co.**
Letts's popular atlas, being a complete series of maps, delineating the whole surface of the globe, with special and original features, and a copious index of 23,000 names.   4 v. in 2.   fol.   London, Letts, son & co. limited, 1881–1883.   900

CONTENTS.
 v. 1. General maps.   2 p. l., 34 maps.
 " 2. British empire.   2 p. l., 39 maps.
 " 3. Europe.   2 p. l., 39 maps.
 " 4. Foreign.   2 p. l., 38 pp., 40 maps.

## 1882

**Cram, G. F.**
Cram's illustrated family atlas of the world.   327 pp. incl. 61 col. maps, 6 pl.   fol.   Chicago, G. F. Cram [1882]   901

## 1882

**Dussieux, L. E.**
Atlas de géographie physique, politique, historique, commerciale et agricole . . . No. 2, Atlas complet de géographie ancienne, du moyen age et moderne a l'usage de toutes les classes. Nouvelle éd. . . .   2 p. l., 75 maps on 117 l., 1 pl.   fol.   Paris, V. Lecoffre [1882]   902
 NOTE.—Date supplied from Journal général de l'imprimerie et de la librairie. Feuilleton. 1882. 2nd sér. v. 26, pt. 2, p. 1776.

## 1882

**Géographie universelle.** Atlas-Migeon, dressé par Desbuisson et A. T. Chartier . . . revu par Vuillemin . . . Historique, scientifique, industriel et commercial a l'usage des lycées, des séminaires et des familles, comprenant la géographie, l'histoire, la statistique, etc., d'après les documents authentiques les plus récents avec une feuille de texte explicatif mis en regard de chaque carte.  Éd. de 1882. 2 p. l., [89] l., 41 maps.   fol.   Paris, J. Migeon [1882]   903
 NOTE.—Maps have inset views.

35799—08——33

**1882**

**Gray, O. W., & son.**

The national atlas, containing elaborate topographical maps of the United States, and the dominion of Canada with plans of cities and general maps of the world . . .   224 pp. incl. 73 col. maps, 12 col. maps.  fol.  Philadelphia, O. W. Gray & son, 1882.   904

**1882**

**Johnston, A. K.**

The royal atlas of modern geograpny exhibiting, in a series of entirely original and authentic maps, the present condition of geographical discovery and research in the several countries, empires, and states of the world . . .  With a special index to each map, New ed.   6 p. l., 154 pp., 51 maps.  fol.  Edinburgh and London, W. & A. K. Johnston, 1882.   905

> NOTE.—See also title 835 and 867.  Contains plans of the following cities: Marseille–Genoa.—Trieste.—Valetta.—Alexandria.—Copenhagen.—Vienna.—S! Petersburg.

**1882**

**Mitchell, S. A.**

Mitchell's new general atlas, containing maps of the various countries of the world, plans of cities, etc. . . .  Together with valuable statistical tables.  Also, a list of post-offices of the United States and territories, census of 1860 and 1870, and also census of 1880 for states, territories and counties, also of cities of over 10,000 inhabitants.   2 p. l., 45, [1] pp., 72 maps.  fol.  Philadelphia, Bradley & co. 1882.   906

> NOTE.—See title 797 for the various editions.  Like the edition of 1881 with the following maps revised:
> no. [17] New Jersey.
> " [18] Pennsylvania.
> " [19] [Plans of] Harrisburg, Williamsport, Erie and Scranton.
> " [22] Delaware, Maryland, Virginia and West Virginia.
> " [27] Florida.
> " [39] Detroit.
> " [42] Montana, Idaho and Wyoming.

**1882**

**Philip, G. & son.**

Philips' student's atlas of ancient & modern geography, with a copious consulting index.  Edited by William Hughes . . .  New and enlarged edition.   3 p. l., 46 pp., 40 maps.  4°.  London, G. Philip & son, 1882.   907

> NOTE.—The following maps relate to America:
> nos. 1-2. The world.
> no. 2ᴬ. The world on Mercator's projection . . .
> " 2ᵇ. British empire throughout the world . . .

no. 30. North America, by W. Hughes.
" 31. United States.
" 32. . . . Canada [and the adjoining provinces of British North America]
" 33. Mexico [and Yucatan]
" 34. The West Indies, and the states of Central America.
" 35. South America.

**1882**

**Rand, McNally & co.**
Rand, McNally & co.'s indexed atlas of the world. Containing large scale maps of every country and civil division upon the face of the globe, together with historical, statistical and descriptive matter relating to each . . . 3d ed.   3 p. l., 904 pp. incl. 70 maps, 21 col. pl.  fol.  Chicago, Rand, McNally & co. 1882.    908

**1882**

**Robiquet, ――**
Atlas hydrographique comprenant les côtes d'Europe, d'Asie et d'Afrique sur l'océan Atlantique, la mer des Indes et l'océan Pacifique les côtes des États-Unis, le golfe du Mexique et les Antilles les côtes du Brésil et de la Patagonie, les côtes du Chili, du Pérou, de l'Amérique centrale, de la Californie &c. . . .   1 p. l., 71 maps. fol.  Paris, Robiquet, 1882.    909

NOTE.—Engraved title.  See also title 795.
A collection of maps by different hydrographers many of whom were officers in the english or french navy: Barnett, Owen, T. Smyth, Scott, Hurd, Haines, Spatt, Slater, Bedford, and Dumoulin, Beautemps-Beaupré, Tardy de Montravel, Lagravière, le baron Roussin, Fisquet, Bérard and Garnault.
Imprint date is 1856, beneath which is the following: edition de 1882.
Maps generally have insets dated 1812–1880.
An earlier edition having maps dated 1844–1851, contains the following maps not found in this atlas:
no. [1] Carte générale de l'océan Atlantique . . .
" [2] Océan Atlantique méridional.
" [3] Carte générale de la mer des Indes . . .
" [15] Carte de la côte méridionale d'Espagne . . .  1848.
" [23] Carte de la côte d'Afrique . . .  1849.
" [25] Plan des îles Bermudes . . .  1844.
" [27] Carte des côtes de la Patagonie et des mers du cap Horn . . . 1849.
The following maps differ from edition with maps dated 1844–1851:
no. [15] . . . carte de la Manche . . .  1878.
" [16] Carte générale du golfe de Gascogne.
" [23] Embouchure de la Gironde . . .
" [24] Carte générale des côtes de Portugal . . .  1882.
" [25] Carte de la Méditerranée . . .
" [26] Méditerranée, partie orientale.
" [31] Carte des côtes de France . .
" [40]-[41] Carte de la côte d'Afrique.
" [43] Carte des îles Açores.
" [45] . . . Îles du cap Vert . . .
" [52] Carte de la côte des Guyanes . . .
" [54]    "   des côtes l'Amerique du Sud.

**Robiquet,** ——Continued.

The following maps relate to America:

no. [1] Carte des terres et des mers connues .
" [2] Planisphère géohydrographique . . .
" [3] Carte générale de l'océan Atlantique . . . 1879.—Insets: Plan des îles Bermudes, par le cap. Th. Hurd.—Madère, par le cap. A. T. E. Vidal, 1847.
" [4] Carte de l'océan Atlantique . . . 1880. Insets: Île Sainte Hélène . . . 1816, par John Barnes.—Île de la Trinidad . . .—Île de l'Ascension . . . 1838, par lieut. G. A. Bedford.—Georgetown (Ascension) . . .—Mouillage de St Hélène.
" [46] Carte générale de l'île et des bancs de Terre-neuve et du golfe du Saint Laurent . . . 1879.—Inset: Plan de la rade de l'île St Pierre . . . 1841, par m. J. de la Roche-Poncié.
" [47] Carte particulière des bancs de Terre-Neuve . . .—Inset: Plan de l'île St Pierre, par m. J. de la Roche-Poncié.
" [48] Carte de la côte des États-Unis comprise entre la Nouvelle-Ecosse et la Floride . . . 1880.—Insets: Baie de New York, par F. R. Hassler et Thomas R. Gedney.—Complément de la partie méridionale des États-Unis.—Charleston . . . 1823 à 1825 . . .—Carte de la baie Delaware . . .
" [49] Carte générale des îles Antilles et du golfe du Mexique.—Insets: Carmen.—Veracruz.—San Juan de Nicaragua, par m. m. Peacock, Barnett et Wheeler.—Port de Chagres, par m. m. Lloyd et Barnett.
" [50] Carte des îles et bancs de Bahama, passages à l'île de Cuba et au golfe du Mexique . . . 1874.—Insets: Porte de Nassau . . .—Bahia Honda . . .—La Havane.—Sagua la Grande, par don Fco. Lavallée.
" [51] Carte réduite de la Guadeloupe et dependances . . . 1842.—Insets: Plan du bourg et du port du Moule . . . 1827.—Plan de la ville et du port de la Pointe à Pitre.—Vue de l'entrée du port de la Pointe à Pitre . . .
" [52] Carte de la côte des Guyanes et de la partie n. e. du Brésil . . .— Insets: Cayenne.—Entrée de la rivière Corentyn, par Robert H. Schomburgk.—Plan du mouillage de la ville du Para . . . 1843 par m. Tardy-de-Montravel.—Port de Vigia, par [le même]— Rivière du Para, par [le même]—Mouillage des îles San Joao, par C. H. M. Buckle.—S. Luiz de Maranham, par m. Tardy-de-Montravel.
" [53] Carte de la côte du Brésil . . .—Insets: Pernambugo, par m. Gressier . . .—Baie de Espirito Santo, par m. m. Givry et Gressier.— Rio-Janeiro, par m. Jehenne.—Bahia, ou San Salvador.—Canal des Abrolhos.—Mouillage de l'île St Sebastiaõ.
" [54] Côte de l'Amérique du Sud . . . 1874. Insets: Montevideo, par m. Barral.—Rade de Buenos-Ayres . . .—Baie de l'Union . . .—Rio Negro . . .—Rade de Maldonado.—Rade de Colonia.—Mouillage de l'île St Catherine, par m. Barral.
" [55] Carte générale de l'océan Pacifique . . . par C. A. V. Dumoulin . . . 1877.
" [56] Carte des mers de Behring . . .—Insets: Baie d'Avatcha . . . par le cap. F. W. Beechey, 1827.—Mouillage de Chamisso (golfe de Kotzebue)—Plan du port Clarence, par le cap. F. W. Beechey.
" [57] Carte des côtes du Chili et de la Bolivie . . . Insets: Iquique.— Arica. — Rade d'Ilo. — Cobija. — Ports Caldera et Yngles. — Copiapo.—Coquimbo.—Valparaiso, par m. de Tessan.—Baie Pichidanque.—Île Mocha.—Baie de la Conception.

no. [58] Carte des côtes du Pérou et de l Équator . . . 1880. Insets: Entrée de la rivière Guayaquil.—Baie de Payta.—Plan du Callao.—Huacho, par m. m. Fisquet et Garnault.—Chilca, par Edward Belcher.—Pisco et îles Chincha.

" [59] Carte des côtes de l'Amérique centrale comprises entre Panama et l'entrée du golfe de Californie . . . 1878.—Insets: Mazatlan.—San Blas.—Acapulco.—Punta-Arenas (golfe de Nicoya)—Realejo.—Baie Salinas.—San Carlos de la Union.—Baie de Panama.—Chemin de fer de Panama.

" [60] Carte générale de l'océan Indien . . . éd. de 1880.

" [67] Carte générale des îles de la Sonde comprenant Sumatra, Java, Borneo, Célèbes . . . [les Philippines] éd. de 1880.

" [68] Mer de Chine et îles Philippines.—Inset: Carte de la baie de Manille. éd. de 1882.

## 1882
**Stieler, A.**

Adolf Stieler's hand atlas über alle theile der erde und über das weltgebäude . . .  4 p. l., 8 pp., 95 (*i. e.* 90) col. maps, 1 col. map on 16 l., 4 col. pl.  fol.  Gotha, J. Perthes [1882]  910

NOTE.—See also title 819. Neu bearb. von Aug. Petermann, Herm. Berghaus u. Carl Vogel. *cf.* Kayser, C. G. Vollstandiges bücher-lexicon.
First published 1817-23.
Wanting:
no. 31. Ober- und Mittel-Italien.
" 32. Süd-Italien.

## 1882
**Colton, G. W.**

Colton's general atlas of the world . . . Accompanied by geographical, statistical, and historical letter-press descriptions.  2 p. l., [282] pp., incl. [104] col. maps, 2 pl.  fol.  New York, G. W. & C. B. Colton & co. 1883.  911

NOTE.—See also title 816, 827, 856, 866, 879 and 886.

## 1883
**Cram, G. F.**

Cram's unrivaled family atlas of the world.  132 pp. incl. 66 col. maps, 10 pl., 6 diagr.  fol.  [Chicago, G. F. Cram, 1883]  912

## 1883
**Johnson, A. J.**

Johnson's new illustrated family atlas of the world . . . with a treatise on physical geography, by professor A. Guyot, with descriptions, geographical, statistical, and historical; revised by A. R. Spofford . . . Also including a dictionary of religious denominations, sects, parties, and associations, compiled by pro-

**Johnson, A. J.**—Continued.

fessor Roswell D. Hitchcock . . . 101, 24 pp., front., 72 maps, 2 pl., diagr. fol. New York, A. J. Johnson, 1883-[1882] 913

  NOTE.—Copyright date is 1882. See also titles 837, 840, 843, and 858.
  Contains plans of the following cities: no. 36–37, Boston.—no. 40–41, New York.—no. 43(a), Philadelphia.—no. 48, Washington.—no. 49-50, A map of the vicinity of Richmond and Peninsular campaign in Virginia; showing also the interesting localities along the James, Chickahominy & York rivers . . .

### 1883

**Rand, McNally & co.**

Rand, McNally & co.'s improved indexed business atlas and shippers' guide . . . 11th ed. 479 pp. incl. 72 maps. fol. Chicago, Rand, McNally & co. 1883. 914

### 1883

**Watson, G.**

New indexed family atlas of the United States, with maps of the world. A compendium of geographical knowledge . . . showing in detail the railway system and post routes . . . 112 pp. incl. 50 col. maps. fol. New York, G. Watson; Chicago, Tenney & Weaver, 1883. 915

### 1883–1908

**Vivien de Saint-Martin, L.** *and* **Schrader, J. D. F.**

Atlas universel de géographie construit d'après les sources originales et les documents les plus récents, cartes, voyages, mémoires, travaux géodésiques, etc. Avec un texte analytique; ouvrage commencé par m. Vivien de Saint-Martin . . . et continué par Fr. Schrader. 90 cartes gravées sur cuivre sous la direction de mm. E. Collin et Delaune. fol. Paris, Hachette & cie. 1883–1908. 916

  NOTE.—All published to date.

#### CONTENTS.

  no. 3. Mappemonde [en deux hémisphères] 1902.
  "  4. Région polaire Arctique. 1904.
  "  5. Région polaire Antarctique. 1883.
  "  6. Europe physique. 1898.
  "  7.  " politique. 1897.
  "  8. France physique. 1897.
  "  9.  " politique. 1897.
  " 10.  " en 6 feuilles, feuille nord-ouest. 1888.
  " 11. France en 6 feuilles, feuille nord-est. 1888.
  " 12.  "   " "   "    " ouest. 1889.
  " 13.  "   " "   "    " est.
  " 14.  "   " "   "    " sud-ouest. 1897.
  " 15.  "   " "   "    " sud-est.
  " 16. Péninsule Ibérique. 1903.

no. 17. Espagne et Portugal, en 4 feuilles par F. Prudent. feuille I. 1902.
" 18. " " " " " " " " II. 1902.
" 19. " " " " " " " " III. 1902.
" 20. " " " " " " " " IV. 1902.
" 21. Italie. 1900.
" 22. Italie septentrionale. 1899.
" 23. Italie méridionale. 1887.
" 24. Suisse. 1896.
" 25. Belgique et Luxembourg. 1886.
" 26. Pays-bas. 1885.
" 27. Iles Britanniques. 1906. [Galles.
" 28. Royaume-Uni de Gr. de Bretagne & d'Irlande. Angleterre & Pays de
" 28 [a] " " " " " " " " Ecosse & Irlande.
" 29. Suède, Norvège, Danemark, feuille septentrionale. 1886.
" 30. " " " " méridionale. 1884.
" 31. Allemagne. 1899.
" 32. Autriche-Hongrie. 1899.
" 33. Europe centrale, en 4 feuilles; feuille I. 1892.
" 34. " " " " II. 1896.
" 35. " " " " II. 1896.
" 36. { " " " " III. 1898.
       " " " " IV. "
" 37. Russie d'Europe. 1899.
" 38. Russie Occidentale et Roumanie. 1883.
" 39. Turquie d'Europe. 1897.
" 40. Russie Orientale et Caucasie. 1900.
" 42. Asie physique. 1900.
" 42ter. Afrique française. (Feuille II) 1899.
" 43. Empire russe. (Asie septentrionale) 1887.
" 44. Asie politique. 1900.
" 46. Asie en dix feuilles. feuille I. Asie Mineure & Caucasie. 1905.
" 49. Asie en dix feuilles. feuille IV. Japon, Corée, Mandjourie, 1904.
" 51. " " " " " VI. Perse, Afghanistan & Inde Nord-Ouest.
" 53. " " " " " IX. Inde Méridionale. 1900.
" 55. Archipel Asiatique. 1897.
" 57. Afrique physique. 1896.
" 57. bis. " politique. 1897.
" 58. Afrique en 3 feuilles, feuille nord-ouest. 1894.
" 59. " " " " " nord-est. 1893.
" 60. " " " " " sud. 1892.
" 64. Afrique française (feuille I)
" 65. " " (feuille II) 1899.
" 65. [a] Amérique septentrionale. 1891.
" 66. Afrique française (feuille III) 1905.
" 66. [a] Puissance du Canada. 1889.
" 68. Afrique australe. 1908.
" 69. Amérique du nord physique. 1899.
" 72. États-Unis. 1904.
" 73. Mexique. 1884.
" 74. États-Unis en 4 feuilles par V. Huot. feuille sud-est. 1908.
" 74[a] " " " " " " " nord-est. 1908.
" 74[b] Amérique Centrale. 1893.
" 75. Antilles. 1898.
" 75a États-Unis. f$^{lle}$ S. O. 1908.

**Vivien de Saint-Martin, L.** *and* **Schrader, J. D. F.**—Continued.
  no. 76. Amérique du Sud, physique. 1898.
  " 76 bis. " " " politique. "
  " 77. " " " en 5 feuilles, feuille 1. 1895.
  " 78. " " " " " " " 2. 1894.
  " 79. " " " " " " " 3. 1893.
  " 80. " " " " " " " 4. 1897.
  " 81. " " " " " " " 5. 1891.
  " 82. Océanie. 1887.
  " 83. Australie. 1889.
  " 84. Principaux archipels d'océanie. 1885.

## 1884

**Ivison, Blakeman, Taylor & co.**
  Handy atlas of the world . . .    32 pp. incl. 27 maps.  4°.
New York, Chicago, Ivison, Blakeman, Taylor & co. [1884]    917

## 1884

**Johnson, A. J. & co.**
  Johnson's new illustrated family atlas of the world . . . With a treatise on physical geography, by prof. A. Guyot . . . with descriptions, geographical, statistical, and historical. Revised by hon. A. R. Spofford . . . Also including A dictionary of religious denominations, sects, parties, and associations, compiled by professor Roswell D. Hitchcock . . .    101, 35 pp., front., 71 col. maps, 2 col. pl., 1 diagr. fol. New York, A. J. Johnson & co. 1884.    918

## 1884

**Kochersperger, H. L.,** *and* **Kochersperger, D. H.**
  The people's illustrated & descriptive family atlas of the world. Indexed. [anon.]    350 pp., incl. 71 col. maps, 6 diagr. fol. Chicago, people's publishing co. ᶜ 1884.    919

## 1884

**Mitchell, S. A.**
  Mitchell's new general atlas, containing maps of the various countries of the world, plans of cities, etc. . . . Together with valuable statistical tables. Also a list of post-offices of the United States and territories, and also census of 1880 for states, territories and counties, also of cities of over 10,000 inhabitants.    2 p. l., 45, [1] pp., 72 maps, 1 pl. fol. Philadelphia, W. M. Bradley & bro. 1884.
    920
    NOTE.—Copyrighted 1883. See title 797, for the various editions.
    Like the edition of 1882 with the following maps revised: no. [11] Maine.—no. [12] Vermont and New Hampshire.—no. [31] Ohio.—no. [32] Indiana.—no. [34] Illinois.—no. [60] France.—no. [61] Spain & Portugal.
    Map of Turkey in Europe (double sheet) is omitted.

### 1884

**Monteith, J.**
The boys' and girls' atlas of the world . . .   1 p. l., 14 col. maps.  sm. 4°.  New York and Chicago, A. S. Barnes & co. [1884]
921

### 1884

**Rand, McNally & co.**
Rand, McNally & co.'s improved indexed business atlas and shippers' guide . . .   13th ed.   498 pp. incl. 73 maps.  fol.  Chicago, Rand, McNally & co. 1884.
922

### 1885

**Bradley, W. M., & bro.**
Bradley's atlas of the world, for commercial and library reference . . . with index to maps.   3 p. l., 132 pp., 74 col. maps. fol.  Philadelphia, W. M. Bradley & bro. 1885.
923

### 1885

**Cram, G. F.**
Illustrated atlas and hand book of the world.  Mechanical news ed. . . .   1 p. l., 203 pp. incl. 21 maps, 17 pl.  12°.  Chicago, H. S. Stebbins, 1885.
924

### 1885

**De Puy, W. H.**
The people's atlas of the world.  Astronomical, historical, political, chronological, statistical, and descriptive . . .   578 pp. incl. 102 col. maps, 48 diagr.  4°.  Boston, Toronto, M. Garrison & co. [1885]
925

### 1885

**Johnson, A. J., & co.**
Johnson's new general cyclopædia and copper-plate hand-atlas of the world . . . being specially adapted for daily use in the family, school, and office.  Editors-in-chief Frederick A. P. Barnard . . . Arnold Guyot . . .   2 v.  4°.  New York, A. J. Johnson & co. 1885.
926

NOTE.—Collation: v. 1, xii, 784 pp., 23 col. maps, 5 pl., illus; v. 2, 1 p. l., 785–1562 pp., 19 col. maps, 1 pl., illus.

### 1885

**Lubrecht, C.**
Charles Lubrecht's pictorial and comprehensive atlas of the world, ne plus ultra.   168 pp. incl. front., 77 col. maps, 5 col. pl. fol.  New York, C. Lubrecht, 1885.
927

## 1885

**Rand, McNally & co.**

Rand, McNally & co.'s improved indexed business atlas and shippers' guide . . .   509 pp. incl. 67 maps.   fol.   Chicago, Rand, McNally & co. 1885.   928

## 1885

**Watson, G.**

Watson's new and complete illustrated atlas of the world. Indexed . . . Showing the entire railroad system in detail, post routes . . .   250 pp. incl. 70 col. maps, plates.   fol.   New York, Chicago, G. Watson [1885]   929

NOTE.—Copyright 1885. Dated 1886 on cover.

## 1886

**Kochersperger, H. L.,** *and* **Kochersperger, D. H.**

The people's illustrated & descriptive family atlas of the world. Indexed. [anon.]   386 pp. incl. 89 maps, 6 diagr.   fol.   Chicago, people's publishing co. [1886]   930

NOTE.—On reverse of title-page: 7th edition, thoroughly revised to march 1886.

## 1886

**Lippincott, J. B., co.**

Popular family atlas of the world.   1 p. l., 26 pp. incl. 23 maps. sq. 4°.   Philadelphia, J. B. Lippincott co. 1886.   931

NOTE.—Maps selected from David M. Warren's Series of school geographies.

## 1886

**Palmer, L. T.**

Gaskell's new and complete family atlas of the world . . .   4 p. l. 11–581 pp. incl. 73 col. maps, 4 pl., 22 tab.   Chicago, Fairbanks & Palmer publishing co. 1886.   932

## 1886

**Rand, McNally & co.**

Rand, McNally & co.'s improved indexed business atlas and shipper's guide . . .   15th ed.   557 pp. incl. 92 maps.   fol.   Chicago, Rand, McNally & co. 1886.   933

## 1886

Rand, McNally & co.'s new indexed atlas of the world, containing large scale maps of every country and civil division upon the face of the globe, together with historical, statistical and descriptive matter relative to each . . .   731 pp., front. incl. 97 maps, 6 pl.   fol.   Chicago, Rand, McNally & co. 1886.   934

## 1886

Rand, McNally & co's pocket atlas of the world. Containing colored maps of each state and territory in the United States; also, maps of the chief grand divisions, with complete index of every country on the face of the globe. 191 pp. incl. 88 maps. 18°. Chicago [etc.] Rand, McNally & co. 1886. 935

## 1887
**Alden, J. B.**
Alden's home atlas of the world. 2 p. l., 70 maps, [18] pp. 4°. New York, J. B. Alden, 1887. 936

## 1887
**Bartholomew, J.**
The pocket atlas of the world. A comprehensive ana popular series of maps illustrating physical and political geography. New ed. ... 24, 60 pp., 54 maps. 32°. New York and London, G. P. Putnam's sons, 1887. 937

## 1887
**Cram, G. F.**
Cram's standard american atlas of the world. Accompanied by a complete and simple index ... 312 pp. incl. 76 col. maps, 6 diagr. fol. Chicago, G. F. Cram [1887] 938

## 1887

Cram's unrivaled atlas of the world. Indexed. [18th ed. rev. to march 1, 1887] 231 pp. incl. 93 col. maps, 9 pl., 5 diagr. fol. Chicago, H. S. Stebbins, 1887. 939

## 1887
**De Puy, W. H.**
The universal guide and gazetteer to the countries, peoples, and governments of the world, including a geographical, historical, astronomical, chronological, statistical, political, and descriptive office and family atlas and blue-book ... 645 pp. incl. 118 maps, 27 diagrs. fol. New York, Phillips & Hunt, 1887. 940

## 1887
**Drioux, C. J., and Leroy, C.**
Atlas universel et classique de géographie ancienne, romaine du moyen âge, moderne et contemporaine a l'usage des établissements d'instruction publique ... Nouvelle éd. 7, [1] pp., 56 maps, 2 pl. sm. fol. Paris, E. Belin, 1887. 940a

NOTE.—Map on l. 25-26 wanting.

### 1887

**Mecutchen, S., *and* Harrower, H. D.**
A pocket atlas of the world: with descriptive text, statistical tables, etc. etc. [anon.]  224 pp. incl. 91 maps.  24°.  New York and Chicago. Ivison, Blakeman & co. [1887]  941

### 1887

**Rand, McNally & co.**
General atlas of the world containing large scale maps of every state, territory and county in the world, with a carefully prepared historical and descriptive sketch of each . . .  216 pp. incl. 94 maps, 3 pls.  4°.  Chicago, continental publishing co. 1887.  942

NOTE.—Copyright by Rand, McNally & co., 1887.

### 1887

Rand, McNally & co.'s improved indexed business atlas and shippers' guide . . .  16th ed.  569 pp. incl. 98 maps.  fol.  Chicago, Rand, McNally & co. 1887.  943

### 1887

**Stanford, E.**
Stanford's London atlas of universal geography, exhibiting the physical and political divisions of the various countries of the world . . .  5 p. l., 25 pp., 90 col. maps.  fol.  London, E. Stanford, 1887.  944

### 1888

**Rand, McNally & co.**
Rand, McNally & co.'s improved indexed business atlas and shippers' guide . . .  17th ed.  597 pp. incl. 101 maps.  fol.  Chicago, Rand, McNally & co. 1888.  945

### 1888

Rand, McNally & co.'s new family atlas of the world, indexed . . .  288 pp. incl. 108 maps, 16 col. pl.  fol.  Chicago, people's publishing co. 1888.  946

### 1888

Same.  288 pp. incl. 108 maps, 16 col. pl.  fol.  Dallas, Tex. Talty & Wiley, 1888.  946a

NOTE.—Copyright aug. 13, 1888 by Rand, McNally & co.

### 1888

**Standard publishing co.**
The standard atlas and gazetteer of the world, specially adapted for commercial and library reference . . . By eminent specialists in each department . . .  615 pp. incl. maps, plates.  fol.  Chicago, standard publishing co. 1888.  947

## 1889

**American express co.**
The American express company's note book and atlas. 1889. 171 [1] pp. incl. 86 maps, 6 l., 1 fold. map, 1 facs. obl. 48°. Chicago, Rand, McNally & co. 1889. 948

## 1889

**Brown, M. R.**
The continental atlas, containing elaborate topographical maps of the several states and territories, of the dominion of Canada, the republics of South America, and all the principal countries of the world . . . 26, [4] 27–225 pp. incl. 92 maps. fol. Philadelphia, M. R. Brown, 1889. 949

NOTE.—The following maps relate to America:
- p. [6–7]. Gray's new map of the world in hemispheres . . . ᶜ1879.
- " 10. Northern regions.
- " 11. Southern regions.
- " 12. North America.
- " 23. Gray's historical maps of the United States.
- " 24–25. Gray's geological map of the United States. By prof. Charles H. Hitchcock . . .
- " 26. Gray's botannical and zoological maps of the United States.
- " [28–29]. . . . United States . . . ᶜ1879.
- " 39. Maine. ᶜ1886.
- " 42–43. . . . New Hampshire and Vermont.
- " 46–47. Massachusetts, Rhode Island, and Connecticut. ᶜ1884.
- " 50–51. Boston and adjacent cities.
- " 54–55. New York City, Brooklyn, Jersey City, Hoboken, etc. ᵒ1886.
- " 58–59. New York. ᶜ1876.
- " 62–63. New Jersey.
- " 66–67. . . . Pennsylvania. ᶜ1883.
- " 70–71. Outline map of the county and city of Philadelphia and vicinity. ᵒ1883.
- " 73. . . . Baltimore.
- " 74–75. Maryland, Delaware and the District of Columbia. City of Washington.
- " 76. . . . Richmond.
- " 78–79. Virginia and West Virginia. ᶜ1877.
- " 82–83. . . . North Carolina and South Carolina. ᶜ1881.
- " 86–87. . . . Georgia. ᶜ1877.
- " 90–91. . . . Florida. ᶜ1886.
- " 94–95. . . . Alabama.
- " 98–99. Mississippi. ᵒ1878.
- " 102–103. . . . Louisiana. City of New Orleans. ᶜ1878.
- " 106–107. Texas and the Indian territory. City of Galveston.—Austin. ᶜ1876.
- " 110–111. Arkansas. ᶜ1876.
- " 113. Indianapolis.—Louisville.
- " 114–115. . . . Kentucky and Tennessee. ᵒ1876.
- " 116. . . . Cinainnati. ᵒ1877.
- " [118–119]. . . . Ohio. City of Columbus.
- " [122–123]. Indiana. ᶜ1882.

**Brown, M. R.**—Continued.
- no. 126-127. North and South Dakota with part of Manitoba, etc. ᵒ1883.
- " 130-131. Michigan. ᵒ1886.
- " 134-135. Lake Superior and the upper peninsula of Michigan.
- " 138-139. Minnesota. ᵒ1886.
- " 141. Iowa.
- " 142-143. Wisconsin. ᵒ1881.
- " 146-147. Illinois. ᵒ1886.
- " 150-151. Missouri. ᵒ1886.
- " 153. Saint Louis.
- " 156.157. Kansas.
- " 160-161. Nebraska.
- " 165. Idaho, Montana and Wyoming.
- " 166. Colorado.
- " 167. Oregon and Washington.
- " 168-169. California. City of San Francisco.
- " 170. Nevada.
- " 171. Utah.
- " 172. Arizona and New Mexico.
- " 175. Dominion of Canada.
- " 176-177. Provinces of Ontario and Quebec.
- " 178. Northern America.
- " 180. Mexico.
- " 181. West Indies and Central America.
- " 183. South America. ᵒ1886.
- " 184. Cuba, Jamaica and Porto Rico. ᵒ1886.
- " 185. Venezuela, united states of Colombia and Ecuador. ᵒ1886.
- " 186. Brazil and Guayana. ᵒ1886.
- " 187. Peru and Bolivia.
- " 188-189. Argentine republic, Chile, Uruguay, Paraguay, Patagonia, etc. ᵒ1879.

### 1889

**Cram, G. F.**

Cram's standard american atlas of the world accompanied by a complete and simple index of the United States showing the true location of all railroads, towns, villages and post offices . . .   390 pp. incl. 127 maps, 6 pl. fol. Chicago, New York, G. F. Cram [1889]   950

### 1889

**Mast, Crowell & Kirkpatrick.**

The peerless atlas of the world.   132 pp. incl. maps, plates. fol. Philadelphia, Springfield, O., Mast, Crowell & Kirkpatrick, 1889.   951

NOTE.—Published at various times under titles, such as "The people's atlas of the world. 1894," "The new peerless atlas of the world. 1897," "The new people's atlas of the world." 1898.

### 1889

**Rand, McNally & co.**

Rand, McNally & co's enlarged business atlas and shippers' guide . . . 18th ed.   1 p. l., 291 pp. incl. 85 maps. fol. Chicago, Rand, McNally & co. 1889.   952

### 1889

Rand, McNally & co.'s model atlas of the world. Containing maps of states and territories in the United States and every country upon the face of the globe . . . 501 pp. incl. 90 maps, 12 col. pl. 12°. Chicago, continental publishing co. 1889.   953

### 1889
**Reed, H. T.**
Pocket atlas of the world.   72 pp. incl. 67 maps.   24°.   Chicago, H. T. Reed, 1889.   954

### 1889
**Turner, C. H.**
Peerless atlas of the world. Arranged for popular use. [anon.] 1 p. l., 97 pp. incl. 46 col. maps, 2 pl. fol. Springfield, O., Mast, Crowell & Kirkpatrick [1889]   955
[Farm and fireside library, no 47]

NOTE.—Republished with title, "The dollar atlas of the world" and "The twentieth century peerless atlas."

### 1890
**Bacon, G. W.**
Complete atlas of the world containing one hundred and twenty-four double page maps, including all the latest discoveries . . . 3 p. l., 56 pp., 49 maps on 61 l., 7 diagr. fol. London, G. W. Bacon, 1890.   956

### 1890
**Bartholomew, J.**
The library reference atlas of the world. 4 p. l., 209 pp., 84 col. maps. sm. fol. London and New York, Macmillan & co. 1890.   957

### 1890
**Philip, G. & son.**
Philips' imperial atlas of the world. A series of eighty maps, illustrating every aspect of geographical science. Engraved from original drawings compiled from the latest surveys and the works of eminent travellers and explorers. Each map, with the exception of the physical and orographical maps, is accompanied by a complete index in which the latitude & longitude of every place is given.   3 p. l., [149] pp., 80 col. maps.   fol.   London, G. Philip & son, 1890.   958

### 1890
**Rand, McNally & co.**
Rand, McNally & co.'s enlarged business atlas and shippers' guide . . . 19th ed.   1 p. l., 312 pp. incl. 89 maps.   fol.   Chicago, Rand, McNally & co. 1890.   959

### 1890

**Rand, McNally & co.**—Continued.
 The Rand, McNally new standard atlas of the world. 196 pp. incl. 79 maps, 17 col. pls. fol. Chicago, the continental publishing co. °[1890] 960
  NOTE.—Copyright 1890 by Rand, McNally & co.

### 1890

**Scribner's, C., sons.**
 The Scribner-Black atlas of the world. Embracing the latest discoveries, new boundaries, and other changes accompanied by a geographical introduction and indexes. Library ed. 2 p. l., 32, 105 pp. incl. front., 81 maps, 2 pl. fol. New York, C. Scribner's sons, 1890. 961

### 1890

**Turner, C. H.**
 The dollar atlas of the world [anon.] 98 pp. incl. 51 col. maps, 2 pl. fol. Philadelphia, Springfield, O., Mast, Crowell & Kirkpatrick [1890] 962
  NOTE.—First published with title "Peerless atlas of the world." Afterwards "The twentieth century peerless atlas."

### 1891

**Appleton, D., & co.**
 Appleton's hand atlas of the world. cover-title, 26 col. maps. fol. [New York] D. Appleton & co. °1891. 963

### 1891

**Desbuissons,** —— *& others.*
 Nouvel atlas illustré. Géographie universelle comprenant la géographie, l'histoire, l'administration, la statistique, etc. Dressé, dessiné et gravé par mm. Desbuissons, Lorsignol . . . Texte par m. A. Martineau. 2 p. l., 62 (*i. e.* 60) l., 64 maps. fol. Paris, direction et administration [J. Migeon] 1891. 964
  NOTE.—Contains a geographical description and a short history of the countries.
  Majority of the maps illustrated by engraved views of important cities.
  The following maps relate to America:
  no. 55. Amérique du Nord.
  " 56. États-Unis.
  " 57. Mexique, Amérique centrale et Antilles.
  " 58. Amérique du Sud.
  " 59. Amérique du Sud (partie septentrionale)
  " 60. "    "   " ( " méridionale)

## 1891

**Garretson, Cox & co.**
The Columbian atlas of the world containing large-scale maps of every country upon the earth . . . Acccmpanied by a new and complete index . . . [anon.]   11 p. l., 5–159 pp., 2 l. incl. 92 col. maps, 12 pl.   fol.   New York, Garretson, Cox & co. 1891.   965
NOTE.—Maps by Rand, McNally & co.

## 1891

**Rand, McNally & co.**
Rand, McNally & co.'s neuer familien atlas der welt.   331 pp. incl. 97 maps.   fol.   Chicago, Rand, McNally & co. 1891.   966

## 1891

Rand, McNally & co.'s new family atlas of the world.   321 pp. incl. 92 maps, 18 col. pl.   fol.   Chicago, Rand, McNally & co. [1891]   967

## 1891

**Schrader, J. D. F., Prudent, F. P. V.** *and* **Anthoine E.**
Atlas de géographie moderne. Accompagnées d'un texte géographique, statisque et ethnographique et d'environ 600 cartes de détail, figures, diagrammes, etc.   2 p. l., 35, [1], [246] pp. incl. 64 col. maps.   fol.   Paris, Hachette & cie. 1891.   968
NOTE.—See also title 1126a.

## 1892

**Appleton, D. & co.**
The library atlas of modern geography . . .   3 p. l., 610, 45, 109 pp. incl. 103 col. maps, 2 pl.   sm. fol.   New York, D. Appleton & co. 1892.   969

## 1892

**Blegen, J.**
Blegen's veileder og verdens–atlas.   2 p. l., 443 pp. incl. 48 maps, xxv, [2] pp.   16°.   Chicago, J. Blegen [1892]   970

## 1892

**Dodd, Mead & co.**
The universal atlas including county and railroad maps of the United States. Together with carefully prepared maps of all other countries from latest surveys. To which are added statistical tables, showing census of the United States from 1790 to 1890, of the dominion of Canada, and larger cities of the whole world, as well as

**Dodd, Mead & co**—Continued.

area and population of the nations of the earth and financial statistics of the main cities of the United States, debts of the different nations, and other interesting and valuable information.   2 p. l., [158] l. incl. 81 maps, [1] l., 42 pp.   4°.   New York, Dodd, Mead & co. 1892.   971

NOTE.—Map no. 19 wanting.

**1892**

Same.   2 p. l., [168] l. incl. 86 maps.   [1] l., 42 pp.   4°.   New York, Dodd, Mead & co. 1892.   971a

**1892**

**Jones, A. W.**
The popular atlas of the world . . . [anon.]   208 pp., incl. 60 maps, pl., diagr.   fol.   Philadelphia, Mast, Crowell & Kirkpatrick [c1892]   972

**1892**

**Mast, Crowell & Kirkpatrick.**
The popular atlas of the world.   212 pp. fold. map, incl. maps & pls.   fol.   Philadelphia, Springfield, O., Mast, Crowell & Kirkpatrick [1892]   973

**1892**

**Rand, McNally & co.**
Rand, McNally & co.'s enlarged business atlas and shippers' guide . . . 22d ed.   351 pp. incl. 88 maps.   fol.   Rand, McNally & co. 1892.   974

**1892**

Rand, McNally & co.'s indexed atlas of the world containing large scale maps of every country and civil division upon the face of the globe, together with historical, descriptive and statistical matter relating to each . . .   581 pp. incl. 126 maps, 18 charts.   fol. Chicago and New York, Rand, McNally & co. 1892.   975

**1892**

The Rand, McNally new standard atlas of the world.   192 pp. incl. 81 maps, 11 col. pl.   fol.   Chicago, Rand, McNally & co. [c1892]   976

**1892**

Same.   196 pp. incl. 79 maps, 14 col. pl.   fol.   Chicago, Rand, McNally & co. [c1892]   977

## 1892

Rand, McNally & co.'s universal atlas of the world. 360 pp. incl. 96 maps, 18 col. pl. fol. Chicago, Rand, McNally & co. 1892  978

## 1892

**White, J. E.,** *& others.*
World's atlas and educational guide. A complete atlas and guide for the business man, and educational compendium for the home, with a treatise on the world's columbian exposition. 442 pp. incl. 42 col. maps, 14 pl. fol. Battle Creek, Mich., world's atlas publishing co. ltd. 1892.  979

## 1893

**Bradley, W. M., & co.**
Bradley's atlas of the world for commercial and library reference . . . With isometric index to each map. 5 p. l., [138] pp., 86 col. maps. fol. Philadelphia, W. M. Bradley & co. 1893.  980
NOTE.—Index interleaved with maps.

## 1893

**Hunt & Eaton.**
The Columbian atlas of the world we live in. Geological, astronomical, geographical . . . [anon.] 380 pp., front. incl. 103 col. maps. 4°. New York, Hunt & Eaton [°1893]  981
NOTE.—Copyrighted 1893.

## 1893-1896

**Kiepert, H.**
Kiepert's grosser hand-atlas mit namensverzeichnissen und bevölkerungsziffern. Statistischer text von dr. Paul Lippert, und M. Busemann. 3. aufl. 3 p. l. [103] l., 45 maps. fol. Berlin, D. Reimer [1893-96]  982

## 1893

**Mitchell, S. A.**
Mitchell's new general atlas, containing maps of the various countries of the world, plans of cities, etc. . . . Together with valuable statistical tables. Also, census of 1890 for states, territories and counties, also of cities of over 10,000 inhabitants. 102 pp., 68 maps, 1 pl. fol. Philadelphia, A. R. Keller co. 1893.  983
NOTE.—Cover title "Mitchell's family atlas of the world." Copyrighted 1892. Maps are like the edition of 1884 with the following maps revised: no. [8] Railroad map of the United States, . . . — no. [34] Chicago. See title 797, for the various editions.
Map of the original thirteen colonies and plan of Milwaukee omitted.

### 1893
**Rand, McNally & co.**
Rand, McNally & co.'s enlarged business atlas and shippers' guide. . . . 23d ed.   361 pp. incl. 93 maps. fol. Chicago, Rand, McNally & co. 1893.   984

### 1893
Rand, McNally & co.'s new handy atlas . . . accompanied by descriptive, statistical, and historical matter.   382 pp. incl. 60 maps, 11 pl.   12°.  Chicago and New York, Rand, McNally & co. 1893.   985

### 1893
Rand, McNally & co.'s universal atlas of the world . . .   412 pp. incl. 97 maps, 27 col. pl.   fol.   Chicago and New York, Rand, McNally & co. 1893.   986

### 1894
**Mast, Crowell & Kirkpatrick.**
The people's atlas of the world.   1 p. l., 124 pp. incl. maps, pls.   fol.   Philadelphia, Springfield, O., Mast, Crowell & Kirkpatrick [1894]   987
[Farm and fireside library, no. 110]

> NOTE.—Published at various times under titles, such as, "The peerless atlas of the world, 1889," "The new peerless atlas of the world, 1897," "The new people's atlas of the world, 1898."

### 1894
**Palmer, L. T.**
The unique album atlas of the world.   665 pp. incl. 125 col. maps, 140 pl.   obl. 18°.   Chicago, Cram standard book co. 1894.   988

### 1894
**Potter, J. E. & co.**
Potter-Bradley atlas of the world, for commercial, educational and library reference . . .   v. 1, no. 1.   3 p. l., [9] pp., 4 maps. fol.   Philadelphia, New York [etc.] J. E. Potter & co. 1894.   989

### 1894
**Rand, McNally & co.**
Rand, McNally & co.'s enlarged business atlas and shippers' guide . . .   24th ed.   399 pp. incl. 109 maps.   fol.   Chicago, Rand, McNally & co. 1894.   990

### 1894
Rand, McNally & co.'s indexed atlas of the world.   Complete in eight parts.   [v. 1, 3–4]   fol.   Chicago, Rand, McNally & co. 1894.   991

CONTENTS.

v. [1] New indexed atlas of Europe, being parts I and II . . .
" [3] "      "      "   " the U. S. "      "   v "   vi
" [4] "      "      "   "   "   "   "      "   vi "  viii

#### 1894

Rand, McNally & co.'s indexed atlas of the world . . . 2 v. 1 p. l., [5]-223 pp. incl. 50 maps, 8 charts; 2 p. l. 225-460 pp. incl. 69 maps, 22 charts. fol. Chicago and New York, Rand, McNally & co. 1894. 992

CONTENTS.

v. 1. Foreign countries. Parts. I, II, III, IV.
" 2. United States.     "    V, VI, VII, VIII.

#### 1894

Rand, McNally & co.'s indexed atlas of the world containing large scale maps of every country and civil division upon the face of the globe, together with historical, descriptive, and statistical matter relative to each . . . 460 pp. incl. 125 maps. fol. Chicago, Rand, McNally & co. 1894. 993

#### 1894

Rand, McNally & co.'s library atlas of the world . . . together with historical, descriptive, and statistical matter . . . 345 pp. incl. 96 maps, 12 col. pl. fol. Chicago and New York, Rand, McNally & co. c[1894] 994

NOTE.—Different from title 995 in the arrangement of the text, plates and maps. Contains maps of the western and eastern hemispheres, not in title. 995.

#### 1894

Rand, McNally & co.'s library atlas of the world . . . together with historical, descriptive, and statistical matter . . . 345 pp. incl. 93 maps, 10 col. pl. fol. Chicago and New York, Rand, McNally & co. [c1894] 995

#### 1894

New handy census gazetteer and atlas of the world containing colored county maps of the United States and the dominion of Canada accompanied by descriptive, statistical, and historical matter . . . 384 pp. incl. 60 maps, 12 diag. 12°. Chicago [etc.] Rand, McNally & co. [1894] 996

#### 1894

**Shewey, A. C.**

The new, handy reference atlas of the world . . . 1 p. l., 128 pp. incl. 111 maps, 2 pl. fol. Chicago, A. C. Shewey [1894] 997

### 1894
**Vidal de La Blache, P.**
  Atlas général Vidal-Lablache . . .   Index alphabétique de plus de 40,000 noms.   4 p. l., 44 pp., 37 col. maps.   fol.   Paris, A. Colin & cie. 1894.   998
  NOTE.—At head of title, "Histoire et géographie."

### 1895
**Garretson, Cox & co.**
  The Columbian atlas of the world, containing large-scale maps of every country upon the earth . . . Accompanied by a new and complete index . . . [anon.]   11 p. l., 5–159 pp., 3 l., incl. 92 col. maps, 12 pl.   fol.   Buffalo, Garretson, Cox & co. 1895.   999
  NOTE.—An extra leaf is found between pp. 150–151. Maps are by Rand, McNally & co.

### 1895
**Gorjan, A., *and* Luncan, I.**
  Atlas-geografic, cunóscerea continentelor, pentru clasele: IV pr. urbană și v pr. rurală de A. Gorjan și I. Luncan.   1 p. l., 37 pp. incl. 8 maps (in text), 2 col. maps.   4°.   Bucuresci, editura librăriei Socecu & co. 1895.   1000

### 1895
**Rand, McNally & co.**
  Rand, McNally & co.'s enlarged business atlas and shippers' guide . . . 25th ed.   384 pp. incl. 88 maps.   fol.   Chicago, Rand, McNally & co. 1895.   1001

### 1895
  Rand, McNally & co.'s library atlas of the world . . . together with historical, descriptive, and statistical matter . . .   444 pp. incl. 101 maps, 52 col. pl.   fol.   Chicago and New York, Rand, McNally & co. [c1895]   1002

### 1895
  Rand, McNally & co.'s new general atlas of the world . . . 18, 17–159 pp. incl. 143 maps, 3 pl.   fol.   Chicago-New York, Rand, McNally & co. [1895]   1003

### 1895
  Rand, McNally & co.'s universal atlas of the world . . .   345 pp. incl. 95 maps, 12 col. pl.   fol.   Chicago and New York, Rand, McNally & co. °1895.   1004

### 1895
  Rand, McNally & co.'s universal atlas of the world . . .   444 pp. incl. 101 maps, 52 col. pl.   fol.   Chicago and New York, Rand, McNally & co. [c1895]   1005

## 1895

**Werner co.**
The people's illustrated and descriptive family atlas of the world. Indexed [21st ed. greatly enlarged and thoroughly revised to jan. 1st, 1895]   3 p. l., 5-534 pp. incl. plates, maps and plans.   fol. Chicago, the Werner co. [1895]   1006

## 1896

**Fort Dearborn publishing co.**
The national standard family and business atlas of the world specially adapted for commercial and library reference . . . With all populations according to 1890 census.   418 (*i. e.* 420) pp. incl. 87 col. maps, 12 plans.   fol.   Chicago, the Fort Dearborn publishing co. [°1896]   1007

## 1896

**Funk & Wagnalls co.**
A standard atlas of the world . . . with a convenient marginal reference index. Also a condensed cyclopedia giving a descriptive and statistical manual of the principal features of the various nations. 1 p. l., [1], xxiv-xxiv[b], xxv-cxxxvi pp. incl. 73 col. maps.   fol. New York, London [etc] Funk & Wagnalls co. [°1896]   1008

## 1896

**Garretson, Cox & co.**
The columbian atlas of the world containing large-scale maps of every country upon the earth . . . Accompanied by a ready reference marginal index . . .   159 pp. incl. 118 col. maps, 3 pl.   fol. Buffalo, N. Y., Garretson, Cox & co. 1896.   1009
  NOTE.—Maps are by Rand, McNally & co. 1896.

## 1896

**Rand, McNally & co.**
New pictorial atlas of the world containing colored maps of every country and civil division, with marginal index together with historical, descriptive, and statistical matter pertaining to each, with city maps and colored statistical diagrams, also a concise review of the world's peoples.   320 pp. incl. 118 maps, 18 pl.   fol.   Chicago, Rand, McNally & co. [1896]   1010
  NOTE.—Copyrighted in 1896.

## 1896

Rand, McNally & co.'s enlarged business atlas and shippers' guide . . .   26th ed.   398 pp. incl. 89 maps.   fol.   Chicago, Rand, McNally & co. 1896.   1011

### 1896

**Rand, McNally & co.**—Continued.

Rand, McNally & co.'s new popular atlas of the world, containing large scale colored maps of each state and territory in the United States, provinces of Canada, the continents and their subdivisions . . . 159 pp. incl. 115 maps, 3 col. pls. fol. Chicago [etc.] Rand, McNally & co. 1896. 1012

### 1896

Rand, McNally twentieth century atlas of the world, containing large scale maps of each state and territory in the United States, provinces of Canada, the continents and their subdivisions . . . 151 pp. incl. 17 maps, 3 col. pl. fol. Chicago [etc.] Rand, McNally & co. 1896. 1013

### 1896

Rand, McNally & co.'s universal atlas of the world . . . With marginal index . . . 456 pp. incl. maps, plans and diagr. fol. Chicago and New York, Rand, McNally & co. 1896. 1014

### 1896

**Stieler, A.**

Adolf Stieler's hand atlas über alle theile der erde und über das weltgebäude. 4 p. l., 201 pp., 95 col. maps. fol. Gotha, J. Perthes [1896] 1015

### 1896

**Waite, J. F., publishing co.**

The new international office and family atlas of the world. Indexed. 482 pp. incl. 154 col. maps, 2 col. pl. fol. Chicago, J. F. Waite publishing co. [1896] 1016

### 1897

**Mast, Crowell & Kirkpatrick.**

The new peerless atlas of the world. contents, title, 219 pp. incl. plates & maps. fol. Springfield, O., Mast, Crowell & Kirkpatrick [1897] 1017
[Farm and fireside library, no. 143]

> NOTE.—Published at various times, under titles, such as, "The people's atlas of the world. 1894," "The peerless atlas of the world. 1889," "The new people's atlas of the world. 1898."

## 1897

**Pennesi, G.**
Atlante scolastico per la geografia fisica e politica. 1 p. l., 49 col. maps, 1 pl. obl. fol. Torino-Roma [etc.] G. B. Paravia & co. [1897] 1018

> NOTE.—"New edition of an atlas by the same author which was published in 1894–95 in two parts. Some alterations and additions have been made which add to the value of the atlas."—The geographical journal. London. June 1897. v. 9. no. 6. See also titles 310 and 311.

## 1897

**Rand, McNally & co.**
Rand, McNally & co.'s enlarged business atlas and shippers' guide . . . 27th ed. 406 pp. incl. 99 maps. fol. Chicago, Rand, McNally & co. 1897. 1019

## 1897

**Smith, B. E.**
The century atlas of the world, prepared under the superintendence of Benjamin E. Smith. 3 p. l., xxx, 382 pp., 134 maps. fol. New York, the century co. [1897] 1020

## 1898

**Black, A.** *and* **C.**
Black's general atlas of the world. 3 p. l., 103 pp., front., 105 col. maps. fol. London, A. & C. Black, 1898. 1021

## 1898

**Mast, Crowell & Kirkpatrick.**
The new peerless atlas of the world. 160 pp. incl. 61 col. maps, 2 pl. fol. Springfield, O., Mast, Crowell & Kirkpatrick, 1898. [Farm and fireside library. no. 166] 1022

## 1898

**Mast, Crowell & Kirkpatrick.**
The new people's atlas of the world. 1 p. l., 134 pp. incl. 57 maps, 1 pl. fol. Springfield, O., Mast, Crowell & Kirkpatrick, 1898. 1023
[Farm and fireside library, no. 110]

> NOTE.—Published at various times under titles, such as "The peerless atlas of the world. 1889." "The people's atlas of the world. 1894." "The new people's atlas of the world. 1898."

### 1898
**Matthews-Northrup co.**
Complete handy atlas of the world and city guide, containing maps of every country on the face of the globe, and the leading cities of this country . . .   239 pp. incl. 82 maps, 15 pl. 12°. Chicago, New York, Orange Judd co. [1898]   1024
  NOTE.—Copyright by the Matthews-Northrup co., 1898.

### 1898
**Rand, McNally & co.**
A household atlas of the world containing large scale colored maps of each state and territory in the United States, provinces of Canada . . .   192 pp. incl. 117 maps, 4 col. pl.   fol.   Philadelphia [etc.] J. Wanamaker, 1898.   1025
  NOTE.—Copyright by Rand, McNally & co., 1897.

### 1898
Rand, McNally & co.'s indexed atlas of the world.   2 v.   3 p. l., 9–224 pp. incl. 57 col. maps; 2 p. l., 225–464 pp. incl. 76 col. maps. fol.   Chicago and New York, Rand, McNally & co. 1898.   1026

CONTENTS.
United States.
Foreign countries.

### 1898
Rand-McNally new international indexed atlas of the world containing large scale maps of every country and civil division upon the face of the globe . . .   361 pp. incl. 129 maps.   fol.   Chicago and New York, Rand, McNally & co. 1898.   1027

### 1898
**Schrader, J. D. F., Prudent, F. P. V.** *and* **Anthoine, E.**
Atlas de géographie moderne . . . accompagnée d'un texte géographique, statistique et éthnographique et d'environ 600 cartes de détail, figures, diagrammes, etc.   2 p. l., [250] 35 [1] pp., incl. 64 col. maps.   fol.   Paris, Hachette & cie. 1898.   1028

### 1898
**Stanford, E.**
Stanford's London atlas of universal geography exhibiting the physical and political divisions of the various countries of the world. Folio edition, 2d issue, revised and enlarged.   5 p. l., 29 pp., 100 maps.   fol.   London, E. Stanford, 1898.   1029

## 1898-1899

**Matthews-Northrup co.**
 The up-to-date handy atlas of the world. [anon.] cover-title, 32 pp. incl. maps. 12°. [Buffalo, N. Y., the Matthews-Northrup co. 1898-1899] 1030

### 1899

**Andree, R.**
 Andrees allgemeiner handatlas . . . 4. völlig neubearb. und verm. aufl. Hrsg. von A. Scobel . . . 2 p. l., [179] pp., 102 col. map, 1 pl. fol. Bielfeld, Leipzig, Velhagen & Klasing, 1899. 1031

### 1899

**Chicago chronicle.**
 Unrivalled atlas of the world . . . with historical, descriptive, and statistical matter . . . Prepared and published especially for the Chicago chronicle. 4 p. l., 336 pp. incl. 123 col. maps, 33 l. fol. Chicago, New York, Rand, McNally & co. 1899. 1032

### 1899

**Cincinnati commercial tribune.**
 Unrivaled atlas of the world, containing colored maps of every country and civil division upon the face of the globe . . . with historical, descriptive and statistical matter . . . Prepared and published especially for Cincinnati commercial tribune. 2 p. l., 336 pp. incl. 123 col. maps, 32 col. pl. fol. Chicago, Rand, McNally & co. 1899. 1033

### 1899

**Fort Dearborn publishing co.**
 The national standard family and business atlas of the world specially adapted for commercial and library reference . . . 420 (*i. e.* 422) pp. incl. 103 col. maps, 5 pl. fol. Chicago, the Fort Dearborn publishing co. [1899] 1034

### 1899

**Larousse, Librairie.**
 Atlas Larousse, illustré. 3 p. l., 387 pp., 42 maps. fol. Paris, librairie Larousse [1899] 1035

### 1899

**Mast, Crowell & Kirkpatrick.**
 The new home atlas of the world . . . 164 pp. incl. 61 col. maps, 2 pl. fol. Springfield, O., Mast, Crowell & Kirkpatrick, 1899.
 [Farm and fireside library. No. 169] 1036

**1899**

**Miller, J. M.**

The twentieth century atlas of the commercial, geographical and historical world, with a description of every known land, both near and remote, ancient and modern . . . Together with useful and timely statistics, educational, industrial, military, naval. 300 pp., front., incl. 19 maps, 1 pl. fol. Chicago, Monarch book co. [1899]
1037

NOTE.—Issued also under title "The world up-to-date." By J. M. Miller. See also title 1038.

**1899**

The world up-to-date. Commercial, geographical and historical with a description of every known land, both near and remote, ancient and modern . . . Together with useful and timely statistics educational, industrial, military, naval. 300 pp., front., incl. 19 maps, 1 pl. fol. Chicago, Monarch book co. [1899]   1038

NOTE.—Issued also under title "The twentieth century atlas." By J. M. Miller. See also title 1037.

**1899**

**Minneapolis tribune.**

The Minneapolis tribune unrivaled atlas of the world, containing colored maps of every country and civil division upon the face of the globe . . . Prepared and published especially for the Minneapolis tribune. 4 p. l., 336 pp. incl. 124 col. maps. fol. Chicago and New York, Rand, McNally & co. 1899.   1039

**1899**

**Pittsburg dispatch.**

The Pittsburg dispatch universal atlas of the world containing colored maps of every country and civil division upon the face of the globe . . . Prepared and published especially for the Dispatch publishing company, Pittsburg, Pa. 344 pp. incl. 120 col. maps, 6 pls. fol. Chicago and New York, Rand, McNally & co. 1899.
1040

**1899**

**Public ledger.**

Philadelphia public ledger's unrivaled atlas of the world . . . with historical, descriptive, and statistical matter. 331 pp. incl. 119 col. maps. fol. Chicago and New York, Rand, McNally & co. 1899.   1041

**1899**

**Rand, McNally & co.**

Rand, McNally & co.'s enlarged business atlas and shippers' guide . . . 29th ed. 425 pp. incl. 95 maps. fol. Chicago, Rand, McNally & co. 1899.   1042

## 1899

Rand-McNally new standard atlas of the world containing large scale maps of every country and civil division upon the face of the globe ... Accompanied by a new and original compilation forming a ready reference index ... 373 pp. incl. plans, maps, diagr. fol. Chicago and New York, Rand, McNally & co. [1899] 1043

## 1899

Rand, McNally & co.'s universal atlas of the world. 3 p. l., 3–456 pp., front, incl. 113 col. maps. 4°. Chicago, New York, Rand, McNally & co. [1899] 1044

## 1899

**Smith, B. E.**
The century atlas of the world, prepared under the superintendence of Benjamin E. Smith. 2 p. l., xxx, [2] pp., [119] l., 402 pp. incl. 135 maps. fol. New York, the century co. [1899] 1045

## 1900?

**Bailly-Baillière & hijos.**
Atlas de las cinco partes del mundo dividido en 28 mapas en dos colores. Con los mapas de los telégrafos, correos y ferrocarriles del mundo. 51 pp. incl. 28 maps. 12°. Madrid, Bailly-Baillière & hijos [1900?] 1046

## 1900

**Andree, R.**
Andrees allgemeiner handatlas in 126 haupt- und 138 nebenkarten nebst vollständigem alphabetischem namenverzeichnis. Herausgegeben von A. Scobel. 4. aufl. 2ʳ. abdruck. 2 p. l., 186 l., 179 pp. fol. Bielefeld und Leipzig, Velhagen & Klasing, 1900. 1047

## 1900

**Crowell & Kirkpatrick co.**
The new popular atlas of the world. 238, [7] pp. incl. 66 col. maps, 2 pl. fol. Springfield, O., the Crowell & Kirkpatrick co. 1900. 1048

## 1900

**Debes, E.**
Neuer handatlas über alle teile der erde in 61 haupt- und 124 nebenkarten mit alphabetischem namenverzeichnis. 2. verm. und verb. aufl. 2. abdruck. 2 p. l., 2–4, 111, [1] pp., 52 maps. fol. Leipzig, H. Wagner & E. Debes, 1900. 1049

### 1900
**Gebbie publishing co.**
Spofford's cabinet cyclopædia atlas of the world containing large scale colored maps of each state and territory in the United States, provinces of Canada, the continents and their subdivisions . . . 2 p. l., 160 pp. incl. 117 col. maps, 3 col. pl. fol. Philadelphia, Gebbie publishing co. 1900. 1050

NOTE.—Copyright by Rand, McNally & co. 1900.

### 1900
**Hickmann, A. L.**
Prof. A. L. Hickmann's geographisch-statistischer universaltaschenatlas. Ausgabe 1900. 1 p. l., 64 pp., 24 maps, 32 pl., 9 l. at end. 16°. Wien, G. Freytag & Berndt, 1900. 1051

### 1900
**Johnston, W. & A. K.**
The world-wide atlas of modern geography, political and physical, containing one hundred and twenty-eight plates and complete index with an introduction by J. Scott Keltie . . . 5th ed. 1 p. l., xvi, 128, 94 pp., 2 front. incl. 128 col. maps. fol. Edinburgh and London, W. & A. K. Johnston, 1900. 1052

### 1900
**Meyers, H. J.**
Meyers hand-atlas. Mit 113 kartenblättern und register aller auf den karten und plänen vorkommenden namen. 2 neub. und verm. aufl. 4 p. l., ii, 210 pp., 113 maps. 8°. Leipzig und Wien, verlag des bibliographischen instituts, 1900. 1053

NOTE.—Maps from Meyers Konversations-lexikon.

### 1900
**Perthes, J.**
Justus Perthes' taschen-atlas. Volkständig neu bearbeitet von Hermann Habenicht. Mit geographisch-statistischen notizen von H. Wichmann. 38. aufl. 68 pp., 24 maps. 16°. Gotha, J. Perthes, 1900. 1054

### 1900
**Rand, McNally & co.**
Cyclopedic atlas of the world containing colored maps of every country and civil division upon the globe . . . Prepared and published especially for Henry G. Allen & company . . . New York city. 4 p. l., 336 pp. incl. 124 col. maps, 37 pls. fol. Chicago, New York, Rand, McNally & co. 1900. 1055

## 1900

Rand, McNally & co.'s enlarged business atlas and shippers guide. 30th ed.   429 pp. incl. 99 maps.   fol.   Chicago, Rand, McNally & co. 1900.   1056

## 1900

Rand-McNally pocket atlas of the world. Historical, political and commercial, etc.   381 pp. incl. 91 maps.   24°.   Chicago and New York, Rand, McNally & co. [1900]   1057

## 1900

**Spamer, O.**
Spamers grosser hand-atlas . . . enthaltend eine geographische, ethnographische und statistische beschreibung aller teile der erde von dr. Alfred Hettner . . . 2te aufl.   vii, [1], 131, [1] pp., 150 l. incl. 77 col. maps, 165 maps in text, illus.   fol.   Leipzig, O. Spamer [1900]   1058

NOTE.—The text, maps, and index are separately paged.

## 1900

**Times, The.** [London daily]
The times atlas containing 132 pages of maps, and comprising 196 maps and an alphabetical index to 150,000 names. New ed.   iv, 132, 120 pp. incl. 196 col. maps.   fol.   London, published at the office of "the Times," 1900.   1059

NOTE.—Mostly taken from and based on Andree's allgemeiner handatlas.

## 1900

**Vidal de la Blache, P.**
Atlas de géographie, physique, politique, économique, géologique, ethnographique.   2 p. l., 53–130 pp. incl. 59 col. maps.   fol.   Paris, A. Colin & cie. 1900.   1060

## 1901

**Bacon, G. W., & co.**
Bacon's new handy atlas of modern geography with index-gazetteer . . .   2 p. l., 36 pp., 31 col. maps on 48 l.   8°.   London, G. W. Bacon & co. 1901.   1061

## 1901

**Crowell & Kirkpatrick co.**
The new people's atlas of the world. New century ed.   153 pp. 1 l. incl. 63 maps, 2 pl.   fol.   Springfield, O., the Crowell & Kirkpatrick co. 1901.   1062

[Farm and fireside library, no. 195]

**1901**

**Crowell & Kirkpatrick co.**—Continued.
   The twentieth century peerless atlas and pictorial gazetteer of all lands.   1 p. l., 166 pp. incl. 63 col. maps, 2 pl.   fol.   Springfield, O., the Crowell & Kirkpatrick co. ᶜ 1901.   1063

**1901**

   The twentieth century pictorial atlas and complete gazetteer of all lands.   1 p. l., 284 pp. incl. 63 col. maps, 2 pl.   fol.   Springfield, O., the Crowell & Kirkpatrick co. ᶜ 1901.   1064

**1901**

   The twentieth century popular atlas and pictorial gazetteer of all lands.   1 p. l., 284 pp. incl. 63 maps, 2 pl.   fol.   Springfield, O., the Crowell & Kirkpatrick co. ᶜ 1901.   1065

**1901**

**Fort Dearborn publishing co.**
   The national standard family and business atlas of the world, specially adapted for commercial and library reference . . .   436 (*i. e.* 438) pp. incl. 103 col. maps, 5 pl.   fol.   Chicago, the Fort Dearborn publishing co. [ᶜ 1901]   1066

**1901**

**Rand, McNally & co.**
   Rand, McNally & co.'s universal atlas of the world.   1900 census. 4 p. l., 461 pp. incl. 121 col. maps.   4°.   Chicago-New York, Rand, McNally & co. 1901.   1067

**1901**

**Los Angeles saturday post.**
   The Los Angeles saturday post unrivalled atlas of the world, containing colored maps of every country and civil division upon the face of the globe . . .   3 p. l., 320 pp. incl. 120 col. maps, 9 pl. fol.   Chicago, Rand, McNally & co. 1901.   1067a

   NOTE.—Prepared and published especially for the Los Angeles saturday post, by Rand, McNally & co.

**1901**

**Rand, McNally & co.**
   Rand, McNally & co.'s enlarged business atlas and shippers' guide . . . 31st ed.   400 pp. incl. 100 maps.   fol.   Chicago, Rand, McNally & co. 1901.   1068

## 1901

Everybody's new census atlas of the world . . . Historical, descriptive, and statistical matter based on the latest available information . . .   1 pl., 244 pp. 1 l., incl. 77 maps, 2 pl. fol. Chicago, New York, Rand, McNally & co. 1901.   1069

## 1901

**Smith, B. E.**
The century atlas of the world, prepared under the superintendence of Benjamin E. Smith.   3 p. l., xxx, [2], 401 pp., 137 maps. fol.  New York, the century co. [1901]   1070
[The century dictionary and cyclopedia. v. 10]

## 1901

**Stieler, A.**
Stieler's hand-atlas, 100 karten in küpferstich mit 162 nebenkarten. Hrsg. von Justus Perthes' geographischer anstalt in Gotha. 9., von grund aus neubearb. und neugestochene aufl. 4 p. l., 237 pp., 98 maps, 2 pl. fol.  Gotha, J. Perthes, 1905.   1071

NOTE.—Issued in parts, 1901–1905.
See also title 1108.

## 1901

**Tunison, H. C.**
Tunison's atlas, encyclopaedia, gazetteer and portfolio of our universe, globe and nation . . .   225 pp. incl. 105 col. maps, 6 col. pl. obl. fol.   Brooklyn, Atlanta, etc., etc., H. C. Tunison, ᶜ 1901.   1072

## 1902

**Bartholomew, J. G.**
The international student's atlas of modern geography. A series of 105 physical, political, and statistical maps compiled from british and foreign surveys and the latest results of international research . . .   viii, 90 pp. incl. 86 maps, 3 pl.  1 l., 69, [1] pp.  fol. London, G. Newnes [1902]   1073

## 1902

**Cram, G. F.**
Cram's atlas of the world, ancient and modern. New census edition.—Indexed geographical, historical and statistical presentation of the world in all its divisions . . . A thoroughly revised, rewritten and newly illustrated edition by George F. Cram, editorially assisted by dr. Eugene Murray-Aaron . . .   4 p. l., 15 pp., 1 l., 11–856 pp. incl. 249 col. maps, 67 pl. fol. New York, Chicago, G. F. Cram, 1902.   1074

## 1902

Cram's ideal reference atlas of the world.  Political, historical, astronomical.  Covering every known portion of the globe, with special maps illustrating the discovery, growth, products, history

**Cram, G. F.**—Continued.

and gradual formation of the greater United States . . . 272 pp. incl. 84 col. maps, 12 pl. fol. Chicago, New York, G. F. Cram, 1902. 1075

**1902**

**Crowell publishing co.**

The twentieth century peerless atlas and pictorial gazetteer of all lands. 1 p. l., 26, 31–166, [2] pp. incl. 61 col. maps, 2 pl. fol. Springfield, O., the Crowell publishing co.ᶜ 1902. 1076

NOTE.—pp. 27–30, containing 2 maps, wanting.

**1902**

**Fort Dearborn publishing co.**

The national standard family and business atlas of the world specially adapted for commercial and library reference . . . With all populations according to 1900 census. 410 pp. incl. 98 col. maps, 4 pl. fol. Chicago, the Fort Dearborn publishing co. [ᶜ1902] 1077

**1902**

**Johnston, W. & A. K.**

The Victoria regina atlas; political, physical & astronomical, containing two hundred plates and complete index. 2d ed. 4 p. l., 150 pp. 196 maps, 4 pl. fol. Edinburgh & London, W. & A. K. Johnston, ltd. 1902. 1078

**1902**

**Rand, McNally & co.**

Rand, McNally & co.'s indexed atlas of the world, with 275 illustrations. Historical, descriptive, statistical. [Rev. ed.] 2 v. 288 pp. incl. 61 maps; 4 l. unp., 289–547 pp. incl. 53 maps. fol. Chicago, Rand, McNally & co. [1902] 1079

NOTE.—Index to West Indies in v. 1.

CONTENTS.

v. 1. United States.
v. 2. Foreign countries.

**1902**

**Smith, B. E.**

The century atlas of the world, prepared under the superintendence of Benjamin E. Smith. 3 p. l., xxx, [2], 401 pp., 137 maps. fol. New York, the century co. [1902] 1080

NOTE.—Separate publication.

**1903**

**Bartholomew, J. G.**

The xxᵗʰ century citizen's atlas of the world, containing 156 pages of maps and plans with an index, a gazetteer and geographical statistics edited. xvi, 69, [3], 133, [1] pp. front., 78 maps on 156 l. fol. London, G. Newnes [1903] 1081

## 1903
**Cram, G. F.**
A complete atlas of the world, containing a series of 106 newly engraved maps, covering every portion of the globe, including special maps of our new possessions, accompanied by a complete index giving locations and area of all divisions. 1903. Published expressly for the northern trust company bank. 112 pp. incl. 106 maps. 12°. Chicago, for the northern trust company bank, 1903. 1082

NOTE.—Copyright by George F. Cram.
Maps same as those in title 1084.

## 1903
Cram's handy reference atlas of the world containing a complete series of 106 newly engraved maps, covering every portion of the globe. Including special maps of our new possessions. Accompanied by a complete index giving location and area of all divisions. 176 pp. incl. 106 maps, 41 pl. 12°. New York, Chicago, G. F. Cram, 1903. 1083

## 1903
**Crowell publishing co.**
The twentieth century peerless atlas and pictorial gazetteer of all lands. 1 p. l., 166, [2] pp. incl. 63 maps, 2 pl. fol. Springfield, O., the Crowell publishing co. 1903. 1084

## 1903
**Encyclopædia britannica.**
The new volumes of the Encyclopædia britannica constituting in combination with the existing volumes of the ninth edition, the tenth edition of that work and also supplying a new, distinctive, and independent library of reference dealing with recent events and developments. The tenth of the new volumes, being volume 34 of the complete work. Maps. vii, [2], 497, [1] pp., 124 col. maps. fol. Edinburgh, London, A. & C. Black, 1903. 1085

## 1903
**Funk & Wagnalls co.**
A standard atlas of the world . . . with a convenient marginal reference index also a condensed cyclopedia giving a descriptive and statistical manual of the principal features of the various nations. xxi-xxiv, xxiva-xxivd, xxv-cxl pp. incl. 75 col. maps. fol. New York, London [etc.] Funk & Wagnalls co. 1903. 1086

**1903**

**Johnston, W. & A. K.**
The unrivalled atlas of modern geography for schools and families. Forty maps with index to twenty two thousand names contained in the atlas. 23d ed. 1 p. l., 35, [1], 4, [4] pp., 40 maps. fol. Edinburgh and London, W. & A. K. Johnston, l^td. [1903]
1087

**1903**

**Rand, M°Nally & co.**
Rand, M?Nally & co.'s enlarged business atlas and shippers guide containing large scale maps of all states and territories in the United States, the dominion of Canada, the republic of Mexico, Central America, the West Indies, Cuba, Porto Rico, Hawaii, the Philippines and China . . . Together with complete reference maps of all countries . . . 33d ed. 453 pp., incl. 102 maps. fol. Chicago, Rand. M°Nally & co. 1903.
1088

**1903**

**Turner, C. H.**
The twentieth century peerless atlas and pictorial gazetteer of all lands. [anon.] 2 p. l., 3–166 pp., 1 l. incl. 63 col. maps, 2 pl. fol. Springfield, O., the Crowell publishing co. [1903]
1089

NOTE.—First published with title "Peerless atlas of the world." Afterwards, "The dollar atlas of the world."

**1904**

**Andree, R.**
Andree's allgemeiner handatlas in 126 haupt- und 139 nebenkarten nebst vollständigem alphabetischem namenverzeichnis. 4^te völlig neubearb. und verm. aufl. . . . Hrsg von A. Scobel . . . 2 p. l., 183 [1] pp., 102 col. maps, 2 pl. fol. Bielefeld und Leipzig, Velhagen & Klasing, 1904.
1089a

**1904**

**Cram, G. F.**
The success handy reference atlas and gazetteer of the world. Containing 105 newly engraved maps and over 40,000 index entries with the latest areas and census statistics . . . edited by dr. Eugene Murray-Aaron. vii, [1], 219–574 pp., 105 fold. maps on 211 pp. 24°. New York, the success company, 1904.
1090

**1904**

**Northern trust company bank.**
A complete atlas of the world, containing every portion of the globe. Including special maps of our new possessions. Accompanied by a complete index giving locations and area of all divisions.

1904. 112 pp. incl. 106 maps. 12°. Chicago, the northern trust company bank, 1904. 1091

NOTE.—Maps copyrighted by Geo. F. Cram.

### 1904
**Rand, McNally & co.**

Rand, McNally & co.'s enlarged business atlas and shippers' guide, containing large scale maps of all states and territories in the United States, of the Dominion of Canada, the republic of Mexico, Central America, the West Indies, Cuba, Porto Rico, Hawaii, the Philippines, and China, showing in detail all existing railroad systems . . . accompanied by a new and original ready-reference shippers' index . . . also alphabetical indexes of steamboat and steamship lines and electric railroads . . . Complete reference maps of all countries . . . 34th ed.   391 pp. incl. 103 maps.  fol.   Chicago, Rand, McNally & co. 1904. 1092

### 1904
**Smith, B. E.**

The century atlas of the world, prepared under the superintendence of Benjamin E. Smith.   3 p. l., xxx pp., 1 l. incl. 16 maps, 401 pp., 120 maps.  fol.  New York, the century co. [1904]   1093
[The century dictionary and cyclopedia.  v. 10]

### 1904
**Stanford, E.**

Stanford's London atlas of universal geography, exhibiting the physical and political divisions of the various countries of the world . . .  3d ed. rev. and enl.   5 p. l., [2] 2-29 pp., 110 (*i. e.* 98) col. maps.  fol.   London, E. Stanford, 1904. 1094

NOTE.—First edition published 1887. See title 944.

Contains fine series of maps of London and its environs.

### 1904-1905
**Marks, A. F.**

Большой всемірный настольный Атласъ Маркса. Подъ редакціей . . . Э. Ю. Петри и Ю. М. Шокальскаго. 12 pts. in 1 v. fol. С.-Петербургъ, А. Ф. Марксъ [1904-]1905.—[Large general table atlas. Edited by . . . E. Y. Petri and Y. M. Shokalsky. St. Petersburg, A. F. Marks, 1904-1905] 1095

NOTE.—"The maps of the russian empire, nineteen in number, are entirely new; but the plates of the well-known atlas published by Wagner & Debes, of Leipzig . . . form the basis of most of the others . . ."

"As in Debes' atlas, the maps are printed in colours; and on all of them the depths of the water adjacent to the coast-line is shown by different tints of blue."—Geographical journal. February, 1904. London, 1904. v. 23, no. 2, pp. 279-280.

### 1905
**Bartholomew, J. G.**
The century atlas of the world; a series of sixty-six maps, with general index and geographical statistics. 2 p. l., [44] pp., front., incl. 66 (*i. e.* 43) maps, 1 pl. 1 l., 44 pp. fol. London, J. Walker & co., ltd. 1905. 1096

NOTE.—Frontispiece shows flags of all nations.

### 1905
The handy shilling atlas of the world. New rev. ed. viii, 160 pp., 120 (*i. e.* 97) maps. 24°. London, G. Newness [1905] 1097

NOTE.—First published in 1903.

### 1905
Physical & political. 3d. ed. rev. and impr. 2 p. l., front., 27 pp., 64 pp. incl. 60 col. maps, 1 col. pl. 4°. London, Meiklejohn & Holden [1905] 1098
[Meiklejohn's geographical series]

### 1905
**Crowell publishing co.**
The twentieth century peerless atlas and pictorial gazetteer of all lands. 1 p. l., 166, [4] pp. incl. 65 col. maps, 3 pl. fol. Springfield, O., the Crowell publishing co. °1905. 1099

### 1905
**Debes, E.**
Neuer handatlas über alle teile der erde in 61 haupt- und 124 nebenkarten mit alphabetischem namen-verzeichnis . . . 3$^{te}$ verb. aufl. 2 p. l., 4 pp., 52 col. maps. fol. Leipzig, H. Wagner & E. Debes, 1905. 1099a

NOTE.—Index, 114, [1] pp., in pocket at end.

### 1905
**Funk & Wagnalls co.**
A standard atlas of the world containing large colored maps of the world, the continents and their subdivisions, including each state and territory of the United States, and maps of Canada, central Europe, the Balkan states, the British Isles, Germany, Japan, Russia, Australia, etc; also maps of Washington, Boston, Chicago, New York city and vicinity, Philadelphia, etc. With a condensed cyclopedia giving a descriptive and statistical manual of the principal features of the various nations. xx$^a$–xx$^h$, xxi–cxl, [3], (*i. e.* 133) pp. incl. 96 col. maps. 4°. New York & London, Funk & Wagnalls co. 1905. 1100

NOTE.—First published in 1903. See title 1086.

### 1905
**Hammond, C. S. & co.**
Hammond's modern atlas of the world. A new series of physical, political and historical maps compiled from government surveys and exhibiting the latest results of geographical research. Accompanied by an index-gazetteer of the principal towns of the world. 1 p. l., 149 pp. incl. 94 maps, 2 diagrs. fol. New York, C. S. Hammond & co. 1905. 1101

### 1905
Hammond's pictorial atlas of the world. A new series of over one hundred maps in colors, based upon the latest official surveys; and accompanied by an index-gazetteer of cities and towns and a descriptive gazetteer of the states, countries and physical features of the globe . . . 256 pp. incl. 97 col. maps, 2 pl. fol. New York, C. S. Hammond & co. 1905. 1102

### 1905
**Johnston, A. K.**
The royal atlas of modern geography exhibiting, in a series of entirely original and authentic maps the present condition of geographical discovery and research in the several countries, empires, and states of the world. By the late Alexander Keith Johnston . . . With additions and corrections to the present date by G. H. Johnston . . . With a special index to each map. New edition. 6 p. l., [184] pp., front. (map), 56 fold. maps. fol. Edinburgh and London, W. & A. K. Johnston, 1905. 1103

### 1905
**Meyers, H. J.**
Meyers geographischer hand-atlas. 3$^{te}$ neubearb. und verm. aufl. Mit 115 kartenblättern, 5 textbeilagen und alphabetischem register aller auf den karten und plänen vorkommenden namen. 4 p. l., [262] pp., 115 (*i. e.* 114) col. maps. 4°. Leipzig und Wien, bibliographisches institut, 1905. 1103a

NOTE.—Various paging.
Maps from Meyers's Konversations-lexikon.

### 1905
**Rand, McNally & co.**
General atlas of the world containing colored maps showing every country and civil division upon the face of the globe. Statistical matter giving area and population of the leading countries of the world. Special ready reference lists showing all places in the United States. 1 p. l., 146 pp., 1 l. incl. 80 maps, 2 pl. fol. Chicago-New York, Rand, McNally & co. 1905. 1104

### 1905

**Rand, McNally & co.**—Continued.

Rand, McNally & co.'s enlarged business atlas and shippers' guide . . . 35th ed.　　xxxv, [1], 319 (*i. e.* 355) pp. incl. 106 maps. fol.　Chicago, Rand, McNally & co. 1905.　　1105

Note.—Slight changes in title.

### 1905

Rand, McNally & co.'s indexed atlas of the world with 275 illustrations.　Historical—descriptive—statistical . . .　2 v. fol. Chicago, London [etc.] Rand, McNally & co. [1905]　　1106

Note.—Paged continuously; v. 1, 1 p. l., 274, (*i. e.* 382) pp. incl. 67 col. maps; v. 2, viii, 275–527, (*i. e.* 277) pp. incl. 55 col. maps.

CONTENTS.

v. 1. United States.
" 2. Foreign countries.

### 1905

Rand, McNally & co.'s new imperial atlas of the world containing large scale colored maps of each state and territory in the United States, provinces of Canada, the continents and their subdivisions. A ready reference marginal index is shown upon the maps of all the countries of the earth.　2 p. l., 172 pp. incl. 121 maps, 2 pl.　fol. Chicago-New York, Rand, McNally & co. 1905.　　1107

### 1905

**Stieler, A.**

Stielers hand-atlas, 100 karten in kupferstich mit 162 nebenkarten. Hrsg. von Justus Perthes' geographischer anstalt in Gotha. 9., von grund aus neubearb. und neugestochene aufl.　4 p. l., 237 pp., 98 maps, 2 pl. fol. Gotha, J. Perthes, 1905.　　1108

Note.—Issued in parts. 1901–1905.

### 1906

**Cram, G. F.**

Cram's quick reference atlas and gazetteer of the world. Containing 105 newly engraved maps and over 40,000 index entries, with the latest areas and census statistics . . . ed. by dr. Eugene Murray-Aaron . . .　vii, [8]–218, [356] pp. incl. 105 col. maps. 24°.　New York, Chicago, G. F. Cram [ᶜ1906]　　1109

### 1906

Cram's superior reference atlas of Illinois and the world.　158 pp. incl. 61 maps, 17 pl.　fol.　New York, Chicago, G. F. Cram, ᶜ1906.　　1110

## 1906

**Hammond, C. S. & co.**
The ready reference atlas of the world.   cover-title, 16 maps. fol.   New York, C. S. Hammond & co. [ᶜ1906]   1111

## 1906

**Rand, McNally & co.**
Rand, McNally & co.'s enlarged business atlas and shippers' guide, containing large scale maps of all states and territories, in the United States of the Dominion of Canada, the republic of Mexico, Central America, the West Indies, Cuba, Porto Rico, Hawaii, the Philippines, Japan and China, showing in detail all existing railroad systems . . . accompanied by a new and original ready-reference shippers' index . . . also alphabetical indexes of steamboat and steamship lines and electric railroads . . . Complete reference maps of all countries . . .   37th. ed.   xxxv, [1], 333 (*i. e.* 369) pp. incl. 101 maps, diagr.   fol.   Chicago, Rand, McNally & co. [1906]   1112

## 1906

**Smith, B. E.**
The century atlas of the world, prepared under the superintendence of Benjamin E. Smith . . .   3 p. l., xxx, 402 pp., 134 col. maps, 2 col. pl.   fol.   New York, the century co. [1906]   1112a
[The century dictionary and cyclopedia. v. 10]

## 1907

**Andree, R.**
Andree's allgemeiner handatlas in 139 haupt- und 161 nebenkarten nebst vollständigem alphabetischem namenverzeichnis.  5ᵗᵉ völlig. neubearb. und verm. aufl. jubiläumsausgabe.   Hrsg. von.' A. Scobel . . .   2 p. l., 186 [1] pp., 108 col. maps, 1 pl.   fol.   Bielefeld und Leipzig, Velhagen & Klasing, 1907.   1112b

## 1907

**Collier, P. F., & son.**
The new encyclopedic atlas and gazetteer of the world (now first published).  Containing an entirely new series of colored maps . . . showing every country and all political or civil divisions . . . also an index gazetteer of the world . . . and a complete physical, commercial and historical analysis of the United States . . .   348 pp., front. (map), 98 col. maps, illus. (incl. maps, pl.)   fol.   New York, P. F. Collier & son, 1907.   1113

NOTE.—Contains numerous plans and views of cities.

**Cram, G. F.**

### 1907

Army and navy edition of Cram's quick reference atlas and gazetteer of the world . . . Containing 111 newly engraved maps and over 42,000 index entries with the latest areas and census statistics. Edited by dr. Eugene Murray-Aaron.   vii, [8], 155 (*i. e.* 259), [367 pp. incl. 111 maps.   24°.   New York, Chicago, G. F. Cram [°1907]
1114

### 1907

Cram's atlas of the world, ancient and modern. Geographical, historical and statistical presentation of the world in all its divisions . . . A thoroughly revised, rewritten, and newly illustrated edition by George F. Cram, editorially assisted by dr. Eugene Murray-Aaron . . .   4 p. l., 16, [9]–856 (*i. e.* 886) pp. incl. 247 col. maps, illus.   fol.   New York, Chicago, G. F. Cram, °1907.
1115

### 1907

Cram's ideal reference atlas of the world.   368 pp. incl. 82 col. maps, 13 pl., 5 diagr.   fol.   New York, Chicago, G. F. Cram, °1907.
1116

### 1907

Cram's modern atlas. The new unrivaled . . . A thoroughly revised, rewritten, and newly illustrated edition by George F. Cram, editorially assisted by dr. Eugene Murray-Aaron . . .   774 (*i. e.* 792) pp. incl. 175 col. maps.   illus.   fol.   New York, Chicago, G. F. Cram, °1907.
1117

### 1907

Cram's standard american railway system atlas of the world. Showing all the railway systems in colors and numbers, express companies doing business over each road, and all banking towns indicated plainly on face of maps. Accompanied by a concise and original ready reference index of the United States, Canada, Mexico and Cuba . . .   628, [22] pp. incl. 152 maps.   fol.   New York, Chicago, G. F. Cram, 1907.
1118

### 1907

Cram's superior reference atlas of Iowa and the world.   159 pp. incl. 68 col. maps, 21 pl.   (1 fold. maps)   fol.   New York, Chicago, G. F. Cram, 1907.
1119

### 1907

Cram's superior reference atlas of Kansas and the world. 160 pp. incl. 68 maps, 24 pl., 1 fold. map.   fol.   New York, Chicago, G. F. Cram, °1907.   1120

NOTE.—pp. 136–160 relate to Kansas.

### 1907

Cram's superior reference atlas of Minnesota and the world. 160, [2] pp., front., incl. 68 maps, 31 pl.   fol.   New York, Chicago, G. F. Cram, °1907.   1121

NOTE.—pp. 136–160 relate to Minnesota.

### 1907

Cram's unabridged atlas of the world. Indexed. A specially prepared atlas . . . with maps of all the american, european, asian, african and oceanic lands . . . Also giving the latest obtainable populations . . . To which is added an encyclopedia of geography . . . edited and revised by dr. Eugene Murray-Aaron . . . 700 (*i. e.* 698) pp. incl. 158 maps. illus.   fol.   New York, Chicago, G. F. Cram [1907]   1122

### 1907

**Hammond, C. S. & co.**

Hammond's handy atlas of the world. Containing new maps of each state and territory in the United States and every country in the world.   105 pp., incl. 66 maps, 4 pl.   8°.   New York, C. S. Hammond & co. 1907.   1123

### 1907

**Rand, McNally & co.**

New atlas of the state of Minnesota [and the world]   100 pp. incl. 42 maps, 3 pl., 3 tab., 1 facs. (2 fold. maps)   fol.   Chicago-New York, Rand, McNally & co. 1907.   1124

NOTE.—Copyright 1906.
pp. 53–59 only relate to Minnesota.

### 1907

Rand, McNally & co.'s enlarged business atlas and shippers' guide, containing large-scale maps of all states and territories, in the United States of the Dominion of Canada, the Republic of Mexico, Central America, the West Indies, Cuba, Porto Rico, Hawaii, the Philippines, Japan, and China, showing in detail all existing railroad systems . . . accompanied by a new and original ready-reference

**Rand, McNally & co.**—Continued.

shippers' index . . . also alphabetical indexes of steamboat and steamship lines and electric railroads . . . Complete reference maps of all countries . . . 38th ed.    379 (*i. e.* 411) pp. incl. 109 maps, diagr.    fol.  Chicago, Rand, McNally & co. 1907.    1125

### 1907

Rand, McNally & co.'s indexed atlas of the world with 275 illustrations.    Historical—descriptive—statistical . . .    2 v.    fol. Chicago, London [etc.] Rand, McNally & co. 1907.    1126

CONTENTS.

v. 1. United States.  298 (*i. e.* 406) pp. incl. 70 col. maps, 1 diagr.
" 2. Foreign countries.  1 p. l., 265 (*i. e.* 289) pp. incl. 59 col. maps.

### 1907

**Schrader, F.,** *i. e.* **J. D. F.**

Atlas de géographie moderne.  Contenant 64 cartes doubles imprimées en couleurs, accompagnées au verso d'un texte géographique, statistique et ethnographique avec 600 cartes de détail et d'un index alphabétique d'environ 50,000 noms.  Nouv. éd. corr. et mise à jour. 2 p. l., 43 [1] pp., 64 fold. maps.    fol.  Paris, Hachette & cie. 1907.
1126a
NOTE:—See also title 968.

### 1907

**Sipman, F.**

Ergänzungsheft für haus- und schulatlanten.  Globus-karte. Weltkarte in teilkarten in einheitlichem flächenmassstabe mit einer statistischen tabelle der selbständigen staaten und der deutschen kolonien.    cover-title, 10 pp., 1 fold. map.  fol.  Berlin, D. Reimer, 1907.    1126b

NOTE.—Text on inside covers.

### 1908?

**Bartholomew, J. G.**

The xx[th] century citizen's atlas of the world containing 156 pages of maps and plans with an index, a gazetteer, and geographical statistics.    [Revised ed.]    xvi, 69, [3], 133, [1] pp., front., 78 maps on 156 l.  fol.  London, G. Newnes [1908?]    1127

NOTE.—First edition published 1903. See title 1081.

### 1908?

**Kopp, J.**

Kopp's taschen-weltatlas . . . cover-title, 20 col. maps.  32°. München, J. Kopp [1908?]    1128

NOTE.—In portfolio.
Text on the reverse of maps.

## 1908

**Cram, G. F.**
Cram's modern atlas of the world . . . A thoroughly revised, rewritten, and newly illustrated edition by George F. Cram, editorially assisted by dr. Eugene Murray-Aaron . . . 774 (*i. e.* 804) pp. incl. 191 col. maps, illus. fol. New York, Chicago, G. F. Cram, ᶜ1908. 1129

## 1908

Cram's standard american railway system atlas of the world . . . Accompanied by a concise and original ready reference index of the United States, Canada, Mexico and Cuba . . . 610, [32] pp. incl. 152 col. maps. fol. New York, Chicago, G. F. Cram, 1908. 1130

## 1908

Cram's superior reference atlas of California, Nevada and the world. 164 pp. incl. 68 col. maps, 3 col. pl., 1 fold. map. fol. Chicago, New York, for E. A. Davis by G. F. Cram, ᶜ1908. 1131

## 1908

Cram's superior reference atlas of Michigan and the world. 160 pp. incl. 68 col. maps, 3 pl., illus. fol. New York, Chicago, G. F. Cram, ᶜ1908. 1131a

## 1908

Cram's superior reference atlas of Missouri and the world. 160 pp. incl. 68 col. maps, 3 col. pl. sm. fol. New York, Chicago, G. F. Cram, ᶜ1908. 1131b

## 1908

Cram's superior reference atlas of Nebraska and the world. 162 pp. incl. 77 col. maps, 3 pl., illus. fol. New York, Chicago, G. F. Gram, ᶜ1908. 1131c

## 1908

Cram's superior reference atlas of Oklahoma and the world. 160 pp. incl. 68 col. maps, 3 pl., illus. fol. New York, Chicago, G. F. Cram, ᶜ1908. 1131d

## 1908

Cram's superior reference atlas of Wisconsin and the world. 2 p. l., 160 pp. incl. 66 col. maps, 3 pl., illus. fol. New York, Chicago, G. F. Cram, ᶜ1908. 1131e

## 1908

**Harmsworth, The,** atlas and gazetteer. 500 maps and diagrams in colour, with commercial statistics and gazetteer index of 105,000 names. 4 p. l., viii, 32, 284 pp., 210 l. incl. 116 col. maps, pls., diagr. fol. London, published at Carmelite house [1908]    1132
NOTE.—Issued in 36 fortnightly parts.
Maps printed by Geo. Philip & son, ltd.

## 1908

**Rand, McNally & co.**
Rand, McNally & co.'s enlarged business atlas and shippers' guide, containing large-scale maps of all states and territories, in the United States, of the dominion of Canada, the republic of Mexico, Central America, the West Indies, Cuba, Porto Rico, Hawaii, the Philippines, Japan, and China . . . 39th ed.    397 pp. incl. 106 col. maps, diagr. fol. Chicago, Rand, McNally & co. 1908.
   1132a

## 1908

Rand, McNally & co.'s new ideal state and county survey and atlas containing a large county and railway map of Indiana printed in colors, also . . . a new, complete and ready reference index to the state of Indiana . . .    104 pp. incl. 70 col. maps, 3 col. pl., 2 diagr. (2 col. fold. maps) sm. fol. Chicago, New York, Rand, McNally & co. 1908.    1132b

## 1908

**Vidal de La Blache, P.**
Atlas général Vidal-Lablache . . .    3 p. l., 131 (*i. e.* 191), 44 pp. incl. 149 col. maps. sm. fol. Paris, A. Colin, 1908.    1133
NOTE.—At head of title: Histoire et géographie.

---

## AMERICA.

### HISTORICAL.

**Bennet, R. G.,** *and* **Wijk Roelandszoon, J. van.**
Verhandeling over de Nederlandsche ontdekkingen in Amerika, Australië, de Indiën en de Poollanden, en de namen, welke weleer aan dezelve door Nederlanders zijn gegeven, door R. G. Bennet en J. van Wijk, Roeldz. . . . Atlas.   cover-title, 8 maps. fol. Utrecht, J. Altheer, 1827.    1134
NOTE.—Atlas accompanying this work is in roll, with title: Atlas behoorende tot de Verhandeling van R. G. Bennet en J. van Wijk, Roelandsz, wegens de

Nederlandsche ontdekkingen, bekroond door het provinciaal Utrechtsch genootschap van kunsten en wetenschappen en opgedragen aan hetzelve genootschap. Dordrecht. J. de Vos & comp. 1829.
Maps described in the " Verhandeling," pp. 187-215.
List of maps given on a " Bericht " attached to map no. [1]

CONTENTS.

no. [1] Spitsbergen.
" [2-3] Kaart der Noodelyke yszee . . . Insets: Nederlandsche ontdekkingen langs de kust van Oost-Groenland . . . van kapt. Scoresby, in 1822.—Mauritius, of Jan Mayen eil, 1611.—Enkhúizen of eil. Waaigat . . .
" [4] Kaart van Nieuw Nederland . . .
" [5] " " straat Magellaan, straat le Maire, het Vuurland en kaap Hoorn. Inset: Kaart van het Dirk Gerrits land . . . Nieuw Suid Shetland.
" [6-a] Kaart van Nieuw Holland, Nieuw Guinea en omliggende eilanden . . .
" [6-b] Kaart der Vriendelyke eilanden . . .
" [6-c] Stille zuid zee no. 2. Inset: Nieuw Zeeland ontdekt door Tasman, 1642.
" [7] Kaart van Japan . . .

REPRODUCTIONS.

**Kohl, J. G.**
Die beiden ältesten general-karten von Amerika. Ausgeführt in den jahren 1527 und 1529 auf befehl kaiser Karl's v. Im besitz der grossherzoglichen bibliothek zu Weimar. 2 pts. in 1 v. x, 185 pp., 2 fold. maps. fol. Weimar, geographisches institut, 1860. 1135

NOTE.—Erster theil: Allgemeine untersuchungen über die beiden karten. Zweiter theil: Specielle analyse der beiden karten.
Only the parts of the two maps relating to America have been reproduced in facsimile.
Map no. 1, entitled, "Carta universal, en que se contiene todo lo, que del mundo se a descubierto fasta aora hizola un cosmographo de su majestad anno M.D.XVII en Sevilla" is attributed by Kohl to Hernando Colon, son of Christopher Columbus.
Map no. 2 is entitled, "Carta universal en que se contiene todo lo que del mundo se ha descubierto fasta agora: Hizola Diego Ribero cosmographo de su majestad: año de 1529. La qual se devide en dos partes conforme a la capitulaçiõ que hizieron los catholicos reyes de españa, y el rey don Juan de portugal ẽ la villa de Tordesillas: año de 1494."

**Kretschmer, K.**
Die entdeckung Amerika's in ihrer bedeutung für die geschichte des weltbildes . . . Mit einem atlas von 40 tafeln in farbendruck. 471 pp. Atlas. 4 p. l., [6] pp., 93 maps. fol. Berlin, W. H. Kühl [etc.] 1892. 1136

NOTE.—Added title: Festschrift der gesellschaft für erdkunde zu Berlin zur vierhundertjährigen feier der entdeckung Amerika's.
Atlas has title: Die entdeckung Amerika's . . . Hierzu ein text band.
Added title: Atlas der festschrift . . .

**Kretschmer, K.**—Continued.

Compiled under the direction of baron Ferdinand von Richthofen, president of the Berlin geographical society.

Dedicated to the emperor of Germany and king of Prussia, Wilhelm II.

Contains the history of the evolution of geography from the time of Strabo to the 16th century.

Twenty-four of the plates are exact reproductions of the originals, not published heretofore. The remaining 16 have been reconstructed or reduced in size. See "Vorwort."

CONTENTS.

Tafel I. Rekonstruirte weltkarten der alten.
  no. 1. Lage der oikumene nach Strabo.
  " 2. Weltkarte nach Pomponius Mela.
  " 3. Weltkarte des Ptolemaeus.
  " 4. Schema des weltbildes nach Macrobius.
  " 5. Erdglobus nach Krates von Mallos.
—— II. Arabische weltkarten.
  no. 1. Weltkarte des Abu Ishak al Farsi al Istachri (um 950) Nach Reinaud.
  " 2. Weltkarte des Abu-Abdallah Muhammad al-Edrisi (1154) Nach Lelewel.
  " 3. Weltkarte des Omar ben Mutfir ibn al Wardi (1349) Nach Lelewel.
—— III. Mittelalterliche weltkarten.
  no. 1. Weltkarte des Kosmas Indikopleustes. VI. jahrhundert. Nach dem codex Laurentianus.
  " 2. Weltkarte von Alby. VIII. jahrhundert. Nach Marinelli.
  " 3. Weltkarte von Saint Sever. XI. jahrhundert. Nach Cortambert.
  " 4. Weltkarte des Ranulfus Hyggeden. XIV. jahrhundert. Nach Santarem.
  " 5. Genuesische weltkarte, 1447. Nach Lelewel.
  " 6. Weltkarte aus eimen Leipziger kodex. XI. jahrhundert. Nach Neumann.
  " 7. Weltkarte des Guido. XII. jahrhundert. Nach Santarem.
  " 8. Weltkarte des Richard von Haldingham. XIII. jahrhundert. Nach Kiepert.
  " 9. Weltkarte von St. Denis. XIV. jahrhundert. Nach Lelewel.
  " 10. Weltkarte des Petrus Vesconte, 1320. Nach dem original.
  " 11. Weltkarte Borgia, nach 1410. Nach Lelewel.
  " 12. Weltkarte des Andreas Bianco. Nach dem original.
  " 13. Weltkarte aus einem kodex der Markus-bibliotek zu Venedig. Nach dem original.
  " 14. Weltkarte des Adreas Walsperger. Nach dem original.
  " 15. Weltkarte des fra Mauro. Nach Kiepert.
—— IV. Die Atlantische küste Europa's auf karten des XV. und XVI. jahrhunderts.
  no. 1. Karte des Graciosus Beninca&ssa;, 1482 (Universitätsbibliotek zu Bologna) Nach dem original.
  " 2. Karte des Andreas Bianco von 1436 (Markusbibliothek zu Venedig) Nach dem original.
  " 3. Aus dem atlas des Jaume Olives von Mallorca, 1514 (Biblioteca nazionale zu Florenz) Nach dem original.
  " 4. Karte des jüngeren Zeno, 1558. Nach Winsor.
  " 5. Karte des Matheus Prunes, 1553. (Biblioteca comunale zu Siena) Nach dem original.

no. 6. Karte de Matheus Prunes, 1553. (Biblioteca comunale zu Siena) Nach dem original.
" 7. Aus dem atlas eines anonymus des XVI. jahrhunderts. (Markusbibliotek zu Venedig). Nach dem original.
" 8. Karte eines katalanen des XV. jahrhunderts. (Biblioteca nationale zu Neapel) Nach dem original.

Tafel v. Karte des Bartolomeo Pareto, 1455. (Biblioteca Vittorio Emanuele zu Rom) Nach dem original.

—— VI. Karten vom Atlantischen ocean vor Columbus.
no. 1. Toscannelli's karte. Rekonstruirt.
" 2. Globus des Martin Behaim, 1492. Nach Ghillany.

—— VII. Aelteste karte von Amerika, gezeichnet von Juan de la Cosa im jahre 1500. Nach Jomard.

—— VIII. Karten von Amerika aus dem ersten jahrzehnt des XVI. jahrhunderts.
no. 1. Karte des Nicolaus de Canerio, nach 1502. Nach Gallois.
" 2. Karte eines anonymus, nach 1502. Nach Kunstmann.

—— IX. Karten von Amerika aus dem ersten jahrzehnt des XVI. jahrhunderts.
no. 1. Karte des Salvat de Pilestrina, 1503–1504. Nach Kunstmann.
" 2. Karte des Pedro Reinel, 1505. Nach Kunstmann.
" 3. Karte des Johannes Ruysch aus der Ptolemaeus-ausgabe von 1508. Nach dem originaldruck.

—— x. Karten von Amerika aus dem zweiten jahrzehnt des XVI. jahrhunderts.
no. 1. Karte des Bernardus Sylvanus in der Ptolemaeus-ausgabe von 1511. Nach dem originaldruck.
" 2. Karte des Joannes de Stobnicza, 1512. Nach Nordenskiöld.
" 3. Karte aus der ersten ausgabe der Decas Oceani des Petrus Martyr. Nach Schumacher.
" 4. Karte aus der Margarita philosophica des Gregorius Reisch, 1515. Nach dem originaldruck.

—— XI. Karten von Amerika aus dem zweiten jahrzehnt des XVI. jahrhunderts.
no. 1. Lenox-Globus (um 1510-1512) Nach de Costa.
" 2. Globus-Karte des Ludovicus Boulenger, 1514. Nach Nordenskiöld.
" 3. Globus-Karte des Leonardo da Vinci (um 1515) Nach Wieser.
" 4. Globus des Johannes Schöner, 1515. Nach Wieser.

—— XII. Karten von Amerika aus dem zweiten jahrzehnt des XVI. jahrhunderts.
no. 1. Tabula Terrae Novae aus der Ptolemaeus—ausgabe von 1513. Nach Varnhagen.
" 2. Portugiesische karte (vor 1520) Nach Kuntsmann.

—— XIII. Globus des Johannes Schöner vom Jahre 1520. Nach Ghillany.

—— XIV. Karten von Amerika aus dem dritten und vierten jahrzehnt des XVI. jahrhunderts.
no. 1. Karte des Laurentius Frisius, 1522. Nach dem originaldruck.
" 2. Karte des Robert Thorne, 1527. Nach Nordenskiöld.
" 3. Karte des Simon Grynaeus, 1532. Nach dem originaldruck.
" 4. Karte des Benedetto Bordone, 1528. Nach dem originaldruck.
" 5. Weltkarte des Pietro Coppo, 1528. Nach dem originaldruck.
" 6. Karte des Mexikanischen golfes (nach Pineda?) Nach Navarrete.
" 7. Karte des Visconte Maggiolo, 1527. Nach dem original.

—— XV. Karte des Diego Ribero vom jahre 1529. Nach Kohl.

—— XVI. Karte des Sebastian Cabot vom jahre 1544. Nach Jomard.

**Kretschmer, K.**—Continued.
 Tafel xvii. Karte Heinrich's ii von Frankreich, gezeichnet von Pierre Desceliers zu Arques im jahre 1546. Nach Jomard.
 —— xviii. Angeblicher kontinental-zusammenhang zwischen Amerika und Asien.
 no. 1. Aus dem atlas des Vaz Dourado, 1580. Nach Kunstmann.
 " 2. Weltkarte des Franciscus Monachus, 1526. Nach dem originaldruck.
 " 3. Weltkarte aus der Ptolemaeus-ausgabe von 1548. Nach dem originaldruck.
 " 4. Weltkarte des Giovanni Battista Caloiro e Oliva, 1673 (Biblioteca nazionale zu Neapel). Nach dem original.
 " 5. Karte des Battista Agnese (Biblioteca nazionale zu Neapel) Nach dem original.
 —— xix. Amerika, ein eigener weltteil.
 " 1. Karte des Sebastian Münster, 1540. Nach dem originaldruck.
 " 2. Karte aus der Cosmographia des Petrus Apianus, 1551. Nach dem originaldruck.
 " 3. Zaltieri's karte, 1566. Nach dem originaldruck.
 " 4. Karte eines Nürnberger anonymus. Nach Nordenskiöld.
 " 5. Karte des Cornelius de Judaeis, 1593. Nach dem originaldruck.
 " 6. Wytfliet's karte, 1597. Nach dem originaldruck.
 —— xx. Aus dem atlas des Angelus Eufredutius von Ancona, 1556 (Biblioteca comunale zu Mantua) Nach dem original.
 —— xxi. Aus dem atlas des Angelus Eufredutius von Ancona, 1556 (Biblioteca comunale zu Mantua) Nach dem original.
 —— xxii. Aus dem atlas des griechen Georgio Sideri, genannt Callapoda, 1563. (Markusbibliotek zu Venedig) Nach dem original.
 —— xxiii. Aus dem atlas des Battista Agnese, xvi. jahrhundert (Zweite hälfte) (Universitätsbibliothek zu Bologna) Nach dem original.
 —— xxiv. Aus dem atlas des Battista Agnese, xvi. jahrhundert (Zweite hälfte) (Universitätsbibliotek zu Bologna) Nach dem original.
 —— xxv. Aus dem atlas des Battista Agnese, xvi. jahrhundert (Zweite hälfte) (Universitätsbibliotek zu Bologna) Nach dem original.
 —— xxvi. Aus dem atlas des Battista Agnese, xvi. jahrhundert (Zweite hälfte) (Universitätsbibliotek zu Bologna) Nach dem original.
 —— xxvii. Aus dem atlas eines anonymus des xvi. jahrhunderts. (Bibliotek des Museo civico zu Venedig) Nach dem original.
 —— xxviii. Aus dem atlas des Aloysius Cesanis, 1574. (Biblioteca Palatina zu Parma) Nach dem original.
 —— xxix. Globus des Franciscus Bassus Mediolanensis, 1570. (Universitäts-Bibliotek zu Turin) Nach dem original.
 —— xxx. Aus dem atlas eines anonymus des xvi. jahrhunderts. (Bibliotek des Museo civico zu Venedig) Nach dem original.
 —— xxxi. Aus dem atlas des Bartolomeo Olives von Mallorca, xvi. jahrhundert. (Vatikanische bibliothek) Nach dem original.
 —— xxxii. Aus dem atlas des Bartolomeo Olives von Mallorca, xvi. jahrhundert. (Vatikanische bibliothek) Nach dem original.
 —— xxxiii. Aus einem portugiesischen atlas der Biblioteca Riccardiana zu Florenz, blatt 18. Nach dem original.
 —— xxxiv. Aus einem portugiesischen atlas der Biblioteca Riccardiana zu Florenz, blatt 19. Nach dem original.
 —— xxxv. Aus einem portugiesischen atlas der Biblioteca Riccardiana zu Florenz, blatt 20. Nach dem original.

Tafel xxxvi. Aus einem portugiesischen atlas der Biblioteca Riccardiana zu Florenz, blatt 21. Nach dem original.
— xxxvii. Aus einem portugiesischen atlas der Biblioteca Riccardiana zu Florenz, blatt 22. Nach dem original.
— xxxviii. Aus einem portugiesischen atlas der Biblioteca Riccardiana zu Florenz, blatt 23. Nach dem original.
— xxxix. Aus einem portugiesischen atlas der Biblioteca Riccardiana zu Florenz, blatt 24. Nach dem original.
— xl. Aus einem portugiesischen atlas der Biblioteca Riccardiana zu Florenz, blatt 25. Nach dem original.

**Kunstmann, F.**
Die entdeckung Amerikas. Nach den ältesten quellen geschichtlich dargestellt . . .   2v.   2 p. l., 151 pp.   4°.  Atlas. 2 p. l., 13 col. maps.  fol.   München, A. Asher & cie. in Berlin, 1859.   1137

NOTE.—Atlas accompanying this work entitled: Atlas zur entdeckungsgeschichte Amerikas. Aus handschriften der k. hof- und staats. bibliothek, der k. universitæt und des hauptconservatoriums der k. b. armee herausgegeben von Friedrich Kunstmann, Karl von Spruner, Georg M. Thomas.
"Maps . . . elucidate many points hitherto obscure in the history of the discovery of America. As specimens of art and perfect fac-similes . . . drawn from sources inaccessible to ordinary research. Maps 6–12 are from a manuscript executed about 1540 and contain very full details of the California coast. Map 13, was made by an englishman named Thomas Hood in 1592, and exhibits the coasts of Florida, Virginia and upper North America. The others are chiefly charts . . . done by portuguese and spaniards at the beginning of the sixteenth century." *cf.* Sabin's Bibliotheca Americana. 1877. v. 9. pp. 554. Inserted is an article by J. G. Kohl, from "National Intelligencer," of Washington, D. C. dated aug. 13th 1859, entitled, "Notes on the atlas for the history of the discovery of America;" published by the Royal academy of Munich, spring of 1859.

CONTENTS.

no. 1. Karte des Pedro Reinel, die ost-küste der insel Neufundland und die küste von Labrador.
"  2. Karte einzelner theile von Nord und Südamerika, im norden ein theil von Canada und der länder an der Davisstrasse, im süden die küste Paria im heutigen Venezuela bis zum flusse Cananea in Brasilien.
"  3. Karte ähnlichen inhaltes; im norden sind die bereits angegebenen länder wiederholt, im süden beschrankt sie sich auf die küste vom cap. S. Roque bis zum flusse Cananea.
"  4. Karte ähnlichen inhaltes; im norden ist auch die küste von Florida angegeben, im süden ist die küste von Yucatan bis zum cap. Sta Maria in Uruguay abgebildet.
"  5. Karte des Vesconte de Majolo, die Antillen und das festland von Honduras bis zum cap Sta Maria in Uruguay.
"  6. Karte einzelner theile von Amerika. Von Nordamerika enthält sie die ostküste von New-york an bis Mexiko, von Mexiko auch die west-küste mit Californien und die länder bis zur landenge von Panama, von Südamerika Neugranada und Venezuela, die küste von Peru und die strasse des Magalhães mit dem Feuerlande.
"  7. Karte der ostküste von Amerika von der Hudsonsbay bis zum Feuerlande.

**Kunstmann, F.**—Continued.
- no. 8bis xii. Karten des Vaz Dourado.
- " 8. Karte der ost- und westküste von Südamerika vom 30–60° s. b.
- " 9. Karte von Südamerika von der landenge von Panama bis zum 34 s. b.
- " 10. Karte der ostküste von Amerika von Neubraunschweig bis zum Amazonenstrome.
- " 11. Karte der ostküste von Nordamerika vom 80° n. b. bis Neubraunschweig.
- " 12. Karte von Californien und der westküste von Mexiko.
- " 13. Karte von Thomas Hood, die ostküste von Nordamerika bis zur landenge von Panama.

**Marcel, G. A.**
Recueil de voyages et de documents pour servir à l'histoire de la géographie. Section cartographique. 1. Reproductions de cartes et de globes . . . 2v. 146 pp., 1 l. 4°. Atlas. 3 p. l., 41 maps. fol. Paris, E. Leroux, 1894. 1138

NOTE.—Atlas accompanying this work, entitled: Reproductions de cartes & de globes relatifs à la découverte de l'Amérique du xvi*e* au xviii*e* siècle avec texte explicatif.

A collection of important fac-similes relating to the discovery of America. Map no. 41 inserted.

Reproduction with the following manuscript statement, "Carte du Marañon du p. Fritz, publiée à Quito en 1707 et réimprimée par la librairie Ch. Chadenat, d'après l'un des deux seuls exemplaires connus. Cette réimpression n'a été tirée qu'à 50 exemplaires."

Contains plans of the following cities: New York, Boston, New Orleans, Montreal and Quebec.

CONTENTS.

- no. 1. Globe vert (Bibliothèque nationale)
- " 2–3. Mappemonde de Canerio (Dépôt des cartes de la marine)
- " 4–5. Carte de Gaspar Viegas. 1534 (Bibliothèque nationale)
- " 6. Plan de Manathes ou Nouvelle Yorc. Vérifiée par le s$^r$ de la Motte (Dépôt . . . de la marine)
- " 7–10. Carte de l'Amérique septentrionale et partie de la méridionale.
- " 11. Mappemonde de 1502 (Appartenant à m. d$^r$ E. T. Hamy)
- " 12. Plan de la ville de Quebec fait à Quebec ce 20 octobre 1722 Chaffegros de Lery (Dépôt . . . de la marine)
- " 13. Brésil français par J. de Vaux de Claye.
- " 14–15. Carte géographique de l'isle de Cayenne et de ses environs, par m. de Préfontaine. 1762.
- " 16. Plan de la ville Marie ou Montréal.
- " 17. Environs de la rivière de Misisipi découuertes par m$^r$ de la Salle en 1683 et reconnues par m. le chevalier d'Heruille en 1698 et 1699. Les chiffres marquent le nombre des villages de chacune de ces nations en ces lieux là . . .—Amériqve Septentrionale.
- " 18–19. Mapa geographica del rio Marañon o Amazonas . . . p. Samuel Fritz . . . 1691.
- " 20. Carta geografica . . . del rio de la Plata . . . J. Ramon.
- " 21. Globe doré (Bibliothèque nationale)
- " 22. Carte de la ville, baye et environs de Baston . . . Par Jean Baptiste Louis Franquelin. 1693 (Dépôt . . . de la marine)

no. 23-24. Description de la première partie dv Perv (Dépôt ... de la marine)
" 25. Carte générale de la Louisiane ou du Miciscipi ... par le s.r Vermale. 1717.
" 26. [Cours du Tocantins] (Bibliothèque nationale)
" 27. Carte de la découverte du s.r Jolliet ou lon uoit la communication du fleuue S.t Laurens auec les lacs Frontenac, Erié, lac des Hurons et Illinois.
" 28. Planche de l'atlas de Le Testu [Carte de la Nouvelle-France par G. Le Testu] (Bibliothèque du ministère de la guerre)
" 29. Lac Supérieur (Dépôt ... de la marine)
" 30. Carte de la nouvelle découverte ... en l'année 1672 ... par le père Jacque Marquette ... qu'on pourra nommer la Manitoumé ... (Bibliothèque nationale)
" 31-34. [Carte de Diego Gutierrez] (Dépôt ... de la marine)
" 35. Plan de la Nouvelle Orléans ... (Archives nationales)
" 36. Parties les plus occidentales du Canada. Carte du père Raffix [Les Grands Lacs]
" 37. Carte des nouvelles découvertes dans l'ouest du Canada [Les découvertes père Gauthier de La Verenderye] (Dépôt ... de la marine)
" 38. Carte du lac Champlain ... pard. le s.r Anger, arpenteur du roy en 1732 fait à Québec le 10 octobre 1748 Chaufsegros de Lery f[ils]
" 39. [Cours du Mississippi 1719-1731] (Dépôt ... de la marine)
" 40. Carte générale de la Nouvelle France ... par ... Franquelin. 1708. [Amérique Septentrionale]
" [41] El gran rio Maranon o Amazonas ... Por e‾ p.e Samuel Fritz ... 1707.

**Stevenson, E. L.**
Maps illustrating early discovery and exploration in America 1502-1530 reproduced by photography from the original manuscripts issued under the direction of Edward Luther Stevenson ... cover-title, 12 maps (in covers) fol. New Brunswick, N. J., 1903.
1139

NOTE.—Maps no. 1, 5 and 7 each accompanied by one leaf of descriptive text.

CONTENTS.

no. 1. Cantino 1502-4.
" 2. Munich—Portuguese 1502-4.
" 3. Pilestrina 1503-5.
" 4. Maggiolo 1519.
" 5. Munich—Portuguese 1516-20.
" 6. Turin—Spanish 1523-25.
" 7. Salviati 1525-27.
" 8. Wolfenbüttel—Spanish 1525-30.
" 9. Weimar—Spanish 1527.
" 10. Maggiolo 1527.
" 11. Ribero 1529.
" 12. Verrazano 1529.

—— Text and key maps.   cover-title, [26] pp. incl. 12 maps. fol. New Brunswick, N. J., 1906.

## GENERAL.

(Arranged chronologically)

### 1597

**Wytfliet, C.**
Descriptionis Ptolemaicæ avgmentvm, siue Occidentis notitia breui commentario illustrata studio et opera Cornely Wytfliet Louaniensis. 2 pts. in 1 v. 4 p. l., 191, [1] pp. incl. 19 maps. 4°. Lovanii, tijpis Iohannis Bogardi, 1597. 1140

NOTE.—Engraved title.
The first edition was printed in 1597 and contained an errata of 6 lines on p. [192] The present copy, a second issue of the same year, omits the errata, although mistakes in the text are not rectified.
Eight lines of manuscript errata are supplied on recto of first fly-leaf following text.
Seven editions were published between 1597 and 1611.
Dedicated to Philip III, "Hispaniarum et Indiarum princeps."
The earliest distinctively american atlas. It is as important in the history of the early cartography of the new world, as Ptolemy's maps are in the study of the old.
Referred to as a continuation or supplement of Ptolemy. See p. l. 3, "In Cornelii Wytfliet . . . Ptolemaicum supplementum . . . epigramma."
Nordenskiöld states that the author has described a part of the globe entirely unknown to the ancients, in a manner completely different from the style of the Alexandrian geographer, and that the work does not contain a map or a single line of Ptolemy, although Ptolemy's name is on the title-page.
pt. 1 contains an account of the history of the discovery, the geography, natural history, and ethnology of the New World; pt. 2 contains maps interspersed with explanatory text.
Map no. 1. "Orbis terrarum" is a copy of Mercator's map of the world of 1584. *cf.* Nordenskiöld, Facsimile atlas, p. 134. The western hemisphere outlines the northern and southern continents. North America is called "America sive India nova" The unknown northwest coast is defined and is separated from Asia by "El streto de Anian." A small inland sea, "mar dulce," is probably Hudson's bay. "No. Francia" is Labrador, north of which is "Estotilant." "Groenlant" is an Arctic island with "Groclant" to the west and "Islant" on the east. The outline of the southern continent is less accurate than that of the northern and it has no general name. Terra del Fuego is represented as part of an indefinite Antarctic region, and is entirely separated from the continent. Maps of special interest and value are: no. 2, "Chica sive Patagonica et Avstralis terra," which Nordenskiöld describes as a "beautiful" map; no. 10, an early map of Cuba; no. 13, "California," represented as a peninsula; no. 17, " Norumbega et Virginia;" and no. 19, "Estotilandia et Laboratoris terra," which is also a most interesting map of the Arctic islands. "Groenlandiæ pars," "Islandiæ pars" and "Frislant" appear to have been much better known than the mainland. The entire map with its accompanying text, shows the author's knowledge of the Zeno chart and the discoveries of the Zeno brothers.

CONTENTS.

no. 1. Orbis terrarum.
" 2. Australis terra & Chica.
" 3. Chili.

no. 4. Plata.
" 5. Brasilia.
" 6. Peruuia.
" 7. Castillia Aurifera.
" 8. Residuū terræ firmæ siue Paria & Cubagua.
" 9. Hispaniola.
" 10. Cuba & Jamaica.
" 11. Iucatana regio & Fondura.
" 12. Hispania noua.
" 13. Nouva Granata & California.
" 14. Anian & Quiuira.
" 15. Conibas regio.
" 16. Florida.
" 17. Virginia.
" 18. Noua Francia & Canada.
" 19. Estotilandia & Laboratoris terra.

## 1601

**Herrera y Tordesillas, A. de**
Descripcion de las Indias Ocidentales de Antonio de Herrera coronista mayor de sv mag.$^{d}$ de las Indias, y sv coronista de Castilla . . . 2 p. l., 96 pp., 14 maps. 4°. Mad[rid] enla emplen$^{ta}$ real, 1601.

1141

NOTE.—Colophon: En Madrid, Por Iuan Flamenco. Año M.DCI.
First edition. Other editions as follows: latin, french and dutch editions of 1622; spanish edition of 1726. See title 1156.
This work is a part of his "Historia general" . . . and is usually found at the end of the second volume after the "Decada quarta" as in the Library of Congress copy. In the edition of 1726-1727, it precedes the "Decada primera," v. 1.
Engraved title-page contains a miniature of the author and representations of mexican deities.
Pagination irregular.

CONTENTS.

no. 1. Descripcion de las Yndias Ocidentales.
" 2. Descripcion de las Yndias del Norte.
" 3. Description del destricto del avdiencia de la Española.
" 4. Description del destricto del avdiencia de Nveva Espana.
" 5. Descripcion del destricto de avdiencia de la Nveva Galicia.
" 6. Descripcion del avdiencia de Gvatimala.
" 7. Descripcion de las Yndias de Mediodia.
" 8. Descripcion del avdiencia de Panama.
" 9. Descripcion del avdiencia del Nvevo Reino.
" 10. Descripcion del avdiencia del Qvito.
" 11. Descripcion del destricto del avdiencia de Lima.
" 12. Descripcion del avdiencia de los Charcas.
" 13. Descripcion de la provincia de Chile.
" 14. Descripcion de las Indias del Poniente.

## 1603

**Wytfliet, C.**
 Descriptionis Ptolemaicæ avgmentvm, siue Occidentis notitia breui commentario illustrata, et hac secunda editione magna sui parte aucta . . . 2 pts. in 1 v. 3 p. l., 191, [1] pp., incl. 20 maps. 4°. Dvaci, apud Franciscum Fabri, 1603. 1142

NOTE.—Engraved title.
Second Edition, according to title, but earlier editions appeared in 1597 and 1598.
Leclerc, Bibl. Amér., 614, Muller, Books on America, 1877, no. 3575, and Winsor, Bibl. of Ptolemy's geographies, respectively, note the ed. of 1603 differs from that of 1598, as follows: change of title and imprint, and the insertion of a blank leaf after the preface in place of "In C. Wytfliet . . . epigramma."
L. C. copy imperfect; the above is omitted and the blank leaf is not inserted. Map no. 1, "Orbis terrarum," called for in the table of contents, is wanting.
The first two maps, "Typvs orbis universalis" and "Altera generalis secvndo Ptol," both Ptolemy's, are inserted here from Sebastian Munster's Cosmographiae universalis, lib. vi. . . . Basileæ, 1559. Text and remaining 18 maps are like the edition of 1597.
For description and list of maps, see title 1140 under Wytfliet's Descriptionis Ptolemaicæ avgmentvm, sive Occidentis . . . Lovanii, tijpis Iohannis Bogardi, 1597.

## 1605

Histoire vniverselle des Indes, Orientales et Occidentales. Divisée en devx livres: le premier par Cornille Wytfliet: le second par Ant. M.[agini] & avtres historiens. 2 pts. in 1 v. 126, [2], 52 (*i. e.* 56), [7] pp., 23 maps. 4°. Douay, F. Fabri, 1605. 1143

NOTE.—Engraved title.
Pagination irregular: pt. 2, pp. 21–56 numbered respectively: 20, 20, 21, 22, 23, 24, 24, 24–52.
pt. 1, is a free translation of Wytfliet's Descriptionis Ptolemaicæ avgmentvm, 1597, with omissions and additions. The maps are like those in the edition of 1597; text of maps not translated.
For description and list of maps, of pt. 1, see title 1140.
pt. 2 comprises a history of the discovery of the Indies and a description of separate islands, by Giovanni Antonio Magini and other historians, and the following maps:
no. [1] India Orientalis.
" [2] Iapaniæ regnvm.
" [3] Chinæ regnvm.
" [4] Insvlæ Philippinæ.

## 1622

**Herrera y Tordesillas, A de.**
 Description des Indes Occidentales, qu'on appelle aujourdhuy le Novveav Monde: . . . tranflatée d'efpagnol en françois. A la quelle font adjoustées quelques autres defcriptions des mefmes

pays, avec la navigation du vaillant capitaine de mer Jaques le Maire, & de plufieurs autres . . . 4 pts. in 1 v. 4 p. l., 254 pp., 2 l., 17 maps, 5 pl. 4°. Amsterdam, M. Colin, 1622. 1144

NOTE.—Added title-page, engraved, reads: Descriptio Indiæ Occidentalis . . . "Cet ouvrage [est] connu sous le nom de 'Collection de Michel Colin.'"— Leclerc, Bibl. amer., 1878.

pt. [1], by Herrera, is a translation of his Descripcion de las Indias Ocidentales, Madrid, 1601.

pts. [2-4] were added when pt. [1] was translated and published by Colijn in 1622, in french, dutch and latin; in latin as "Novvs orbis, sive Descriptio Indiae Occidentalis", and in dutch under title, Nievwe wereldt, anders ghenaempt West-Indien."

The maps of pt. [1] are like those in the original edition of 1601.

CONTENTS.

pt. [1] no. 1. Descripcion de las Yndias Ocidentales.
" " 2. Descripcion de las Yndias del Norte.
" " 3. Description del destricto del avdiencia dela Española.
" " 4. Description del destricto del avdiencia de Nveva Espana.
" " 5. Descripcion del destricto de avdiencia de la Nveva Galicia.
" " 6. Descripcion del avdiencia de Gvatimala.
" " 7. Descripcion de las Yndias de Mediodia.
" " 8. Descripcion del avdiencia de Panama.
" " 9. Descripcion del avdiencia del Nvevo Reino.
" " 10. Descripcion del avdiencia del Qvito.
" " 11. Descripcion del destricto del avdiencia de Lima.
" " 12. Descripcion del avdiencia de los Charcas.
" " 13. Descripcion de la provincia de Chile.
" " 14. Descripcion de las Indias del Poniente.

Three additional maps from Le Maire's Jovrnal, & miroir de la navigation, titles in dutch, latin and french, as follows:

pt. [2], no. [1] Carte du destroict trouvé et paffé par Iacq. le Maire au dela du destroict de Magallanas vers le zudeft.
" " [2] Carte du chemin ou de la route tenuë par Iacq. le Maire en son voyage par la mer Australe, et quand[!] et quand monstrant les isles et terres, par iceluy defcouvertes.
" " [3] Cartes des terres des Papouas ou de Guinee Neuve ainfi que Iacq. le Maire les a defcouvertes en fon voijage faict en l'an 1616.

**1622**

Nievwe werelt, anders ghenaempt VVest-Indien. 3 pts. in 1 v. fol. t' Amsterdam, M. Colijn, 1622. 1145

NOTE.—Collation: [pt. 1], 4 p. l., 111 pp., 14 maps; [pt. 2], 29 pp.; [pt. 3], 8 p. l., 72 pp., 73-85 numb. l., 3 maps.

Added title-page engraved and colored, reads: Descriptio Indiæ Occidentalis Gothic type . . .

Maps and plates hand colored.

"Cet ouvrage [est] connu sous le nom de 'Collection de Michel Colin.'"— Leclerc, Bibl. amer., 1878.

This collection was published by Colijn the same year in latin as "Novvs orbis, sive Descriptio Indiae Occidentalis," and in french with title, "Descrip-

**Herrera y Tordesillas, A. de**—Continued.
tion des Indes Occidentales." The brief account of America by Petrus Bertius, found in the french and latin versions, is not included in the dutch edition. [pt.1], by Herrera, is a translation of his "Descripcion de las Indias Ocidentales, Madrid, 1601," and contains 14 maps.

CONTENTS.

pt. [1], no. 1. Descripcion de las Yndias Ocidentales.
" " 2. Descripcion de las Yndias del Norte.
" " 3. Description del destricto del avdiencia dela Española.
" " 4. Description del destricto del avdiencia de Nveva Espana.
" " 5. Descripcion del destricto de avdiencia de la Nveva Galicia.
" " 6. Descripcion del avdiencia de Gvatimala.
" " 7. Descripcion de las Yndias de Mediodia.
" " 8. Descripcion del avdiencia de Panama.
" " 9. Descripcion del avdiencia del Nvevo Reino.
" " 10. Descripcion del avdiencia del Qvito.
" " 11. Descripcion del destricto del avdiencia de Lima.
" " 12. Descripcion del avdiencia de los Charcas.
" " 13. Descripcion de la provincia de Chile.
" " 14. Descripcion de las Indias del Poniente.

Three additional maps from Le Maire's Spieghel der avstralische navigatie, titles in dutch, latin and french, as follows:

pt. [3], no. [1] Caerte van de strate ende paffage by Iacob le Maire ghevonden ende befeylt in 't zuydooften van de Magallanfche Straet.
" " [2] Caerte van de zeylage van Iacob le Maire over de Zuydzee, vertonende de eylanden ende landen aldaer by hem ghesien ende aenghedaen.
" " [3] Caerte van de landen vande Papouas ofte Nova Guinea nae de befeijlinge en ondecking van Iacob le Maire gedaen in den iare 1616.

**1622**

Novvs orbis, sive Descriptio Indiæ Occidentalis, auctore Antonio de Herrera . . . Metaphrafte C. Barlæo. Accefferunt & aliorum Indiæ Occidentalis defcriptiones, & navigationis nuperæ auftralis Jacobi le Maire hiftoria, uti & navigationum omnium per Fretum Magellanicum fuccincta narratio. 4 pts. in 1 v. fol. Amstelodami, M. Colinivm, 1622. 1146

NOTE.—Collation: pts. [1–2], 4 p. l., 81 l., 17 maps, 6 pl.; pt. [3], 9 l.; pt. [4], 11 l.
Added title-page, engraved, reads: Descriptio Indiæ Occidentalis . . .
Pagination irregular: pts. [1–2], l. 21, 40, 81 bis; pt. [3] l. 5 bis.
"Editione latine de la collection du libraire Michel Colin." Leclerc, Bibl. amer. 1878.
This collection which for convenience is entered under the name of the author of the first work included in it, was published by Colin the same year in dutch as "Nievwe werelt, anders ghenaempt VVest-Indien," and in french as "Description des Indes Occidentales, qu'on appelle aujourdhuy le Novveav Monde."

pt. [1], by Herrera, is a translation of his "Descripcion de las Indias Ocidentales, Madrid, 1601."
pts. [2-4], were added when pt. [1] was published in latin. Maps to pt. [2] were in dutch, latin and french.

CONTENTS.

pt. [1], no. 1. Descripcion de las Yndias Ocidentales.
" " 2. Descripcion de las Yndias del Norte.
" " 3. Description del destricto del avdiencia de la Española.
" " 4. Description del destricto del avdencia de Nveva Espana.
" " 5. Descripcion del destricto de avdencia de la Nveva Galicia.
" " 6. Descripcion del avdiencia de Gvatimala.
" " 7. Descripcion de las Yndias de Mediodia.
" " 8. Descripcion del avdiencia de Panama.
" " 9. Descripcion del avdiencia del Nvevo Reino.
" " 10. Descripcion del avdiencia del Qvito.
" " 11. Descripcion del destricto del avdiencia de Lima.
" " 12. Descripcion del avdencia de los Charcas.
" " 13. Descripcion de la provincia de Chile.
" " 14. Descripcion de las Indias del Poniente.
pt. [2], " [1] Tabula exhibens fretum, quod Iac. le Maire trans Fretum Magallanicum Euro Auftrum verfus reperit prinuis et navigavit.
" " [2] Tabula, ductum navigationis, quem in mari Auftrali tenuit Iacobus Le Maire, simulq. insulas ac terras sive regiones ab eo primum detectas, delineans.
" " [3] Tabula exhibens Papouarum feu Nova Guineæ regiones prout illas Iac. le Maire cum eafdem a° 1616 legeret detexit.

**1625**

**Laet, J. de.**

Nieuvve wereldt, ofte Beschrijvinghe van West-Indien, wt veelderhande schriften ende aen-teeckeninghen van verscheyden natien by een versamelt door Ioannes de Laet, ende met noodighe kaerten ende tafels voorsein. 12 p. l., 510, [16] pp., 10 maps. fol. Tot Leyden, I. Elzevier, 1625. 1147

NOTE.—First edition. Other editions and translations as follows: 2d., in dutch, 1630; latin ed., 1633; french ed., 1640; spanish ed. (abridged), text only, translated from the french ed., 1640. cf. Tapia y Rivera, Biblioteca historica de Puerto Rico. 1854. pp. 123–447.
Maps by Hessel Gerritsz.
Gothic type.
Printer's mark, the eagle, on title-page.
"This invaluable work has much improved in subsequent editions and translations." Asher's comment on the first edition. cf. Essay No. 1.
"It would have been difficult to produce anything better at the time when he wrote; and we must accept this book as the standard work on New Netherland of the 17th century" . . . cf. Winsor, Narrative and critical history. v. 4, p. 417.

CONTENTS.
Text.

pt. 1. West Indische eylanden.
" 2. Nova Francia.
" 3. Virginia.

**Laet, J. de**—Continued.
  pt. 4. Florida.
  " 5. Nova Hispania.
  " 6. Nova Galicia ofte Guadalaiara.
  " 7. Guatemala.
  " 8. Terra Firma.
  " 9. Neuvo reyno de Granada.
  " 10. Peru.
  " 11. Chile.
  " 12. Rio de la Plata.
  " 13. Brazil.
  " 14. Guiana.
  " 15. Nova Andaluzia.

Maps.

  no. [1] De groote ende kleyne eylanden van West Indien.
  " [2] Nova Hispania, Nova Galacia, Gvatimala.
  " [3] Tierra Firma met nvevo reyno de Granada ende Popayan.
  " [4] Perv.
  " [5] Chili.
  " [6] Provincien vande straet van Magallanes ende vande straet le Maire.
  " [7] Paragvay, ó prov. de rio de la Plata: . . .
  " [8] Tlandt van Brasil met de aengelegene provincien.
  " [9] Gvaiana ofte de provincien tusschen rio de las Amazonas ende rio de Yviapari ofte Orinoqve.
  " [10] Venezvela ende het westelyckste gedeelte van Nveva Andalvsia.

**1630**

Beschrijvinghe van West-Indien . . . Tweede druck: in ontallijke plaetsen verbetert, vermeerdert, met eenige nieuwe caerten, beelden van verscheyden dieren ende planten verciert.    14 p. l., 622, [17] pp., 14 maps. fol. Tot Leyden, bij de Elzeviers, 1630.    1148

NOTE.—Half-title: Nieuvve wereldt, ofte Beschrijvinghe van West-Indien door Joannes de Laet.
Second edition of "Nieuvve wereldt" corrected and augmented with 4 new maps and accompanying text.
Engraved title, with miniature portraits of Peter P. Heyn and Hendrick C. Lonck.    Cornelis Claessen Dusent, sculpsit.
Maps by Hessel Gerritsz.
Gothic type.
Dedicated to the states general of the United Netherlands.

CONTENTS.

Text.

  pt. 1. West-Indische eylanden.
  " 2. Nova Francia.
  " 3. Virginia.
  " 4. Florida.
  " 5. Nova Hispania.
  " 6. Nova Galicia ofte Guadalaiara.
  " 7. Guatemala.
  " 8. Terra Firma.
  " 9. Nuevo reyno de Granada.

pt. 10. Peru.
" 11. Chile.
" 12. Magallanica.
" 13. Rio de la Plata.
" 14. Brasil.
" 15. Guaiana.
" 16. Nova Andaluzia.

**Maps.**

no. [ 1] Americæ . . . tabula generalis.
" [ 2] Maiores minoresque insvlæ Hispaniola, Cvba, Lucaiæ et Caribes.
" [ 3] Nova Francia et regiones adiacentes.
" [ 4] Nova Anglia, Novvm Belgivm et Virginia.—Inset: Bermuda majori mole expressa.
" [ 5] Florida et regiones vicinæ.
" [ 6] Nova Hispania, Nova Galicia, Gvatimala.
" [ 7] Tierra Firma item nvevo reyno de Granada atque Popayan.
" [ 8] Peru.
" [ 9] Chili.
" [10] Provinciæ sitæ ad fretvm Magallanis itemque fretvm Le Maire.
" [11] Paragvay, ó prov. de rio de la Plata . . .
" [12] Provincia de Brasil cum adiacentibvs provinciis.
" [13] Gvaiana siue provinciæ intra rio de las Amazonas atqve rio . . . Orinoqve.
" [14] Venezvela atque occidentalis pars Novæ Andalvsiæ.

## 1633

**Laet, J. de.**

Novvs orbis, seu Descriptionis Indiæ Occidentalis, libri xviii . . . Novis tabulis geographicis et variis animantium, plantarum fructuumque iconibus illustrati. Cvm privilegio. 16 p. l., 690, [18] pp., 14 maps. fol. Lvgd. Batav., apud Elzevirios, 1633. 1149

NOTE.—Translated from the 1630 edition of his "Nieuvve wereldt."
Engraved title, maps and subject matter of text, like the edition of 1630.
Half-title: Joannis de Laet. Americae utriusque descriptio.
Dedication: Carolo I. Magnæ Britanniæ, Franciæ, atque Hiberniæ regi, fidei defensori, &c.
For description and list of maps see title 1148.

## 1640

L'histoire dv Nouveau Monde ou description des Indes Occidentales, contenant dix-huict liures . . . enrichi de nouvelles tables géographiques & figures des animaux, plantes & fruicts. 14 p.l., 632, [12] pp., 14 fold. maps. fol. Leyde, B. & A. Elfeuiers, 1640. 1150

NOTE.—Title-page in red and black.
Printer's mark, the hermit, on title-page.
First edition published in dutch with title "Nieuvve wereldt" . . . Leyden, 1625.
Translated from the dutch edition of 1630, with additions, chiefly vocabularies of indian tribes, in text: pp. 52, 57, 81, 153, 406, 536, 582 and 583.

**Laet, J. de**—Continued.

"Full details of natural history, and the character, manners and customs of the american aborigines, derived from reports of the european mission established in America." *cf.* Charlevoix. v. 1, p. 77. "Les cartes géographiques . . . sont celles de l'édition flamande de 1630." *cf.* Willems, Les Elzevirs. 1880. no. 497.

CONTENTS.

Text.

pt. 1. Des isles de l'océan.
" 2. Nouuelle France.
" 3. Virginie.
" 4. Floride.
" 5. Nouuelle Espagne.
" 6. Nouuelle Galice.
" 7. Guatimala.
" 8. Terra Firma.
" 9. Nouueau royaume de Granade.
" 10. Peru.
" 11. Peru ou Charca.
" 12. Chile.
" 13. Magallanque.
" 14. Rio de la Plata.
" 15. Brasil.
" 16. Brasil Septentrional.
" 17. Guaiana.
" 18. Nouuelle Andaluzie.

Maps.

no. [1] Americæ sive Indiæ Occidentalis. Tabula generalis.
" [2] Maiores minoresqve insvlæ Hispaniola, Cuba, Lucaiæ et Caribes.
" [3] Nova Francia et regiones adiacentes.
" [4] Nova Anglia, Novvm Belgium et Virginia.
" [5] Florida et regiones vicinae.
" [6] Nova Hispania, Nova Galicia, Gvatimala.
" [7] Tierra Firma item nvevo reyno de Granada atque Popayan.
" [8] Perv.
" [9] Chili.
" [10] Provinciæ sitæ ad fretvm Magallanis itemque fretvm le Maire.
" [11] Paragvay, ó prov. de rio de la Plata . . .
" [12] Provincia de Brasil cum adiacentibvs provinciis.
" [13] Gvaiana . . .
" [14] Venezvela, atque occidentalis pars Novæ Andalvsiæ.

**1657**

**Sanson, N.,** *d'Abbeville.*

L'Amériqve en plvsievrs cartes, & en divers traittés de géographie, et d'histoire. Là où font defcripts fuccinctement, & avec vne belle méthode, & facile ses empires, ses pevples, ses colonies, levrs moevrs, langves, religions, richesses &c. Et ce qu'il y a de plus beau, & de plus rare dans toutes fes parties, & dans fes ifles. Dediée a monseignevr Fovcqvet conseiller dv roy en tovs ses conseils

et chancelier des ordres de sa maiesté . . . 2 p. l., [40] l., 15 fold.
maps. 8°. Paris, chez l'avthevr, dans le cloiftre de Sainct Germain
de l'Auxerrois joignant la grande porte du cloiftre, 1657. 1151

NOTE.—"Avec privilege pour vingt ans."
Maps dated 1657; nos. 1, 8, signed "A. Peyrounin fculp."
The text of this edition differs in several chapters from that of the edition without date [1667?] The 4 pages comprising "Islande" and "Gronelande" are not here included.

CONTENTS.

no. [1] Américqve Septentrionale . . .
" [2] Le Canada, ou Nouvelle France, &c. . . .
" [3] La Floride . . .
" [4] Audience de Mexico . . .
" [5] Audience de Guadalajara, Nouveau Mexique, Californie, &c. . . .
" [6] Audience de Guatimala . . .
" [7] Les isles Antilles, &c. . . .
" [8] Amérique Méridionale . . .
" [9] Terre Ferme, Nou$^{veau}$ roy$^{me}$ de Grenade, &c. . . .
" [10] Guiane divisée en Guiane, et Caribane . . .
" [11] Le Pérou, et le cours de la riv$^{re}$ Amazone . . .
" [12] Le Chili . . .
" [13] Le Brésil . . .
" [14] Le Paraguay subdivisé en ses principales parties, fuivant les dernieres relãons . . .
" [15] Destroit de Magellan, Terre, et Isles Magellanicques, &c. . . .

1662

L'Amériqve en plvsievrs cartes novvelles, et exactes; & en divers traictés de géographie, et d'histoire. Là où font defcrits fuccinctement, & auec vne belle méthode, & facile ses empires, ses monarchies, ses estats, &c. les moevrs, les langves, les religions, le negoce, et la richesse de ses pevples &c. et ce qu'il y a de plus beau, & de plus rare dans toutes fes parties, & dans fes ifles. 1 p. l., [40] l., 15 fold. maps. 8°. Paris, chez l'avthevr, dans le cloiftre de Sainct Germain l'Auxerrois joignant la grande porte du cloiftre, 1662. 1152

NOTE.—"Avec privilege pour vingt ans."
Text similar to 1657 edition but with errors in arrangement. The maps of the 1657 edition are here issued without date and with the imprint of "Pierre Mariette, rue S$^t$ Iacques a l'Esperance." Slight changes are noticed such as the addition of "la Trinidad" on "Guiane" and "Rio de la Plata, Paraguay ó Rio de la Plata" on "Le Paraguay."

CONTENTS.

no. [1] Américqve Septentrionale . . .
" [2] Le Canada, ou Nouvelle France, &c. . . .
" [3] La Floride . . .
" [4] Audience de Guadalajara, Nouveau Mexique, Californie, &c. . . .
" [5] Audience de Guatimala . . .

**Sanson, N.** *d'Abbeville*—Continued.
  no. [6] Audience de Mexico . . .
  " [7] Les Isles Antilles, &c. . . .
  " [8] Amériqve Meridionale . . .
  " [9] Terre Ferme, Nou$^{reau}$ roy$^{me}$ de Grenade, &c. . . .
  " [10] Guiane divisée en Guiane, et Caribane . . .
  " [11] Le Pérou, et le cours de la riv$^{re}$ Amazone . . .
  " [12] Le Chili . . .
  " [13] Le Brésil . . .
  " [14] Le Paraguay subdivisé en ses principales parties, fuivant les dernieres relāons . . .
  " [15] Destroit de Magellan, Terre, et Isles Magellanicques, &c. . . .

**1667?**
**Sanson, N.** *d'Abbeville.*
L'Amériqve en plvsievrs cartes novvelles, et exactes, &c., en divers traitez de géographie, et d'histoire. Là où font defcrits fuccinctement, & auec vne belle méthode, & facile ses empires, ses monarchies, ses estats, &c. les moevrs, les langves, les religions, le negoce et la richesse de ses pevples, &c. et ce qu'il y a de plus beau & de plus rare dans toutes fes parties, & dans fes ifles . . . 1 p. l., 112 pp., 16 fold. maps. 8°. Paris, chez l'avthevr, ruē S. Iacques, á l'Efperance [1667 ?] 1153

NOTE.—"Avec privilège du roy pour vingt ans."
This edition, published without date, bears evidence of an issue later than 1656, the year usually credited. The date 1656 is contained in the text, page 8; the map of "Islande" is dated 1667. Like the 1662 edition, the dedication on title and the laudatory remarks on the following leaf of the 1667 edition, are omitted, owing, probably, to the fall of Fouquet in 1661.
Text is on numbered pages and contains changes and the following new chapters not in the previous editions: pp. 9-12, "Islande."—pp. 17-20, "Novvelle Angleterre."—"Niev Niderland, ov N. Pays Bas."—"Virginie."—pp. 21-24, "Bermvdes."—pp. 29-32," "Apalachites."—pp. 53-64, "Isles Caraibes ou Cannibales āls Antiles.—Saint Chreftofle Isle.—Gvadalovpe."—pp. 65-68," La Martinique."
Maps are the same as those in 1662 edition except that of "Islande," dated 1667, probably inserted to accompany the new chapter on that country. Maps numbered in lower right hand corner; nos 1, 8, signed "A. Peyrouin fculp."

CONTENTS.

  no. 1 Américqve Septentrionale . . .
  " 2. Le Canada, ou Nouvelle France, &c. Tirée de diverses relationes des François, Anglois, Hollandois, &c. . . .
  " [2a] Isle d'Islande, divisée en ses quatre principales parties . . . 1667.
  " 3. La Floride . . .
  " 4. Audience de Mexico . . .
  " 5. Audience de Guadalajara, Nouveau Mexique, California, etc. . . .
  " 6. Audience de Gautimala . . .
  " 7. Les isles Antiles, &c. . . .
  " 8. Amérique Méridionale . . .
  " 9. Terre Ferme, Nou$^{reau}$ roy$^{me}$ de Grenade, &c. . . .
  " 10. Guiane divisée en Guiane, et Caribane . . .

no. 11. Le Perou et le cours le la riv^re Amazone . . .
" 12. Le Chili . . .
" 13. Le Brésil . . .
" 14. Le Paraguay.
" 15. Déstroit de Magellan, Terre, et Isles Magellanicques, &c. . . .

**1696**

**La Guilbaudière, J. de.**

Description des principaux endroits de la Mer du fud, depuis les 52 dégrez 30 minutes fud, où est le d'estroit du Magelland jusqu'au 41 dégrez nord, qui est l'jsle de Californe faite fur les lieux par le s.^r Iouhan de la Guilbaudière. Dressé et dessiné les plans qui l'accompagnent, fur fes mémoires par le sieur Hanicle, ingénieur ordinaire du roy.     313 (*i. e.* 324) pp. incl. 35 maps.    fol.    [1696]
1154

NOTE.—Manuscript. Paged 1 to 313, with some errors.

Contains 35 maps, plans and views of towns, islands, ports, harbors, anchorages, forts etc., along the west coast of America from the straits of Magellan to the gulf of California. Six maps are double page, 12½ x 16½; the remainder are 7 x 11½.

Maps are beautifully drawn, colored and shaded in elevation and perspective. The manuscript text, 223 pp., comprises an introduction, a vocabulary of the "buccaneer" or native language at Magellan, and explanatory notes preceding each map.

pp. 310-313, " Route partant du port Acapoul pour aller aux jsles Philippines."

"The author of this extremely valuable and important manuscript was one of the celebrated band of buccaneers under the command of m. de Gennes . . . He was shipwrecked in the straits of Magellan about 1688 and shortly afterwards joined the buccaneering expedition of m. de Beauchesne-Gouin as second in command" . . . *cf.* "Les Fuégiens à la fin du XVII siècle d'après des documents français inédits" par m. G. Marcel.  Paris, 1892.

CONTENTS.

no. [1] Détroit du Magellan et de ses environs.
" [2] Isle de Chilloué [*i. e.* Chiloe, an island on the west coast of Chili]
" [3] P. de Baldive
" [4] Port de S.^t Vincent [coast of Brasil]
" [5] Baye de la Conception [Chili]
" [6] Port de Qu°quimbo [showing Tortuga, an island in the gulf of California]
" [7] Port de Morne Morene [Morro Moreno, Chili]
" [8] Baye de Ricque [showing "Sama R," Chili]
" [9] Port de Hillo
" [10] P. de la Nasque [Coast of Peru]
" [11] P. de Pisco [Coast of Peru]
" [12] P. du Caillau [Lima, showing plan of "Lima ville," Peru]
" [13] P. de Casma [Town, coast of Peru]
" [14] P. de Paite [showing "La pointe Parina," coast of Peru]
" [15] Baye de Gouyaquil [Guayaquil]
" [16] B. de Bonnavêture.
" [17] B. de Panama.

**La Guilbaudière J. de**—Continued.
- no. [18] B. de Chiriquitte [Chiriqui, Panama]
- " [19] Port de la Realegue [Realejo, Nicaragua]
- " [20] Golf de Fonseca ou de Mapalle [in the west of Central America] Soufrière de S! Michel.
- " [21] P. de Acaxulte ou de Sansonette [Acajutla, seaport town of San Salvador]
- " [22] P. de Gouatimala.
- " [23] P. de Gouatoules.
- " [24] P. de Angeles [s. California, coast of]
- " [25] P. Escondido [cape s coast of Mexico]
- " [26] Fallaises.
- " [27] P. de Acapoul [Acapulco, Mexico]
- " [28] P. de Plitaplan.—P. d'Oignatanexo autrem. le Sacatanosque.
- " [29] B. de Santiogue.
- " [30] P. de Chametlan [Chametla, Mexico]
- " [31] B. des Banderes.
- " [32] P. de Mantaquel.
- " [33] P. St Sébastien [on "Isles S! Sébastien" in "Détroit de Magellan"]
- " [34] Le port de S! Jean [coast of California]
- " [35] P. de la Paix.

## 1706

**English pilot, The.** The fourth book. Describing the Weft-India navigation from Hudfon's-bay to the river Amazones. Particularly delineating the sea-coafts, capes, head-lands, rivers, bays, roads, havens, harbours, streights, rocks, sands, shoals, banks, depths of water, and anchorage. With all the iflands therein, as Jamaica, Cuba, Hifpaniola, Barbadoes, Bermudoes, Porto Rico, and the reft of the Carribe and Bahama iflands. Also a new description of Newfoundland, New-England, New-York, eaft and weft New-Jerzey, Dellewar-bay, Virginia, Mary-land, and Carrolina, &c. Shewing the courfes and diftances from one place to another, the ebbing and flowing of the sea, the setting of the tides and currents, &c. With many other things neceffary to be known in navigation. The whole being very much enlarged and corrected, with the additions of feveral new charts and defcriptions, not before publifh'd. By the information of divers able navigators of our own and other nations.    1 p. l., 69 pp., 24 maps.    fol.    London, for J. Thornton; & R. Mount, 1706.    ç1155

NOTE.—See also titles 1157, 1158, 1160, 1162, 1163, 1164, 1168, and 1171.
The first edition of "The english pilot" was printed in London, for W. Fisher and J. Thornton, 1689.

CONTENTS.

- no. [1] A new and correct chart of the north part of America from New Found Land to Hudsons bay.    By John Thornton . . .
- " [2] A new and correct chart from England to Guinea with all the trading part of the West Indies.    According to m! Edw! Wrights projection vulgarly called Mercator's chart.    By John Thoruton . . .

no. [3] A new chart of the sea coaſt of Newfound land, new Scotland, new England, new Jerſey, Virginia, Maryland, Pennſilvania, and part of Carolina. By John Thornton . . .
" [4] A chart of y$^e$ iland of New Found Land with y$^e$ particular harbors at larg. by John Thornton . . . —Insets: Catalina harbor.—Trinity harbor.—Port Bonavista.—St. Johns harbor.—Bay of Bulls.—Harbor Grace.
" [5] A new chart of the trading part of New Found Land. By John Thornton . . .
" [6] Cattalina harbor.
" [7] Port Bonavista.
" [8] Harbor Grace.
" [9] Bay Bulls.
" [10] A large draught of New England, New York, and Long Island. By John Thornton . . . —Inset: Boston harbour.
" [11] Part of New England. Sold by I. Thornton . . . and by Will: Fiſher . . .
" [12] Part of New England, New York, east New Iarsey and Long Iland.
" [13] Virginia, Maryland, Pennsilvania, east & west New Jarsey. By John Thornton . . . and by Will: Fiſher . . .
" [14] A new mapp of Carolina. By John Thornton . . . and Will: Fiſher . . . —Inset: A large draught of Aſhly and Coopers rivers.
" [15] A large draught of Port Royall harbour in Carolina. By Iohn Thornton . . .
" [16] A large draft of South Carolina from Cape Roman to Port Royall. By John Thornton . . .
" [17] A chart of the Caribe Ilands. By John Thornton . . .
" [18] The iland of Bermudas.—The iland of Barbados. By John Thornton . . . and by Will: Fisher . . .
" [19] A large chart of the iſland Antegua. By Iohn Thornton . . . Corrected by capt Bryan 1701.
" [20] A new mapp of the iſland of S$^t$ Christophers being an actuall survey taken by m$^r$ Andrew Norwood. By John Thornton . . . —Insets: A new mapp of the island Guardalupa.—A new mapp of the island Martineca.
" [21] A chart of the iland of Hispaniola. With the Windward pafsage . . .
" [22] A new chart of the Bahama Islands and the Windward pafsage. By John Thornton . . .
p. 45 The draught of the bay of Honda.
no. [23] The iſland of Jamaica.—Inset: A draft of the harbor of Port Royall and of all ⅌ Kees.
" [24] A new and correct large draught of the tradeing part of the West Indies. By John Thornton . . .

**1726**

**Herrera y Tordesillas, A. de.**

Descripcion de las Indias Ocidentales de Antonio de Herrera coronista mayor de sv mag.$^d$ de las Indias, y su coronista de Castilla . . . 20 p. l., 78 pp., 14 maps. 4°. Madrid, N. R. Franco, 1726. 1156

**Herrera y Tordesillas, A de**—Continued.
[ *With his* Historia general. Madrid, 1726-[28] v. 1]
NOTE.—Engraved title-page. See also titles 1141, 1144-1146.
The date on title-page has been altered from 1726 to 1730.
In the first edition of the "Historia general", Madrid, 1601, the "Descripcion de las Indias Ocidentales" is found after the "Decada quarta", at the end of v. 2. In the present copy, quoted as the 2d edition by some bibliographers, by others as the 3d, the "Descripcion de las Indias Ocidentales" precedes the "Decada primera", v. 1. It is accompanied by 14 maps like the original edition.

CONTENTS.

no. 1. Descripcion de las Yndias Ocidentales.
" 2. Descripcion de las Yndias del Norte.
" 3. Description del destricto del avdiencia de la Española.
" 4. Description del destricto del avdiencia de Nveva Espana.
" 5. Descripcion del destricto de avdiencia de la Nveva Galicia.
" 6. Descripcion del avdiencia de Gvatimala.
" 7. Descripcion de las Yndias de Mediodia.
" 8. Descripcion del avdiencia de Panama.
" 9. Descripcion del avdiencia del Nvevo Reino.
" 10. Descripcion del avdiencia del Qvito.
" 11. Descripcion del destricto del avdiencia de Lima.
" 12. Descripcion del avdiencia de los Charcas.
" 13. Descripcion de la provincia de Chile.
" 14. Descripcion de las Indias del Poniente.

### 1737

**English pilot, The.** The fourth book. Describing the Weft-India navigation, from Hudfon's-Bay to the river Amazones. Particularly delineating the sea-coafts, capes, head-lands, rivers, bays, roads, havens, harbours, straits, rocks, sands, shoals, banks, depths of water and anchorage, with all the iflands therein, as Jamaica, Cuba, Hifpaniola, Barbadoes, Antigua, Bermudas, Porto-Rico, and the reft of the Caribbee and Bahama iflands. Also, a new defcription of Newfoundland, New-England, New York, Eaft and Weft New-Jerfey, Dellevar-bay, Virginia, Maryland, and Carolina, &c. Shewing, the courfes and distances from one place to another, the ebbing and flowing of the sea, the setting of the tides and currents, &c. With many other things neceffary to be known in navigation. The whole being much enlarged and corrected with the additions of feveral new charts and descriptions, not publifhed before this edition. By the information of divers able navigators of our own and other nations. 1 p. l., 66 pp., 25 maps, 6 maps in text. fol. London, for W. Mount & T. Page, 1737. 1157

NOTE.—See title 1155, for numbers to other editions.
Map no. 13, "A correct map of the coast of New England. 1731", contains the inset, "Boston harbour."
Maps engraved by I. Harris, Em. Bowen, Ia. Clark and S. Parker.

CONTENTS.

no. [1] A new and correct chart shewing the variations of the compass in the Western & Southern oceans as observed in y<sup>e</sup> year 1700 by . . . Edm. Halley. Border text on each side "The description and uses of a new and correct sea-chart of the Weftern and Southern ocean, shewing the variations of the compas. Signed E. Halley.
" [2] A new and correct chart of the north part of America from New Found Land to Hudsons bay. By [John] Thornton . . .
" [3] A new generall chart for the West Indies of E. Wright's projection vul Mercators chart.
" [4] A generall chart of the Western ocean . . .
" [5] A chart of the sea coast of New Found Land, New Scotland, New England, New York, New Jersey, with Virginia and Maryland . . .
" [6] The harbour of Casco bay and islands adjacent. By capt. Cyprian Southicke . . . 1720.
" [7] The coaft of New Found-Land from Cape-Raze to Cape S<sup>t</sup> Francis.— The coast of New-Found-Land from Salmon Cove to Cape Bonavista . . . Described by Henry Southwood.
" [8] A chart shewing part of the sea coast of New Foundland from ye Bay of Bulls to Little Plecentia exactly and carefully lay'd down by Iohn Gaudy. Inset.—A draught of the harbour of Trepassey in Newfoundland.
" [9] Cattalina harbor.
" [10] Port Bonavista.
" [11] Bay Bulls.
" [12] Harbor Grace.
p. 18. Ifland of St. Peters.
no. [13] A correct map of the coaft of New England. 1731. Inset: Boston harbour.
" [14] A draught of New York from the Hook to New York town . . .
" [15] Virginia, Maryland, Pennsilvania, East & West New Jarsey.
" [16] A draught of Virginia from the Capes to York in York river and to Kuiquotan or Hamton in James river. By Mark Tiddeman . . .
p. 25. Tabago road.
" [26] Barbados.
" [30] A large draft of the ifland Antegua.
no. [17] A new mapp of Carolina.—Inset: A large draught of Afhly and Coopers river.
" [18] A chart of the Caribe islands.
" [19] A chart of the ifland of Hispaniola. With the Windward pafsage from Iamaica betwene ye east end of Cuba & weft end of Hifpaniola.
" [20] A new and correct draught of the bay of Mantanzas on ye north side of ye ifland Cuba done from a survey in the year 1729 by Robt. Pearfon.
p. 44. A draught of the bay of Honda.
no. [21] The ifland of Jamaica. Inset: A draft of the harbor of Port Royall and of all ye kees . . .
" [22] A new chart of the Bahama islands and the Windward pafsage.
p. 50. Bermudas.
no. [23] A draught of the coaft of Guiana, from the river Oronoque, to the river Amazones.—The river Oronoque from the entrance thereof to St. Thomas's.—The river of Surinam and places adjacent.
" [24] A new and correct chart of the trading part of the West Indies . . .
" [25] A large draught of the gulf of Darien with the coaft to Porto Bella with a particular draught of the scotch settlement in Calledonia . . .

## 1758

**English pilot, The.** The fourth book. Describing the West India navigation, from Hudfon's-bay to the river Amazones. Particularly delineating the sea-coafts, capes, head-lands, rivers, bays, roads, havens, harbours, straits, rocks, sands, shoals, banks, depths of water and anchorage, with all the islands therein, as Jamaica, Cuba, Hifpaniola, Barbadoes, Antigua, Burmudas, Porto-Rico, and the reft of the Caribbee and Bahama iflands. Also, a new defcription of Newfoundland, New-England, New York, eaft and west New-Jerfey, Dellavar-bay, Virginia, Maryland, and Carolina, &c. Shewing the courfes and diftances from one place to another, the ebbing and flowing of the sea, the setting of the tides and currents, &c. With many other things neceffary to be known in navigation. The whole being much enlarged and corrected, with the additions of feveral new charts and descriptions. By the information of divers able navigators of our own and other nations. 4, 3-66 pp., 25 maps, 6 maps in text. fol. London, for W. & J. Mount, T. Page & son, 1758. 1158

NOTE.—See title 1155, for numbers to other editions.
Map no. 13, "A correct map of New England," contains the inset, "Boston harbour." Without date.
Maps engraved by Em. Bowen and S. Parker.

### CONTENTS.

no. [1] A new and correct chart of the Western and Southern oceans showing the variations of the compass according to the latest and best observations . . . Without signature of Halley. Border as in title 1157.
" [2] A new and correct chart of the north part of America from New Found Land to Hudsons bay . . .
" [3] A new general chart for the West Indies of E. Wright's projection vut. Mercators chart . . .
" [4] A general chart of the Western ocean . . .
" [5] A chart of the sea coast of New Foundland, New Scotland, New England, New York, New Jersey with Virginia and Maryland . . .
" [6] The harbour of Casco bay and islands adjacent. By capt. Cyprian Southicke . . . 1720.
" [7] A new and correct chart of the coaft of New Foundland from Cape Raze to Cape Bonavifta, with Chebucto Harbour in Nova Scotia. Done from the latest observations . . .—Inset: Chebucto harbour, in Nova Scotia . . .
" [8] A chart showing part of the sea coast of New Foundland. From ye bay of Bulls to little Placentia exactly and carefully lay'd down by Iohn Gaudy.—Inset: A draught of the harbour of Trepafsey in Newfoundland . . .
" [9] Harbor Grace.
" [10] Bay Bulls.
" [11] Cattalina harbor.
" [12] Port Bonavista.
p. 18. Ifland of St. Peters.

no. [13] A correct map of the coaſt of New England.—Inset: Boston harbour.
" [14] A draught of New York from the Hook to New York town by Mark Tiddeman . . .
" [15] Virginia, Maryland, Pennsylvania, east & west New Jársey . . .
" [16] A draught of Virginia from the Capes to York in York river and to Kuiquotan or Hamton in James river by Mark Tiddeman . . .
p. 25. Tabago road.
" [26] Barbados.
" [30] A large draft of the iſland Antegua.
no. [17] A large draft of South Carolina from Cape Roman to Port Royal 1 . . .
" [18] A correct chart of the Carribbee islands . . .
" [19] A correct chart of Hispaniola with the Windward passage . . . by C. Price . . .
" [20] A new and correct draught of the bay of Matanzas, on y$^e$ north side of y$^e$ iſland Cuba done from a survey in the year 1729 by Robt. Pearson.
p. 44. A draft of the bay of Honda.
no. [21] The iſland of Jamaica.—Inset: A draft of the harbor of Port Royall . . .
" [22] A new chart of the Bahama islands and the Windward paſsage . . .
p. 50. Bermudas.
no. [23] A draught of the coaſt of Guiana, from the river Oronoque, to the river Amazones.—The river Oronoque from the entrance thereof to St. Thomas's.—The river of Surinam and places adjacent.
" [24] A new and correct chart of the trading part of the West Indies . . .
" [25] An exact draught of the gulf of Darien & the coast to Porto Bello with Panama in the South sea & the scotch settlement in Calledonia . . .

**1758**
**López, L. de V. M. T.**

Atlas geographico de la America Septentrional y Meridional; dedicado a la catholica sacra real magestad de el rey nuestro señor don Fernando vi, por su mas humilde vasallo Thomas Lopez pensionista de s. m. en la corte de Paris año de 1758 . . .   7 p. l., 116 pp., port., 38 maps. 24°. Madrid, A. Sanz, 1758.   1159

NOTE.—Contains portrait of Fernando vi, king of Spain.

CONTENTS.

no. [1] Mapa general de la America.
" [2] Plano de Mexico.
" [3] Provincias de Mexico, Mechoacan y Panuco.
" [4] Provincias de Yucatan, Tabasco Guaxaca y Tlascala.
" [5] Provincias de Guadalæcara, Xalisco, Chiametlan y Zacatecas.
" [6] Provincias dë Nueva Vizcaya; Culvacan y Cinaloa.
" [7] El Nuevo Mexico proprio.
" [8] California. Nuevo reyno de Leon.
" [9] Neuva Navarra, Pimeria, Sonora, Hiaqui, y Mayo.
" [10] Provincias de Guatemala, Soconusco, Chiapa y Vera Paz.
" [11] La Florida.
" [12] Provincias de Honduras, Nicaragua, Costa Rica y Veragua.
" [13] Isla de Cuba.
" [14] El puerto de San Agustin.—La Havana.—Bahia de Santiago.
" [15] Isla de Santo Domingo.—Puerto Rico.
" [16] Plano de la bahia y ciudad de Portovelo . . .
" [17] Plano de la ciudad de Carthagena.

**López, L. de V. M. T.**—Continued.
- no. [18] Provincias de Panama, Darien, Choco y Carthagena.
- " [19] Provincias de S.ta Martha, y Rio de la Hacha.
- " [20] Govierno de Venezuela.
- " [21] Provincias de Cumana, Paria, la isla de la Trinidad y el rio Orinco.
- " [22] Nuevo reyno de Granada.
- " [23] Popayan.
- " [24] Plano de Lima.
- " [25] Parte septentrional de la audiencia de Lima.
- " [26] Meridional de la audiencia de Lima.
- " [27] Plano de la ciudad de Quito . . .
- " [28] Parte occidental de la audiencia de Quito.
- " [29] Parte oriental de la audiencia de Quito.
- " [30] Las Charcas el obispado de N. sén de la Paz; y el S.ta Cruz de la Sierra.
- " [31] El opispado de Tucuman.
- " [32] el [!] Paraguay.
- " [33] Parte del Paraguay, y el obispado de Buenos-Ayres.
- " [34] Plano de la ciudad de Santiago capital del Chile.
- " [35] Plano de la villa de la Serena . . .—Vista de la Serena.
- " [36] Reyno de Chile.
- " [37] Plano de la ciudad de Penco ó la concepcion . . .—Vista de Penco.
- " [38] Parte del reyno de Chile la Tierra del Fuego, el estrecho Magallanes y el del Maire.

## 1760

**English pilot, The.** The fourth book. Describing the West-India navigation, from Hudſon's-bay to the river Amazones. Particularly delineating the sea-coaſts, capes, head-lands, rivers, bays, roads, havens, harbours, straits, rocks, sands, shoals, banks, depths of water and anchorage, with all the iſlands therein, as Jamaica, Cuba, Hiſpaniola, Barbadoes, Antigua, Bermudas, Porto-Rico, and the reſt of the Caribbee and Bahama iſlands. Also a new deſcription of Newfoundland, New-England, New-York, eaſt and west New-Jerſey, Dellavar-bay, Virginia, Maryland and Carolina, &c. Shewing the courſes and diſtances from one place to another, the ebbing and flowing of the sea, the setting of the tides and currents, &c. With many other things neceſſary to be known in navigation. The whole being much enlarged and corrected, with the additions of ſeveral new charts and descriptions. By the information of divers able navigators of our own and other nations. 4, 3-66 pp., 25 maps, 6 maps in text. fol. London, for W. & J. Mount, T. Page & son, 1760. 1160

NOTE.—Map no. 13, "A correct map of the coaſt of New England," contains the inset, "Boston harbour." Without date.
Same maps in edition of London, 1758, with the exception of "A correct chart of the coast of Portugal & Barbaria . . . by C. Price," which is substituted for "A correct chart of Hispaniola . . . by C. Price" found in edition of 1758.
Map no. 6, engraved by Em. Bowen; no. 8, by S. Parker. See title 1155, for numbers to other editions.

CONTENTS.

no. [1] A new and correct chart of the Western and Southern oceans shewing the variations of the compass according to the latest and best observations . . . Without signature of Halley. Border text as in title 1157.
" [2] A new and correct chart of the north part of America from New Found Land to Hudsons bay . . .
" [3] A new generall chart for the West Indies of E. Wright's projection vut. Mercator's chart . . .
" [4] A general chart of the Western ocean . . .
" [5] A chart of the sea coast of New Foundland, New Scotland, New England, New York, New Jersey with Virginia and Maryland . . .
" [6] The harbour of Casco bay and islands adjacent. By cap! Cyprian Southicke . . . 1720.
" [7] A new and correct chart of the coaft of New Foundland from Cape Raze to Cape Bonavifta, with Chebucto harbour in Nova Scotia, done from the latest observations . . .—Inset: Chebucto harbour, in Nova Scotia, done from the latest observations.
" [8] A chart shewing part of the sea coast of New Foundland from ye bay of Bulls to little Placentia exactly and carefully lay'd down by Iohn Gaudy.—Inset: A draught of the harbour of Trepafsey in Newfoundland.
" [9] Harbor Grace.
" [10] Bay Bulls.
" [11] Cattalina harbor.
" [12] Port Bonavista.
p. 18. Ifland of St. Peters.
no. [13] A correct map of the coaft of New England.—Inset: Boston harbour.
" [14] A draught of New York from the Hook to New York town by Mark Tiddeman . . .
" [15] Virginia, Maryland, Pennsilvania, east & west New Jarsey . . .
" [16] A draught of Virginia from the Capes to York in York river and to Kuiquotan or Hamton in James river by Mark Tiddeman . . .
p. 25. Tobago road.
" 26. Barbados.
" 30. A large draft of the ifland Antegua.
no. [17] A large draft of South Carolina from Cape Roman to Port Royall . . .
" [18] A correct chart of the Caribbee islands . . .
" [19] A correct chart of the coast of Portugal & Barbaria from C. Finisterra to C. Baydor, with the Canarie isles . . . by . . . C. Price . . .
" [20] A new and correct draught of the bay of Matanzas, on ye north side of ye ifland Cuba done from a survey in the year 1729, by Robt. Pearson . . .
p. 44. A draft of the bay of Honda.
no. [21] The ifland of Jamaica.—Inset: A draft of the harbor of Port Royall and of all ye kees . . .
" [22] A new chart of the Bahama islands and the Windward pafsage . . .
p. 50. Bermudas.
no. [23] A draught of the coast of Guiana, from the river Oronoque, to the river Amazones.—The river Oronoque from the entrance thereof to St. Thomas's.—The river of Surinam and places adjacent.
" [24] A new and correct chart of the trading part of the West Indies . . .
" [25] An exact draught of the gulf of Darien & the coast to Porto Bello with Panama in the South sea & the scotch settlement in Calledonia . . .

## 1763

**Gazzettiere americano, Il**, contenente un distinto ragguaglio di tuttle le parte del Nuovo mondo . . . Tradotto dall' inglese e arricchito di aggiunte, note, carte, e rami . . .   3 v.  sm. fol.  Livorno, M. Cottelini, 1763.   1161

NOTE.—Translation of the "American gazetteer," London, 1762, with different maps.
Maps in this edition reproduced in Atlante dell' America. Livorno, G. T. Masi & comp., 1777. See also title 1167.

CONTENTS.

v. 1, no. 2. Nuova ed esatta carta della America . . .
"    " 3. Planata del porto d'Acapulco . . .
"    " 5. Piano della città, e porto di Sant'. Agostino.
"    " 6. Carta del corso del Maragnone o sia del gran fivme dell' Amazzoni.
"    " 9. Carta esatta rappresentante l' isola di Barbados.
"    " 10. Carta rappresentante il porto di Boston.
"    " 14. Carta rappresentante la baia de Campeggio e l' Jucatan.
"    " 20. Piano della città, e sobborghi di Cartagena.
"    " 21. Piano della città, rada, e porto di Chagre.
"    " 24. Carta essatta rappresentante l' isola di Cuba estratta dalle carte del sig: Poppler.
"    " 25. Piano di Guantanimo chiamato dagl' Inglesi porto di Cumberland.
"    " 26. Pianta di Cusco.
"    " 27. Carta rappresentante l' istmo di Darien o' siadi Panama.
"    " 28. Piano della città di S. Domingo.
"    " 29. Vedvsta di S. Evstachio.
"    " 30. Carta rappresentante la penisola della Florida.
v. 2, no. 1. Nuova e corretta carta dell' Indie Occidentali . . .
"    " 2. Carta esatta rappresentante l' isola di Granata.
"    " 3. Carta esatta rappresentante l' isola della Guadalupa.
"    " 5. Piano della città e porto dell' Havana.
"    " 6. Carta efatta rappresentante l' isola di S. Domingo o sia Hispaniola.
"    " 7. Carta rapprefentante una parte dlla[!] baja d' Hudson . . .
"    " 10. Pianta della citta di Sant' Iago capitale del regno del Chili.
"    " 11. Carta rappresentante l' isola della Giammaica.
"    " 17. Carte della Nuova Inghilterra, Nuova Iork, e Pensilvania.
"    " 18. Piano scenografico della città dei re ò di Lima capitale del regno del Perù.
"    " 20. Carta rapprefentante l' isola della Martinicca.
"    " 22. Nuovo Messico.
"    " 23. Carta rappresentante i cinque laghi del Canadà.
v. 3, no. 1. Carte rappresentate l' America Meridionale.
"    " 2. Caduta di Niagara.
"    " 3. Carte rappresentante il golfo del fiume S. Lorenzo.
"    " 4. Carta esatta rappresentante il corso del fiume Paraguay . . .
"    " 5. Piano del porto, e degli stabilimenti di Pensacola.
"    " 6. Piano di Porto Bello.
"    " 7. Veduta della citta, e della montagna del Potosi.
"    " 8. Piano della città di Quebec.
"    " 9. Quebec [View]
"    " 10. Piano della città e contorni di S. Francesco di Quito.

v. 3, no. 13. Pianta della città di Salvadore. Inset: Venduta della città di S. Salvadore.
" " 16. Nuova, e corretta carta dell' isola di Terra Nuova.
" " 19. Carta rappresentante le provincie di Cartagena, S. Marta, e Venezuela.
" " 20. Pino della rada, e della città della vera Cruz.
" " 24. Porti della Nuova York e Perthamboy.

**1767**

**English pilot, The.** The fourth book. Describing the Weft-India navigation, from Hudſon's bay to the river Amazones. Particularly delineating the sea-coafts, capes, headlands, rivers, bays, roads, havens, harbours, straits, rocks, sands, shoals, banks, depths of water, and anchorage. With all the iflands therein, as Jamaica, Cuba, Hifpaniola, Barbadoes, Antegua, Barmudas, Porto Rico and the reſt of the Caribbe and Bahama iflands. Also a new description of Newfound-land, New-England, New York, eaſt and weft New Jerzey, Dellawar-bay, Virginia, Mary land and Carolina, &c. Shewing the courſes and diſtances from one place to another, the ebbing and flowing of the sea, the setting of the tides and currents, &c. With many other things neceſſary to be known in navigation. The whole being very much enlarged and corrected, with the additions of feveral new charts and descriptions, by the information of divers able navigators of our own and other nations. 68 pp., 22 maps, 6 maps in text. fol. Dublin, B. Grierson, 1767. 1162

NOTE.—This edition contains maps of Boston harbor not found in the editions of London, 1758, 1767. See title 1155, for numbers to other editions.
Maps no. 3, 4, 37, engraved by James Barlow; no. 14 probably inserted.

CONTENTS.

no. [1] A new and correct chart shewing the variations of the compass in the Western & Southern oceans as observed in ye year 1700 by . . . Edm. Halley. No border text.
" [2] A chart shewing part of the sea coaſt of Newfoundland from the bay of Bulls to Little Placentia exactly and carefully lay'd down by John Gaudy anno 1715.—Inset: A draught of the harbour Trepaſſey in Newfoundland.
" [3] The coaſt of New Found Land from Salmon Cove to Cape Bonaviſta . . .
" [4] The coaſt of New Found-Land from Cape Raze to Cape St. Francis . . .
" [5] Harbor Grace.
" [6] Bay Bulls.
" [7] Port-Bonavista.
" [8] Cattalina harbor.
p. 20. Iſland of St. Peters.
no. [9] A new suruey of the barbour of Boston in New England. Done by order of the principall officers and comiſsioners of his ma[ties] navy [No date. Variation west 10° observed an? 1700 by capt. Edm. Halley]

**English pilot, The**—Continued.
  no. [10] A large draught of New England, New York and Long Island . . .
       Inset: Boston harbour [No date]
  "   [11] A draught of New York from the Hook to New York town . . .
  "   [12] Virginia, Maryland, Pennsilvania, east & west New Jarsey . . .
  "   [13] The harbour of Casco bay and islands adjacent. By capt. Cyprian Southicke.
  "   [14] A map of the south part of Nova Scotia and its fishing banks.—A plan of Halifax survey'd by M[oses] Harris.—Bedford formerly called Torrington Bay . . .—A view of Halifax drawn from ye top maſt head. Cartouche. "To the right honb.le the lords comiſsionrs for trade and plantations this plate is most humbly presented by your lordships most obedient and devoted humble servant." No author given.
  "   [15] A chart of the sea coast of New Found Land, New Scotland, New York, New Jersey with Virginia and Maryland and New England . . .
  "   [16] A draught of Virginia from the capes to York in York river and to Kuiquotan or Hamton in James river. By Mark Tiddeman . . .
  "   [17] A new mapp of Carolina by John Thornton at ye Platt in ye Minories and by Will: Fisher at ye Poſtorn Gate on Tower Hill London . . .—Inset: A large draught of Aſhly and Coopers rivers.
  "   [18] A chart of the Caribe ilands . . .
  p.    27. Tobago road.
  "     28. Barbados.
  "     32. A large draft of the iſland Antegua . . .
  no. [19] A chart of the iland of Hispaniola with the Windward paſsage from Iamaica betwene ye eaſt end of Cuba & the weſt end of Hispaniola . . .
  p.    46. A draft of the bay of Honda.
  no. [20] The iſland of Jamaica . . .
  "   [21] A new chart of the Bahama islands and the Windward paſsage by Saml. Thornton . . .
  p.    52. Bermudas.
  no. [22] A draught of the coaſt of Guiana from the river Oronoque to the river Amazones.—The river Oronoque from the entrance to St. Thomas's.—The river of Surinam and places adjacent.
  "   [23] A generall chart for the West Indies according to mr. Edw: Wrights projection commonly called Mercators chart.
  "   [24] A new generall chart for the West Indies of E. Wrights projection vut Mercators chart . . .

## 1767

**English pilot, The.** The fourth book. Describing the West India navigation, from Hudſon's-bay to the river Amazones. Particularly delineating the sea-coaſts, capes, headlands, rivers, bays, roads, havens, harbours, straits, rocks, sand, shoals, banks, depths of water and anchorage, with all the iſlands therein, as Jamaica, Cuba, Hiſpaniola, Barbadoes, Antigua, Bermudas, Porto-Rico, and the reſt of the Carribbee and Bahama islands. Also a new deſcription of Newfoundland, New-England, New-York, east and west New-Jerſey, Dellawar-bay, Virginia, Maryland, and Carolina, &c. Shewing the courſes and diſtances from one place to another, the ebbing and flowing of the sea, the setting of the tides and currents, &c. With many other things necessary to be known in navigation. The whole being much enlarged and corrected, with the additions of feveral new charts and descriptions. By the information of divers able navigators of our own and other nations. 4, 3–36 pp., 22 maps, 6 maps in text. fol. London, for J. Mount, & T. Page, 1767. 1163

NOTE.—Map no. 8 engraved by S. Parker. See title 1155, for numbers to other editions.

CONTENTS.

no. [1] A new and correct chart of the Western and Southern oceans shewing the variations of the compass according to the latest and best observations . . . Without signature of Halley. Border text as in title 1157.
" [2] A new and correct chart of the north part of America from New Found Land to Hudsons bay . . .
" [3] A new generall chart for the West Indies of E. Wright's projection vut. Mercators chart . . .
" [4] A general chart of the Western ocean . . .
" [5] A chart of the sea coast of New Foundland, New Scotland, New England, New York, New Jersey with Virginia and Maryland . . .
" [6] The harbour of Casco bay, and islands adjacent . . .
" [7] A new and correct chart of the coaſt of New Foundland from Cape Raze to Cape Bonaviſta, with Chebucto harbour in Nova Scotia, done from the latest observations . . .
" [8] A chart shewing part of the sea coast of New Foundland from ye bay of Bulls to little Placentia exactly and carefully lay'd down by Iohn Gaudy . . .—Inset: A draught of the harbour of Trepaſsey in Newfoundland.
p. 18. Iſland of St. Peters.
no. [9] A new and correct chart of the sea coast of New-England from Cape Codd to Casco bay, lately survey'd by capt. Henry Barnsley . . .
" [10] A draught of New York from the Hook to New York town by Mark Tiddeman . . .
" [11] Virginia, Maryland, Pennsilvania, east & west New Jarsey . . .
" [12] A draught of Virginia from the Capes to York in York river and to Kuiquotan or Hamton in James River, by Mark Tiddeman . . .
p. 25. Tabago road.
" 26. Barbados.
no. [13] A new mapp of the iſland of St. Christophers being an actuall survey taken by mr. Andrew Norwood, survey[r]. gen[l].[1] . . .—A new mapp of the iſland Martineca.—A new map of the iſland Guardalupa.
p. 30. A large draft of the iſland Antegua.
no. [14] A large draft of South Carolina from Cape Roman to Port Royall . . .
" [15] A correct chart of the Caribbee islands . . .
" [16] A correct chart of Hispaniola with the Windward passage . . . by C. Price . . .
" [17] A draught of the west end of the island of Porto Rico and the island of Zachee . . .—A draught of the island of Beata on the south side of Hispaniola.—The west end of the island of Heneago.—Platform bay, on the south side of Cape Nicolas.—A draught of Sam bay on the south side of Hispaniola.

**English pilot, The**—Continued.

 no. [18] A new & correct chart of Cuba, streights of Bahama, Windward passage, the current through the gulf of Florida, with the soundings &c. By an officer in the navy . . .—Inset: A plan of the harbour & town of Havana . . .
 " [19] A new and correct draught of the bay of Matanzas on ye north side of ye iſland Cuba done from a survey by Robt. Pearson.
 p. 44. A draught of the bay of Honda.
 no. [20] A new & correct chart cf the island of Jamaica, with its bays, harbours, rocks, soundings &c . . .—Inset: The river Orinoco, from the entrance thereof to S! Thomas.—The river of Surinam and places adjacent.
 p. 50. Bermudas.
 no. [21] A chart of the coast of Guayana, from the entrance of the river Orinoco . . . to the entrance of the river Amazones, by R. Waddington.
 no. [22] A new and correct chart of the trading part of the West Indies . . .

### 1775

**English pilot, The.** The fourth book. Describing the West-India navigation, from Hudſon's bay to the river Amazones. Particularly delineating, the sea coaſts, capes, headlands, rivers, bays, roads, havens, harbours, streights, rocks, sands, shoals, banks, depths of water, and anchorage, with all the iſlands therein, as Jamaica, Cuba, Hiſpaniola, Barbadoes, Antigua, Bermudas, Porto Rico, and the reſt of the Caribbee and Bahama iſlands. Also, a new deſcription of Newfoundland, New England, New York, eaſt and weſt New Jerſey, Dellawar bay, Virginia, Maryland, Carolina, &c. Shewing the courſes and diſtances from one place to another; the ebbing and flowing of the sea, the setting of the tides and currents, &c. With many other things neceſſary to be known in navigation. The whole being much enlarged and corrected, with the additions of ſeveral new charts and descriptions. By the information of divers able navigators of our own and other nations. 4, 3–66 pp. incl. 20 maps, 6 maps in text. fol. London, for J. Mount, T. Page, & W. Mount, 1775.          1164

 Note.—See title 1155, for numbers to other editions.

#### CONTENTS.

 no. [1] A new and correct chart of the Western and Southern oceans, shewing the variations of the compass according to the latest and best observations . . . Without signature of Halley. Border text as in title 1157.
 " [2] A new and correct chart of the north part of America from New Found Land to Hudsons bay . . .
 " [3] A new generall chart for the West Indies of E. Wright's projectſon vut. Mercators chart . . .
 " [4] A chart of the sea coast of New Foundland, New Scotland, New England, New York, New Jersey with Virginia and Maryland . . .

no. [5] The harbour of Casco bay and islands adjacent.
" [6] A new and correct chart of the coaſt of New Foundland from Cape Raze to Cape Bonaviſta with Chebucto harbour in Nova Scotia . . .
p. 18. Iſland of S! Peters.
no. [7] A chart showing part of the sea coast of New Foundland from y^e Bay of Bulls to little Placentia exactly and carefully lay'd down by Iohn Gaudy . . .
" [8] A map of the coaſt of New England, from Staten Iſland to the iſland of Breton; as it was actually survey'd by cap! Cyprian Southack . . .—Inset: A chart of the Atlantic ocean shewing the situation of Nova Scotia with reſpect to the British Iſles.—The town of Boston in New England.
" [9] A draught of New York from the Hook to New York town, by Mark Tiddeman . . .
" [10] Virginia, Maryland, Pennsilvania, eaſt & weſt New Jersey . . .
p. 25. Tobago road.
" 26. Barbados.
no. [11] A draught of Virginia from the capes to York in York river and to Kuiquotan or Hamton in James river by Mark Tiddeman . . .
p. 30. Bermudas.
no. [12] A new mapp of the iſland of S! Christophers being an actuall survey taken by m! Andrew Norwood, survey! gen!! . . .—A new mapp of the iſland Martineca.—A new mapp of the iſland Guardalupa.
" [13] A large draft of South Carolina from Cape Roman to Port Royall . . .
" [14] A correct chart of the Caribbee islands . . .
" [15] A correct chart of Hispaniola with the Windward passage . . . by C. Price . . .
" [16] A draught of the west end of the island of Porto Rico, and the island of Zachee.—A draught of the island of Beata, on the south side of Hispaniola.—The west end of the island of Heneago.—Platform bay, on the south side of Cape Nicholas.—A draught of Sam bay, on the south side of Hispaniola.
" [17] A new & correct chart of Cuba, streights of Bahama, Windward paſsage . . . current through the gulf of Florida, with the soundings &c. By an officer in the navy.—Inset: A plan of the harbour & town of Havana . . .
p. 44. A draught of the Bay of Honda.
no. [18] A new and correct draught of the bay of Matanzas on ye north side of y^e iſland Cuba, done from a survey by Rob! Pearſon.
p. 50. A large draft of the iſland Antegua.
no. [19] A new & correct chart of the island of Jamaica with its bays, harbours, rocks, soundings &c. . . .
" [20] A chart of the coast of Guayana from the entrance of the river Orinoco . . . to the entrance of the river Amazones, by R. Waddington.—Inset: The river Orinoco from the entrance thereof to S! Thomas's.—The river of Surinam and places adjacent.
" [21] A new and correct chart of the trading part of the West Indies . . .

**1775**

**Jefferys, T.**

The american atlas: or, a geographical deſcription of the whole continent of America. Wherein are delineated at large, its several regions, countries, states, and islands; and chiefly the british colo-

**Jefferys, T.**—Continued.

nies. Engraved on forty-eight copper-plates . . . 2 p. l., 23 maps on 29 sheets. fol. London, R. Sayer & J. Bennett, 1775.

1165

NOTE:—Some copies of map no. 15-16, A map of the most inhabited part of New England, contain inset of Fort Frederik, in place of the plan of Boston, a copy of which is in Library of Congress. See also titles 1166 and 1169.

CONTENTS.

no. 1-3. A chart of North and South America, including the Atlantic and Pacific oceans, with the neareſt coaſts of Europe, Africa and Asia [Comprehending the Icy-sea . . . the russian discoveries between Aſia and America, taken from the map publiſhed at Peterſburg in 1774 by mr. J. von Stæhlin . . . [By John Green anon.] 3 sheets.

" 4. The russian discoveries [previous to . . . 1763] from the map published by the imperial academy of S$^t$. Petersburg. 1775.

" 5-6. An accurate map of North America, describing . . . the british and spanish dominions . . . according to the . . . treaty concluded at Paris 10$^{th}$ feb$^y$. 1763 . . . By Eman Bowen . . . and John Gibson. 1775. 2 sheets.—Insets: A particular map of Baffin and Hudson's bay.—The passage by land to California discover'd by . . . Eusebius Francis Kino between the years 1698 and 1701 . . .

" 7. North America from the french of m$^r$ d'Anville, improved with the english surveys made since the peace. 1775.

" 8. A map of the british empire in North America; by Samuel Dunn. 1774.

" 9. An exact chart of the river S$^t$. Laurence from fort Frontenac to the island of Anticosti. 1775.—Insets: The Seven islands.—S$^t$. Nicholas or English harbor.—A view of the lands from the traverse or passage from Cape Torment into the south channel of Orleans island.—The road of Tadousac.

" 10. A chart of the gulf of S$^t$. Laurence composed from a great number of actual surveys and other materials. 1775.

" 11. A map of the island of St. John in the gulf of S$^t$. Laurence . . . improved from the survey of captain Holland. 1775.—Inset: Gulf of S$^t$. Laurence.

" 12. A general chart of the island of Newfoundland . . . by James Cook and Michael Lane . . . and others. 1775.

" 13. A chart of the banks of Newfoundland drawn from a great number of . . . surveys, chiefly those of Chabert, Cook and Fleurieu. 1775.

" 14. A new map of Nova Scotia and Cape Breton island with the adjacent parts of New England and Canada . . . by Thomas Jefferys. 1775.

" 15-16. A map of the most inhabited part of New England containing the provinces of Massachusetts bay and New Hampshire with the colonies of Conecticut and Rhode Island. 1774. 2 sheets.—Insets: sheet 1. A plan of the town of Boston.—sheet 2. A plan of Boston harbor [by John Green. anon.]

" 17. A map of Pennsylvania . . . laid down from actual surveys and chiefly from the late map of W. Scull published in 1770. London, 1775.

no. 18. The provinces of New York and New Jersey, with part of Pensilvania . . . by cap‍ᵗ. Holland. 1775.
" 19. A general map of the middle british colonies in America . . . published by Lewis Evans . . . Corrected and improved . . . by Thos. Jefferys. 1775.—Inset: A sketch of the remaining part of Ohio r. &c.
" 20-21. A map of the most inhabited part of Virginia containing the whole province of Maryland with part of Pennsilvania, New Jersey and North Carolina . . . by Joshua Fry & Peter Jefferson, 1775. 2 sheets. Revised in 1755 by John Dalrymple.
" 22-23. An accurate map of North and South Carolina with their indian frontiers . . . the whole from actual surveys by Henry Mouzon and others, 1775. 2 sheets.—Insets: The harbour of Port Royal— The bar and harbour of Charleston.
" 24. The coast of West Florida and Louisiana . . . the peninsula and gulf of Florida or channel of Bahama . . . by Thoˢ. Jefferys. 1775.
" 25. Course of the river Mississipi, from the Balise to Fort Chartres taken on an expedition to the Illinois in the latter end of the year 1765 by lieuᵗ. Ross . . . improved from the surveys . . . made by the french. 1775.
" 26. The bay of Honduras. By Thoˢ. Jefferys. 1775.
" 27-28. A map of South America . . . from mʳ. d'Anville with several improvements and additions . . . 1775. 2 sheets.—Inset, sheet 1: A chart of Falkland's islands named by the french Malouine islands, and discovered by Hawkins in the year 1593.
" 29. A chart of the straits of Magellan. Inlarged from the chart published at Madrid in 1769 by don Juan de la Cruz Cano y Olmedilla . . . improved from the observations and surveys of capᵗⁿˢ. Byron, Wallis and Carteret compared with those of monʳ. de Bougainville. 1775.—Inset: A chart of Magellania with Falkland's islands.

## 1776

**Jefferys, T.,** *& others.*

The american atlas: or, a geographical defcription of the whole continent of America: wherein are delineated at large, its several regions, counties, states, and islands; and chiefly the British colonies, compofed from numerous surveys, feveral of which were made by order of Government. By major Holland, Lewis Evans, William Scull, Henry Mouzon, lieut. Ross, J. Cook, Michael Lane, Joseph Gilbert, Gardner, Hillock, &c. &c. Engraved on forty-nine copperplates . . . 2 p. l., 34 maps on 41 sheets. fol. London, R. Sayer & J. Bennett, 1776. 1166

NOTE.—See also titles 1165 and 1169. Maps with bracketed numbers are not found in the "Index to the maps," and are evidently insertions.

CONTENTS.

no. [1a] A chart of the world upon Mercator's projection defcribing the tracks of capt. Cook in the years 1768, 69, 70, 71, and in 1772, 73, 74, 75, with the new difcoveries. Published . . . 1775, by William Faden.

**Jefferys, T.,** & *others*—Continued.

no. 1-3. A chart of North and South America, including the Atlantic and Pacific oceans, with the neareſt coaſts of Europe Africa, and Asia [Comprehending the Icy-sea, with adjacent coaſts of Asia and America . . . the russian discoveries between Aſia and America, taken from the map publiſhed at Peterſburg in 1774, by mr. J. von Staehlin, secretary to the imperial academy . . . [By John Green. anon.] 1775. 3 sheets.

" 4. The russian discoveries from the map published by the imperial academy of St. Petersburg. 1775.

" 5-6. A new and correct map of North America, with the West India islands, divided according to the last treaty of peace concluded at Paris, 10$^{th}$ feb$^y$, 1763 . . . laid down according to the latest surveys, and corrected from the original materials, of gover$^r$. Pownall, mem$^{br}$. of parlia$^{mt}$· 1777. 2 sheets.—Insets: sheet 1: A particular map of Baffin and Hudson's bay.—sheet 2: The paſsage by land to California discover'd by father Eusebius Francis Kino . . . between the years 1698 and 1701 . . .

" 7. North America from the french of m$^r$. d'Anville, improved with the english surveys made since the peace. 1775.

" 8. A map of the britiſh empire in North America by Samuel Dunn . . . improved from the surveys of cap$^t$. Carver. 1776.

" 9. An exact chart of the river S$^t$. Lawrence, from Fort Frontenac to the island of Anticoſti showing the soundings, rocks . . . and all neceſsary instructions for navigating that river to Quebec . . . by . . . Thos. Jefferys. 1775.—Insets: The Seven islands.—A continuation of the river from Quebec to lake Ontario taken from the original . . . by m$^r$. d'Anville. 1755.—S$^t$. Nichols or English harbor.—A view of the lands from Cape Torment to the Butt . . .— The traverse or paſsage from Cape Torment into the south channel of Orleans island.—The road of Tadousac.

" 10. A chart of the gulf of St. Laurence. 1775.

" 11. A map of the iſland of S$^t$. John . . . improv'd from the late survey of captain Holland. 1775.—Inset: Gulf of S$^t$. Laurence.

" 12. A general chart of the island of Newfoundland with the rocks and soundings. By James Cook and Michael Lane . . . and others. 1775.

" 13. A chart of the banks of Newfoundland, drawn from a great number of hydographical surveys, chiefly from thoſe of Chabert, Cook, and Fleurieu. 1775.

" 14. A new map of Nova Scotia and Cape Breton island with the adjacent parts of New England and Canada. 1775.

" 15-16. A map of the moſt inhabited part of New England containing the provinces of Massachuſets bay and New Hampshire with the colonies of Conecticut and Rhode Island . . . 1774 [By John Green, anon.] 2 sheets.—Insets: A plan of the town of Boston.—A plan of Boston harbor from an accurate survey.

" 17. The provinces of New York and New Jersey with part of Penſilvania, and the province of Quebec. Drawn by major Holland . . . Corrected and improved from the original materials by govern. Pownall . . . 1776.—Insets: A chart of the mouth of Hudson's river from Sandy Hook to New York.—A plan of the city of New York.—Plan of Amboy, with its environs . . .

no. [17a] A chorographical map of the province of New-York in North America. Divided into counties, manors, patents and townships . . . By Claude Joseph Sauthier . . . Engraved and published by William Faden . . . 1779.

" 18. A survey of lake Champlain including lake George, Crown point and Sͭ John . . . by William Brassier. 1762. London, printed . . . 1776.—Inset: A particular plan of lake George. Surveyed in 1756 by capͭ Jackson.

" 19. A new map of the province of Quebec, according to the royal proclamation of the 7th of october 1763 . . . by captain Carver and other officers . . . 1776.—Insets: A particular survey of the isles of Montreal.—The city of Quebec.—Course of the river Sͭ Laurence from La Valterie to Quebec.—Plan of Montreal or Villemarie.

" 20. A map of Pennsylvania exhibiting not only the improved parts of that province, but alſo its extensive frontiers: laid down from actual surveys and chiefly from the late map of W. Scull, published in 1770. London, 1775.

" [20a] The province of New Jersey divided into east and west commonly called the Jerseys. Engraved and publiſhed by W͞m Faden. 1777.

" 21-22. A map of the moſt inhabited part of Virginia containing the whole province of Maryland, with part of Pensilvania, New Jersey, and North Carolina. Drawn by Joshua Fry & Peter Jefferson in 1775. 2 sheets. Edition revised by John Dalrymple in 1755.

" 23, 24. An accurate map of North and South Carolina with their indian frontiers, shewing . . . all the mountains, rivers, swamps . . . with the roads and indian paths . . . the whole from actual surveys by Henry Mouzon and others. 1775. 2 sheets.—Insets: The harbour of Port Royal.—The bar and harbour of Charlestown.

" [24a] A map of South Carolina and a part of Georgia . . . Composed from surveys taken by the hon. William Bull . . . captain Gascoign, Hugh Bryan . . . and William De Brahm . . . Republished with considerable additions from the surveys made & collected by John Stuart . . . by William Faden. 1780.

" [24b] A plan of the town, bar, harbour and environs of Charlestown in South Carolina . . . from the surveys made in the colony. Engraved by William Faden. 1780.

" 25. The coast of West Florida and Louisiana . . . The peninsula and gulf of Florida or channel of Bahama with the Bahama islands, by Tho͡ Jefferys. 1775.

" [25a] Sketch of the northern frontiers of Georgia, extending from the mouth of the river Savannah to the town of Augusta, by Archibald Campbell . . . engraved by Will͞m Faden. 1780.—Insets: Continuation of Savanna river from Ebenezer to Auguſta. [Contains " References to the attack of Savannah on the 28ᵗʰ december 1778] .

" 26. Course of the river Mississipi from the Balise to Fort Chartres, taken on an expedition to the Illinois in the latter end of the year 1765, by lieut. Roſs, improved from the surveys of that river made by the french. 1775.

" 27. The bay of Honduras, by Tho͡ Jefferys. 1775.

" [27a] L'isle de la Jamaïque, par m. T. J[efferys] Paris, chez Lattré, 1779.—Insets: Port de Bluefields.—Les ports de Kingston et de Port Royal.

**Jefferys, T.,** *& others*—Continued.
- no. [27b] La Grenade divisée par quartiérs avec ses ports et mouïllages d'après cette levée par ordre du gouverneur Scott. Paris, chez Lattré, 1779.
- " [27c] L'isle de la Dominique par m. J. M. Paris, chez Lattré, 1779.—Inset: Grande anse ou baye du prince Ruperts.
- " 28–29. A map of South America . . . from mr. d'Anville, with several improvements and additions, and the newest discoveries. 1775. 2 sheets.—Inset: A chart of Falkland's islands named by the french Malouine islands, and discovered by Hawkins in . . . 1593.
- " 30. A chart of the straits of Magellan. Inlarged from the chart published at Madrid in 1769 by don Juan de la Cruz Cano y Olmedilla . . . and improved from the observations and surveys of cap$^{tns}$ Byron, Wallis, and Carteret compared with those of mon$^{sr}$ de Bougainville. 1775.—Inset: A chart of Magellania with Falkland's islands.
- " [31] Hawkins's Maiden-land called afterwards, Falkland's islands, then by the french, Isles Nouvelles & Isles Malouines, by the dutch Nova Belgia . . . by Thomas Jefferys . . .
- " [32] A chart of the southern hemisphere according to the lateft difcoveries: with the tracks of the Resolution, cap$^n$ Cook; and the Adventure, cap$^n$ Furneaux; from 1772, to 1775. By George Forster. Engraved by William Whitchurch. 1777.

## 1777

**Atlante** dell' America contenente le migliori carte geografiche, e topografiche delle principali città, laghi, fiumi, e fortezze del nuovo mundo . . . 15 pp., 38 maps, 6 pl. fol. Livorno, G. T. Masi e comp. 1777. 1167

NOTE.—Maps taken from "Il Gazzettiere Americano" . . . Livorno, M. Cotellini, 1763, the text of which is a translation of the "American gazetteer," London, 1762. See also title 1161.
The names of the following engravers appear on the various maps: Andrea Scacciati, G. M. Terreni, Guiseppe Pazzi, D. V. Rossi, Violante Vanni, and N. Mabraini.
Page 15 numbered 8.
Plate no. [7½], Quebec, not given in list of contents.

CONTENTS.

- no. 1. Nuova ed esatta carta della America .
- " 2. Carta della Nuova Inghilterra, Nuova Jork, e Pensilvania.
- " 3. Carta rappresentante il porto di Boston.
- " 4. Porti della Nuova Jork, e Perthamboy.
- " 5. Carta rappresentante i cinque laghi del Canadà.
- " 6. Caduta di Niagara.
- " 7. Piano della città di Quebec.
- " 7½. Quebec.
- " 8. Carta rappresentante il golfo del fiume S. Lorenzo.
- " 9. Nuova, e corretta carta dell' isola di Terra Nuova.
- " 10. Carta rappresentante una parte dlla baja d' Hudson . . .
- " 11. Piano di Guantanimo . . .
- " 12. Carta reppresentante la penisola della Florida.
- " 13. Piano del porto, e degli stabilimenti di Pensacola.
- " 14. Piano della città, e porto di Sant'. Agostino.

no. 15. Nuovo Messico.
" 16. Nuova e corretta carta dell' Indie Occidentali ...
" 17. Carta e satta rappresentante l' isola di Cuba estratta dalle carte del sig: Poppler.
" 18. Piano della città, e porto dell' Havana.
" 19. Carta esatta rappresentante l' isola di S. Domingo ...
" 20. Piano della citta di S. Domingo.
" 21. Carta rappresentante l' isola della Giammaica.
" 22. Vedvta di S. Evstachio.
" 23. Carta esatta rappresentante l' isola della Guadalupa.
" 24. Carta rappresentante l' isola della Martinicca.
" 25. Carta esatta rappresentante l' isola di Barbados.
" 26. Carta esatta rappresentante l' isola di Granata.
" 27. Piano della rada, e della città della Vera Cruz.
" 28. Pianta del Porto d' Acapulco ...
" 29. Carta rappresentante la baia di Campeggio e l' Jucatan.
" 30. Carta rappresentante l' istmo di Darien ...
" 31. Piano di Porto Bello.
" 32. Piano della città rada, e porto di Chagre.
" 33. Carta rappresentante l' America Meridionale.
" 34. Carta rappresentante le provincie di Cartagena, S. Marta, e Venezula.
" 35. Piano della città, e sobborghi di Cartagena.
" 36. Piano della città e contorni di S. Francesco di Quito.
" 37. Carta del corso del Maragnone o sia del gran fivme dell' Amazzoni.
" 38. Piano scenografico della città dei Re, o' sia di Lima ...
" 39. Pianta di Cusco ...
" 40. Veduta della città, e della montagna del Potosi.
" 41. Pianta della città di Sant' Iago ...
" 42. Carta esatta rappresentante il corso del fiume Paraguay ...
" 43. Pianta della città di S. Salvadore.—Inset: Venduta della città di S. Salvadore.

**1780**

**English pilot, The.** The fourth book. Describing the West-India navigation, from Hudfon's bay to the river Amazones. Particularly delineating the coafts, capes, headlands, rivers, bays, roads, havens, harbours, streights, rocks, sands, shoals, banks, depths of water and anchorage, with all the iflands therein; as Jamaica, Cuba, Hifpaniola, Barbadoes, Antigua, Bermudas, Porto Rico and the reft of the Caribbee and Bahama iflands. Also a new defcription of Newfoundland, New England, New York, eaft and weft New Jerfey, Dellawar bay, Virginia, Maryland, Carolina, &c. Shewing the courfes and distances from one place to another; the ebbing and flowing of the sea, the setting of the tides and currents, &c. With many other things neceffary to be known in navigation. The whole being much enlarged and corrected, with the addition of feveral new charts and descriptions. By the information of divers able navigators of our own and other nations. 4, 3-66 pp., 21 maps, 9 maps in text. fol. London, for J. Mount, T. Page, W. Mount, & T. Page, on Towerhill, 1780. 1168

NOTE.—See title 1155, for numbers to other editions.

**English pilot, The**—Continued.

CONTENTS.

no. [1] A new and correct chart of the north part of America from New Found Land to Hudsons bay . . .
" [2] A new generall chart for the West Indies of E. Wright's projection vut. Mercators chart . . .
" [3] A new and accurate chart of the vast Atlantic or Western ocean . . . by Eman: Bowen . . .
" [4] A chart of the sea coast of New Foundland, New Scotland, New England, New York, New Jersey with Virginia and Maryland.
" [5] The harbour of Casco bay, and islands adjacent.
" [6] A new and correct chart of the coast of New Foundland from Cape Raze to Cape Bonavifta, with Chebucto harbour in Nova Scotia, done from the latest observations . . .—Chebucto harbour, in Nova Scotia, done from the latest observations.
p. 18. Ifland of St. Peters.
no. [7] A chart of the south-east coast of Newfoundland . . .
" [8] A map of the coaft of New England, from Staten Ifland to the ifland of Breton; as it was actually survey'd by capt. Cyprian Southack . . .—Insets: A chart of the Atlantic ocean fhewing the situation of Nova Scotia with refpect to the Britifh Ifles.—The town of Boston in New England.
" [9] A draught of New York from the Hook to New York town by Mark Tiddeman . . .
" [10] Virginia, Maryland, Pennsilvania, eaft & weft New Jersey . . .
p. 25. Tobago road.
" 26. Barbados.
no. [11] A draught of Virginia from the capes to York in York river and to Kuiquotan or Hamton in James river, by Mark Tiddeman . . .
p. 30. A large draft of the ifland Antegua.
no. [12] A new mapp of the ifland of St. Christophers being an actuall survey taken by mr. Andrew Norwood . . .—A new mapp of the ifland Martineca.—A new mapp of the ifland Guardalupa.
" [13] A draught of South Carolina and Georgia from Sewee to St. Estaca by Andrew Hughes . . .
" [14] A correct chart of the Caribbee islands . . .
" [15] A correct chart of Hispaniola with the Windward Passage . . , by C. Price . . .
" [16] A draught of the west end of the island of Porto Rico and the island of Zachee.—A draught of the island of Beata, on the south side of Hispaniola.—The west end of the island of Heneago.—Platform bay, on the south side of Cape Nicholas.—A draught of Sam bay, on the south side of Hispaniola.
" [17] A new & correct chart of Cuba, streights of Bahama, Windward passage, the current through the gulf of Florida, with the soundings &c. By an officer in the navy . . .—Inset: A plan of the harbour & town of Havana . . .
p. 44. A draught of the bay of Honda.
no. [18] A new and correct draught of the bay of Matanzas, on ye north side of ye ifland Cuba done from a survey by Robt Pearfon.
p. 50. Bermudas.
no. [19] A new & correct chart of the island of Jamaica, with its bays, harbours, rocks, soundings &c . . .

Another edition of his "The world in miniature . . . Western hemisphere . . . 1857" and "The Diamond atlas . . . Western hemisphere . . . 1857." See titles 820 and 824.

Descriptive text and maps "Connecticut, Rhode Island and Long Island" and "Texas" omitted.

**1864**

**Colton, G. W.**

Colton's atlas of America, illustrating the physical and political geography of North and South America and the West India Islands . . . Accompanied by descriptions geographical, statistical and historical, by Richard Swanson Fisher. 2 p. l., 149 pp. incl. 57 maps. fol. New York, J. W. Colton, 1864. 1182

NOTE.—Contains maps of the following cities: Washington and Georgetown.—Boston.—New York.—Philadelphia.—Baltimore.—Charleston, Savannah.—Louisville, New Orleans.—Pittsburg, Cincinnati.—Chicago, St. Louis.

**1874**

**Mitchell, S. A.**

Mitchell's new atlas of America, containing maps of the United States and territories, Canada, Central America, Sandwich islands, Mexico, Cuba, West Indies and South American states, plans of cities, etc., embraced in sixty-three quarto maps forming a series of eighty-three maps and plans, together with valuable statistical tables. Also, a list of post-offices of the United States and territories, and census of 1860 and 1870. 2 p. l., [64], 27, [4] pp. incl. 47 col. maps, 1 tab. fol. Philadelphia, S. A. Mitchell, 1874.
1183

NOTE.—Pagination irregular.

**1879**

**Bartholomew, J.**

Philip's handy general atlas of America, comprising a series of detailed maps of the United States, Canada, etc. With index and statistical notes . . . 18 pp., 23 col. maps. fol. London, G. Philip & son [1879] 1184

## NORTH AMERICA.

### CITIES.

**Le Rouge, G. L.**

Recueil des plans de l'Amérique Septentrionale. 1 p. l., 18 maps, 2 pl. 8°. Paris, Le Rouge, 1755. 1185

NOTE.—Engraved title.

Maps nos. [3-5] numbered respectively 87, 88, 89, are the same as those with corresponding numbers in his Recueil des fortifications, forts et ports

**LeRouge, G. L.**—Continued.

de mer de France [1760?]
no. 13 inserted owing to change in title in no. 12.
See title 2973.

CONTENTS.

no. [1] Plan de la ville de Quebec.
" [2] Vue de Quebec, capitale du Canada.
" [3] en [!] Amérique Quebec.—Louisbourg.
" [4] Cayenne.—Ville Marie.
" [5] Nouvelle Orleans.—Fort Dauphin projetté.
" [6] Fort S! Frederic . . .—Nouvelle ville de Halifax.
" [7] Fort Halifax bati en 1754.—Fort Western en 1754.—Fort Francfort en 1752.
" [8] Charles-Town, capitale de la Caroline.
" [9] Kingston, capitale de la Jamaique, bâtie par les anglois en 1692.
" [10] Port Royal, de Jamaique.
" [11] Carte des bayes, rades et port de Plaisance dans l'isle de Terre Neuve . . .
" [12] Port Royal, appellé aujourd' par les anglois Annapolis Royal . . .
" [13] Port Royal dans l'Acadie appellé aujourd' par les anglois . . .
" [14] Vera-Cruz, dans le golfe du Mexique.
" [15] S! Domingo, capitale de l'isle du même nom.
" [16] Havane.
" [17] Sault du Niagara . . .
" [18] Plan de Boston . . .

**CITIES AND FORTS.**

**Rocque, J.**

A set of plans and forts in America, reduced from actual surveys.
1763.   1 p. l., 30 maps.   obl. 24°.   [London] 1763.   1186

NOTE.—First edition.
Engraved title.
John, or Jean Rocque was a native of France and eventually became topographer to the king of England. He published various plans and views but this set was not issued until the year after his death, in 1762, presumedly by Mary Ann Rocque whose name here appears on the map of New York as publisher and later on the title page of the 1765 edition. This copy contains the rare plan of New York very similar to that originally drawn in 1755 by F. Maerschalck, city surveyor, and known from its publisher as the Duyckinck map. Comparison with an original engraved copy in the Library of Congress shows differences in names and slight changes in the outline. The general outline and key are like this copy which may have been taken from another survey by Maerschalck. The maps are usually credited to P. Andrews as engraver, although only nos. 1, 7, 10 and 30 are signed.
Bound by Zaehnsdorf.

CONTENTS.

no. [1] A plan of the city of New-York, reduced from an actual survey, by T. Maerfchalckm, 1763.   P. Andrews sculp.   Publish'd according to act of parliament by M. A. Rocque . . .
" [2] Plan of Quebec . . . 1763.

no. [3] Plan of the city and fortress of Louisbourg with the attacks.
" [4] Plan of the town and fortifications of Montreal . . .
" [5] Plan of Schenectady . . .
" [6] A plan of the city of Albany . . .
" [7] A plan of the town of Halifax in Nova Scotia . . . P. Andrews, sculp.
" [8] Plan of Fort Frontenac . . .
" [9] Sketch of Fort Brewerton at the west end of Oneda [!] lake.
" [10] Sketch of the stockade fort, at Oswego Falls. P. Andrews, sculp.
" [11] Fort William Henry.
" [12] Plan of the Narrows about 10 miles from New York . . .
" [13] Plan and profile of retrenched work round Harkemeis house at ye German Flats 1756.
" [14] Scetch [!] of the blockhouse at the east of Oneda [!] lake.
" [15] A plan of the royal block house, with the environs at Fort Edward.
" [16] A plan of Fort William Henry and the English camps & retrenchments with the French different camps and attacks thereupon . . .
" [17] A plan of the fort at Saratoga . . .
" [18] Plan of part of Fort George, with the barracks &c. Erected in the year 1759 . . .
" [19] Plan of the retrench'd camp, at Fort Ligonier . . .
" [20] Plan of Fort Fredrick at Albany . . .
" [21] A plan of the new fort at Pitts-Burgh or Du Quesne. Nov! 1759 . . .
" [22] Plan of Fort Edward . . .
" [23] Fort Bedford.
" [24] Plan of the new fort & redoubts at Crown Point . . .
" [25] Plan of the new fort and redoubts at New Crown Point.
" [26] Plan of Fort Stanwix built at Oneida station by provincial troops in 1758 . . .
" [27] A plan of Fort Frederick, situated at the entrance of S! Johns river . . .
" [28] Plan of Fort Niagara, with its environs . . .
" [29] Plan of the fort at Tienderoga [!] . . . 1759.
" [30] A plan of Fort Ontario . . . P. Andrews sculp.

### FORESTRY.
**Sargent, C. S.**
Sixteen maps accompanying report on forest trees of North America. 1 p. l., 16 maps. fol. [Washington, government printing office, 1884]
[United States. Department of the interior. Census office. 10th census]    1187

### HISTORICAL.
**Hart, A. B.**
Epoch maps illustrating american history. [1st ed.] . . . 3 p. l., 14 maps. obl. 16°. New York, Longmans, Green & co. 1891.    1188

CONTENTS.

no. 1. Physical features of the United States of America . . .
" 2. North America, 1650. Showing claims arising out of exploration and occupancy.
" 3. English colonies, 1700. Showing extent of actual jurisdiction.

**Hart, A. B.**—Continued.
>no. 4. North America, 1750. Showing claims arising out of exploration and occupancy.
>" 5. English colonies, 1763-1775.
>" 6. The United States, 1783. Subdivisions as claimed by the states.
>" 7. Territorial growth of the United States. 1783-1866.
>" 8. Status of slavery in the United States. 1775-1865.
>" 9. The United States, march 4th, 1801.
>" 10. The United States, march 4th, 1825.
>" 11. Territorial controversies settled by the United States. 1840-1850.
>" 12. The United States, march 4th, 1855.
>" 13. The United States, july 4th, 1861.
>" 14. The United States, march 4th, 1891.

Epoch maps illustrating american history . . .   3 p. l., 14 maps.  obl. 16°.   New York, Longmans, Green & co. 1899.   1189

Epoch maps illustrating american history . . .  New ed.  3 p. l., 14 maps.  obl. 16°.  New York, Longmans, Green & co. 1904.
1190

>Note.—Map no. [14] in this edition, entitled: The United States, march 4th, 1897. First edition, nov., 1891. Reprinted, july, 1892, aug., 1893, june, 1897, feb., 1898, dec., 1898 (revised), oct., 1901, aug., 1902, feb., 1904 (revised)

### REPRODUCTIONS.

**Hulbert, A. B.,**
>The crown collection of photographs of american maps selected and edited by Archer Butler Hulbert . . .   5 v.  fol.  Cleveland, the A. H. Clark co. 1904-1908.   1191

>>Note.—Issue limited to twenty-five sets, of which v. 1 is no. 6; v. 2 no. 8; v. 3 no. 8; v. 4 no. 8. v. 5, received too late to note contents.

>> CONTENTS.

>>v. 1: 8 p. l., 48 maps, 2 pl.
>>Fifty photographs of maps of american rivers in the crown collection of manuscripts in the British Museum.
>>>no. 1. A new mappe of a part of Hutson's or the North river . . . survoyed in the yare 1700, by col: W. W. Römer.
>>>" 2. A plan of the great falls on Hudson's River . . . [Drawn about 1758]
>>>" 3. [Map of the county of Albany; with a continuation of the Mohawk river . . . down to Oswego about 1756]
>>>" 4. Map of the county of Albany.
>>>" 5. Continuation of the Mohawk river, Wood creek & down to Oswego.
>>>" 6. The course of the Wood creek . . . to the Onoida lake . . . [drawn about 1758]
>>>" 7. [Same continued]
>>>" 8. A sketch of lake Ontario, between Oswego and Niagara, and from thence up the river . . . taken by George Dember . . .
>>>" 9. View of the lesser fall at Niagara . . . july 1765.
>>>" 10. View of the great fall at Niagara . . . july 1765.

no. 11. Plan of [fort] Niagara . . . [drawn by Francis Pfister . . . 28 sept., 1773 . . . and a sketch of the communication between lake Ontario and lake Erie]
" 12. Plan of a survey from lake Ontario to lake Erie [Niagara river, 1773?]
" 13. [Chart of lake Erie, with route southward, Allegheny river, 1756?]
" 14. [Same continued—Monongahela and Youghiogheny rivers]
" 15. [A map of part of New York . . . the river Connecticut &c., to shew the way from Albany to Canada . . . drawn about 1720]
" 16. A French draught of lake Champlain and lake George . . . [1758?]
" 17. [Same continued—lake Champlain]
" 18. [Same continued—Richelieu and St. Lawrence]
" 19. A sketch of lake George [drawn by capt. Abercrombie, about 1756 . . .]
" 20. [A "plan of part of lake Champlain with the communication down to St. John's," drawn by Gather Mann . . . Quebec, 13 june, 1791]
" 21. Plan of part of lake Champlain with the communication down to S. Johns.
" 22. A correct map of the province of New Hampshire together with part of Hudson's river . . . june, 1756.
" 23. Pascatway river in New England by I. S.
" 24. [A plan of Kennebeck river . . . dated Boston, nov. 12, 1754]
" 25. [Same continued]
" 26. [A plan of the bay and port of the river Penobscot, or Penobsceag . . . by Jones, capt. North . . . in 1758, and lieut. Scarborough]
" 27. [A . . . chart of the entrance of Chesapeake bay, with King James' river, Prince Henry's river . . . and Rapahanoc river . . . the draught by Robarte Tindall of Virginia, anno 1608]
" 28. [Same continued]
" 29. [A large . . . chart of Albemarle river drawn by W. Hack, about 1684]
" 30. [Map of route from fort Cumberland . . . to fort Erie 1755]
" 31. Carte . . . du fleuve Mississippi, ou de St. Louis, depuis la Nouvelle orleans . . . fait en 1731; [drawn by sr. Gonichon]
" 32-35. [Same continued]
" 36. [A draught of the river Mississippi, from its entrance to the river Iberville]
" 37-39. [Same continued]
" 40. [Carte du cours du fleuve St. Louis . . . drawn about 1740]
" 41. [Same continued]
" 42. Plan of the proposed new town, also the proposed cut from the Mississippi, to the Iberville. [1772]
" 43-44. [Same continued]
" 45. Map of Ohio company's lands—1753? showing upper Ohio river and tributaries]
" 46. [A . . . map of the Grand Pass from New York to Montreal . . . drawn about 1756]
" 47. [Same continued]
" 48. [Part of . . . map of the route between Albany and Oswego . . . drawn about 1756]
" 49-50. [Same continued]
v. 2: 7 p. l., 49 maps, 1 fac-sim.
Fifty photographs of maps and plans in the southern states, western Pennsylvania, and New York . . .

**Hulbert, A. B.**—Continued.
- no. 1-2. Chart of lake Borgne and the neighboring islands . . . [By lieut. col.] C. R. Forrest, 1815. 2 sheets.
- " 3. Plan of Mobile. Survey'd by P. Pitman . . .
- " 4. A plan of the fort at Pensacola. Copy W. Brasier.
- " 5. [A plan of the coast of East Florida from fort William to Anstatia island: with a bird's-eye view of the town of St. Augustine, to shew the attack and capture of the place by the English forces under general Oglethorpe in 1740]
- " 6. Plan of the fortified canal across the neck from Ashley to Cooper river [Surveyed about 1770, by W. G. de Brahm . . .]
- " 7. Same continued. Explanation.
- " 8. Plan and profiles of Loudoun upon Tanaísee river . . . [Surveyed about 1770, by W. G. de Brahm]
- " 9. Plan of the town Ebenezer and its fort [Surveyed about 1770, by W. G. de Brahm]
- " 10. The environs of fort Barrington [Surveyed about 1770, by W. G. de Brahm]
- " 11. [Plan of the fort in St. Simon's island and of the adjacent redoubt]
- " 12. Plan d'un petit fort pour l'isle de St Andre . . . [or Cumberland island]
- " 13. View of Cockspur fort at the entrance of Savanna river in Georgia. decr: 1764.
- " 14. Plan and profile of fort George, on Coxpur island . . . [Surveyed about 1770, by W. G. de Brahm]
- " 15-16. Plan of the city Savannah and fortification [Surveyed about 1770, by W. G. de Brahm]
- " 17. Plan of the city and fortification of Charlestown . . . [Surveyed about 1770, by W. G. de Brahm]
- " 18. Plan and profile of Fort Johnston . . . [near Charlestown, surveyed about 1770, by W. G. de Brahm]
- " 19. A plan of fort Cumberland on Will's creek & Potomack river, with a view of the store houses belonging to the Ohio company . . . [1755]
- " 20. A plan of the fort and barracks at Mount Pleasant in Maryland . . . [Fort Cumberland, drawn about 1755]
- " 21. A plan of fort De Quesne.
- " 22. Rough plan of fort Du Quesne, such as it was before it was demolish'd, 1758 . . . [Drawn by J. C. Pleydell]
- " 23. A plan of the fort for 220 men built in December 1758 within 400 yards of fort Du Quesne . . .
- " 24-27. Plan of fort Pitt and parts adjacent with both rivers . . . [Drawn by] B. Ratzer, 1761. 4 sheets.
- " 28. [A plan of] fort Augusta . . . [on the Susquehanna river, drawn about 1756]
- " 29. Profil coupé par une face d'un bastion du fort Augusta . . .
- " 30. [Plan of] fort Bedford [on the Juniata creek]
- " 31. Rough plan of fort Ligonier [on the Loyal Hanon creek]
- " 32. Plan of fort Ligonier with part of the retranchment . . .
- " 33. [A military sketch, imperfect, of the disposition of some of the english and american troops and of general Howe's headquarters, after the affair of White Plains, 25 oct., 1776]
- " 34. [A plan of the town of Albany . . . drawn in 1695, by John Miller]
- " 35. Plan of the city of Albany . . . [drawn about 1756]

no. 36. Plan of the city of Albany, with the designs for securing it . . . [Drawn in 1756]
" 37–38. Plan of the city of Albany, in the province of New York . . . shewing designs for fortifications etc., drawn by Thos. Sowers, engr., 1756]  2 sheets.
" 39. Plan of the city of Albany, fhowing the several works & buildings made there in the years 1756 & 57 . . .
" 40. Plan of fort Frederick at Albany . . . [drawn by Thomas Sowers, engr., 1756]
" 41. The Indian fort at y$^e$ Flats [four miles from Albany; drawn in 1695, by John Miller]
" 42. [Plan of the river Schohary, showing] Plan of the Indian Castel.— Plan of the new fort. [Drawn about 1758]
" 43. Plan of the post at the Half Moon [at the junction of the rivers Hudson and Mohawk]
" 44. Plan of the buildings at the Half-Moon . . . [drawn by capt. Abercromby?]
" 45. The fort at Scanecthade [drawn in 1695, by John Miller]
" 46. Plan of Schenectady . . . [Drawn by capt. Abercromby? about 1756]
" 47. Plan of the entreckment made round Herkhumer's house, 1756.
" 48. Plan of the forts at the Onoida . . . in the province of New York . . . built by major general Charles Craven . . . and destroyed by major general Webb, 31 august, 1756 . . .
" 49. Plan of fort Stanwix, built at Onieda station . . . in 1758 . . . [Drawn by John Williams]
" 50. Plan of fort Stanwix, built at the Onnida station, 1758 . . .
v. 3: 7 p. l., 42 maps, 6 pl.
Fifty-three photographs of maps and fortifications of the Niagara frontier, Hudson valley, and lakes George and Champlain . . .
no. 1. [Chart of the upper part of lake Erie . . . with a plan of fort Erie, built under the direction of John Montresor, engineer, 1764 . . . drawn by Francis Pfister, 1764]
" 2. Plan of fort Niagara with its environs, and the attack made thereupon, in the month of july 1759 . . .
" 3. [Plan du fort Niagara; cette place a été commencée le 14 janvier, 1756, et finie le 12 october, 1757, avec 80 travailleurs par jours, par mr. de Pouchot . . .]
" 4. [Same continued]
" 5. Plan of fort Niagara, with a design for contracting the fame, by Iohn Montresor . . . Dated june 1768 . . .
" 6. Elevation, plan and section, of the new draw-bridge built at Niagara 1769. By captain Tho$^s$. Sowers, eng$^r$. 1769.
" 7. Section and elevation of a stone redout [being one of those built in fort Niagara in 1770 . . .]
" 8. [A plan of Oswego, at the mouth of the river Onondaga, on lake Ontario, shewing the positions of fort Ontario and fort Oswego; drawn by capt. Abercromby? about 1756 . . .]
" 9. Plan of Oswego with a projected fort for to contain 500 men . . . Albany may 29th 1759. W. B[rasier] del.
" 10. [A plan and sections of a quadrangular fort, being a design made in 1759? . . . Drawn by capt Abercrombie?]
" 11. Fort Ontario. Built by Thomas Sowers engin$^r$. 1760.
" 12. [Same continued]
" 13. Perspective view of fort Ontario by **Francis Pfister** . . . **1761.**

**Hulbert, A. B.**—Continued.

no. 14. Carte du lac ontario nouvelleman[!] rellevé, avec ces port à grand poit abittée, l'escadre engloisse & francoisse, leur gremamt, leur cantitée de canon faitte à frontenac ce 4 october, 1757, part. Labrogueril.
" 15. A mappe of colonel Römer's voyage to y$^e$ 5 indian nations . . . anno do. 1700.
" 16. Plan of Still-Water [on Hudson's river] with its block house, & c$^a$.
" 17. Plan of Saratogha, 36 miles n. by e. from Albany [on Hudson's river, shewing the lines made in the summer of 1756 . . .]
" 18. Plan of the fort at Saratoga, 1757.
" 19. Plan of fort Miller and the environs on the west-side of Hudsons river [1759]
" 20. Plan of fort Miller with the barraks.
" 21. Plan of fort Edward . . . [on Hudson's river] nov. 13$^{th}$ 1755.
" 22. Sketch of fort Edward and the propofed improvements [drawn about 1728]
" 23. Plan of fort Edward with the environs . . . [drawn about 1758]
" 24. Rapport of the fort Edward with a deffein of a chemin couvert, a larger ditch, a sluice, and a detached work of the large jland with remarqs of the fort and his defence.
" 25. Fort Edward [drawn about 1760, by Francis Pfister]—Plan of the city of Albany, [drawn about 1760, by Francis Pfister]
" 26. [A plan for a military post on Wood creek, at the junction of the Cannada creek; drawn by Wm. Eyre . . .]
" 27. View of Harlaem, from Morisania in the province of New York, septem! 1765.
" 28. Plan of the country from fort Edward to Crown Point [shewing the marches of the french under baron Dieskau, and of the english under colonel Williams, in august, 1755 . . . drawn by Harry Gordon, engineer]
" 29. Plan of the city of Albany; [drawn by capt. T. Abercrombie, in 1758]—Fort Edward [drawn about 1760, by Francis Pfister]—Fort William Henry and the attack thereupon [drawn in 1758, by capt. Th. Abercrombie]
" 30. Lake George. Laid down by me in the month of october, 1756, G. C. Wetterström . . .
" 31. [Same continued]
" 32. A draught of lake George, with all the islands & soundings [drawn about 1760]
" 33. Plan of fort William Henry and camp at lake George . . . [shewing the attack by the french troops and canadians, 8 sept., 1755]
" 34. Plan of fort William-Henry. Will Eyre eng$^r$. [about 1755]
" 35. Plan of fort Wm. Henry with a design to strengthen that part the most liable to be attacked . . . [drawn by Wm. Eyre about 1756]
" 36. [Plan of the environs of fort William Henry on lake George, shewing the proceedings of the siege by the french under m. Montcalm in august, 1757]
" 37. Defigned plan of a fort and batterys of the ground of the retranchment in 1758, for the defence of the head waters of lake George, and for a poft to be eftablished there.
" 38. [A map of lake Champlain and lake George, shewing the route from Fort Edward to Montreal]

no. 39. [A plan of the southern part of lake Champlain, from "Tienderoga fort" to Crown Point; drawn about 1758]
" 40-41. [Same continued]
" 42. A plan of fort Frederic situate on the south side of lake Champlain, and on the west side of Wood creek, said to be built within the bounds of the province of New York, by the french anno domini 17$\frac{31}{32}$.
" 43. A survey of the country between the upper part of lake George and fort Ticonderoga, drawn about 1756]
" 44. [Survey of the ground about fort Carillon, Ticonderoga, copied by W. B. from the original, drawn about 1756, by John Burghard]
" 45. Montreal [drawn by capt. Th. Abercrombie, in 1758]—Fort Frederic or Crown point [drawn by capt. T. Abercrombie in 1758]—Fort Ticonderoga [drawn by capt. T. Abercrombie, in 1758]
" 46. Plan of the fort at Tienderoga and environs, at the head of lake Champlain, november 1759 . . . The fort and lines survey'd by lieut. Bream assist engin$^r$. the ground by Wm. Brasier.
" 47. A view of Ticonderoga from the middle of the channel in lake Champlain. James Hunter. 1777.
" 48. A view of Ticonderoga from a point on the north shore of lake Champlain. James Hunter. 1777.

v. 4: 7 p. l., 36 maps, 1 l., 24 pl.
Thirty-six photographs of maps and forts and fortifications of lake Champlain, eastern New York and New England, and twenty-four photographs of Simcoe views of the Niagara frontier, in the crown collection of manuscripts in the British Museum.

no. 1. A draught of the fortrefs building at Crown Point 22 oct$^r$ 1759 . . . Scale of 100 feet to an inch.
" 2-3. Plan of the new fort, and redouts at Crown Point called . . . The fort . . . Grenadier fort . . . Light infantry of regiments fort . . . Scale . . . 40 feet to an inch. 2 sheets.
" 4. Project for taking post at Crown Point. may 13$^{th}$, 1774, by John Montresor. Scale for the plan, 40 feet to an inch.
" 5-6. A map of the province of New York, part of New Jersey with a part of New France. Composed from actual surveys [by major Christie, in 1759; drawn by] Francis Pfister, by a scale 16 miles to a [!] inch. 2 sheets.
" 7-8. To his excellency major general Abercrombie . . . this map of the scene of action [in 1758] is humbly submitted. [Shows that part of the state of New York situated between lake Ontario and Massachusetts, northward to the St. Lawrence, drawn by capt. Thomas Abercrombie . . . with drawings of Montreal, fort Crown Point, fort Ticonderoga, Albany, fort Edward, fort William Henry and Oswego] 2 sheets.
" 9-10. To his excellency William Shirly esq$^r$ . . . this draught of the northern english colonies, together with the french neighbouring settlements; taken partly from actual surveys and partly from the most approved draughts and other accounts, done at your excellency's request; is most humbly dedicated by . . . Charles Morris. Boston, aug. 16$^{th}$ 1749. 2 sheets.
" 11. A small map of the sea coast of New England, together with the outlines of several of the provinces lying thereon. 1738.
" 12. The south boundary line of the Mafsachusetts [!] as run in 1713. The line as said to have been run by Woodward and Safery in 1642.

**Hulbert, A. B.**—Continued.

no. 13-14. A map of the country adjacent to the north part boundary line of the colony of Rhode Island as the same was run by commifsioners appointed for that purpose by the general afsembly of the said colony in the year 1750. Drawn by Joseph Harrison. 2 sheets.

" 15-19. [An iconographic draft of Castle Island whereupon is built her majesty's castle and by her majesty's special command named Castle William, situated on the bay of Boston south ¾ of a mile of the mean, made and survaied [!] by collonel Römer, in the yeare 1705] 5 sheets.

" 20. [Plan of the town and environs of Boston, the capital of New England, with six colored views; drawn by lieut. William Pierie, of the royal regiment of artillery, in 1773]

" 21. View of Boston, the capitol of New England; from col. Hatch's houfe, on the road to Dorchester. 2 sheets.

" 22. View from Dorchester neck, at station A.—View from Charlestown, at station B. 2 sheets.

" 23. View of Castle William, at station C.—View of Castle William, at station D. 2 sheets.

" 24. View of Castle William, a; Dorchester Neck, b; Light house, c; sailing out of the harbour. 2 sheets.

" 25-27. No. 1. A view of the country round Boston taken from Beacon hill by lieut. Williams . . .—no. 2-6. Shewing the lines, redouts & diffferent encampments of the rebels allso those of his majesty's troops under the command of . . . lieut. general Gage . . . These drawings are most humbly inscribed to colonel James of the royal artillery, by . . . R.d Williams . . . 3 sheets.

" 28-29. A plan of Boston and its environs shewing the true situation of his majesty's troops and also those of the rebels; likewise all the forts, redouts and entrenchments erected by both armies. Drawn by an engineer at Bofton . . . 2 sheets.

" 30. Draft of fort William & Mary on Piscatagua river in y.e province of New-Hampshire on the continent of America . . .

" 31-32. Draft of her maj.ties fort William & Mary, on Piscataqua river, America, 1705. 2 sheets.

" 33. [A map of New Hampshire, shewing the settlement of the boundaries between it and Massachusetts as determined by his majesty]

" 34-35. [Two plans, shewing the disputed boundaries of the townships of Suncook, Rumford, and Bon, on the river Merrimack, now forming part of the counties of Rockingham and Hillsborough] 2 sheets.

" 36. View of Oswegatchee on the river S.t Laurence, july, 1765.

Supplement, comprising a collection of views in Upper Canada, drawn on birch bark by mrs. Simcoe; collected by her husband, governor Simcoe, and presented to king George III.

no. 37. York [Toronto] harbour.—The garrison at York.

" 38. Navy Hall opposite [fort] Niagara.—Queenston or landing near Niagara.

" 39. Spray of the falls of Niagara seen from the Welland [river]—Scene near fort Erie.

" 40. Mohawk village on the Grand river or Ouse.—Waterfall near Burlington bay.

" 41. Castle Frank near York.—Mill on the Appamée river.—Bay of Quinty.

" 42. Fifteen Mile creek on lake Ontario.—Twenty Mile creek on lake Ontario.

no. 43. Cootes Paradise near Burlington bay.—From the King's Inn on the beach at Burlington bay.
" 44. Fort Chippewa on the river Welland.—Mouth of the Welland.
" 45. Point á Bodet.—Kingston.
" 46. Bass Island in lake Erie.—Scite [!] of Charlotteville near Long Point on lake Erie.
" 47. Bridge on the Donn near York.—Bridge on the Donn.
" 48. View of lake Ontario, and entrance of Burlington bay.—Entrance of Burlington bay.

**Boundary** between the dominion of Canada and the territory of Alaska. . . . Appendix to the case of his majesty's government before the Alaska boundary tribunal. v. 2. Atlas. 2 p. l., 37 maps. fol. London, McCorquodale & co. limited, 1903. 1192

NOTE.—v. 2, contains portions of maps of North America relating chiefly to Alaska, Canada and the north coast.
Atlas entitled: British case. Alaska boundary. Atlas. Appendix vol. II.

CONTENTS.

no. 1-3. . . . Chart shewing part of the coast of n. w. America . . . Vancouver, 1798.
" 4. Parts of charts VII & XII, Vancouver's atlas.
" 5. [Russian map] Translation of title: Map of marine discoveries by russian navigators in the Pacific and Frozen oceans . . . 1802.
" 6. Part of map no. 5 i. e. карта морскихъ открытіи . . .
" 7. Map of the world illustrating the voyages and travels of G. H. von Langsdorff.
" 8. Map of America by A. Arrowsmith . . . 1822 (colored)
" 9. [Part of Arrowsmith's map of America] (uncolored)
" 10. Map of North America from 20°-80° north latitude . . . 1823.
" 11. Same. 1824.
" 12. [Part of Arrowsmith's map of America] 1824.
" 13. Part of colonial office manuscript map. By L. Hebert senior. 1831.
" 14. The British dominions in North America. Bouchette. 1831.
" 15. карта ледовитаго моря . . . Translation of title: Part of map of the Frozen ocean and the Eastern ocean . . . 1844.
" 16. Map of the western and middle portions of North America . . . by Robert Greenhow. 1844.
" 17. Map showing sir George Simpson's route. 1847.
" 18. [Russian map] Translation of title: Part of map of the straits of the north-west coast of America, from latitude 54° to 56°. . . . 1849.
" 19. Map of North America. John Arrowsmith. Ordered by the house of commons. 1850.
" 20. [Russian map] Translation of title: [Part of] Mercator map of the southern half of the Koloshenski archipelago . . . 1853.
" 21. Map of North America. Drawn by J. Arrowsmith . . . 1857.
" 22. Part of map of British North America. Drawn by J. Arrowsmith. 1863.
" 23. N. W. America. British Columbia. Portland canal. From the admiralty survey of 1868.
" 24. N. W. America. British Columbia. Observatory inlet, from the admiralty survey of 1868.
" 25. . . . Port Simpson to Nass village. fr. the admiralty survey of 1868.

**Boundary** between the dominion of Canada and the territory of Alaska—Continued.
  no. 26. Plan of the Stachine or Stickeen river . . . 1877.
  "   27. Tracing of part of "Alaska" shewing "Stakeen river;" from U. S. coast survey of 1869.
  "   28. Map of Alaska and adjoining regions. Compiled by Ivan Petroof . . . 1880.
  "   29. Same (reduced)
  "   30. Same (reduced and colored)
  "   31. Map of the province of British Columbia . . . by Edward Mohun . . . 1884.
  "   32. Map of the dominion of Canada. Geologically colored from surveys made by the geological corps, 1842-1882.
  "   33. Part of british admiralty chart no. 2431. Cordova bay to Cross sound. 1865. Corrections to 1884.
  "   34. Dawson's canadian map, 1887, showing conventional lines proposed by Canada.
  "   35. Portland inlet, Alaska. U S. coast and geodetic survey. 1888.
  "   36. N. W. shore of Portland inlet Alaska. U. S. coast and geodetic survey. 1888.
  "   37. Southern Alaska and part of British Columbia. . . . Canadian boundary commission . . . 1893-1898.

**Alaskan** boundary tribunal. The case of the United States before the tribunal convened at London under the provisions of the treaty between the United States of America and Great Britain, concluded january 24, 1903. Atlas. 3 p. l., 25 maps. fol. Washington, government printing office, 1903.     1193

  NOTE.—Atlas entitled: . . . Atlas accompanying the case of the United States . . .
  Supplemented by "Atlas accompanying the counter case of the United States." Another edition, with imprint date 1904, has atlas and supplement in one volume.
  Portions of maps of North America, relating chiefly to Alaska, Canada and the north coast.
  Contains also biographical notes of some of the cartographers whose maps are reproduced.
  Maps nos. 6-9, 11-13 and 24 were photographed from the originals in the Library of Congress.

CONTENTS.

  no. 1. General map. Adjacent parts of North America and Asia . . . 1903.
  "  2-3. Southeastern Alaska . . . 1903.
  "  4-5. Charts of part of the coast of n. w. America . . . nos. 7, 12 Vancouver, 1798.
  "   6. Part of a map published at St. Petersburg in 1802. [Pacific & Icy seas]
  "   7. Part of a map of North America, published at Augsburg in 1807 by Johann Walch. [Tr. fr. german title]
  "   8. The northwest part of a "Map of British North America, after mr. Arrowsmith," from Pinkerton's Modern atlas . . . Philadelphia, 1818.
  "   9. Part of Brué's map of North America, 1815-1819 . . .

no. 10. Part of the "Map of America by A. Arrowsmith, hydrographer to his majesty, 1822. Additions to 1823" . . .
" 11. Part of russian admiralty chart no. 1266 . . . Translated the title reads: General chart of the South sea, sheet 2, from the equator to latitude 72° 30′ north and from longitude 112° 30′ to 192° 30′ east. 1826.
" 12. Part of A. Arrowsmith's map of North America . . . 1795 . . . revised to 1833 . . .
" 13. Part of Bruć's map of North America . . . Paris, 1833 . . .
" 14. Part of "A map of North America, constructed according to the latest information, by H. S. Tanner, 1839."
" 15. Part of the "Map of the western and middle portions of North America, to illustrate the history of California, Oregon and the other countries on the northwest coast of America, by Robert Greenhow . . . 1844."
" 16. Part of a map of the western coast of America . . . m. Duflot de Mofras, Paris, 1844.
" 17. The greater part of a map of "The british dominions in North America," which appears as an inset map on the large "Map of the provinces of Canada" . . . by Joseph Bouchette . . . 1853.
" 18. Part of a Mercator map of the world, pub. by the spanish admiralty in 1857.
" 19. The greater part of the "Map of the northwest part of Canada, Hudson's bay and Indian territories . . . 1857." Drawn by T: Devine . . .
" 20. Part of the "Map of the russian dominions on the shores of the Eastern ocean 1861" . . .
" 21. Part of a Mercator's map of the world, by Hermann Berghaus and Fr. v. Stülpnagel . . . 1863.
" 22. Part of russian admiralty chart no. 1345 . . . Translated, the title reads: "Chart of the Icy sea and the Eastern ocean . . . 1844." Foot note reads: "Corrected to 1864."
" 23. Part of the british admiralty chart no. 2461. "Pacific ocean, Cook river to gulf of California, 1861." Corrected to 1866.
" 24. Part of the map of northwestern America, prepared for the dept. of state at the office of the U. S. coast survey in 1867.
" 25. Southeastern Alaska, with sites of various Indian villages as located by lieut. G. T. Emmons . . . prepared at the office of the U. S. coast and geodetic survey, 1903.

**Alaskan** boundary tribunal. The counter case of the United States before the tribunal convened at London under the provisions of the treaty between the United States of America and Great Britain concluded january 24, 1903. Atlas. 2 p. l., 34 maps. fol. Washington, government printing office, 1903. 1194

NOTE.—Atlas entitled: . . . Atlas accompanying the counter case of the United States . . .
Contains portions of maps of North America relating chiefly to Alaska, Canada and the north coast.
Maps are numbered 26–47, the atlas being a supplement to "Atlas accompanying the case of the United States" . . .

**Alaskan** boundry tribunal—Continued.

CONTENTS.

no. 26. Southeastern Alaska, a reprint of no. 2 of "Atlas accompanying the case of the United States," with the addition of the line now claimed by Great Britain.
" 27. Southeastern Alaska and part of British Columbia. Map presented to the joint high commission at Quebec in 1898 by the british commissioners.
" 28. A series of eight maps of the Alaskan lisière, from british sources. (a) Official map of British Columbia, 1884. (b) [Same] Dated 1884 but presumably later than (a). (c) Dawson's map, sessional papers, 1887, from senate ex. doc. 146, 50th cong. 2d. sess. (d) Official map of British Columbia, 1893. (e) . . . British Columbia, 1895. (f) Map presented to the joint high commission in 1898 by british commissioners. (g) Map from year book of British Columbia, 1897. (h) Official british government map, 1903.
" 29. A series of six maps of the lower part of the of the Stikine river. (a) prof. W. P. Blake's sketch map, of the Stikine river. 1863. (b) Wright's map of the Cassiar district, 1876. (c) General map of Alaska by U. S. coast survey, 1869. (d) Hunter's survey of the lower Stikine, 1877. (e) Surveyor-general Dennis's map of the Stikine, 1878. (f) Canadian geological survey, 1884.
" 30. Clarence strait, Revillagigedo channel and Portland canal . . . 1903.
" 31. Sketch map of Portland channel and vicinity . . . 1867.
" 32. Map of Pyramid harbour and vicinity . . . 1891.
" 33. Part of sir George Simpson's map from his narrative of a journey round the world . . . 1847.
" 34. Part of a map of the russian empire, compiled to accompany Mr. Hill's Travels.
" 35. Official map of North America. Drawn by J. Arrowsmith. 1857. Ordered by the house of commons.
" 36. The provinces of British Columbia and Vancouver island . . . by John Arrowsmith, 1859.
" 37. Part of Imray's chart of the North Pacific ocean, 1869.
" 38. Part of british admiralty chart no. 787 *i. e.* Pacific ocean, eastern part. Cape Corrientes, Mexico to Kodiak island . . . 1876.
" 39. Part of official canadian map *i. e.* Map of the dominion of Canada . . . 1878.
" 40. Part of map of Manitoba, Keewatin, British Columbia and North West territory . . . 1880.
" 41. Part of map of British Columbia and the North West territory, by the canadian geological survey, 1881.
" 42. Part of official canadian map of the dominion of Canada . . . 1882.
" 43. Part of official canadian map of the dominion of Canada and part of the United States . . . 1883.
" 44. Part of map of British Columbia and the North West territory . . . 1887.
" 45. Part of map of the dominion of Canada (western sheet) . . . By T. B. Johnston . . .
" 46. Part of a map of the western part of the dominion of Canada . . . J. B. Bartholomew. 1898.
" 47. Part of map of British Columbia . . . 1898.

## GENERAL.

(Arranged chronologically)

### 1604-1772

**Robert de Vaugondy, D.**

[Recueil de 10 cartes . . . traitant particulièrement de l'Amérique du Nord et des regions arctiques, d'après les relations les plus authentiques depuis le commencement du 17° siècle, réproduites . . .] 1 p. l., 10 fold. maps. 8°. [Livourne, 1779]  1195

NOTE.—Atlas to accompany articles on America, Asia and Arctic regions in Diderot's Encyclopaedie; ou dictionaire raisonné des sciences . . . 1770-1779. The same maps are in the "Supplement." 1779. v. 5, pp. 179-198. Without title-page. Title as given above occurs in K. W. Hiersemann, Catalog no. 327.

CONTENTS.

no. 1. Carte des parties nord et ouest de l'Amérique . . . 1772.
" 2. Carte des parties nord et est de l'Asie . . . 1772.
" 3. Nouvelle représentation des côtes nord et est de l'Asie . . . 1712.
" 4. Carte de la Californie et des pays nord-ouest, séparés de l'Asie par le détroit d'Anian.
" 5. Carte de la Californie suivant—I. La carte manuscrite de l'Amérique de Mathieu Néron Pecci olen dressés à Florence en 1604.—II. Sanfon, 1656.—III. De l'Isle, Amérique sept., 1700.—IV. Le père Kino jésuite en 1705.—V. La Société des Jésuites en 1767.
" 6. Carte des nouvelles découverts . . . par P. Buache . . .—Extrait d'une carte japonoise de l'univers.
" 7. Carte générale des découvertes de l'amiral de Fonte et autres navigateurs espagnols, anglois et russes pour la recherche du passage à la mer du Sud par m. De l'Isle, 1752.
" 8. Carte générale des découvertes de l'amiral de Fonte representant la grande probabilité d'un passage au nord ouest par T. Jefferys . . . 1768.
" 9. Carte qui represente les différentes connoissances que l'on à eues des terres Arctiques depuis 1650 jusqu'en 1747 . . . selon Sanson en 1750; Delisle en 1700 et 1703.—Carte de baye d'Hudson parcourue en 1746 et 1747 par Henri Ellis pour la recherche du passage par le nord-ouest.
" 10. Partie de la carte du capitaine Cluny . . .

### 1768

**Jefferys, T.**

A general topography of North America and the West Indies. Being a collection of all the maps, charts, plans, and particular surveys, that have been published of that part of the world, either in Europe or America . . . 4, 4 pp., 100 maps on 109 sheets. fol. London, for R. Sayer & T. Jefferys, 1768.  1196

NOTE.—Title and contents also in french.
Map no. 102, "Plan of the french attacks upon the island of Grenada . . . 1779," and map no. 109, "Attack of the rebels upon fort Penobscot in the province of New England . . . 1779," inserted.
nos. 46-51, entitled in table of contents, "Six plans of the different disposi-

**Jefferys, T.**—Continued.
tions of the british army, under the command of the late general Braddock in North America, by an aid de camp to the general [capt. William Orme. anon.] Operations against fort Du Quesne."

CONTENTS.

no. 1–6. A chart of North and South America . . . [By John Green. anon.] 6 sheets.
" 7. North America, from the french of mr. d'Anville.
" 8–11. An accurate map of North America . . . 1763. By Eman. Bowen . . . and John Gibson.—Insets: A particular map of Baffin and Hudson's bay.—The passage by land to California discover'd by . . . Eusebius Francis Kino between the years 1698 and 1700.
" 12. A map of the discoveries made by the russians on the north west coast of America. Published by the royal academy of sciences at Petersburg. Republished by Thomas Jefferys . . .
" 12a. A map of the n. e. parts of Asia, and n. w. parts of America . . . taken from a japanese map of the world.
" 12b. A general map of the discoveries of admiral de Fonte. [Bartholomé de Fuentes] By mr. De l'Isle, 1752.
" 13. Chart of the Atlantic ocean, with the british, french & spanish settlements in North America, and the West Indies . . .
NOTE.—With two extension leaves.
" 14. A map of Canada and the north part of Louisiana . . . 1762.
" 15–16. An exact chart of the river St. Laurence from Frontenac to the island of Anticosti . . . 2 sheets.—Insets: St. Nicholas harbor. [The road of Tadousac]—The Seven islands.—A continuation of the river from Quebec to Ontario . . . 1755.—A view of the lands from Cape Torment to the Butt.—The traverse or passage from Cape Torment into the South channel of Orleans island.
" 17. An authentic plan of the river St. Laurence from Sillery, to the fall of Montmorenci. 1759 . . .—Insets: Part of the upper river of St. Laurence.—A view of the action . . . 1759 near Quebec.
" 17a. A plan of Quebec . . . 1758.—Inset: The course of St. Laurence river from Chaudiere fall to Orleans island.
" 18. A correct plan of the environs of Quebec, and of the battle fought on the 13th september, 1759.
NOTE.—With extension leaf.
" 19. A map of the several dispositions of the english fleet & army on the river St. Laurence, to the taking of Quebec.
" 20. Plan of the town and fortifications of Montreal or Villemarie . . . 1758.
" 21. A new map of Nova Scotia and Cape Britain . . . 1755.
" 22a. Carte d'une partie de l'Amérique Septentrionale . . .—Exact copy from the french original.
" 22b. A map exhibiting a view of the english rights, relative to the ancient limits of Acadia . . . By Thomas Jefferys.
" 23. A plan of the city and harbour of Louisburg from a survey made by Richard Gridley . . . in 1745.—Insets: A plan of the city and harbour of Louisburg . . . in 1758.—A map of Gabarus bay . . .
" 24. A large and particular plan of Shegnekto bay . . . 1755.
" 25. A chart of the harbour of Halifax . . . with Jebucto bay and Cape Sambro . . . By Charles Morris . . . 1759.

no. 26–29. A map of the most inhabited part of New England containing the provinces of Massachusetts bay and New Hampshire . . . [By John Green. anon.] 1755.—Insets: A plan of the town of Boston.—A plan of Boston harbor . . .

" 30–31. An accurate map of his majesty's province of New-Hampshire . . . by col. [Joseph] Blanchard, and the rev'd mr. [Samuel] Langdon. 1761.—Inset: A general map of the river S! Lawrence above Montreal to lake Ontario . . .

" 32. A general map of the middle british colonies in America . . . by Lewis Evans. 1758.—Inset: A sketch of the remaining part of Ohio r. &c.

" 33–34. A chorographical map of the country between Albany, Oswego . . . and les Trois rivières.—The provinces of New York and New Jersey; with part of Pensilvania . . . Drawn by capt. [Samuel] Holland.

" 35. A plan of the city of New-York & its environs . . . [By] John Montresor. 1766.—Inset: A chart of the entrance to New York . . .

" 36. A plan of the town and fort of Carillon at Ticonderoga; with the attack made by the british army . . . 8 july 1758.

" 37. A prospective view of the battle fought near lake George, on the 8th of september 1755. Samuel Blodget delin. Published . . . 1756.—Inset: A plan of fort William Henry.—A plan of Lymans now called fort Edward.

NOTE.—L. C. has a copy of the pamphlet (1755) written by Samuel Blodget to accompany the original edition of the view.

" 38–43. . . . Map of the improved part of the province of Pennsylvania . . . by Nicholas Scull. 1759.

" 44. An east prospect of the city of Philadelphia: taken by George Heap . . . under the direction of Nicholas Scull.

" 45. Plan of fort Le Quesne . . . 1754. [By Robert Stobo. anon.]

" 46. A plan of the line of march with the whole baggage.

" 47. A plan of the disposition of the advanced party consisting of 400 men.

" 48. A plan of the line of march of the detachment from the Little Meadows.

" 49. A plan of the encampment of the detachment from the Little Meadows.

" 50. A plan of the field of battle and disposition of the troops, as they were on the march at the time of the attack on the 9th of july, 1755.

" 51. A map of the country between Will's creek & Monongahela river . . . 1755.

" 52. A map of the country on the Ohio & Muskingum rivers . . . A survey of that part of the indian country through which colonel Bouquet marched in 1764. By Thomas Hutchins.

" 53. Plan of the battle near Bushy-Run 1763 . . . by Tho's Hutchins. [Also diagram]

" 54–57. A map of the most inhabited part of Virginia containing the whole province of Maryland . . . Drawn by Joshua Fry & Peter Jefferson in 1751. Revised by John Dalrymple in 1755.

" 58. A survey of the coast about Cape Lookout in North Carolina, taken the 29th of june, 1756. By Arthur Mackay.

**Jefferys, T.**—Continued.
- no. 59–62. A map of South Carolina and a part of Georgia from surveys taken by ... William Bull ... captain Gascoign, Hugh Bryan and ... William De Brahm.
- " 63. A new and exact plan of Cape Fear river from the bar to Brunswick, by Edward Hyrne, 1749.
- " 64. A draught of the Cherokee country ... taken by Henry Timberlake ... march 1762.
- " 65. Florida from the latest authorities, by T. Jefferys.
- " 66. Païs Cedés, sheet I$^{st}$ containing the coast of Louisiana and Florida.
- " 67. Païs Cedés, sheet II$^d$ containing the peninsula & gulf of Florida, with the Bahama islands.
- " 68. A north view of Pensacola, on the island of Santa Rosa, drawn by Dom. Serres.
- " 68a. Plan of the harbor and settlement of Pensacola.
- " 69. Plan of New Orleans ... by mr. de la Tour, 1720. Published, 1759.—Insets: The course of Mississipi river from Bayagoulas to the sea.—The east mouth of the Mississipi with the plan of fort la Balise ...
- " 70–71. The West Indies exhibiting the english, french, spanish, dutch & danish settlements, by Thomas Jefferys. 2 sheets.
- " 71a. Jamaica. [A new and correct map of Jamaica]
- " 72. A new chart of the West Indies, drawn from the best spanish maps. NOTE.—"To front the title" [of Jefferys' A description of the Spanish ids. 4°. London, 1762]
- " 72a. Plan of the road and port of La Vera Cruz [by le sieur Bully]
- " 73. Plan of La Vera Cruz, from spanish draughts.
- " 73a. Plan of Port Royal laguna, commonly called the Logwood creeks.
- " 74. Plan of the harbour of San Fernando de Omoa [drawn by lieut. Young]
- " 74a. A map of the isthmus of Panama, drawn from spanish surveys.
- " 75. Plan of the town, road, and harbour of Chagre [by Fran. Math. Celi]
- " 75a. Plan of Porto Belo [by Fran. Math. Celi]
- " 76. Plan of Zispata bay [by Juan de Herrera]
- " 76a. Plan of the harbour of Carthagena [by Juan de Herrera]
- " 77. Plan of the city and suburbs of Carthagena.
- " 77a. Plan of the bay & town of S$^{ta}$ Martha. By Fran. Math. Celi.
- " 78. Plan of Puerto Cavello on the coast of the Caracas.
- " 78a. Plan of Puerto de la Guaira on the coast of the Caracas.
- " 79. A map of the isle of Cuba with the Bahama islands, gulf of Florida ...
- " 80. Plan of the city and harbour of the Havana.
- " 80a. Plan of bahia de Matanzas. [Fran. Math. Celi]
- " 81. The Grand bay of Nipe ... [Fran. Math. Celi]
- " 81a. Plan of Puerto de Baracoa.
- " 82. Plan of Guantanimo.
- " 82a. Plan of the city and harbour of St. Jago de Cuba.
- " 83. Plan de bahia Xagua [by F. M. Celi]
- " 83a. Plan of the Colorado Rocks, near the west end of Cuba.
- " 84. Plan of bahia Honda [by F. M. Celi]
- " 84a. Plan of Puerto de Cavañas [by F. M. Celi]
- " 85. Plan de Puerto de Mariel [by F. M. Celi]
- " 86. The island of Hispaniola.

no. 87. An authentic plan of the town and harbour of Cap-François.
" 88. Plan of the city of San Domingo.
" 89. Plan of the town and harbour of San Juan de Puerto Rico [by sieur Bully]
" 90. Plan of the Aguada Nueva de Puerto Rico [by F. M. Celi]
" 91. The Caribbee islands and Guayana. Drawn by L. Delarochette.
" 92. St. Christophers, surveyed by Anthony Ravell.
" 93. Antigoa.
" 94. A map of the island of Guadaloupe, drawn from an accurate survey by lieut! Archibald Campbell.
" 95. Guadaloupe one of the Caribbee islands.
" 96. Plan of the town of Basse Terre the capital of Guadaloupe.
" 97. Plan of the attack against Basseterre . . . 1759 drawn on the spot by lieut. col. Rycaut. 1760.—Inset: Plan of fort-Royal.
" 98. Plan of the attack against fort Louis now fort George on the island of Guadeloupe. 1759. Drawn on the spot by lieut. col. Rycaut.— Inset: Plan of the harbour of Point à pitre on the island of Guadeloupe.
" 99. Dominica, by Thomas Jefferys.—Inset: Prince Ruperts bay.
" 100. Martinico . . . according to the observations of mr. Houel . . . by Tho'. Jefferys.
" 101. Plan of the town and citadel of Fort Royal . . . with the bay of Cul de sac royal, by mr. de Caylus. 1760.—Inset: Port du Carenage.
" 102. Plan of the french attacks upon the island of Grenada, with the engagement between the english . . . and the french fleet. 1799.
" 103. Plan of the town and fort of Grenada. By. mr. de Caylus.—Inset: The isle of Grenada.
" 104. Plan de l'isle de la Grenade. 1763.
" 105. Tobago. 1765.—Insets: A survey of great & little Courland bays. By D. Ross. 1760.—Man of War bay.
" 106. The island and colony of Cayenne . . . 1760.
" 107. Plan of the town of Cayenne and fort St. Michael. Drawn by the chevalier de Mareechais [R. de Marchais] 1760.
" 108. The dutch colony of Surinam, as laid down by l! colonel Spiering.
" 109. Attack of the rebels upon fort Penobscot. 1779.

**1772**

**De Brahm, J. G. W.**
The Atlantic pilot. viii, 25, [1], pp., 3 fold. maps, 1 tab. 8°. London, for the author by T. Spilsbury, 1772. 1197

NOTE.—Full title as entered in Sabin and Rich as follows: The Atlantic pilot. Calculated for the safe conduct of ships in their navigation from the gulph of Mexico along Cuba and the Martieres through the new Bahama channel, to the northern parts of his majesty's dominions on the continent of America, and from thence to Europe. London, 1772.

No record of an earlier edition in english, but a french edition dated 1771, has title, "Recherches pour perfectionner la navigation du canal de Bahama— trad. de l'anglais"—which leads us to suppose that there was an english edition prior to 1772.

Another french edition published in 1788 has change of title, "Recherches faites par ordre de sa majesté britannique, depuis 1765 jusqu'en 1771, pour

**De Brahm, J. G. W.**—Continued.

 rectifier les cartes et perfectionner la navigation du canal de Bahama—trad. de l'anglais par Ch. Romme.''

 Atlantic pilot, 1722 in British Museum catalogue must be a typographical error.

CONTENTS.

Maps.

 no. [1] Hydrographical map of the Atlantic ocean, extending from the southernmost part of North America to Europe . . . 1771.
 " [2] The ancient Tegesta, now promontory of East Florida . . . 1771.
 " [3] Chart of the south end of East Florida, and Martiers . . .

### 1774-1781

**The Atlantic Neptune**, published for the use of the royal navy of Great Britain, by Joseph F. W. Des Barres . . . under the directions of the right hon$^{ble}$ the lords commissioners of the admiralty. 3 v. fol. [London, 1774-1781]     1198

 NOTE.—Copy no. 1. In his Bibliotheca Americana, v. 1, p. 249, Rich describes the Atlantic Neptune as "The most splendid collection of charts, plans, and views ever published. It was executed at the expense of the british government for the use of the british navy, and no expense appears to have been spared in the execution in order to render it a monument worthy of the nation."

 The copy Rich gives is in 2 v.; v. 1 in 1 pt.; v. 2 in 3 pts.

 L. C. copy no. 1 is in 3 v.; v. 1 in 1 pt.; v. 2 in 1 pt.; v. 3 in 2 pts.

 Several maps and views not listed in Rich's description are found in v. 3.

 This copy lacks the following:

 v. 1, Engraved general title.
  Title to Nova Scotia.
  Table of contents.
  View of Port Hood.
  Two views (on 1 pl.)
  Four views (on 1 pl.) following map of Isle of Sables.
 " 2, Index of charts, which has been supplied in manuscript.
  View of Cape-Breton.
 " 3, Indexes of charts, which has been supplied in manuscript.

CONTENTS.

v. 1, References.
 "  General remarks.
 "  no. 1. The coast of Nova Scotia, New England, New York, Jersey, the gulph and river of St Lawrence. 1780.
 "  "  2. A chart of Nova Scotia . . . 1780.—Inset view: [The entrance of the river St. John]
 "  "  4. A view of Partridge island from the west. 1777.
 "  "  5. The isthmus of Nova Scotia. 1780.
 "  "  6. [Views of:] The Isle Haut . . . and Cape Chignecto.— . . . Cape Dore.— . . . Cape Baptist.— . . . Entrance into the Bason of mines.—The Isle Haute.—Cape Blowmendown . . . with Cape Split.
 "  "  7. [Views of:] Cape Blowmedown.—Cape Split.—The entrance of Mines bason.—Isle Haut and cape Chegnecto. 1779.
 "  "  8. [Chignecto bay] 1781.

v. 1, no. 9. The environs of Fort Cumberland in the bay of Fundy. 1781.
" " 10. Annapolis Royal.—S! Mary's bay. 1781.—Inset: View of Gulivers Hole.
" " 11. [View of:] Annapolis royal. 1781.
" " 12. A view of the entrance of Petit Passage.—Grand passage in the Bay of Fundy. 1780.
" " 13. [Views of:] Cape S! Mary.— . . . Grand passage.—S! Marys bay. 1781.
" " 14–15. South east part of the Bay of Fundy. 1780.
" " 16–17. The southwest coast of the peninsula of Nova Scotia. 1780.
" " 18. Barrington bay. 1781.
" " 19. [Views of:] Cape Prospect.—Cape Sambro.—The High lands of Haspotagoen.—The Ovens.—Cape Sable.—Entrance of Barrington bay.
" " 20. Port Amherst—Port Haldimand. 1781.
" " 21. Port Campbell. 1781.
" " 22–23. Port Mills, Port Mansfield.—Gambier harbour. 1781.
" " 24. [Views of:] Mechios river near the mills. A sketch of Mechios mills. 1777.
" " 25. Liverpool bay. 1781.
" " 26. Port Jackson. 1781.
" " 27. King's bay.—Lunenburg. 1781.
" " 28. Mecklenburgh bay. 1779.
" " 29. Charlotte bay. 1781.
" " 30. Leith harbour.—Prospect harbour.—Prospect harbour.—Bristol bay.—Sambro harbour. 1781.
[View of:] Hopson's Nose.
" " 31–32. The south east coast of Nova Scotia. 1776.
" " 33. Halifax harbour. 1781.—Insets: [Col. views of:] Light house.—Chebucto head.—Citadel hill.
" " 34. The harbour of Halifax. 1781.
" " 35. A view of the town & harbour of Halifax. [1781]
" " 36. [Views of:] Halifax harbour.—Sambro light house.—Chebucto head.
" " 37. Egmont harbour. 1779.—2 insets, views.
" " 38. Keppell harbour.—Knowles harbour.—Tangier harbour.—Saunder's harbour.—Deane harbour.—Insets: [Views of:] Entrance of Keppel harbour.—Cape Southampton.
" " 39. [Views of:] . . . Cape Egmont and Winter.—The entrance of Keppel harbor.—Falls of Hinchinbroke river.—The entrance into Chisetcook inlet.—Darmouth shore in the harbor of Halifax. 1781.
" " 40. Spry harbour.—Port Pallisser.—Port North.—Port Parker.—Beaver harbour.—Fleming river. 1779.—Insets: [Views of:] Cape Spry.—Beaver isles.— . . . Pegasus wing.
" " 41. [Views of:] . . . land from the White islands to S! Marys river.—Milford haven.—Port Bickerton.—Entrance of Beaver harbor.—Canso, Cranberry isle.—S. E. point of Nova Scotia. 1781.
" " 42. White islands harbour.—Port Stephen's Liscomb harbour.—Houlton harbour.—River S! Mary. 1779.
" " 43. Sandwich bay. 1781.
" " 44. [Torbay] 1781.
[View of:] Berry head . . . & White head island.

**The Atlantic Neptune**—Continued.

v. 1, no. 45. White Haven.—Port Howe  1774.—Inset: view.
" " 46. [Canso harbour.—Port George.—Glasgow harbour]  1781.—Inset: View of Port George.
" " 47. Crow harbor.—Philip inlet.  1779.
" " 48. [St. Peter's bay]—View of Cape Round.  1781.
" " 49. Milford Haven.—[View]  1781.
" " 50. Conway harbour—Port Aylesbury.  1781.
" " 51. [Richmond Isles (alias Isles Madame), Lenox Passage.—Part of Cape Breton island.—Conway harbour.—Chedabucto bay.  1781.
" " 52. The Gut of Canso.  1781.
" " 53. [Northeastern district of Nova Scotia].—Northumberland streights.—Part of the island of S! John]  1781.
" " 54. [North east coast of Nova Scotia.—Northumberland streights.—Part of the island of S! John]  1779.
" " 55. Port Hood.  1780.
" " 56–57. Frederick bay—Ramsheg harbour.—Pictou harbour.—Port Luttrell.  1781.
" " 58. A view of the Plaister Cliffs.
" " 59. Port Shediack–Cocagne.  1781.
" " 60. [Isle of Sable]  1779.
" " 61–62. The isle of Sable surveyed . . . in 1766–1767. Published . . . 1779.
" " 63. Remarks on the isle of Sable.
" " 64. A view of the east end of the isle of Sable . . .  1779.
" " 65. A view from the camp at the east end of the Naked Sand hills . . . Isle of Sable.  1781.

v. 2, Charts of the coasts and harbours in the gulf and river of St. Lawrence, from surveys taken by major Holland, surv!-gen! of the north! diftrict of North America, and his afsistants, pursuant to orders from the right hon^ble the lords commifos^rs fortrade & plantations in the years 1765, 1766, 1767 and 1768. Composed and published by command of government, for the ufe of the royal navy of Great Britain, by J. F. W. Des Barres esq.  1781.

" References.
" Manuscript index.
" no. 1. [General chart of the gulph and river St. Lawrence]  1780.
" " 2–4. River of St. Lawrence, from Chaudiere to lake St. Francis, &c. Surveyed . . . [by] S. Holland.  1781.
" " 5. A plan of Quebec and environs with its defences and the occasional entrenched camps of the French.  1759.
" " 6. A view of Quebec from the south east.
" " 7–8. [River St. Lawrence up to Quebec]  1781.
" " 9. [Bay of Seven islands]  1778.
" " 10–11. [Coast from River S! John to S! Genevieve island]  1777.
" " 12. [Gaspee bay, Maul bay, &c.]
" " 13. [Bay of Chaleurs]  1777.
" " 14. [Miramichi bay]  1781.
" " 15. The harbours of Rishibucto & Buctush.  1781.
" " 16. A chart of Cape Breton and St. John's islands, &c.
" " 17–18. The south east coast of the island of St. John. Surveyed . . . by Sam! Holland.  1781.

v. 2, no. 19. The Magdalen isles in the gulph of St. Lawrence. 1781.
" " 20. A chart of the island of Cape Breton.
" " 21. A chart of the n. e. coast of Cape Breton island from St. Ann bay to Cape Morien. 1781.
" " 22–23. The south east coast of Cape Breton island. By S. Holland. 1781.
" " 24. A chart of the harbour of Louisbourg in the island of Cape Breton. 1781.
" " 25. [Views of:] Louisbourg.—Gabarrus bay.—Richmond isle.—S.W. shore of Cape Breton island.—Kamea isles.—S$^{ta}$ Maria island] 1777.
" " 26. A view of Louisbourg from the north east.
v. 3, Charts of the coast and harbors of New England from surveys taken by Sam! Holland . . . surv! gen! of lands for the northern district of North America and Geo? Sproule, Cha? Blascowitz, Jam? Grant and tho? Wheeler his assistants pursuant to orders from the right hon$^{ble}$ the Lords commifs? for trade & plantations together with several usefull additional surveys, soundings, views &c. taken by various officers on the spot. Collected composed & published by command of government at the request of the right hon$^{ble}$ vice admiral lord vis! Howe for the use of the royal navy of Great Britain, by J. F. W. Des Barres . . . surveyor of the coast and harbours of North America.  2 p. l., [7] l., 49 maps on 104 l., 12 pl. nar. fol. [London] J. F. W. Des Barres, 1780.
" Manuscript index.
" no. 1. The coast of New England. 1781.
" " 2–3. [Grand bay of Passamaquody, St. Croix river, Copscook bay, Campo Bello harbour, Dear island harbour, Etang harbour, Beaver harbour &c.—Grand Manan island]
" " 4. The Wolves, a cluster of isles, lying s. e. of the entrance of Pafsamaquodi bay.—Grand Manan Island . . .—View of the shore westward of St. John's river . . . [Views]
" " 5. The north point of Grandmanan island in the Bay Fundy . . .—A view of Campo Bello at the entrance of Passamaquady bay.
" " 6. [Coast from Moose harb! to Gouldsborough] 1776.
" " 7. [Coast from Moose Point to Frenchmans bay] 1776.
" " 8. [Mount Desart island.—Frenchmans bay] 1776.
" " 9–10. Belfast bay.—Penobscot bay.—Isle Haute bay.—Great Blue Hill bay] 1776.
" " 11. [Coast from Cape Elizabeth to Moose pt.] 1776.
" " 12. [Coast from Penmaquid point to Seal harbour] 1776.
" " 13. [Coast of Portland sound to Rodgers bay] 1776.
" " 14. [Falmouth harbour] 1781.
" " 15. [Coast from Newbury harbour to Cape Elizabeth] 1776.
" " 16. [Piscataqua harbour] 1779.
" " 17. Castle William.—A view of New Castle with the fort and light house on the entrance of Pisquataqua river.
" " 18. [View of Portsmouth]
" " 19. [Coast from Marblehead harb. to Hampton harbor] 1781.
" " 20. [Massachusets bay] 1781.
" " 21. [Boston bay] 1781.
" " 22. [Boston harbour] 1781.
" " 23. [Text to accompany map no. 22]

**The Atlantic Neptune**—Continued.

v. 3, no. 24. Boston, seen between Castle Williams and Governors island . . .—Appearance of the high lands of Agameticus, n. e. with Penobscot hills . . .—Boston bay.—The entrance of Boston harbor. [Views]
" " 25. A view of Boston from Dorchester neck.—1775.—Long Island open on the north side of Nicks Mate island.—Boston from Willis creek. 1775. [Views]
" " 26. A front view of the lines taken from the advanced post near Browns house.—A view of the harbour of Boston taken from Fort hill.—A view of the country towards Dorchester, taken from the advanced works on Boston Neck.
" " 27. A view of Boston. 1779.
" " 28. [Plymouth bay] 1781.
" " 29. [From Nantucket to Rhode Island] 1781.
" " 30. [From Shelter Island to Point Judith] 1781.
" " 31. [Part of Martha's Vineyard and Nantucket island] 1781.
" " 32. [Buzzard's bay. The Elizabeth islands.—Vineyard sound] 1781.
" " 33. Cape Poge . . .—Sandy point . . .—Gay Head . . .—Gay Head . . .—Sankoty Head . . . [Views]
" " 34. A chart of the harbor of Rhode Island and Narraganset bay . . . 1776.
" " 35. A plan of the town of Newport . . . 1781.
" " 36. Title to pt. 2:
Charts of several harbours, and divers parts of the coast of North America, from New York fouth weftwards to the gulph of Mexico. Collected from surveys depofited at the office of the right hon'ble the lords com'rs for trade & plantations, and others. Compofed and publifhed by command of government, for the ufe of the royal navy of Great Britain by J. F. W. Des Barres, 1780.
" " 37. Manuscript index.
" " 38. A chart of the coast of New York, New Jersey, Pensilvania, Maryland, Virginia, North Carolina . . . with soundings and nautical remarks from lt. Jno. Knight . . . 1780.
" " 39. A chart of New York harbour . . . Compofed from surveys and observations of lieutenants John Knight, John Hunter . . . —Insets: Bond Hollow . . . —Mount Pleasant . . .
" " 40. Nautical directions to sail into the harbour of New York, &c.
" " 41. A view of the Highland of Neversunk.—The south shore of Long Island . . . —New York . . . —The light house on Sandy Hook . . . —The Narrows . . . 1777. [Views]
" " 42. A sketch of the operations of his majesty's fleet and army under the command of vice admiral . . . Howe and gen! sir Wm. Howe . . . 1776.
" " 43. Text to accompany map. no. 42.
" " 44. Part of Hudsons river, fhewing the position of fort Montgomery and fort Clinton . . . by lieut. John Knight . . . in 1777.—A plan of fort Montgomery & fort Clinton . . . Survey'd by major Holland . . . 1779.
" " 45. [Coast of Long Island from Yellow hook to Cow harbour]
" " 46. Oyster bay and Huntington . . . —Huntington bay . . . —Hell Gate . . . 1778.

v. 3, no. 47. A chart of Delawar bay, with soundings taken by cap$^t$ sir Andrew Snape Hammond . . . 1779.
" " 48. A chart of Delawar river from Bombay hook to Ridley creek with soundings &c. taken by l$^t$ Knight . . . 1779.—A plan of Delawar river from Chester to Philadelphia . . . on the 15$^{th}$ nov$^r$ 1777. Surveyed and sounded by lieutenant John Hunter . . .
" " 49. [Pensilvania and part of New Jersey] 1777.
" " 50. A plan of York and Gloucester in the province of Virginia . . . on the 17$^{th}$ of october 1781. Surveyed by capt$^n$ Fage . . . 1782.—Inset: [Country bordering on James and York rivers]
" " 50½. [Before Yorktown] The position of the army between the ravines on the 28$^{th}$ and 29$^{th}$ of sept. 1781.
" " 51. The harbour of Charles Town in South Carolina from the surveys of s$^r$ Ja$^s$ Wallace . . . with a view of the town . . . 1777.
" " 52. A sketch of the operations before Charlestown the capital of South Carolina . . . 1780.—Inset: [Charlestown harbour]
" " 53. A sketch of the environs of Charlestown in South Carolina . . .
" " 54. A sketch of the battle near Camden in South Carolina, 16. aug$^{st}$ 1780.
" " 55. Port Royal in South Carolina . . . 1777.
" " 56. [Coast of South Carolina and Georgia from Tono river to Inlet S$^t$ Mary] Inset: Plan of the siege of Savannah . . . 1779 . . . Surveyed by John Wilson . . .
" " 57. The coast, rivers and inlets of the province of Georgia, surveyed by Joseph Avery and others . . . 1780.
" " 58. A plan of the harbour of S$^t$ Augustin in the province of Georgia . . .
" " 59-60. [The north east shore of the gulf of Mexico] 1780.
" " 61. A chart of the bay and harbour of Pensacola in the province of West Florida. Surveyed by George Gould . . . 1780.
" " 62. [The coast of West Florida from Apelousa river to Pensacola]
" " 63-64. Mifsifsipi river, from Iberville to Yazous. 1779.
" " 65. A chart of Port Royal and Kingston harbours in the island of Jamaica . . .
" " 66. A chart of Montego bay on the north west shore of the island of Jamaica.—Port Antonio on the north eaft shore of the island of Jamaica.
" " 67. The entrance of Havannah from within the harbour.—The harbour and part of the town of Havannah. [Views]

## 1774—1781

**The Atlantic Neptune,** published for the use of the royal navy of Great Britain, by Joseph F. W. Des Barres, under the directions of the right hon'ble the lords commissioners of the admiralty 3 v. fol. [London, 1774-1781] 1199
NOTE.—Copy no. 2.

CONTENTS.

v. 1, no. 1. The coast of Nova Scotia, New England, New York, Jersey, the gulph and river of S$^t$. Lawrence. 1778. Publish'd . . . 1779.
" " 2. [The isle of Sable]
" " 3. Remarks on the isle of Sable.

**The Atlantic Neptune**—Continued.

v. 1, no. 4. A chart of Nova Scotia. 1775.
" " 5-6. [Grand bay of Passamaquody, S! Croix river, Copscook bay, Campo bello harbour, Dear island harbour, Etang harbour, Beaver harbour, &c.—Grand Manan island] 1778.
" " 7. The river S! John. 1776.—Inset: [View of] the entrance of the river S! John.
" " 8. The isthmus of Nova Scotia. 1779.
" " 9. [Chignecto bay]
" " 10. Annapolis Royal.—St. Mary's bay. 1776.—Inset: View of Gulivers hole.
" " 11. [South east part of the bay of Fundy] 1776.
" " 12. The south west coast of the peninsula of Nova Scotia. 1776.
" " 13. The south east coast of Nova Scotia. 1776.
" " 14. Barrington bay. 1776.
" " 15. Port Amherst—Port Haldimand. 1775.
" " 16. Port Campbell. 1776.
" " 17. Port Mills.—Port Mansfield.—Gambrier harbour. 1776.
" " 18. Liverpool bay. 1777.
" " 19. Port Jackson. 1777.
" " 20. King's bay—Lunenburg. 1776.
" " 21. Mecklenburgh bay. 1776.
" " 22. Charlotte bay. 1776.
" " 23. Leith harbour.—Prospect harbour.—Bristol bay.—Sambro harbour. 1775.—Inset: [View of] Hopsons nose.
" " 24. Halifax harbour. 1776.—Insets: [Views of] Chebucto head.—Light-house.
" " 25. Egmont harbour.—2 inset views.
" " 26. Keppell harbour.—Knowles harbour.—Tangier harbour.—Saunder's harbour.—Deane harbour.—Insets: [Views of] Entrance of Keppel harbour.—Cape Southampton.
" " 27. Spry harbour.—Port Pallisser.—Port North.—Port Parker.—Beaver harbour.—Fleming river. 1776.—Insets: [Views of] Cape Spry.—Beaver isles.— . . . Pegasus wing.
" " 28. White islands harbour.—Port Stephen's.—Liscomb harbour.—Houlton harbour.—River S! Mary. 1776.
" " 29. Sandwich bay. 1776.
" " 30. [Torbay] 1776.—Inset: [View of] Berry head . . . & White head island.
" " 31. White haven.—Port Howe. 1774.—Inset view.
" " 32. [Canso harbour.—Port George.—Glasgow harbour] 1775.—Inset: [View of] Port George.
" " 33. Canso harbour. [Letter-press]
" " 34. Crow harbor.—Philip inlet.
" " 35. Milford haven.—[View]
" " 36. [St. Peter's bay] View of Cape Round. 1775.
" " 37. Conway harbour—Port Aylesbury. 1776.
" " 38. The Gut of Canso. 1776.
v. 2, no. 1. The coast of Nova Scotia, New England, New York, Jersey, the gulph and river of S! Lawrence. 1778. Publish'd . . . 1779.
" " 2. [General chart of the gulph and river St. Lawrence]
" " 3. A chart of Cape Breton and St. John's islands, &c.
" " 4. The Magdalen isles in the gulph of St. Lawrence. 1778.

| | | |
|---|---|---|
| v. 2, no. | 5. | [Richmond isles (alias Isles Madame) Lenox passage, Inhabitants river, Arishat, Conway harbour, Petit Degrat, Aylesbury harbour, &c. Cape Breton island] 1779. |
| " " | 6. | The south east coast of Cape Breton island surveyed . . . by Samuel Holland. 1781. |
| " " | 7. | A chart of the n. e. coast of Cape Breton island . . . 1781. |
| " " | 8. | A chart of the island of Cape Breton. |
| " " | 9. | A chart of the harbour of Louisbourg in the island of Cape Breton. 1781. |
| " " | 10. | Port Hood. 1779. |
| " " | 11. | Frederick bay.—Ramsheg harbour.—Pictou harbour.—Port Luttrell. 1779. |
| " " | 12-13. | The south east coast of the island of St. John. Surveyed . . . by Sam! Holland. 1781. |
| " " | 14. | [North east coast of Nova Scotia.—Northumberland streights.—Part of the island of S! John] 1779. |
| " " | 15. | Port Shediack—Cocagne. 1779. |
| " " | 16. | The harbours of Rishibucto & Buctush. 1778. |
| " " | 17. | [Miramichi bay] 1777. |
| " " | 18. | [Bay of Chaleur's] 1777. |
| " " | 19. | [Chaleur's bay, Mal bay, Gaspey &c.] |
| " " | 20. | [Bay and harbour of the Seven islands] 1778. |
| " " | 21. | [Coast from River S! John to S! Genevieve island] 1777. |
| " " | 22. | [River St. Lawrence up to Quebec] |
| " " | 23. | [Northeastern district of Nova Scotia.—Northumberland streights.—Part of the island of St. John] 1777. |
| v. 3, " | 1. | The coast of Nova Scotia, New England, New York, Jersey, the gulph and river of S! Lawrence. 1780. |
| " " | 2. | The coast of New England. 1781. |
| " " | 3. | [Coast from Moose harb! to Gouldsborough] 1776. |
| " " | 4. | [Coast from Moose point to Frenchmans bay] 1776. |
| " " | 5. | [Frenchmen's bay.—Mount Desart island] 1776. |
| " " | 6-7. | [Belfast bay.—Penobscot bay—Isle haut bay.—Great blue hill bay] 1776. |
| " " | 8. | [Coast from Penmaquid point to Seal harbour] 1776. |
| " " | 9. | [Coast from Portland Sound to Rodgers bay] 1776. |
| " " | 10. | [Coast from Cape Elizabeth to Moose p!] |
| " " | 11. | [Falmouth harbour] |
| " " | 12. | [Piscataqua harbour] 1779. |
| " " | 13. | [Coast from Newbury harbour to Cape Elizabeth] 1776. |
| " " | 14. | [Coast from Marblehead harb. to Hampton harbor] 1776. |
| " " | 15. | [Massachusets bay] 1776. |
| " " | 16. | [Part of Martha's Vineyard—Nantucket island] 1776. |
| " " | 17. | [Boston bay] 1776. |
| " " | 18. | [Boston harbour] 1775. |
| " " | 19. | [Plymouth bay] |
| " " | 20. | [Coast from Nantucket island to Rhode Island] 1779. |
| " " | 21. | [Coast of Long Island from Yellow Hook to Cow harbour] |
| " " | 22. | [Buzzard's bay, Elizabeth islands, Vineyard Sound] 1781. |
| " " | 23. | A chart of the harbour of Rhode Island and Narraganset bay. 1776. |
| " " | 24. | A chart of the coast of New York, New Jersey, Pensilvania Maryland, Virginia, North Carolina . . . with soundings and nautical remarks from 1! Jno. Knight. 1780. |

**The Atlantic Neptune**—Continued.

v. 3, no. 25. A chart of New York harbour . . . composed from surveys and observations of . . . John Knight, John Hunter.—Insets: [Views of] Bond Hollow.—Mount Pleasant.
" " 26. Part of Hudsons river shewing the position of fort Montgomery and fort Clinton . . . by lieut John Knight . . . 1777.—A plan of fort Montgomery & fort Clinton . . . by major Holland. 1779.
" " 27. Oyster bay and Huntington.—Huntington bay.—Hell gate.
" " 28. [Coast of Connecticut.—Gardners bay] 1779.
" " 29. A chart of Delaware bay . . . with soundings . . . taken by capt sir Andrew Snape Hammond. 1779.
" " 30. A chart of Delawar river from Bombay hook to Ridley creek with soundings &c. taken by lt Knight. 1779.—A plan of Delawar river from Chester to Philadelphia shewing the situation of his majesty's ships &c. on the 15th novr 1777.
" " 31. [Pensilvania.—Part of New Jersey] 1777.
" " 32. A sketch of the operations before Charlestown . . . 1780.—Inset: [Charleston harbour]
" " 33. The harbour of Charles Town in South Carolina, from the surveys of sr Jas Wallace. 1777. Inset: [View]
" " 34. Port Royal in South Carolina. 1777.
" " 35. A plan of the harbour of St. Augustin, in the province of Georgia.
" " 36. [The north east shore of the gulph of Mexico] 1780.
" " 37. [Gulph of Mexico. Northern coast]
" " 38. A chart of the bay and harbour of Pensacola. Surveyed by George Gould. 1780.
" " 39. A plan of the town of Newport. 1776.
" " 40. A chart of Port Royal and Kingston harbours in the island of Jamaica.

## 1774–1781

**The Atlantic Neptune,** published for the use of the royal navy of Great Britain, by Joseph F. W. Des Barres, under the directions of the right hon'ble the lords commissioners of the admiralty. 3 v. fol. [London, 1774–1781]  1200

CONTENTS.

NOTE.—Copy no. 3.

v. 1, no. 1. The coast of Nova Scotia, New England, New York, Jersey, the gulph and river of St Lawrence. 1778 . . . Publish'd . . . 1779.
" " 2. [The isle of Sable]
" " 3. Remarks on the isle of Sable.
" " 4. A chart of Nova Scotia.
" " 5–6. [Grand bay of Passamaquody, St Croix river, Copscook bay, Campo bello harbour, Dear island harbour, Etang harbour, Beaver harbour, &c.—Grand Manan island]
" " 7. [River St John] 1776.
" " 8. The isthmus of Nova Scotia. 1777.
" " 9. [Chignecto bay]
" " 10. Annapolis Royal.—St. Mary's bay. 1776.—Inset: View of Guliver's hole.

v. 1, no. 11. [South east part of the Bay of Fundy] 1776.
" " 12. The south west coast of the peninsula of Nova Scotia. 1780.
" " 13. The south east coast of Nova Scotia. 1776.
" " 14. Barrington bay.
" " 15. Port Amherst—Port Haldimand. 1775.
" " 16. Port Campbell. 1776.
" " 17. Port Mills.—Port Mansfield.—Gambier harbour. 1776.
" " 18. Liverpool bay. 1777.
" " 19. Port Jackson. 1779.
" " 20. King's bay—Lunenburg. 1776.
" " 21. Mecklenburgh bay. 1776.
" " 22. Charlotte bay. 1776.
" " 23. Leith harbour.—Prospect harbour.—Bristol bay.—Sambro harbour. 1775.—Inset: [View of] Hopsons nose.
" " 24. Halifax harbour.—Insets: [Views of Chebucto head.—Light house]
" " 25. Egmont harbour.—2 Inset views.
" " 26. Keppell harbour.—Knowles harbour.—Tangier harbour.—Saunder's harbour.—Deane harbour.—Insets: [Views of] Entrance of Keppel harbour.—Cape Southampton.
" " 27. Spry harbour.—Port Pallisser.—Port North.—Port Parker.—Beaver harbour.—Fleming river. 1776.—Insets: [Views of] Cape Spry.—Beaver isles.— . . . Pegasus wing.
" " 28. White islands harbour.—Port Stephen's Liscomb harbour.—Houlton harbour.—River S! Mary. 1776.
" " 29. Sandwich bay. 1776.
" " 30. [Torbay] 1775.—Inset: [View of] Berry head . . . & White head island.
" " 31. White Haven.—Port Howe. 1774.—Inset view.
" " 32. [Canso harbour.—Port George.—Glasgow harbour] 1775.—Inset: View of Port George.
" " 33. Crow harbor.—Philip inlet.
" " 34. Milford haven. [View]
" " 35. [St. Peter's bay]—View of Cape Round.
" " 36. Conway harbour.—Port Aylesbury. 1776.
" " 37. The Gut of Canso [1776]
v. 2, no. 1. The coast of Nova Scotia, New England, New York, Jersey, the gulph and river of S! Lawrence. 1780.
" " 2. [General chart of the gulph and river St. Lawrence] 1781.
" " 3. A chart of Cape Breton and St. John's islands, &c.
" " 4. The Magdalen isles in the gulph of St. Lawrence. 1781.
" " 5. [Richmond isles (alias Isles Madame) Lenox passage, Inhabitants river, Arishat, Conway harbour, Petit Degrat, Aylesbury harbour, &c. Cape Breton island] 1781.
" " 6. The South east coast of Cape Breton island surveyed . . . by Samuel Holland. 1781.
" " 7. A chart of the n. e. coast of Cape Breton island. 1781.
" " 8. A chart of the island of Cape Breton.
" " 9. A chart of the harbour of Louisbourg in the island of Cape Breton. 1781.
" " 10. Port Hood [1776]
" " 11. Frederick bay.—Ramsheg harbour.—Pictou harbour.—Port Luttrell. 1779.

**The Atlantic Neptune**—Continued.

v. 2, no. 12-13. The south east coast of the island of St. John surveyed . . . by Sam¹. Holland. 1781.
" " 14. [North east coast of Nova Scotia.—Northumberland streights. Part of the island of S! John] 1779.
" " 15. Port Shediack-Cocagne. 1781.
" " 16. The harbours of Rishibucto & Buctush. 1781.
" " 17. [Miramichi bay] 1781.
" " 18. [Bay of Chaleurs] 1781.
" " 19. [Chaleur's bay.—Mal bay.—Gaspey, &c.]
" " 20. [Bay and harbour of the Seven islands] 1781.
" " 21. [Coast from river S! John to S! Genevieve island] 1777.
" " 22. [River St. Lawrence up to Quebec] 1781.
" " 23. [Northeastern district of Nova Scotia.—Northumberland streights.—Part of the island of S! John] 1781.
v. 3, no. 1. The coast of Nova Scotia, New England, New York, Jersey, the gulph and river S! Lawrence. 1780.
" " 2. The coast of New England. 1776.
" " 3. [Coast from Moose harb^r. to Gouldsborough] 1776.
" " 4. [ " " Moose point to Frenchmans bay] 1776.
" " 5. [Frenchmens bay.—Mount Desart island] 1776.
" " 6-7. [Penobscot bay.—Belfast bay—Isle Haut bay.—Great Blue Hill bay] 1770.
" " 8. [Coast from Penmaquid point to Seal harbour] 1776.
" " 9. [ " " Portland sound to Rodgers bay] 1776.
" " 10. [ " " Cape Elizabeth to Moose p!] 1776.
" " 11. [Falmouth harbour] 1781.
" " 12. [Piscataqua harbour] 1779.
" " 13. [Coast from Newbury harbour to Cape Elizabeth] 1776.
" " 14. [ " " Marblehead harb. to Hampton harbor] 1776.
" " 15. [Massachusets bay] 1776.
" " 16. [Part of Martha's Vineyard.—Nantucket island] 1776.
" " 17. [Boston bay]
" " 18. [Boston harbour] 1775.
" " 19. A chart of the harbour of Boston. [Letterpress]
" " 20. [Plymouth bay]
" " 21. [Coast from Nantucket island to Rhode Island] 1779.
" " 22. A chart of New York island and North river, East river, passage through Hell Gate, Flushing bay . . .
" " 23. [Buzzard's bay, Elizabeth islands, Vineyard sound] 1776.
" " 24. A chart of the harbour of Rhode Island and Narraganset bay 1776.
" " 25. A chart of the coast of New York, New Jersey, Pensilvania, Maryland, Virginia, North Carolina, &c. . . . with soundings & nautical remarks from 1! Jn? Knight. 1780.
" " 26. A chart of New York harbour . . . composed from surveys and observations of . . . John Knight, John Hunter.—Insets: [Views of] Bond hollow.—Mount Pleasant.
" " 27. Part of Hudson's river shewing the position of fort Montgomery and fort Clinton . . . by lieu! John Knight . . . 1777.—A plan of fort Montgomery & fort Clinton . . . by major Holland. 1779.
" " 28. Oyster bay and Huntington.—Huntington bay.—Hell Gate. 1778.
" " 29. [Coast of Connecticut.—Gardners bay] 1781.

v. 3, no. 30. A chart of Delawar bay . . . with soundings . . . taken by capt sir Andrew Snape Hammond. 1779.
" " 31. A chart of Delawar river from Bombay hook to Ridley creek with soundings &c. taken by lt Knight. 1779.—A plan of Delawar river from Chester to Philadelphia shewing the situation of his majesty's ships &c. on the 15th of nov. 1777. By lieutenant John Hunter.
" " 32. [Pensilvania.—Part of New Jersey] 1777.
" " 33. A sketch of the operations before Charlestown. 1780.—Inset: [Charlestown harbour]
" " 34. The harbour of Charles Town in South Carolina, from the surveys of st Jas. Wallace. 1777.—Inset: [View]
" " 35. Port Royal in South Carolina. 1777.
" " 36. A plan of the harbour of St. Augustin in the province of Georgia.
" " 37. [The north east shore of the gulph of Mexico] 1780.
" " 38. [Gulph of Mexico. Northern coast]
" " 39. A chart of the bay and harbour of Pensacola . . . surveyed by George Gould. 1780.
" " 40. A plan of the town of Newport. 1776.
" " 41. A chart of Port Royal and Kingston harbours in the island of Jamaica.

## 1774–1781

**The Atlantic Neptune**, published for the use of the royal navy of Great Britain, by Joseph F. W. Des Barres, under the directions of the right hon'ble the lords commissioners of the admiralty. 3 v. fol. [London, 1774–1781] 1201

CONTENTS.

NOTE.—Copy No. 4.
v. 1, no. 1. The coast of Nova Scotia, New England, New York, Jersey, the gulph and river of St. Lawrence. 1780.
" " 2. [Isle of Sable]
" " 3. Remarks on the isle of Sable.
" " 4. A chart of Nova Scotia. 1775.
" " 5-6. [Grand bay of Passamaquody, St. Croix river, Copscook bay, Campo bello harbour, Dear island harbour, Etang harbour, Beaver harbour &c.—Grand Manan island]
" " 7. The river St. John. 1776.—Inset: [View of] the entrance of the river of St. John.
" " 8. The isthmus of Nova Scotia. 1777.
" " 9. [Chignecto bay] 1779.
" " 10. Annapolis Royal.—St. Mary's bay. 1776.—Inset: View of Gulivers hole.
" " 11. [South east part of the Bay of Fundy]. 1776.
" " 12. The south west coast of the peninsula of Nova Scotia. 1776.
" " 13. The south east coast of Nova Scotia. 1776.
" " 14. Barrington bay. 1776.
" " 15. Port Amherst.—Port Haldimand. 1775.
" " 16. Port Campbell. 1776.
" " 17. Port Mills.—Port Mansfield.—Gambier harbour. 1776.
" " 18. Liverpool bay. 1777.
" " 19. Port Jackson. 1779.

**The Atlantic Neptune**—Continued.

v. 1, no. 20. King's bay—Lunenburg. 1776.
" " 21. Mecklenburgh bay. 1776.
" " 22. Charlotte bay. 1776.
" " 23. Leith harbour.—Prospect harbour.—Bristol bay.—Sambro harbour. 1775.—Inset: [View of] Hopsons nose.
" " 24. Halifax harbour. 1776.—Insets: [Views of] Chebucto head.—Light house.—Citadel hill.
" " 25. Egmont harbor.—2 inset views.
" " 26. Keppell harbour.—Knowles harbour.—Tangier harbour.—Saunder's harbour.—Deane harbour.—Insets: [Views of] Entrance of Keppel harbour.—Cape Southampton.
" " 27. Spry harbour.—Port Pallisser.—Port North.—Port Parker.—Beaver harbour.—Fleming river. 1776.—Insets: [Views of] Cape Spry.—Beaver isles.—. . . Pegasus wing.
" " 28. White islands harbour.—Port Stephen's.—Liscomb harbour.—Houlton harbour.—River S$^t$ Mary. 1776.
" " 29. Sandwich bay. 1776.
" " 30. [Torbay] 1775.—Inset: [View of] Berry head . . . & White head island.
" " 31. White haven.—Port Howe. 1774.—Inset view.
" " 32. [Canso harbour.—Port George.—Glasgow harbour] 1775.—Inset: View of Port George.
" " 33. Crow harbor.—Philip inlet.
" " 34. Milford haven.—[View] 1777.
" " 35. [S$^t$. Peter's bay].—View of Cape Round. 1775.
" " 36. Conway harbour.—Port Aylesbury. 1776.
" " 37. The gut of Canso [1776]
v. 2, no. 1. The coast of Nova Scotia, New England, New York, Jersey, the gulph and river of S$^t$. Lawrence. 1778. Publish'd . . . 1779.
" " 2. [General chart of the gulph and river of St. Lawrence]
" " 3. A chart of Cape Breton and St. John's islands, &c.
" " 4. The Magdalen isles in the gulph of St. Lawrence. 1778.
" " 5. [Richmond isles (alias Isles Madame). Lenox passage, Inhabitants river, Arishat, Conway harbour, Petit Degrat, Aylesbury harbour, &c. Cape Breton island] 1777.
" " 6. The south east coast of Cape Breton island. Surveyed . . . by Samuel Holland. 1781.
" " 7. A chart of the n. e. coast of Cape Breton island.
" " 8. A chart of the island of Cape Breton.
" " 9. A chart of the harbour of Louisbourg in the island of Cape Breton. 1781.
" " 10. Port Hood. 1776.
" " 11. Frederick bay—Ramsheg harbour—Pictou harbour—Port Luttrell. 1776.
" " 12-13. The south east coast of the island of St. John. Surveyed . . . by Sam$^l$. Holland. 1781.
" " 14. [North east coast of Nova Scotia]—Northumberland streights.—Part of the island of S$^t$. John. 1777.
" " 15. [Port Shediack—Cocagne] 1776.
" " 16. The harbours of Rishibucto & Buctush. 1778.
" " 17. [Miramichi bay] 1777.
" " 18. [Bay of Chaleurs] 1777.
" " 19. [Chaleur's bay, Mal bay, Gaspey, &c.]

v. 2, no. 20. [Bay and harbour of the Seven islands] 1778.
" " 21. [Coast from river S‍t. John to S‍t. Genevieve island]
" " 22. [River St. Lawrence up to Quebec] 1781.
" " 23. [Northeastern district of Nova Scotia.—Northumberland streights.—Part of the island of S‍t. John] 1777.
v. 3, no. 1. The coast of Nova Scotia, New England, New York, Jersey, the gulph and river of S‍t Lawrence. 1777.
" " 2. The coast of New England. 1776.
" " 3. [Coast from Moose harb‍r to Gouldsborough] 1776.
" " 4. [ " " Moose point to Frenchmans bay] 1776.
" " 5. [Frenchmens bay.—Mount Desart island] 1776.
" " 6-7. [Penobscot bay.—Belfast bay.—Isle Haut bay.—Great Blue Hill bay] 1776.
" " 8. [Coast from Penmaquid point to Seal harbour] 1776.
" " 9. [ " " Portland sound to Rodgers bay] 1776.
" " 10. [ " " Cape Elizabeth to Moose p‍t] 1776.
" " 11. [Falmouth harbour] 1781.
" " 12. [Piscataqua harbour] 1779.
" " 13. [Coast from Newbury harbour to Cape Elizabeth] 1776.
" " 14. [ " " Marblehead harb. to Hampton harbor] 1776.
" " 15. [Massachusets bay] 1776.
" " 16. [Part of Martha's Vineyard—Nantucket island] 1776.
" " 17. [Boston bay]
" " 18. [Boston harbour] 1775.
" " 19. A chart of the harbour of Boston [Letter-press]
" " 20. [Plymouth bay] 1781.
" " 21. [Coast from Nantucket island to Rhode Island] 1779.
" " 22. [Coast of Long Island from Yellow hook to Cow harbour]
" " 23. [Buzzard's bay, Elizabeth islands, Vineyard sound] 1781.
" " 24. A chart of the harbour of Rhode Island and Narraganset bay. 1776.
" " 25. A chart of the coast of New York, New Jersey, Pensilvania, Maryland, Virginia, North Carolina &c. . . . with soundings & nautical remarks from 1‍t Jn‍o Knight. 1780.
" " 26. [Coast of Connecticut.—Gardners bay] 1781.
" " 27. A chart of Delawar river from Bombay hook to Ridley creek with soundings &c. taken by 1‍t Knight. 1779.—A plan of Delawar river from Chester to Philadelphia shewing the situation of his majesty's ships &c. on the 15‍th of nov‍r 1777 . . . By lieutenant John Hunter.
" " 28. Same as 27.
" " 29. A sketch of the operations before Charlestown. 1780.—Inset: [Charlestown harbour]
" " 30. [The North east shore of the gulph of Mexico] 1780.
" " 31. A chart of the bay and harbour of Pensacola . . . surveyed by George Gould. 1780.
" " 32. A plan of the town of Newport. 1781.
" " 33. A chart of Port Royal and Kington harbours in the island of Jamaica.

## 1774–1781

**The Atlantic Neptune**, published for the use of the royal navy of Great Britain, by Joseph F. W. Des Barres, under the directions of the right hon'ble the lords commissioners of the admiralty   3 v.   fol. [London, 1774–1781]   1202

CONTENTS.

NOTE.—Copy no. 5.

v. 1, no. 1. The coast of Nova Scotia, New England, New York, Jersey, the gulf and river of S.! Lawrence. 1780.
" " 2. [Isle of Sable]
" " 3. Remarks on the isle of Sable.
" " 4. A chart of Nova Scotia. 1775.
" " 5–6. [Grand bay of Passamaquody, S.! Croix river, Copscook bay, Campo Bello harbour, Dear island harbour, Etang harbour, Beaver harbour, &c.—Grand Manan island]
" " 7. The river S.! John. 1780.—Inset: [View of] The entrance of the river S.! John.
" " 8. The isthmus of Nova Scotia. 1779.
" " 9. [Chignecto bay]
" " 10. Annapolis Royal, St. Mary's bay. 1781.—Inset: View of Gulivers hole.
" " 11. [South east part of the Bay of Fundy] 1780.
" " 12. The south west coast of the peninsula of Nova Scotia. 1780.
" " 13. The south east coast of Nova Scotia. 1776.
" " 14. Barrington bay. 1781.
" " 15. Port Amherst—Port Haldimand. 1781.
" " 16. Port Campbell. 1781.
" " 17. Port Mills.—Port Mansfield.—Gambier harbour. 1781.
" " 18. Liverpool bay. 1781.
" " 19. Port Jackson. 1781.
" " 20. King's bay—Lunenburg. 1776.
" " 21. Mecklenburgh bay. 1776.
" " 22. Charlotte bay. 1781.
" " 23. Leith harbour.—Prospect harbour.—Bristol bay.—Sambro harbour. 1781.—Inset: [View of] Hopsons nose.
" " 24. Halifax harbour. 1781.—Insets: [Colored views of] Light house—Chebucto head.—Citadel hill.
" " 25. Egmont harbor. 1779.—Insets: 2 views.
" " 26. Keppell harbour.—Knowles harbour.—Tangier harbour.—Saunder's harbour.—Deane harbour.—Insets: [Views of] Entrance of Keppel harbour.—Cape Southampton.
" " 27. Spry harbour.—Port Pallisser.—Porth North.—Port Parker.—Beaver harbour.—Fleming river. 1776.—Insets: [Views of] Cape Spry.—Beaver isles.—. . . Pegasus wing.
" " 28. White islands harbour.—Port Stephen's.—Liscomb harbour.—Houlton harbour.—River S.! Mary. 1779.
" " 29. Sandwich bay. 1776.
" " 30. [Torbay] 1775.—Inset: [View of] Berry head . . . & White head island.
" " 31. White haven.—Port Howe. 1774.—Inset view.
" " 32. [Canso harbour.—Port George.—Glasgow harbour] 1775.—Inset: View of Port George.

v. 1, no. 33. Crow harbor.—Philip inlet.
" " 34. Milford haven.—[View] 1777.
" " 35. [S! Peter bay]—View of Cape Round. 1775.
" " 36. Conway harbour.—Port Aylesbury. 1779.
" " 37. The gut of Canso 1781.
v. 2, no. 1. The coast of Nova Scotia, New England, New York, Jersey, the gulph and river of S! Lawrence. 1778. Publish'd . . . 1779.
" " 2. [General chart of the gulph and river St. Lawrence]
" " 3. A chart of Cape Breton and St. John's islands, &c.
" " 4. The Magdalen isles in the gulph of St. Lawrence. 1778.
" " 5. [Richmond Isles (alias Isles Madame) Lenox passage, Inhabitants river, Arishat, Conway harbour, Petit Degrat Aylesbury harbour &c. Cape Breton island] 1781.
" " 6. The south east coast of Cape Breton island. Surveyed . . . by Samuel Holland. 1779.
" " 7. A chart of the n. e. coast of Cape Breton island.
" " 8. A chart of the island of Cape Breton.
" " 9. A chart of the harbour of Louisbourg in the island of Cape Breton. 1781.
" " 10. Port Hood. 1776.
" " 11. Frederick bay-Ramsheg harbour—Pictou harbour.—Luttrell. 1776.
" " 12-13. The south east coast of the island of St. John. Surveyed . . . by Sam! Holland. 1781.
" " 14. [North east coast of Nova Scotia] — Northumberland streights.—Part of the island of S! John. 1777
" " 15. [Fort Shediack—Cocagne] 1776.
" " 16. The harbours of Rishibucto & Buctush. 1778.
" " 17. [Miramichi bay] 1777.
" " 18. [Bay of Chaleurs] 1777.
" " 19. [Chaleur's bay, Mal bay, Gaspey, &c.]
" " 20. [Bay and harbour of the Seven islands] 1778.
" " 21. [Coast from river S! John to S! Genevieve island]
" " 22. [Northeastern district of Nova Scotia, Northumberland streights.—Part of the island of S! John] 1777.
v. 3, no. 1. The coast of Nova Scotia, New England, New York, Jersey, the gulph and river of S! Lawrence. 1778. Publish'd . . . 1779.
" " 2. The coast of New England. 1776.
" " 3. [Coast from Moose harb! to Gouldsborough] 1776.
" " 4. [ " " Moose point to Frenchmans bay] 1776.
" " 5. [Frenchmens bay.—Mount Desart island] 1776.
" " 6-7. [Belfast bay.—Penobscot bay.—Isle Haut bay.—Great Blue Hill bay] 1776.
" " 8. [Coast from Penmaquid point to Seal harbour] 1776.
" " 9. [ " " Portland sound to Rodgers bay] 1776.
" " 10. [ " " Cape Elizabeth to Moose p!] 1776.
" " 11. [Falmouth harbour]
" " 12. [Piscataqua harbour] 1779.
" " 13. [Coast from Newbury harbour to Cape Elizabeth] 1776.
" " 14. [ " " Marblehead harb. to Hampton harbor] 1776.
" " 15. [Massachusets bay] 1776.
" " 16. [Part of Martha's Vineyard—Nantucket island] 1776.
" " 17. [Boston bay] 1776.

**The Atlantic Neptune**—Continued.
    v. 3, no. 18. A chart of the harbour of Boston composed from surveys . . . taken in 1769 by mr. George Callendar. 1775.
    "   " 19. [Plymouth bay]
    "   " 20. [Coast from Nantucket island to Rhode Island]
    "   " 21. [Coast of Connecticut.—Gardner's bay] 1779.
    "   " 22. [Buzzard's bay, Elizabeth islands, Vineyard Sound] 1776.
    "   " 23. [A chart of the harbour of Rhode Island and Narraganset bay. 1776.]
    "   " 24. A chart of the coast of New York, New Jersey, Pensilvania, Maryland, Virginia, North Carolina, &c . . . with soundings & nautical remarks from lt. Jno. Knight. 1780.
    "   " 25. Part of Hudsons river shewing the position of fort Montgomery and fort Clinton . . . by lieut. John Knight . . . 1777.—A plan of fort Montgomery & fort Clinton . . . surveyed by major Holland . . . 1779.
    "   " 26. Hell gate.—Oyster bay and Huntington.—Huntington bay.
    "   " 27. Same as 21.
    "   " 28. A chart of Delawar bay with soundings and nautical observations . . . by cap: sir Andrew Snape Hammond . . . 1779.
    "   " 29. A chart of Delawar river from Bombay hook to Ridley creek with soundings &c taken by lt. Knight. 1779.—A plan of Delawar river from Chester to Philadelphia shewing the situation of his majesty's ships &c on the 15th of novr. 1777 . . . By lieutenant John Hunter.
    "   " 30. A chart of the coast of New York, New Jersey, Pensilvania, Maryland, Virginia, North Carolina &c . . . with soundings &c nautical remarks from lt. Jno. Knight. 1780.
    "   " 31. The harbour of Charles Town in South Carolina from the surveys of st. Jas. Wallace . . . 1777.—Inset: Colored view.
    "   " 32. Port Royal in South Carolina. 1777.
    "   " 33. [The north east shore of the Gulph of Mexico] 1780.
    "   " 34. [North coast of the gulph of Mexico]
    "   " 35. A chart of the bay and harbour of Pensacola . . . surveyed by George Gould. 1780.
    "   " 36. A plan of the town of Newport. 1776.
    "   " 37. A chart of Fort Royal and Kingston harbours in the island of Jamaica.

## 1774–1781

**The Atlantic Neptune,** published for the use of the royal navy of Great Britain, by Joseph F. W. Des Barres . . . under the directions of the right honble. the lords commissioners of the admiralty. 3 v. fol. [London, 1774–1781]     1203

CONTENTS.

Note.—Copy no. 6.
    v. 1, no. 1. The coast of Nova Scotia, New England, New York, Jersey, the gulf and river of St. Lawrence . . . 1778.
    "   " 2. [Isle of Sable]
    "   " 3. Remarks on the isle of Sable.
    "   " 4. A chart of Nova Scotia . . . 1775.

v. 1, no. 5-6. [Grand bay of Passamaquody, S! Croix river, Copscook bay, Campo Bello harbour, Dear island harbour, Etang harbour, Beaver harbour etc. Grand Manan island] 1778.
" " 7. The river St. John . . . 1776.—Inset: Entrance of the river St. John.
" " 8. The isthmus of Nova Scotia . . . 1777.
" " 9. [Chignecto bay] 1776.
" " 10. Annapolis Royal . . . St. Mary bay . . .—Inset: View of Gulivers hole. 1776.
" " 11. [South east part of the Bay of Fundy] 1776.
" " 12. The south west coast of the peninsula of Nova Scotia . . . 1776.
" " 13. The south east coast of Nova Scotia. 1776.
" " 14. Barrington bay. 1776.
" " 15. Port Amherst . . .—Port Haldimand. 1775.
" " 16. Port Campbell. 1776.
" " 17. Port Mills . . . Port Mansfield . . . Gambier harbour. 1776.
" " 18. Liverpool bay. 1777.
" " 19. Port Jackson. 1779.
" " 20. King's bay . . .—Lunenburg. 1776.
" " 21. Mecklenburgh bay. 1776.
" " 22. Charlotte bay. 1776.
" " 23. Leith harbour . . . Prospect harbour . . . Bristol bay . . . Sambro harbour. 1775.—Inset: Hopsons nose . . . [View]
" " 24. Halifax harbour.—Insets: Light house . . .—[View of the entrance of Halifax harbour]
" " 25. Egmont harbour.—Insets: Two views.
" " 26. Keppell harbour . . . Knowles harbour . . . Tangier harbour . . . Saunder's harbour . . . Deane harbour.—Insets: Entrance of Keppell harbour.—Cape Southampton.
" " 27. Spry harbour . . . Port Palliser . . . Port North . . . Port Parker . . . Beaver harbour . . . Fleming river. 1776.— Insets: Cape Spry . . . Beaver isles . . . Pegasus wing. [View]
" " 28. White island harbour . . . Port Stephen's . . . Liscomb harbour . . . Houlton harbour . . . River S! Mary. 1776.
" " 29. Sandwich bay. 1776.
" " 30. [Torbay] 1775.—Inset: Berry head . . . White head island. [View]
" " 31. White Haven . . . Port Howe. 1774.—Inset: [View]
" " 32. [Canso harbour . . . Port George . . . Glasgow harbour] 1775.—Inset: View of Port George.
" " 33. Crow harbor . . . Philip inlet.
" " 34. Milford Haven.—Inset: [View]
" " 35. [St Peters bay] 1775.—Inset: View of Cape Round.
" " 36. Conway harbour . . . Port Aylesbury. 1776.
" " 37. The Gut of Canso. 1776.
v. 2, no. 1. The coast of Nova Scotia, New England, New York, Jersey, the gulph and river of S! Lawrence . . . 1777.
" " 2. [General chart of the gulph and river St. Lawrence]
" " 3. A chart of Cape Breton and St. John's island, &c . . .
" " 4. The Magdalen isles in the gulph of St. Lawrence. 1778.
" " 5. [Richmond isles, alias Isles Madame, Lenox passage, Inhabitants river, Arishat, Conway harbour, Petit Degrat, Aylesbury harbour, &c] 1777.

**The Atlantic Neptune**—Continued.

v. 2, no. 6. The south east coast of Cape Breton island. Surveyed . . . by Samuel Holland. 1779.
" " 7. A chart of the n. e. coast of Cape Breton island . . .
" " 8. A chart of the island of Cape Breton.
" " 9. A chart of the harbour of Louisbourg in the island of Cape Breton. 1781.
" " 10. Port Hood. 1776.
" " 11. Frederick bay . . . Ramsheg harbour . . . Pictou harbor . . . Port Lutterell. 1776.
" " 12–13. The south east coast of the island of St. John. Surveyed . . . by Sam¹ Holland. 1781.
" " 14. [North east coast of Nova Scotia] 1779.
" " 15. [Port Shediack, Cocagne] 1776.
" " 16. The harbours of Rifhibucto & Buctufh. 1778.
" " 17. [Miramichi bay] 1777.
" " 18. [Bay of Chaleurs] 1777.
" " 23. [Northeastern district of Nova Scotia . . . Northumberland streights . . . Part of the island of St. John] 1781.
v. 3, no. 1. [The coast from river S! John to S! Genevieve island] 1777.
" " 2. The coast of New England. 1776.
" " 3. [Coast from Moose harb! to Gouldsborough] 1776.
" " 4. [Coast from Moose point to Frenchman's bay] 1776.
" " 5. [Mount Desart island, Frenchmans bay] 1776.
" " 6–7. [Belfast bay.—Penobscot bay.—Isle Haute bay.—Great Blue Hill bay]
" " 8. [Coast from Penmaquid point to Seal harbour] 1776.
" " 9. [Coast from Portland sound to Rodgers bay] 1776.
" " 10. [Coast from Cape Elizabeth to Moose pt.] 1776.
" " 11. [Falmouth harbour]
" " 12. [Piscataqua harbour] 1779.
" " 13. [Coast from Newbury harbour to Cape Elizabeth] 1776.
" " 14. [Coast from Marblehead harb. to Hampton harbour] 1776.
" " 15. [Massachusets [!] bay] 1776.
" " 16. [Part of Martha's Vineyard, Nantucket island] 1776.
" " 17. [Boston bay] 1776.
" " 18. [Boston harbour] 1775. Text to accompany map.
" " 19. Duplicate of map, no. 10.
" " 20. [Plymouth bay]
" " 21. [From Nantucket to Rhode Island]
" " 22. [Coast from Shelter island. to Point Judith] 1779.
" " 23. [Buzzards' bay, Elizabeth islands, Vineyard sound] 1776.
" " 24. A chart of the harbour of Rhode Island and Narraganset bay. 1776.
" " 25. A chart of the coast of New York, New Jersey, Pensilvania, Maryland, Virginia, North Carolina . . . with soundings and nautical remarks from l¹. Jnọ Knight. 1780.
" " 26. Oyster bay and Huntington . . . Huntington bay . . . Hell Gate.
" " 27. [Same as map no. 22, with more detail]
" " 28. A chart of Delawar bay with soundings and nautical observations taken by cap¹. sir Andrew Snape Hammond . . . 1779.

v. 3, no. 29. A chart of Delawar river from Bombay hook to Ridley creek, with soundings &c taken by l$^t$. Knight . . . 1779.—A plan of Delawar river from Chester to Philadelphia . . . Surveyed and sounded by lieutenant John Hunter . . .
" " 30. A sketch of the operations before Charlestown, the capital of South Carolina . . . 1780. Inset: Charlestown harbour.
" " 31. The harbour of Charles Town in South Carolina from the survey of s$^r$. Ja$^s$. Wallace . . . with a view of the town. 1777.
" " 32. [The north east shore of the gulph of Mexico] 1780.
" " 33. A chart of the bay and harbour of Pensacola in the province of West Florida. Surveyed by George Gould. 1780.
" " 34. A plan of the town of Newport. 1776.
" " 35. A chart of Port Royal and Kingston harbours in the island of Jamaica . . .

## 1776–1781

**The Atlantic Neptune,** published for the use of the royal navy of Great Britain, by Joseph F. W. Des Barres, under the directions of the right hon'ble the lords commissioners of the admiralty. 3 v. fol. [London, 1776–1781]      1204

NOTE.—Copy no. 7. Volume 1 and 3 wanting.

### CONTENTS.

v. 2, no. 1. The coast of Nova Scotia, New England, New York, Jersey, the gulph and river of S$^t$ Lawrence. 1778. Publish'd. 1779.
" " 2. [General chart of the gulph and river St. Lawrence]
" " 3. A chart of Cape Breton and St. John's islands, &c.
" " 4. The Magdalen isles in the gulph of St. Lawrence. 1778.
" " 5. The south east coast of Cape Breton island. Surveyed . . . by Samuel Holland. 1779.
" " 6. A chart of the n. e. coast of Cape Breton island.
" " 7. A chart of the island of Cape Breton.
" " 8. A chart of the harbour of Louisbourg in the island of Cape Breton. 1781.
" " 9. Port Hood. 1776.
" " 10. Frederick bay.—Ramsheg harbour.—Pictou harbour.—Port Luttrell. 1776.
" " 11–12. The south east coast of the island of St. John. Surveyed . . . by Sam$^l$ Holland. 1781.
" " 13. [North east coast of Nova Scotia.—Northumberland streights.—Part of the island of S$^t$ John] 1777.
" " 14. [Port Shediack.—Cocagne] 1776.
" " 15. The harbours of Rishibucto & Buctush. 1778.
" " 16. [Miramichi bay] 1777.
" " 17. [Plymouth bay]
" " 18. [Chaleur's bay, Mal bay, Gaspee, &c.]
" " 19. [Bay of Seven islands] 1778.
" " 20. [Coast from river S$^t$ John to S$^t$ Genevieve island]
" " 21. [Northeastern district of Nova Scotia.—Northumberland streights.—Part of the island of S$^t$ John]

## 1775-1781

**The Atlantic Neptune**, published for the use of the royal navy of Great Britain, by Joseph F. W. Des Barres, under the directions of the right hon'ble the lords commissioners of the admiralty. 3 v. fol. [London. 1775-1781]  1205

Note.—Copy no. 8.

CONTENTS.

v. 1, no. 1. The coast of Nova Scotia, New England, New York, Jersey, the gulf and river of S$^t$ Lawrence ... 1777.
" " 2. [Isle of Sable] 1779.
" " 3. [Views of Sable island] 1779.
" " 4. The isle of Sable survey'd ... in 1766–1767. Published ... 1779.
" " 5. A view from the camp at the east end of the Naked Sand hills ... isle of Sable. 1781.
" " 6. Remarks on the isle of Sable.
" " 7. A chart of Nova Scotia. 1775.
" " 8-9. [Grand bay of Passamaquody, S$^t$. Croix river, Copscook bay, Campo Bello harbour, Dear Island harbour, Etang harbour, Beaver harbour &c.—Grand Manan island]
" " 10. The river St. John. 1776.—Inset: [View of] the entrance of the river S$^t$. John.
" " 11. The isthmus of Nova Scotia. 1777.
" " 12. [Chignecto bay] 1777.
" " 13. Annapolis Royal, St. Mary's bay. 1776.—Inset: View of Gullivers hole.
" " 14. [South east part of the bay of Fundy] 1776.
" " 15. The south west coast of the peninsula of Nova Scotia. 1776.
" " 16. The south east coast of Nova Scotia. 1779.
" " 17. Barrington bay. 1776.
" " 18. Port Amherst.—Port Haldimand. 1775.
" " 19. Port Campbell. 1776.
" " 20. Port Mills.—Port Mansfield.—Gambier harbour. 1776.
" " 21. Liverpool bay. 1777.
" " 22. Port Jackson. 1777.
" " 23. King's bay.—Lunenburg. 1776.
" " 24. Mecklenburgh bay. 1776.
" " 25. Charlotte bay. 1776.
" " 26. Leith harbour.—Prospect harbour.—Bristol bay.—Sambro harbour. 1775.—Inset: Hopsons nose.
" " 27. Halifax harbour. 1779.—Insets: Light house.—[View of the entrance of Halifax harbour]
" " 28. Egmont harbour. 1779. Inset: 2 views.
" " 29. Keppell harbour.—Knowles harbour.—Tangier harbour.—Saunder's harbour.—Deane harbour. 1779.—Insets: Entrance of Keppel harbour.—Cape Southampton.
" " 30. Spry harbour.—Port Pallisser.—Port North.—Port Parker.—Beaver harbour.—Fleming river. 1779.—Insets: [View of] Cape Spry.—Beaver Isles.—Pegassus wing.
" " 31. White island harbour.—Port Stephen's.—Liscomb harbour.—Houlton Harbour.—River S$^t$. Mary. 1779.
" " 32. Sandwich bay. 1779.

| | | |
|---|---|---|
| v. 1, no. | 33. | Torbay.—Inset: [View of] Berry head . . . & White head island. 1779. |
| " " | 34. | White haven.—Port Howe. 1779.—Inset view. |
| " " | 35. | [Canso harbour.—Port George.—Glasgow harbour . . . ]—View of Port George. 1779. |
| " " | 36. | Crow harbor.—Philip inlet. 1779. |
| " " | 37. | Milford haven.—[View] 1779. |
| " " | 38. | [S$^t$ Peters bay]—View of Cape Round. 1779. |
| " " | 39. | Conway harbour.—Port Aylesbury. 1779. |
| " " | 40. | The gut of Canso. 1776. |
| v. 2, no. | 1. | The coast of Nova Scotia, New England, New York, Jersey, the gulph and river of S$^t$. Lawrence . . . 1777. Rev. ed. |
| " " | 2. | [General chart of the gulph and river St. Lawrence] |
| " " | 3. | A chart of Cape Breton and St. John's island, &c. |
| " " | 4. | The Magdalen isles in the gulph of St. Lawrence. 1778. |
| " " | 5. | [Richmond Isles (alias Isles Madame)] Lenox Passage, Inhabitants river, Arishat, Conway harbour, Petit Degrat, Aylesbury harbour, &c. |
| " " | 6. | The south east coast of Cape Breton island. Surveyed . . . by Samuel Holland. 1779. |
| " " | 7. | A chart of the n. e. coast of Cape Breton island . . . 1781. |
| " " | 8. | A chart of the island of Cape Breton. |
| " " | 9. | A chart of the harbour of Louisbourg in the island of Cape Breton. 1781. |
| " " | 10. | Port Hood. 1776. |
| " " | 11. | Frederick bay.—Ramcheg harbour.—Pictou harbour.—Port Luttrell. 1776. |
| " " | 12-13. | The south east coast of the island of St. John. Surveyed . . . by Sam$^l$. Holland. 1781. |
| " " | 14. | [North east coast of Nova Scotia]—Northumberland streights. 1779. |
| " " | 15. | Port Shediack.—Cocagne. 1781. |
| " " | 16. | The harbours of Rishibucto & Buctush . . . 1778. |
| " " | 17. | [Miramichi bay] 1777. |
| " " | 18. | [Bay of Chaleurs] 1777. |
| " " | 19. | [Chaleur's bay, Mal bay, Gaspey, &c.] |
| " " | 20. | [Bay and harbour of the Seven islands] 1778. |
| " " | 21. | [Coast from river S$^t$. John to S$^t$. Genevieve island] 1781. |
| " " | 22. | [River St. Lawrence up to Quebec] 1781. |
| " " | 23. | [Northeastern district of Nova Scotia . . . Northumberland streights.—Part of the island of St. John] 1777. |
| v. 3. no. | 1. | The coast of Nova Scotia, New England, New York, Jersey, the gulph and river of S$^t$. Lawrence. 1778. |
| " " | 2. | The coast of New England. 1776. |
| " " | 3. | [Coast from Moose harb$^r$. to Gouldsborough] 1776. |
| " " | 4. | [ " "   Moose point to Frenchmans bay] 1776. |
| " " | 5. | [The north east shore of the gulph of Mexico] 1780. |
| " " | 6. | [Mount Desart island.—Frenchman's bay] 1776. |
| " " | 7-8. | [Belfast bay.—Penobscot bay.—Isle haut bay.—Great blue hill bay] 1776. |
| " " | 9. | [Coast from Penmaquid point to Seal harbour] 1776. |
| " " | 10. | [ " "   Portland sound to Rodgers bay] 1776. |
| " " | 11. | [ " "   Cape Elizabeth to Moose pt.] 1776. |
| " " | 12. | [Falmouth harbour] |

**The Atlantic Neptune**—Continued.

v. 3, no. 13. [Coast from Newbury harbour to Cape Elizabeth] 1776.
" " 14. [Piscataqua harbour] 1779.
" " 15. [Coast from Marblehead harbour to Hampton harbor] 1776.
" " 16. [Massachusets bay] 1776.
" " 17. [Part of Martha's Vineyard.—Nantucket island] 1776.
" " 18. [Boston bay] 1776.
" " 19. [Boston harbour] 1775.
" " 20. Text to accompany sheet no. 19.
" " 21. [Plymouth bay]
" " 22. [Coast from Nantucket island to Rhode island] 1779.
" " 23. [ " " Shelter island to Point Judith]
" " 24. [Buzzard's bay.—Elizabeth islands.—Vineyard sound] 1776.
" " 25. A chart of the harbour of Rhode Island and Narraganset bay. 1776.
" " 26. A chart of the coast of New York, New Jersey, Pensilvania, Maryland, Virginia, North Carolina . . . with soundings and nautical remarks from l$^t$. Jn$^o$. Knight. 1780.
" " 27. A chart of New York harbour . . . composed from surveys and observations of . . . John Knight, John Hunter.—Insets: [Views of] Bond hollow.—Mount Pleasant.
" " 28. Part of Hudson's river shewing the position of fort Montgomery and fort Clinton . . . by lieu$^t$. John Knight . . . 1777.—A plan of fort Montgomery & fort Clinton . . . by major Holland. 1779.
" " 29. Oyster bay and Huntington.—Huntington bay.—Hell gate.
" " 30. [Coast of Long Island from Yellow hook to Cow harbour.]
" " 31. A chart of Delawar bay . . . with soundings . . . taken by cap$^t$. sir Andrew Snape Hammond. 1779.
" " 32. A chart of Delawar river from Bombay hook to Ridley creek with soundings &c. taken by l$^t$. Knight. 1779—A plan of Delawar river from Chester to Philadelphia shewing the situation of his majesty's ships &c. on the 15$^{th}$ nov$^r$. 1777.
" " 33. [Pensilvania.—Part of New Jersey] 1777.
" " 34. A sketch of the operations before Charlestown . . . 1780.—Inset: [Charlestown harbour]
" " 35. The harbour of Charles Town in South Carolina, from the surveys of s$^r$. Ja$^s$. Wallace. 1777.—Inset: [View]
" " 36. Port Royal in South Carolina. 1777.
" " 37. A plan of the harbour of S$^t$. Augustin in the province of Georgia.
" " 38. [The north east shore of the gulph of Mexico] 1780.
" " 39. [Gulph of Mexico. Northern coast]
" " 40. A chart of the bay and harbour of Pensacola . . . surveyed by George Gould. 1780.
" " 41. A plan of the town of Newport. 1776.
" " 42. A chart of Port Royal and Kingston harbours in the island of Jamaica.

## 1776

**Sayer, R.,** *and* **Bennet, J.**
 The american military pocket atlas; being an approved collection of correct maps, both general and particular, of the british colonies; efpecially thofe which now are, or probably may be the theatre of war: taken principally from the actual surveys and judicious obfervations of engineers De Brahm and Romans; Cook, Jackson, and Collet; maj. Holland, and other officers, employed in his majesty's fleets and armies.    viii pp., 1 l., 6 fold. maps.   8°.   London, for R. Sayer & J. Bennet [1776]    1206

   NOTE.—Known as the "Holster atlas," owing to its being made for the use of the mounted british officers.

   CONTENTS.

   no. 1. North America, as divided amongst the european powers. By Samuel Dunn . . . 1774.
   " 2. A compleat map of the West Indies, containing the coasts of Florida, Louisiana, New Spain, and Terra Firma . . . By Samuel Dunn . . . 1774.
   " 3. A general map of the northern british colonies in America which comprehends . . . Quebec . . . Newfoundland, Nova Scotia, New-England and New-York . . . Regulated by the . . . observations of major Holland and corrected from governor Pownall's late map 1776 . . . 1776.
   " 4. A general map of the middle british colonies, in America. Containing Virginia, Maryland, the Delaware counties, Pennsylvania and New Jersey . . . improved from several surveys made after the latwar, and corrected from governor Pownall's late map 1776 . . . 1776.
   " 5. A general map of the southern british colonies, in America. Comprehending North and South Carolina, Georgia, East and West Florida . . . From the modern surveys of engineer de Brahm, capt. Collet, Mouzon & others; and from the large hydrographical survey of the coasts of East and West Florida. By B. Romans, 1776. . . . 1776.—Insets: Plan of Charlestown.—Plan of S! Augustine.
   " 6. A survey of lake Champlain, including lake George, Crown Point and St. John . . . By William Brassier, 1762 . . . Inset: A particular plan of lake George. Surveyed in 1756. By cap! Jackson. 1776.

## 1777

**Faden, W.**
 The North American atlas, selected from the most authentic maps, charts, plans, &c. hitherto published.    1 p. l., 27 col. maps on 63 l. fol.   London, for W. Faden, 1777.    1207

   NOTE.—Copy A. Copies A and B differ. See title 1208.

   CONTENTS.

   no. [1–2] A new and correct map of North America, with the West India islands . . . Laid down according to the latest surveys . . . of gove! Pownall . . . 1777. 2 sheets.—Inset: A particular map of Baffin and Hudson's bay.—The passage by land to California . . .

**Faden, W.**—Continued.
no. [3] A new map of the province of Quebec . . . By captain Carver and other officers . . . 1776.—Inset: A particular survey of the isles of Montreal.—The city of Quebec.—Course of the river S$^t$ Laurence from la Valterie to Quebec..—Plan of Montreal or Villemarie.
" [4] A map of the inhabited part of Canada . . . with the frontiers of New York and New England . . . By C. J. Sauthier. 1777.
" [5] Plan of the city of Quebec . . . Engraved by W$^m$. Faden. 1776.
" [6–7] A map of Nova Scotia . . . by capt$^n$. Montresor . . 1768.—Insets: A plan of the town of Boston.—A plan of Boston harbor . . . 2 sheets.
" [8–9] A map of the inhabited part of New England . . . [By John Green. anon.] 1774. 2 sheets.
" [10] A topographical chart of the bay of Narraganset . . . By Charles Blaskowitz . . . 1777.
" [11] A plan of the town of Newport in Rhode Island. Surveyed by Charles Blaskowitz . . . 1777.
" [12] A map of the province of New York . . . By C. J. Sauthier . . . 1776.
" [13–14] A map of the province of New York, with part of Pensilvania, and New England . . . by captain Montresor . . . 1775. 2 sheets.— Insets: . . . Continuation of lake Champlain . . .—Continuation of Connecticut river . . .
" [15] A topographical map of Hudsons river . . . By C. J. Sauthier . . . 1776.
" [16] The attack and defeat of the american fleet . . . by the kings fleet . . . upon lake Champlain, the 11$^{th}$ of october, 1776. Engraved by W$^m$ Faden . . . 1776.
" [17] A plan of the operations of the king's army . . . in New York and east New Jersey against the american forces . . . from the 12$^{th}$ of october, to the 28$^{th}$ of november, 1776 . . . By C. J. Sauthier . . . 1777.
" [18] A plan of New York island, with part of Long island, Staten island & east New Jersey . . . Engraved . . . by W$^m$. Faden . . . 1776.
" [19] A topographical map of the north$^n$ part of New York island. Exhibiting the plan of fort Washington . . . By C. J. Sauthier . . . 1777.
" [20–21] Plan of the city of New York . . . Surveyed in . . . 1766 & 1769. [By] B. Ratzer. 1776. Inset: A south west view of the city of New York.
" [22] The province of New Jersey . . . Engraved . . . by W$^m$ Faden. 1777.
" [23] Plan of the operations of gen. Washington, against the king's troops in New Jersey, from the 26$^{th}$ of december 1776, to the 3$^d$ january 1777, by William Faden. 1777.
" [24] A map of Pennsylvania . . . from the late map of W. Scull published in 1770 . . . 1775.
" [25] Plan of the city and environs of Philadelphia. Surveyed by N. Scull and G. Heap . . . 1777.
" [26] A chart of Delaware bay and river . . . Taken from the original chart . . . by Joshua Fisher . . . 1776.
" [27–28] A map of the most inhabited part of Virginia . . . **Drawn by Joshua Fry & Peter Jefferson in 1775. 2 sheets.**
NOTE.—Revised in 1755 by John Dalrymple.

no. [29-30] An accurate map of North and South Carolina . . . By Henry Mouzon and others. 1775. 2 sheets. Insets: The harbour of Port Royal.—The bar and harbour of Charlestown.
" [31] A plan of the attack of fort Sulivan . . . on the 28th of june, 1776 . . . Engraved by W$^m$. Faden. 1776.—Inset: Plan of the platform in Sulivans fort by . . . Thos. James
" [32-33] A map of South Carolina and part of Georgia . . . [By] William De Brahm . . . 1757. 2 sheets.
" [34] The coast of west Florida and Louisiana. By Tho$^s$ Jefferys. 1775.
" [35] The bay of Espiritu Santo, and the western coast of east Florida.— Plan of the town of S$^t$ Augustine . . . [By] T. Jefferys.

**1777**

The North American atlas, selected from the most authentic maps, charts, plans, &c. hitherto published.    1 p. l., 23 fold. maps on 54 l. fol. London, for W. Faden, 1777.    1208

NOTE.—Copy B. Copies A and B differ. See title 1207.

CONTENTS.

no. 1. The british colonies in North America. Engraved by William Faden. 1777.
" 2. A chart of part of the coast of Labradore . . . by Michael Lane . . . 1777.
" 3. A map of the inhabited part of Canada . . . with the frontiers of New York and New England . . . By C. J. Sauthier. 1777.
" 4. A chart of the gulf of S$^t$. Lawrence . . .
" 5. A general chart of the island of Newfoundland . . . by James Cook and Michael Lane . . . 1775.
" 6. A plan of the island of S$^t$. John . . . Surveyed by cap$^t$. Holland. 1775.—Inset: gulf of S$^t$. Laurence.
" 7. A new map of Nova Scotia and Cape Breton island . . . by Thomas Jefferys . . . 1775.
" 8-9. A map of the most inhabited part of New England . . . [By John Green. anon.] 1774.—Insets: A plan of Boston harbor . . .—A plan of the town of Boston.
" 10. Boston its environs and harbour, with the rebel works raised against that town in 1775 from the observations of lieut. Page . . . and from the plans of cap$^t$. Montresor. 1777.
" 11. A topographical chart of the bay of Narraganset . . . By Charles Blaskowitz. 1777.
" 12. A map of the province of New York . . . By C. J. Sauthier . . . 1776.
" 13-14. A map of the province of New York, with part of Pensilvania, and New England . . . by cap$^t$. Montresor . . . 1775. Republished . . . 1777.—Insets: . . . Continuation of lake Champlain . . .— . . . Continuation of Connecticut river . . .
" 15. A topographical map of Hudsons river . . . By C. J. Sauthier . . . 1776.
" 16. A plan of the operations of the king's army . . . in New York and east New Jersey against the american forces, from the 12$^{th}$ of october, to 28$^{th}$ of november 1776. . . . By C. J. Sauthier . . . 1777.

**Faden, W.**—Continued.

   no.   17. A plan of New York island, with part of Long island, Staten island & east New Jersey . . . Engraved by W$^m$. Faden . . . 1776.
   "   18. A map of Pennsylvania . . . from the late map of W. Scull published in 1770 . . . 1775.
   "   19. A plan of the city and environs of Philadelphia. Surveyed by N. Scull and G. Heap . . . 1777.
   "   20. A chart of Delaware bay and river . . . Taken from the original chart . . . by Joshua Fisher . . . 1776.
   "   21-22. A map of the most inhabited part of Virginia . . . Drawn by Joshua Fry & Peter Jefferson in 1775.
         Note.—Revised in 1755 by John Dalrymple.
   "   23-24. An accurate map of North and South Carolina . . . By Henry Mouzon and others. 1775.—Insets: The harbour of Port Royal.—The bar and harbour of Charlestown.
   "   25. The coast of west Florida and Louisiana. By Tho$^s$. Jefferys. 1775.
   "   26. A chart of the entrance into S$^t$. Mary's river taken by capt$^n$. W. Fuller in november 1769. 1770.—Insets: Plan of Amelia island in east Florida.—A chart of the mouth of the Nassau river.
   "   27. The Carribbee islands and Guayana. Drawn by L. Delarochette . . . 1776 . . .

### 1777

**North-American, The, pilot** for Newfoundland, Labradore, the gulf and river St. Laurence: being a collection of sixty accurate charts and plans, drawn from original surveys: taken by James Cook and Michael Lane . . . and Joseph Gilbert . . . Chiefly engraved by the late mr. Thomas Jefferys . . .    2 v. 4 p. l., 22 maps; 1 p. l., 13 maps. fol. London, R. Sayer & J. Bennett, 1777.    **1209**

    Note.—See also title 1220.

    Capt. James Cook's letter fronting title, addressed to Sayer, dated feb. 26, 1776, and dedication to sir Hugh Palliser, signed Robert Sayer, Fleet—street, 1775. Sabin, in his A dictionary of books relating to America, v. 13, title 55557, describes an edition similar to this, dated 1775.

    Title varies, v. 2: (Part the second) The North-American pilot for New England, New York, Pensilvania, Maryland, and Virginia; also, the two Carolinas, and Florida. Drawn from original surveys, taken by capt. John Gascoigne, Joshua Fisher, Jacob Blamey, and other officers and pilots in his majesty's service . . .

        CONTENTS.

   v. 1, no. 1. A general chart of the island of Newfoundland . . . 1775 . . .
   "   "   2. A chart of the banks of Newfoundland . . .
   "   "   3. A chart of south-east part of Newfoundland, containing the bays of Placentia, S$^t$ Mary, Trespassey and Conception . . . 1770.
   "   "   4. Trinity harbour.—Carboniere and Harbour Grace.—S$^t$ Johns harbour. 1770.
   "   "   5. The harbour of Trespassey with Mutton and Biscay bays.—The road and harbour of Placentia . . .—S$^t$ Mary's harbour. 1770.

v. 1, no. 6. A chart of part of the south coast of Newfoundland including the islands of Langley, S! Peter's and Miquelon . . . 1774 . . . Insets: Port aux Basque.—S! Peter's island. Survey'd . . . 1763.—Great Jervis harbour.—Harbour Briton.—Harbours of S! Laurence.

" " 7. A new map of Nova Scotia, and Cape Breton island with the adjacent parts of New England and Canada . . . 1775.

" " 8. The island of Sable . . . 1770.

" " 9. A chart of the harbour of Halifax, in Nova Scotia; with Jebucto bay and Cape Sambrô . . . 1775.

" " 10. A plan of Port Dauphin on the eastern side of Cape Breton Island. Surveyed in 1743.—A plan of Murgain or Cow bay, on the eastern side of Cape Breton island. Surveyed in 1760.—A draught of the gut of Canso, between Nova Scotia and Cape Breton island. Surveyed . . . 1761.

" " 11. A chart of the gulf of S! Laurence . . . 1775.

" " 12. A chart of the Magdalen islands in the gulf of S! Laurence. Surveyed in 1765.

" " 13. A map of the island of S! John, in the gulf of S! Laurence . . . 1775.—Inset: gulf of S! Laurence.

" " 14. A plan of Chaleur bay, in the gulf of S! Laurence, surveyed . . . 1760 . . . 1775.

" " 15. A plan of Ristigouche harbour in Chaleur bay, surveyed in 1760 . . . 1775.

" " 16. A chart of the west coast of Newfoundland . . . by James Cook . . . 1770.—Insets: A plan of Hawkes harbour, Port Saunders, and Keppel harbour.—A plan of York and Lark harbours.

" " 17. A chart of the straights of Bellisle with part of the coast of Newfoundland and Labradore . . . Surveyed . . . in 1766 and . . . 1769 . . . 1770.—Insets: Bradore harbour.—Red bay.—York, or Chateaux bay.—Old Ferolle harbour.—Quirpon harbour.—Croque harbour.

" " 18. A chart of part of the coast of Labradore, from the straights of Bell Isle, to Cape Bluff. Surveyed . . . 1767 . . . 1770.—Insets: Petty harbour.—The three harbours of Sophia, Charlotte and Mecklenburg.

" " 19. A chart of part of the coast of Labradore from Grand Point to Shecatica. Surveyed by Michael Lane in 1768 . . . 1770.—Insets: Plan of Mecatina harbour.—Plan of S! Augustine.—Plan of Cumberland harbour.

" " 20-23. A new chart of the river S! Laurence from the island of Anticosti to the falls of Richelieu . . . 1775.—Insets: Parokett islands, Mingan island.—Mingan harbour.—Gaspee bay.—English channel . . . Havre S! Nicholas, by Desjardins.—Bay of the Seven islands.—Pointe aux Allouettes . . . by Desjardins.—Quebec. 2 sheets.

v. 2, no. 1. A chart of the Atlantic ocean. 1 sheet . . . 1775.

" " 2. A chart of the harbour of Boston . . .

" " 3. Chart of the entrance of Hudson's river, from Sandy Hook to New York . . . 1776.

" " 4. A chart of Delaware bay and river . . . by Joshua Fisher . . . 1776.

**North American pilot, The**—Continued.

    v. 2, no. 5-6. A new and accurate chart of the bay of Chesapeake . . . as far as the navigable part of the rivers Patowmack, Patapsco and North-east . . . 1776.—Inset: A plan of Herring bay in Maryland. 2 sheets.
    " " 7. A plan of Cape Fear river from the bar to Brunswick. 1776.
    " " 8. An exact plan of Charles-town-bar and harbour . . . 1776.
    " " 9. A plan of Port Royal in South Carolina . . . Survey'd by cap$^{\text{n}}$ John Gafcoigne. 1776.
    " " 10. A plan of the river and sound of D'Awfoskee in South Carolina. Survey'd by Cap$^{\text{t}}$ John Gascoigne . . . 1776.
    " " 11. A plan of Amelia harbour and barr [!] in east Florida. Surveyed in 1775 . . . by Jacob Blamey . . . 1776.
    " " 12. The coast of west Florida and Louisiana . . .—The peninsula and gulf of Florida or channel of Bahama with the Bahama islands . . . 1775.
    " " 13. The coast of Yucatan from Campeche to Bahia del Ascension; with the west end of Cuba . . .—The island of Cuba with part of the Bahama banks & the Martyrs . . . 1775.

## 1778

**Le Rouge, G. L.**

    Pilote Américain Septentrional pour les côtes de Labrador, N$^{\text{lle}}$ Ecosse, N$^{\text{lle}}$ Angleterre, New-York, Pensilvanie, Maryland, Virginie, les 2 Carolines et Florides. Par Jefferys, Lane, Morris, chevalier des Barres, Smith, Blaskowitz, Scull. Publié à Londres en 1776. Traduit de l'anglais. 2 p. l., 20 maps. fol. Paris, Le Rouge, 1778.      1210

    NOTE.—Engraved title.
    Map no. 1, La Manche contenant les côtes de France . . . les côtes méridionales d'Angletterre . . . 1778, wanting.

        CONTENTS.

    no. 2. Carte de l'océan Atlantique, traduite de Jefferis.
    " 3. Océan Atlantique . . . en quatre feuilles, contenant les côtes de l'Europe, de l'Afrique et de l'Amérique . . . 1778.
    " 4. Partie des côtes de Labrador . . . Par M. Lane, publié à Londres en 1777. Traduit de l'anglais. 1778. 2 sheets.
    " 5. Port de Halifax de la Nouvelle Ecosse . . . Levé . . . par Morris premier arpenteur, publié à Londres en 1775 . . . 1778.
    " 6. Plan de Boston avec les sondes et les directions pour la navigation. Traduit de l'anglais.
    " 7. Port de Rhode Island et Narraganset baye. Publié . . . par le chevalier des Barres Londres 1776. Traduit de l'anglais et augmenté d'après celui de Blaskowitz. Publié à Londres en 1777. 1778.—Inset: Plan de Newport en Rhode Island, levé par Blaskowitz. Publié à Londres par Faden 1777. 1778. 2 sheets.
    " 8. Entrée de la rivière d'Hudson depuis la pointe Sandy Hook, les bancs, les sondes, les guides &c. Traduit de l'anglais . . . 1778.
    " 9. Baye de la Delaware . . . d'après la carte de Joshua Fisher publiée à Philadelphia . . . 1777.

no. 10. Environs de Philadelphie par Scull et Heap, publie à Londres par Faden en 1777. Traduit de l'anglais . . . 1778.
" 11. Baye de Chesapeake en 4 feuilles . . . publié à Londres en juillet 1776. Traduit de l'anglais . . . 1778.
" 12. Rivière du Cap Fear de la bare a Brunswick. Traduit de l'anglais . . . 1778.
" 13. Nouvelle carte des côtes des Carolines Septentrionales et Méridionales du Cap Fear a Sud Edisto. Levées et sondées par N. Pocock en 1770. Traduites de l'anglois . . . 1777.
" 14. Barre et port de Charles-Town, levé en 1776 . . . 1778.
" 15. Port Royal dans la Caroline Méridionale. Levé par le cap:$^e$ Gascoigne. Publié à Londres en 1776 . . . 1778.
" 16. Rivière et détroit de D'Awfoskee en Caroline Mérid$^{le}$ par le cap$^e$ Gascoigne. Publié à Londres en mai 1776. Traduit de l'anglois . . . 1778.
" 17. Port et barre d'Amelia de la Floride orientale, levé en 1775 par Blamey . . . Traduit correctement de Langlais . . . 1778.
" 18. Entrée de la rivière S$^{te}$ Marie, levée par cap$^t$ Fuller en 1769.—Isle Amelia en Floride.—Bouche de la rivière Nassau . . . Fuller dédia cette carte au comte d'Egmont, la sit publier par Gefferys à Londres en 1770. Traduitte de l'anglais . . . 1778.
" 19. La baye de Spiritu Santo côte occidentale de la Floride.—S. Augustin capitale de la floride orientale.
" 20. Carte de la Floride occidentale et Louisiane. Traduite de Jefferys, à Paris par le Rouge, 1777.—La peninsule et golfe de la Floride ou canal de Bahama avec les isles de Bahama, traduit de Gefferys . . . 1777.

**1778–1780**

**France.** *Dépôt des cartes et plans de la marine.*

Neptune Americo-Septentrional contenant les côtes, îles et bancs, les baies, ports, et mouillages, et les sondes des mers de cette-partie du monde, depuis le Groenland inclusivement, jusques et compris le golfe du Mexique . . . ou recuil de cartes hydrographiques à l'usage des vaisseaux du roi . . . Dressé au dépôt général des cartes, plans et journaux de la marine . . . 1 p. l., 25 maps. fol. [Paris, 1778–1780] 1211

CONTENTS.

no. 1-2. Carte réduite des côtes orientales de l'Amérique Septentrionale. . . . 1778–1780.
" [3] Carte d'une partie des côtes de la Floride et de la Louisiane . . . 1778.
" [4] Carte réduite des côtes et de l'intérieur de la presqu'ile de la Floride . . . 1780.
" [5] Plan de l'île de S$^t$ Jean . . . Suivant l'arpentage du capitaine anglois Holland . . . 1778.
" [6] Carte de la baie des Chaleurs . . . Levé en 1724 par m$^r$ l'Hermite . . . 1780.
" [7] Plans particulièrs dépendans de l'île Royale.
" [8] Carte réduite de l'île Royale . . . Faites par m. le marquis de Chabert . . . 1780.

**France**—Continued.

no. [9] Plan de la ville du port de Louisbourg. Levé en 1756 . . . 1779.
" [10] Plan de la baie de Gabarus . . . 1779.
" [11] Plan de la baie de Nérichac . . . 1779.—Plan du Port Toulouse, . . . 1779.
" [12] Plan du Port Dauphin . . . 1778 . . .
" [13] Plan du port de Chibouctou . . . Levée par m. le m!ª de Chabert, . . . 1779.
" [14] Plan du port de la revière S! Jean . . . 1779.—Plan du port de la Heve . . .—Plan du Port Rochelois . . .
" [15] Plan de l'isthme de l'Acadie . . . 1779.
" [16] Plan de la baie et du havre de Casco . . . Par le cap? Cyprian Southack. . . . 1779.
" [17] Plan du bassin et de la revièr du Port Royal . . . 1779.
" [18] Carte particulière du havre de Boston . . . Réduite de la carte anglaise de J. E. S. Des Barres . . . 1780.
" [19] Plan de la baie de Narragansett . . . Levé par Charles Blaskowitz . . . 1777 . . . 1780.
" [20] Carte de la baye et rivière de Delaware . . . par Josué Fischer . . . 1778.
" [21] Carte de l'entrée de la rivière d'Hudson . . . 1778.
" [22] Carte de la baie de Chesapeake . . . 1778.
" [23] Plan de la rivière du Cap Fear . . . 1778.
" [24] Plan de la barre et du havre de Charlestown . . . 1776 . . . Rédigé, en 1778 . . .
" [25] Plan de Port Royal et de la rivière et détroit d'Awfskée . . . Levé par cap? John Gascoine . . . 1778.
" [26] Plan de la barre et du port d'Amelia . . . Levé en janvier 1775. Par Jacob Blamey . . . 1779.

### 1778-1792

**Le Rouge, G. L.**

Atlas Amériquain Septentrional contenant les details des differentes provinces, de ce vaste continent. Traduit des cartes levées par ordre du gouvernement britannique. Par le major Holland, Evans, Scull, Mouzon, Ross, Cook, Lane, Gilbert, Gardner, Hillock &c. &c.   1 p. l., front., 20 maps. fol. Paris, le Rouge, 1778-[1792]   1212

NOTE.—Contains maps nos. [4a] and [23a] not called for by index, and probably no. 3, inserted.

#### CONTENTS.

no. 1. Guillaume Penn traite avec les indiens.
" 2. Titre et table.
" 3. Amérique . . . par C. F. Delamarche . . . 1792.
" 4. Amérique suivant le r. p. Charlevoix . . . 1777.
" [4a] Theatre de la guerra en Amérique. Par s! le Rouge . . . 1777.— Inset: Sault du Niagara.
" 5-8. Amérique Septentrionale . . . Par le docteur [John] Mitchel . . . Traduit de l' anglois. Corigée en 1776 par M. Hawkins. [Title also in german] 1777. [Corrected to 1783]—Inset: Nouvelle carte de la baye d'Hudson et de Labrador.

no. 9. Nouvelle carte de la province de Quebec selon l'édit du roi d' Angleterre du 7. 8.$^{bre}$ 1763. par le capitaine Carver et autres. Traduites de l'anglois . . . 1777.—Insets: Isle Montreal.—Plan de Quebec.—Plan de Montreal ou Villemarie.—Fleuve S$^t$ Laurent depuis la Valterie à Quebec.

" 10. Nouvelle Ecosse ou partie orientale du Canada. Traduit de l'angloi. de la carte de Jefferys publiée à Londres en mai 1755 . . .

" 11-12. La Nouvelle Angleterre . . .—A map of the moft inhabited part of New England containing the provinces of Massachusets bay and New Hampshire with the colonies of Conecticut and Rhode Island . . . [By John Green. anon.] After the original . . . 1777. 2 sheets. Insets: Plan de Boston.—A plan of Boston harbor . . .

" 13-14. Province de New-York . . . par [John] Montresor . . . 1777. Inset: . . . Continuation of Connecticut river.

" 15. Carte des troubles de l'Amérique levée par ordre du chevalier Tryon . . . Par Sauthier et Ratzer. Traduit de l'anglais . . . 1778.

" 16. La Pensilvanie . . . Traduite des meilleures cartes anglaises . . .— A map of Pennsylvania . . . and chiefly from the late map of W. Scull published in 1770.

" 17. Baye de la Delaware . . . d'après la carte de Joshua Fisher . . . 1777.

" 18. Virginie, Maryland . . . par Fry et Jefferson. Traduit, corrigé, augmente . . . 1777.

" 19-20. Caroline Méridionale et partie de la Georgie. Par le chev$^r$ Bull . . . le capitaine Gascoign, chev$^r$ Bryan, et de Brahm . . . 1777.—Insets: Cours de la rivière d'Hudson et la cofñunication avec la Canada par le lac Champlain jusqu' au fort Chambly, par Sauthier . . . 1777.

" 21. An accurate map of North and South Carolina . . . By Henry Mouzon and others . . . 1777.

" 22. Caroline Septentrionale et Méridionale . . . Traduite de anglois . . . 1777.—Insets: Attaques de fort Sullivan . . . 1776.—Port de Port Royal.—Barre et port de Charles-town.

" 23. Entrée de Charles-town par Dessans . . . 1777.—Barre et porte de Charles-town. Levé en 1776 avec les attaques du fort Sulivan . . . Commandée par P. Parker . . . 1778.

" [23a] Nouvelle carte des côtes des Carolines Septentrionales et Méridionales du cap Fear a Sud Edifto. Levées et sondées par N. Pocock, en 1770. Traduites de l'anglois . . . 1777.

" 24. Carte de la Floride Occidentale et Louisiane. Traduite de Jefferys.— La peninsule et golfe de la Floride ou Canal de Bahama avec les isles de Bahama . . . 1777.

" 25. La Martinique . . . par Jefferys 1775 . . . 1779.—Inset: Cul de sac Royal.

" 26. La Guadeloupe . . . 1753.—Inset: L'Isle de Bourbon ou Mascareigne.

## 1795

**Carey, M.**
Carey's american atlas . . .     1 p. l., 21 maps. fol. Philadelphia, M. Carey, 1795.     1213

NOTE.—All maps except nos. 3, 7, 8, and 14 carry the following: Engraved for Carey's american edition of Guthrie's Geography improved.
See also title 1222.

**Carey, M.**—Continued.

CONTENTS.

no. 1. The british possession in North America . . . by Samuel Lewis. 1794.
" 2. The province of Maine . . . by Samuel Lewis. 1794.
" 3. The state of New Hampshire. Compiled . . . by Samuel Lewis. 1794.
" 4. Vermont . . . delineated . . . by Amos Doolittle.
" 5. The state of Massachusetts. Compiled . . . by Samuel Lewis.
" 6. Connecticut . . . delineated . . . by A. Doolittle . . .
" 7. The state of Rhode Island; compiled from the surveys . . . of Caleb Harris. By Harding Harris.
" 8. The state of New York, compiled . . . by Samuel Lewis. 1795.
" 9. The state of New Jersey . . . Compiled by Samuel Lewis [1794]
" 10. The state of Pennsylvania. reduced . . . from Reading Howells map by Samuel Lewis [1794]
" 11. Delaware . . . [1795]
" 12. The state of Maryland . . . by Samuel Lewis [1794]
" 13. The state of Virginia . . . by Samuel Lewis. 1794.
" 14. The state of North Carolina . . . by Samuel Lewis.
" 15. The state of South Carolina . . . by Samuel Lewis. 1795.
" 16. Georgia . . .
" 17. Kentucky, reduced from Elihu Barker's large map.
" 18. A map of the Tennassee government formerly part of North Carolina taken chiefly from surveys by gen! D. Smith & others.
" 19. A map of South America . . .
" 20. A map of the discoveries made by capt$^s$ Cook & Clerke in the years 1778 & 1779 between the eastern coast of Asia and the western coast of North America . . . also mr. Hearn's discoveries to the north westward of Hudson's bay, in 1772.
" 21. A chart of the West Indies . . .

**1796**

**Collot, V.**, *i. e.* **G. H. V.**

Voyage dans l'Amérique Septentrionale, ou description des pays arrosés par le Mississipi, l'Ohio, le Missouri, et autres rivières affluentes; observations exactes sur le cours et les sondes de ces rivières; sur les villes, villages, hameaux et fermes de cette partie du Nouveau-Monde. Par feu le général Collot. Atlas. 2 p. l., 25 maps, 11 pl.   fol. Paris, A. Bertrand, 1826.   1214

NOTE.—To accompany the author's work of same title, in 2 v.
Gen. Collot undertook the journey in 1796. Work published posthumously.
Table of contents in french. Maps, views, and plates have english titles.
Maps and views engraved by Tardieu l'aîné.

CONTENTS.

no. 1. General map of North America.
" 2. General map of the course of the Ohio from its source to its junction with the Mississipi.
" 3. Plan of fort Erie.
" 4. Plan of fort Niagara.
" 5. View of Pittsbourgh.

no. 6. Plan of the town of Pittsburg.
" 8-11. A general map of the river Ohio. 4 sheets.
" 12. Plan of an old fort in the state of Kentucky.
" 13. View of the fort of the Natchez.
" 14. View of Marietta on the banks of the Ohio.
" 15. View of Long-Reach.
" 17. Plan of the rapids or falls of the Ohio latitude of Louisville.
" 18. View of the rapids of the Ohio and of Louisville taken from the village of Clarkesville.
" 22. Road from Limestone to Frankfort in the state of Kentucky.
" 23. Passage o fa branch of the river Juniata across a chain of mountains uninhabited and covered with wood.
" 25. Map of the course of the Mississipi from the Missouri and the country of the Illinois to the mouth of this river.
" 26. Plan of cape Girardo.
" 27. Plan of S! Lewis with the project of an intrenced camp French.
" 28. Map of the country of the Illinois.
" 29. Map of the Missouri; of the higher parts of the Mississippi . . .
" 30. Plan of the fort of New Madrid or Anse à La Graisse.
" 31. Plan of fort des Ecores at Margot.
" 32. Plan of Nogales.
" 33. Chart of the sources of the Mobile and of the river Yazoo . . .
" 34. Town and fort of Natchez.
" 35. Plan of fort Baton Rouge.
" 36. Sketch of new Orleans taken from fort S! Charles.—Sketch of Plaquemine.

**1796**

A journey in North America, containing a survey of the countries watered by the Mississipi, Ohio, Missouri and other affluing rivers . . . Atlas. 4 p. l., 25 maps, 11 pl. fol. Paris, A. Bertrand, 1826. 1215

NOTE.—Contains the same maps as in the french edition. See title 1214.

**1796**

**Winterbotham, W.**
The american atlas . . . 1 p. l., 20 maps (partly fold.) 8°. New York, J. Reid, 1796. 1216

NOTE.—Cover-title: The atlas for Winterbotham's history of America. 1796. Maps to accompany, "An historical, geographical, commercial, and philosophical view of the United States of America . . . By William Winterbotham."
Inserted after map no. 20: Plan of the city of Washington in the territory of Columbia ceded by the states of Virginia and Maryland to the United States of America and by them established as their seat of government after the year 1800. Rollinson sculpt. N. York. Publish'd by I. Reid, L. Wayland and C. Smith. 1795. "The Ellicott map with Potomac river soundings."—P. L. Phillips, A list of maps of America.

**Winterbotham, W.**—Continued.

CONTENTS.

no. 1. A general map of North America drawn from the best surveys 1795. Scoles, sc.
" 2. A general map of South America from the best surveys, 1796. B. Tanner sculpt
" 3. An accurate map of the United States of America, according to the treaty of peace of 1783. A. Anderson sculp.
" 4. The state of New Hampshire, compiled chiefly from actual surveys. 1796. B. Tanner sculpt
" 5. The province of Maine, from the best authorities. 1795.
" 6. The state of Massachusetts from the beft information. 1796.
" 7. Vermont from the latest authorities. Roberts fc.
" 8. the [!] state of Rhode Island, from the latest surveys. 1796. B. Tanner del. & sculpt
" 9. Connecticut from the beft authorities. B. Tanner del. & sculpt
" 10. The state of New York, compiled from the moft authentic information. 1796. Martin sculpt
" 11. The state of New Jersey, compiled from the most accurate surveys. Martin fculpt
" 12. The state of Pennsylvania, from the lateft surveys. D. Martin fct
" 13. The states of Maryland and Delaware, from the lateft surveys. 1795. D. Martin fculpt
" 14. the [!] state of Virginia, from the best authorities, 1796.
" 15. Map of the state of Kentucky; with the adjoining territories. 1795. A. Anderson sculp.
" 16. the [!] state of North Carolina from the best authorities. Tanner sculpt.
" 17. The state of South Carolina: from the beft authorities. 1796.
" 18. a [!] map of the Tennassee [!] government formerly part of North Carolina from the latest surveys. 1795. B. Tanner delt. & sculpt
" 19. Georgia, from the lateft authorities. B. Tanner sculpt
" 20. An accurate map of the West Indies with the adjacent coaft of America. 1796. D. Martin sculpt

### 1798

**Norman, W.**

The american pilot containing the navigation of the sea coaft of North America, from the streights of Belle-Ifle to Effequebo, including the ifland and banks of Newfoundland, the West-India iflands, and all the iflands on the coaft. With particular directions for sailing to, and entering the principal harbours, rivers, &c. Describing also the capes, head lands, rivers, bays, roads, havens, harbours, straits, rocks, sands, shoals, banks, depths of water and anchorage. Shewing the courses and diftances from one place to another, the ebbing of the sea, the setting of the tides and currents, &c. With many other things neceffary to be known in navigation. Likewise neceffary directions for those who are not fully acquainted with the use of charts ... 3 p. l., 9 maps. fol. Boston, W. Norman, 1798. 1217

NOTE.—"Certificate," on title page, signed by Osgood Carleton, dated sept. 10th, 1794.

### CONTENTS.

no. [1] A chart of Nantucket shoals surveyed by capt. Paul Pinkham ... 1791.
" [2] A new general chart of the West Indies from the lateſt marine journals and surveys ... 1789.
" [3] A chart of South Carolina and Georgia.—Inset: A chart of the bar and harbour of Charles Town.
" [4] Chart of the coast of America from Cape Hateras to Cape Roman from the actual surveys of Dr Dunbibin esqr
" [5] A new and accurate chart of the bay of Chesapeak including Delaware bay ... Drawn from ſeveral draughts ... chiefly from those of Anthony Smith, pilot of St Marys ...
" [6] A chart of the coast of New England from the south shoal to Cape Sable ... from Hollands actual surveys ...—Inset: A plan of Boston harbour from Hollands actual surveys.
" [7] [Coast of Maine]
" [8] Part of Newfoundland.
" [9] A chart of the banks of Newfoundland drawn from ... surveys, chiefly from thoſe of Chabert, Cook and Fleurieu ...

### 1798

**Vancouver, G.**

Voyage of discovery to the North Pacific ocean and round the world; in which the coast of north-west America has been carefully examined and accurately surveyed ... Atlas. 10 maps, 6 pl. fol. London, for G. G. & J. Robinson & J. Edwards, 1798. 1218

NOTE.—Without title.
Atlas to accompany Vancouver's Voyage of discovery ... London, 1798.
Published also in french. See title 1219.
Another edition bears date 1801.
The following map relates to America:
no. [3-9] A chart shewing part of the coast of n. w. America ...

### 1799

Voyage de découvertes, à l'océan Pacifique du nord, et autour du monde; dans lequel la côte nord-ouest de l'Amérique a été ... reconnue et ... relevée ... Atlas. 4 pp., 10 maps, 6 pl. fol. Paris, imprimerie de la république, an VIII [1799] 1219

NOTE.—Without title.
Atlas to accompany Vancouver's Voyage de découvertes ...
Like the english edition of 1798. See title 1218.
The following map relates to America:
no. [3-9] A chart shewing part of the coast of n. w. America.

## 1800
**North American pilot, The.**

A new edition, much enlarged, of the second part of the North American pilot, for New England, New York, Pennsylvania, New Jersey, Maryland, Virginia, North and South Carolina, Georgia, Florida, and the Havanna: including general charts of the British channel, and the Atlantic ocean. From original surveys taken by captain Holland, John Gascoigne, Joshua Fisher, Jacob Blamey, and other officers and pilots in his majesty's service, &c. ... 1 p. l., 17 maps on 20 sheets. fol. London, R. Laurie & J. Whittle, 1800. 1220

NOTE.—"The first part of the North American pilot contains all Newfoundland, Nova Scotia from Cape Breton and Bay of Fundy to Penobſcot bay, Labradore, the gulf and river St. Lawrence, and straits of Belle-Iſle, &c." See titles 1209 and 1236.

CONTENTS.

no. [1] The British channel, with a part of the Atlantic ocean ... By Thomas Jefferys ... With numerous improvements and emendations to the year 1800 ...

" [2-3] A new general chart of the Atlantic or Western ocean and adjacent seas ... 1794. 2 sheets.—Inset: Hudsons bay.

" [4] Chart of the Açores (Hawks) islands, called also Flemish and Western islands ... 1797.—The roads of Punta Delgada and Villa Franca, in the iſle of S. Miguel.—The road of Fayal, with Porto Pin ...

" [5-6] A new and correct chart of the coast of New England and New York with the adjacent parts of Nova Scotia and New Brunswick from Cape Sable to the entrance of Hudsons or North River, by captain Holland ... 1794. 2 sheets.—Insets: View of Hell Gate, by W. A. Williams 1777.—Plan of Hell Gate.—The rivers Kennebeck and Sheepscut, by capt. Joseph Huddart.

" [7] A chart of the harbour of Boston, with soundings, sailing marks and other directions ...

" [8] Chart of the entrance of Hudson's river, from Sandy Hook to New York, with the banks, depths of water, sailing marks, &c. ... 1794.

" [9] A new chart of the coast of North America, from New York to Cape Hatteras ... By captain Holland ... 1794.

" [10] A chart of Delaware bay and river ... Faithfully coppied [!] from that published at Philadelphia by Joshua Fisher ... 1794.

" [11-12] A new and accurate chart of the bay of Chesapeake ... Drawn from several draughts ... chiefly from those of Anthony Smith ... 1794. 2 sheets—Inset: A plan of Herring bay in Maryland.

" [13] A new chart of the coast of North America, from Currituck inlet to Savannah river ... By captain N. Holland ... 1794.

" [14] A plan of Cape Fear river from the Bar to Brunswick ... 1794.

" [15] An exact plan of Charleston bar and harbour. From an actual survey ... 1791.

" [16] A plan of Port Royal in South Carolina. Survey'd by capn. John Gaſcoigne ... 1794.

no. [17] A plan of the river and sound of D'Awfoskee, in South Carolina. Surveyed by captain John Gascoigne . . . 1794.
" [18] A new chart of the coast of North America from Port Royal entrance to Matanza inlet, exhibiting the coast of Georgia &c. . . . By captain N. Holland . . . 1794.—Insets: The mouth of Nassau river.—The mouth of St. Mary's river.—Plan of the harbour of St. Augustin . . .
" [19] A plan of Amelia harbour and barr in East Florida. Survey'd in jan[r] 1775. By Jacob Blamey . . . 1794.
" [20] The peninsula and gulf of Florida, or New Bahama channel with the Bahama islands . . . By Tho[s] Jefferys . . . 1794.

## 1802

**Espinosa y Tello, J.**

Relacion del viage hecho por las goletas Sutil y Mexicana en el año de 1792: para reconocer el estrecho de Fuca . . . Atlas.  2 p. l., 9 maps, 8 pl. fol. Madrid, imprenta real, 1802.   1221

NOTE.—Atlas has title: Atlas para el viage de las goletas Sutil y Mexicana al reconocimiento del estrecho de Juan de Fuca en 1792, publicado en 1802. Dionisio Alcalá Galiano is not the author, as supposed by some bibliographers. "Vocabulario del idioma de los habitantes de Nutka," pp. 178–184 of text.

CONTENTS.

no. 1-2. Carta esférica de los reconocimientos hechos en la costa n. o. de América en 1791 y '92 . . .
"   3. Continuacion de los reconocimientos hechos en la costa n. o. de América . . .
"   4. Carta de los reconocimientos chechos en 1602. Por el capitan Sebastian Vizcayno . . .
"   5. Plano del puerto de S. Diego en la costa setent[l] de Californ[l] Levantado por el 2.° piloto de la armada d. Juan Pantola . . . 1782.
"   6. Plano del puerto y bahia de Monte Rey . . . 1791.
"   7. Plano de la cala de los Amigos . . . 1791.
"   8. Plano del puerto de Mulgrave . . . 1791.
"   9. Plano del puerto del Desengaño . . . 1791.
"   10. Fiesta celebrada en Nutka por su Xefe Macuina á causa de haber dado su hija indicios de entrar en la pubertad.
"   11. Vista de lo interior de la Cala de los Amigos en la entrada de Nutka.
"   12. Macuina, xefe de Nutka.
"   [13] Tetacú, xefe de la entrada del estrecho de Juan de Fuca.
"   [14] Maria, muger de Fetacú.
"   [15] Oratorio del fays de Nutka.
"   [16] Plancha de Madera hallada en el canal á que por ésta razón se dió el nombre de canal de la Tabla.
"   17. El peje que bimos semejava á estos aun que no devisamos si tenia escama ó no, que parescia la color de tonina: . . .

## 1809

**Carey, M.**

Carey's american atlas. 26 maps. fol. Philadelphia, M. Carey, 1809.

1222

NOTE.—Title-page wanting. See also title 1213.
All maps except nos. [2, 4, 7, 9, 12, 15, 18, 23-26] carry the following: Engraved for Carey's american edition of Guthrie's Geography improved.

### CONTENTS.

no. [1] The british possessions in North America . . . by Samuel Lewis. 1809.
" [2] A map of the United States . . . by Sam! Lewis. 1809.
" [3] Vermont . . . delineated & engraved by Amos Doolittle . . .
" [4] The state of New Hampshire. Compiled . . . by Samuel Lewis. 1794.
" [5] The province of Maine . . . by Samuel Lewis. 1794. W. Barker sculp.
" [6] The state of Massachusetts. Compiled . . . by Samuel Lewis.
" [7] The state of Rhode Island; compiled from the surveys . . . of Caleb Harris. By Harding Harris. J. Smither sculp.
" [8] Connecticut . . . delineated & engraved by A. Doolittle . . .
" [9] The state of New York, compiled . . . by Samuel Lewis. 1809.
" [10] The state of New Jersey . . . Compiled by Samuel Lewis. Engraved by W. Barker.
" [11] The state of Pennsylvania. reduced with permission from Reading Howells map by Samuel Lewis. Smither sculp.
" [12] Delaware . . . W. Barker sculp.
" [13] The state of Maryland . . . by Samuel Lewis. W. Barker sculp.
" [14] The state of Virginia . . . By Samuel Lewis. 1809. Smither sculp.
" [15] The state of North Carolina . . . by Samuel Lewis. Engraved by Vallance.
" [16] The state of South Carolina . . . by Samuel Lewis. 1795. W. Barker sculp.
" [17] Georgia . . . W. Barker sculp.
" [18] Kentucky, reduced from Elihu Barker's large map. W. Barker sculp.
" [19] A map of the Tennassee state formerly part of North Carolina taken chiefly from surveys by gen! D. Smith & others. J. T. Scott sculp.
" [20] A map of South America . . .
" [21] A chart of the West Indies . . . W. Barker sculp.
" [22] A map of the discoveries made by capt! Cook & Clerke in the years 1778 & 1779 between the eastern coast of Asia and the western coast of North America . . . Also m! Hearn's discoveries to the north westward of Hudson's bay, in 1772. J. T. Scott sculp.
" [23] Plat of the seven ranges of townships being part of the territory of the United States n. w. of the river Ohio . . . Surveyed in conformity to an ordinance of congress of may 20th. 1785, under direction of Tho! Hutchins.
" [24] A map of part of the N: W: territory of the United States: compiled . . . by Samuel Lewis. 1796. W. Barker sc.
" [25] Carte de la partie Françoise de S! Domingue faite par Bellin . . . et depuis augmentée par P. C. Varlè et autres ing<sup>rs</sup>—A map of the french part of S! Domingo. J. T. Scott sculp.
" [26] Louisiana.

## 1809

**Spain.** *Ministerio de marina. Dirección de hidrografia.*
Portulano de la América Setentrional. Construido en la dirección de trabajos hidrograficos. Divido en quarto partes. 2 p. l., [3] l., 111 maps. obl. 4°. Madrid, 1809. 1223

NOTE.—First edition.
Each part has separate index. The title of map no. 15 has been added with pen to the index of pt. 1.
L. C. also has edition to the title of which is added: Aumentado y corregido en 1818, and edition of 1825 published in Mexico. See also titles 1224 and 1226.

CONTENTS.

pt. 1, no. 1. Puerto de S. Juan de Puerto Rico.
" " 2. Plano de la Aguadilla. Puerto Rico.
" " 3. Plano de la ensenada de Mayaguez.
" " 4. Plano del Puerto de Guanica.
" " 5. Plano del Pto. de San Tómas [Islas Virgenes]
" " 6. Plano del puerto principal de la Tortola.
" " 7. Plano del Puerto de Normand.
" " 8. Plano de Pt̃o. Grande. Iª Virgen Gorda.
" " 9. Rada y Puerto de S. Juan de Antigua.
" " 10. Bahía de Fte. Real de Martinica.
" " 11. Plano del Puerto del Carenero. Iª Stª Lucia.
" " 12. Plano de la rada y Carenero de San Jorge. Iª Granada.
" " 13. Plano de la rada de Rockly. Iª de Tábago.
" " 14. Plano del Puerto de Chaguaramas. Iª de Trinidad.
" " 15. Plano del fondeadero de la Punta del Toco.
pt. 2, no. 1. Ensenª de Unare. Costa de Tierra Firme.
" " 2. Ensenadas de Pto Santo.
" " 3. Ensda de Carupano.
" " 4. Ensenada de la Esmeralda.
" " 5. Plano de las ensenadas de Pampatar y Pto. Moreno en la Iª Margaríta.
" " 6. Plano del puerto nombrado laguna grande del Obispo, en el golfo de Cariaco.
" " 7. Plano del fondeadero de Cumaná.
" " 8. Puerto de Mochima.
" " 9. Ensenada de Barcelona.
" " 10. Plano del fondeadero de Corsarios.
" " 11. Fondeadero de la Guayra.
" " 12. Pto de Turiamo.
" " 13. Puerto Cabello.
" " 14. Puerto de Chichirivichi.
" " 15. Ensenada de San Juan.
" " 16. Plano del canal y Bahía Stª Ana en la Iª de Curazac.
" " 17. Plano de Bahía Honda en la costa Guajira.
" " 18. Plano del puerto y ciudad de Santa Marta.
" " 19. Plano del Puerto de Cartagena de Indias.
" " 20. Plano del Puerto de Cispata.
" " 21. Bahía de Candelaria en el golfo del Darien.
" " 22. Plano del Puerto Carreto. Costa del Darien del Norte.

**Spain**—Continued.

pt. 2, no. 23. Plano del fondeadero de Carolína y del Puerto Escocés.
" " 24. Plano del Pto. y ciudad de Porto-velo. Istmo de Panamá.
" " 25. Plano del Puerto de Naos.
" " 26. Plano de la boca del rio de Chagres.
" " 27. Puerto y boca del rio de S. Juan de Nicaragua. Costa de Mosquitos.
" " 28. P$^{to}$ de Blewfields.
" " 29. Ensenada del cabo de Gracias á Dios.
" " 30. Plano de la ensenada del Triunfo de la Cruz. Costa de Honduras.
" " 31. Bahía y Puerto de Omóa.
" " 32. Plano del Puerto de Veracruz. Seno Mexicano.
" " 33. Bahía de S. Bernardo.
" " 34. Bahía de Galvez-Towm.
" " 35. Puerto de Panzacola.
" " 36. Bahía de Tampa. Florida ocidental.
" " 37. Barra y puerto de S$^{n}$ Agustin. Florida oriental.
" " 38. Boca y barra del rio S$^{n}$ Juan.
" " 39. Boca y barra del rio Nasau.
" " 40. Boca y barra del rio S$^{ta}$ Maria.
pt. 3, no. 1. Plano del Puerto de Cuba. Cuba.
" " 2. Puerto Escondido.
" " 3. Puerto de Baitiqueri.
" " 4. Pto. de Mata.
" " 5. Puerto de Baracoa.
" " 6. Puerto de Maraví.
" " 7. Puerto de Navas.
" " 8. Puerto de Cayaguaneque.
" " 9. Puerto de Taco.
" " 10. Puerto de Jaragua.
" " 11. Puerto de Cayo Moa.
" " 12. Plano del Puerto de Yaguaneque.
" " 13. Puerto de Cananova.
" " 14. Plano del Puerto de Cebollas.
" " 15. Puerto de Tanamo.
" " 16. Plano de los Puertos de Cabonico y Livisa.
" " 17. Puerto de Nipe.
" " 18. Plano del Puerto de Banes.
" " 19. Puerto de Sama.
" " 20. Puerto de Naranjo.
" " 21. Plano del P$^{to}$ de Vita.
" " 22. Puerto de Bariai.
" " 23. Plano del P$^{to}$ de Jururu.
" " 24. Pto. de Gibara.
" " 25. Puerto del Padre.
" " 26. Puerto de Manatí.
" " 27. Puerto de Nuevas Grandes.
" " 28. Plano del Puerto de las Nuevitas del Principe.
" " 29. Puerto de Matanzas.
" " 30. Puerto del Mariel.
" " 31. Bahía Honda.
" " 32. Puerto de la Havana.
" " 33. Bahía de Jagua.
" " 34. Puerto del Guantanamo.

pt. 4, no. 1. Puerto de S.ᵗᵃ Barbara de Samaná. I.ᵃ de S.ᵗᵒ Domingo.
" " 2. Plano de las ensenadas de Monte-Cristi y Manzanillo.
" " 3. Plano del Puerto del Delfin.
" " 4. Puerto del Guarıco.
" " 5. Fondeadero de Chouchou.—Bahía de la Granja.
" " 6. Rada de Tierra-Baja en la Isla Tortuga.—Puerto de Paz.
" " 7. Bahía Mosquito.—Puerto Escudo.
" " 8. Fondeadero de Juan Rabel.—Bahía de Tiburon.
" " 9. Puerto del Mole de S.ⁿ Nicolas.
" " 10. Bahía de las Gonaives.
" " 11. Plano de la bahía del Pequeño Guave.
" " 12. Plano del puerto y fuerte de S.ⁿ Luis.
" " 13. P.ᵗᵒ de la Caldera.
" " 1. Puerto Antonio. Jamayca.
" " 2. Bahía de Sta. Ana.
" " 3. Bahía de Montego.
" " 4. Puerto de Musquito.
" " 5. Bahía de Lucea.
" " 6. Plano del fondeadero de Bleufields.
" " 7. Plano de Bahía Antigua.
" " 8. Plano del puerto de Kingston y P.ᵗᵒ Real.
" " 9. Plano del P.ᵗᵒ Morante.

**1818**

Portulano de la America Setentrional. Construido en la dirección de trabajos hidrograficos. Dividido en quatro partes. Madrid, 1809. Aumentado y corregido en 1818. 2 p. l., [3] l., 121 maps. obl. 4°. [Madrid, 1818]     **1224**

NOTE.—Contains 9 maps which do not appear in the mexican reproduction of 1825. See also titles 1223 and 1226.

CONTENTS.

pt. 1, no. 1. Puerto de S. Juan de Puerto Rico.
" " 2. Plano de la Aguadilla. Puerto Rico.
" " 3. Plano de la ensenada de Mayaguez.
" " 4. Plano del Puerto de Guanica.
" " 5. Plano del P.ᵗᵒ de San Tómas [Islas Virgenes]
" " 6. Plano del puerto principal de la Tortola.
" " 7. Plano del Puerto de Normand.
" " 8. Plano de P.ᵗᵒ Grande. I.ᵃ Virgen Gorda.
" " 9. Rada y Puerto de S. Juan de Antigua.
" " 10. Bahía de Fte. Real de Martiníca.
" " 11. Plano del Puerto del Carenero. I.ᵃ S.ᵗᵃ Lucia.
" " 12. Plano de la rada y Carenero de San Jorge. I.ᵃ Granada.
" " 13. Plano de la rada de Rockly. I.ᵃ de Tábago.
" " 14. Plano del Puerto de Chaguaramas. I.ᵃ de Trinidad.
" " 15. Plano del fondeadero de la Punta del Toco.
" " 16. Plano de la Bahía del Almirantazgo. Granadillos.
pt. 2, no. 1. Ensen.ᵃ de Unare. Costa de Tierra Firme.
" " 2. Ensenadas de P.ᵗᵒ Santo.
" " 3. Ens.ᵈᵃ de Carupano.

35799—08——43

**Spain**—Continued.

pt. 2, no. 4. Ensenada de la Esmeralda.
" " 5. Plano de las ensenadas de Pampatar y P.to Moreno en la I.ª Margarita.
" " 6. Plano del puerto nombrado laguna Grande del Obispo en el golfo de Cariaco.
" " 7. Plano del fondeadero de Cumaná.
" " 8. Puerto de Mochima.
" " 9. Ensenada de Barcelona.
" " 10. Plano de fondeadero de Corsarios.
" " 11. Fondeadero de la Guayra.
" " 12. P.to de Turiamo.
" " 13. Puerto Cabello.
" " 14. Puerto de Chichirivichi.
" " 15. Ensenada de San Juan.
" " 16. Plano del canal y Bahía S.ta Ana en la I.ª de Curazao.
" " 17. Plano de Bahía Hondia en la costa Guajira.
" " 18. Plano del puerto y ciudad de Santa Marta.
" " 19. Plano del Puerto de Cartagena de Indias.
" " 20. Plano del Puerto de Cispata.
" " 21. Bahía de Candelaria en el golfo del Darien.
" " 22. Plano del Puerto Carreto. Costa del Darien del Norte.
" " 23. Plano del fondeadero de Carolina y del Puerto Escocés.
" " 24. Plano del Pto. y ciudad de Porto-Velo. Istmo de Panamá.
" " 25. Plano del Puerto de Naos.
" " 26. Plano de la boca del rio de Chagres.
" " 27. Puerto y boca del rio de S. Juan de Nicaragua. Costa de Mosquitos.
" " 28. P.to de Blewfields.
" " 29. Ensenada del cabo de Gracias á Dios.
" " 30. Plano de la ensenada del Triunfo de la Cruz. Costa de Honduras.
" " 31. Bahía y Puerto de Omóa.
" " 32. Plano del Puerto de Veracruz. Seno Mexicano.
" " 33. Bahía de S. Bernardo.
" " 34. Bahía de Galvez-Town.
" " 35. Puerto de Panzacola.
" " 36. Bahía de Tampa. Florida ocidental.
" " 37. Barra y puerto de S.ⁿ Agustin. Florida oriental.
" " 38. Boca y barra del rio S.ⁿ Juan.
" " 39. Boca y barra del rio Nasau.
" " 40. Boca y barra del rio Sta Maria.
" " 41. Plano de la Bahía de Movila. Seno Mexicano.
" " 42. Plano de las yslas de Sta. Catalína y Providencia. Costa de Mosquitos.
" " 43. Plano del Alacran. Seno Mexicano.
" " 44. Plano del baxo de las Arcas.
" " 45. Plano del fondeadero de Anton Lizardo.
" " 46. Plano de la isla de Arenas.
pt. 3, no. 1. Plano del Puerto de Cuba. Cuba.
" " 2. Puerto Escondido.
" " 3. Puerto de Baitiqueri.
" " 4. Pto. de Mata.
" " 5. Puerto de Baracoa.
" " 6. Puerto de Maraví.

pt. 3, no. 7. Puerto de Navas.
"   "   8. Puerto de Cayaguaneque.
"   "   9. Puerto de Taco.
"   "  10. Puerto de Jaragua.
"   "  11. Puerto de Cayo Moa.
"   "  12. Plano del Puerto de Yaguaneque.
"   "  13. Puerto de Cananova.
"   "  14. Plano del Puerto de Cebollas.
"   "  15. Puerto de Tanamo.
"   "  16. Plano de los Puertos de Cabonico y Livisa.
"   "  17. Puerto de Nipe.
"   "  18. Plano del Puerto de Banes.
"   "  19. Puerto de Sama.
"   "  20. Puerto de Naranjo.
"   "  21. Plano del P.to de Vita.
"   "  22. Puerto de Bariai.
"   "  23. Plano del Pto. de Jururu.
"   "  24. Pto. de Gibara.
"   "  25. Puerto del Padre.
"   "  26. Puerto de Manatí.
"   "  27. Puerto de Nuevas Grandes.
"   "  28. Plano del Puerto de las Nuevitas del Príncipe.—Canal de la entrada del Puerto.
"   "  29. Puerto de Matanzas.
"   "  30. Puerto del Mariel.
"   "  31. Bahía Honda.
"   "  32. Puerto de la Havana.
"   "  33. Bahía de Jagua.
"   "  34. Puerto del Guantanamo.
pt. 4, no. 1. Puerto de S.ta Barbara de Samaná. I.a de S.to Domingo.
"   "   2. Plano de las ensenadas de Monte-Cristi y Manzanillo.
"   "   3. Plano del Puerto del Delfin.
"   "   4. Puerto del Guarico.
"   "   5. Fondeadero de Chouchou.—Bahía de la Granja.
"   "   6. Rada de Tierra-Baja en la Isla Tortuga.—Puerto de Paz.
"   "   7. Bahía Mosquito.—Puerto Escudo.
"   "   8. Fondeadero de Juan Rabel.—Bahía de Tiburon.
"   "   9. Puerto del Mole de S.n Nicolas. ——. [Inserted, small manuscript map, entitled, Plan of the anchorage of S.t Nicholas Mole]
"   "  10. Bahía de las Gonaives.
"   "  11. Plano de la Bahía del Pequeño Guave.
"   "  12. Plano del puerto y fuerte de S.n Luis.
"   "  13. P.to de la Caldera.
"   "  14. Plano de la Bahía de Acul, situada la Isla de Ratas.
"   "  15. Plano de la embocadura del rio Ozama y ciudad de S.to Domingo.
"   "  16. Plano de la Bahía de S. Lorenzo.
"   "   1. Puerto Antonio, Jamayca.
"   "   2. Bahía de Sta. Ana.
"   "   3. Bahía de Montego.
"   "   4. Puerto de Mosquito.
"   "   5. Bahía de Lucea.
"   "   6. Plano del fondeadero de Bleufields.

**Spain**—Continued.
  pt. 4, no. 7. Plano de Bahía Antigua.
  "    "    8. Plano del Puerto de Kingston y Ptō. Real.
  "    "    9. Plano del P$^{to}$ Morante.

## 1824-1829

**Weiland, C. F.**
  [Atlas von America. Mit beigedruckter geographisch-statistisch und historischer beschreibung von G. Hassel]   30 maps. fol.
  [Weimar, geograph. institut, 1824–1828]   1225
  NOTE.—Title-page wanting.
  Imperfect. Perfect copy calls for 45 maps, 1824–1829.
  Maps have border text, were published separately, and were evidently copied from H. C. Carey & I. Lea. A complete historical, chronological and geographical american atlas, 1822 and 1827. See titles 1175 and 1177.

CONTENTS.

  no. 1. Geographisch-statistische und historische charte von Nord-America. 1828.
  "  2.   "   "   "   "   "   "   " Maine. 1826.
  "  3.   "   "   "   "   "   "   " Neuhampshire. 1825.
  "  4.   "   "   "   "   "   "   " Massachusetts. 1825.
  "  5.   "   "   "   "   "   "   " Rhodeisland. 1826.
  "  6.   "   "   "   "   "   "   " Connecticut. 1825.
  "  7.   "   "   "   "   "   "   " Vermont. 1826.
  "  8.   "   "   "   "   "   "   " Neuyork. 1824.
  "  9.   "   "   "   "   "   "   " Neu-Jersey. 1825.
  " 10.   "   "   "   "   "   "   " Pennsylvanien. 1825.
  " 11.   "   "   "   "   "   "   " Delaware. 1825.
  " 12.   "   "   "   "   "   "   " Maryland. 1826.
  " 13.   "   "   "   "   "   "   " Columbia. 1828.
  " 14.   "   "   "   "   "   "   " Virginia. 1828.
  " 15.   "   "   "   "   "   "   " Nordcarolina. 1826.
  " 16.   "   "   "   "   "   "   " Süd-carolina. 1825.
  " 17.   "   "   "   "   "   "   " Georgia. 1825.
  " 18.   "   "   "   "   "   "   des Staates Ohio. 1825.
  " 19.   "   "   "   "   "   "   von Kentucky. 1826.
  " 20.   "   "   "   "   "   "   " Tennessee. 1825.
  " 21.   "   "   "   "   "   "   " Mississippi. 1826.
  " 22.   "   "   "   "   "   "   " Louisiana. 1824.
  " 23.   "   "   "   "   "   "   " Alabama. 1825.
  " 24.   "   "   "   "   "   "   " Indiana. 1826.
  " 25.   "   "   "   "   "   "   " Illinois. 1826.
  " 26.   "   "   "   "   "   "   " Missury. 1826.
  " 27.   "   "   "   "   "   "   " Arkansas. 1828.
  " 28.   "   "   "   "   "   "   " Michigan. 1828.

no. 29. Geographisch-statistische und historische charte von Missouri und Oregan. 1828.
" 30. " " " " " " Florida. 1828.

## 1825

**Spain.** *Ministerio de marino. Dirección de hidrografía.*
Portulano de la America Setentrional. Dividido en quatro partes. Publicado por orden del esemo sor d, Guadalupe Victoria, primer presidente de la republica Mexicana. 2 p. l., [3] l., 112 maps. obl. 4°. Mexico, 1825. 1226

NOTE.—Correct reprint of the spanish publication of 1809. One map, pt. 2, no. 33, has been added. This map appears in the enlarged edition of 1818 as no. 45 of pt. 2. See also titles 1223 and 1224.

CONTENTS.

pt. 1, no. 1. Puerto de S. Juan de Puerto Rico.
" " 2. Plano de la Aguadilla. Puerto Rico.
" " 3. Plano de la ensenada de Mayaguez.
" " 4. Plano del Puerto de Guanica.
" " 5. Plano del Pto. de San Tómas. [Islas Virgenes]
" " 6. Plano del puerto principal de la Tortola.
" " 7. Plano del puerto de Normand.
" " 8. Plano del Pto. Grande. I$^a$ Virgen Gorda.
" " 9. Rada y Puerto de S. Juan de Antigua.
" " 10. Bahía de Fte. Real de Martinica.
" " 11. Plano del Puerto del Carenero. I$^a$ S$^{a1}$ Lucia.
" " 12 Plano de la rado y Carenero de San Jorge. I$^a$ Granada.
" " 13. Plano de la rada de Rockly. I$^a$ de Tábago.
" " 14. Plano del Puerto de Chaguaramas. I$^a$ de Trinidad.
" " 15. Plano del fondeadero de la Punta del Toco.
pt. 2, no. 1. Ensen$^a$ de Unare. Costa de Colombia.
" " 2. Ensenadas de P$^{to}$. Santo.
" " 3. Ens$^{da}$ de Carupano.
" " 4. Ensenada de la Esmeralda.
" " 5. Plano de las ensenadas de Pampatar y Pto. Moreno.
" " 6. Plano del Puerto nombrado laguna grande del Obispo en el golfo de Cariaco.
" " 7. Plano del fondeadero de Cumana.
" " 8. Puerto de Mochima.
" " 9. Ensenada de Barcelona.
" " 10. Plano del fondeadero de Corsarios.
" " 11. Fondeadero de la Guayra.
" " 12. P$^{to}$ de Turiamo.
" " 13. Puerto Cabello.
" " 14. Puerto de Chichirivichi.
" " 15. Ensenada de San Juan.
" " 16. Plano del canal y Bahía S$^{ta}$ Ana en la I$^a$ de Curazao.
" " 17. Plano de Bahía Honda en la costa Guajira.
" " 18. Plano del Puerto y ciudad de Santa Marta.
" " 19. Plano del Puerto de Cartagena de Indias.
" " 20. Plano del Puerto de Cispata.

**Spain**—Continued.

pt. 2, no. 21. Bahía de Candelaria.
" " 22. Plano del Puerto Carreto. Costa del Darien del Norte.
" " 23. Plano del fondeadero de Carolina y del Puerto Escocés.
" " 24. Plano del pto. y ciudad de Porto-Velo. Istmo de Panamá.
" " 25. Plano del puerto de Naos.
" " 26. Plano de la boca del rio de Charges.
" " 27. Puerto y boca del rio de S. Juan de Nicaragua.
" " 28. Pto. de Blewfields. Costa de Mosquitos.
" " 29. Ensenada del cabo de Gracias a Dios.
" " 30. Plano de la ensenada del Triunfo de la Cruz. Costa de Honduras.
" " 31. Bahía y puerto de Omóa.
" " 32. Plano del puerto de Veracruz. Seno Mexicano.
" " 33. Plano del fondeadero de Anton Lizardo.
" " 34. Bahía de S. Bernardo.
" " 35. Bahía de Galvez-town.
" " 36. Puerto de Panzacola.
" " 37. Bahía de Tampa. Florida ocidental.
" " 38. Barra y puerto de S$^a$ Agustin. Florida oriental.
" " 39. Boca y barra del rio S$^a$ Juan.
" " 40. Boca y barra del rio Nasau.
" " 41. Boca y barra del rio S$^{ta}$ Maria.
pt. 3, no. 1. Plano del Puerto de Cuba. Cuba.
" " 2. Puerto Escondido.
" " 3. Puerto de Baitiqueri.
" " 4. Pto. de Mata.
" " 5. Puerto de Baracoa.
" " 6. Puerto de Maraví.
" " 7. Puerto de Navas.
" " 8. Puerto de Cayaguaneque.
" " 9. Puerto de Taco.
" " 10. Puerto de Jaragua.
" " 11. Puerto de Cayo Moa.
" " 12. Plano del puerto de Yaguaneque.
" " 13. Puerto de Cananova.
" " 14. Plano del puerto de Cebollas.
" " 15. Puerto de Tanamo.
" " 16. Plano de los puertos de Cabonico y Livisa.
" " 17. Puerto de Nipe.
" " 18. Plano del puerto de Banes.
" " 19. Puerto de Sama.
" " 20. Puerto de Naranjo.
" " 21. Plano del p$^{to}$ de Vita.
" " 22. Puerto de Bariai.
" " 23. Plano del pto. de Jururu.
" " 24. Pto. de Gibara.
" " 25. Puerto del Padre.
" " 26. Puerto de Manati.
" " 27. Puerto de Nuevas Grandes.
" " 28. Plano del puerto de las Nuevitas del Principe. Canal de la entrada del puerto.
" " 29. Puerto de Matanzas.
" " 30. Puerto del Mariel.

pt. 3, no. 31. Bahía Honda.
" " 32. Puerto de la Havana.
" " 33. Bahía de Jagua.
" " 34. Puerto del Guantanamo.
pt. 4, no. 1. Puerto de S$^{ta}$ Barbara de Samaná. I$^a$ de Haity.
" " 2. Plano de las ensenadas de Monte-Cristi y Manzanillo.
" " 3. Plano del puerto del Delfin.
" " 4. Puerto del Guarico.
" " 5. Fondeadero de Chouchou.—Bahía de la Grania.
" " 6. Rada de Tierra-Baja en la isla Tortuga.—Puerto de Paz.
" " 7. Bahía Mosquito.—Puerto Escudo.
" " 8. Fondeadero de Juan Rabel.—Bahía de Tiburon.
" " 9. Puerto del Mole de S$^n$ Nicolas.
" " 10. Bahía de las Gonaives.
" " 11. Plano de la bahía del Pequeño Guave.
" " 12. Plano del puerto y fuerte de S$^n$ Luis.
" " 13. P$^{to}$ de la Caldera.
" " 1. Puerto Antonio. Jamayca.
" " 2. Bahía de Sta. Ana.
" " 3. Bahía de Montego.
" " 4. Puerto de Mosquito.
" " 5. Bahía de Lucea.
" " 6. Plano del fondeadero de Bleufields.
" " 7. Plano de Bahía Antigua.
" " 8. Plano del puerto de Kingston y Pto. Real.
" " 9. Plano del p$^{to}$ Morante. 1827.

**1827**

**Carey, H. C.**, *and* **Lea, I.**
A complete historical, chronological, and geographical american atlas, being a guide to the history of North and South America, and the West Indies: exhibiting an accurate account of the discovery, settlement, and progress, of their various kingdoms, states, provinces, &c. together with the wars, celebrated battles, and remarkable events, to the year 1826. According to the plan of Le Sage's [pseud. of M. J. A. E. D. comte de Las Cases] atlas, and intended as a companion to Lavoisne's improvement of that celebrated work. 3d ed. cor. and impr.  3 p. l., [109] l. incl. 46 maps, 2 pl. fol. Philadelphia, H. C. Carey & I. Lea, 1827.  1227

NOTE.—First edition published 1822. See also title 1175.
Maps have border text.

CONTENTS.

no. 1. N. America.—S. America. Drawn by J. Finlayson.
" 3. North America. Drawn by J. Finlayson.
" 4. British possessions in North America. Drawn by F. Lucas jr.
" 5. United States of America. Engraved by B. Tanner.
· 10. Maine. J. Yeager sculp.
" 11. New Hampshire. Engrav'd by Young & Delleker.
" 12. Massachusetts. Drawn by F. Lucas.
" 13. Rhode Island. Drawn by F. Lucas jr.
" 14. Connecticut. Engrav'd by Young & Delleker.
" 15. Vermont. Drawn by F. Lucas jr.

**Carey, H. C.,** *and* **Lea, I.**—Continued.
  no. 16. New York. Drawn by F. Lucas jr.
  " 17. New Jersey. Kneass sc.
  " 18. Pennsylvania. Engr? by J. Yeager.
  " 19. Delaware. Drawn by F. Lucas jr.
  " 20. Maryland. Drawn by F. Lucas jr.
  " 21. District of Columbia. Engraved by Young & Delleker.
  " 22. Virginia. Engrav'd by Young & Delleker.
  " 23. North Carolina. Drawn by F. Lucas jr.
  " 24. South Carolina. Reduced by J. Drayton from the state map by J. Wilson.
  " 25. Georgia. Drawn by F. Lucas jr.
  " 26. Ohio. Drawn by F. Lucas jr.
  " 27. Kentucky. Drawn by F. Lucas jr.
  " 28. Tennessee. Drawn by F. Lucas jr.
  " 29. Mississippi. Drawn by F. Lucas jr.
  " 30. Alabama. J. Drayton del.
  " 31. Louisiana. Kneass sc.
  " 32. Indiana. Drawn by F. Lucas jr.
  " 33. Illinois. J. Yeager sculp.
  " 34. Missouri. Engraved by Young & Delleker.
  " 35. Map of Arkansa and other territories of the United States . . . by S. H. Long . . .
  " 36. Michigan territory. Drawn by J. Finlayson.
  " 37. Florida. Drawn by J. Drayton.
  " 38. Mexico and internal provinces. Prepared from Humbolt's map & other documents by J. Finlayson.
  " 39. West Indies. Drawn by F. Lucas jr.
  " 40. Cuba and the Bahama islands. B. Tanner sc.
  " 41. Jamaica. Drawn by J. Finlayson.
  " 42. Hayti . . . Drawn by F. Lucas jr.
  " 43. Porto Rico and Virgin islands. Drawn by F. Lucas.
  " 44. Windward islands. Drawn by F. Lucas jr.
  " 45. Leeward islands. J. Yeager sculp.
  " 46. South America. Drawn by E. Paguenaud.
  " 47. Colombia. Drawn by J. Finlayson.
  " 48. Brazil. Drawn by J. Finlayson.
  " 49. United provinces of South America. Drawn by J. Finlayson.
  " 50. Peru. Drawn by J. Finlayson.
  " 51. Chili. Drawn by J. Finlayson.

## 1842–1845

**Morse, S. E.,** *and* **Breese, S.**
  Morse's North American atlas.   1 p. l., 36 col. maps. fol. New York, Harper & brothers, 1842–[45]     1228

  Note.—Issued in parts.
  Cover-title dated 1845 reads as follows: Morse's cerographic maps. Plan of publication . . . The subjects illustrated will embrace the whole field of ancient and modern, including sacred geography, chronology, and history.—The work will be edited by Sidney E. Morse . . . and when finished, it is intended, shall be a universal atlas in the most comprehensive sense of the term . . . .—The first ten numbers will form a comprehensive and elegant North American atlas . . .

CONTENTS.

no. 1. North America.
" 2. Canada, east. 1845.
" 3. Canada, west. 1845.
" 4. Nova Scotia, New Brunswick &c. 1843.
" 5. Maine.
" 6. Vermont and New Hampshire.
" 7. Massachusetts and Rhode Island.
" 8. Connecticut.
" 9. New York. 1842.
" 10. New York and vicinity. 1842.
" 11. City of New York. 1842.
" 12. New Jersey. 1841. Reduced from T. Gordon's map.
" 13. Pennsylvania. 1843.
" 14. Maryland and Delaware.—District of Columbia.
" 15. Virginia.
" 16. North Carolina. 1843.
" 17. South Carolina. 1843.
" 18. Georgia. 1842.
" 19. Florida. 1842.
" 20. Alabama. 1842.
" 21. Mississippi. 1842.
" 22. Louisiana. 1842.
" 23. Texas. 1844.
" 24. Arkansas. 1844.
" 25. Kentucky and Tennessee. 1845.
" 26. Ohio.
" 27. Michigan. 1844.
" 28. Indiana. 1842.
" 29. Illinois. 1844.
" 30. Iowa and Wisconsin, chiefly from the map of J. N. Nicollet. 1844.
" 31. Wisconsin, southwestern part. 1845.
" 32. Missouri. 1844.
" 33. A map of the Indian territory, northern Texas and New Mexico . . . by Josiah Gregg. 1844.
" 34. Map of the Californias by T. J. Farnham . . . 1845.
" 35. Mexico.--Central America and Yucatan.
" 36. West India islands.

**1852**

**Tebien'kov, M. D.**

Атласъ сѣверозападныхъ береговъ Америки отъ Берингова пролива до мыса Корріэнтесъ и острововъ Алеутскихъ . . . 3 p. l., 39 maps. fol. [Санктпетербургъ] 1852. 1229

NOTE.—Atlas of the northwestern coast of America from Behrings straits to cape Corrientes and the Aleutian islands.
Maps dated 1848, 1849 and 1850.
This atlas is accompanied by the following: Гидрографическія замѣчанія къ Атласу сѣверозападныхъ береговъ Америки, острововъ Алеутскихъ и нѣкоторыхъ другихъ мѣстъ сѣвернаго Тихаго океана. 8°. Санктпетербургъ, въ типографіи Морскаго кадетскаго корпуса.—Hydrographic notes to the atlas of the northwestern shores of America, the Aleutian islands and other places of the Pacific ocean. 4, 148, 17 pp., 1 l. 1852.

## Tebīen'kov, M. D.—Continued.

CONTENTS.

1. Генеральная карта сѣверной части Тихаго океана 1849. [General map of the northern part of the Pacific ocean]
2. Карта Берингова пролива. [Map of the Behring straits]
3. Карта залива Нортонъ. [Map of Norton bay]
4. Карта очерка берега около о. Пунивокъ. [Map of Nunivok island]
5. Карта залива Бристоль. [Map of Bristol bay]
6. Карта залива Кенайскаго. [Map of Kenai bay]
7. Карта залива Чугацкаго. [Map of Chugatsky bay]
8. Карта залива Якутатъ. [Map of Yakutat bay]
9. Карта сѣверныхъ проливовъ N W берега Америки. [Map of the northwest passages of North America]
10. Карта проливовъ отъ шир. 54° до шир. 56°. [Map of the coast]
11. Карта проливовъ отъ шир. 51° да щир. 54°. [Map of the coast]
12. Карта острова Квадра и Ванкувера. [Map of Quadra and Vancouver islands]
13. Карта береговъ около рѣки Колумбіи. [Map of Columbia river]
14. Карта береговъ отъ шир. 44° до шир. 39°. [Map of the coast]
15. Карта заливовъ Бодего, С. Францыско и Монтерей. [Map of Bodego, San Francisco and Monterey bays]
16. Карта берегевъ отъ шир. 37° до шир. 32½°. [Map of the coast]
17. Карта сѣверной части полу-о. Калифорніи. [Map of the northern part of the peninsula of California]
18. Карта южной части полу-о. Калифорніи. [Map of the southern part of the peninsula of California]
19. Карта входа въ Калифорнскій заливъ. [Map of the entrance to the bay of California]
20. Карта острова С. Лаврентія. [Map of St. Laurence island]
21. Карта пространства между о-ми С. Павла и С. Матѳѣя. [Map of St. Paul and St. Matthew islands]
22. Карта острововъ Прибылова. [Map of Pribiloff islands]
23. Карта острова Кадьяка и сѣвер. час. Аляски. [Map of Kadiak and northwestern Alaska]
24. Карта сѣверовосточной стороны о. Кадьякъ. [Map of the northeastern part of Kadiak]
25. Карта югозападной части полу-о. Аляски. [Map of the southwestern part of Alaska]
26. Карта острововъ Лисьихъ Восточныхъ. [Map of eastern Fox islands]
27. Карта острововъ Лисьихъ Западныхъ. [Map of western Fox islands]
28. Карта острововъ Андреяновскихъ Восточныхъ. [Map of eastern Andrianoff islands]
29. Карта острововъ Андрелновскихъ Западныхъ. [Map of western Andriana islands]
30. Карта острововъ Крысьихъ. [Map of Rat islands]
31. Карта острововъ Ближнихъ. [Map of Near islands]
32. Карта острововъ Командорскихъ. [Map of Commander islands]
33. Карта берега Камчатки между шир. 51½° и 54¾°. [Map of Kamtschatka]
34. Карта острововъ Курильскихъ Сѣверныхъ. [Map of northern Kurile islands]
35. Карта острововъ Курильскихъ Южныхъ. [Map of southern Kurile islands]

36. Карта сѣверной части о. Сахалинъ. [Map of northern Saghalin island]
37. Карта Удской губы. [Map of Uda bay]
38. Карта берега Охотоскаго моря отъ р. Охоты до з. Аянъ. [Map of the sea Okhotsk from Okhota river to the bay of Ayan]
39. Карта частная входа въ заливъ Ситха. [Map of the entrance to the bay Sitka]

## 1854

**Lange, H.**
Atlas von Nord-Amerika. Nach den neuesten materialien, mit besonderer rücksicht auf physikalische verhältnisse und genauer angabe der county-eintheilung, der eisenbahnen, canäle, poststrassen und dampfschiffahrt, in 18 blättern mit erläuterndem texte. 3 p. l., 28 pp., 18 maps. obl. 4°. Braunschweig, G. Westermann, 1854. 1230

  Note.—Issued also under title: Kartenwerk zu dr. Karl Andree's Nord-Amerika.
  See also title 1231.

### CONTENTS.

no. 1. Karte von Nord-Amerika . . .
" 2. Die staaten Maine, Vermont, New-Hampshire, Massachusetts, Connecticut und Rhode Island.
" 3. Die staaten New-York, Pennsylvania und New-Jersey. Umgegend von New-York.
" 4. Die staaten Virginia, North-Carolina, Delaware und bundesdistrict Columbia.
" 5. Die staaten Alabama, Georgia, South-Carolina und Florida.
" 6. Die staaten Arkansas, Louisiana und Mississippi.
" 7. Die staaten Kentucky und Tennessee.
" 8. Die staaten Jowa, Missouri und Illinois.
" 9. Die staaten Indiana und Ohio.
" 10. Der staat Michigan.—Geologische karte der insel Royal.
" 11. Die staaten Minnisota [!] und Wisconsin.
" 12. Der staat Texas.
" 13. Die staaten Oregon, California, Utah, New-Mexico, und die territorien Nebraska (North-West territory) und Indian-territory.
" 14. Das britische Amerika.
" 15. Ethnographische karte von Nord-Amerika . . .
" 16. Verbreitung und vertheilung der säugethiere (mammalia) in Nord-Amerika.
" 17. Verbreitung der nahrungs- und kleidungsstoffe liefernden pflanzen von Nord-Amerika.
" 18. Die bay v. San Francisco, der Sacramento u. San Joaquin.

## 1854

Kartenwerk zu dr. Karl Andree's Nord-Amerika. Nach den neuesten materialien . . . in 18 blättern mit erläuterndem texte hrsg. von Henry Lange . . .   2 p. l., 28 pp., 18 maps. obl. 4°. Braunschweig, G. Westermann, 1854. 1231

  Note.—To accompany Andree's Nord-Amerika in geographische und geschichtlichen umrissen. v. 1, 1851.
  Issued also under title: Atlas von Nord-Amerika. **Maps the same as** contained in title 1230.

## 1856
**Black, A. & C.**
Black's atlas of North America. A series of twenty maps constructed and engraved by John Bartholomew. With introductory letter-press and a complete index. 40 pp., 20 maps. fol. Edinburgh, A. & C. Black, 1856. 1232
NOTE.—For contents see title 1385.

## 1879
**Bartholomew, J.**
Philip's handy general atlas of America, comprising a series of detailed maps of the United States, Canada, etc. With index and statistical notes . . . 18 pp., 23 col. maps. fol. London, G. Philip & son [1879] 1233

## CANADA.

### PHYSICAL.
**Hurlbert, J. B.**
Physical atlas with coloured maps, showing the geographical distribution of plants yielding food; climates; flora; soils; regions of summer rains, geological formations and hydrography of the dominion of Canada. 37 pp. incl. 10 maps. sm. fol. [Ottawa, 1880] 1234

### REPRODUCTIONS.
**Pinart, A. L.**
Recueil de cartes, plans et vues relatifs aux États-Unis et au Canada, New York, Boston, Montréal, Québec, Louisbourg, 1651–1731. Reproduits d'après les originaux manuscrits, et inédits, etc., exposés à la Bibliothèque Nationale à l'occasion du quatrième centenaire de la découverte de l'Amérique sous la direction de A. L. Pinart. 3 p. l., 13 maps on 19 l., 11 pl., 2 diagr. fol. Paris, E. Dufossé, 1893. 1235

CONTENTS.

no. 1. Vue de New-York, tirée de la *Beschrijvinghe van Virginia, Nieuw-Nederlandt, Nieuw-Engelandt, en de Eylanden Bermudes, Barbados en S. Christoffel. Amsterdam, Joost Hartgers, 1651* . . . (Sur le titre)

" 2. Carte de la Nieuw-Nederlandt avec une vue de Nieuw-Amsterdam (New York) tirée de l'ouvrage de: *Adriaen van der Donck, Beschryvinge van Nieuw-Nederlant (gelijck het Tegenwoordigh in staet is), begrijpende de nature, aert . . . Den tweede Druck. t' Aemsteldam, Evert Nieuwenhof, 1656* . . .

" 3. Le plan de Manathes ou Nouvelle-Yorc, vérifié par le sieur de La Mothe, 1693. Ce plan, fort curieux, fait partie de la *Carte de la côte de la Nouvelle-Angleterre, depuis le cap Anne jusqu'à la pointe Nevresing, où est compris le chemin par terre et par mer de Baston à Manathes, par J. B. L. Franquelin* . . .

" 4. Carte de la ville, baie et environs de Baston, par Jean-Baptiste-Louis Franquelin . . . 1693, *vérifiée par le sieur de la Motte* . . .

no. 5–6. Plan de la ville Marie ou Montréal, au Canada, sans date ni nom d'auteur. Les indications qui s'y trouvent portées nous font supposer, à raison croyons-nous, qu'il est de 1720 . . .

" 7. Carte figurative du prompt secours envoyé par l'ordre de monseigneur le marquis de Beauharnois . . . le 2<sup>e</sup> septembre 1729. Dessigné par Mahier, à Québec, le 15 octobre 1729 . . .

" 8. Vue de Québec prise de l'est . . . Cette vue est tirée d'une carte manuscrite de la Nouvelle-France, etc., qui porte en cartouche: à monseigneur, monseigneur le comte de Maurepas . . . par son très humble et très obéissant serviteur de Fonville . . . 1699 . . .

" 9. Vue de Québec, prise du nord-ouest. Cette vue est tirée de la carte indiquée sous le numéro précédent, où elle se trouve dans le coin du bas, à droite . . .

" 10. Vue de Québec, comme il se voit du côté de l'est . . . Belle pièce tirée d'une carte intitulée: Carte de l'Amérique, entre les 25<sup>e</sup> et 65<sup>e</sup> degrés de latitude, et depuis environ les 240<sup>e</sup> jusqu'aux 340<sup>e</sup> de longitude, contenant les pays de la Nouvelle-France, la Louisiane, Floride, Virginie, Nouvelle-Yorck, Nouvelle-Angleterre, Acadie, etc., par Jean-Baptiste-Louis Franquelin, 1699 . . .

" 11. Vue de Québec . . . Jolie vue tirée d'une carte intitulée: Partie de l'Amérique septentrionale où est compris la Nouvelle-France, la Nouvelle-Angleterre, la Nouvelle-Albanie et la Nouvelle-Yorc, la Pensylvanie, la Virginie, la Caroline, la Floride, la Louisiane, etc., par Jean-Baptiste-Louis Franquelin . . . 1699 . . .

" 12. Partie de la Carte de l'Amérique septentrionale entre 27 et 64 degrés de latitude, et environ 250 et 340 degrés de longitude, où est compris le pays de la Nouvelle-France, la Nouvelle-Angleterre, la Virginie, la Caroline, la Floride et tous les environs du grand fleuve Mississipi . . . par Jean-Baptiste-Louis Franquelin, dessiné et écrit par F. de La Croix. Cette carte, bien que non datée, est peu postérieure à l'expédition de Beaujeu et à la mort de Cuvelier de la Salle, 1687.

" 13. Carte des grands lacs (1679) attribuée à J.-B.-L. Franquelin . . .

" 14. Carte de la rivière de Saint-Laurent depuis Québec et la rivière du Sault de la Chaudière . . . Curieuse carte qui, bien que non datée, ne peut être postérieure à 1679 . . .

" 15. Carte de la région située aux environs du lac Ontario ou de Fontenac, la rivière des Outaouais depuis le Sault de la Chaudière, le lac Shekoven ou Nipissing et les portages entre ce lac et la rivière des Outaouais et avec le lac des Hurons par la rivière des Français . . . Cette carte, dont la date peut être fixée à 1679 . . .

" 16. Carte du lac Huron, Karegnondi ou mer des Hurons où sont indiqués les tribus, les villages indiens ainsi que la route qu'ils suivaient . . . Curieuse carte qui, bien que non datée, ne paraît pas postérieure à 1679 . . .

" 17. Carte des lacs Tracy ou Supérieur, des Illinois et des Hurons avec la rivière Colbert et le pays au nord du lac Tracy jusqu'à la baie ou golfe de Hudson et la rivière des Assinipoul . . . Cette . . . carte, bien que non datée, ne paraît pas postérieure à 1680 . . .

" 18. Carte des lacs et des régions à l'ouest de la baie d'Hudson . . .

" 19–20. Carte générale des paroisses et missions établies des deux côtés du fleuve Saint-Laurent, depuis Rimousky en montant jusqu'au coteau des Cèdres . . . Cette carte . . . date de la fin du XVII<sup>e</sup> siècle . . .

" 21–22. Carte des côtes habitées du Canada par paroisses et par seigneuries, signée Deshaies . . .

**Pinart, A. L.**—Continued.
>    no. 23. Carte des régions entre le Saint-Laurent et la baie d'Hudson de la main de L. Jolliet, sous ce titre: *Cette carte montre le chemin que Louis Jolliet a fait depuis Tadoussac jusqu'à la mer du Nord dans la baie d'Hudson et du destroit* . . . 1679 . . .
>    " 24–25. Vue de la ville de Louisbourg, prise en dedans du port, Verrier fils, *fecit* 1731 . . .
>    " 26–27. Plan de la ville de Louisbourg avec les fortifications du côté des terres, vers 1731 . . .

### GENERAL.
(Arranged chronologically)
### 1806

**North American pilot, The.**

The first part of the North American pilot; for Newfoundland, Labradore, and the gulf and river St. Lawrence: being a collection of sixty-one accurate charts and plans, drawn from original surveys, taken by captain James Cook, and Michael Lane, surveyor, Joseph Gilbert, and other experienced officers in the king's service . . . Chiefly engraved by the late Thomas Jefferys . . . on thirty-seven large copper-plates. A new ed. 3 p. l., 23 maps on 25 sheets. fol. London, R. Laurie & J. Whittle, 1806.    1236

> NOTE.—For 1777 edition, see title 1209. The second part, title 1220.
>
> CONTENTS.
>
> no. 1. A general chart of the island of Newfoundland . . . By James Cook and Michael Lane . . . and others . . . 1794.
> " 2. A chart of the banks of Newfoundland, drawn from . . . hydrographical surveys, chiefly from those of Chabert Cook, Fleurieu and recent observations of Fran$^s$ Owen. 1803.
> " 3. A chart of the south-east part of Newfoundland, containing the bays of Placentia, St. Mary, Trepassey and Conception . . . 1794.
> " 4. Trinity harbour.—Carboniere and Harbour Grace.—St. John's harbour.—Cape Broyle harbour.—Ferryland harbour.—Aquafort harbour.—Fermouse harbour. 1794.
> " 5. A new survey of Trinity harbour in Newfoundland . . . by . . . Francis Owen . . . 1801.
> " 6. A chart of St. John's harbour in Newfoundland, surveyed in October, 1798, by Francis Owen . . . 1799.
> " 7. A chart of the road and harbour of Great Placentia, in Newfoundland. Surveyed in august, 1800, by Francis Owen . . . 1801.
> " 8. The harbour of Trepassey with Mutton and Biscay bays.—The road and harbour of Placentia. By James Cook.—St. Mary's harbour . . . 1794.
> " 9. A chart of part of the south coast of Newfoundland . . . By James Cook . . .—Inset: Port aux Basque.—S$^t$ Peters island . . . 1763.—Great Jervis harbour.—Harbour Briton.—Harbours of S$^t$ Laurence.
> " 10. A new chart of the coast of Nova Scotia with the south coast of New Brunswick . . . By capt. Holland. 1798.—Inset: Plan of river S$^t$ John.—Plan of the entrance or harbour of river S$^t$ John.—Plan of Port Roseway harbour.
> " 11. The island of Sable . . . 1794.
> " 12. The harbour of Halifax in Nova Scotia, by Thos. Backhouse. 1798.

no. 13. A plan of Port Dauphin . . . surveyed in 1743.—A plan of Murgain or Cow bay . . . Surveyed in . . . 1760 . . .—A draught of the gut of Canso . . . Surveyed by the king's ships in 1761 . . . 1794.

" 14. A chart of the gulf of St. Laurence . . . 1794.

" 15. A chart of the Magdalen islands in the gulf of St. Laurence. Surveyed in 1765. 1794.

" 16. A map of the island of St. John . . . Improved from the late survey of captain Holland . . .—Inset: Gulf of St. Laurence. 1794.

" 17. A plan of Chaleur bay . . . Surveyed by his majefty's ship Norwich in 1760. 1794.

" 18. A plan of Ristigouche harbour in Chaleur bay. Surveyed in 1760 by the king's ship Norwich. 1794.

" 19. A chart of the West coast of Newfoundland . . . By James Cook. 1794.—Inset: A plan of Hawkes harbour, Port Saunders and Keppel harbour.—A plan of York and Lark harbours, in the Bay of Iflands.

" 20. A chart of the straights of Bellisle . . . Taken in 1766 by James Cook . . . and by Michael Lane in 1769 . . . 1794.—Inset: Bradore harbour.—Red Bay.—York, or Chateaux Bay.—Quirpon harbour.—Croque harbour.

" 21. A chart of part of the coast of Labradore . . . Surveyed by Joseph Gilbert in 1767 and engraved by Thomas Jefferys . . . —Inset: Petty Harbour.—The three harbours of Sophia, Charlotte, and Mecklenburg.

" 22. A chart of part of the coast of Labradore, from Grand Point to Shecatica. Surveyed by Michael Lane in 1768 and engraved by Thomas Jefferys . . .—Inset: Plan of Mecatina harbour.—Plan of S! Augustine.—Plan of Cumberland harbour.

" 23–25. A new chart of the river St. Laurence, from the island of Anticosti to the falls of Richelieu . . . Taken by order of Charles Saunders . . . commander in chief of his majesty's ships in the expedition againft Quebec in 1759. Engraved by Thomas Jefferys. 1794. 3 sheets.—Inset: Havre S! Nicholas . . .—Bay of the Seven islands.—Pointe aux Allouettes or Larks Point . . .—Mingan harbour.—Mingan island.—Gaspee bay.

## 1875

**Walker & Miles.**

The new standard atlas of the dominion of Canada . . . comprising a . . . series of the topographical, geological, postal, railway and timber-land maps of Canada . . .   lvi, 151, x pp. incl. 48 maps. fol. Montreal and Toronto, Walker & Miles, 1875.   1237

## 1875

**Walling, H. F.**

Atlas of the dominion of Canada with general descriptions by T. Sterry Hunt, Robert Bell, A. R. C. Selwyn & others.   251 pp. incl. 52 maps. fol. Montreal, Toronto and London, G. N. Tackabury, 1875.   1238

NOTE.—Contains plans of Toronto, Montreal, Ottawa, Hamilton, London, Kingston, Quebec.

## 1880
**Roe brothers.**
Atlas of the maritime provinces of the dominion of Canada, with historical and geological descriptions. 102 pp. incl. 35 maps. fol. St. John, N. B., Roe bros., 1880. 1239

NOTE.—Contains plans of the following cities: S! John, Halifax, Chatham, Newcastle, Charlottetown, Fredericton, Moncton, Woodstock, S! Stephen, S! Andrews, Yarmouth, Truro, Amherst, Pictou, Windsor.

## 1890
**Bartholomew, J. G.**
The pocket atlas and gazetteer of the dominion of Canada. Edited by J. M. Harper . . . xxiv, 276 pp., 36 fold. maps. 24°. London, J. Walker & co. 1890. 1240

## 1899
**Canada.** *Department of the interior.*
Descriptive atlas of western Canada. Showing maps of the provinces of Manitoba and British Columbia and districts of Assiniboia, Alberta and Saskatchewan. Also the world and the dominion of Canada. Issued by authority of hon. Clifford Sifton, m. p. minister of the interior, Can. 10 pp., 3 l. incl. 5 maps. 4°. [Chicago, Rand, McNally & co. 1899] 1241

NOTE.—Maps copyrighted by Rand, McNally & co. 1895-9.

## 1899
Beschreibender atlas des westlichen Canada enthaltend karten der provinzen Manitoba und British-Columbia . . . Hrsg. unter autorität des achtb. Clifford Sifton, minister des inneren. German ed. cover-title, 10 pp. incl. 5 maps. fol. [Chicago, Rand, McNally & co.] 1899. 1242

NOTE.—Descriptive text on inside covers in german; maps in english.

## 1900
Concise school atlas of the dominion of Canada. Historical and physical features of provinces, districts, and territories of the dominion. Issued by direction of honorable Clifford Sifton, minister of the interior. 32 pp. incl. 15 maps. 16°. Ottawa, 1900.
1243

NOTE.—Maps copyrighted by Rand, McNally & co., Chicago.

## 1900
Descriptive atlas of western Canada, showing maps of the provinces of Ontario, Quebec, New Brunswick, Nova Scotia, Prince

Edward Island, Manitoba, British Columbia, and districts of Assiniboia, Alberta, Saskatchewan, and Athabasca, also of the world and the dominion of Canada . . . Issued by direction of hon. Clifford Sifton, minister of the interior.   11, [2] pp. incl. 8 maps.   fol. Ottawa, 1900.   1244

NOTE.—Maps copyrighted by Rand, McNally & co., Chicago.

### 1902

Atlas of western Canada, showing maps of the provinces of Ontario, Quebec, New Brunswick, Nova Scotia, Prince Edward Island, Manitoba, British Columbia, and districts of Assiniboia, Alberta, Saskatchewan, Athabasca, New Ontario, lake St. John, Great Britain and Ireland, the world and the dominion of Canada. Issued by direction of hon. Clifford Sifton, minister of the interior. Census edition 1901.   52 pp. incl. 14 maps.   fol.   Ottawa, 1902.
1245

NOTE.—Maps copyrighted 1901 by Rand, McNally & co., Chicago.

### 1903

Atlas of western Canada, showing maps of the provinces of Ontario, Quebec, New Brunswick, Nova Scotia, Prince Edward island, Manitoba, British Columbia and districts of Assiniboia, Alberta, Saskatchewan, the dominion of Canada. Issued by direction of hon. Clifford Sifton, minister of the interior.   41 pp. incl. 11 maps.   4°.   Ottawa [1903]   1246

NOTE.—Maps copyrighted 1901, 1902, 1903, by Rand, McNally & co., Chicago.

### 1904
**Rand, McNally & co.**

Toronto mail and empire atlas of Canada and the world showing map of the world, dominion of Canada, Ontario, Quebec, maritime provinces, Manitoba, British Columbia, Europe, Asia, Africa, United States and South America.   16 pp. incl. 11 maps.   fol.   [Chicago] published specially for the mail and empire by Rand, McNally & co. [1904]   1247

### 1905

The Rand-McNally indexed atlas of the dominion of Canada, with one hundred illustrations. Physical-political-commercial, containing detail maps of the colonies and possessions of the British empire and of all the more important foreign countries and states of the world; with a comprehensive index for each map and special geographical statistics.   174 pp. incl. 51 maps.   fol.   Chicago, Rand, McNally & co. [1905]   1248

## 1906

**Canada.** *Department of the interior.*
    Atlas of Canada. Prepared under the direction of James White
. . .    1 p. l., 21 pp., 46 col. maps, 44 tab. fol. [Toronto] 1906.
                                                                                              1249

    NOTE.—At head of title: Department of the interior, Canada, honourable Frank Oliver, minister. No. 2212 on first p. l.
    Reviewed by H. Baulig, in Annales de géographie, 15 juillet, 1908, pp. 360-363.

## NOVA SCOTIA.

### 1775-1778

**Atlantic Neptune, The.** The sea coast of Nova Scotia; exhibiting the diversities of the coast, and face of the country near it: the banks, rocks, shoals, soundings, &c. together with remarks and directions for the conveniency of navigation and pilotage. Survey'd by order of the right honorable the lords commissioners of the admiralty, by J. F. W. Des Barres . . . 2 v. fol. [London, 1775-1778]                                                                1250

    NOTE.—v. 1, of The Atlantic Neptune, in 2 pts. For full description of the various copies of "The Atlantic Neptune," see titles 1198-1205.
    Collation: pt. 1, 7 p. l., 11 maps; pt. 2, 4 p. l., 32 maps.
    Imperfect: map no. 3 of pt. 1, wanting.
    Maps correspond with the contents of v. 1, of the french edition of this atlas, described in "L'esprit des journaux" v. 3, 1784, except that the latter contains many views as well as maps.
    Like v. 1 of copy no. 1, with the following exceptions: map of "The coast of Nova Scotia, New England, New York, Jersey . . . &c" wanting; five small views of Sable island, map of the "Grand bay of Pasamaquody" and of "Grand Manan island," omitted.
    Contains a plan of "The harbor of Halifax" and maps of "port Hood," "Frederick bay and Pictou harbour," and "port Shediack," not found in v. 1 of copy 1.

### 1798

**Backhouse, T.**
    A new pilot for the south east coast of Nova Scotia, Chedabucto bay, gut of Canso, bay of Fundy, and round the isle of Cape Breton, with the principal harbours . . . With an entire new book of sailing directions. 2 p. l., 15 maps. fol. London, R. Laurie & J. Whittle, 1798.                                               1251

    NOTE.—The "Directions," wanting.

CONTENTS.

    no. 1. A new chart of the coast of Nova Scotia . . .
    "   2. The harbour or river St. John in New Brunswick . . .
    "   3. A survey of Shelburne, or Port Roseway harbour . . .

no. 4. A survey of Lunenburg harbour on the coast of Nova Scotia . . .
" 5. The harbour of Halifax, in Nova Scotia . . .
" 6–7. A survey of Country harbour on the coast of Nova Scotia . . .
" 8. The harbour of Canso . . .
" 9. Crow harbour, on the south side of Chedabucto bay . . .
" 10. Part of the isle, of Cape Breton, Inhabitant bay, and, harbour . . .
" 11. The island of Cape Breton, with the gut of Canso, and Chedabucto bay . . .
" 12. Port Hood on the north west side of Cape Breton . . .
" 13. St. Ann's bay and harbour, on the north east side of Cape Breton island . . .
" 14. A survey of Spanish river or Sydney harbour . . .
" 15. A survey of Louisburg harbour . . .

### 1818

**Lockwood, A.**

A brief description of Nova Scotia, with plates of the principal harbors; including a particular account of the island of Grand Manan . . .   2 p. l., 134 pp., 8 maps. 4°. London, for the author, 1818.   1252

NOTE.—Maps engraved by J. Walker.
Contains also the following map, "The lands round the North Pole, shewing the intended track's of h. m. ships to discover a n. w. passage to the Pacific ocean," on a polar projection.

### ONTARIO.

#### YORK.

**Miles & co.**

Illustrated historical atlas of the county of York and the township of West Gwillimbury & town of Bradford in the county of Simcoe, Ont. Compiled, drawn and published from personal examinations and surveys.   xxii, 75 pp. incl. 35 maps, 12 pl., 7 l. at end.   fol.   Toronto, Miles & co. 1878.   1253

### LABRADOR.

**Cook, J., Lane, M.**, *& others.*

A collection of charts of the coasts of Newfoundland and Labradore, &c. . . .  Drawn from original surveys taken by James Cook and Michael Lane, surveyors, Joseph Gilbert, and other officers in the king's service . . .  Chiefly engraved by Thomas Jefferys . . .   1 p. l., 9 maps.   fol.   London, T. Jefferys [1765–1768]   1254

NOTE.—Inclusive dates from maps nos. [2], [5] and [8]
Map no. 9 has border text.
Foot-note on title-page states that the "Newfoundland pilot" contains a "collection of directions" for each chart.

## QUEBEC.

**Sulte, B.**
    Album de l'histoire des Trois-Rivières . . .     18 l. incl. 11 maps. obl. 4°.    Montréal, G. E. Desbarats, 1881.          1255

    NOTE.—Le volume, qui contient de belles reproductions de plans et de documents manuscrits anciens, n'a été tiré qu'à 150 ex., au prix de $5.00 par exemplaire. *cf.* Philéas Gagnon's Essai de bibliographie canadienne, for works of Sulte.

CONTENTS.

    1634. Première page des registres de l'église.
    1648. Election d'un syndic.
    1648–90. Signatures des habitants.
    1685. Plan de la ville.
    1685–1709. Cadastre des seigneuries du gouvernement des Trois-Rivières.
    1700. La ville et les terres dans un circuit d'une lieue.
    1704. Plan de la ville, avec légende.
    1721. Vue de la ville.

## NEWFOUNDLAND.

**Cook, J., Lane, M.,** & *others.*
    A collection of charts of the coasts of Newfoundland and Labradore, &c. . . . Drawn from original surveys taken by James Cook and Michael Lane, surveyors, Joseph Gilbert, and other officers in the king's service . . . Chiefly engraved by Thomas Jefferys . . .    1 p. l., 9 maps.   fol.   London, T. Jefferys [1765–1768]                                               1256

    NOTE.—Inclusive dates on maps nos. [2], [5] and [8]
    Map no. [9] has border text.
    Foot-note on title-page states that the "Newfoundland pilot" contains a "collection of directions" for each chart.

# UNITED STATES.

### AGRICULTURAL.

**United States.** *Department of agriculture.*
    Album of agricultural graphics. Values per acre of crops of the United States, based on results of investigation under the direction of the statistician. Published by authority of the secretary of agriculture.    3 p. l., 10 col. maps.   obl. fol.   Washington, [Bell lith. co.] 1890.                                                    1257

### BANKERS AND BROKERS.

**Grant, A. A.**
    Grant's bankers' and brokers' railway system atlas . . . Accompanied by a concise and original ready reference index of the United States, Canada, Mexico and Cuba . . .    628 (*i. e.* 626), [32] pp. incl. 151 col. maps.   fol.   New York, for A. A. Grant by G. F. Cram [°1907]                                           1258

## BOUNDARY.

### Alaska.

**Alaskan boundary tribunal.**
The case of the United States before the tribunal convened at London under the provisions of the treaty between the United States of America and Great Britain concluded january 24, 1903. Atlas. 3 p. l., 25 maps. fol. Washington, government printing office, 1903. 1259

> NOTE.—Atlas has title: . . . Atlas accompanying the case of the United States . . .
> Supplemented by, "Atlas accompanying the counter case of the United States." Another edition, with imprint date 1904, has atlas and supplement in one volume.
> Portions of maps of North America, relating chiefly to Alaska, Canada and the north coast.
> Contains also biographical notes of some of the cartographers whose maps are reproduced.
> Maps no. 6–9, 11–13 and 24 were photographed from originals in the Library of Congress.
>
> CONTENTS.
>
> no. 1. General map. Adjacent parts of North America and Asia . . . 1903.
> " 2–3. Southeastern Alaska . . . 1903.
> " 4–5. Charts of part of the coast of n. w. America . . . nos. 7 & 12 of Vancouver's atlas, 1798.
> " 6. [The Pacific and Icy seas] Part of a map published at St. Petersburg in 1802.
> " 7. Part of a map of North America published at Augsburg in 1807 by Johann Walch.
> " 8. The northwest part of a "Map of British North America, after mr. Arrowsmith," from Pinkerton's Modern atlas . . . Philadelphia, 1818.
> " 9. Part of Brué's map of North America, 1815–1819 . . .
> " 10. Part of the "Map of America by A. Arrowsmith . . . 1822. Additions to 1823 " . . .
> " 11. Part of russian admiralty chart no 1266 . . . Translated the title reads: General chart of the South sea, sheet 2, from the equator to latitude 72° 30′ north and from longitude 112° 30′ to 192° 30′ east. 1826.
> " 12. Part of A. Arrowsmith's map of North America . . . 1795 . . . revised to 1833. . . .
> " 13. Part of Brué's map of North America . . . Paris, 1833 . . .
> " 14. Part of "A map of North America, constructed according to the latest information by H. S. Tanner, 1839."
> " 15. Part of the " Map of the western and middle portions of North America, to illustrate the history of California, Oregon and the other countries on the northwest coast of America, by Robert Greenhow . . . 1844."
> " 16. Part of a map of the western coast of America . . . m. Duflot de Mofras, Paris, 1844.
> " 17. The greater part of a map of "The british dominions in North America," which appears as an inset on the large "Map of the provinces of Canada " . . . by Joseph Bouchette . . . 1853.

**Alaskan boundary tribunal**—Continued.

    no. 18. Part of a Mercator map of the world, pub. by the spanish admiralty in 1857.
    " 19. The greater part of the "Map of the north west part of Canada Hudson's bay and Indian territories . . . 1857. Drawn by T: Devine.
    " 20. Part of the "Map of the russian dominions on the shores of the Eastern ocean, 1861" . . .
    " 21. Part of Mercator's map of the world, by Hermann Berghaus and Fr. v. Stülpnagel . . . 1863.
    " 22. Part of russian admiralty chart no. 1345 . . . Translated, the title reads: "Chart of the Icy sea and the Eastern ocean . . . 1844." Foot note reads: "Corrected to 1864."
    " 23. Part of the british admiralty chart no. 2461 "Pacific ocean, Cook river to gulf of California, 1861." Corrected to 1866.
    " 24. Part of the map of northwestern America, prepared for the dept. of state at the office of the U. S. coast survey in 1867.
    " 25. Southeastern Alaska, with sites of various indian villages as located by lieut. G. T. Emmons . . . prepared at the office of the U. S. coast and geodetic survey, 1903.

——— The counter case of the United States before the tribunal convened at London under the provisions of the treaty between the United States of America and Great Britain concluded january 24, 1903. Atlas. 2 p. l., 34 maps. fol. Washington, government printing office, 1903.     1260

    NOTE.—Atlas has title: . . . Atlas accompanying the counter case of the United States . . .
    Contains portions of maps of North America relating chiefly to Alaska, Canada and the north coast.
    Maps are numbered 26–47, the atlas being a supplement to "Atlas accompanying the case of the United States" . . .

CONTENTS.

    no. 26. Southeastern Alaska, a reprint of no. 2 of "Atlas accompanying the case of the United States" with the addition of the line now claimed by Great Britain.
    " 27. Southeastern Alaska and part of British Columbia. Map presented to the joint high commission at Quebec in 1898 by the british commissioners.
    " 28. A series of eight maps of the Alaskan lisière, from british sources: (a) Official map of British Columbia, 1884.
    " 28. (b) [Same] Dated 1884 but presumably later than (a) (c) Dawson's map, sessional papers, 1887, from senate ex. doc. 146, 50th cong. 2d. sess. (d) Official map of British Columbia, 1893. (e) . . . British Columbia, 1895. (f) Map presented to the joint high commission in 1898 by british commissioners. (g) Map from year book of British Columbia, 1897. (h) Official british government map 1903.
    " 29. A series of six maps of the lower part of the Stikine river. (a) Prof. W. P. Blake's sketch map, of the Stikine river, 1863. (b) Wright's map of the Cassiar district, 1876. (c) General map of Alaska by U. S. coast survey, 1869. (d) Hunter's survey of the lower Stikine, 1877. (e) Surveyor-general Dennis's map of the Stikine, 1878. (f) Canadian geological survey, 1884.

no. 30. Clarence strait, Revillagigedo channel and Portland canal . . . 1903.
" 31. Sketch map of Portland channel and vicinity . . . 1867.
" 32. Map of Pyramid harbour and vicinity . . . 1891.
" 33. Part of sir George Simpson's map from his narrative of a journey round the world . . . 1847.
" 34. Part of a map of the russian empire, compiled to accompany mr. Hill's travels.
" 35. Official map of North America. Drawn by J. Arrowsmith. 1857. Ordered by the house of commons.
" 36. The provinces of British Columbia and Vancouver island . . . by John Arrowsmith, 1859.
" 37. Part of Imray's chart of the North Pacific ocean, 1869.
" 38. Part of british admiralty chart no. 787 i. e. Pacific ocean, eastern part. Cape Corrientes, Mexico to Kodiak island . . . 1876.
" 39. Part of official canadian map i. e. Map of the dominion of Canada . . . 1878.
" 40. Part of map of Manitoba, Keewatin, British Columbia and North West territory . . . 1880.
" 41. Part of map of British Columbia and the North West territory, by the canadian geological survey, 1881.
" 42. Part of official canadian map of the dominion of Canada . . . 1882.
" 43. Part of official canadian map of the dominion of Canada and part of the United States . . . 1883.
" 44. Part of map of British Columbia and the North West territory . . . 1887.
" 45. Part of map of the dominion of Canada (western sheet) . . . By T. B. Johnston . . .
" 46. Part of a map of the western part of the dominion of Canada . . .
" 47. Part of map of British Columbia . . . 1898.

——— Boundary between the dominion of Canada and the territory of Alaska . . . Appendix to the case of his majesty's government before the Alaska boundary tribunal. v. 2. Atlas. 2 p. l., 37 maps. fol. London, McCorquodale & co. limited, 1903.   1261

Note.—v. 2, portions of maps of North America relating chiefly to Alaska, Canada and the north coast.
Atlas has title: British case. Alaska boundary. Atlas. Appendix vol. ii.

CONTENTS.

no. 1-3. . . . Chart shewing part of the coast of n. w. America . . . Vancouver, 1798.
" 4. Parts of charts vii & xii, from Vancouver's atlas.
" 5. [Russian map] Translation of title: Map of marine discoveries by russian navigators in the Pacific and Frozen oceans . . . 1802.
" 6. Part of map no. 5, i. e. карта морскихъ открытіи . . .
" 7. Map of the world illustrating the voyages and travels of G. H. von Langsdorff.
" 8. Map of America by A. Arrowsmith . . . 1822 (colored)
" 9. [Part of Arrowsmith's Map of America] (uncolored)
" 10. Map of North America from 20°-80° north latitude . . . 1823.
" 11. Same. 1824.
" 12. [Part of Arrowsmith's Map of America] 1824.
" 13. Part of colonial office manuscript map. By L. Hebert, senior. 1831.
" 14. The british dominions in North America. Bouchette. 1831.

**Alaskan boundary tribunal**—Continued.
 no. 15. Карта ледовитаго моря . . . Translation of title: Part of map of the Frozen ocean and the Eastern ocean . . . 1844.
 " 16. Map of the western and middle portions of North America . . . by Robert Greenhow. 1844.
 " 17. Map showing sir George Simpson's route. 1847.
 " 18. [Russian map] Translation of title: Part of map of the straits of the north-west coast of America, from latitude 54°-56° . . . 1849.
 " 19. Map of North America. John Arrowsmith. Ordered by the house of commons. 1850.
 " 20. [Russian map] Translation of title: [Part of] Mercator map of the southern half of the Koloshenski archipelago . . . 1853.
 " 21. Map of North America. Drawn by J. Arrowsmith . . . 1857.
 " 22. Part of map of British North America . . . A. Arrowsmith. 1863.
 " 23. N. W. America. British Columbia. Portland canal. From the admiralty survey of 1868.
 " 24. N. W. America. British Columbia. Observatory inlet, from the admiralty survey, of 1868.
 " 25. . . . Port Simpson to Nass village fr. the admiralty survey of 1868.
 " 26. Plan of the Stachine or Stickeen river . . . 1877.
 " 27. Tracing of part of "Alaska" shewing "Stakeen river;" from U. S. coast survey of 1869.
 " 28. Map of Alaska and adjoining regions. Compiled by Ivan Petroof . . . 1880.
 " 29. Same. (Reduced)
 " 30. " ( " and colored)
 " 31. Map of the province of British Columbia . . . by Edward Mohun . . . 1884.
 " 32. Map of the dominion of Canada. Geologically colored . . . 1842-1882.
 " 33. Part of british admiralty chart no. 2431. Cordova bay to Cross sound. 1865. Corrections to 1884.
 " 34. Dawson's canadian map, 1887, showing conventional lines proposed by Canada.
 " 35. Portland inlet, Alaska. U. S. coast and geodetic survey. 1888.
 " 36. N. W. shore of Portland inlet. Alaska. U. S. coast and geodetic survey. 1888.
 " 37. Southern Alaska and part of British Columbia . . . Canadian boundary commission . . . 1893-1898.

Mexico.

**International boundary commission. United States and Mexico, 1882.**
Boundary between the United States and Mexico, as surveyed and marked by the international boundary commission, under the convention of july 29th, 1882. Revived february 18th, 1889. 1 p. l., 26 maps. fol. [Washington, 1898]   1262

NOTE.—Published to accompany the "Report of the boundary commission," 1898, by the Norris Peters co. litho., Washington, D. C.
Published also as U. S. 55th cong., 2d sess. senate. doc. no. 247 (v. 25)

CONTENTS.

A and B. Index map of the boundary.
no. 1-4. California line.
" 5. Colorado line.
" 6-11. Arizona—Sonora oblique line.
" 12-16. Parallel 31° 30′ north latitude.
" 16-17. Meridian section.
" 17-19. Parallel 31° 47′ north latitude.
" 20-24. Profile of the boundary.

―――― Línea divisoria entre México y los Estados Unidos al oeste del río Grande leventada y marcada, bajo la dirección por parte de México del ingeniero Jacobo Blanco, por la comisión internacional de límites creada por la convención de julio 29 de 1882, renovada por la de febrero 18 de 1889.   1 p. l., 19 maps.   fol. [Nueva York, impr. de J. Polhemus & co. 1901?]   1263

NOTE.—Lettered, "Planos vol. II."
Atlas to accompany "Memoria de la sección mexicana de la comisión internacional de límites entre México y los Estados Unidos."

CONTENTS.

no. 1-3. Paralelo 31° 47′.
" 3-4. Sección meridiana.
" 4-8. Paralelo 31° 20′.
" 9-14. Linea azimutal entre Sonora y Arizona.
" 15-18. Linea azimutal entre la baja y Alta Californias.
" 19. Rio Colorado (en dos colores)

**Northern.**

**United States.**   *Department of state.*
Joint maps of the northern boundary of the United States, from the Lake of the Woods to the summit of the Rocky mountains. United States northern boundary commission. Archibald Campbell, esq., commissioner. W. J. Twining, capt. of engrs. U. S. A. chief astronomer. Her majesty's North American boundary commission. D. R. Cameron, maj. royal engrs., chief astronomer.   1 p. l., 24 sheets.   obl. 4°.   [Washington, government printing office, 1878]
1264

NOTE.—To accompany "Reports upon the survey of the boundary between the territory of the United States and the possessions of Great Britain. 1878." By Archibald Campbell.

**CANALS.**

**Poussin, G. T.**
Travaux d'améliorations intérieures projetés ou exécutés par le gouvernement général des États-Unis d'Amérique, de 1824-1831. 2 p. l., 10 maps.   fol.   Paris, Anselin [&] Carilian-Goeury, 1834.
1265

NOTE.—To accompany his work of same title.

**Poussin, G. T.**—Continued.

CONTENTS.

no. 1. Carte générale des États-Unis d'Amérique. 1834.
" 2. Canal de la Chesapeake à l'Ohio.
" 3. Canal de la Chesapeake à la Delaware.—Canal de Louisville. (État du Kentucky)—Canal de jonction du Mississippi au lac Pontchartrain.
" 4. Canal Morris.
" 5. Canal du Cap Cod.
" 6. Breakwater de la Delaware.
" 7. Canal des Florides.—Carte générale.
" 8. Canal des Florides.—Plans hydrographiques des baies, rades etc.
" 9. Canal du Muscle-Shoal.
" 10. Grand-canal de New-York—Port de Presqu'ile.—Ponts en bois de m. J. Cown.

**Chevalier, M.**
Histoire et description des voies de communication aux États-Unis et des travaux d'art qui en dépendent.   Atlas.   cover-title, 19 pl. incl. 4 maps.   fol.   Paris, C. Gosselin, 1841.   1266

NOTE.—To accompany his work of the same title.
Plates engraved by Tardieu, Adam and Lemaitre.

CONTENTS.

no. 1. Carte générale des États-Unis. 1849.
" 2. Carte des canaux et des chemins de fer des états de New York, Pensylvanie, New Jersey et Maryland.
" 3. Fig. 1. Plan topographique du terrain traversé par le chemin de fer du portage.—Fig. 2. Profil du tracé définitif du chemin de fer du portage.—Fig. 3. Profil du canal Érié et du canal Champlain.—Fig. 4. Profil de la ligne de Philadelphie à Pittsburg.—Fig. 5. Locomotive américaine.
" 4. Canal du Schuylkill . . .
" 5. Chemin de fer de Baltimore à l'Ohio.
" 6. Fig. 1. Plan de Philadelphie avec ses faubourgs.—Fig. 2. Plan topographique du terrain traversé par le canal de la Chesapeake à l'Ohio.—Fig. 3. Profil du canal de la Chesapeake à l'Ohio.
" 7–11. Pont-aqueduc de Georgetown sur le Potomac.   5 sheets.
" 12. Canal latéral au S? Laurent.
" 13. Plan incliné du canal Morris.
" 14–15. Plans inclinés du chemin de fer de Pottsville à Sunbury.   2 sheets.
" 16. Fig. 1. Viaduc Thomas sur le Patapsco, chemin de fer de Baltimore à l'Ohio.—Fig. 2. Pont du Schuylkill, chemin de fer de Columbia.—Fig. 6. Pont sur la Delaware, à New-hope.—Fig. 7. Pont sur la Delaware, à Trenton . . .—Fig. 8. Pont sur le Schuylkill à Philadelphia . . .—Fig. 9. Pont de Trenton.—Fig. 10. Pont sur le Schuylkill à Philadelphie.—Fig. 11. Pont dans le système de Burr.—Fig. 12. Pont dans le système de town.—Fig. 13. Pont de Portsmouth . . .—Fig. 14–19. [Details]
" 17. Fig. 2.—Point sur le Will's creek.—Fig. 9. Pont situé sur le chemin de fer de Philadelphie à Mount Carbon au dessous de Reading . . .—Fig. 1, 3–8, 10–19. [Details]

no. 18. Fig. 2. Pont sur le Nottoway, chemin de fer de Petersburg au Roanoke . . .—Fig. 8. Pont sur l'Opequon, chemin de fer de Winchester à Harper's Ferry.—Fig. 1, 3 to 7, 9-22. [Details]
" 19. Fig. 1. Pont du Richmond. Chemin de fer de Richmond à Petersburg . . .—Fig. 7. Pont des ecluses de Peacock, chemin de fer de Mount Carbon à Philadelphie . . .—Fig. 13-15. Rail et coussinet du chemin de fer de Mount Carbon à Philadelphie . . .—Fig. 2-6, 8-12, 14. [Details]

## CITIES.
**Köllner, A.**
[Views of cities, prominent buildings, &c., in the United States and Canada. Drawn from nature by Aug. Köllner] 54 col. pl. obl. fol. [New York & Paris, Goupil, Vilbert & co. 1848-51] 1267

NOTE.—No title-page.
Copyrighted separately from 1848 to 1851, nos. 1-48 by Aug. Köllner, nos. 49-54 by William Schauss.

### CONTENTS.
no. 1. Baltimore. N. west view. 1848.
" 2. " Washington's monument. 1848.
" 3. " Hospital. 1848.
" 4. " Green Mount cemetery.
" 5. " Battle monument. 1848.
" 6. " City spring. 1848.
" 8. Philadelphia. Merchant's exchange. 1848.
" 9. " Girard college. 1848.
" 7. " S. E. view. 1848.
" 10. " Laurel Hill cemetery. 1848.
" 11. " State-house. 1848.
" 12. " U. S. custom-house. (formerly U. S. bank) 1848.
" 13. " Fairmount water-works. 1848.
" 14. Mount Vernon. Residence of Washington. 1848.
" 15. " " Tomb of Washington. 1848.
" 16. " " Virginia. Natural bridge. 1848.
" 17. Niagara Falls. The falls of Niagara. 1848.
" 18. " " The rapids at Niagara. 1848.
" 19. " " American side. 1848.
" 20. " " Horseshoe fall (from the Canada side) 1848.
" 21. " " American falls (from Table rock) 1848.
" 22. " " Horseshoe fall. 1848.
" 23. " " General view. 1848.
" 24. " " Suspension bridge. 1848.
" 25. Saratoga. Part of Saratoga. 1848.
" 26. " United States hotel. 1848.
" 27. " Highrock-Iodine and Empire springs. 1848.
" 28. " Pavillon fountain. 1848.
" 29. " Congress spring. 1848.
" 30. " Saratoga lake. 1848.
" 31. Washington. President's house. 1848.
" 32. " Capitol (east view) 1848.
" 33. " Senate chamber. 1848.
" 34. " Chamber of representatives. 1848.
" 35. " Capitol (west side) 1848.

**Köllner, A.**—Continued.

    no. 36. Washington.   General post-office. 1848.
    " 37. New York.   New York bay and the narrows. 1850.
    " 38.   "   "   Grace-church (Broad-way) 1850.
    " 39. Albany.   General view. 1850.
    " 40.   "   City-hall. 1850.
    " 41. Troy.   General view. 1850.
    " 42.   "   Court house. 1850.
    " 43. New York.   General view (from Governor's island) 1850.
    " 44.   "   Broad-way. 1850.
    " 45.   "   City-hall. 1850.
    " 46.   "   General view (from Brooklyn) 1850.
    " 47.   "   Wall street. 1850.
    " 48.   "   The narrows and part of Staten Island. 1850.
    " 49. Canada.   Quebec & fort. 1851.
    " 50.   "   Montmorency river (near Quebec) 1851.
    " 51.   "   Kingston on Kings river. 1851.
    " 52.   "   Thousand islands (lake Ontario & river S$^t$ Lawrence) 1851.
    " 53.   "   Montreal. 1851.
    " 54.   "   Toronto. 1851.

### COAL.

**Peabody coal company.**
    The Peabody atlas. Shipping mines and coal railroads in the central commercial district of the United States, accompanied by chemical, geological, and engineering data by A. Bement. 149 pp., incl. 26 maps. fol. Chicago, Peabody coal co. 1906.     1268

    NOTE.—Maps showing location of coal mines in the following states: Illinois, Indiana, Iowa, Michigan, Missouri, Ohio (western) Kentucky.
    pp. 137-149 contain text: Smokeless furnaces and smoke suppression.—Improvements in boilers for the purpose of securing high efficiency.—Analysis of combustion gases and manipulation of fires.

### COAST.

**United States.** *Treasury department. Coast and geodetic survey.*
    Maps and charts of the United States coast survey. A. D. Bache, superintendent. To july, 1854. 2 p. l., 58 maps on 59 fold. sheets. 4°. [Washington] 1854.     1269

    CONTENTS.

    no. [1] Richmond's Island, Maine . . . 1851.
    " [2] Wellfleet harbor, Massachusetts . . . 1853.
    " [3] Nantucket harbor . . . 1848.
    " [4] . . . Davis's shoals and other dangers . . . 1853.
    " [5] The harbor of Hyannis . . . 1850.
    " [6] Edgartown harbor . . . 1848.
    " [7] The harbor of Holmes' Hole . . . 1847.—. . . The harbor of Tarpaulin Cove . . . 1847.
    " [8] The harbor of New Bedford. 1850.
    " [9] General chart of the coast from Gay Head to Cape Henlopen . . . 1852.
    " [10] Fisher's Island sound [Long Island sound] . . . 1847.
    " [11] The harbor of New London . . . 1848.

DO. [12] Mouth of Connecticut river . . . 1853.
" [13] New Haven harbor . . . 1846.
" [14] Harbors of Black Rock and Bridgeport . . . 1848.
" [15] Huntington bay [Long Island] . . . 1849.
" [16] Oyster or Syosset bay [Long Island] . . . 1847.
" [17] Harbors of Captain's Island east and Captain's Island west . . . 1849.
" [18] Hart & City islands . . . 1851.—Sachem's Head harbor . . . 1851.
" [19] Hell Gate and its approaches . . . 1851.
" [20] . . . New York bay and harbor, and the environs . . . 1845.
" [22] . . . Little Egg harbor [New Jersey] . . . 1846.
" [21, 23, 24] . . . Delaware bay and river . . . 1848. 3 sheets.
" [25] Sea coast—Delaware, Maryland, and part of Virginia . . . 1852.
" [26] The harbor of Annapolis . . . 1846.
" [27] Mouth of Chester river . . . [Chesapeake bay] . . . 1849.
" [28] Pasquotank river [Albemarle sound] . . . 1850.
" [29] . . . Hatteras inlet, North Carolina . . . 1853.
" [30] . . . Ocracoke inlet, North Carolina . . . 1852.
" [31] . . . Beaufort harbor, North Carolina . . . 1851.
" [32] . . . New River and bar, North Carolina . . .
" [33] . . . Frying-Pan shoals . . . and Cape Fear river . . . 1851.
" [34] . . . North Edisto river [S. Carolina] . . . 1853.
" [35] . . . Savannah river [Georgia] . . . 1851.
" [36] . . . Key West harbor and approaches . . . 1852.
" [37] . . . Reconnoissance of vicinity of Cedar Keys, coast of Florida . . . 1851.
" [38] . . . Channel, no. 4, Cedar-Keys, Florida . . . 1852.
" [39] Entrance to Mobile bay [Alabama] . . . 1851.
" [40] . . . Mobile bay [Alabama] 1852.
" [41] . . . Horn island pass, Mississippi sound . . . 1853.
" [42] Cat and Ship island harbors [Mississippi sound] . . . 1850.
" [43] Reconnoissance of the passes of the delta Mississippi, Louisiana . . . 1852.
" [44] . . . Galveston bay, Texas . . . 1852.
" [45] Reconnoissance of the Western coast of the United States, from San Francisco to San Diego [Cal.] 1853.
" [46] . . . San Diego entrance and approaches, California . . . 1853.
" [47] . . . Catalina harbor [California] 1852.—View of Catalina harbor.
" [48] . . . Santa Barbara, California . . . 1853.
" [49] Santa Cruz, San Simeon, Coxo, and San Luis Obispo, California . . . 1852.
" [50] Monterey harbor, California . . . 1852.
" [51] . . . San Pedro harbor, California . . . 1852.
" [52] . . . City of San Francisco and vicinity, California . . . 1853.
" [53] . . . Mare Island straits, California . . . 1851.
" [54] . . . Humboldt bay, California . . . 1852.—Sketch of Humboldt bay . . .
" [55] . . . Trinidad bay, California . . . 1851.
" [56] . . . Shoalwater bay, Washington . . . 1853.
" [57] . . . Reconnoissance . . . from Gray's Harbor to . . . Admiralty inlet . . . [Washington] . . . 1853.—[Views of] Duncan's Rock.—Flattery Rocks.—Destruction i.—Sail Rock.
" [58] . . . Cape Flattery and Neé-Ah harbor, Washington . . . 1853. Inset: View of Cape Flattery . . .
" [59] False Dungeness, Washington . . . 1853.

## COMMERCIAL.

**Asher & Adams.**

Asher & Adams's new commercial, topographical, and statistical atlas and gazetteer of the United States: with maps showing the dominion of Canada, Europe and the world . . . 2 p. l., 120, 6–253 pp., 5 l. incl. 29 maps. fol. New York, Asher & Adams [1872]     1270

Asher & Adams' new commercial and statistical atlas and gazetteer of the United States, exhibiting a clear topographical view of the entire country, including portions of the provinces of Ontario and Quebec, with their lines of travel and avenues of trade, and comprising a concise description and the location of cities, villages, post offices, railroad stations, etc., etc., in the United States. Compiled drawn and engraved by the publishers' own engineers, topographers, and artists, from authentic and recent astronomical observations, government surveys, and records of the United States and territories, and the several states, surveys of railroads, official reports, etc. 2 v. 2 p. l., 7–52, 131 pp., 3 l. incl. 13 maps; 2 p. l., 59–120 pp., 1 l., 6–121 pp., 4 l. incl. 15 maps. fol. New York, Asher & Adams, 1872.     1271

Asher & Adams' new commercial, topographical, and statistical atlas and gazetteer of the United States: with maps showing the dominion of Canada, Europe and the world . . . Compiled, drawn, and engraved under the supervision of the publishers . . . 2 p. l., 6–251 (*i. e.* 260), [8] pp., 39 maps. fol. New York, Asher & Adams [1873]     1272

NOTE.—Pagination irregular. Maps of Texas, California and Nevada, Montana, are in two sheets.

"Geological map. United States and territories," pp. 143–144.

Asher & Adams's new commercial, topographical, and statistical atlas and gazetteer of the United States: with maps showing the dominion of Canada, Europe and the world . . . 2 p. l., 3–152, 6–284, [15] pp. incl. 41 maps. fol. New York, Asher & Adams [1874]     1273

Asher & Adams' new commercial and statistical gazetteer of the United States and the dominion of Canada. Comprising a concise description and the location of cities, villages, post-offices, railroad stations, etc., with populations of such as are officially reported by the latest government census, conveniently arranged in alphabetical order. Compiled under the supervision of the publishers, by their own corps, from the most recent official reports, records, and documents of the United States, the dominion of Canada, the several states, railroad companies, etc.   2–241, [19] pp.   fol.   New York, Asher & Adams [1875] 1274

>  NOTE.—Copyrighted in 1874.
>  Text only. To accompany the atlas.

**Cram atlas company.**

New commercial atlas of the United States and territories: (scale, 21 miles to the inch)  Showing all railroads, stations, cities, towns, villages, congressional townships, etc., etc. A complete shippers' guide. Drawn and engraved from the very latest government surveys.   2 p. l., 75 pp. incl. 35 col. maps.   fol.   New York & Chicago, the Cram atlas co. [1875] 1275

>  NOTE.—Copyrighted in 1875 by the Cram atlas co.
>  Pagination irregular.

**Fraser, S. L.**

Fraser's mercantile guide, for the use of commission, grain, and produce merchants . . . contains a catalogue, with key and index, of all products, vegetable, animal and mineral, of every county in each state of the United States; showing where they are produced, shipped and received, and names of all places, on rail or water route, with post office address . . . Names of dealers in each place . . . also a complete and reliable atlas, embracing a map of the United States; and of each state and territory with counties . . . 14 p. l., 12 col. maps.   4°.   New York, J. W. Pratt & son, 1886. 1276

### DIPLOMATIC.

**United States.** *Department of state.*

Maps showing the location of the diplomatic and consular offices of the United States of America. March 1, 1888. Prepared under the direction of the secretary of state.   2 p. l., 8 col. maps.   fol.   Washington, government printing office, 1888. 1277

### FORESTRY.

**Sargent, C. S.**

Report on the forests of North America (exclusive of Mexico) . . . Atlas in portfolio.   cover-title, 16 maps.   fol.   Washington, government printing office, 1884. 1278
[U. S. Census office. 10th census, 1880. Census reports. v. 9]

>  NOTE.—At head of title: Department of the interior. Census office . . .

## GEOLOGICAL.

**United States.** *War department. Engineer department. Geological exploration of the fortieth parallel.*

Atlas accompanying volume III on mining industry. 1 p. l., 14 maps. obl. fol. New York, J. Bien, 1870–80.      1279

NOTE.—To accompany, Report of the U. S. geological exploration of the fortieth parallel made by order of the secretary of war according to acts of congress of march 2, 1867 and march 3, 1869, under the direction of A. A. Humphreys chief of engineers, by Clarence King, U. S. geologist. Washington, government printing office, 1870–80.

Plates 3 to 12 inclusive were compiled and drawn by R. H. Stretch.

### CONTENTS.

- no. 1. General map, showing location of mining districts, U. S. engineer department.
- " 2. Geological map of the Washoe mining district, geology: C. King; topography: J. T. Gardiner.
- " 3. Horizontal map Gold hill mine workings, Comstock lode.
- " 4. Horizontal map Virginia mine workings, Comstock lode.
- " 5. Horizontal map North Virginia mines, Comstock lode.
- " 6. Longitudinal elevation Gold hill mines, Comstock lode.
- " 7. Longitudinal elevation Virginia mines, Comstock lode.
- " 8. Cross sections Gold hill mines, Comstock lode.
- " 9. Cross sections Virginia mines, Comstock lode.
- " 10. Cross sections Virginia mines, Comstock lode.
- " 11. Horizontal sections Virginia mines, Comstock lode.
- " 12. Sections, Comstock lode.
- " 13. Geological map of the Toyabe mountains, geology: S. F. Emmons; topography A. D. Wilson.
- " 14. Geological map of the White Pine mining district: A. Hague; topography: F. A. Clark.

Geological and topographical atlas accompanying the report of the geological exploration of the fortieth parallel made by the authority of the honorable secretary of war under the direction of brig. and brvt. major-general A. A. Humphreys . . . by Clarence King . . . 2 p. l., 11 maps, 1 pl. fol. New York, J. Bien, 1876.      1280

NOTE.—To accompany, Report of the U. S. geological exploration of the fortieth parallel made by order of the secretary of war according to acts of congress of march 2, 1867 and march 3, 1869, under the direction of A. A. Humphreys, chief of engineers, by Clarence King, U. S. geologist. Washington, government printing office, 1870–80.

### CONTENTS.

- no. 1. Cordilleras.
- " 2. Rocky mountains.
- " 3. Green river basin.
- " 4. Utah basin.
- " 5. Nevada plateau.
- " 6. Nevada basin.
- " 7. Rocky mountain [Geological]
- " 8. Green river basin [Geological]

no. 9. Utah basin [Geological]
" 10. Nevada plateau [Geological]
" 11. Nevada basin [Geological]
" 12. General sections [Geological]

**United States.** *War department. Engineer department. Geographical surveys west of the 100th meridian.*
Geological atlas projected to illustrate geographical explorations and surveys west of the 100th meridian of longitude prosecuted in accordance with acts of Congress, under the authority of the honorable the secretary of war, and the direction of brig. genl. A. A. Humphreys, chief of engineers, U. S. army. Embracing results of the different expeditions under the command of 1st. lieut. Geo. M. Wheeler, corps of engineers. fol. [Washington, 1876–81] 1281

NOTE.—*Cf.* United States. Geographical surveys west of the 100th meridian. List of reports and maps. Washington, government printing office, 1881. The following valuable and exhaustive bibliography relating to this atlas, was compiled by major Gilbert Thompson, of the U. S. geological survey.
Four typewritten copies were made and deposited in the following libraries:
Library, Army war college, Washington.
Library, United States military academy, West Point, N. Y.
Library, United States geological survey.
Library of Congress.
Bibliographical list of maps and atlas sheets, published by the office of explorations west of the 100th meridian, captain George M. Wheeler, corps of engineers, U. S. A., in charge. 1869–1882.

*Introduction.*

This list is derived from an atlas in the library of the U. S. geological survey, Washington, D. C. This atlas is the result of long and careful collection by mr. Charles C. Darwin, librarian, and major Gilbert Thompson, geographer of that bureau; the latter serving as topographer in the office of "explorations west of the 100th meridian," from 1872 to 1880, and being familiar with its publications. This atlas is believed to be as complete a collection as can be brought together, and contains all varities and different editions. Some proofs were included on account of their fine quality or rarity. Such sheets as were printed in duplicate on thin paper, for annual or special reports, are included in such cases where they were the only edition.
In this list, no more description of sheets has been gone into than is absolutely necessary for their identification. The average size of atlas sheets is 14½ inches x 17½ inches, that of special sheets will be found in the text. The variety of the seal of the corps of engineers, U. S. A. as found on these sheets is also given, and the various under-tints are given with a view to distinction rather than exactness.

GILBERT THOMPSON.

WASHINGTON, D. C., *november 22, 1907.*
U. S. G. S.
Atlas Page. Title (character of the sheet)
1. Topographical Atlas. Large seal, with words "war department." "Hon. Wm. W. Belknap, secretary of war. By the corps of engineers, U. S. A." Light cream under-tint. Landscape in crayon; (a scene on the Colorado river) Julius Bien, lith.

**United States.** *War department. Engineer department. Geographical surveys west of the 100th meridian*—Continued.

2. Same as (1) Seal without words, "war department." Very few, if any, issued. Made into computation blocks.
3. Same as (2) except "The honorable the secretary of war," instead of "hon. Wm. W. Belknap," etc.
4. General title for issue of sheets 49-50-57-58-59-65-66-and 67. Large seal. White paper. "Hon. Wm. Belknap, secretary of war."
5. Title. Geological atlas. Large seal. "Hon. Wm. W. Belknap, secretary of war," landscape in crayon, "headlands of Paria creek, Utah," Dark cream under-tint, shaded for clouds and landscape effect. The only print known is in the U. S. geological survey atlas. The words "headlands of Paria creek, Utah," are written under the landscape in India ink. (The upper headlands of Paria creek are in Utah) There is an office stamp on this print of date of february 17, 1876.
6. Same title as (5) for "hon. Wm. W. Belknap, secretary of war," it has "the honorable secretary of war" Light cream under-tint. "Headlands of Paria creek, Arizona."
7. Legend. Seal enclosed in the words "war department, corps of engineers, U. S. A." Gives list of officers and topographers for years 1869, 1871, 1872 and 1873.
8. Legend. Small seal with wreath. List to 1873. The subject matter is different from (7) "The travelled lines" in (7) and "The traveled lines" in this legend.
9. Note. A progress map, 1873 was issued with annual report of october, 1873 for fiscal year ending june 30, 1873. No seal above title, and no numbers for atlas sheets except as preliminary for areas as occupied to date. Routes of explorers are indicated with names and dates. Probably this progress map was never issued separately and comes in the class of illustrations to monographs and annual reports.
10. Conventional signs. Small seal as (8) with wreath. Topography is hachures. Seasons 1869 to 1874. Dark cream under-tint.
11. Same as (10) except topography is in crayon.
12. (Vacant slip)
13. Same as (11) White paper. Mining districts omitted, and signs for "Mines" added. Topography in crayon. Season 1869-1875.
14. Same as (11) in crayon. No seasons of survey. Light cream under-tint. "Signal Peak" in place of "Belknap Peak" of (13)
15. Conventional signs. Diagrams and lettering. Small seal with wreath. Topography in contours of Mount Taylor, N. M. Dark cream under-tint.
16. Conventional signs. Topography in contours and of the "Needle" and "Donner Lake," California. Small seal. Light brown under-tint. From a new drawing.
17. Index map. Giving scheme of arrangement of atlas sheets 1 to 95 of the area "west of the 100th meridian." Large seal with words "war department, etc.," date 1873. Light brown tint.
18. Index map similar to (17) Topography in crayon. Light brown tint. Dated 1874. From a newer drawing than (17)
19. Skeleton Map. Seal above title. Diagram of atlas sheets, and surveyed areas indicated for seasons 1869-1871 and 1872. Routes of explorers. To accompany report of 1872.

20. Progress map. Similar to (19) but a new compilation and drawing, 1869 to 1873. Small seal with wreath, encircled by words "war department" "corps of engineers, U. S. A." Light brown under-tint.

NOTE.—These maps were issued each year and indicated surveyed areas at date, with arrangement of atlas sheets west of the 100th Meridian. Each atlas sheet extended over 2 degrees 45 minutes in longitude, and 1 degree 40 minutes in latitude. These were designated by the order of numbering from left to right as given on the progress maps. Some were familiarly known by a noted natural feature as "Lake Tahoe sheet," "Grand Canyon sheet," etc. When any sheet was one-fourth of any atlas sheet it was designated as 41a, 41b, 41c, or 41d. Any sheet of a special area was known by the name of the locality, and as a "special map." Some variation in the method of delineation of the topography, or form of publication, or a portion of an atlas sheet, was also designated, e. g. "Special map 61A," etc. The scale is 8 miles to 1 inch, the dimensions being the same. The topography was generally given by the method of hachures but contouring and crayon shading were also used to a less extent. The majority of these sheets were produced by photolithography from original drawings. The amount of reduction being about one-sixth.

21. Progress map, very light tint. To 1873 (1st ed. 1874)
22. Progress map, small seal at top. To 1874 (2d ed. 1874)
23. Progress map. To 1875.
24. Progress map. To 1876.
25. Progress map. To 1877.
26. Progress map. Dark tint. To 1877.
27. Progress map. Light tint. To 1878.
28. Progress map. Dark tint. To 1878.
29. Progress map. "In response to resolution house of representatives, march 8, 1878." Surveyed areas in tints.
30. Progress map to 1879. Exterior areas of the sheet dark under-tint.
31. Progress map to 1879, on white drawing paper. Outlines and explorer's routes only.
32. Progress map, tinted areas. To 1879. To accompany the annual report: similar to (30)
33. Progress map, tinted areas. To 1880. Similar style to (30)
34. Progress map, tinted areas. To 1881. To accompany report of 1st lt. M. M. Macomb, 4th U. S. Artillery. Style similar to (30).
35. Same as (34) "To accompany 2d edition of list of reports and maps, june 30, 1881."
36. Progress map. "To accompany the annual report of 1st lieutenant M. M. Macomb, 4th U. S. Artillery," to 1882. (The last edition of the series of progress maps)

NOTE.—The total areas surveyed from 1869 to 1879 inclusive, amounted to 359065 square miles; topographic sheets were issued that delineated 326891 square miles while material comprising small areas and insufficient to publish as complete atlas sheets plotted and drawn amounted to 32174 square miles (see Geographical report, vol. I, for additional details and descriptions of field and office work, and publications)

NOTE.—Office was closed february 29, 1884. Annual reports were issued for 1883 and 1884 but without progress maps, that of 1884 being the last.

37. Maps of areas of drainage, west of the Mississippi river. River basins in in tint. 1869–1873. Seal with names.

**United States.** *War department. Engineer department. Geographical surveys west of the 100th meridian*—Continued.

38. Same subject as (37) "By order of the honorable Wm. W. Belknap, secretary of war." 1869-1874. Small narrow seal. The words "The lakes," larger letters than on (37)
39. Atlas sheet (32) C (s. w. quarter of atlas sheet (32) In hachures, with light brown tint. Issued january 10, 1881. Small seal.
40. Same as (39) giving classification of land in various tints and also per cent of each. Small seal. Issued january 10, 1881.
41. Atlas sheet 32 (D) (S. E. quarter of atlas sheet 32) In hachures, small narrow seal; light gray under tint. Expeditions 1877.
42. Same as (41) showing land classification. Issued june 30, 1879. Small broad seal.
43. Atlas sheet 38 (B) (N. E. quarter of atlas sheet 38) In hachures; small seal; light cream under-tint; lakes without tint. Issued june 30, 1882.
44. Atlas sheet 38 (D) In hachures; small seal; light cream under-tint. Lakes without tint. Issued november 15, 1880.
45. Same as (44) showing land classification. Issued november 15, 1880.
46. Atlas sheet 41 (A) In hachures. No seal; very light under-tint. Issued june 30, 1880.
47. Same as (46) showing land classification; small seal. Issued june 30, 1880.
48. Atlas sheet 41 (B) In hachures; small seal very light grey under-tint. Issued june 30, 1878.
49. Same as (48) showing land classification. Issued june 30, 1878.
50. Atlas sheet 47 (A) In hachures; small seal; dark cream under-tint. Issued june 30, 1881.
51. Same as (50) showing land classification. Issued june 30, 1881.
52. Atlas sheet 47 (B) and 47 (D) in one sheet. Outline in black; drainage in blue; small seal; light tint. Printed for immediate use. Seasons 1876 and 1877.
53. Atlas sheet 47 (B) and 47 (D) joined as one sheet. In hachures; light tint; small seal. Issued june 30, 1879.
54. Same as (53) showing land classification. Issued june, 1879.
55. Atlas sheet 47 (B) In hachures; gray under-tint; lakes without tint; small seal. Issued june 30, 1882.
56. Atlas sheet 47 (D) In hachures; gray under-tint; lakes without tint; small seal. Issued june 30, 1882.
57. Atlas sheet 48 (C) In hachures; small seal; light gray under-tint. Issued april 29, 1882.
58. Atlas sheet 48 (D) Northeast portion not surveyed. In hachures; light gray under-tint; small seal. Issued june 30, 1882.
59. Atlas sheet 49. In hachures; light neutral under-tint. Small broad seal. Seasons 1869 and 1872 (Graphic co., New York, N. Y.) Lakes lined.
60. Same as (59) In crayon; small narrow seal; light ground tint.
61. Atlas sheet 50. In hachures; large seal with names; cream under tint; lakes in blue. "Sevier lake 4600 above sea level." "Expeditions 1872 and 1873." "Salt Lake City" outside the border.
62. Same as (61) In hachures; small seal; no altitude for Sevier Lake; lakes shaded by black lines; light neutral under-tint. "Salt Lake City" omitted. (Graphic co. photo-lith., New York.)
63. Same as (62) Light neutral under-tint. No imprint of Graphic co., N. Y.
64. Same as (63) in crayon. Small narrow seal. "Salt Lake City" outside the border as (61). Cream under-tint and lightened for high lands.

NOTE.—Sheet 50 in crayon. There are two varieties of this at Lib. of Congress including (64)

The second has a light gray tint; "Salt Lake City" omitted; also names of "Weyss, Herman and Aguirre, del."

In the Library of Congress is a crayon (50) light grey tint; "Salt Lake City" omitted, also the names of the draftsmen. This is the only print known.

65. Same as (64) in crayon; showing areas of different geological formations in various tints. "Salt Lake City" outside the border as (61)
66. Atlas sheet 52 (D) In hachures; small seal; light gray under-tint. Expeditions 1873, 1876 and 1879.
67. Same as (66) showing land classification.
68. Atlas sheet 53 (C) In hachures; small broad seal; light grey under tint. Issued may 7, 1877.
69. Atlas sheet 56 (B) In hachures; small narrow seal; dark cream under tint. Issued march 31, 1883.
70. Atlas sheet 56 (D) In hachures; small seal; warm grey under-tint. Expeditions 1878 and 1879.
71. Atlas sheet 57. Same style and seal as (62) lakes black lined, light neutral under-tint. Expedition, 1871. (Graphic co., N. Y.)
72. Atlas sheet 58. In hachures; lakes in blue tint; cream yellow under-tint; seal with encircling names. Expeditions 1869, 1871 and 1872.
73. Atlas sheet 58. In hachures; lakes black lined; small seal with wreath; bluish grey tint (same style as 71). Expeditions 1869, 1871 and 1872. (Graphic co., N. Y.)
74. Atlas sheet 58. (Same as 73) Light neutral under-tint. (Graphic co., N. Y.)
75. Atlas sheet 58. In crayon; light yellow under-tint. Small narrow seal.
76. Atlas sheet 58 (in part) and atlas sheet 66 (in part on one sheet) In crayon and showing geological formations in tints. Small seal. (Such sheets comprise the geological atlas, as distinctive from the topographical atlas)
77. Atlas sheet 59. Not designated and without seal; blue lakes; in hachures; dark cream tint; no scale. (Probably a proof)
78. Atlas sheet 59. Designated; Seal with names; lakes blue and scale furnished; light cream tint; Expeditions 1872 and 1873.
79. Atlas sheet 59. In hachures; small broad seal; lakes lined; greenish neutral under-tint. Altitude of Sevier lake given.
80. Atlas sheet 59. In hachures; small seal; very light grey under-tint.
81. Atlas sheet 59. Similar to (80) (A good print on better quality of paper)
82. Atlas sheet 59. In crayon. Cream under-tint, lightened for high land.
83. Atlas sheet 59. In crayon, and showing geological formations in tints.
84. Atlas sheet 61 (A) In contours; a proof on drawing paper for land classification; small seal; no under-tint.
85. Atlas sheet 61 (A) In hachures; small seal.
86. Atlas sheet 61 (A) Land classification sheet; base same as (84)
87. Atlas sheet 61 (B) In hachures; small broad seal; light grey tint. Issued march 3, 1876. Graphic co., N. Y.
88. Atlas sheet 61 (B) In hachures and a new drawing. Small narrow seal, light cream under-tint.
89. Atlas sheet 61 (B) In hachures; base same as (87); for land classification.
90. Atlas sheet 61 (B) Land classification; base map same as (87) Issued march 3, 1876.
91. Atlas sheet 61 (C) In outline; small seal; light grey under-tint. Printed for immediate use. Scale 1 inch to 4 miles.

**United States.** *War department. Engineer department. Geographical surveys west of the 100th meridian*—Continued.

92. Atlas sheet 61 (C) In hachures; small seal light grey under-tint. Issued june 30, 1878. Scale 1 inch to 4 miles.
93. Atlas sheet 61 (C) Base map for land classification, proof print on thick drawing paper, small broad seal.
94. Atlas sheet 61 (C) In hachures; small seal, giving land classification. Scale 1 inch to 4 miles. Issued june 30, 1878. Base same as (92) and (93).
95. Atlas sheet 61 (C) Comprising a portion of 61 (C) in the San Juan mining region, s. w. Colorado. In black contours and outline; small seal; cream under-tint. The sheets comprising this area are sometimes designated as "61 (C) sub." Scale 1 inch to 2 miles. Issued april 24, 1876, for immediate use.
96. Atlas sheet 61 (C) Same area as (95) Proof print on drawing paper; no seal; contours in reddish brown; drainage in blue; outlines in black.
97. Atlas sheet 61 (C) Base same as (96) In reddish brown and green contours; drainage in blue; highest peaks in hachures. Scale 1 inch to 2 miles. Small seal.
98. Atlas sheet 61 (C) Same base and area as (96) In black contours; drainage and outlines; small seal; shows land classification. Scale 1 inch to 2 miles.
99. Atlas sheet 61 (D) In hachures; reddish cream under-tint; small seal. Issued january 10, 1878.
100. Atlas sheet 61 (D) Same base as (99) showing land classification. Issued january 10, 1878.
101. Atlas sheet 62 (A) In hachures; small seal; dark cream under-tint, lightened for high land. Issued march 14, 1878.
102. Atlas sheet 62 (A) Proof print on white drawing paper, as base for land classification sheet. Same otherwise as (101).
103. Atlas sheet 62 (A) Same as (102) and a land classification sheet. Issued march 14, 1878.
104. Atlas sheet 62 (C) In hachures; small seal; deep cream under-tint lightened at highpeaks and ridges. Issued march 14, 1878.
105. Atlas sheet 62 (C) Same as (104) except as a base for land classification; proof on white drawing paper.
106. Atlas sheet 62 (C) A land classification sheet; base map as (105) Issued march 14, 1878.
107. Atlas sheet 62 (D) In hachures; small seal; cream under-tint. Issued june 30, 1882.
108. Atlas sheet 65. In hachures; grayish cream under-tint; small broad seal. 1 inch to 8 miles. (Graphic co., N. Y.) (This edition was withdrawn and cut up for computation blocks)
109. Atlas sheet 65 (D) In hachures; small broad seal; gray cream under-tint and omitted for flats and areas below sea-level. Scale 1 inch to 4 miles. Issued may 7, 1877. (Graphic co., N. Y.)
110. Atlas sheet 65 (D) same base as (109) and as a land classification sheet. Issued may 7, 1877.
111. Atlas sheet 65 (D) Proof of experimental tints for (109) Low areas in altitude given a dark neutral tint.
112. Atlas sheet 65 (D) Base same as (109) and as a land classification sheet, with darker tints than (110)

NOTE.—Atlas sheets 65 and 65 (D) include the low areas of Death valley, California. Issued may 7, 1877.

113. Atlas sheet 66. In hachures; dark cream under-tint; large seal with names. Expeditions 1869, 1872 and 1873. The Colorado river shown in blue. Scale 1 inch to 8 miles. Same style as (61)
114. Atlas sheet 66. In hachures; same drawing as (113) Very light neutral under-tint. Extra large with wreath, height $1\tfrac{9}{16}$ inches. No blue for Colorado river.
115. Atlas sheet 66. Same drawing as (113) Dark cream under-tint; small broad seal. (Graphic co., N. Y.)
116. Atlas sheet 66. In crayon, small narrow seal.
117. Atlas sheet 67. In hachures; light gray under-tint; small broad seal. (Graphic co., N. Y.) "Grand Canyon sheet."
118. Atlas sheet 67. In crayon; light shaded under-tint.
   NOTE.—The outlines for the crayon sheet were drawn on stone by the lithographer.
119. Atlas sheet 67. In crayon as (118) and with added tints indicating geological formations.
120. Atlas sheet 69. In hachures; small seal; gray under-tint. Issued june 30, 1882.
121. Atlas sheet 69 (B) In hachures; small seal; light shaded gray under-tint. Issued january 8, 1878.
122. Atlas sheet 69 (B) In hachures as (121) and showing land classification. Issued january 8, 1878.
123. Parts of atlas sheets 69 (B) 69 (D) 77 (B) and 78 (A) In hachures; small seal; showing geological formations. Issued june 30, 1881.
124. Atlas sheet 69 (D) In hachures; small broad seal; gray cream tint. (Graphic co., N. Y.) Issued april 26, 1876. Special edition on extra thick paper.
125. Atlas sheet 69 (D) Same as (124) An edition on usual paper for issue.
126. Atlas sheet 69 (D) In hachures as (124) as base for land classification sheet, proof on thick drawing paper.
127. Atlas sheet 69 (D) Same as (126) and showing land classification. Issued april 26, 1876.
128. Atlas sheet 70 (A) In hachures; small seal; gray cream under-tint. (Graphic co., N. Y.) Issued may 7, 1877.
129. Atlas sheet 70 (A) In hachures as (128) Proof of trial land classification tints and base.
130. Atlas sheet 70 (A) Same as (129) with other and final tints showing land classification. Issued may 7, 1877.
131. Atlas sheet 70 (A) Same as (128) and showing geological formations. Second edition, june 30, 1881 of (128)
132. Atlas sheet 70 (C) In hachures; small seal; light cream under-tint. (Graphic co., N.Y.) Issued may 7, 1877.
133. Atlas sheet 70 (C) In hachures as (132) and showing land classification. Issued may 7, 1877.
134. Atlas sheet 70 (C) In hachures as (132) and showing geological formations. Second edition of (132) Issued june 30, 1881.
135. Atlas sheet 73. In hachures; cream under-tint omitted for water-surfaces; small seal. Issued november 30, 1883. Scale 1 inch to 8 miles.
136. Atlas sheet 73 (A) In hachures; shaded cream under-tint; small seal. Expeditions 1875 and 1878. Scale 1 inch to 4 miles. (No date of issue.)
137. Atlas sheet 73 (A) In hachures as (136) and showing land classifications. Issued june 30, 1879.
138. Atlas sheet 73 (C) In hachures; gray under-tint; omitted on water-surfaces; small seal. Issued february 23, 1881.

**United States.** *War department. Engineer department. Geographical surveys west of the 100th meridian*—Continued.

139. Atlas sheet 73 (C) Showing land classification, base map as (138) Issued february 23, 1881.
140. Atlas sheet 75. In hachures; light gray under-tint. Scale 1 inch to 8 miles. Issued march 8, 1876.
141. Atlas sheet 75. Showing geological formations. Base map as (140) Issued february 15, 1877.
142. Atlas sheet 76. In hachures; light gray under-tint; small seal. Issued march 18, 1876. (Graphic co., N. Y.)
143. Atlas sheet 76. Base map as (142) showing geological formations. Issued february 18, 1877.
144. Atlas sheet 77. In hachures; light gray cream under-tint; small seal. Issued june 30, 1882.
145. Atlas sheet 77. Base map as (144) showing land classification. Issued june 30, 1882.
146. Atlas sheet 77 (B) In hachures; cream under-tint; small seal. Issued may 7, 1877. (Graphic co., N. Y.)
147. Atlas sheet 77 (B) Base map as (146) showing land classification. Issued may 7, 1877.
148. Atlas sheet 77 (D) In hachures; light cream under-tint; small seal. Issued june 30, 1878.
149. Atlas sheet 77 (D) Base map as (148) showing land classification. Issued june 30, 1878.
150. Atlas sheet 78 (A) In hachures; light cream under-tint; small seal. Issued june 30, 1879.
151. Atlas sheet 78 (A) Base map as (150) showing land classification. Issued june 30, 1879.
152. Atlas sheet 83. In hachures; light gray under-tint; small broad seal. "C. Lowell," and "C. Bowie" outside lower border (Graphic co., N. Y.) Issued march 18, 1876.
153. Atlas sheet 83. Base map as (152) showing geological formations. Issued february 15, 1877.
154. Atlas sheet 84. In hachures; small seal; cream under-tint. Portions unsurveyed. Issued june 30, 1881.
155. Atlas sheet 84. Base as (154) showing land classification. Issued june 30, 1881.
156. Atlas sheet 84 (B) A beautiful print on drawing paper. In hachures; greenish gray under-tint; small seal; east half in outline.
157. Atlas sheet 84 (B) In hachures; cream gray under-tint; small seal. Entire sheet surveyed. Issued june 30, 1879.
158. Atlas sheet 84 (B) Base as (157) showing land classification. Issued june 30, 1879.
159. Atlas sheet 84 (C) In hachures; cream gray under-tint; small seal. Issued october 30, 1881.
160. Atlas sheet 84 (C) Base map as (159) showing land classification. Issued october 30, 1881.
161. Restored outline of lake Bonneville. In crayon with blue tints for lakes and drainage; cream under-tint. (Scale as printed is wrong and some copies have correct scale on slip pasted over the map scale.) Small seal $1\frac{13}{30}$ inch height. Size $14\frac{3}{10}$ by $18\frac{1}{4}$ inches.
162. Same as (161) with correct scale placed over the map scale.
163. Cover, for issue of topographical sheets. Warm neutral tint paper; large seal with encircling names. $2\frac{1}{4}$ inch diameter. 1873. Size 18 by 23 inches; folded once.

164. Cover, for issue of several geological sheets. Seal 1⅛ inches in height. 1874. Paper of warm neutral tint; folded once.
165. Cover, for geological sheets. Paper a dark neutral tint; same style as (164) 1874.
166. Cover, for issue of crayon sheets of the topographical atlas; seal with wreath; paper neutral tint. (Crayon) 1875.
167. Cover, for topographical sheets. Paper light neutral green tint; large seal and wreath with names. 1878.
168. Department of California. Military map no. 1, 1869. P. W. Hamel, chief topographer. In hachures and tints; no seal; also an insert to Report for 1869. Size $18\frac{7}{16}$ by $24\frac{5}{8}$ inches.
169. Map to accompany report for 1871. Louis Nell, chief topographer. In hachures and outlines. Size 21¼ by 28 inches.
170. Map to accompany "Lists of distances 1872; and for office use." In black hachures and outlines. A number of copies of this map were printed upon cloth. Size $16\frac{3}{16}$ by $20\frac{15}{16}$ inches.
171. Outline map of Washoe district, Nevada. Small seal with wreath; cream under-tint. Size 17¼ by $20\frac{5}{8}$ inches.
172. Map of Washoe district, Nevada. Brown contours and black outlines. 1879. Size $24\frac{11}{16}$ by $33\frac{9}{16}$ inches.
173. Topographical map of Washoe district, Nevada. North half of two sheet map (173) and (174) Brown contours; black outlines and drainage. Each half sheet $32\frac{15}{16}$ by $21\frac{3}{4}$ inches.
174. South half of map described in (173).
175. Outline map of S. W. New Mexico. For immediate use. Louis Nell, del. Size $15\frac{5}{16}$ by 18¼ inches.
 NOTE.—Library of Congress copy is a blue print. The office edition is printed in black.
176. Lake Tahoe, California. In hachures. One large sheet $33\frac{9}{16}$ by 40 inches Scale 1 inch to 1 mile.
177. Lake Tahoe, California. Heliogravure reduction at Imperial royal geographical Institute, Vienna, 1881. From (176) Scale 1 inch to 2 miles. Size $21\frac{5}{8}$ by $26\frac{5}{8}$ inches.
178. Yosemite valley, California. In hachures; cream under-tint. Size 20½ by $13\frac{3}{4}$ inches. Drawn from topographical plats, by lieut. M. M. Macomb, november 30, 1883.
179. Same as (178) with deep cream under-tint. (Issued probably in 1883)

## Becker, G. F.

Atlas to accompany a monograph on the geology of the quicksilver deposits of the Pacific slope.   2 p. l., 13 maps.  fol.  Washington, 1887.   1282

[United States.   Department of the interior.   Geological survey]

NOTE.—House miscellaneous documents. 1st sess. 50th Cong. 1887-88. v. 24.

**United States.** *Department of the interior.   Geological survey.*

Geologic atlas of the United States.   Library ed.   Folios 1-161. fol.  Washington, engraved and printed by the survey, 1894-1908.

1283

NOTE.—Contents given both numerically and by subjects according to states. Scale given in numerical contents only. "Under the plan adopted for the preparation of a geologic map of the United States the entire area is divided

**United States.** *Department of the interior. Geological survey*—Con.
into small quadrangles bounded by certain meridians and parallels, and these quadrangles, which number several thousand, are separately surveyed and mapped. The unit of survey is also the unit of publication, and the maps and descriptions of each quadrangle are issued in the form of a folio. When all the folios are completed, they will constitute a geologic atlas of the United States. A folio is designated by the name of the principal town or of a prominent natural feature within the quadrangle. It contains topographic, geologic, economic, and structural maps of the quadrangle, and in some cases other illustrations, together with a general description." *cf.* United States. Geological Survey. Bulletin 340, p. 9.

CONTENTS.

(SUBJECTS)

Alabama.—Gadsden. fol. 35.
    Stevenson. fol. 19.
Arizona.—Bisbee. fol. 112.
    Bradshaw mountains. fol. 126.
    Clifton. fol. 129.
    Globe. fol. 111.
Arkansas.—Fayetteville. fol. 119.
    Tahlequah. fol. 122.
    Winslow. fol. 154.
California.—Bidwell Bar. fol. 43.
    Big Trees. fol. 51.
    Colfax. fol. 66.
    Downieville. fol. 37.
    Jackson. fol. 11.
    Lassen Peak. fol. 15.
    Marysville. fol. 17.
    Mother Lode. fol. 63.
    Nevada City. fol. 29.
    Placerville. fol. 3.
    Pyramid Peak. fol. 31.
    Redding. fol. 138.
    Sacramento. fol. 5.
    San Luis. fol. 101.
    Smartsville. fol. 18.
    Sonora. fol. 41.
    Truckee. fol. 39.
Colorado.—Crested Butte. fol. 9.
    Elmoro. fol. 58.
    Fennile district. fol. 48.
    La Plata. fol. 60.
    Needle mountains. fol. 131.
    Nepesta. fol. 135.
    Ouray. fol. 153.
    Pikes Peak. fol. 7.
    Pueblo. fol. 36.
    Rico. fol. 130.
    Silverton. fol. 120.
    Spanish Peaks. fol. 71.
    Telluride. fol. 57.
    Walsenburg. fol. 68.

Connecticut.—Holyoke. fol. 50.
Delaware.—Dover. fol. 137.
District of Columbia.—Patuxent. fol. 152.
    Washington. fol. 70.
Georgia.—Ringgold. fol. 2.
    Rome. fol. 78.
    Stevenson. fol. 19.
Idaho.—Boise. fol. 45.
    Nampa. fol. 103.
    Silver City. fol. 104.
Illinois.—Chicago. fol. 81.
    Danville. fol. 67.
    Lancaster—Mineral Point. fol. 145.
    Patoka. fol. 105.
Indiana.—Chicago. fol. 81.
    Danville. fol. 67.
    Ditney. fol. 84.
    Patoka. fol. 105.
Indian Territory.—Atoka. fol. 79.
    Coalgate. fol. 74.
    Tahlequah. fol. 122.
    Tishomingo. fol. 98.
    Muscogee. fol. 132.
    Winslow. fol. 154.
Iowa.—Elk Point. fol. 156.
    Lancaster—Mineral Point. fol. 145.
Kansas.—Cottonwood Falls. fol. 109.
    Independence. fol. 159.
    Joplin. fol. 148.
Kentucky.—Estillville. fol. 12.
    London. fol. 47.
    Richmond. fol. 46.
Maine.—Penobscot bay. fol. 149.
    Rockland. fol. 158.
Maryland.—Dover. fol. 137.
    Fredericksburg. fol. 13.
    Harpers Ferry. fol. 10.
    Nomini. fol. 23.
    Patuxent. fol. 152.
    Piedmont. fol. 28.
    St. Marys. fol. 136.
    Washington. fol. 70.
Massachusetts.—Holyoke. fol. 50.
Michigan.—Ann Arbor. fol. 155.
    Menominee. fol. 62.
Minnesota.—Casselton-Fargo. fol. 117.
Missouri.—Fayetteville. fol. 119.
    Joplin. fol. 148.
Montana.—Aladdin. fol. 128.
    Butte. fol. 38.
    Three Forks. fol. 24.
    Fort Benton. fol. 55.
    Little Belt mountains. fol. 56.
    Livingston. fol. 1.

**United States.** *Department of the interior.* *Geological survey*—Con.
    Nebraska.—Camp Clarke. fol. 87.
        Edgemont. fol. 108.
        Elk Point. fol. 156.
        Oelrichs. fol. 85.
        Scotts Bluff. fol. 88.
    New Jersey.—Dover. fol. 137.
        Franklin Furnace. fol. 161.
        Passaic. fol. 157.
        New York city. fol. 83.
    New York.—Gaines. fol. 92.
        New York city. fol. 83.
        Passaic. fol. 157.
    North Carolina.—Asheville. fol. 116.
        Cranberry. fol. 90.
        Greeneville. fol. 118.
        Knoxville. fol. 16.
        Mount Mitchell. fol. 124.
        Nantahala. fol. 143.
        Norfolk. fol. 80.
        Pisgah. fol. 147.
        Roan mountain. fol. 151.
    North Dakota.—Casselton-Fargo. fol. 117
    Ohio.—Huntington. fol. 69.
    Oregon.—Coos bay. fol. 73.
        Nampa. fol. 103.
        Port Orford. fol. 89.
        Roseburg. fol. 49.
    Pennsylvania.—Amity. fol. 144.
        Beaver. fol. 134.
        Brownsville-Connellsville. fol. 94.
        Ebensburg. fol. 133.
        Elders Ridge. fol. 123.
        Elkland-Tioga. fol. 93.
        Gaines. fol. 92.
        Indiana. fol. 102.
        Kittanning. fol. 115.
        Latrobe. fol. 110.
        Masontown-Uniontown. fol. 82.
        Rogersville. fol. 146.
        Rural Valley. fol. 125.
        Waynesburg. fol. 121.
    South Carolina.—Pisgah. fol. 147.
    South Dakota.—Aladdin. fol. 128.
        Alexandria. fol. 100.
        De Smet. fol. 114.
        Edgemont. fol. 108.
        Elk Point. fol. 156.
        Huron. fol. 113.
        Mitchell. fol. 99.
        Newcastle. fol. 107.
        Oelrichs. fol. 85.
        Olivet. fol. 96.
        Parker. fol. 97.
        Sundance. fol. 127.

Tennessee.—Asheville. fol. 116.
    Briceville. fol. 33.
    Bristol. fol. 59.
    Chattanooga. fol. 6.
    Cleveland. fol. 20.
    Columbia. fol. 95.
    Cranberry. fol. 90.
    Estillville. fol. 12.
    Greeneville. fol. 118.
    Kingston. fol. 4.
    Knoxville. fol. 16.
    Loudon. fol. 25.
    McMinnville. fol. 22.
    Maynardville. fol. 75.
    Morristown. fol. 27.
    Mount Mitchell. fol. 124.
    Nantahala. fol. 143.
    Pikesville. fol. 21.
    Ringgold. fol. 2.
    Roan mountain. fol. 151.
    Sewanee. fol. 8.
    Standingstone. fol. 53.
    Stevenson. fol. 19.
    Wartburg. fol. 40.
Texas.—Austin. fol. 76.
    Nueces. fol. 42.
    Uvalde. fol. 64.
Utah.—Tintic. fol. 65.
Virginia.—Bristol. fol. 59.
    Estillville. fol. 12.
    Franklin. fol. 32.
    Fredericksburg. fol. 13.
    Harpers Ferry. fol. 10.
    Monterey. fol. 61.
    Nomini. fol. 23.
    Norfolk. fol. 80.
    Pocahontas. fol. 26.
    St. Marys. fol. 136.
    Staunton. fol. 14.
    Tazewell. fol. 44.
    Washington. fol. 70.
Washington.—Ellensburg. fol. 86.
    Mount Stuart. fol. 106.
    Snoqualmie. fol. 139.
    Tacoma. fol. 54.
West Virginia.—Buckhannon. fol. 34.
    Charleston. fol. 72.
    Franklin. fol. 32.
    Harpers Ferry. fol. 10.
    Huntington. fol. 69.
    Monterey. fol. 61.
    Piedmont. fol. 28.
    Pocahontas. fol. 26.
    Raleigh. fol. 77.

**United States.** *Department of the interior.* *Geological survey*—Con.
   West Virginia.—Staunton. fol. 14.
     Tazewell. fol. 44.
   Wisconsin.—Lancaster—Mineral Point. fol. 145.
     Milwaukee. fol. 140.
   Wyoming.—Absaroka. fol. 52.
     Aladdin. fol. 128.
     Bald mountain—Dayton. fol. 141.
     Cloud Peak—Fort McKinney. fol. 142.
     Devils Tower. fol. 150.
     Hartville. fol. 91.
     Newcastle. fol. 107.
     Sundance. fol. 127.
     Yellowstone. fol. 30.

CONTENTS.

(Numerical)

Folio 1. Montana.—Livingston. Scale $\frac{1}{250000}$.
" 2. Georgia.—Tennessee. Ringgold. $\frac{1}{125000}$.
" 3. California.—Placerville. $\frac{1}{125000}$.
" 4. Tennessee.—Kingston. $\frac{1}{125000}$.
" 5. California.—Sacramento. $\frac{1}{125000}$.
" 6. Tennessee.—Chattanooga. $\frac{1}{125000}$.
" 7. Colorado.—Pikes Peak. $\frac{1}{250000}$.
" 8. Tennessee.—Sewanee. $\frac{1}{250000}$.
" 9. Colorado.—Crested Butte. $\frac{1}{62500}$.
" 10. Virginia-Maryland-West Virginia.—Harpers Ferry. $\frac{1}{125000}$.
" 11. California.—Jackson. $\frac{1}{125000}$.
" 12. Kentucky-Virginia-Tennessee.—Estillville. Scale $\frac{1}{125000}$.
" 13. Virginia-Maryland.—Fredericksburg. Scale $\frac{1}{125000}$.
" 14. Virginia-West Virginia.—Staunton. Scale $\frac{1}{125000}$.
" 15. California.—Lassen Peak. Scale $\frac{1}{125000}$.
" 16. Tennessee-North Carolina.—Knoxville. Scale $\frac{1}{125000}$.
" 17. California.—Marysville. Scale $\frac{1}{125000}$.
" 18. " Smartsville. Scale $\frac{1}{125000}$.
" 19. Alabama-Georgia-Tennessee.—Stevenson. Scale $\frac{1}{125000}$.
" 20. Tennessee.—Cleveland. Scale $\frac{1}{125000}$.
" 21. " Pikeville. Scale $\frac{1}{125000}$.
" 22. " McMinnville. Scale $\frac{1}{250000}$.
" 23. Maryland-Virginia.—Nomini. Scale $\frac{1}{125000}$.
" 24. Montana.—Three Forks. Scale $\frac{1}{125000}$.
" 25. Tennessee.—Loudon. Scale $\frac{1}{250000}$.
" 26. Virginia-West Virginia.—Pocahontas. Scale $\frac{1}{125000}$.
" 27. Tennessee.—Morristown. Scale $\frac{1}{125000}$.
" 28. West Virginia-Maryland.—Piedmont. Scale $\frac{1}{125000}$.
" 29. California.—Nevada City. Scale $\frac{1}{14400}$.
" 30. Wyoming.---Yellowstone. Scale $\frac{1}{125000}$.
" 31. California—Pyramid Peak. Scale $\frac{1}{125000}$.
" 32. West Virginia-Virginia.—Franklin. Scale $\frac{1}{125000}$.
" 33. Tennessee.—Briceville. Scale $\frac{1}{125000}$.
" 34. West Virginia.—Buckhannon. Scale $\frac{1}{125000}$.
" 35. Alabama.—Gadsden. Scale $\frac{1}{125000}$.
" 36. Colorado.—Pueblo. Scale $\frac{1}{125000}$.

Folio 37. California.—Downieville. Scale $\frac{1}{125000}$.
" 38. Montana.—Butte. Scale $\frac{1}{15000}$.
" 39. California.—Truckee. Scale $\frac{1}{125000}$.
" 40. Tennessee.—Wartburg. Scale $\frac{1}{125000}$.
" 41. California.—Sonora. Scale $\frac{1}{125000}$.
" 42. Texas.—Nueces. Scale $\frac{1}{125000}$.
" 43. California.—Bidwell Bar. Scale $\frac{1}{125000}$.
" 44. Virginia-West Virginia.—Tazewell. Scale $\frac{1}{125000}$.
" 45. Idaho.—Boise. Scale $\frac{1}{125000}$.
" 46. Kentucky.—Richmond. Scale $\frac{1}{125000}$.
" 47. " London. Scale $\frac{1}{125000}$.
" 48. Colorado.—Fennile district. Scale 1:13680.
" 49. Oregon.—Roseburg. Scale $\frac{1}{125000}$.
" 50. Massachusetts-Connecticut.—Holyoke. Scale $\frac{1}{125000}$.
" 51. California.—Big Trees. Scale $\frac{1}{125000}$.
" 52. Wyoming.—Absaroka. Scale $\frac{1}{125000}$.
" 53. Tennessee.—Standingstone. Scale $\frac{1}{125000}$.
" 54. Washington.—Tacoma. Scale $\frac{1}{125000}$.
" 55. Montana.—Fort Benton. Scale $\frac{1}{250000}$.
" 56. " Little Belt mountains. Scale $\frac{1}{250000}$.
" 57. Colorado.—Telluride. Scale $\frac{1}{62500}$.
" 58. " Elmoro. Scale $\frac{1}{125000}$.
" 59. Virginia-Tennessee.—Bristol. Scale $\frac{1}{125000}$.
" 60. Colorado.—La Plata. Scale $\frac{1}{62500}$.
" 61. Virginia-West Virginia.—Monterey. Scale $\frac{1}{125000}$.
" 62. Michigan.—Menominee. Scale $\frac{1}{62500}$.
" 63. California.—Mother Lode. Scale $\frac{1}{63360}$.
" 64. Texas.—Uvalde. Scale $\frac{1}{125000}$.
" 65. Utah.—Tintic. Scale $\frac{1}{62500}$.
" .66. California—Colfax. Scale $\frac{1}{125000}$.
" 67. Illinois-Indiana.—Danville. Scale $\frac{1}{62500}$.
" 68. Colorado.—Walsenburg. Scale $\frac{1}{125000}$.
" 69. West Virginia-Ohio.—Huntington. Scale $\frac{1}{125000}$.
" 70. District of Columbia-Maryland-Virginia.—Washington. Scale $\frac{1}{62500}$.
" 71. Colorado.—Spanish Peaks. Scale $\frac{1}{125000}$.
" 72. West Virginia.—Charleston. Scale $\frac{1}{125000}$.
" 73. Oregon.—Coos Bay. Scale $\frac{1}{125000}$.
" 74. Indian territory.—Coalgate. Scale $\frac{1}{125000}$.
" 75. Tennessee.—Maynardville. Scale $\frac{1}{125000}$.
" 76. Texas.—Austin. Scale $\frac{1}{125000}$.
" 77. West Virginia.—Raleigh. Scale $\frac{1}{125000}$.
" 78. Georgia.—Rome. Scale $\frac{1}{125000}$.
" 79. Indian territory.—Atoka. Scale $\frac{1}{125000}$.
" 80. Virginia-North Carolina.—Norfolk. Scale $\frac{1}{125000}$.
" 81. Illinois-Indiana.—Chicago. Scale $\frac{1}{62500}$.
" 82. Pennsylvania. Masontown-Uniontown. Scale $\frac{1}{62500}$.
" 83. New York-New Jersey.—New York city. Scale $\frac{1}{62500}$.
" 84. Indiana.—Ditney. Scale $\frac{1}{125000}$.
" 85. South Dakota-Nebraska.—Oebuchs. Scale $\frac{1}{125000}$.
" 86. Washington.—Ellensburg. Scale $\frac{1}{125000}$.
" 87. Nebraska.—Camp Clarke. Scale $\frac{1}{125000}$.
" 88. " Scotts Bluff. Scale $\frac{1}{125000}$.
" 89. Oregon.—Port Orford. Scale $\frac{1}{125000}$.
" 90. North Carolina-Tennessee.—Cranberry. Scale $\frac{1}{125000}$.

**United States.** *Department of the interior.   Geological survey*—Con.

no. 91. Wyoming.—Hartville. Scale $\frac{1}{125000}$.
" 92. Pennsylvania-New York.—Gaines. Scale $\frac{1}{62500}$.
" 93. " Elkland-Tioga. Scale $\frac{1}{62500}$.
" 94. " Brownsville-Connellsville. Scale $\frac{1}{62500}$.
" 95. Tennessee.—Columbia. Scale $\frac{1}{125000}$.
" 96. South Dakota.—Olivet. Scale $\frac{1}{125000}$.
" 97. " Parker. Scale $\frac{1}{125000}$.
" 98. Indian territory. Tishomingo. Scale $\frac{1}{125000}$.
" 99. South Dakota.—Mitchell. Scale $\frac{1}{125000}$.
" 100. " Alexandria. Scale $\frac{1}{125000}$.
" 101. California.—San Luis. Scale $\frac{1}{125000}$.
" 102. Pennsylvania.—Indiana. Scale $\frac{1}{62500}$.
" 103. Idaho-Oregon.—Nampa. Scale $\frac{1}{125000}$.
" 104. Idaho.—Silver City. Scale $\frac{1}{125000}$.
" 105. Indiana-Illinois.—Patoka. Scale $\frac{1}{125000}$.
" 106. Washington.—Mount Stuart. Scale $\frac{1}{125000}$.
" 107. Wyoming-South Dakota.—Newcastle. Scale $\frac{1}{125000}$.
" 108. South Dakota-Nebraska.—Edgemont. Scale $\frac{1}{125000}$.
" 109. Kansas.—Cottonwood Falls. Scale $\frac{1}{125000}$.
" 110. Pennsylvania.—Latrobe. Scale $\frac{1}{62500}$.
" 111. Arizona.—Globe. Scale $\frac{1}{62500}$.
" 112. " Bisbee. Scale $\frac{1}{62500}$.
" 113. South Dakota.—Huron. Scale $\frac{1}{125000}$.
" 114. " De Smet. Scale $\frac{1}{125000}$.
" 115. Pennsylvania.—Kittanning. Scale $\frac{1}{62500}$.
" 116. North Carolina-Tennessee.—Asheville. Scale $\frac{1}{125000}$.
" 117. North Dakota-Minnesota.—Casselton-Fargo. Scale $\frac{1}{125000}$.
" 118. Tennessee-North Carolina.—Greeneville. Scale $\frac{1}{125000}$.
" 119. Arkansas-Missouri.—Fayetteville. Scale $\frac{1}{125000}$.
" 120. Colorado.—Silverton. Scale $\frac{1}{62500}$.
" 121. Pennsylvania.—Waynesburg. Scale $\frac{1}{62500}$.
" 122. Indian territory-Arkansas.—Tahlequah. Scale $\frac{1}{125000}$.
" 123. Pennsylvania.—Elders Ridge. Scale $\frac{1}{62500}$.
" 124. North Carolina-Tennessee.—Mount Mitchell. Scale $\frac{1}{125000}$.
" 125. Pennsylvania.—Rural Valley. Scale $\frac{1}{62500}$.
" 126. Arizona.—Bradshaw mountains. Scale $\frac{1}{125000}$.
" 127. Wyoming-South Dakota.—Sundance. Scale $\frac{1}{125000}$.
" 128. Wyoming-South Dakota-Montana.—Aladdin. Scale $\frac{1}{125000}$.
" 129. Arizona.—Clifton. Scale $\frac{1}{62500}$.
" 130. Colorado.—Rico. Scale $\frac{1}{62500}$.
" 131. " Needle mountains. Scale $\frac{1}{62500}$.
" 132. Indian territory.—Muscogee. Scale $\frac{1}{125000}$.
" 133. Pennsylvania.—Ebensburg. Scale $\frac{1}{62500}$.
" 134. " Beaver. Scale $\frac{1}{62500}$.
" 135. Colorado.—Nepesta. Scale $\frac{1}{125000}$.
" 136. Maryland-Virginia.—St. Marys. Scale $\frac{1}{125000}$.
" 137. Delaware-Maryland-New Jersey.—Dover. Scale $\frac{1}{125000}$.
" 138. California.—Redding. Scale $\frac{1}{125000}$.
" 139. Washington.—Snoqualmie. Scale $\frac{1}{125000}$.
" 140. Wisconsin.—Milwaukee. Scale $\frac{1}{62500}$.
" 141. Wyoming.—Bald mountain—Dayton. Scale $\frac{1}{125000}$.
" 142. Wyoming.—Cloud Peak-Fort McKinney. Scale $\frac{1}{125000}$.

no. 143. North Carolina-Tennessee.—Nantahala. Scale $\frac{1}{125000}$.
" 144. Pennsylvania.—Amity. Scale $\frac{1}{62500}$.
" 145. Wisconsin-Iowa-Illinois.—Lancaster-Mineral Point. Scale $\frac{1}{125000}$.
" 146. Pennsylvania.—Rogersville. Scale $\frac{1}{62500}$.
" 147. North Carolina-South Carolina.—Pisgah. Scale $\frac{1}{125000}$.
" 148. Missouri-Kansas.—Joplin district. Scale $\frac{1}{62500}$.
" 149. Maine.—Penobscot bay. Scale $\frac{1}{125000}$.
" 150. Wyoming.—Devils Tower. Scale $\frac{1}{125000}$.
" 151. Tennessee-North Carolina.—Roan mountain. Scale $\frac{1}{125000}$.
" 152. Maryland-District of Columbia.—Patuxent. Scale $\frac{1}{125000}$.
" 153. Colorado.—Ouray. Scale $\frac{1}{62500}$.
" 154. Arkansas-Indian territory.—Winslow. Scale $\frac{1}{125000}$.
" 155. Michigan.—Ann Arbor. Scale $\frac{1}{125000}$.
" 156. South Dakota-Nebraska-Iowa.—Elk Point. Scale $\frac{1}{125000}$.
" 157. New Jersey-New York.—Passaic. Scale $\frac{1}{125000}$.
" 158. Maine.—Rockland. Scale $\frac{1}{62500}$.
" 159. Kansas.—Independence. Scale $\frac{1}{125000}$.
" 161. New Jersey.—Franklin Furnace. Scale $\frac{1}{62500}$.

## HIEROGLYPHIC.

**Heermans, A. A.**

A hieroglyphic geography of the United States. Designed and drawn by Anna A. Heermans. Engraved by Charlotte B. Cogswell. Part 1. 24 pp., illus. 4°. New York, E. P. Dutton & co. 1875.

1284

NOTE.—No more published.

### CONTENTS.

pt. 1. Maine, New Hampshire, Vermont, Massachusetts, Rhode Island, Connecticut, and New York.

## HISTORICAL.

**Foster, E. G.**

Forty maps illustrating United States history . . .   1 p. l., 40 maps. obl. fol. Topeka, Kan., historical publishing company, °1905.

1285

### CONTENTS.

no. 1. Commercial routes prior to 1492 and voyages of Columbus.
" 2. Routes of early discoverers.
" 3. Spanish explorations.
" 4. French explorations.
" 5. The London and Plymouth companies, 1606.
" 6. The London co., 1609. Plymouth co., 1620.
" 7. The dutch and swedes in America.
" 8. The New England grants and the development of the New England states.
" 9. Grants to the middle colonies and the development of the middle states.
" 10. The southern grants and the development of the southern states.
" 11. North America from 1755-1763.
" 12. The result of the french and indian war, 1763.
" 13. The thirteen colonies, proclamation line 1763 and Quebec act 1774.
" 14. The early campaigns of the revolutionary war.

**Foster, E. G.**—Continued.
  no. 15. Washington's campaigns.
  "  16. Northern campaigns of the revolutionary war.
  "  17. Southern campaigns of the revolutionary war.
  "  18. The United States, 1783.
  "  19. Territorial claims of the thirteen colonies.
  "  20. The northwest territory and the territory southwest of the Ohio river.
  "  21. Drainage map.
  "  22. Political parties.
  "  23. The Louisiana purchase, 1803.
  "  24. Campaigns of the war of 1812.
  "  25. The Missouri compromise and Florida treaty.
  "  26. The United States, 1837 and the republic of Texas.
  "  27. The Maine boundary, and Webster-Ashburton treaty.
  "  28. The Oregon country.
  "  29. Our country, 1846.
  "  30. Campaigns of the mexican war.
  "  31. Our country at the close of the mexican war, 1848.
  "  32. The compromise of 1850.
  "  33. The United States, 1850.
  "  34. The Kansas-Nebraska act, 1854.
  "  35. Our country during the civil war, 1861–65.
  "  36. Grant's campaigns in the west.
  "  37. Campaigns of Buell and Bragg.
  "  38. Sherman's march to the sea and Hood's retreat.
  "  39. Lee's campaigns in Virginia vs. the army of the Potomac.
  "  40. United States and her possessions, 1904.

Foster's historical outline maps and note book for students in United States history.   cover-title, 2 p. l., 40 maps.   obl. 12°. Topeka, Kan., the historical publishing company, c1904.   1286

**Hardesty, H. H.**
 Hardesty's historical and geographical encyclopedia, illustrated . . . Special history of northwestern Ohio, and the geological history of the state.  Outline map and history of Meigs county, Ohio, containing a condensed history of the county; biographical sketches; general statistics; miscellaneous matters, &c.   xxiv, 15–294, 40 pp. incl. 56 col. maps, 1 fold. map, 50 pl. on 21 l., 61 port. on 5 l. fol.  Chicago and Toledo, H. H. Hardesty & co. 1883.   1287

 Hardesty's historical and geographical encyclopedia, illustrated . . . Special military history of Ohio giving its part in the indian wars, border annals, the war of 1812, the mexican war, the war of the rebellion . . .   454 pp. 1 l. incl. 82 col. maps, 75 pl. on 34 l., 86 port. on 26 l.  fol.  New York, Richmond, etc., H. H. Hardesty & co. 1884.   1288

 NOTE.—This edition contains only an extract relating to the battles of the civil war, from Brock's "History of the Virginias." The remainder is omitted and replaced by military history of Ohio.

**Hart, A. B.**
　Epoch maps illustrating american history. [1st ed.]　3 p. l., 14 maps.　obl. 16°.　New York, Longmans, Green and co. 1891.　　1289

　　　　　CONTENTS.

　no. 1. Physical features of the United States of America . . .
　" 　2. North America, 1650. Showing claims arising out of exploration and occupancy.
　" 　3. English colonies, 1700. Showing extent of actual jurisdiction.
　" 　4. North America, 1750. Showing claims arising out of exploration and occupancy.
　" 　5. English colonies, 1763-1775.
　" 　6. The United States, 1783. Subdivisions as claimed by the states.
　" 　7. Territorial growth of the United States, 1775-1866.
　" 　8. Status of slavery in the United States, 1775-1865.
　" 　9. The United States, march 4th, 1801.
　" 　10. The United States, march 4th, 1825.
　" 　11. Territorial controveries settled by the United States, 1840-1850.
　" 　12. The United States, march 4th, 1855.
　" 　13. The United States, july 4th, 1861.
　" 　14. The United States, march 4th, 1891.

　Epoch maps illustrating american history . . .　3 p. l., 14 maps.　obl. 16°.　New York, Longman, Green and co. 1899.
　　　　　　　　　　　　　　　　　　　　　　　　　　　　　1290

　Epoch maps illustrating american history . . .　New ed.　3 p. l., 14 maps.　obl. 16°.　New York, Longmans, Green and co. 1904.　　　　　　　　　　　　　　　　　　　　　　　1291

　　NOTE.—Map no. [14] in this edition entitled: The United States, march 4th, 1907. First edition, nov., 1891. Reprinted, july, 1892, aug., 1893, june, 1897, feb., 1898, dec., 1898 (revised) oct., 1901, aug., 1902, feb., 1904 (revised)

**Hodder, F. H.**
　Outline maps for an historical atlas of the United States, illustrating territorial growth and development.　2 p. l., 24 maps. obl. 4°.　Boston, Ginn & co. 1901.　　1292

**MacCoun, T.**
　An historical geography of the United States . . . [1st ed.] vi pp., 1 l., 46 pp., 44 maps on 23 l.　16°.　New York, T. MacCoun, 1889.　　1293

　　NOTE.—Explanatory text follows maps.

　An historical geography of the United States. Rev. ed.　4 pp., 1 l., 46 pp., 43 maps on 23 l.　sq. 16°.　New York, Boston, Chicago, Silver, Burdett & co. 1890.　　1294

　An historical geography of the United States . . . Rev. ed. vi pp., 1 l., 48 pp., 45 maps on 24 l.　sq. 12°.　New York, Boston [etc.] Silver, Burdett & co. [1901]　　1295

**Smith, L. H.**

Historical and chronological atlas of the United States. [19] l. incl. 8 maps. 4°. Washington, national republican printing and publishing co. 1881.    1296

### LAKES.

**Thompson, T. S.**

Thompson's coast pilot for the upper lakes, on both shores, from Chicago to Buffalo, Green bay, Georgian bay and lake Superior . . . also, a description of all the lights and lighthouses, on both shores, from Ogdensburg to Superior City. Including correct charts of the south shore of lake Superior . . . viii, 74, 6 pp., 6 maps. 8°. Chicago, J. Barnet, 1861.    1297

### POLITICAL.

**Hewes, F. W.**

Citizen's atlas of american politics 1789–1888. A series of colored maps and charts. 56 pp. incl. 11 col. maps, 5 diagr. fol. New York, C. Scribner's sons, 1888.    1298

CONTENTS.

Political parties.
The tariff rate.
Duty, revenue, and importation.
Wages and cost of living compared.
Presidential elections.
Foreign population.
Distribution of manufactures.
Distribution of wool product.
Historical epitome.

Citizen's atlas of american politics 1789–1892. A series of colored maps and charts. 56 pp. incl. 12 col. maps, 5 diagr. fol. New York, C. Scribner's sons [1892]    1299

### RAILROADS.

**Asher & Adams.**

Asher & Adams' new columbian railroad atlas and pictorial album of american industry, comprising a series of new copper plate maps exhibiting the thirty-seven states, the provinces of Ontario, Quebec, New Brunswick, and the nine territories (not including Alaska) delineating the railway system from the Atlantic to the Pacific, on a uniform scale of twenty miles to an inch, with general maps showing the United States, Europe and the world together with illustrations and descriptions of mercantile and manufacturing establishments, machinery, works of art, mechanism, trade-marks, etc., etc. Compiled, written, drawn and engraved under the supervision of the publishers, by their own corps of editors, engineers, topographers, and artists. 1 p. l., 3–152, [59] pp. incl. 42 maps. fol. New York, Asher & Adams, 1875.    1300

NOTE.—Pagination irregular.

**Atlas** of western, northwestern, and middle western states with maps of the island possessions, Japan, China, United States, and the world showing location of railway lines of the Chicago, Burlington & Quincy railway, Great Northern railway, Northern Pacific railway. Issued by the passenger departments of the Burlington route, Great Northern railway, Northern Pacific railway. 1 p. l., 56 pp. incl. 23 maps. fol. [Chicago and New York, Rand, McNally & co. °1905] 1301

NOTE.—Maps copyrighted by Rand, M°Nally & co.

**Cram, G. F.**
Cram's standard american railway system atlas of the world. Showing all the railway systems in colors. Accompanied by a complete and simple index of the United States . . . 604 (*i. e.* 614), [30] pp. incl. 157 col. maps. fol. New York, Chicago, G. F. Cram, 1905. 1302

Cram's standard american railway system atlas of the world. Showing all the railway systems in colors and numbers . . . Accompanied by a concise and original ready reference index of the United States, Canada, Mexico and Cuba . . . 628, [22] pp. incl. 152 col. maps. fol. New York, Chicago, G. F. Cram, 1907. 1303

Cram's standard american railway system atlas of the world . . . Accompanied by a concise and original ready reference index of the United States, Canada, Mexico and Cuba . . . 610, [32] pp. incl. 152 col. maps. fol. New York, Chicago, G. F. Cram, 1908. 1304

**Pennsylvania railroad.**
Ticket agents atlas containing complete maps of the Pennsylvania system of railways with index to all stations and key to their locations. 21 pp. incl. 10 maps. fol. [Chicago, Rand, McNally & co.] 1905. 1305

**Poor, H. V.**
Poor's manual. Maps for 1883. 2 p. l., 49 maps. 8°. Chicago, Rand, McNally & co. 1883. 1306

NOTE.—For Poor's manual of railroads for 1883, by Rand, McNally & co.

### REPRODUCTIONS.
**Pinart, A. L.**
Recueil de cartes, plans et vues relatifs aux États-Unis et au Canada, New York, Boston, Montréal, Québec, Louisbourg. 1651–1731. Reproduits d'après les originaux manuscrits et inédits, etc. exposés à la Bibliothèque Nationale à l'occasion du quatrième centenaire de la découverte de l'Amérique sous la direction de A. L. Pinart. 3 p. l., 13 maps on 16 l., 11 pl., 2 diagr. fol. Paris, E. Dufossé, 1893. 1307

**Pinart, A. L.**—Continued.

### CONTENTS.

no. 1. Vue de New-York, tirée de la *Beschrijvinghe van Virginia, Nieuw-Nederlandt, Nieuw-Engelandt, en de Eylanden Bermudes, Barbados en S. Christoffel.* Amsterdam, Joost Hartgers, *1651* . . . (Sur le titre)

" 2. Carte de la Nieuw-Nederlandt avec une vue de Nieuw-Amsterdam (New York) tirée de l'ouvrage de: *Adriaen van der Donck, Beschryvinge van Nieuw-Nederlant (gelijck het Tegenwoordigh in staet is), begrijpende de nature, aert* . . . *Den tweede Druck. t'Aemsteldam, Evert Nieuwenhof, 1656* . . .

" 3. Le plan de Manathes ou Nouvelle-Yorc, vérifié par le sieur de La Mothe, 1693. Ce plan, fort curieux, fait partie de la *Carte de la côte de la Nouvelle-Angleterre, depuis le cap Anne jusqu'à la pointe Nevresing, où est compris le chemin par terre et par mer de Baston à Manathes, par J. B. L. Franquelin* . . .

" 4. Carte de la ville, baie et environs de Baston, par Jean-Baptiste-Louis Franquelin . . . 1693, *vérifiée par le sieur de la Motte* . . .

" 5–6. Plan de la ville Marie ou Montréal, au Canada, sans date ni nom d'auteur. Les indications qui s'y trouvent portées nous font supposer, à raison croyons-nous, qu'il est de 1720 . . .

" 7. *Carte figurative du prompt secours envoyé par l'ordre de monseigneur le marquis de Beauharnois* . . . *le 2ᵉ septembre 1729.* Dessigné par Mahier, *à Québec, le 15 octobre 1729* . . .

" 8. Vue de Québec prise de l'est . . . Cette vue est tirée d'une carte manuscrite de la Nouvelle-France, etc., qui porte en cartouche: *à monseigneur, monseigneur le comte de Maurepas* . . . *par son très humble et très obéissant serviteur de Fonville* . . . 1699 . . .

" 9. Vue de Québec, prise du nord-ouest. Cette vue est tirée de la carte indiquée sous le numéro précédent, où elle se trouve dans le coin du bas, à droite . . .

" 10. Vue de Québec, comme il se voit du côté de l'est . . . Belle pièce tirée d'une carte intitulée: *Carte de l'Amérique, entre les 25ᵉ et 65ᵉ degrés de latitude, et depuis environ les 240ᵉ jusqu'aux 340ᵉ de longitude, contenant les pays de la Nouvelle-France, la Louisiane, Floride, Virginie, Nouvelle-Yorck, Nouvelle-Angleterre, Acadie, etc., par Jean-Baptiste-Louis Franquelin,* 1699 . . .

" 11. Vue de Québec . . . Jolie vue tirée d'une carte intitulée: *Partie de l'Amérique septentrionale où est compris la Nouvelle-France, la Nouvelle-Angleterre, la Nouvelle-Albanie et la Nouvelle-Yorc, la Pensylvanie, la Virginie, la Caroline, la Floride, la Louisiane, etc., par Jean-Baptiste-Louis Franquelin* . . . 1699 . . .

" 12. Partie de la *Carte de l'Amérique septentrionale entre 27 et 64 degrés de latitude, et environ 250 et 340 degrés de longitude, où est compris le pays de la Nouvelle-France, la Nouvelle-Angleterre, la Virginie, la Caroline, la Floride et tous les environs du grand fleuve Mississipi* . . . *par Jean-Baptiste-Louis Franquelin, dessiné et écrit par F. de La Croix.* Cette carte, bien que non datée, est peu postérieure à l'expédition de Beaujeu et à la mort de Cuvelier de la Salle, 1687.

" 13. Carte des grands lacs (1679) attribuée à J.-B.-L. Franquelin . . .

" 14. Carte de la rivière de Saint-Laurent depuis Québec et la rivière du Sault de la Chaudière . . . Curieuse carte qui, bien que non datée, ne peut être postérieure à 1679 . . .

no 15. Carte de la région située aux environs du lac Ontario ou de Fontenac, la rivière des Outaouais depuis le Sault de la Chaudière, le lac Shekoven ou Nipissing et les portages entre ce lac et la rivière des Outaouais et avec le lac des Hurons par la rivière des Français . . . Cette carte, dont la date peut être fixée à 1679 . . .

" 16. Carte du lac Huron, Karegnondi ou mer des Hurons où sont indiqués les tribus, les villages indiens ainsi que la route qu'ils suivaient . . . Curieuse carte qui, bien que non datée, ne paraît pas postérieure à 1679 . . .

" 17. Carte des lacs Tracy ou Supérieur, des Illinois et des Hurons avec la rivière Colbert et le pays au nord du lac Tracy jusqu'à la baie ou golfe de Hudson et la rivière des Assinipoul . . . Cette . . . carte, bien que non datée, ne paraît pas postérieure à 1680 . . .

" 18. Carte des lacs et des régions à l'ouest de la baie d'Hudson . . .

" 19-20. Carte générale des paroisses et missions établies des deux côtés du fleuve Saint-Laurent, depuis Rimousky en montant jusqu'au coteau des Cèdres . . . Cette carte . . . date de la fin du xvii° siècle . . .

" [21-22] Carte des côtés habitées du Canada par paroisses et par seigneuries, signée Deshaies . . .

" [23] Carte des régions entre le Saint-Laurent et la baie d'Hudson de la main de L. Jolliet, sous ce titre: *Cette carte montre le chemin que Louis Jolliet a fait depuis Tadoussac jusqu'à la mer du Nord dans la baie d'Hudson et du destroit* . . . 1679.

" [24-25] Vue de la ville de Louisbourg, prise en denans du port, Verrier fils, fecit 1731 . . .

" [26-27] Plan de la ville de Louisbourg avec les fortifications du côté des terres, vers 1731 . . .

### RIVERS.

#### Mississippi and Ohio.

**Conclin, G.**

Conclin's new river guide, or, a gazetteer of all the towns on the western waters . . . on the Ohio and Mississippi rivers . . . 128 pp. incl. front., 44 maps. 8°. Cincinnati, H. S. & J. Applegate, 1849. 1308

NOTE.—Frontispiece, "View of Cave-in-Rock, on the Ohio river, near Shawneetown."
Illustrated cover with "Table of distances" bound at end.

——— Same. illus. cover, 128 pp. incl. front., 44 maps. 8°. Cincinnati, H. S. & J. Applegate, 1850. 1309

NOTE.—Frontispiece, "View of Cave-in-Rock, on the Ohio river, near Shawneetown."

——— Same. illus. cover, 128 pp. incl., front., 44 maps. 8°. Cincinnati, J. A. & U. P. James, 1851. 1310

NOTE.—Table of distances on second and third p. of covers.
Frontispiece, "View of Cave-in-rock, on the Ohio river, near Shawneetown."

——— Same. 128 pp. incl. front., 44 maps. 8°. Cincinnati, U. P. James, 1855. 1311

NOTE.—Table of distances on second and third p. of covers at end.
Frontispiece, View of "Maiden's Rock, on the Mississippi."

**Cramer, Z.**

The navigator: or the traders' useful guide in navigating the Monongahela, Allegheny, Ohio, and Mississippi rivers; containing an ... account of these ... waters ... of their towns ... &c. with particular directions how to navigate them, in all stages of the water ... 5th ed., much ... enl. To which is added, an account of Louisiana ... 2 p. l., [3]—94 pp. incl. 12 maps. 16°. Pittsbugh, Z. Cramer, 1806. 1312

> NOTE.—First edition published 1801.

The navigator: containing directions for navigating the Monongahela, Alleghany, Ohio, and Mississippi rivers; with an ... account of these ... waters ... of their towns ... &c. ... To which is added ... an account of Louisiana, and of the Missouri and Columbia rivers, as discovered by ... captains Lewis and Clark. 6th ed. impr. and enl. 3 p. l., 5—156 pp. incl. 28 maps. 16°. Pittsbugh, Z. Cramer, 1808. 1313

> NOTE.—p. [3] "Map of Pittsburgh."

—— Same. 7th ed. impr. and enl. 296 pp. incl. 28 maps. 16°. Pittsburgh, Cramer, Spear & Eichbaum, 1811. 1314

> NOTE.—p. [11] "Map of Pittsburgh."

—— Same. 8th ed. impr. and enl. 360 pp. incl. 28 maps. 16°. Pittsburgh, Cramer, Spear & Eichbaum, 1814. 1315

> NOTE.—p. [11] "Map of Pittsburgh."

—— Same. 9th ed. 1 p. l., 307 pp. incl. 28 maps. 16°. Pittsburgh, Cramer, Spear & Eichbaum, 1817. 1316

> NOTE.—p. [11] "Map of Pittsburgh."

—— Same. 10th ed. 305 pp. incl. 28 maps. 16°. Pittsburgh, Cramer & Spear, 1818. 1317

**Cumings, S.**

The western navigator; containing charts of the Ohio river in its whole extent and of the Mississippi river, from the mouth of the Missouri to the gulf of Mexico. Accompanied by directions for the navigation of the Ohio and Mississippi ... 2 v. 1 p. l., 27 maps; 4, 232 pp., 3 l. Text. 8°; atlas. fol. Philadelphia, E. Littell, 1822. 1318

> NOTE.—Imperfect: atlas sheet no. 7 wanting.

The western pilot, containing charts of the Ohio river, and of the Mississippi, from the mouth of the Missouri to the gulf of Mexico ... 143 pp., 44 maps. 8°. Cincinnati, Morgan, Lodge & Fisher, 1825. 1319

—— Same.  1 p. l., 151 pp. incl. 44 maps, 2 pl.  8°.  Cincinnati, N. & G. Guilford & co. 1832. 1320

> NOTE.—Engraved title. A revised and altered edition of the author's "Western navigator."

—— Same.  1 p. l., 152 pp. incl. 44 maps.  2 pl., port.  8°. Cincinnati, N. & G. Guilford & co. 1834. 1321

> NOTE.—Engraved title: The western pilot for 1834.
> A revised and altered edition of the author's "Western navigator."
> "Cumings' editions of the 'Navigator' and 'Pilot' and another work by Jas. C. Gilleland were amplifications of Cramer, without acknowledgment of the main source of their material."—Sabin, Bibl. amer., v. 5, p. 126.
> The charts are projected on a uniform scale of four miles to the inch.
> Contains views of Pittsburg and Cincinnati and portrait of Gabrielle Menou.

—— Same.  New edition.  144 pp. incl. 44 maps.  8°.  Cincinnati, G. Conclin, 1838. 1322

## Gilleland, J. C.

The Ohio and Mississippi pilot, consisting of a set of charts of those rivers . . . To which is added a geography of the states and territories west and south of the Allegheny mountains . . .  2 pts. in 1 v. 44 pp. 1 l. incl. 16 maps; 1 p. l., 49–274 pp.  12°.  Pittsburgh, R. Patterson & Lambdin, 1820. 1323

> NOTE.—See title 1321. "The first six of the preceding charts were drawn upon the scale of five miles to the inch and all the rest on the scale of eight miles to the inch except that of the falls. This proportion, however, is observed only lengthwise; because from the necessity of the case, the river is made to appear much wider than it is in reality."

## Ockerson, J. A., *and* Stewart, C. W.

The Mississippi river from St. Louis to the sea . . .  4 p. l., 42 maps. obl. fol.  St. Louis, Mo., J. A. Ockerson & C. W. Stewart, 1892. 1324

## United States.  *War department.*

[Reconnoissance of the Mississippi & Ohio rivers]  1 p. l., 65 maps. fol. [Washington, engineer department, 1875] 1325

> NOTE.—"This reconnoissance of the Mississippi & Ohio rivers was made during the months of october, november & december 1821, by capt. H. Young—capt. W. T. Pousin of the topog! engrs. and lieut. S. Tuttle of the engrs. under the direction of the board of engineers. The soundings on the bars were made during the months of october and november, and it is believed that they are accurate for the lowest stage of waters in common years, in very dry seasons the lowest stage of waters would be about 10 inches lower."
> Comprises plans no. 1–2, mentioned by gen. Simon Bernard in his report of the board of engineers on the Ohio & Mississippi rivers, made in 1821 and read january 22, 1823. (Doc. no. 35. State papers, 17th cong., 2d sess. ser. no. 78) It is also known as gen. Bernard's map.

## ROADS.

**Blanchard, F. S., & co.**

The "pilot" sectional road maps of New England and Hudson river district covering 53,600 square miles ... [2], 133 pp. incl. 117 maps. sq. 8°. Worcester, Mass., F. S. Blanchard & co. c1908. 1325a

**Colles, C.**

A survey of the roads of the United States of America ... C. Tiebout, sculpt. 1789. 1 p. l., 83 maps. 8°. [New York] 1789.
1326

NOTE.—Title page and 83 plates (numbered 1-33 and 40-86) were probably never engraved as they are wanting in each of the copies in the following libraries and catalogues: New York state; Lenox; New York historical society; Library of Congress (2 copies); Brinley, Catalogue, vol. 3, no. 4818; Church, Catalogue, vol. v, no. 1236; and Sabin, vol. 4, no. 14411, which mentions only 74 plates.

Church states that the set is complete without these plates and suggests that these numbers may have been reserved for a map of the roads from Newburgh to New York, along the west bank of the Hudson.

"In drawing these plans, Colles has taken New York, Philadelphia and Annapolis as his starting points." The set is reclassified in the Church catalogue, into ten series; the original titles are discarded, being considered somewhat misleading. It is noted that plate 86 is continued some 3½ miles beyond Hooe's ferry, showing that the author contemplated continuing the series still farther.

L. C. copy no. 1, contains two original wrappers in manuscript; the first reads in part as follows: Colles' road maps for col. Force ... [signed] G[eorge] H. M[oore] nov. 10, 1846; the second is a title-slip pasted on a fly-leaf and reads: Survey of the roads of the United States by Christopher Colles. A. D, 1789. Then follows the folding sheet of "Proposals" found in Library of Congress copies no. 1 and 2, containing the additional paragraph beginning: "These surveys are made from actual mensuration" ...

*Proposals for publishing a survey of the roads of the United States of America. By Christopher Colles, of New York.*

CONDITIONS.

That the work shall be neatly engraved upon copper, each page containing a delineation of near 12 miles of the road upon a scale of about one inch and three quarters to the mile, and particularly specifying all the cross roads and streams of water which intersect it, the names of the most noted inhabitants of the houses contiguous to or in view of the road; the churches and other public buildings; the taverns, blacksmith's shops, mills, and every object which occurs to render it a useful and entertaining work, and in every respect equal to the specimen of the three first pages annexed.

That a set of general maps shall be made upon a small scale with references from them to the particular page where the description of any road is to be found; these maps will then answer as an index and will be found more convenient than any other index that can be made.

That each subscriber shall pay one quarter dollar at the time of subscribing (to defray several incidental charges necessary for the work) and one eighth of a dollar upon the delivery of every six pages of the work: but such gentlemen as are willing to advance one dollar will be considered as patrons of the work, and will not be entitled to pay any more till the value thereof is delivered in.

That subscribers shall pay 20 cents for each of the general maps and three cents for each sheet of letter press in the alphabetical lists of other necessary explanation of the drafts.

That each subscriber shall be considered as engaging to take 100 pages.

That non-subscribers shall pay three cents for each page of the work.

These surveys are made from actual mensuration, by a perambulator of a new and convenient construction, invented by said Colles, and very different from any hitherto used, which determines the number of revolutions of the wheel of a carriage to which it is fixed, and it is found by experiment to ascertain the distance to a much greater degree of accuracy than could be expected; the direction of the road is determined by a compass likewise affixed to the surveying carriage.

### ACCOUNT OF THE ADVANTAGES OF THESE SURVEYS.

A traveller will here find so plain and circumstantial a description of the road, that whilst he has the draft with him it will be impossible for him to miss his way: he will have the satisfaction of knowing the names of many of the persons who reside on the road; if his horse should want a shoe, or his carriage be broke, he will by the bare inspection of the draft be able to determine whether he must go backward or forward to a blacksmith's shop: Persons who have houses or plantations on the road may in case they want to let, lease, or sell the same, advertise in the public newspapers that the place is marked in such a page of Colles's Survey of the roads; this will give so particular a description of its situation that no difficulty or doubt will remain about it. If a foreigner arrives in any part of the Continent and is under the necessity to travel by land, he applies to a bookseller, who with the assistance of the index map chooses out the particular pages which are necessary for his direction. It is expected many other entertaining and useful purposes will be discovered when these surveys come into general use.

Subscription papers will be sent to most of the Booksellers on the continent.

### CONTENTS.

no. 1–7. From New York to Stratford.
" 8–13. From New York to Poughkeepsie.
" 14. From Poughkeepsie to Albany.
" 15–20. From Stratford to Poughkeepfie.
" 21–25. From Pougkeepsie to Albany.
" 26–33. From Albany to Newborough.
" 34–39. Wanting.
" 40. From New York to Elizabeth town.
" 41–42. From New York to Brunswick.
" 43. From New York to Kingston.
" 44. From New York to Trenton.
" 45. From New York to Briftol.
" 45.* From New York to Cranberry.
" 46. From New York to Frankford.
" 46.* From New York to Allen town.
" 47. From New York to Philadelphia.
" 47.* From New York to the Blackhorse.
" 48. From New York to Mount holly.

**Colles, C.**—Continued.

  no. 49–50. From New York to Philadelphia.
  "   51–61. From Philadelphia to Annapolis, Md.
  "   62–63. From Annapolis to Bladensburg.
  "   64–65. From Annapolis to Alexandria.
  "   66. From Annapolis to Dumfries.
  "   67–68. From Annapolis to Fredericksburg, Va.
  "   69. From Annapolis to Todd's Ordinary.
  "   70. From Annapolis to Bowling-green Ordry
  "   71. From Annapolis to Head Lynchs Ordry
  "   72. From Annapolis to Hanover Court-house.
  "   73. From Annapolis to Hanover & Newcaftle.
  "   74–75. From Annapolis to New Kent Court-house.
  "   76–77. From Annapolis to Williamfburgh.
  "   78–79. From Annapolis to York.
  "   80–81. From Williamsburgh to Ayletts Warehouse.
  "   82. From Williamsburgh to Sneed's Ordinary.
  "   83–84. From Williamsburgh to Port-Royal.
  "   85–86. From Williamsburgh to Hooe's ferry.

**Moore, S. S.** *and* **Jones, T. W.**

The traveller's directory, or a pocket companion: shewing the course of the main road from Philadelphia to New York, and from Philadelphia to Washington. With descriptions of the places through which it passes, and the intersections of the cross roads. Illustrated with an account of such remarkable objects as are generally interesting to travellers. From actual survey . . .  3 p. l., 52 pp., 38 maps on 22 l. 8°. Philadelphia, printed for, and published by M. Carey, 1802.          1327

  NOTE.—Maps engraved by F. Shallus, W. Harrison jr., James Smither, and I. Draper.

CONTENTS.

  no. 1. Philadelphia and the commencement of the road to New York.
  " 2–15. Road from Philadela to New York.
  " 1–22. Road from Philadelphia to Washington.
  " 23. Washington city [Plan]

——— Same. 2d. ed.  1 p. l., 37, 19 (*i. e.* 17) pp., 38 maps on 22 l. 8°. Philadelphia, for M. Carey, 1804.          1328

  NOTE.—Preface omitted; descriptive text rewritten. Maps the same as in title 1327.

STATISTICAL.

**Asher & Adams.**

Asher & Adams' new statistical and topographical atlas of the United States. With maps showing the dominion of Canada, Europe and the world. Exhibiting a clear topographical view of the United States, from fine copper-plate maps, delineating rivers, landings, railroads, stations, distances, etc. Populations of cities and villages containing three hundred inhabitants and upward, as reported by government census for 1870; population of counties in the several states, the territories, and the dominion of Canada, together with comprehensive statistical tables of the United States and the various countries of the world. Compiled, drawn, and engraved under the supervision of the publishers, by their own engineers, topographers, and artists, from the most recent official reports, astronomical observations, surveys, records and documents of the United States and territories, the dominion of Canada, the several states, railroad companies, etc.   2 p. l., 7–132 pp., 14 l. incl. 29 maps.  fol.  New York, Asher & Adams [1872]   1329

NOTE.—Pagination irregular.

**United States.** *Census office. 9th census, 1870.*
Statistical atlas of the United States based on the results of the ninth census 1870, with contributions from many eminent men of science and several departments of the government. Compiled under authority of Congress by Francis A. Walker.   [158] pp. incl. 38 maps, 16 pl.  fol.  [New York] J. Bien, 1874.   1330

**Hewes, F. W.** *and* **Gannett, H.**
Scribner's statistical atlas of the United States showing by graphic methods their present condition and their political, social and industrial development.   cxx pp., 151 col. pl. incl. 111 maps.  fol.  New York, C. Scribner's sons [°1883]   1331

Scribner's statistical atlas of the United States, showing by graphic methods their present condition and their political, social and industrial development.   cxx pp. 117 maps, 34 pl.  fol.  New York, C. Scribner's sons [1885]   1332

**United States.** *Census office. 11th census, 1890.*
Statistical atlas of the United States, based upon results of the eleventh census. By Henry Gannett. 69 pp., 63 pl. incl. maps, diagr.  fol.  Washington, government printing office, 1898.   1333

NOTE.—To accompany 52d cong. 1st sess. House misc. doc. no. 340, part 29.

**United States.** *Census office. 12th census, 1900.*
Statistical atlas. Prepared under the supervision of Henry Gannett, geographer of the twelfth census.   57 pp., 86 maps, 121 pl. 4°.  Washington, United States census office, 1903.   1334

NOTE.—At head of title: Twelfth census, taken in the year 1900. William R. Merriam, director.

### WARS.

#### Revolutionary.

**Rochambeau, J. B. D. de V.**, *comte de*.

Amérique campagne, 1782. Plans des différents camps occupés par l'armée aux ordres de m.<sup>r</sup> le comte de Rochambeau. 1 p. l., 54 col. maps. fol. 12½ x 8. [1782]     1335

NOTE.—The 54 plans are colored and each measures 12½ × 8 inches.

This volume of manuscript plans, which explain themselves, was purchased by the government from among the military papers, maps, etc., of the comte de Rochambeau, general of the french army in America during the revolution. A detailed manuscript description of this collection is in the Manuscripts Division of the Library of Congress.

The following is copied from the Magazine of american history, may, 1882, v. 8, pages 349-350:

"For similar reasons the purchase of this collection is to be urged, and it is gratifying to find that it has likewise secured the favorable attention of the joint library committee. The papers of the count de Rochambeau, it will be recalled, were first offered for sale to our government by their present owner, the marquis of Rochambeau, in 1877, and were finally brought over by him last fall upon the occasion of his visit as a member of the french delegation to the Yorktown celebration. This was done at the request of the library committee with a view to their inspection before purchasing them; and that the committee have become impressed with their value is apparent in their unanimous recommendation that the collection be secured. The papers embrace:

First. The original letter-books of the count de Rochambeau, in nine volumes, covering the period from 1780 to 1784, and containing copies of multitudes of letters to and from that general, relating principally to the conduct of the war in America.

Second. About fourteen hundred original letters and documents, covering the years 1780 to 1794, and embracing letters and military papers by french and american officers, besides numerous letters of instruction, etc., from the french government to the count de Rochambeau, concerning the details of outfit, payment of troops, rank and military operations generally. Among these interesting documents are one hundred and fifty-two letters from general Washington to the count, all upon military affairs or topics of public interest. Of this great mass of documents it has been found that less than sixty have been printed.

Third. A manuscript "Mémoire pour l'histoire de la guerre en Amérique," with corrections in the hand of count de Rochambeau.

Fourth. A "Mémoire du roi pour servir à l'instruction particulière à m. le chevalier de Ternay, chef d'escadre des armées navales."

Fifth. A "Journal des opérations du corps français."

Sixth. A series of sixty-nine military and topographical maps, all of the period covered by the operations of the french land and naval forces in America. Of these, thirty-eight are original charts or maps, carefully drawn to scale by engineers of the french army, and colored, with accompanying legends. This precious and unique series of maps, delineating as it does all the movements in which the french forces were engaged from Rhode Island to Virginia, presents authentic contemporaneous memorials of battlefields, camps, marches, and sieges of the highest interest and value to the historian of the war of the revolution. They serve to fill many omissions or breaks in the chartography of that war, and may even be regarded as more valuable than even the manuscripts. Maps and documents together constitute a mine of historical lore worthy of the government's possession. The price asked for the collection is $20,000, and that sum the committee recommends should be appropriated for their purchase."

CONTENTS.

no. 1. Camp à Drinking-Spring  Le 1$^{er}$ Juillet  8 milles de Williamsburg.
"  2. Camp 2 milles au de la de Byrd's Tavern  Le 2 Juillet  8 milles de Drinking Spring.
"  3. Camp à Rattelaffe House  Le 3 Juillet  7 Milles de Byrds Tavern.
"  4. Camp à Hartfield  Le 4 Juillet  7 Milles ½ de Rattelaffe house.
"  5. Camp à New Castle 7 Milles endeça de la Ville  Le 5 Juillet 19 milles de Martfield.  Le 6 Séjour.
"  6. Camp à Hannover Town un Mille au de la de la Ville  Le 7 Juillet  7 Milles de New-Castle.
"  7. Camp à Peage's Bridge ou Graham's house.  Le 8 Juillet  10 Milles de Hannover town.
"  8. Camp à Burck bridge ou Kenner's Tavern  Le 9 Juillet  12 Milles de Peages Bridge.
"  9. Camp à Bowling-green  Le 10 Juillet  9 Milles de Burck bridge.
"  10. Camp à Charles Thoon's-Ton's house  Le 11 Juillet  8 Milles ½ de Bowling-green.
"  11. Camp à Falmouth le 12 Juillet  14 milles de Charles Thoon's-Ton's house  le 13 Séjour.
"  12. Camp à Garrot's Tavern  Le 14 Juillet  13 milles de Falmouth (les Eaux n'étans pas assez abondantes, les divisions suivantes campèrent trois milles plus loing à — à Peyton's tavern.
"  13. Camp à Dumphris  le 15 Juillet  10 Milles de Peyton's Tavern Et 13 milles de Garrot's Tavern.
"  14. Camp à Colchester  Le 16 Juillet  10 Milles de Dumphris.
"  15. Camp à Alexandrie  le 17 Juillet  15 Milles de Clochester.
"  16. Camp à 1 Mille ½ au de la de George's Town.
"  17. Camp à Blanden'sburg  Le 19 Juillet  8 Milles de Georges Town  le 20 et 21 Séjour.
"  18. Camp à Snowden-iron-Work  le 22 Juillet  13 Milles de Blanden'sburg.
"  19. Camp à Spurier's Tavern  Le 23 Juillet  9 Milles de Snowden iron Work's.
"  20. Camp à Baltimore  Le 23 Juillet  13 Milles ½ de Spurier's Tavern.  Séjour jusquau 24 Aoust.
"  21. Camp à la forges de White marsh  Le 24 Aoust, 12, Milles ½ de Baltimore.
"  22. Camp à Bush Town  Le 25 Aout  12 milles ½ de la forge de White Marsh.
"  23. Camp à Lower Ferry  Le 26 Aoust, 12, Milles de Bush Town.  Le 27 Séjour.
"  24. Camp à Head-of-Elk  Le 28 Aoust  15 milles de de Lower Ferry.
"  25. Camp à Newport  Le 29 Aoust  16 Milles ½ d'Head-of-Elk.
"  26. Camp à Chester  Le 30 Aoust. 15 Milles de Newport.
"  27. Camp à Philadelphie Le 31 Aoust 16 Milles de Chester, Le 1$^{re}$ Septembre Séjous.
"  28. Camp à Read Lion T. Le 2, Septembre  15 milles de Philadelphie, manq[ue]

**Rochambeau, J. B. D. de V.**, *comte de*—Continued.

no. 29. Camp à Trenton Le 3 Septembre, 16 Milles de Read lion Voyez Campagne 1781, 25ᵉᵐᵉ Camp. Le 4, 5, et 6 Séjour.
" 30. Camp à Prince-Town le 7, Septembre, 12 Milles de Trentown. Voyez Campagne 1781, 24ᵉ camp.
" 31. Camp à Sommerset Court house le 8 Septembre 16 milles de Prince-Town.
" 32. Camp à Bullion's Tavern Le 19 Septembre 13 milles de Sommerset-Court-house.
" 33. Camp à Wyspany le 10 Septembre 16 milles de Bullion's Tavern. Voyez la Campagne 1781, 21ᵉ. Camp. (Le 11 Séjour)
" 34. Camp à Pompton-Meeting house Le 12 Septembre, 15 milles de Wyspany.
" 35. Camp à Suffrantz le 13 Septembre 15 milles de Pompton-Meeting-house.
" 36. Camp à Hawer-Straw le 14 Septembre, 15 milles ½ de Suffrantz Le 15 et 16 Séjour.
" 37. Camp à Peak's Kill, le 17 Septembre 9 milles ½ de hawer Straw Séjour jusquau 23 Septembre.
" 38. Camp à Huntz Tavern le 24 Septembre, 8 milles de Peak's Kill Séjour jusquau 21 Octobre.
" 39. Camp à Salem le 22 Octobre, 13 milles ½ de Huntz Tavern.
" 40. Camp à Dambury le 23 Octobre, 11 milles de Salem.
" 41. Camp à New Town le 24 Octobre. 12 milles de Dambury; Voyez la Campagne 1781 10ᵉ Camp. (Le 25 Séjour)
" 42. Camp à Break Neck le 26 Octobre, 15 milles de New Town, Voyez, Campagne 1781 9ᵉ Camp.
" 43. Camp à Barn's Tavern, le 27 Octobre, 13 milles de Break-Neck Voyez Campagne 1781. 8ᵉ Camp.
" 44. Camp à Farmington le 28 Octobre, 13 milles de Barn's Tavern.
" 45. Camp à East Hartford Le 29 Octobre, 12 milles ½ de Farmingtown Séjour jusqu'au 4 Novembre.
" 46. Camp à deux Milles au de là de Bolton Meeting house le 4 Novembre 14 Milles d'East Hartford.
" 47. Camp à Windham le 5 Novembre 16 Milles ½ de Bolton Le 6 Séjour.
" 48. Camp à Cantorbery le 7 Novembre, 10 milles de Windham.
" 49. Camp à Walen Town le 8 Novembre, 10 Milles de Cantorbery.
" 50. Camp à Waterman's Tavern, le 9 Novembre 10 Milles de Walen Town, Voyez Campagne 1781, 2º Camp.
" 51. Camp à Providence le 10 Novembre 15 milles de Waterman's Tavern, l'armée sur deux lignes dans lancien camp de la Brigade de Soiffonnois, Voyez les campagnes 1781 1º Camp
" 52. Camp à Providence sur Le chemin de Boston, le 13 Novembre, 4 milles de Lancien Camp.
" 53. Camp à Wrentham 1ʳ Décembre 16 milles du Camp de Providence.
" 54. Camp à Dedam le deux Décembre, 16 milles de Wrentham.

**Carrington, H. B.**

Battle maps and charts of the american revolution, with explanatory notes and school history references ... 88 pp. incl. 33 maps, front. (port.) 1 pl. 8°. New York, Chicago, A. S. Barnes & co. [1881]  1336

NOTE.—Same maps used in his work entitled: Battles of the american revolution.

CONTENTS.

p. [7] Outline of Atlantic coast.
" [9] The battle of Breeds hill, or Bunker hill [June 17th, 1775]
" [11] Assault upon Quebec [December 30, 1775]
" [13] Boston and vicinity [From june 20th, 1775 to march 17th, 1776]
" [15] Operations in Canada [From sept. 1755, to july 1776]
" [17] Battle of Long Island [August 27, 1776]
" [19] Operations near New York [1776]
" [21] Capture of Fort Washington [November 16th, 1776]
" [23] Trenton and vicinity [1777]
" [25] Trenton.—Princeton [December 26th, 1776]
" [27] Operations in New Jersey [1777]
" [29] Burgoynes Saragota campaign [From june 20th to oct. 19th, 1777]
" [31] Battle of Hubbardton [July 7th, 1776]
" [33] Battle of Bennington [August 16th, 1777]
" [35] Battle of Freeman's Farm [September 17th, 1777]
" [37] Battle of Bemis heights [October 7th, 1777]
" [39] Surrender of Burgoyne [October 19th, 1777]
" [41] Attack of forts Clinton and Montgomery [October 6th, 1777]
" [43] Battle of Brandywine [September 11th, 1777]
" [45] Battle of Germantown [October 4th, 1777]
" [47] Operations on the Delaware [1777]
" [49] Operations near Philadelphia [1776–8]
" [51] Encampment at Valley Forge [1777–8]
" [53] Lafayette at Barren hill [1778]
" [55] Battle of Monmouth [June 29th, 1778]
" [57] Siege of Newport [August 1778]
" [59] Siege of Savannah [September 16th to october 9th 1780]
" [61] Siege of Charleston [May 12th 1780]
" [63] Operations from Staten Island.—Battle of Springfield [June, 1780]
" [05] Outline map of Hudson river highlands.
" [67] Battle of Camden [August 16th, 1780]
" [69] Arnold at Petersburg.—Arnold at Richmond [April 25th, 1781—January 5th, 1780]
" [71] Battle of Cowpens [January 7th, 1781]
" [73] Operations in southern states [1779–81]
" [75] Battle of Guilford [March 15th, 1781]
" [77] Hobkirk hill [April 25th, 1781]
" [79] Battle of Eutaw Springs [September 8th, 1781]
" [81] Operations in Chesapeake bay [1777–81]
" [83] La Fayette in Virginia [1781]
" [85] Benedict Arnold at New London [September 6th, 1781]
" [87] Siege at Yorktown [1781]

**Faden, W.**

Atlas of battles of the american revolution, together with maps showing the routes of the british and american armies, plans of cities, surveys of harbors, &c., taken during that eventful period by officers attached to the royal army. 2 p. l., 36 maps on 55 l. fol. [New York, Bartlett & Welford, 1845?] 1337

NOTE.—This atlas sometimes contains 16, 24 or 33 maps.
The original atlas published in London, 1793, was a collection of maps varying in number from seventeen to twenty-two, published at different times with

**Faden, W.**—Continued.

this title. Bartlett & Welford purchased a large remainder of these maps and issued them with the above title-page. Their edition is distinguished by the broad letters with which the title is printed, and the omission of the place and date of publication. *cf.* Sabin's. Dictionary of books relating to America. v. 1, p. 309.

CONTENTS.

no. 1. A plan of the action at Bunkers hill, on the 17th of june 1775 . . . Engraved for Stedman's history of the american war. Published by the author april 12th 1793.

" 2. Plan of the city and environs of Quebec with its siege and blockade by the americans, from the 8th of december 1775 to the 13th of may 1776. Published 12 sept. 1776.

" 3. Plan of the siege of Savannah, with the joint attack of the french and americans on the 9th october 1779 . . . Printed feb. 2d 1784.

" 4. A plan of the surprise of Stoney Point . . . on the 15th july, 1779. Also of the works erected on Verplanks Point, for the defence of Kings ferry by the british forces in july, 1779, from the surveys of W$^m$ Simpson . . . and D. Campbell . . . by John Hills . . Printed march 1st 1784.

" 5. British camp at Trudruffrin from the 18th to the 21st of september 1777 . . . Engraved & published july 1st 1778.

" 6. Plan of the siege of York Town in Virginia. Published march 1st, 1787.

" 7. Battle of Guilford . . . 15th of march 1781. Published march 1st, 1787.

" 8. Plan of the battle fought near Camden, august 16th 1780. Published march 1st 1787.

" 9. Sketch of the battle of Hobkirks hill . . . on the 25th april, 1781. Drawn by C. Vallancey . . . Engraved and published, aug. 1st 1783.

" 10. Plan of the siege of Charlestown in South Carolina. Published march 1st 1787.

" 11. A plan of the town of Newport in Rhode Island. Surveyed by Charles Blaskowitz . . . Engraved and published sept. 1st 1777.

" 12. Sketch of the surprise of German Town, by the american forces . . . october 4th 1777; by J. Hills. Published march 12th 1784.

" 13. A plan of the city and environs of Philadelphia. Survey'd by N. Scull and G. Heap . . . Engraved by Will$^m$ Faden 1777. Published march 12th 1777.

" 14. Sketch of part of the island of S$^{te}$ Lucie [1778] Published by James Wyld.

" 15. A plan of York Town and Gloucester . . . 1781. From an actual survey in the possession of Jn$^o$ Hills. Printed oct. 7th 1785.

" 16. Sketch of the position of the british forces at Elizabeth Town Point . . . on the 8th june 1780 . . . By John Hills . . . Published april 12th 1784.

" 17. Plan of the attack of the forts Clinton & Montgomery upon Hudsons river . . . the 6th of oct. 1777 . . . By John Hills. Published june 1st 1784.

no. 18. A plan of the town of Boston, with the intrenchments &c. of his majestys forces in 1775: from the observations of lieut. Page . . . and from the plans of other gentlemen. Engraved and printed 1st oct. 1777.

" 19. A plan of the town, bar, harbour and environs, of Charlestown in South Carolina. Published june 1st 1780.

" 20. The course of Delaware river from Philadelphia to Chester . . . Printed jany 1st 1785.

" 21. A plan of the city and environs of Philadelphia . . . Engraved and published jan. 1st 1779.

" 22. A topographical chart of the Bay of Narraganset in the province of New England . . . By Charles Blaskowitz . . . Engraved & printed july 22d 1777.

" 23. A plan of part of the provinces of Pensylvania, and East & West New Jersey . . . in 1777 . . . 1778. By John Hills . . . Published june 1st 1784.

" 24. A plan of the entrance of Chesapeak bay, with James and York rivers . . . Publish'd nov. 26th 1781.

" 25. Plan of the action at Huberton . . . on the 7th july 1777. Publifhed feby 1st 1780.

" 26. . . . View of the fort on the western end of Sullivans island . . . during the attack on the 28th of june 1776 . . . Engraved & published augt 10th 1776.

" 27. A birds eye view from part of Mount Pleasant . . . Engraved & published augt 10th 1776.

" 28. . . . View of Charles Town . . . Engraved & published augt 10th 1776.

" 29. Plan of Amelia island.—A chart of the entrance into St Mary's river taken by captn W. Fuller in november 1769.—A chart of the mouth of Nassau river. Published 26 march, 1770.

" 30. Position of the detachment under lieut col. Baum at Walmscock near Bennington . . . on the 16th august 1777. Drawn by lieut. Durnford. Engraved 1780.

" 31. A chart of Delaware bay and river . . . by Joshua Fisher . . . Published march 12, 1776.

" 32. Plan of the encampment and position of the army under his excelly lt general Burgoyne at Swords House on Hudson's river near Stillwater on sept 17th with the positions of that part of the army engaged on the 19th septr 1777. Drawn by W. C. Wilkinson . . . Published feby 1st 1780.

" 33. Plan of the encampment and position of the army under his excelly lt general Burgoyne at Bræmus heights on Hudson's river near Stillwater on the 20th septr . . . & 7th . . . & 8th oct. 1777. Drawn by W. C. Wilkinson . . . Published feby 1st 1780.

" 34. A plan of the operations of the king's army . . . in New York and east New Jersey . . . from the 12th of october, to the 28th november 1776 . . . By Claude Joseph Sauthier . . . 1777. Published feby 25th 1777.

" 35. A map of the country in which the army under lt general Burgoyne acted in the campaign of 1777 . . . Drawn by mr Medcalfe . . . Published feby 1st 1780.

" 36. Battle of Brandywine . . . september the 11th 1777 . . . Published, april 13th 1778.

**Guizot, F. P. G.**

Vie correspondance et écrits de Washington, publiés d'après l'édition américaine et précédés d'une introduction sur l'influence et le caractère de Washington dans la révolution des États-Unis d'Amérique . . . Atlas. 2 p. l., 16 maps, 3 facs. fol. Paris, C. Gosselin, 1840. 1338

CONTENTS.

- no. 1. George Washington d'après le tableau de Stuart.
- " 2. George Washington d'après le buste de Houdon.
- " 3. Title page of "A book of surveys, began july 22$^d$ 1749."
- " 4. Bataille des Grandes Prairies, 3 juillet, 1754.
- " 5. Portrait of Martha Washington.
- " 6. Médaille d'honneur offerte à George Washington par le congrès.
- " 7. Signatures of Washington.
- " 8. Défaite du général Braddok 9 juillet 1755.
- " 9. Opérations militaires en Virginie.
- " 10. Boston avec les environs en 1775 & 1776.
- " 11. Positions de l'armée américaine et bataille de Long Island, le 27 août 1776.
- " 12. Plan du fort de Washington.
- " 13. Bataille de Trenton et de Princeton.
- " 14. Bataille de Germantown.
- " 15. Campement à Valley Forge.
- " 16. Bataille de Monmouth.
- " 17. Travaux à Stony Point.
- " 18. Opérations militaires sur l'Hudson.
- " 19. Plan du siège de Yorktown.
- " 20. Plan du domaine de Mont Vernon.
- " 21. Carte des États-Unis.
- " 22. Declaration of independence.

**Hills, J.**

A collection of plan's &c. &c. &c. in the province of New Jersey . . . 2 p. l., 20 col. maps on 15 l. fol. [1776-1782] 1339

NOTE.—In manuscript maps showing sir Henry Clinton's operations in the Jerseys; by various draftsmen including John Hills, A. Dunham, J. Rue, J. Fisher, James Grant, T. Milliadge, B. Morgan, A. Sutherland, J. Williams, A. Dennis.

Twelve of this collection are by John Hills. Some are signed, "Lieut. J. Hills, 23$^d$ reg$^t$." In the british army lists of 1781-84 is the following: " — Hill, 23$^d$ reg$^t$ foot. America. 5 Oct. 1781. Second lieut." Records of the 23$^d$ regt. after 1784 do not contain his name. It is probable that he settled in Philadelphia at the close of the revolution. "John Hills, surveyor and draftsman" appears in the Philadelphia directory from 1795 to 1817. The same John Hills made plans of the city of Philadelphia in 1796 and 1801-1807; that of 1796 is signed, "John Hills, surveyor and draughtsman."

no. 14, A map of Monmouth county, is dedicated "To his excellency sir Henry Clinton . . . general and commander of his majesty's forces &c. &c. &c. in North America . . . by . . . Iohn Hills, afs$^t$ engineer."

### CONTENTS.

no. 1. Plan of Perth Amboy from an Actual Survey [By James Grant] 9 x 8.
" 2. Sketch of Bonham Town [showing] Redoubts for its Defence in the Winter. 1776. 77. [By A. Sutherland] 7½ x 12.
" 3. Sketch of Brunswick [By A. Sutherland] 8½ x 10½.
" 4. Sketch of the Ground near M[r] Low's at Rariton Landing [By John Hills] 8½ x 10¾.
" 5. Sketch of Haddonfield March. 1778 [By John Hills] Scale 400 paces to an inch 6½ x 8½.
" 6. Sketch of the Roads from Penny Hill to Black Horse through Mount Holly. By I Hills June 1778 Scale 400 paces to an inch 19 x 27.
" 7. Sketch of the Road from Black Horse to Crosswick. By I Hills June 1778 Scale 400 paces to an inch 19 x 21½.
" 8. Sketch of Allens Town June. 1778 [By John Hills] Scale 400 paces to an inch 8 x 7.
" 9. Sketch of Part of the Road from Freehold to Middle Town shewing the Skirmish between the Rear of the British Army under the Command of his Excellency Gen[l] Sir Henry Clinton and the advanced Corps of the Rebel Army June 28. 1778. By I Hills Scale 400 paces to an inch 17¼ x 22¾.
" 10. Sketch of Middle Town June [By John Hills] Scale 400 paces to an inch 8 x 7¼.
" 11. A Map of Part of the Province of Jersey [By Morgan, Williams, Dennis, Rue, Dunham, Taylor, Skinner, &c.] Compiled from the Original Surveys. By I. Hills Afs[t] Engineer 1781 N. B. The Doted [!] Red Line is the Line of March of the Royal Army under the Command of His Excellency Gen[l] Sir Henry Clinton K. B. &c &c &c 1778 20 x 27.
" 12. A Map Somerset County [By B. Morgan] Reduced from the Original Survey By I. Hills, Afs[t] Engineer 1781 19 x 26½.
" 13. A Map Middlesex County [By A. Dunham and J. Rue] Reduced from the Original Survey. By I Hills Afs[t] Engineer. 1781 24 x 27.
" 14. A Map of Monmouth County [By I. Williams and A. Dennis] Reduced from the Original Survey By I. Hills Afs[t] Engineer 1781 ... 28½ x 53¼.
" 15. A Sketch of the Northern Parts of New Jersey [By T. Milliadge] Copied from the Original By Lieu[t] I Hills 23[d] Reg[t] 1781. Scale 2 miles to an inch 38½ x 33.
" 16. A Chart of Delaware Bay and River, from the Cape's to Philadelphia, being Part of the Province of New Jersey & Pennsylvania. [By Joshua Fisher] Copied from the Original By I. Hills 1777. 24 x 56.
" 17. Sketch of the Road from Paulus Hook and Hobocken to New Bridge By I. Hills 1778 Scale 800 paces to an inch 28 x 23½.
" 18. A Plan of Paulus Hook with the Road to Bergen and Parts adjacent in the Province of New Jersey. Survey'd by I Hills Afs[t] Engineer 1781 Inset: A Plan of Paulus Hook shewing the Works erected for its Defence 1781-2 26¾ x 27½.
" 19. Plan of Paulus Hook shewing the Works erected for its Defence 1781-2 Survey'd [!] By I Hills Lieu[t] in the 23[d] Reg[t] Scale 200 feet to an inch 18½ x 14.
" 20. Plan of the Road from Elizabeth Town Point to Elizabeth Town Shewing the Rebel Works Raised for its Defence Survey'd By I Hills Afsistant Eng[r] 1780 Scale 400 feet to an inch 17¾ x 27¾.

**Le Boucher, O. J.**

Atlas pour servir à l'intelligence de l'histoire de la guerre de l'indépendence des États-Unis.   cover-title, 7 maps.  fol. [Paris, Anselin, 1830]

1340

NOTE.—These maps were published in the first edition of this work, entitled: Histoire de la dernière guerre, entre la Grande-Bretagne et les États-Unis de l'Amérique, la France, l'Espagne et la Hollande . . . 1775–1783. Paris, chez Brocas, 1787.

CONTENTS.

no. 1. Carte réduite du nord des États-Unis . . . Copiée . . . sur le no. 1$^{er}$ du Neptune, Américo-Septentrional.
" 2. Carte réduite du sud des États-Unis . . . Copiée . . . sur le no. 2 du Neptune, Américo-Septentrional.
" 3. Carte réduite des Isles du Vent . . . Copiée . . . sur le no. 75 de l'Hydrographie françoise, tom. II.
" 4. Carte du golfe de Bengale . . . sur le no. 34 de l'Atlas maritime de Belin, tome III.
" 5. Carte réduite du golfe du Mexique . . . Copiée . . . sur la carte de Belin, insérée dans sa description géographique des Isles Antilles.
" 6. Carte de l'isle S$^t$. Christophe . . . Copiée . . . sur la carte de Belin.
" 7. Plan de la baye de Trinquemalay . . . Copiée . . . sur celui du petit Atlas maritime de Belin, tome, III, no. 32.

**Marshall, J.**

Life of George Washington.   Maps and subscribers' names.   1 p. l., [21] pp., 10 maps.  4°.  Philadelphia, C. P. Wayne, 1807.

1341

NOTE.—To accompany his: Life of George Washington. Compiled under the inspection of the hon. Bushrod Washington, from original papers . . . Philadelphia, C. P. Wayne, 1804–1807.
Maps on a larger scale than in edition of 1832. See title 1342.
A view of Washington city in 1800 is found in the atlas to accompany the french translation of Marshall's life of Washington by S. F. Henry.

CONTENTS.

no. 1. Boston with its environs. Eng$^d$ by J. Vallance. 8¾ x 12¼.
" 2. A plan of New York island, part of Long island &c. shewing the position of the american and british armies, before, at, and after engagement on the heights, August 27$^{th}$ 1776. Drawn by S. Lewis. J. H. Seymour sculp. 16 x 10.
" 3. A plan of the country from Frogs point to Croton river shewing the positions of the american and british armies from 12$^{th}$ of october 1776 until the engagement on the White Plains on the 28$^{th}$   Drawn by S. Lewis    B. Jones sc.   16 x 8½.
" 4. A plan of the northern part of New Jersey, shewing the positions of the american and british armies after crossing the North river in 1776. Drawn by S. Lewis from surveys by order of gen. Washington. Engrav'd by F$^s$ Shallus. 15¾ x 10.
" 5. A map of the country from Rariton river in East Jersey to Elk Head in Maryland shewing the several operations of the american and british armies, in 1776 & 1777. Drawn by S. Lewis from surveys made by orders of G. Washington. Engraved by I. H. Seymour. 9¾ x 15½.

" 6. A map of the country which was the scene of operations of the northern army; including the Wilderness through which general Arnold marched to attack Quebec. Engraved by F. Shallus. 10¼ x 8½.
" 7. A map of part of Rhode Island shewing the positions of the american and british armies at the siege of Newport, and the subsequent action on the 29th of august 1778. Drawn by S. Lewis Engraved by Benjⁿ Jones. 16½ x 10.
" 8. A map of those parts of Virginia, North Carolina, South Carolina, & Georgia which were the scenes of the most important operations of the southern armies. Compiled by S. Lewis. Engraved by Frances Shallus. 14¼ x 10¼.
" 9. Plan of the investment and attack of York in Virginia. Engraved by Frances Shallus. 9 x 8½.
" 10. Plan of the siege of Charleston in S. Carolina. Drawn by S. Lewis. Tanner sc. 9½ x 14¼.

Atlas to Marshall's Life of Washington. 1 p. l., 10 maps. 8°. Philadelphia, J. Crissy [1832] 1342

NOTE.—To accompany his: Life of George Washington. Compiled under the inspection of the hon. Bushrod Washington, from original papers . . . Philadelphia, J. Crissy, 1832.
Engraved title.
Same maps as title 1341, but smaller scale.

**Sayer, R.,** *and* **Bennet, J.**
The american military pocket atlas; being an approved collection of correct maps, both general and particular, of the british colonies; efpecially thofe which now are, or probably may be the theatre of war. Taken principally from the actual surveys and judicious obfervations of engineers De Brahm and Romans; Cook, Jackson, and Collet; maj. Holland, and other officers, employed in his majesty's fleets and armies. viii pp., 1 l., 6 maps. 8°. London, for R. Sayer & J. Bennet [1776] 1343

NOTE.—Known as the "Holster atlas," owing to its being made for the use of the mounted british officers.

CONTENTS.

no. 1. North America as divided amongst the european powers. By Samuel Dunn . . . 1774.
" 2. A compleat map of the West Indies, containing the coasts of Florida, Louisiana, New Spain, and Terra Firma: with all the islands. By Samuel Dunn . . . 1774.
" 3. A general map of the northern british colonies, in America . . . corrected from governor Pownell's late map. 1776.
" 4. A general map of the middle british colonies, in America . . . corrected from governor Pownell's late map. 1776.
" 5. A general map of the southern british colonies, in America . . .—Insets: Plan of Charlestown.—Plan of Sᵗ Augustine. From the modern surveys of engineer de Brahm, capt. Collet, Mouzon & others; and from the large hydrographical survey of the coasts of East and West Florida, by B. Romans. 1776.
" 6. A survey of lake Champlain, including lake George, Crown Point and Sᵗ John . . . by William Brassier . . . 1762.—Inset: A particular plan of lake George; surveyed in 1756. By capᵗ Jackson. Printed, aug. 5, 1776.

### Revolutionary and War of 1812.

**Wilkinson, J.**

Diagrams and plans, illustrative of the principal battles and military affairs, treated of in Memoirs of my own times ... 2 p. l., 2 l., 20 (*i. e.* 19) maps. 4°. Philadelphia, A. Small, 1816.    1344

> NOTE.—To accompany his "Memoirs of my own times." 3 v. 8°. Philadelphia, A. Small, 1816.
> "The following diagrams and plans were sketched by the author from his own recollection, or the information of military friends actually engaged in the several affairs to which they relate ... The author, however, disclaims the intention of offering them to the public, as the result of actual and accurate surveys." *cf.* "Advertisement," signed J. W.

*Contents.*

- no. 1. Sketch of the rivers S! Lawrence and Soriel ...
- " 2. Sketch of Trenton as it was, dec! 26th 1776.
- " 3-5. Part of New Jersey embracing Trenton & Princeton; to exhibit the operations of the american & british armies, jan! 1st·, 2nd & 3rd· 1777 with gen! Washington's previus [!] movements against the hessians, under col! Rahl ... 1776.
- " 6. Affair of Princeton, january 3rd. 1777.
- " 7. Part of the river S! Lawrence.
- " 8. Sketch of the S! Lawrence from Cornwall to Grand river.
- " 9. Disposition of the american troops on the 30th march 1814, before La Cole mill ...
- " 10. Sackets harbor.
- " 11. [Action at Fleet's creek]
- " 12. Battle of Bridgewater. View 1st
- " 13.    "    "    "    "    2nd
- " 14.    "    "    "    "    3rd
- " 14.a    "    "    "    "    4th
- " 15. Map of the straights of Niagara from lake Erie to lake Ontario.
- " 16. Map of maj: gen: Ross's route, with the british column, from Benedict ... to the city of Washington, august, 1814.
- " 17. The affair of Bladensburg, august 24th 1814.
- " 18. [Philadelphia]
- " 19. Plan of Rouses point at the fort of lake Champlain.
- " 20. Part of Vermont.

### War of 1812.

**Latour, A. L.**

Atlas to the historical memoir of the war in West Florida and Louisiana ... 1 p. l., 8 maps, 1 pl. 8°. Philadelphia, J. Conrad & co. 1816.    1345

> NOTE.—Plate no. 1, is the portrait of general Jackson, bound with the historical memoir.

CONTENTS.

- no. 2. A general map of the seat of war in Louisiana & West Florida ...
- " 3. Plan shewing the attack made by a british squadron on fort Bowyer at Mobile Point on the 15th sep.tr 1815 ...
- " 4. Plan of the attack made by the british barges on five american gunboats on the 14th december 1814 ...

no. 5. Map shewing the landing of the british army, its several encampments . . . on the Mississippi . . . 1815.
" 6. Plan of the attack made by major gen. Jackson on a division of the british army . . . on the 23rd december 1814 . . .
" 7. Plan of the attack and defence of the american lines below New Orleans, on the 8th. january, 1815 . . .
" 8. Plan of fort S$^t$. Philip at Plaquemines, shewing the position of the british vessels when bombarding the fort . . . 1815.
" 9. Map of Mobile Point & part of the bay, & of Dauphine island . . . 1815.

**Melish, J.**

A military and topographical atlas of the United States; including the british possessions & Florida . . . to which is added, a list of the military districts, a register of the army, and a list of the navy of the United States . . .   6, 3–34, 3–18, 3–29, 44 pp., 8 maps. 8°.  Philadelphia, G. Palmer, 1813.   1346

CONTENTS.

no. 1. Map of the seat of war in North America. 2$^{nd}$ ed. . . . H. S. Tanner direx$^t$
" 2. View of the country round the falls of Niagara. J. Vallance sculp$^t$
" 3. East end of lake Ontario. H. S. Tanner sc.
" 4. Plan of Montreal, with a map of the islands & adjoining country. H. S. Tanner sc.
" 5. A map of the southern section of the United States including the Floridas & Bahamas islands shewing the seat of war in that department . . . 1813. Engraved by H. S. Tanner.
" 6. Map of the american coast, from Lynhaven bay to Narraganset bay . . . 1813. Engraved by H. S. Tanner.
" 7. Map of Detroit river and adjacent country, from an original drawing, by a british engineer. 1813. H. S. Tanner sc.
" 8. Plan of Quebec and adjacent country shewing the principal encampments & works of the british & french armies during the siege by general Wolfe in 1759. Reduced from the m. s. s. map of capt. J. B. Glegg.—Inset: View of Quebec from Point Levi.

A military and topographical atlas of the United States; including the british possessions & Florida . . .   6 pp., 1 l., [3]–34, 3–20 pp., 1 l., [3]–29 pp., 12 fold. maps.  8°.  Philadelphia, J. Melish, 1815.
1347

CONTENTS.

no. 1. Map of the seat of war in North America. 2nd ed. . . . H. S. Tanner direx$^t$
" 2. View of the country round the falls of Niagara. J. Vallance sculp$^t$
" 3. East end of lake Ontario. H. S. Tanner sc.
" 4. Plan of Montreal, with a map of the islands & adjoining country. H. S. Tanner sc.
" 5. A map of the southern section of the United States including the Floridas & Bahama islands shewing the seat of war, in that department . . . 1813. Improved 11th nov$^r$ 1814. Engraved by H. S. Tanner.
" 6. Map of the american coast, from Lynhaven bay to Narraganset bay . . . 1813.

**Melish, J.**—Continued.
- no. 7. Map of Detroit river and adjacent country, from an original drawing, by a british engineer. 1813. H. S. Tanner sc.
- " 8. Plan of Quebec and adjacent country shewing the principal encampments & works of the british & french armies during the siege by general Wolfe in 1759 . . . Reduced from the m. m. s. map of cap? J. B. Glegg.—Inset: View of Quebec from Point Levi.
- " 9. East end of lake Ontario and river St. Lawrence from Kingston to French mills. Reduced from an original drawing in the naval department . . . 1814. H. S. Tanner sc.
- " 10. Map of the river St. Lawrence and adjacent country from Williamsburg to Montreal. From an original drawing in the war department. 1814. H. S. Tanner sc.
- " 11. Map of the seat of war among the Creek indians. From the original drawing in the war department. 1814. H. S. Tanner sc.
- " 12. Map of New Orleans and adjacent country . . . 1815.

### Civil.

**Bechler, G. R.**

Atlas showing battles, engagements, and important localities connected with the campaigns in Virginia, completing the Campaign map . . .  4 p. l., 16 pl. obl. 12°. Philadelphia, G. R. Bechler [1864]  1348

NOTE.—L. C. has also his Campaign map, 1864.

#### CONTENTS.

- no. 1. [Washington and its forts]
- " 2. Harper's ferry and the main features of Bolivar, Loudon & Maryland heights.
- " 3. Battlefield of Manassas plains or Bull Run, july 21'', 1861.
- " 4. F? Monroe, Norfolk and vicinity.
- " 5. Defensive positions of the Confederates near Yorktown. Peninsula campaign.
- " 6. Main features of the country between Williamsburg, West Point, Charles city & White House, relative to the peninsula campaign.
- " 7. Richmond and eastern environs, relative to the peninsula campaign.
- " 8. Entrenchments of the Union army after the battle of Malvern Hill's. Peninsula campaign.
- " 9. Plan of Cedar mountain and north east vicinity with references to gen! Pope's campaign.
- " 10. Map of Rappahannock and Brandy station in connection with Beverly's, Freeman's, Lee's & Fox's ford. In reference to gen! Pope's campaign in Va.
- " 11. Vicinity of Sulphur springs and Waterloo bridge with reference to gen! Pope's campaign.
- " 12. Plan of the battle of Groveton near Bull Run fought on the 30th of august 1862. Gen! Pope's campaign.
- " 13. Plan of the battlefield of Antietam. Fought on the 16 & 17 september, 1862.
- " 14. Principal features of the battle of Fredericksburgh, december 13, 1862. Burnside's campaign.
- " 15. Topographical features near Ely's, Bank's & U. S. ford on the Rappahannock river, including the main positions of the U. S. army at the battle of Chancellorsville, Va. Gen! Hooker's campaign.
- " 16. The battle of Gettysburg before the final assault.

**Cowles, C. D.**
    Atlas of the war of the rebellion. Giving Union and Confederate armies by actual surveys by the Union and Confederate engineers, and approved by the officers in command, of all the maps herein published. Approved by secretary of war, and by major George B. Davis. Revised for publication by J. A. Caldwell.   1 p. l., 2 l., 35 maps, 12 pl.  fol.  New York, atlas publishing co. 1892. [United States. War department]                    1349

    NOTE.—An official publication of the first 40 plates of the "Atlas to accompany the official records of the Union and Confederate armies. Washington, 1891-95." See also title 1353.

**Fisher, R. S.**
    A chronological history of the civil war in America. Illustrated with A. J. Johnson's and J. H. Colton's steel plate maps and plans of the southern states and harbors.   160 pp., 10 maps.  8°.  New York, Johnson & Ward, 1863.                                    1350

    NOTE.—Cover-title: Chronological history of the civil war in America and hand atlas of the slave states.

**Gaston, S. N.**
    The campaign atlas, for 1861 . . .   2 p. l., 14 maps.  12°. New York, S. N. Gaston, 1861.                                               1351

CONTENTS.

    no. [1] United States.
    "  [2] Delaware and Maryland.
    "  [3] Virginia.
    "  [4] North Carolina.
    "  [5] South Carolina.
    "  [6] Georgia.
    "  [7] Florida.
    "  [8] Mississippi.
    "  [9] Alabama.
    "  [10] Louisiana.
    "  [11] Arkansas.
    "  [12] Missouri.
    "  [13] Kentucky and Tennessee.
    "  [14] Texas.

**Paris, L. P. A. d'Orléans,** *comte* de.
    [Histoire de la guerre civile en Amérique]  Atlas.   30 maps.  fol. [Paris, M. Lévy, 1874-90]                                                               1352

    NOTE.—Originally published in parts: 6 pts. in 3 v. Title-pages of pts. 1-2 wanting.
    Work in 7 v. dated 1874-90; maps not dated; imprint date on title-page of pts. 3-4, 1886; pts. 5-6, 1883.

CONTENTS.

    no. 1. Carte générale du théâtre de la guerre. Inset: Côte de la Georgie.
    "  2. Virginie et Maryland. Insets: Environs de Leesburg.—Carnifex ferry d'après Lossing.

**Paris, L. P. A. d'Orleans,** *comte* **de**—Continued.
no. 3. Kentucky et Tennessee. Inset: Champ de bataille de Mill spring.
" 4. Missouri et Arkansas. Inset: Environs de Lexington d'après Lossing.—Champ de bataille de Wilson's creek d'après Lossing.
" 5. Environs de Washington et du Bull Run.
" 6. Pamlico sound (Caroline du Nord)
" 7. Sea islands (Caroline du Sud)
" 8. Belmont.—Pea Ridge.—Hampton roads.—Isle No. 10 et ses abords.
" 9. Fort Henry.—Fort Donelson.—Shiloh.
" 10. Yorktown et Williamsburg (Virginie) Inset: Environs de Yorktown.
" 11. Bouches du Mississippi et Nouvelle Orléans.
" 12. Environs de Richmond. Insets: Gaines mill.—Fair Oaks.—Glendale.
" 13. Winchester.—Suffolk (Virginie)—Environs de Corinth (Mississippi) Inset: Corinth.
" 14. Charleston (Caroline du Sud) Inset: Fort Pulaski.
" 15. Environs de Warrenton (Virginie)
" 16. Cedar Mountain (Virginie)—Harpers Ferry et South Mountain.—Antietam (Maryland)
" 17. Iuka.—Chickasaw bayou (Mississippi)—Murfreesborough (Tennessee)
" 18. Brashear city (Louisiane)—Nashville (Tennessee)—Galveston (Texas)
" 19. Les champs de bataille du Rappahannock. Inset: Environs de Fredericksburg.
" 20. Cours du Mississippi de Vicksburg à Bâton-Rouge.
" 21. Environs de Vicksburg.
" 22. Champion hill.—Big Black river bridge (Mississippi)—Port Hudson (Louisiane)
" 23. Vicksburg (Mississippi)
" 24. Vallée du Monocacy et contrées voisines.
" 25. Gettysburg (Pennsylvanie)
" 26. Vallée du Shenandoah (Virginie)
" 27. Bristow Station.—Manassas Gap.—Brandy Station (Virginie)
" 28. Carnifex Ferry (Virginie occidentale)—Mill spring.—Logan cross roads (Kentucky)—Pea Ridge (Arkansas)
" 29. Perryville (Kentucky) Insets: Thompson's station.—Iuka (Mississippi)
" 30. Cours inférieur du Mississipi.

**United States.** *War department.*
    Atlas to accompany the official records of the Union and Confederate armies. Published under the direction of the . . . secretaries of war, by maj. George B. Davis . . . mr. Leslie J. Perry . . . mr. Joseph W. Kirkley . . . Compiled by capt. Calvin D. Cowles . . . 2 v. 29 pp., 82 maps, 2 pl., 72 maps, 19 pl. fol. Washington, government printing office, 1891-95.    **1353**
    NOTE.—House documents v. 40. 52d congress. 1st session. 1891-92.
    See also title 1349.

    Atlas of the battlefield of Antietam, prepared under the direction of the Antietam battlefield board, lieut. col. Geo. W. Davis, U. S. A., president, gen. E. A. Carman, U. S. V., gen. H. Heth, C. S. A. Surveyed by lieut. col. E. B. Cope, engineer, H. W. Mattern, assistant engineer, of the Gettysburg national park. Drawn by

Charles H. Ourand, 1899. Position of troops by gen. E. A. Carman. Published by authority of the secretary of war, under the direction of the chief of engineers, U. S. army, 1904. 2 p. l., 14 fold. maps. fol. Washington, government printing office, 1904.
1354

Atlas of battlefields of Chickamauga, Chattanooga, and vicinity. cover-title, [6] pp., 14 maps. fol. Washington, government printing office, 1900–1901. 1355

NOTE.—56 Congress. 2d sess. House doc. 514. In v. 101, 4175.
A duplicate sheet of pages 3 and 4 inserted.

**Whitney, W. H.**
Union and Confederate campaigns in the lower Shenandoah valley illustrated. Twenty years after—at the first reunion of Sheridan's veterans on the fields and in the camps of the valley. 1 p. l., 66 pp. incl. 25 maps. fol. Boston, W. H. Whitney, 1883. 1356

NOTE.—Blue prints.

### Spanish American.

**Armstrong, L.**
Pictorial atlas illustrating the Spanish-American war: comprising a history of the great conflict of the United States with Spain. 184 pp. incl. col. front., 44 col. maps, illus. fol. Washington, R. A. Dinsmore [°1898] 1357

**Rand, McNally & co.**
History of the Spanish-American war with handy atlas maps. 16 pp. incl. 6 col. maps, 13 port. 4°. Chicago and New York, Rand, McNally & co. 1898.
[ *With* Rand, McNally & co.'s universal atlas of the world. 1899]
1358

### WEATHER.

**United States.** *Department of agriculture. Weather bureau.*
Summary of international meteorological observations. By H. H. C. Dunwoody, major, signal corps, U. S. army. Published by authority of the secretary of agriculture. xl., 53 maps. obl. fol. Washington, weather bureau, 1893. 1359

NOTE.—Bulletin A.

Rainfall and snow of the United States, compiled to the end of 1891, with annual, seasonal, monthly, and other charts. By Mark W. Harrington, chief of the weather bureau. Published by authority of the secretary of agriculture. 1 p. l., 23 maps. obl. fol. Washington, weather bureau, 1894. 1360

NOTE.—Bulletin C—Atlas.

## GENERAL.

(Arranged chronologically)

### 1794

**Morse, J.**

The american geography; or, a view of the present situation of the United States of America: containing aftronomical geography, geographical definitions, difcovery, and general defcription . . . A particular description of Kentucky, the western territory, the territory south of Ohio, and Vermont . . . with a view of the british, spanish, portuguese, and dutch dominions, on the continent, and in the West Indies, and of Europe, Asia, and Africa . . . New ed. rev., cor., and greatly enlarged . . . and illustrated by twenty-five maps.   1 p. l., vi, [4], 715 pp., 25 maps. 4°. London, for J. Stockdale, 1794.   1361

NOTE.—Another edition, published in London, 1794, has slight variation in title and only 3 maps. While this work can not be regarded as an atlas, it contains a collection of the earliest maps of the states in the union.

CONTENTS.

no. 1. A new map of North America.
" 2. " " " " Upper & Lower Canada.
" 3. " " " " Nova Scotia, New Brunswick and Cape Breton.
" 4. A map of Newfoundland.
" 5. A map of the northern and middle states; comprehending the western territory and the british dominions in North America. 1792.
" 6. A map of Vermont.
" 7. " " " New Hampshire.
" 8. " " " Massachusetts.
" 9. " " " Rhode Island.
" 10. " " " Connecticut.
" 11. " " " the state of New York.
" 12. " " " New Jersey.
" 13. " " " Pennsylvania.
" 14. A map of the states of Virginia, North Carolina, South Carolina and Georgia; comprehending the spanish provinces of east and west Florida: exhibiting the boundaries as fixed by the late treaty of peace between the United States and spanish dominions. Compiled from late surveys & observations by Joseph Purcell. 1792.
" 15. Plan of the city of Washington.
" 16. Map of Virginia, Maryland and Delaware.
" 17. A map of the back settlements.
" 18. A map of Kentucky. Drawn from actual observations. By John Filson.—Inset: A plan of the rapids in the river Ohio. 1793.
" 19. A map of North Carolina.
" 20. " " " the Tennessee government.
" 21. " " " South Carolina.
" 22. " " " east and west Florida.
" 23. " " " South America and the adjacent islands.
" 24. " " " the West Indies.
" 25. " " " world exhibiting all the new discoveries.

### 1795

**Carey, M.**
Carey's american atlas . . .   1 p. l., 21 maps.   fol.   Philadelphia, M. Carey, 1795. 1362

NOTE.—All maps, except nos. 3, 6, 7, and 14, carry the following: Engraved for Carey's american edition of Guthrie's geography improved.

#### CONTENTS.

no. 1. The british possessions in North America . . . by Samuel Lewis, 1794.
" 2. The province of Maine . . . by Samuel Lewis, 1794.
" 3. The state of New Hampshire. Compiled by Samuel Lewis. 1794.
" 4. Vermont . . . delineated . . . by Amos Doolittle . . .
" 5. The state of Massachusetts. Compiled . . . by Samuel Lewis.
" 6. Connecticut . . . delineated . . . by A. Doolittle . . .
" 7. The state of Rhode Island; compiled from the surveys . . . of Caleb Harris. By Harding Harris.
" 8. The state of New York, compiled . . . by Samuel Lewis. 1795.
" 9. The State of New Jersey . . . compiled by Samuel Lewis · [1794]
" 10. The state of Pennsylvania, reduced . . . from Reading Howell's map by Samuel Lewis [1794]
" 11. Delaware . . . [1795]
" 12. The state of Maryland . . . by Samuel Lewis [1794]
" 13. The state of Virginia . . . by Samuel Lewis. 1794.
" 14. The state of North Carolina . . . by Samuel Lewis.
" 15. The state of South Carolina . . . by Samuel Lewis. 1795.
" 16. Georgia . . .
" 17. Kentucky, reduced from Eilhu Barker's large map.
" 18. A map of the Tennassee government formerly part of North Carolina taken chiefly from surveys by gen! D. Smith & others.
" 19. A map of South America . . .
" 20. A map of the discoveries made by capt! Cook & Clerke in the years 1778 & 1779 between the eastern coast of Asia and the western coast of North America . . . also m! Hearn's discoveries to the north westward of Hudson's bay, in 1772.
" 21. A chart of the West Indies . . .

### 1795

**Russell, J.**
An american atlas . . . and a plan of the city of Washington . . .   1 p. l., 9 maps.   fol.   London, H. D. Symonds & J. Ridgway, 1795. 1363

#### CONTENTS.

no. 1. A general map of North America . . . 1794.
" 2. A general map of South America . . . 1794.
" 3. An accurate map of the West Indies with the adjacent coast of America . . .
" 4. An accurate map of the United States of America, according to the treaty of peace of 1783.
" 5. Map of the northern, or, New England states of America, comprehending Vermont, New Hampshire, district of Main [!] Massachusetts, Rhode-Island, and Connecticut . . .

**Russell, J.**—Continued.
    no. 6. Map of the middle states, of America. Comprehends New-York, New-Jersey, Pennsylvania, Delaware and the territory n. w. of Ohio . . .
    " 7. Map of the southern states of America, comprehending Maryland, Virginia, Kentucky, territory s$^{th}$ of the Ohio, North Carolina, Tennessee governm$^t$, South Carolina, & Georgia . . .
    " 8. Map of the state of Kentucky; with the adjoining territories . . . 1794.
    " 9. Plan of the city of Washington, in the territory of Columbia, ceded by the states of Virginia and Maryland to the United States of America, and by them established as the seat of their government, after the year 1800.

## 1796

**Carey, M.**
    Carey's american pocket atlas . . . with a concise description of each state. 118 pp., 19 maps. 16°. Philadelphia, for M. Carey, 1796.     1364
    NOTE.—Maps engraved by W. Barker, J. H. Seymour, A. Doolittle.

### CONTENTS.

    no. 1. The United States of America.
    " 2. Vermont, from actual survey.
    " 3. The state of New Hampshire, by Sam! Lewis.
    " 4. Province of Maine.
    " 5. Massachusetts.
    " 6. Rhode Island.
    " 7. Connecticut.
    " 8. New York.
    " 9. New Jersey.
    " 10. Pennsylvania.
    " 11. Delaware.
    " 12. N. W. Territory.
    " 13. Maryland.
    " 14. Virginia.
    " 15. Kentuckey [!]
    " 16. North Carolina.
    " 17. Tennassee, lately the s. w? territory.
    " 18. South Carolina.
    " 19. Georgia.

## 1796

    Carey's general atlas . . . 1 p. l., 45 maps. fol. Philadelphia, M. Carey, 1796.     1365
    NOTE.—The following maps relate to America:
    no. 1. A map of the world . . .
    " 2. A chart of the world . . .
    " 23. The british possessions in North America . . . by Samuel Lewis. 1794.
    " 24. A map of the United States . . . by Samuel Lewis. 1795.
    " 25. Vermont . . . Delineated & engraved by Amos Doolittle . . .
    " 26. The state of New-Hampshire. Compiled . . . by Samuel Lewis, 1794.
    " 27. The province of Maine . . . by Samuel Lewis, 1794.
    " 28. The state of Massachusetts. Compiled . . . by Samuel Lewis.

no. 29. The state of Rhode Island; compiled, from the surveys . . . of Caleb Harris. By Harding Harris.
" 30. Connecticut . . . Delineated & engraved by A. Doolittle . . .
" 31. The state of New-York, compiled . . . by Samuel Lewis. 1795.
" 32. The state of New Jersey . . .
" 33. The state of Pennsylvania, reduced . . . from Reading Howell's map, by Samuel Lewis.
" 34. Delaware . . .
" 35. The state of Maryland . . . by Samuel Lewis.
" 36. The state of Virginia . . . by Samuel Lewis. 1794.
" 37. The state of North Carolina . . . by Samuel Lewis.
" 38. The state of South Carolina . . . by Samuel Lewis. 1795.
" 39. Georgia . . .
" 40. Kentucky, reduced from Elihu Barker's large map.
" 41. A map of the Tennasee state . . . taken chiefly from surveys by gen! D. Smith & others.
" 42. A map of South America . . .
" 43. A chart of the West Indies . . .
" 44. A map of the countries situated about the north pole.
" 45. A map of the discoveries made by capt? Cook & Clerke in . . . 1778 & 1779 between the eastern coast of Asia and the western coast of North America . . . Also m! Hearn's discoveries to the north westward of Hudson's bay, in 1772.

## 1796

**Winterbotham, W.**

The american atlas . . . 1 p. l., 20 maps (partly fold.) 8°. New York, J. Reid, 1796. 1366

NOTE.—Cover-title: The atlas for Winterbotham's history of America. 1796. Maps to accompany "An historical, geographical, commercial, and philosophical view of the United States of America . . . By William Winterbotham."

Inserted after map no. 20: Plan of the city of Washington in the territory of Columbia ceded by the states of Virginia and Maryland to the United States of America and by them established as their seat of government after the year 1800. Rollinson sculpt. N. York. Publish'd by I. Reid, L. Wayland, and C. Smith. 1795. "The Ellicott map with Potomac river soundings."—P. L. Phillips, A list of maps of America.

CONTENTS.

no. 1. A general map of North America drawn from the best surveys. 1795. Scoles, sc.
" 2. A general map of South America from the best surveys, 1796. B. Tanner sculp!
" 3. An accurate map of the United States of America, according to the treaty of peace of 1783. A. Anderson sculp.
" 4. The state of New Hampshire, compiled chiefly from actual surveys. 1796. B. Tanner sculp!
" 5. The province of Maine, from the best authorities. 1795.
" 6. The state of Massachusetts from the beft information.
" 7. Vermont from the latest authorities . . . Roberts fc.
" 8. the [!] state of Rhode Island, from the latest surveys. 1796. B. Tanner del & sculp!

**Winterbotham, W.**—Continued.
- no. 9. Connecticut from the beſt authorities. B. Tanner del. & sculpᵗ
- " 10. The state of New York, compiled from the moſt authentic imformation. 1793. Martin sculpᵗ
- " 11. The state of New Jersey, compiled from the most accurate surveys. Martin ſculpᵗ
- " 12. The state of Pennsylvania, from the lateſt surveys. D. Martin fᵗ
- " 13. The states of Maryland and Delaware, from the lateſt surveys. 1795. D. Martin ſculpᵗ
- " 14. the [!] state of Virginia, from the best authorities, 1796.
- " 15. Map of the state of Kentucky; with the adjoining territories. 1795. A. Anderson sculp.
- " 16. the [!] state of North Carolina from the best authorities. Tanner sculpᵗ
- " 17. The state of South Carolina: from the beſt authorities. 1796.
- " 18. a [!] map of the Tennassee [!] government formerly part of North Carolina from the latest surveys. 1795. B. Tanner delᵗ & sculpᵗ
- " 19. Georgia, from the lateſt authorities. B. Tanner sculpᵗ
- " 20. An accurate map of the West Indies with the adjacent coaſt of America. 1796. D. Martin sculpᵗ

## 1801

**Carey, M.**

Carey's american pocket atlas; containing nineteen maps ... with a brief description of each state. 2d ed. greatly improved and enlarged. 4 p. l., 114 pp., 19 maps. 12°. Philadelphia, for M. Carey, 1801. 1367

NOTE.—Maps engraved by W. Barker, J. H. Seymour and A. Doolittle.

CONTENTS.

- no. 1. The United States of America.
- " 2. Vermont, from actual survey.
- " 3. The state of New Hampshire, by Samˡ Lewis.
- " 4. Province of Maine.
- " 5. Massachusetts.
- " 6. Rhode Island.
- " 7. Connecticut.
- " 8. New York.
- " 9. New Jersey.
- " 10. Pennsylvania.
- " 11. Delaware.
- " 12. N. W. territory.
- " 13. Maryland.
- " 14. Virginia.
- " 15. Kentuckey[!]
- " 16. North Carolina.
- " 17. Tennassee[!] lately the S. Wⁿ territory.
- " 18. South Carolina.
- " 19. Georgia.

## 1805

Carey's american pocket atlas; containing twenty maps ... with a brief description of each state, and of Louisiana, also, the census of the inhabitants of the United States, for 1801. The exports from the United States for ten years. 3d ed. greatly improved and enlarged. 2 p. l., 114 pp., 19 maps. 12? Philadelphia, M. Carey, 1805. 1368

NOTE.—Maps engraved by W. Barker, J. H. Seymour and A. Doolittle. Map no. 20, Louisiana, wanting. See title 1370.

CONTENTS.

no. 1. The United States of America.
" 2. Vermont, from actual survey.
" 3. The state of New Hamshire, by Sam! Lewis.
" 4. Province of Maine.
" 5. Massachusetts.
" 6. Rhode Island.
" 7. Connecticut.
" 8. New York.
" 9. New Jersey.
" 10. Pennsylvania.
" 11. Delaware.
" 12. Ohio and N. W. territory.
" 13. Maryland.
" 14. Virginia.
" 15. Kentuckey.
" 16. North Carolina.
" 17. Tennassee: lately the S. W? territory.
" 18. South Carolina.
" 19. Mississippi territory and Georgia.
" 20. Louisiana [Wanting]

**1809**

Carey's american atlas. 26 maps. fol. Philadelphia, M, Carey, 1809. 1369

NOTE.—Title-page wanting.
All maps except nos. 2, 4, 7, 9, 12, 15, 18, 23–26 carry the following: Engraved for Carey's american edition of Guthrie's geography improved.

CONTENTS.

no. [1] The british possessions in North America . . . by Samuel Lewis. 1809.
" [2] A map of the United States . . . by Sam! Lewis. 1809.
" [3] Vermont . . . delineated & engraved by Amos Doolittle . . .
" [4] The state of New Hampshire. Compiled . . . by Samuel Lewis. 1794.
" [5] The province of Maine, . . . by Samuel Lewis. 1794.
" [6] The state of Massachusetts. Compiled . . . by Samuel Lewis.
" [7] The state of Rhode Island; compiled from the surveys . . . of Caleb Harris. By Harding Harris.
" [8] Connecticut . . . delineated & engraved by A. Doolittle . . .
" [9] The state of New York, compiled . . . by Samuel Lewis. 1809.
" [10] The state of New Jersey . . . Compiled by Samuel Lewis.
" [11] The state of Pennsylvania, reduced with permission from Reading Howells map by Samuel Lewis.
" [12] Delaware . . .
" [13] The state of Maryland . . . by Samuel Lewis.

**Carey, M.**—Continued.
no. [14] The state of Virginia . . . By Samuel Lewis. 1809.
" [15] The state of North Carolina . . . by Samuel Lewis.
" [16] The state of South Carolina . . . by Samuel Lewis. 1795.
" [17] Georgia . . .
" [18] Kentucky, reduced from Elihu Barker's large map.
" [19] A map of the Tennassee state formerly part of North Carolina taken chiefly from surveys by gen! D. Smith & others.
" [20] A map of South America . . .
" [21] A chart of the West Indies . . .
" [22] A map of the discoveries made by capt! Cook & Clerke in the years 1778 & 1779 between the eastern coast of Asia and the western coast of North America . . . Also m!. Hearn's discoveries to the north westward of Hudson's bay, in 1772.
" [23] Plat of the Seven Ranges of townships being part of the territory of the United States n. w. of the river Ohio. Surveyed may 20th 1785, under direction of Tho! Hutchins.
" [24] A map of part of the N: W: territory of the United States: compiled . . . by Samuel Lewis. 1796.
" [25] Carte de la partie françoise de S! Domingue faite par [Jacques Nicolas] Bellin . . . et depuis augmentée par P. C. Varlè et autres ing!.ˢ—A map of the french part of S! Domingo. J. T. Scott, sculp.
" [26] Louisiana.

## 1814

Carey's american pocket atlas; containing twenty maps . . . with a brief description of each state and territory. Also, the census of the inhabitants of the United States, for 1810; the exports from the United States for twenty years. 4th ed. greatly improved and enlarged. iv, 162, [2] pp., 23 maps. 12°. Philadelphia, M. Carey, 1814. 1370

NOTE.—Index on title-page; atlas contains three maps, Upper territories of the United States, Mississippi territory, and Missouri territory, which do not appear in the index.
Maps engraved by W. Barker, J. H. Seymour and A. Doolittle.
Map no. 3, New Hampshire, by Saml. Lewis.

CONTENTS.

no. 1. United States.
" 2. Vermont from actual survey.
" 3. The state of New Hampshire . . .
" 4. Maine.
" 5. Massachusetts.
" 6. Rhode Island.
" 7. Connecticut.
" 8. New York.
" 9. New Jersey.
" 10. Pennsylvania.
" 11. Delaware.
" 12. Ohio.
" 12a. Upper territories of the United States.
" 13. Maryland.

no. 14. Virginia.
" 15. Kentuckey.
" 16. North Carolina.
" 17. Tennessee.
" 18. South Carolina.
" 19. Georgia.
" 19a. Mississippi territory.
" 20. Louisiana.
" 20a. Missouri territory formerly Louisiana.

## 1814?

[Carey's general atlas, improved and enlarged: being a collection of maps of the world and quarters, their principal empires, kingdoms, &c. . . .]   2 p. l., 58 maps. fol. [Philadelphia, M. Carey, 1814?]   1371

NOTE.—Title-page wanting.
This copy corresponds to the 1814 edition except in map no. 39, Russian empire, and in the preface signed M. Carey, march 17, 1814.
For list of maps of America, see title 1372.

## 1814

Carey's general atlas, improved and enlarged: being a collection of maps of the world and quarters, their principal empires, kingdoms, &c. . . .   3 p. l., 58 maps. fol. Philadelphia, M. Carey, 1814.   1372

NOTE.—The following maps relate to America:
no. 1. A map of the world . . .
" 2. A chart of the world . . .
" 3. A new and accurate map of North America . . .
" 4. The british possessions in North America . . . 1814.
" 5. A map of the United States of America.
" 6. Vermont . . . Delineated & engraved by Amos Doolittle . . .
" 7. The state of New Hampshire. Compiled . . . by Samuel Lewis, 1813.
" 8. The district of Maine.
" 9. The state of Massachusetts.
" 10. The state of Rhode Island; compiled, from the surveys . . . of Caleb Harris. By Harding Harris.
" 11. Connecticut . . . Delineated & engraved by A. Doolittle . . .
" 12. The state of New York. S. Lewis del.
" 13. The state of New Jersey . . .
" 14. Pennsylvania.
" 15. Delaware . . .
" 16. Maryland.
" 17. A correct map of Virginia.
" 18. North Carolina. S. Lewis del.
" 19. The state of South Carolina . . . by Samuel Lewis.
" 20. The state of Georgia.
" 21. Kentucky.
" 22. The state of Tennessee.
" 23. Mississippi territory.

**Carey, M.**—Continued.
- no. 24. The state of Ohio with part of upper Canada, &c.
- " 25. The upper territories of the United States.
- " 26. Louisiana.
- " 27. Missouri territory . . .
- " 28. Plat of the Seven Ranges of townships, being part of the territory n. w. of the river Ohio . . . Surveyed may 20th 1785, under direction of Tho: Hutchins.
- " 29. Mexico . . .
- " 30. A chart of the West Indies . . .
- " 31. Carte de la partie françoise de S! Domingue. Faite par [Jacques Nicolas] Bellin . . . —A map of the french part of S! Domingo. J. T. Scott, sculp.
- " 32. A new map of South America . . .
- " 33. A map of the Caracas.
- " 34. Peru.
- " 35. Chili and part of the viceroyalty of La Plata.
- " 36. A map of Brazil . . .
- " 57. A map of the countries situated about the North pole.
- " 58. A map of the discoveries made by capt! Cook & Clerke in the years 1778 & 1779 between the eastern coast of Asia and the western coast of North America . . . Also m! Hearn's discoveries to the northwestward of Hudson's bay, in 1772.

## 1818

Carey's general atlas, improved and enlarged; being a collection of maps of the world and quarters; their principal empires, kingdoms, &c. . . .    3 p. l., 58 maps. fol. Philadelphia, M. Carey & son, 1818.    1373

NOTE.—The following maps relate to America:
- no. [1] A map of the world . . .
- " [2] A chart of the world . . .
- " 3. A new and accurate map of North America . . .
- " 4. The british possessions in North America . . . 1814.
- " 5. Map of the United States of America.
- " 6. Vermont . . . Delineated & engraved by Amos Doolittle . . .
- " 7. The state of New Hampshire. Compiled . . . by Samuel Lewis. 1813.
- " 8. The district of Maine.
- " 9. The state of Massachusetts.
- " 10. The state of Rhode Island; compiled, from the surveys . . . of Caleb Harris. By Harding Harris.
- " 11. Connecticut . . . Delineated & engraved by A. Doolittle . . .
- " 12. The state of New York. S. Lewis del.
- " 13. The state of New Jersey . . .
- " 14. Pennsylvania.
- " 15. Delaware . . .
- " 16. Maryland.
- " 17. A correct map of Virginia.
- " 18. North Carolina . . . by Samuel Lewis.
- " 19. The state of South Carolina . . . by Samuel Lewis.
- " 20. The state of Georgia.

no. 21. Kentucky.
" 22. The state of Tennessee.
" 23. The state of Mississippi and Alabama territory.
" 24. The state of Ohio with part of upper Canada, &c.
" [25] The upper territories of the United States.
" 26. Louisiana.
" 27. Missouri territory formerly Louisiana.
" 28. Plat of the Seven Ranges of townships . . . n. w. of the river Ohio . . . Surveyed may 25$^{th}$ 1785. Under direction of Tho$^s$ Hutchins.
" 29. Mexico . . .
" [30] West Indies.
" 31. Carte de la partie Françoise de S$^t$ Dominque. Faite par [Jacques Nicolas] Bellin . . . et depuis augmentée par P. C. Varlé et autres ing$^{rs}$—A map of the french part of S$^t$ Domingo. J. T. Scott sculp.
" 32. A new map of South America . . .
" 33. A map of the Caracas.
" 34. Peru.
" 35. Chili and part of the viceroyalty of La Plata.
" 36. A map of Brazil . . .
" 57. A map of the countries situated about the North pole.
" 58. A map of the discoveries made by capt$^s$ Cook & Clerke in the years 1778 & 1779 between the eastern coast of Asia and the western coast of North America . . . Also m$^r$ Hearn's discoveries to the north westward of Hudson's bay, in 1772.

**1822**

**Carey, H. C.**, *and* **Lea, I.**

A complete historical, chronological, and geographical american atlas, being a guide to the history of North and South America, and the West Indies: exhibiting an accurate account of the discovery, settlement, and progress, of their various kingdoms, states, provinces, &c. together with the wars, celebrated battles, and remarkable events, to the year 1822. According to the plan of Le Sage's [pseud. of M. J. A. E. D. comte de Las Cases] atlas, and intended as a companion to Lavoisne's improvement of that celebrated work. 3 p. l., [118] l. incl. 46 maps, 2 pl. fol. Philadelphia, H. C. Carey & I. Lea, 1822.　　1373a

NOTE.—See also title 1177. Maps have border text.

CONTENTS.

no. 1. North America.—South America. Young & Delleker sc.
" 3. North America. Drawn by J. Finlayson.
" 4. British possessions in North America. Drawn by F. Lucas jr.
" 5. United States of America. Engraved by B. Tanner.
" 10. Maine. J. Yeager sculp.
" 11. New Hampshire. Engrav'd by Young & Delleker.
" 12. Massachusetts. Drawn by F. Lucas.
" 13. Rhode Island. Drawn by F. Lucas jr.
" 14. Connecticut. Engrav'd by Young & Delleker.
" 15. Vermont. Drawn by F. Lucas jr.
" 16. New York. Drawn by F. Lucas jr.

**Carey, H. C.**, *and* **Lea I.**—Continued.
- no. 17. New Jersey. Kneass sc.
- " 18. Pennsylvania. Engr'd by J. Yeager.
- " 19. Delaware. Drawn by F. Lucas jr.
- " 20. Maryland. Drawn by F. Lucas jr.
- " 21. District of Columbia. Engraved by Young & Delleker.
- " 22. Virginia. Engrav'd by Young & Delleker.
- " 23. North Carolina. Drawn by F. Lucas jr.
- " 24. South Carolina. Reduced by J. Drayton from the state map by J. Wilson.
- " 25. Georgia. Drawn by F. Lucas jr.
- " 26. Ohio. Drawn by F. Lucas jr.
- " 27. Kentucky. Drawn by F. Lucas jr.
- " 28. Tennessee. Drawn by F. Lucas jr.
- " 29. Mississippi. Drawn by F. Lucas jr.
- " 30. Alabama. Drawn by F. Lucas jun.r
- " 31. Louisiana. Kneass sc.
- " 32. Indiana. Drawn by F. Lucas jr.
- " 33. Illinois. J. Yeager sculp.
- " 34. Missouri. Engraved by Young & Delleker.
- " 35. Map of Arkansas and other territories of the United States . . . by S. H. Long . . .
- " 36. Michigan territory. Drawn by J. Finlayson.
- " 37. Florida. Drawn by F. Lucas jr.
- " 38. Mexico and internal provinces. Prepared from Humbolt's map & other documents by J. Finlayson.
- " 39. West Indies. Drawn by F. Lucas jr.
- " 40. Cuba and the Bahama islands. B. Tanner sc.
- " 41. Jamaica. Drawn by J. Finlayson.
- " 42. Hispaniola . . . Drawn by F. Lucas jr.
- " 43. Porto Rico and Virgin islands. Drawn by F. Lucas.
- " 44. Windward islands. Drawn by F. Lucas jr.
- " 45. Leeward islands. J. Yeager sculp.
- " 46. South America. Drawn by E. Paguenaud.
- " 47. Colombia. Drawn by J. Finlayson.
- " 48. Brazil. Drawn by J. Finlayson.
- " 49. United provinces of South America. Drawn by J. Finlayson.
- " 50. Peru. Drawn by J. Finlayson.
- " 51. Chili. Drawn by J. Finlayson.

### 1823

**Tanner, H. S.**

A new american atlas containing maps of the several states of the North American union. Projected and drawn on a uniform scale from documents found in the public offices of the United States and state governments, and other original and authentic information. 2 p. l., 18 pp., 22 maps. fol. Philadelphia, H. S. Tanner, 1823.

1374

NOTE.—The geographical memoir preceeding the maps contains the sources from which the maps were made, with criticisms. See also titles 1376, 1380 and 1382.

CONTENTS.

- no. 1. The world on Mercators projection.
- " 2. Europe.
- " 3. Asia.

no. 4. Africa.
" 5. America.
" 6–7. South America with improvements to 1823 . . .
" 8–11. A map of North America . . .
" 12. Map of the states of Maine, New Hampshire, Vermont, Massachusetts, Connecticut, & Rhode Island . . .
" 13. New York . . .
" 14. Map of Pennsylvania and New Jersey . . .
" 15. Virginia, Maryland, and Delaware . . .
" 16. Ohio and Indiana . . .
" 17. Kentucky and Tennessee . . .
" 18. Map of North & South Carolina . . .
" 19. Georgia and Alabama . . .
" 20. Louisiana and Mississippi . . .
" 21. Illinois and Missouri . . .
" 22. Map of Florida . . .

**1824**

**Klinckowström, A. L.**, *friherre*.
Atlas til friherre Klinckowströms bref om de Förente Staterne. 1 p. l., 5 maps, 10 pl. obl. fol. [Stockholm] C. Müller [1824]  1375

NOTE.—To accompany his: Bref om de Förenta Staterna, författade under en resa till Amerika åren 1818, 1819, 1820. 8°. Stockholm, Ecksteinska tryckeriet, 1824.

CONTENTS.

no. [1] Presidentons i de Förente Staterna recidence i Washington. [View on title-page]
" [3] New York med trakten däromkring.
" [4] Ruiner efter en gammal fastning i Tenessee staten.
" [6] Flyglarna af capitolen i Washington år 1819.
" [7] Plan af Philadelphia.
" [8] Hoboken midt emot New York.
" [10] Third street i Philadelphia.
" [12] New Yorks hamn och redd från Brooklyn på Longisland.
" [13] Bro öfver Skuylkill strömmen nära Philadelphia.
" [15] Southern section of the United States including Florida &c. by John Melish. 1816.
" [16] Northern section of the United States including Canada &c. by John Melish. 1816.

**1825–1833**

**Tanner, H. S.**
A new american atlas containing maps of the several states of the North American union . . .  2 p. l., 18 pp., 18 col. maps on 42 l. fol. Philadelphia, H. S. Tanner, 1825–[1833]  1376

NOTE.—Engraved title.
Geographical memoir, pp. 1–18, contains a list and criticism of the early state maps.
Like the edition of 1823 except maps nos. [4, 6, 7, 10, 11, 13, 14, 17] See titles 1374, 1380 and 1382.
The following maps dated 1833:
no. [10] A map of the canals and railroads of Pennsylvania and New Jersey.
" [11] Virginia, Maryland and Delaware . . .
" [17] Illinois and Missouri . . .

**Tanner, H. S.**—Continued.
The following maps relate to America:
no. [1] The world on Mercator's projection.
" [3] Asia [Philippine islands]
" [5] America.
" [6] South America and West Indies. 1818. 2 sheets.
" [7] A map of North America . . . improved to 1829. 4 sheets.
" [8] Map of the states of Maine, New Hampshire, Vermont, Massachusetts, Connecticut & Rhode Island.
" [9] New York.
" [10] Map of the canals and railroads of Pennsylvania and New Jersey and the adjoining states . . . 1833.
" [11] Virginia, Maryland and Delaware. 1833.
" [12] Ohio and Indiana.
" [13] Kentucky and Tennessee . . . 1827.
" [14] Map of North & South Carolina . . . 1827.
" [15] Georgia and Alabama.
" [16] Louisiana and Mississippi.
" [17] Illinois and Missouri.
" [18] Map of Florida.

## 1825–1843

**United States.** *War department.*
Internal improvements. A collection of maps and drawings engraved by order of congress, connected with a portion of the surveys &c. made under the engineer bureaus of the war department from 1825 to 1843. 1 p. l., 139 maps. obl. fol. [Washington, 1825–1843] 1377

NOTE.—Manuscript title-page. 7 pp. manuscript index inserted.
Mainly to accompany documents.

CONTENTS.

no. [1] Burlington bay, Vermont . . . 1833.
" [2–3] Chart of part of the Savannah river. 1833 . . . 2 sheets.
" [4] Map of the mouth of Genessee river, New York . . . 1829 . . .— Map of the Mouth of the Great Sodus bay, New York . . . 1829 . . .—Map of the mouth of Big Sandy Creek, New York . . . 1829 . . .—Map of the mouth of Little Sodus bay, New York . . . 1829 . . .—Map of Pultneyville bay, New York . . . 1829 . . .
" [5] Spindle rock, Black Rock harbor, Connecticut . . .—Survey of the entrance of the Teche. Louisiana . . . 1829.
" [6] Canal line on the eastern bank of the Suwanee river, Florida, 1827 . . .
" [7] Survey across the isthmus of Cape Cod, state of Massachusetts and town of Sandwich of a proposed canal between Buzzards and Barnstable bays 1825.
" [8] Plattsburg harbor, New York . . . 1833.—Port Kent, New York . . . 1833.
" [9] Profiles of a canal survey between the waters of Narraganset & Boston bays, Massachusetts . . . 1831.—Part of Taunton & Assonet rivers, with the location of the tide locks at the southern extremity of the canal uniting Boston harbor with Taunton river . . . 1831.— Part of Weymouth Fore river and Quincy bay with the location of tide locks at the northern extremities of the two routes of the canal joining Boston harbor with Taunton river. 1831 . . .

no. [10] Chart shewing the site of light house proposed for the Brandywine choal, Delaware bay . . . 1832 . . . no. 1.
" [11] Michigan & Illinois canal, 1830 & 1831 [Profiles]
" [12] Map of the proposed route for the Michigan and Illinois canal . . . 1831. Maps no. 3, 6-9.
" [13] Map of proposed route of the Michigan and Illinois canal . . . 1830-1831. Maps no. 1, 2, 4, 5.
" [14-15] Florida canals. Profiles. 1826-1827.
" [16] Florida canal. Line from the forks of the Suwanee to St. Marks, 1827 . . .
" [17] Map of reconnaissance exhibiting the survey and line of level of the Tennessee river from Browns Ferry to Waterloo . . . Alabama . . . 1827-1828 . . .—Sheet no. 4. Profile of the Muscle shoals in Tennessee river from South Florence to Browns Ferry.—Sheet no. 5 profile of map no. 3 from Waterloo to Florence.
" [18] Cumberland road. Map of the country through which it is proposed to extend the National road . . . to the . . . District of Columbia. 1826 . . .
" [19-20] North river, N. Y. 1831 . . . no. 1-7.
" [21] Hudson & Ohio rail road . . . 1832.—Profiles.
" [22] Hudson & Ohio rail road. Experimental line from Monticello, Sullivan co. to the dividing line of Rockland and Orange counties . . . 1832.
" [23] Hudson and Ohio rail road. Experimental line from Ramapo to Patterson . . . 1832. Experimental line from the dividing line of Rockland and Orange counties N. Y. to Tappan landing . . . 1832.—Profiles. Experimental line from Monticello . . . to the dividing line of Orange and Rockland counties, N. Y. . . . 1832.
" [24] The north end of the island of Nantucket . . . no. 2.
" [25] Harbor of St. Augustine . . .—Copy of a plan of the city of St. Augustine, Florida . . . 1833.
" [26] Plan of a survey of the Cochecho river, New Hampshire 1829.—Harbor of Stamford, Connecticut . . . 1829.—Survey of Vermilion river, with a view to the construction of a harbor at its mouth. 1833 . . .
" [27] Michigan road, town of Monroe, river rasin [!] to Miami river . . .—Harbor of Norwalk, Connecticut. 1829 . . .
" [28] [Louisville canal, Ohio river, by J. Brooks]
" [29] Town and harbor of Nantucket . . . 1826. no. 4.—Plan and sections of a breakwater and pier designed to form an artificial harbor near Great Point, Nantucket island. 1826. no. 3.
" [30] Survey shewing the obstructions to the navigation at Ocracoke inlet, N. C. 1827 . . .
" [31] Map of reconnaissance exhibiting the country between Washington and New Orleans with the routes examined in reference to a contemplated national road between these two cities.
" [32] A map of the country betwixt Chowan and Nansemond rivers, shewing the track of a canal proposed to be cut from Bennetts creek to Suffolk. Vide acts of the Virginia and North Carolina assemblies passed at the session of 1804-5.—Sketch of the country between the waters of Potomac and those of Youghiogeny and Monongahela.—Drafts of the comparative heights and distances of the principal districts of anthracite coal in Pennsylvania to market.—Barnstable bay.—Elizabeth river . . .—Section of the proposed canal through the great marsh.

**United States.** *War department*—Continued.

no. [33] Harbor of Westbrook, Connecticut, shewing the position of the proposed breakwater. 1829.—Sag Harbor, New York. 1829 . . .
" [34] Map of the mouth of Chicago river, Illinois, with the plan of the proposed piers for improving the harbor. 1830 . . .—Survey of Tuckers island, New Jersey . . . 1829.—Map of Silver Creek bay, New York . . . 1830.—Plan of a survey of the Penobscot river, Maine. 1829 . . .
" [35] The harbor of Hyannis, county of Barnstable, Massachusetts. 1826 . . .
" [36] Harbor of Newbury Port and the mouth of Merrimack river, county of Essex . . . Massachusetts . . . 1826 . . .
" [37] Maryland canal. Profiles . . . 1827.
" [38] Maryland canal . . . 1827.—Map no. 1. From Georgetown to Paint Branch . . .—Map no. 2. From Paint Branch to Saw Mill Branch . . .—Map no. 3. From Saw Mill Branch to Deep Run.—Map no. 4. From Deep Run to Spring Gardens.
" [39] Map of the county embracing the several routes examined with a view to a national road from Washington to lake Ontario. 1828.—Portland harbor, New York.—Map of Portland harbor, New York, exhibiting a plan of a breakwater for its security and protection . . . 1829 . . .—Harbor of Mill river, Fairfield county, Connecticut . . .
" [40-43] Plat of the United States road from Detroit to Chicago . . . 1829. 4 sheets.
" [44] Map of Goat island and the harbor of Newport, Newport county, Rhode Island . . . 1827 . . .
" [45] Plan of an artificial channel to connect lake Erie with Presqu'ile bay, Penn. . . . 1825.—Plan of Lovejoys Narrows from a survey of the Kennebeck river 1826 . . .—Plan of New Castle harbor . . . 1836.
" [46] Canal route from Georgetown to Alexandria. Surveyed in 1827 . . .—Map exhibiting the country between Okoa [Toccoa] and Connessauga . . .
" [47] Profiles. Montpelier canal, Wells river route . . . 1829.
" [48-53] Ohio and Erie canal. 1825-1827. 6 sheets.
" [54] Ohio and Erie canal. no. 1. Experimental and location lines from the end of the Deep Cut to lake Erie. no. 2. Horizontal curves around Conneaut lake. Experimental lines location of the summit and of the line thence to Greenville on the Shenango . . .
" [55] Ohio and Erie canal. Experimental survey. From Conneaut lake to Franklin on the Allegheny river . . .
" [56] Ohio and Erie canal. n° 1. Experimental survey from the head of French creek feeder by the valley of French creek. 1827.—n° 2. Experimental survey by the Waterford summits . . . 1827.
" [57] Ohio and Erie canal. Line of location from Elk creek to the bay of Presqu'ile and survey of the shore of lake Erie within said limits . . . no. 1 . . . From lock XII near the valley of Elk river to the harbor of Erie. 1827 . . .
" [58] Ohio and Erie canal. Section of location Big Beaver creek; from New Castle, on the Shenango to the Ohio river . . . 1826.—. . . From Pittsburgh to the Big Beaver . . . 1826.
" [59] Ohio and Erie canal. n° 3. Big Bend of Shenango. 1826.—n° 4. Valley of Shenango. 1826 . . .

no. [60] Ohio and Erie canal.—Conneaut reservoir, 1825.—Feeder from French creek to Conneaut lake 1825 . . .
" [61] Ohio and Erie canal. Line of examination from . . . Williamsons run by Jno. Hills to Harveys near the head waters of the Big Shenango . . .—Big Beaver Creek from the mouth of the Mahoning to the Ohio river . . . 1826
" [62] Internal improvement Pennsylvania and Ohio. 1824 . . . Map of the country between Pittsburgh and lake Erie showing the proposed route of the Ohio and Erie canal.
" [63-67] James & Kenhawa canal . . . 1826-27. 5 sheets.
" [68] James & Kenhawa canal. Map n? 1. Exhibiting the experimental lines between Dunlaps creek & Greenbrier river. 1826 . . .
" [69] Chart of the entrance of Sandusky bay. In the state of Ohio, 1826 . . .—Inset: Sandusky bay.
" [70-71] Profiles of the proposed route for a canal to connect lake Erie with the Wabash river . . . 1826-27. 2 sheets.
" [72] Map embracing a part of the different routes of the proposed Erie and Wabash canal. Exhibiting the valley of the Wabash from the mouth of Eel river to Tippecanoe. 1827 . . .—From the Mississinewa to Eel river. 1827 . . .
" [73] Map on an enlarged scale exhibiting the junction of Eel river with the Wabash, the Grand Rapids and the soundings as they were found the latter end of july 1827 . . .
" [74] Erie and Wabash canal. 1828 . . .
" [75] Erie canal. 1828.—Map of part of the proposed route of a canal to connect lake Erie and the Wabash river 1827 . . .
" [76] Map of the different routes to connect lake Erie with the Wabash river by a canal. Exhibiting the valley of the Wabash from the forks of the Mississinewa river. 1827 . . .
" [77] Sandy bay, Massachusetts. 1829 . . .—That part of Thames river, Connecticut including the obstructions below Norwich. 1829 . . . —Inset: Survey. A view of Howes ditch on the Shetucket river showing the effects of the freshets of 1788 or 1789 and 1807.
" [78] Profile of the route examined between White Water and White river with a view to ascertain the practicability of uniting them by a canal.—Profile of a line for determining the practicability of uniting by a canal the rivers S! Joseph's, S! Mary's and Wabash with the Ohio through the valley of the White Water . . . 1826.
" [79-80] Map of part of a line for determining the practicability of uniting by a canal the rivers St. Josephs, St. Marys, & Wabash with the Ohio through the valley of the White Water 1826 . . . 2 sheets.
" [81] Map and profile of the contemplated canal around the falls of the Ohio river on the Indiana side . . .—Washington canal. 1827 . . .—Map of the United States road from Detroit in the territory of Michigan to fort Gratiot 1827 . . .—Chart of Laplaisance bay in the territory of Michigan. 1826 . . .
" [82-84] Cape Fear river, N. C., below the town of Wilmington 1827 . . . 3 sheets.
" [85] Sections of the Dismal Swamp canal.
" [86] Plan & profile of the Dismal Swamp canal . . . 1826.
" [87] Harbor of Edgertown in Marthas Vineyard state of Massachusetts. 1826 . . .—Map of Warren river, Bristol county Rhode Island . . . 1827.—Harbor and borough of Stonington . . . Connecticut 1827 . . .

**United States.** *War department*—Continued.

no. [88] Map of the country between Washington and Pittsburgh referring to the contemplated Chesapeake and Ohio canal and its general route and profile . . . 1826.
" [89] Cape May Roads, including Crow Shoal, Del. bay . . . 1836 . . . —Inset: Plan of the artificial harbor.
" [90] Map of the river Sabine from its mouth on the gulf of Mexico in the sea to Logan's Ferry . . . 1840.—Potomac aqueduct . . . 1838.
" [91] Potomac aqueduct. Shewing the condition of the work at the close of the year 1839.—Potomac aqueduct. Shewing the condition of the work at the close of the year 1840.
" [92] Potomac aqueduct. Interior framing of the cofferdam for pier no. 8 . . . 1839.
" [93] Chart of the head of navigation of the Potomac river. Shewing the route of the Alexandria canal . . . 1838 . . .
" [94] Potomac aqueduct. Cofferdam for the northern abutment.
" [95] N° 2. Map of the Rock Island rapids of the Mississippi river . . . 1837.
" [96] N° 1. Map of the Des Moines rapids of the Mississippi river . . . 1837.
" [97] Plat of the falls of the Ohio river, exhibiting the route of the Louisville and Portland canal . . . 1843 . . .
" [98] Plat of the falls of the Ohio at extreme low water, also sections of rock composing the bed of the falls . . . 1843 . . .
" [99] Hydrographical basin of the upper Mississippi river . . . 1843 . . .
" [100] Chicago river copy of a drawing . . . Improvement of the harbor of Chicago, Illinois, at the close of the year 1837.—Michigan city. Showing the present condition of the work at Michigan city, Indiana; also the proposed improvements . . . 1839.—A map of the public works at St. Joseph, Michigan. Showing the present condition of the harbor and the proposed improvements . . . 1839.—Map of the Chicago river . . . 1839.
" [101] No. 3. Map of the harbor of St. Louis, Mississippi river . . . 1837.
" [102] Chart of Kennebeck river from Augusta to Gardiner. 1837.
" [103] Proposed canal on Indiana side of Falls of the Ohio to be fed from the Ohio . . . 1843 . . .
" [104] Plan of Chicago harbor . . . 1839. no. 3.—Plan of Chicago harbor, lake Michigan. no. 1 . . . 1839. Sen. doc. 140, 1st sess., 26th Cong.
" [105] Cataraugus harbor and the public works in progress therein . . . 1838.—Map of Portland harbor . . . 1838 . . .
" [106] Design for Flinns Knoll light . . . 1838.
" [107] No. 5. Proposed improvement of Louisville and Portland canal.—Proposed canal route no. 2 around the falls of the Ohio, on Indiana side . . .—no. 17. Proposed canal route no. 1 around the falls of the Ohio on Indiana side . . .
" [108] No. 4. Proposed improvement of Louisville and Portland canal . . .—no. 8. Proposed improvement of Louisville and Portland canal . . .—no. 6. Proposed improvement of Louisville and Portland canal. Plan of estimate for passing place for boats in Louisville and Portland canal.—no. 10. Natural channel of the falls of the Ohio . . .

no. [109] Proposed canal on Indiana side of the falls of the Ohio to be fed from the interior of Indiana . . .
" [110] Proposed improvement of the natural channel of the falls of the Ohio. 1838 . . .—no. 7. Proposed improvement of Louisville and Portland canal. Plan and estimate for new locks and for improvement of canal at head of the locks of the Louisville & Portland canal . . .—no. 12. Natural channel of the falls of the Ohio . . .—no. 16. Proposed improvement of the natural channel of the falls of the Ohio . . .
" [111] No. 11. Natural channel of the falls of the Ohio. Stages of water and capacity of boats to ascend middle chute.—no. 14. Proposed improvement of the natural channel of the falls of the Ohio . . .— no. 1. Proposed improvement of Louisville and Portland canal . . .
" [112] No. 2. Proposed improvement of Louisville and Portland canal. Mean longitudinal profile of present bottom of canal . . .—no. 3. Proposed improvement of Louisville and Portland canal . . .— no. 15. Proposed improvement of the natural channel of the falls of the Ohio by locks & sluice . . .—no. 13. Proposed improvement of the natural channel of the falls of the Ohio . . .
" [113] Plat of a survey exhibiting a portion of the Ohio river where navigation would be affected by removing the rock barrier of the falls near Louisville . . . 1843.
" [114] Sabine Pass and mouth of the river Sabine in the sea . . . 1840 . . .
" [115] Survey of the mouth of Sheboygan river, Wisconsin. 1836 . . .
" [116] General map to accompany the report of capt. T. J. Cram . . . on the survey of the boundary between Michigan and Wiskonsin . . .
" [117] Chart of the eastern part of Presqu'Ile bay showing the changes of outline of shore going on in consequence of the erection of the U. S. works . . . 1838.
" [118] Survey of the entrance to Milwaukie, Wisconsin, 1836 . . .
" [119] Mouth of Kewaunee river, Wisconsin . . . 1836.
" [120] Survey of Havre bay, Michigan . . . 1826 . . .
" [121] Map of Dunkirk harbor showing the works erected by the United States . . . 1838 . . .
" [122] Mouth of Manitowoc river, Wisconsin . . . 1836.
" [123] Part of the boundary between the United States and Texas from Sabine river, northward to the 36$^{th}$ mile mound . . . — to the 72$^{nd}$ mile mound . . . — to Red river . . . 1838.
" [124] Mouth of Root river, Wisconsin . . . 1836.
" [125] A map of Ocracock inlet . . . 1835 . . .
" [126] Map exhibiting the conditions of U. S. works at the head of Presqu'Ile bay . . . 1838 . . . Inset.—Sketch of Presqu'Ile harbor.
" [127] Map of the Des Moines rapids of the Mississippi . . . 1836.
" [128] Map of the Rock River rapids of the Mississippi . . . 1836.
" [129] Sketch of the Rock Island rapids . . . 1837.—Sketch of the harbor of St. Louis . . . 1837.
" [130] Map of the falls of the Ohio.—Survey for ship canal around the falls of St. Mary . . . 1837 . . .
" [131] Plan of Croatan and Roanoke sounds . . . 1820.
" [132] Map of Presqu'Ile bay or Erie harbor . . . 1839.

**United States.** *War department*—Continued.
 no. [133] Map of the vicinity of Buffalo . . .
 " [134] [Map of Arkansas river at fort Smith in relation to site for a militiary port] 1837.—Survey of the mouth of Fort creek (City.—West) Indiana . . . 1837.
 " [135] Cobscook bay, Maine . . . 1836 . . .
 " [136] Owl's Head harbor, Maine . . . 1836.
 " [137] Sketch of an iron pile light for Bartlett's reef, Long Island Sound . . .
 " [138] Chart of Owlshead harbour and projections of a breakwater . . . 1837.
 " [139] Plan of a portion of the pier, in water of less depth than four feet, at the mouth of Salmon river, Richland, Oswego cy. New York. 1837.

## 1826

**Finley, A.**
 A new american atlas, designed principally to illustrate the geography of the United States of North America; in which every county in each state and territory of the Union is accurately delineated, as far as at present known: the whole compiled from the latest and most authentic information.   2 p. l., 15 maps.   fol.   Philadelphia, A. Finley, 1826.   1378

CONTENTS.

 no. 1. North America.
 " 2. United States.
 " 3. Maine, New Hampshire and Vermont.
 " 4. Massachusetts, Connecticut and Rhode Island.
 " 5. New York.
 " 6. Pennsylvania, New Jersey and Delaware.
 " 7. Virginia and Maryland.
 " 8. North and South Carolina and Georgia.
 " 9. Louisiana, Mississippi and Alabama.
 " 10. Kentucky and Tennessee.
 " 11. Ohio, Indiana, Illinois and part of Michigan ter.
 " 12. Missouri and territory of Arkansas.
 " 13. Florida, and elevation of mountains.
 " 14. West Indies.
 " 15. South America.

## 1827

**Carey, H. C.** *and* **Lea, I.**
 A complete historical, chronological, and geographical american atlas, being a guide to the history of North and South America, and the West Indies: exhibiting an accurate account of the discovery, settlement, and progress, of their various kingdoms, states, provinces, &c. together with the wars, celebrated battles, and remarkable events, to the year 1826. According to the plan of Le Sage's [pseud. of M. J. A. E. D. comte de Las Cases] atlas, and intended as a companion to Lavoisne's improvement of that celebrated work.   3d

ed. cor. and impr. 3 p. l., [109] l. incl. 46 maps, 2 pl. fol. Philadelphia, H. C. Carey & I. Lea, 1827. 1379

NOTE.—First edition published 1822.
See title 1373a.
Maps have border text.

CONTENTS.

- no. 1. N. America. S. America. Drawn by J. Finlayson.
- " 3. North America. Drawn by J. Finlayson.
- " 4. British possessions in North America. Drawn by F. Lucas jr.
- " 5. United States of America. Engraved by B. Tanner.
- " 10. Maine. J. Yeager sculp.
- " 11. New Hampshire. Engrav'd by Young & Delleker.
- " 12. Massachusetts. Drawn by F. Lucas.
- " 13. Rhode Island. Drawn by F. Lucas jr.
- " 14. Connecticut. Engrav'd by Young & Delleker.
- " 15. Vermont. Drawn by F. Lucas jr.
- " 16. New York. Drawn by F. Lucas jr.
- " 17. New Jersey. Kneass sc.
- " 18. Pennsylvania. Engr'd by J. Yeager.
- " 19. Delaware. Drawn by F. Lucas jr.
- " 20. Maryland. Drawn by F. Lucas jr.
- " 21. District of Columbia. Engraved by Young & Delleker.
- " 22. Virginia. Engrav'd by Young & Delleker.
- " 23. North Carolina. Drawn by F. Lucas jr.
- " 24. South Carolina. Reduced by J. Drayton from the state map by J. Wilson.
- " 25. Georgia. Drawn by F. Lucas jr.
- " 26. Ohio. Drawn by F. Lucas jr.
- " 27. Kentucky. Drawn by F. Lucas jr.
- " 28. Tennessee. Drawn by F. Lucas jr.
- " 29. Mississippi. Drawn by F. Lucas jr.
- " 30. Alabama. J. Drayton del.
- " 31. Louisiana. Kneass sc.
- " 32. Indiana. Drawn by F. Lucas jr.
- " 33. Illinois. J. Yeager sculp.
- " 34. Missouri. Engraved by Young & Delleker.
- " 35. Map of Arkansa and other territories of the United States . . . by S. H. Long . . .
- " 36. Michigan territory. Drawn by J. Finlayson.
- " 37. Florida. Drawn by J. Drayton.
- " 38. Mexico and internal provinces. Prepared from Humbolt's map & other documents by J. Finlayson.
- " 39. West Indies. Drawn by F. Lucas jr.
- " 40. Cuba and the Bahama Islands. B. Tanner sc.
- " 41. Jamaica. Drawn by J. Finlayson.
- " 42. Hayti . . . Drawn by F. Lucas jr.
- " 43. Porto Ricó and Virgin islands. Drawn by F. Lucas.
- " 44. Windward islands. Drawn by F. Lucas jr.
- " 45. Leeward islands. J. Yeager sculp.
- " 46. South America. Drawn by E. Paguenaud.
- " 47. Colombia. Drawn by J. Finlayson.
- " 48. Brazil. Drawn by J. Finlayson.
- " 49. United provinces of South America. Drawn by J. Finlayson.
- " 50. Peru. Drawn by J. Finlayson.
- " 51. Chili. Drawn by J. Finlayson.

## 1831–1835
**Burr, D. H.**

A new universal atlas; comprising separate maps of all the principal empires, kingdoms & states throughout the world: and forming a distinct atlas of the United States. Carefully compiled from the best authorities extant . . . 2 p. l., 63 maps. fol. New York, D. S. Stone [1835?]     1379a

    Note—Several maps dated 1835.
    The following maps relate to America:
    no.  [2] Western hemisphere.
    "  [30] Lower Canada. 1834.
    "  31. Upper Canada. 1833.
    "  [32] Newfoundland, Nova Scotia and New Brunswick. 1833.
    "  33. United States. 1833.
    "  34. Maine. 1835.
    "  35. Vermont and New Hampshire. 1835.
    "  36. New York. 1832.
    "  37. New York city. 1831.
    "  38. Massachusetts, Rhode Island and Connecticut. 1835.
    "  39. Pennsylvania. 1834.
    "  40. New Jersey. 1835.
    "  41. Delaware and Maryland. 1833.
    "  [42] Virginia. 1834.
    "  43. Ohio. 1831.
    "  44. Michigan. 1831.
    "  45. Indiana. 1833.
    "  46. Illinois. 1834.
    "  47. Missouri. 1834.
    "  48. Oregon territory. 1833.
    "  49. Kentucky and Tennessee. 1834.
    "  50. Arkansas. 1835.
    "  51. North and South Carolina. 1834.
    "  [52] Georgia. 1834.
    "  53. . . . Alabama. 1834.
    "  54. Mississippi. 1835.
    "  55. Louisiana. 1834.
    "  56. . . . Florida. 1834.
    "  57. . . . Mexico. 1832.
    "  58. West Indies. 1834.
    "  59. South America. 1833.
    "  60. Columbia. 1834.
    "  61. Peru and Bolivia. 1833.
    "  [62] Brazil with Guiana & Paraguay. 1834.
    "  63. United provinces, Chili & Patagonia. 1833.

The following circular was issued by Burr, relating to his post-office and post-road maps, all of which are in the Library of Congress:

MAPS OF THE UNITED STATES, EXHIBITING THE POST OFFICES AND POST ROADS.

    I have been several years engaged in compiling and preparing for publication a set of maps, arranged as follows, to wit:
    No. 1. A General Map of the United States.
    No. 2. A Map of the New-England States.

No. 3. A Map of New-York.
No. 4. Do. New-Jersey and Pennsylvania.
No. 5. Do. Delaware, Maryland, & Virginia.
No. 6. Do. North and South-Carolina.
No. 7. Do. Georgia and Alabama.
No. 8. Do. Kentucky and Tennessee.
No. 9. Do. Ohio and Indiana.
No. 10. Do. Illinois and Missouri.
No. 11. Do. Louisiana, Mississippi & Alabama.
No. 12. Do. Michigan and Wisconsin.
No. 13. Do. Florida.

The Maps are of the same size, three and a half by four and a half feet. The Scales of the last named twelve, are uniform of ten miles to an inch. They were drawn under the direction of the Post Office Department, and are designed to show every Post Office in the United States, with the distances between every Office. The four-horse post-coach routes, the two-horse stage routes, and the horse and sulky routes, are each distinctly marked. They also contain the Canals and Rail-Roads, the Surveys of the Public Lands, with the subdivisions into Ranges and Townships, with their numbers; the boundaries of the Counties, the location of the Mountains, the courses of the Rivers, and all other information relative to the geography of the Country, which the size of the Maps will admit of.

The above is a brief description of the Maps which are respectfully submitted to the public for their patronage, and for which orders are solicited on the following terms, to wit:

The Maps will be finished in the best style, neatly colored, and mounted on cloth in a port folio, at $75 a set. One or more of the separate Maps, in sheets, colored, at $5 each. If colored and mounted on cloth, with rollers, or in a case, at $7. The Maps will be finished by the first of November.

DAVID H. BURR, *Geographer, &c.*

WASHINGTON, *September* 1, 1839.

WASHINGTON, *September* 1, 1839.

SIR: Above is the Prospectus of a set of Maps of the United States, designed expressly to exhibit the Post Offices and Post Roads. In consideration of their importance to the Postmasters, the better to enable them to discharge their duties, I am authorized to say, that if you wish to obtain either of the above Maps for the use of your office, by sending me the price, and naming the Map, it will be forwarded to you by the Department. The Maps to be sent through the mail must be in sheets, or mounted on cloth, and folded in a case. Let me ask you to frank any letters that you may send me on the subject. I am, with respect, yours, &c.,

DAVID H. BURR, *Geographer, &c.*

P. S.—Congress has not yet passed any law authorizing the Postmasters to be furnished with these Maps; and the Department does not feel at liberty, without a special law, to supply, at its own expense, any, except a very few of the largest Offices, with them. As you know the importance of such Maps to every Postmaster, by seeing or writing to your Members of Congress, giving them your views on the subject, they would probably aid in the passage of a law to supply all the Postmasters.

D. H. B.

### 1835

**Tanner, H. S.**

Atlas of the United States, containing separate maps of each state and territory of the North American union. 2 p. l., 24 col. maps. fol. Philadelphia, the author, 1835. 1380

NOTE.—See also titles 1374, 1376 and 1382.

CONTENTS.

- no. 1. Maine.
- " 2. Vermont and New Hampshire.
- " 3. Massachusetts and Rhode Island.
- " 4. Connecticut.
- " 5. New York.
- " 6. New Jersey.
- " 7. Pennsylvania.
- " 8. Maryland and Delaware.
- " 9. Virginia.
- " 10. North Carolina.
- " 11. South Carolina.
- " 12. Georgia.
- " 13. Florida.
- " 14. Alabama.
- " 15. Mississippi.
- " 16. Louisiana.
- " 17. Arkansas.
- " 18. Tennessee.
- " 19. Kentucky.
- " 20. Ohio.
- " 21. Michigan.
- " 22. Indiana.
- " 23. Illinois.
- " 24. Missouri.

### 1838

**Bradford, G. T.**

An illustrated atlas, geographical, statistical, and historical, of the United States, and the adjacent countries . . . 3 p. l., 170 pp., 39 maps. fol. Philadelphia, E. S. Grant & co. [°1838]

1381

NOTE.—Engraved title-page by Jas. Archer.
Plans of Baltimore, Boston, Cincinnati, Louisville, New Orleans, New York and Washington.
Plan of New York city used as frontispiece.
In addition to maps of the various states, there are two of Canada, and one of North America.
Each map is followed by several pages of descriptive text.

### 1839

**Tanner, H. S.**

A new american atlas containing maps of the several states of the North American union. Projected and drawn on a uniform scale from documents found in the public offices of the United States and state governments, and other original and authentic information. 1 p. l., 18 maps on 24 sheets. fol. Philadelphia, H. S. Tanner, 1839.

1382

NOTE.—First edition published in 1823. See also titles 1374, 1376 and 1380.

CONTENTS.

no. [1–4] A map of North America . . . 1839.
" [5] Map of the states of Maine, New Hampshire, Vermont, Massachusetts, Connecticut & Rhode Island . . . 1839.
" [6] New York . . . 1839.
" [7] Map of the canals and railroads of Pennsylvania and New Jersey . . . 1839.
" [8] Virginia, Maryland, and Delaware. 1839.
" [9] Map of North & South Carolina . . . 1839.
" [10] Georgia and Alabama . . . 1839.
" [11] Map of Florida . . . 1839.
" [12] Kentucky and Tennessee . . . 1839.
" [13] Louisiana and Mississippi . . . 1839.
" [14] A new map of the state of Arkansas . . . 1839.
" [15] Illinois and Missouri . . . 1839.
" [16] Ohio and Indiana . . . 1839.
" [17] A new & authentic map of the state of Michigan and the territory of Wisconsin . . . by Thomas R. Tanner. 1830.
" [18] A map of the United States of Mexico . . . 2d ed. 1830.
" [19] Map of Texas . . . Compiled by Stephen F. Austin . . . 1839.
" [20] Map of the West India & Bahama islands . . .
" [21–24] Map of South America . . . 1839.

**1842**

**Morse, S. E.,** *and* **Breese, S.**

The cerographic atlas of the United States. Supplement to the New-York observer. cover-title, 32 maps. fol. New-York, S. E. Morse & co. 1842.

1383

NOTE.—Manuscript index. Maps dated 1841–1845.
Bound with this atlas is "The cerographic bible atlas. By Sidney E. Morse. New York, 1845."
Maps same as those in Morse and Breese, North American atlas. New York, Harper & brothers, 1842–45. See also title 1228.

CONTENTS.

no. 1. Mississippi. 1842.
" 2. Louisiana. 1842.
" 3. New York. 1842.
" 4. City of New York. 1843.
" 5. New York and vicinity. 1842.
" 6. Florida. 1842.
" 7. Georgia. 1842.
" 8. Alabama. 1842.
" 9. Maine. 1841.
" 10. Vermont and New Hampshire.
" 11. Connecticut.
" 12. New Jersey. 1841. Reduced from T. Gordon's map.

**Morse, S. E.,** *and* **Breese, S.**—Continued.
- no. 13. Maryland and Delaware.—District of Columbia.
- " 14. Virginia.
- " 15. Ohio.
- " 16. Iowa.
- " 17. North Carolina. 1843.
- " 18. South Carolina. 1843.
- " 19. Indiana. 1842.
- " 20. Illinois. 1844.
- " 21. Pennsylvania. 1843.
- " 22. Kentucky and Tennessee. 1845.
- " 23. Missouri. 1844.
- " 24. Arkansas. 1845.
- " 25. Michigan. 1844.
- " 26. Iowa and Wisconsin, chiefly from the map of J. N. Nicollet. 1844.
- " 27. Texas. 1844.
- " 28. Map of the Californias by T. J. Farnham.
- " 29. A map of the Indian territory, northern Texas and New Mexico . . . by Josiah Gregg. 1844.
- " 30. Mexico.—Central America and Yucatan.
- " 31. Oregon.
- " 32. Massachusetts and Rhode Island.

## 1843

**Collection, A,** of maps, charts, drawings, surveys, etc. Published from time to time, by order of the two houses of congress . . . 4 p. l., 189 maps. fol. Washington, 1843.    1384

NOTE.—On title-page: "This is not a complete collection of maps, charts, &c. published by order of congress. It contains such only as could be collected when this volume was bound—1843." Mostly to accompany documents. Two incomplete tables of contents.

CONTENTS.

no. [1] Letter from the secretary of state, transmitting, pursuant to a resolution of the house of representatives, of the nineteenth ultimo, a copy of the maps and report of the commissioners under the Treaty of Ghent, for ascertaining the northern and northwestern boundary between the United States and Great Britain. 2 p. l., 8 maps. Washington, printed by Gales & Seaton, 1828. Three maps entitled Detroit, 1820; one map entitled lake Huron, 1820 & 1821; other 4 maps without special titles.

" [2] Pensacola harbor and bar. Florida. Surveyed in 1822 by major James Kearney . . .

" [3] 25th Congress. 2nd sess. Ho. of reps. doc. no. 459. Potomac aqueduct. 81 pp., 28 maps. 1838. Text in 8°. Map entitled, Hydrographic survey of the Potomac river near Georgetown . . . Survey made in fall of 1832 . . . William Turnbull, capt. U. S. top. eng$^{rs}$

" [4] Map of the country embracing the several routes examined with a view to a national road, from Zanesville to Florence, for lt. col. Long's brigade compiled from the most authentic maps del. by lt. Walter Gwynn . . . [1827–1828?]

no.  [5] Design for Flinn's Knoll light: oct. 1838 . . . Governors Island, N. Y., oct. 29, 1838, Jn. L. Smith, major corps of E.

" [6] Map of the mouth of Big Sandy creek. Exhibiting the obstructions at its entrance with a plan for their removal by T. W. Maurice, cap? eng! corps [1829?]

" [7] Putneyville bay [N. Y.] with the plan of a breakwater . . . By T. W. Maurice . . . 1829.

" [8] Map of the mouth of Great Sodus bay [N. Y.] Exhibiting a plan for removing the obstructions at its entrance by T. W. Maurice . . . [1829?]

" [9] Map of Dunkirk harbor [N. Y.] showing the works erected by the United States and the plan of those projected for its further improvement; together with the changes of outline of shore caused by their erection up to sep. 30th 1838. Copied in part from lt. T. S. Brown's map of 1835 by I. H. Simpson 1st lieut. U. S. topog! engr* Accompanying annual report 1838. W. G. Williams, cap! U. S. topo. engs.

" [10] Chart of the eastern part of Presqu'ile bay showing the changes of outline of shore going on in consequence of the erection of the U. S. works; copied in part from lieu! T. S. Brown's map of 1835 by I. H. Simpson . . . Oct. 1838. Accomp* annual report 1838. W. G. Williams . . .

" [11] Map exhibiting the condition of U. S. works at the head of Presqu'ile bay 30th sep. 1838. Copied in part from lt. T. S. Brown's survey and map of sep. 1837 . . . Accompanying annual rept. 1838. W. C. Williams . . .

" [12] Cataraugus harbor and the public works in progress therein . . . J. H. Simpson . . . Accomp* annual report 1838. W. G. Williams . . .

" [13] Map of Portland harbor. Copied in part from H. Lovejoy's survey & map of 1836. J. H. Simpson . . . Accompanying annual report 1838. W. G. Williams . . .

" [14] Portland harbour, with the plan of a proposed breakwater. By T. W. Maurice . . . 1829.

" [15] Map exhibiting the country between lakes Michigan and Erie and the contested boundary lines by David H. Burr.

" [16] Profile with the spirit level, of the due north line from the monument at the source of the river S! Croix to the river S! John. Surveyed in 1840 & 1841 under the direction of major J. D. Graham, U. S. top. engineers . . . To accompany 27th congress. 3d session. House of rep! doc. no. 31.

" [17] [Mississippi river from St. Louis to Chauteau's island]

" [18] Plan of Lovejoy's narrows from a survey of the Kennebeck river . . . under the orders of lieu! col. I. I. Abert. 1826.

" [19] Map of the territory of Wisconsin by David H. Burr. Draughtsman to the house of rep! U. S. 1836. To accompany the hon. Z. Casey's report.

" [20-21] Map shewing the lands assigned to emigrant indians west of Arkansas & Missouri. Prepared at the topographical bureau, feb. 23d 1836. R. Jones, adj. gen.

" [22] Map of the harbor of St. Louis, Mississippi river. Oct. 1837. Surveyed by lt. R. E. Lee, corps of engineers . . . Copied from the original by M. C. Ewing . . .

**Collection, A,** of maps, charts, drawings, surveys, etc.—Continued.

no. [23] The Kennebec river and adjacent country showing the routes examined for a road from Augusta to the Canada line in the direction of Quebec. Reconnoissance made in 1834 by Hartman Bache, t. e. & bt. major . . .

" [24–26] Chart shewing site of light house proposed for the Brandywine shoal, Delaware bay. Hartman Bache . . . 25 jan! 1836. Wash: Hood, lt . . .

" [27–30] [Survey of the Kennebec] nos. [29–30] Drawn by lt. J. Macomb. U. S. A.

" [31] Map of the routes examined and surveyed for the Winchester and Potomac railroad, state of Virginia under the direction of cap! J. D. Graham, U. S. top. eng. 1831 and 1832.

" [32] Map illustrating the plan of the defences of the western & northwestern frontier, as proposed by Charles Gratiot, in his report of oct. 31, 1837. Compiled in the U. S. topographical bureau under the direction of col. J. J. Abert . . . by W. Hood.

" [33] Map illustrating the plan of the defences of the western & northwestern frontier, as proposed by the hon. J. R. Poinsett, sec. of war, in his report of dec. 30, 1837. Compiled in U. S. topographical bureau under the direction of col. J. J. Abert . . . by W. Hood. 25 congress 2 session s. no. 1, doc 65.

" [34] Chart of the entrance of Sandusky-bay bureau of U. S. topographical engineers, 1838. Reduced from original survey of lieu! C. Graham of 1826, under the direction of col. Jn? J. Abert . . . by Wash: Hood. 25th congress. 2 session. h. r. doc. no. 399.

" [35] Profile of breakwater on Stanford's ledge. Topographical bureau. feb. 22ᵈ 1834. Copied by Rob! Fowler . . .

" [36] Elevation of the lantern of the light house at Barfleur.

" [37–39] [Charleston harbour and Fort Sumter]

" [40] Map of the Neenah or Fox river . . . Langtree & O. Sullivan, Washington, D. C. To accompany doc. 102. Ho. of rep! 25 cong! 3ᵈ sess. [1839]

" [41] Map of the northern parts of Ohio, Indiana and Illinois with Michigan and that part of the Ouisconsin territory lying east of the Mississippi river. By David H. Burr . . . 1836.

" [42] Mouth of 18 mile creek, Niagara county, New York [1838?] Rough sketch of that part of Red rivir [!] in which the great raft is situated, and the bayous, lakes, swamps &c. belonging to, or in its vicinity [1833?]

" [43] Map of the Cumberland river from the falls to Nashville. Made to accompany a report on the improvement of that stream for the navigation of it by steam boats; in obedience to a resolution of congress dated april 26th 1834, by Howard Stansbury. Taken from Matthew Rheas map of Tennessee.

" [44] [Survey of Cumberland river from Cowan's shoals to Bartletts creek island] White and Hazard's lock [1834?]

" [45–49] Survey of the Cumberland river from falls to Nashville with a view to the removal of the obstruction between those points. Made under the direction of Howard Stansbury, U. S. ass! civ. eng. 1834.

" [50–52] Plan of Marine hospital to accomodate 50 patients besides officers &c. 7 plans. [1823?]

no. [53] Diagram of the state of Illinois. No. 2, C. Surveyors office. S! Louis, 30th of october 1837. Accompanying report of 30th october, 1837. 25th congress 2ᵈ session. doc! 11, no. 3.
" [54] Diagram of the state of Illinois. Referred to in report of the 27ˢᵗ october, 1841. Surveyors office. Saint Louis, 27ˢ! october, • 1841 . . . Jos. C. Brown . . .
" [55] Diagram of the state of Illinois. Surveyor generals office, Saint Louis, 1ˢᵗ october, 1839 . . . William Milburn . . .
" [56] Diagram of the state of Missouri. Surveyors office. St. Louis, 30th of october 1837. 25 congress 2ⁿᵈ session. h. r. doc. 23, no. 4.
" [57] Diagram of the state of Missouri. Referred to in report of the 27ˢ!t of october, 1841. Surveyors office. St. Louis, 27th oct. 1841 . . . Jos. C. Brown, surveyor . . . 27th con. 2ⁿ.d sess.
" [58] Diagram of the state of Missouri. Surveyor general's office. Saint Louis. 1ˢ! october, 1839. 26th congress. 1ˢ! sess.
" [59] Diagram of the surveying district south of Tennessee [1839] 26th congress. 1ˢᵗ sess.
" [60] Diagram of the surveying district south of Tennessee. Surveyors office. oct! 1ˢ! 1841, Jackson, Mississippi. B. A. Ludlow, surveyor . . . 27th congress 2ⁿᵈ sess.
" [61] Sketch of the public surveys in the north part of Michigan [1839] 26th congr. 1ˢᵗ sess.
" [62] Sketch of the public surveys in the north part of Michigan [1841?] 27th congress. 2ᵈ session.
" [63] S! Helena district, La.—South eastern district, Louisiana. 25th congress. 2ⁿᵈ session, doc. 11, nos. 8–9.
" [64] Map of the south western district Louisiana. 1ˢ! october, 1841. 27 con. 2 ses. s. doc. 22.
" [65] South eastern district Louisiana [1839?]—Sketch of the public surveys in Iowa territory [1839?]
" [66] Sketch of the public surveys in Iowa territory [1841?] s. 27th con. 2ᵈ ses.
" [67] Map of the district north of Red river, La. [1839?]—Sketch of the public surveys in Iowa territory [1839?]
" [68] Arkansas. Map of Arkansas surveying district shewing the extent of public surveys in said district on the 30th september, 1839 . . . Surveyor's office. Little Rock, 30th sep! 1839. David Fulton, sur . . . 26 congress 1ˢᵗ sess.
" [69] Arkansas. Map of Arkansas surveying district shewing the extent of public surveys in said district on the 31ˢ! october, 1837 . . . Surveyor's office. Little Rock, 31 october 1837. Signed, Eʷᵈ Cross, sur . . .
" 70. A plat exhibiting the surveys as they are in the territory of Florida . . . Surveyor generals office, Tallahassee oct! 1839. Approved Robert Butler, surv! gen! . . .
" [71] A plat exhibiting the state of the surveys in the territory of Florida . . . Surveyor generals office, Talahassee oc! 1841. Approved Robert Butler, sur! gen!
" [72] Map of the district north of Red river, La. [1837?]—Map of the south western district Louisiana [1837?] 25th congress 2ᵈ sessⁿ. doc. 11, no. 6–7.
" [73] South eastern district, Louisiana. 1ˢ! october, 1841—Map of the district north of Red river, La. 1ˢ! october, 1841.—S! Helena district, La. 1ˢ! october, 1841.—s. 27th con. 2ᵈ ses.

**Collection, A,** of maps, charts, drawings, surveys, etc.—Continued.

no. [74] Map of the south western district, Louisiana [1839] 26th congr. 1st sess. h. doc.

" [75] Sketch of the public surveys in Wisconsin territory . . . [1839]—St Helena district La. [1839] 26th congr. 1st sess. h. doc.

" [76] Sketch of the public surveys in Wisconsin territory . . . [1841?] 27 cong. 2 sess.

" [77] Sketch of the public surveys in the north part of Michigan . . . [1837?]—Sketch of the public surveys in Wisconsin territory . . . 25th congress. 2d sessn doc. 11, nos. 1-2.

" [78] Map of the Cherokee cession in Alabama . . . [1837]—A plat exhibiting the state of the surveys in the territory of Florida . . . surveyors office, Tallahassee, oct. 20th 1837. Sd Robert Butler . . . 25th congress. 2d session. h. doc. 11, nos. 10-11.

" [79] Core sound, North Carolina, surveyed, under the direction of lieut. col. J. Kearney . . . 1837 . . . by Wash: Hood.

" [80-83] . . . Core sound, N. C. surveyed under the direction of J. Kearney lt. col. . . . 1837. 25 cong. 2 sess. h. rep. doc. 445.

" [84] Map of Portland harbor, Maine. Surveyed under the direction of lt: col: John Anderson, U. S. top. engineer . . . 1833.

" [85] Map of a part of the south shore of lake Erie in the vicinity of the Twenty mile creek, Pennsylvania. Surveyed and executed by Thos Forster and James Maurice, jr. Erie, Penna jan. 31st 1830.

" [86] Sketch of the mouth of Elk creek. James Kearny lt col. & top. e. Copied in bureau top. eng.

" [87] Sketch of the country embracing several routes from Portsmouth, Ohio, to Linville, N. C. . . . Drawn by lieut F. L. Dancy . . . under the direction of lieut. col. S. H. Long . . . U. S. topographical bureau, Washington city, D. C. 26 feb. 1836 . . .

" [88] Pensacola harbor & bar. Surveyed in 1822 by major James Kearney . . . Reduced from the original and drawn by lieuts. Wash. Hood, and Richd S. Smith . . . 1835.

" [89] Survey of the mouth of Galien river, Michigan. Surveyed by lieuts J. M. Berrien and E. Rose.

" [90] Charleston harbour and the adjacent coast and country, South Carolina. Surveyed at intervals in 1823, 1824 and 1825 by Hartman Bache . . .

" [91] Cape Fear river North Carolina. Surveyed in conformity to an act of congress and executed by lieutenant James Glynn, commanding . . . july 1839 . . . Washington city.

" [92] Chart of the bar and bay of St Joseph, West Florida. Surveyed april, 1841, by L. M. Powell . . . under instructions from the hon. the Board of navy commissioners.

" [93] Ship island inlet to Mississippi sound. Surveyed in january and february, 1841, by L. M. Powell, lt . . . under instruction from the hon. the board of navy commissioners . . . Wash. city.

" [94] Map of the delta of the St Clair, surveyed projected and drawn by lieutenants J. N. Macomb and W. H. Warner under the direction of captain W. G. Williams, U. S. corps of topl engrs 1842 . . . Wash. city.

" [95] Beaufort harbour, North Carolina. Surveyed by order of the honorable J. K. Paulding, secy of the navy. Executed by lieutenant James Glynn, commanding . . . dec. 9th 1839.

" [96] Chart of the southern coast from Tybee bar to Hunting id, May river. Surveyed by Charles Wilkes lieutenant commandant . . . in U. S. brig Porpoise, 1838 no. [97] Chart of Georges shoal & bank, surveyed by Charles Wilkes, lieut. commandant . . . in U. S. brig Porpoise, schooners Maria & Hadassah. By order of the hon. Mahlon Dickerson, secretary of the navy. 1837.

" [98] Extract from the U. S. coast survey. Chart of Newark bay [1839] 25th cong. 3d sess. h. rep. doc. 182.

" [99] A map of the extremity of Cape Cod, including the townships of Provincetown & Truro; with a chart of their sea coast and of Cape Cod harbour, state of Massachusetts. Executed under the direction of mayor J. D. Graham . . . During portions of the years 1833, '34 & '35. Engraved by order of the house of representatives . . . to accompany doc. 121, 25th congress, 2nd session.

" [100–101] A chart of the entrance of Cape Fear river. Surveyed by order of the honorable J. K. Paulding, sec. of the navy. Executed by lieutenant James Glynn, commanding . . . 1839.

" [102] Chart of Narraganset bay surveyed in 1832, by capt. Alex S. Wadsworth . . . of the U. S. navy. By order of honr. Levi Woodbury, secretary of the navy.

" [103] Map of the territory of Florida. From its northern boundary to lat: 27°, 30′ n, connected with the delta of the Mississippi. Annexed to the report of the board of internal improvement, dated feby 1829 . . . [Insets: Central America]—Entrance to Mobile bay.—Entrance to Pensacola bay.—Eastern entrance to St. Rosa sound.—Entrance to St. Andrew's sound.—Entrance to St. Joseph's bay.—Entrance to Appalachicola bay.—Main entrance to St. George's sound.—Middle entrance to St. George's sound.—Entrance to Ocklockony bay.—Eastern entrance to St. George's sound.—Entrance to St. Augustine.—Entrance to St. John's river.—Entrance to St. Mary's harbour.

" [104] Map of the river Sabine from its mouth on the gulf of Mexico in the sea to Logan's ferry in latitude 31°. 58′. 24″. north. Shewing the boundary between the United States and Texas between said points . . . Surveyed in 1840 by, on the part of the United States, J. D. Graham, major . . . On the part of Texas, J. J. Pillans . . .

" [105] Map of the river Sabine from Logan's ferry to 32nd degree of north latitude. Shewing the boundary between the United States of America and the republic of Texas between said points, as marked and laid down by survey in 1841 . . .

" [106] Sabine Pass and mouth of the river Sabine in the sea. Surveyed under the direction of major J. D. Graham . . . 1840.

" [107] Map of the seat of war in Florida. Compiled by order of the honble Joel R. Poinsett, secretary of war, under the direction of col. J. J. Abert . . . by Wash: Hood. Bureau of topographical engineer's, Washington city, 1838.

" [108–110] Part of the boundary between the United States and Texas; A? from the Sabine river, northward, to the 36th. mile mound; B? north of Sabine river from 39th to the 72nd mile mound; C? north of Sabine river from the 72nd mile mound to Red river. Drawn from the notes of survey . . . by J. Edmd Blake, 1st. lieut. U. S. topog. engs.

" [111] Maps & profiles, of the Pennsylvania and Ohio canal, from Akron on the Ohio canal by the ballies of the Cuyahoga and Mahoning on the Shenango. Located in 1828 under the direction of lieut. col. Kearney . . .

**Collection, A,** of maps, charts, drawings, surveys, etc.—Continued.
no. [112-115] 26th congress. 2d session. senate. Explanations of the maps accompanying the report from the secretary of the treasury . . . january 18, 1841. 1 p., 9 maps on 4 l. no. 1, Indiana; no. 2, Michigan; no. 3, Illinois; no. 4, Florida; no. 5, Missouri; no. 6, Arkansas; no. 7, Louisiana; no. 8, Mississippi; no. 9, Alabama.
" [116] Map of the Rock Island rapids of the Mississippi river. Surveyed by lt. R. E. Lee . . . in sept! & oct! 1837.
" [117-118] Duplicates of no. [22]
" [119-125] [Lakes Superior, Huron & Michigan] 19 maps on 7 l. Maps copied for the board of commission under the 6. C. 7 article of the treaty of Ghent [1828?]
" [126] Profile of that section of country situated between lake Nicaragua and the South sea . . . Bureau U. S. topographical engineers. Wash. Hood, del. 1838. 25th cong'. 3d session. h. r. doc. 322.
" [127] Map exhibiting the position of the several lines connected with the settlement of the Ohio boundary question . . . [1836?]
" [128] Plan of that part of the isthmus of Panama eligible for effecting a communication between the Atlantic & Pacific . . . 1828 & 1829 by J. A. Lloyd . . .—Map of the western coast of America with the intended track of the steamers from New York to the Isthmus of Panama and from Panama along the western coast northerly as far as California and southerly as far as Conception.
" [129] Mapa corografica de un camino carretero en el Istmo de Panama levantado de orden del gobierno. Por Maur? Palmark . . . [1839].—Map shewing the route from New-York to the isthmus of Panama and from Lima to Australia . . . [1839] 25th cong. 3d ses$^n$. h. r. doc. 322.
" [130] Isthme de Tehuantepec dans lequel se trouve la concefsion faite en 1828 . . .
" [131-138] Survey of Kennebeck river by lt'. J. K. Findlay . . . 8 maps. [1826?]
" [139] Map of the northern part of the state of Maine and of the adjacent british provinces . . . Reduced . . . by S. L. Dashiell, Washington, 1830.
" [140] Map of the United States territory of Oregon . . . Compiled in the bureau of topographical engineers . . . under the direction of col. J. J. Abert, by Wash: Hood. 1838.
" [141] Chart of the Columbia river for 90 miles from its mouth. Drawn by M. C. Ewing . . . [1837] 25 congress. 2 session. s. doc. no. 470.
" [142] Cape May roads, including Crow shoal, Del. bay. September 1836 . . . Hartman Bache . . .
" [143] Survey of a road route from Saginaw to Mackinac M. T. Executed by lieut. Poole 3d. arty.
" [144] Map of the Des Moines rapids of the Mississippi river. Surveyed by lt. R. E. Lee . . . september 1837. no. 1. 25 congress. 2 sessn. senate doc. 139.
" [145] Map of the country embracing the various routes surveyed for the Western & Atlantic rail road of Georgia. Under the direction of lieut. col. S. H. Long . . .—Profiles of the principal routes surveyed for the W. & A. rail road of Georgia. Col. S. H. Long . . . 1837. 25 congress. 2 session. doc. no. 57.

no. [146] Owl's head harbor, Maine. Surveyed in august, 1836, under the direction of lt. col. S. H. Long . . .—Chart of Owlshead harbour and projections of a breakwater. Drawn by T. A. Barton and A. R. Flint. 25 congress. 2 session. s. doc. no. 73.
" [147] Cobscook bay, Maine. Surveyed in 1836 under the direction of lt. col. S. H. Long . . . 25 congress. 2 session. s. doc. no. 73.
" [148] Map of the mouth of Little Sodus bay . . . [1829?]—Extract from a map of the british and french dominions in North America. By Jnº. Mitchell. 1755.
" [149] Map of the west coast of Africa . . . Compiled mostly from the map of John Arrowsmith, 1842.
" [150] Chart of Kennebeck river from Augusta to Gardiner. 1837. 25 congress. 2 session. doc. no. 114.
" [151] Plan of the northern boundary line of the state of Indiana . . . 1827
" [152] A diagram for the triangulation for the survey of the coast of the United States, made in 1817 and 1833, and the secondary triangle made in 1833 & 1834 in Connecticut & upon Long Island.
" [153] Survey of Roanoke inlet and sound . . . Under the direction of Hartman Bache . . . [1829?]
" [154] Map of Illinois with parts of Indiana, Wisconsin, &c. By David H. Burr . . . 1836.
" [155] Sketch of the Illinois river . . . Surveyed under the direction of Howard Stansbury . . . 1837.—Plat of the Milwaukee and Rock river canal. 25 congress. 2 session. s. doc. nos. 272-271.

## 1856

**Black, A. & C.**

Black's atlas of North America. A series of twenty maps constructed and engraved by John Bartholomew. With introductory letter-press and a complete index. 40 pp., 20 maps. fol. Edinburgh, A. & C. Black, 1856.   1385

CONTENTS.

no. 1. North America.
" 2. British America, containing all discoveries . . . up to 1856.
" 3. Canada, west sheet.
" 4. Canada, New Brunswick, Nova Scotia &c. east sheet.
" 5. New York, Vermont, New Hampshire, Rhode Island, Massachusetts & Connecticut.—Inset: City of New York.
" 6. Maine.
" 7. Pennsylvania and New Jersey.
" 8. Ohio, Indiana & Illinois.
" 9. Michigan, Wisconsin, Iowa & Minnesota.
" 10. Virginia, Maryland & Delaware.
" 11. North & South Carolina.
" 12. Kentucky and Tennessee.
" 13. Missouri and Arkansas.
" 14. Georgia & Florida.—Inset: Continuation of Florida.
" 15. Alabama.
" 16. Mississippi & Louisiana.
" 17. Texas, part of New Mexico &c.
" 18. Western states, including California, Oregon, Utah . . .
" 19. Central America, Mexico & West Indies.—Inset: Panama railway.
" 20. Chart shewing the communication between Europe, North America and the Pacific.

### 1864

**Colton, G. W.**

Colton's atlas of America, illustrating the physical and political geography of North and South America and the West India Islands ... Accompanied by descriptions geographical, statistical, and historical, by Richard Swanson Fisher ...   2 p. l., [149] pp., incl. 65 (*i. e.* 57) maps. fol. New York, J. W. Colton, 1864.   1386

NOTE.—Illustrated added title.

### 1864

**Colton, J. H.**

Colton's condensed octavo atlas of the Union: containing maps of all the states and territories of the United States of America.   7, 51 pp. incl. 25 col. maps. 8°. New York, J. H. Colton, 1864.

1387

### 1866

**United States.** *Department of the interior.   General land office.*

Maps accompanying the report of the commissioner of the general land office. 1866. pt. 2.   cover-title, 2 p. l., 23 maps.   sm. fol. [Washington, 1866]   1388

NOTE:—"Showing the progress of public surveys accompanying the annual report of the commissioner dated october 2, 1866."

CONTENTS.

no. 1. Map of Ohio.
"   2. "   " Indiana.
"   3. "   " Illinois.
"   4. "   " Michigan.
"   5. "   " Wisconsin.
"   6. "   " Minnesota.
"   7. "   " Iowa.
"   8. "   " Dakota.
"   9. "   " Missouri.
"  10. "   " Arkansas.
"  11. "   " Louisiana.
"  12. "   " Mississippi.
"  13. "   " Alabama.
"  14. "   " Florida.
"  15. "   " Kansas and Nebraska.
"  16. "   " Colorado.
"  17. "   " New Mexico and Arizona.
"  18. "   " Utah.
"  19. "   " Nevada.
"  20. "   " California.
"  21. "   " Oregon.
"  22. "   " Washington territory.
"  23. Connected map of the land states and territories [*i. e.* Map of the United States and territories]

## 1868

**Walling, H. F.**
Atlas of the state of Ohio, to which is added an atlas of the United States.  2 p. l., 6–101 pp. incl. 35 maps, 2 l. at end.  fol.  New York, H. H. Lloyd & co. 1868.     1389

## 1873

**Gray, O. W.**
Gray's atlas of the United States, with general maps of the world, accompanied by descriptions geographical, historical, scientific, and statistical.  175 pp. incl. 65 maps.  fol.  Philadelphia, Stedman, Brown & Lyon, 1873.     1390

>NOTE.—Contains plans of the principal cities in the United States.

## 1875

**Gray, O. W., & son.**
The national atlas, containing elaborate topographical maps of the United States and the dominion of Canada, with plans of cities and general maps of the world; also, descriptions and tables, historical and statistical, with a reference list . . .  2 p. l., 6–179 pp., 1 l. incl. 72 col. maps.  fol.  Philadelphia, O. W. Gray & son, 1875.     1391

>NOTE.—In addition to plans of the principal cities of the United States, the following relate to Maryland: Cumberland, Frostburg, Lonaconing, Barton, Westernport.

## 1875

**Watson, G.**
Watson's new commercial, county and railroad atlas of the United States and territories, and british provinces.  Giving all railroads, names and stations, distances between stations, proposed railroads, express guide, populations by counties and states, etc., being the most complete mercantile guide ever published, compiled from the latest official sources.  1 p. l., 113 pp. incl. 28 col. maps.  fol. [New York, G. Watson, 1875]     1392

>NOTE.—Pasted over the imprint, "Published by Perry & Spaulding, 147 Court Street, Boston, Mass.," is a piece of paper upon which is written in ink "Published by Gaylord Watson, 16 Beekman St. New York [1875]"

## 1876

**Gray, O. W.**
Gray's atlas of the United States, with general maps of the world.  Accompanied by descriptions geographical, historical, scientific, and statistical . . .  2 p. l., 7–204 pp. incl. 70 maps.  fol.  Philadelphia, J. W. Lyon & co. 1876.     1393

>NOTE.—Contains plans of the principal cities in the United States.

### 1876
**Gray, O. W. & son.**
 The national atlas, containing elaborate topographical maps of the United States and the dominion of Canada, with plans of cities and general maps of the world; also, descriptions and tables, historical and statistical, with a reference list . . .   2 p. l., 7-204 pp., 2 l. incl. 70 col. maps. fol. Philadelphia, O. W. Gray & son, 1876.   1394

> NOTE.—Contains historical maps of the United States.—Geological map, by Charles H. Hitchcock.—Climatological map, by Lorin Blodget.—Botanical map, by Thomas C. Porter.—Zoological map, by Edward D. Cope.

### 1876
**Harrison & Warner.**
 Illustrated historical atlas of Adair county, Missouri, in connection with a general atlas of the United States and the state of Missouri. 2 p. l., [3]-54, 57-89 pp. incl. 35 maps. fol. Philadelphia, Harrison & Warner, 1876.   1395

### 1876
**United States.** *Department of the interior. General land office.*
 Geographical and political atlas of the states and territories of the United States of America in which the public land surveys are now in operation. S. S. Burdett, commissioner.  1 p. l., 18 maps. obl. fol. [New York] J. Bien, photo. lith. & print., 1876.   1396

CONTENTS.

| | | | |
|---|---|---|---|
| no. [ 1] . . . New Mexico. | Scale: | 16 miles to 1 inch. |
| " [ 2] . . . Idaho. | " | 16 " " " " |
| " [ 3] . . . Kansas. | " | 15 " " " " |
| " [ 4] . . . Washington. | " | 12 " " " " |
| " [ 5] . . . Louisiana. | " | 14 " " " " |
| " [ 6] . . . Dakota. | " | 18 " " " " |
| " [ 7] . . . Nebraska. | " | 15 " " " " |
| " [ 8] . . . Wyoming. | " | 15 " " " " |
| " [ 9] . . . Arizona. | " | 18 " " " " |
| " [10] . . . Utah. | " | 12 " " " " |
| " [11] . . . Nevada. | " | 16 " " " " |
| " [12] Indian territory. | " | 12 " " " " |
| " [13] Oregon. | " | 15 " " " " |
| " [14] Montana. | " | 20 " " " " |
| " [15] Florida. | " | 20 " " " " |
| " [16] California. 2 sheets. | " | 20 " " " " |
| " [17] Minnesota. | " | 15 " " " " |
| " [18] Colorado. | " | 16 " " " " |

### 1876-1877
**Rand, McNally & co.**
 Rand, McNally & co.'s business atlas containing large scale maps of each state and territory of the great Mississippi valley and

Pacific slope. Accompanied by a new and original compilation and ready reference index, showing in detail the entire railroad system . . . 112 pp. incl. 27 maps. fol. Chicago, Rand, McNally & co. 1876–1877. 1397

### 1877
**Gray, O. W. & son.**
The national atlas containing elaborate topographical maps of the United States and the dominion of Canada, with plans of cities and general maps of the world. Also descriptions and tables, historical and statistical, with a reference list containing the names of the cities, towns, villages, and post-offices in the United States with their location. Accompanied by special, railway, and scientific maps and articles. 2 p. l., 7–204 pp. incl. 75 col. maps. fol. Philadelphia, O. W. Gray & son, 1877. 1398

> NOTE.—The following maps are inserted: pl. 69a, Richmond.—pl. 88a, Nashville.—pl. 88b, Kentucky (railroad).—pl. 88c, Indianapolis.—pl. 88d, Indiana (railroad) .
> Contains historical maps of the United States.—Geological map, by Charles H. Hitchcock.—Climatological map, by Lorin Blodget.—Botanical map, by Thomas C. Porter.—Zoological map, by Edward D. Cope.

### 1877
**Rand, McNally & co.**
Rand, McNally & co's business atlas containing large scale maps of each state and territory of the United States, the provinces of Canada, West India islands . . . 212 pp. incl. 46 maps. fol. Chicago, Rand, McNally & co. 1877. 1399

### 1878
**Bradstreet, The, co.**
Bradstreet's pocket atlas for the use of commercial travelers. [80] pp. incl. 76 maps. obl. 24°. New York, the Bradstreet co. 1878. 1400

### 1878
**Rand, McNally & co.**
Rand, McNally & co.'s business atlas containing large scale maps of each state and territory of the United States, the provinces of Canada, West India islands . . . 234 pp. incl. 47 maps. fol. Chicago, Rand, McNally & co. 1878. 1401

### 1878–1879
Rand, McNally & co.'s business atlas containing large scale maps of each state and territory of the United States, the provinces of Canada, West India Islands . . . 234 pp. incl. 50 maps. fol. Chicago, Rand, McNally & co. 1878–1879. 1402

### 1879

**Bartholomew, J.**
Philip's handy general atlas of America, comprising a series of detailed maps of the United States, Canada, etc. With index and statistical notes by John Bartholomew. 18 pp., 23 col. maps. fol. London, G. Philip & son [1879] 1403

### 1879

**Macullar, Parker & co.**
Macullar, Parker & co.'s atlas sample book. 1 p. l., 23 maps. obl. 12°. Boston, Macullar, Parker & co. [1879] 1404

### 1879

**United States.** *Department of the interior. General land office.*
[Atlas of the states and territories over which land surveys have been extended, 1879] cover-title, 1 p. l., 29 maps. fol. [New York, J. Bien, 1879] 1405

CONTENTS.

- no. 1. Ohio.
- " 2. Indiana.
- " 3. Illinois.
- " 4. Michigan.
- " 5. Wisconsin.
- " 6. Minnesota.
- " 7. Iowa.
- " 8. Missouri.
- " 9. Arkansas.
- " 10. Louisiana.
- " 11. Mississippi.
- " 12. Alabama.
- " 13. Florida.
- " 14. Dakota.
- " 15. Nebraska.
- " 16. Kansas.
- " 17. Indian territory.
- " 18. Montana.
- " 19. Wyoming.
- " 20. Colorado.
- " 21. New Mexico.
- " 22. Idaho.
- " 23. Utah.
- " 24. Arizona.
- " 25. Nevada.
- " 26. Washington territory.
- " 27. Oregon.
- " 28. California (lower sheet)
- " 29.    "    (upper sheet)

### 1880

**Rand, McNally & co.**
Rand, McNally & co.s business atlas containing large scale maps of each state and territory of the United States, the provinces of Canada, West India islands . . .  2 p. l., 7–257 pp. incl. 51 maps. fol. Chicago, Rand, McNally & co. 1880.  1406

### 1880

Rand, McNally & co.'s new indexed atlas of the northwest. 76 pp. incl. 15 maps. fol. [Chicago, Rand, McNally & co. 1880]
1407

### 1881

Rand, McNally & co.'s new indexed business atlas and shippers' guide . . . 8th ed.  427 pp. incl. 54 col. maps. fol. Chicago, Rand, McNally & co. 1881.  1408

### 1881

Rand, McNally & co.s new indexed business atlas and shippers' guide . . . 9th ed.  429 pp. incl. 54 col. map. fol. Chicago, Rand, McNally & co. 1881.  1409

### 1881

Rand, McNally & co.'s new indexed business atlas and shippers' guide. Containing large scale maps of each state and territory of the Mississippi valley and northwest. Accompanied by a new and original compilation and ready reference index, showing in detail the entire railroad system . . .  2, [5]–180 pp. incl. 23 maps. fol. Chicago, Rand, McNally & co. 1881.  1410

### 1881

**Van Antwerp, Bragg & co.**
The eclectic atlas and hand-book of the United States.  4°. Cincinnati, New York, Van Antwerp, Bragg & co. [1881]
[Eclectic series of geographies. Supplements]  1411
NOTE.—Supplements preceded by 2 p. l., 9 maps on 10 l., and followed by 1 l.

CONTENTS.

Sup. 1. Geography of Alabama. By prof. E. R. Dickson. 14 pp. incl. 1 map.
" 2. Geography of Colorado. [anon.] 10 pp. incl. 2 maps.
" 3. Geography of Georgia. By George Little. 16 pp. incl. 1 map.
" 4. Geography of Illinois. By E. C. Hewett. 12 pp., 1 map.
" 5. Geography of Indiana. [anon.] 10 pp., 1 map.
" 6. Geography of Iowa. By prof. C. E. Bessey. 12 pp., 1 map.
" 7. Geography of Kansas. By H. C. Speer. 14 pp. incl. 1 map.

**Van Antwerp, Bragg & co.**—Continued.

Sup. 8. Geography of Kentucky. By William J. Davis. 16 pp. incl. 1 map.
" 9. Geography of Maine. By Albert P. Marble. 10 pp. incl. 1 map.
" 10. Geography of Maryland. By M. A. Newell. 12 pp. incl. 1 map.
" 11. Geography of Massachusetts. By Albert P. Marble. 16 pp. incl. 1 map.
" 12. Geography of Michigan. By Joseph Estabrook. 12 pp., 1 map.
" 13. Geography of Mississippi. By Eug. W. Hilgard. 10 pp. incl. 1 map.
" 14. Geography of Missouri. By Edward B. Neely. 16 pp. incl. 1 map.
" 15. Geography of New York city and vicinity. By J. S. Newberry. 14 pp. incl. 1 map.
" 16. Geography of Ohio. [anon.] 12 pp., 1 map.
" 17. Geography of Tennessee. By E. C. Hewett. 16 pp. incl. 1 map.
" 18. Geography of Virginia. By Jed. Hotchkiss. 16 pp. incl. 1 map.
" 19. Geography of West Virginia. [anon.] 10 pp., 1 map.
" 20. Geography of Wisconsin. By prof. Robert Graham. 12 pp., 1 map.

### 1882

**Gray, O. W. & son.**
The national atlas, containing elaborate topographical maps of the United States and the dominion of Canada, with plans of cities and general maps of the world; also, descriptions and tables, historical and statistical, with a reference list . . .   2 p. l., 7–224 pp., 20 l. incl. 85 col. maps.  fol.  Philadelphia, O. W. Gray & son, 1882.
1412

NOTE.—Contains historical maps of the United States.—Geological map, by Charles H. Hitchcock.—Climatological map, by Lorin Blodget.—Botanical map, by Thomas C. Porter.—Zoological map, by Edward D. Cope. In addition to plans of the principal cities, the following relate to North Carolina: Wilmington, Raleigh, Tarboro, Washington, Warrenton, Wilson, Beaufort, Oxford, Louisburg, Henderson, Greensboro, Durham.

### 1883

**Rand, McNally & co.**
Rand, McNally & o.'s new indexed business atlas and shippers guide . . . 11th ed.   479 pp. incl. 72 col. maps.  fol.  Chicago, Rand, McNally & co. 1883.
1413

### 1883

**Watson, G.**
New indexed family atlas of the United States, with maps of the world. A compendium of geographical knowledge . . . showing in detail the railway system and post routes . . .  112 pp. incl. 50 col. maps.  fol.  New York, G. Watson; Chicago, Tenney & Weaver, 1883.
1414

### 1884

**Bower, R. A.**
New handy atlas of the United States and Canada, containing new colored maps of each state and territory in the United States,

with special maps of provinces in the dominion, together with full descriptive matter . . . 127 pp. incl. 49 maps, 14 diagr. 4°. Chicago, Rand, McNally & co. 1884. 1415

### 1884
**Rand, McNally & co.**
Rand, McNally & co.'s new dollar atlas of the United States and dominion of Canada . . . together with full descriptive matter . . . 128 pp. incl. 49 maps, 14 diagr. 8°. Chicago, Rand, McNally & co. 1884. 1416

NOTE.—Continental publishing co., Chicago, sole subscription agents.

### 1884
Rand, McNally & co.'s new indexed business atlas and shippers' guide . . . 13th ed. 498 pp. incl. 73 col. maps. fol. Chicago, Rand, McNally & co. 1884. 1417

### 1884
Rand, McNally & co.'s new indexed business atlas and shippers' guide. Containing large scale maps of each state and territory of the Mississippi valley, northwest and Pacific coast. Accompanied by a new and original compilation and ready reference index, showing in detail the entire railroad system . . . 1 p. l., 250 pp. incl. 39 maps. fol. Chicago, Rand, McNally & co. 1884. 1418

### 1884
**Swinton, W.** *and* **Harrower, H. D.**
A descriptive atlas of the United States for reference and general information. [anon.] 2 p. l., 292 pp. incl. 54 col. maps. 4°. New York, and Chicago, Ivison, Blakeman, Taylor & co. [1884]
1419

### 1884-1888
**Atwood, Holmes & Read.**
The pocket atlas of the United States, containing separate copperplate maps of each state and territory . . . 244 pp. incl. 49 maps. 24°. Philadelphia, Atwood, Holmes & Read, 1884. 1420

### 1885
**Bower, R. A.**
The new handy family atlas of the United States and Canada, containing new colored maps of each state and territory in the United States, with special maps of provinces in the dominion, together with full descriptive matter, relative to the topography, climate, history, population by sex, race and color, etc., etc. [anon.] 1 p. l., 208 pp. incl. 48 maps, 12 diagr. 8°. Detroit, F. B. Dickerson & co. 1885. 1421

## 1885
**Rand, McNally & co.**
Rand, McNally & co.'s improved indexed business atlas and shippers' guide . . . 509 pp. incl. 67 col. maps. fol. Chicago, Rand, McNally & co. 1885.    1422

## 1886
Rand, McNally & co.'s improved indexed business atlas and shippers' guide . . . 15th ed. 557 pp. incl. 92 maps. fol. Chicago, Rand, McNally & co. 1886.    1423

## 1887
Rand, McNally & co.'s improved indexed business atlas and shippers' guide . . . 16th ed. 569 pp. incl. 98 col. maps. fol. Chicago, Rand, McNally & co. 1887.    1424

## 1888
**Atwood, Holmes & Read.**
The pocket atlas of the United States, containing separate copperplate maps of each state and territory . . . 244 pp. incl. 49 maps. 24°. Philadelphia, W. M. Bradley & bro. 1888.    1425

## 1888
**Ferris, G. T.**
Appleton's atlas of the United States consisting of general maps of the United States and territories and a county map of each of the states, together with descriptive text outlining the history, geography, and political and educational organizations of the states with latest statistics of their resources and industries. 2 p. l., 49 pp. incl. 5 maps, 40 maps. 4°. New York, D. Appleton & co. 1888.    1426

NOTE.—Text illustrated with seals of the states.

## 1888
**Rand, McNally & co.**
Rand, McNally & co.'s improved indexed business atlas and shippers' guide . . . 17th ed. 597 pp. incl. 101 maps. fol. Chicago, Rand, McNally & co. 1888.    1427

## 1889
**Brown, M. R.**
The continental atlas, containing elaborate topographical maps of the several states and territories, of the dominion of Canada, the republic of South America, and all the principal countries of the world . . . 225 pp., 2 l. incl. 92 maps. fol. Philadelphia, M. R. Brown, 1889.    1428

NOTE.—Contains plans of the principal cities in the United States.

### 1889

**Rand, McNally & co.**
Rand, McNally & co.'s enlarged business atlas and shippers' guide ... 18th ed. 1 p. l., 291 pp. incl. 85 maps. fol. Chicago, Rand, McNally & co. 1889.     1429

### 1890

Rand, McNally & co.'s enlarged business atlas and shippers' guide ... 19th ed. 1 p. l., 312 pp. incl. 39 maps. fol. Chicago, Rand, McNally & co. 1890.     1430

### 1892

Family atlas of the United States. Compiled from the latest official sources; containing a county and railroad map of each state and territory in the United States, printed in chromatic colors. Compiled for the world's fair educational association, and sold only to the participants in the map-drawing contest. 99 pp. incl. 47 maps. 4°. Chicago, Rand, McNally & co. 1892.     1431

### 1892

Rand, McNally & co.'s enlarged business atlas and shippers' guide ... 22d ed. 351 pp. incl. 88 maps. fol. Chicago, Rand McNally & co. 1892.     1432

### 1892

Rand, McNally & co.'s new handy atlas containing colored county maps of the United States and the dominion of Canada, accompanied by descriptive, statistical, and historical matter ... 380 pp. incl. 60 maps, 11 diagr. 12°. Chicago [etc.] Rand, McNally & co. 1892.     1433

### 1892

Rand, McNally & co.'s new pocket atlas containing colored county maps of all states and territories in the United States, and the provinces of the dominion of Canada ... 2 p. l., [9]–171 pp. incl. 60 maps. 12°. Chicago and New York, Rand, McNally & co. 1892.     1434

### 1893

**Matthews-Northrup co.**
The Matthews-Northrup adequate travel-atlas of the United States ... 244 pp. incl. 71 maps. 12°. Buffalo, N. Y., the Matthews-Northrup co. [1893]     1435

## 1893

**Rand, McNally & co.**
Rand, McNally & co.'s enlarged business atlas and shippers' guide . . . 23d ed.     361 pp. incl. 93 maps. fol. Chicago, Rand, McNally & co. 1893.                                                        1436

## 1893

Rand, McNally & co.'s new pocket atlas containing colored county maps of all states and territories in the United States, and the provinces of the dominion of Canada . . .     2 p. l., [9]–173 pp. incl. 60 maps.  12°.  Chicago and New York, Rand, McNally & co. 1893.                                                       1437

## 1894

Rand, McNally & co.'s enlarged business atlas and shippers' guide . . . 24th ed.     399 pp. incl. 109 maps. fol. Chicago, Rand, McNally & co. 1894.                                                       1438

## 1894

Rand, McNally & co.'s indexed atlas of the world . . . 2 v. fol. Chicago and New York, Rand, McNally & co. 1894.   1439
   NOTE.—Paged continuously; v. 1, 5–223 pp. incl. 58 col. maps; v. 2, 2 p. l., 225–460 pp. incl. 91 col. maps.

CONTENTS.

v. 1. Foreign countries.   pts. 1–5.
"  2. United States.        "   6–8.

## 1894

Rand, McNally & co.'s new indexed atlas of the world . . . Complete in eight parts.   4 v.  v. 1, 3–4.  fol. Chicago and New York, Rand, McNally & co. 1894.                     1440

CONTENTS.

v. 1. Europe.   pts. 1–2.
"  2. Wanting.
"  3. United States.  East.  pts. 5–6.
"  4.      "         West.  "   7–8.

## 1895

**Davis, W. M.**
The New England states . . . Supplement to Frye's Complete geography.   31 pp. incl. 4 maps.   4°.  Boston and London, Ginn & co. 1895.                                                             1441
[ *With* Frye, Alexis Everett.  Home and school atlas.  1896]

## 1895
**Rand, McNally & co.**
Rand, McNally & co.'s enlarged business atlas and shippers' guide . . . 25th ed.   384 pp. incl. 88 maps.   fol. Chicago, Rand, McNally & co. 1895.   1442

## 1896
Rand, McNally & co.'s enlarged business atlas and shippers' guide . . . 26th ed.   398 pp. incl. 89 maps.   fol. Chicago, Rand, McNally & co. 1896.   1443

## 1896
**Werner, co.**
The Werner pocket atlas of the United States, Cuba, Ontario, and Quebec.   [48] l. incl. 47 maps.   24°.   Chicago, the Werner co. 1896.   1444

## 1897
**Rand, McNally & co.**
Rand, McNally & co.'s enlarged business atlas and shippers' guide . . . 27th ed.   406 pp. incl. 99 maps.   fol. Chicago, Rand, McNally & co. 1897.   1445

## 1898
Rand, McNally & co.'s indexed atlas of the world . . .   2 v. fol. Chicago and New York, Rand McNally & co. [1898]   1446

NOTE.—Paged continuously; v. 1, 3 p. l., 9–224 pp. incl. 57 col. maps; v. 2, 2 p. l., 225–464 pp. incl. 76 col. maps.

CONTENTS.
v. 1. Foreign countries.
" 2. United States.

## 1902
Rand, McNally & co.'s indexed atlas of the world, with 275 illustrations. Historical, descriptive, statistical.  [Rev. ed.]   2 v. 288 pp. incl. 61 maps; [4] l., 289–547 pp. incl. 53 maps.   fol. Chicago, Berlin [etc.] Rand, McNally & co. [1902]   1447

NOTE.—Index to West Indies in v. 1.

CONTENTS.
v. 1. United States.
v. 2. Foreign countries.

## 1908
Rand, McNally & co.'s enlarged business atlas and shippers' guide, containing large-scale maps of all states and territories, in the United States, of the dominion of Canada, the republic of Mexico, Central America, the West Indies, Cuba, Porto Rico, Hawaii, the Philippines, Japan, and China . . . 39th ed.   397 pp. incl. 106 col. maps, diagr.   fol.   Chicago, Rand, McNally & co. 1908.   1448

# STATES.

## ALABAMA.

### Cities.

#### BIRMINGHAM.

**Beers, Ellis & co.**
 Atlas of city of Birmingham and suburbs, Alabama. Compiled from actual surveys and records . . . 55 pp. incl. 16 maps. fol. New York, Beers, Ellis & co. 1887–1888. 1449

**Baist, G. W.**
 Baist's property atlas of the city of Birmingham and suburbs, Alabama. Complete in one volume, compiled and published from official records, private plans and actual surveys. 1 p. l., 25 maps. fol. Philadelphia, G. W. Baist, 1902. 1450

#### MOBILE.

**Hopkins, G. M.**
 City atlas of Mobile, Alabama. From actual surveys and records. Published for the Southern and southwestern surveying and pub. co. 97 pp. incl. 24 maps. fol. [Philadelphia, G. M. Hopkins, 1878] 1451

## ALASKA.

Proceedings of the Alaskan boundary tribunal, convened at London, under the treaty between the United States of America and Great Britain, concluded at Washington, january 24, 1903, for the settlement of questions between the two countries with respect to the boundary line between the territory of Alaska and the british possessions in North America. Atlas. 3 v. fol. Washington, government printing office, 1904. 1452
[U. S. 58th cong., 2d sess. Senate. Doc. no. 162]

> NOTE.—Titles of atlas vary:—v. 1 . . . United States atlas. Maps and charts accompanying the case and counter case of the United States. . . . v. 2 . . . British atlas. Maps and charts accompanying the case of Great Britain . . . v. 3 . . . Atlas of award. Twenty-five sectional maps and index map showing the line fixed by the tribunal.
> Maps contained in v. 1 are identical with those of "Atlas accompanying the case of the United States," and its supplement, "Atlas accompanying the counter case of the United States." v. 2 is like atlas having title: "British case. Alaska boundary. Atlas. Appendix vol. II," except that the maps have been reduced in scale, and that nos. 2 and 3 have been omitted, being duplicates of 4 and 5 of v. 1.
> For contents of v. 1 and 2, see cards under: United States. Boundary. Alaska. Titles 1259, 1260 and 1261.

## ARKANSAS.

### Counties.

#### JEFFERSON.

**Beauman, G.**
20th century atlas of Jefferson county, Arkansas . . . 102 pp. incl. 36 maps (1 map in text), 1 pl. fol. Pine Bluff, Ark., G. Beauman, 1905. 1453

#### PULASKI.

**Beauman, G.**
20th century atlas of Pulaski county, Arkansas. 3 p. l., [3]-95 (*i. e.* 97), [2] pp. incl. 37 maps. fol. Little Rock, G. Beauman, 1906. 1454

#### SEBASTIAN.

**Hayes, E. L.**
Atlas of Sebastian county, Arkansas. Compiled and drawn from U. S. official surveys, county records and personal observations . . . 55 pp. incl. 21 maps. fol. Chicago, E. L. Hayes & co. [1887] 1455

#### WASHINGTON.

**Skelton, G. V.**
Atlas map of Washington county, Arkansas. Compiled, drawn and published from official records, personal examinations and surveys. 2 p. l., 34 maps, 1 pl. fol. [Cedar Rapids, Iowa, G. V. Skelton, 1894] 1456

## CALIFORNIA.

### State.

#### EXPLORATION.

**Duflot de Mofras, E.**
Exploration du territoire de l'Orégon, des Californies et de la mer Vermeille executée pendant les années 1840, 1841 et 1842. Atlas. 2 p. l., front., 22 maps on 15 l., 2 pl., diagr. fol. Paris, A. Bertrand, 1844. 1457

NOTE.—Atlas accompanying this work has same title.
Plate 23 is bound in as frontispiece.

CONTENTS.

no. 1. Carte de la côte de l'Amérique sur l'océan Pacifique septentrionale comprenant le territoire de l'Orégon, les Californies, la mer Vermeille, partie des territoires de la compagnie de la baie d'Hudson et de l'Amérique Russe. 1844.
" 2. Carte de l'océan Pacifique au nord de l'équateur.
" 3. Isthme de Tehuantepec.

**Duflot de Mofras, E.**—Continued.
 no. 4. Plan du port d'Acapulco sur la côte occidentale du Mexique.
 " 5. Plan du port del Manzanillo . . .
 " 6. Plan de San Blas.
 " 7. Plan de Mazatlan.
 " 8. Plan de la baie de la Paz et du port de Pichilingue.
 " 9. Plan du port de Guaymas sur la mer Vermeille.
 " 10. Plan de l'embouchure du rio Colorado . . .
 " 11. Plan du port de S. Diego.
 " 12. Mouillage de San Pedro.
 " 13. Mouillage de la mission de Sta. Bárbara.
 " 14. Plan du port et de la baie de Monte-Rey . . .
 " 15. Baie de la Trinidad.
 " 16. Port de San Francisco . . .—Entrée du port de San Francisco . . .
 " 17. Carte détaillée du mouillage du fort Ross et du port de la Bodega ou Romanzoff.
 " 18. Carte du rio Colombia . . .
 " 19. Port de Quadra ou de la découverte.
 " 20. Plan du port de Nutka . . .
 " 21. Plan du port de la nouvelle Archangel dans l'île de Sitka . . .
 " 22. Plan du port Mulgrave.

## GEOLOGICAL.

**Becker, G. F.**
 Geology of the quicksilver deposits of the Pacific slope . . . Atlas. 2 p. l., 8 maps, 5 pl. fol. Washington, government printing office, 1888. 1458
 [United States. Department of the interior. Geological survey. Monographs. v. 13 50th cong., 1st sess. House. Mis. doc. 610 v. 24]

 NOTE.—Atlas entitled: Atlas to accompany a monograph on the geology of the quicksilver deposits of the Pacific slope. Washington, 1887.

## 1908

**Cram, G. F.**
 Cram's superior reference atlas of California, Nevada and the world. 164 pp. incl. 68 col. maps, 3 col. pl., 1 fold. map. fol. Chicago, New York, for E. A. Davis by G. F. Cram, ᶜ1908. 1459

## Counties.

### ALAMEDA.

**Thompson & West.**
 Official and historical atlas map of Alameda county, Cal. Compiled, drawn and published from personal examinations and surveys. 170 pp. incl. 36 maps, 75 pl. fol. Oakland, Cal., Thompson & West, 1878. 1460

 NOTE.—pp. 67–68 wanting.

## KERN.

**Randall & Denne.**
Index atlas of Kern county, Cal., containing over five million acres of land, consisting of agricultural, grazing, fruit and mineral lands and its wonderful oil producing lands. Showing the boundary and ownership of each piece of land separately. Issued under the patronage of the board of supervisors.   70 pp. incl. 24 maps, 6 pl. fol. San Jose, Cal., Randall & Denne [1901]   1461

## LOS ANGELES.

**Rueger, H.**
Rueger's atlas showing county properties of Los Angeles county, California. Drawn on various scales, 10 to 20 chains to the inch, showing acreage, subdivisions, townships and ranges, town plats, owner's name of property containing five acres or more; also showing railroads and electric roads . . . Compiled from public records. 4 p. l., 79 maps. fol. Los Angeles, H. Rueger [1903]   1462

Rueger's atlas of Los Angeles city and county, Los Angeles, Cal. Copyrighted 1906.   cover-title, 76 maps, 2 l., 92 maps.   fol. [Los Angeles, Cal., H. Rueger] 1906.   1463

## SANTA CLARA.

**Thompson & West.**
Historical atlas map of Santa Clara county, Cal. Compiled, drawn and published from personal examinations and surveys.   110, [4] pp. incl. 21 maps, 54 pl. fol. San Francisco, Thompson & West, 1876.   1464

## SONOMA.

**Thompson, T. H., & co.**
Historical atlas of Sonoma county, California. Compiled, drawn and published from personal examinations and actual surveys. 102, [2] pp. incl. 15 maps, 44 pl. fol. Oakland, Cal., T. H. Thompson & co. 1877.   1465

**Reynolds & Proctor.**
Illustrated atlas of Sonoma county, California . . .   80, 64 pp. incl. 66 maps. fol. Santa Rosa, Cal., Reynolds & Proctor [1898]   1466

## Cities.

### LOS ANGELES.

**Rueger, H.**
Rueger's atlas of Los Angeles city and county, Los Angeles, Cal. Copyrighted 1906.   cover-title, 76 maps, 2 pp., 92 maps.   fol. [Los Angeles, Cal., H. Rueger] 1906.   1467

### SAN FRANCISCO.

**Hicks-Judd company.**

The San Francisco block book; comprising Fifty Vara survey, One Hundred Vara survey, Mission, Western addition, Richmond district, Sunset district, Flint tract and Horner's addition. Showing size of lots and blocks and names of owners, compiled from latest official records. October, 1901. [2d ed.] xx, 33–736 pp. incl. maps. fol. San Francisco, the Hicks-Judd co. 1901. 1468

NOTE.—pp. xviii-xx, 731-736 blank.

The San Francisco block book; comprising Fifty Vara survey, One Hundred Vara survey, South Beach, Mission, Horner's addition, Potrero, Western addition, Richmond district, Sunset district, Flint tract, etc. Showing size of lots and blocks and names of owners, compiled from latest official records. January, 1906. 3d ed. xix, 887 pp. incl. maps. fol. San Francisco, the Hicks-Judd co. 1906. 1469

The San Francisco block book . . . Homesteads. Comprising Park Lane tract, Market street homestead ass'n, Stanford Heights, Sunnyside, City land ass'n, Lakeview, West End homestead, University Mound homestead ass'n, Excelsior homestead, Reis tract, South San Francisco homestead and railroad ass'n, Tide lands, etc. Showing size of lots and blocks and names of owners compiled from latest official records. 1 p. l., [v]-xiii, [2], 8–722 (*i. e.* 726) pp. incl. maps. fol. San Francisco, the Hicks-Judd co. 1907. 1470

## COLORADO

### GEOLOGICAL.

**Dutton, C.**

Tertiary history of the Grand cañon district, with atlas. Atlas. 2 p. l., 8 maps on 12 l., 10 pl. fol. Washington, J. Bien & co. 1882. 1471

[United States. Department of the interior. Geological survey. Monographs. v. 2]

NOTE.—Atlas entitled: Atlas to accompany the monograph on the Tertiary report of the Grand cañon district by capt. C. E. Dutton . . .

**Emmons, S. F.**

Geology and mining industry of Leadville, Colorado with atlas by Samuel Franklin Emmons. Atlas. 3 p. l., 31 maps. fol. Washington, Gov't. print. off., 1882. 1472

[United States. Department of the interior. Geological survey. Monographs. v. 12]

NOTE.—Atlas entitled: . . . Atlas to accompany a monograph on the geology and mining industry of Leadville, Colorado . . . Washington, 1883.

**Hayden, F. V.**
 Geological and geographical atlas of Colorado and portions of adjacent territory. 2 p. l., 84 pp. incl. 16 maps, 4 pl. fol. New York, J. Bien, 1877. 1473
 [United States. Department of the interior. Geological and geographical surveys of the territories]

**Spurr, J. E.**
 Atlas to accompany monograph XXXI on the geology of the Aspen district, Colorado, by Josiah Edward Spurr. Samuel Franklin Emmons, geologist in charge. 3 p. l., 13 maps, 14 pl. fol. Washington, 1898. 1474
 [United States. Department of the interior. Geological survey]

### Cities

#### DENVER.
**Robinson, E.** & *others.*
 Robinson's atlas of the city of Denver, Colorado. Embracing all territory within the corporate limits . . . 1 p. l., 32 maps. fol. New York, E. Robinson, 1887. 1475

## CONNECTICUT.

### State

### 1893
**Hurd, D. H., & co.**
 Town and city atlas of state of Connecticut. 223 pp. incl. 98 maps. fol. Boston, D. H. Hurd & co. 1893. 1476

### Counties

#### FAIRFIELD.
**Hyde, E. B.**
 Atlas of the rural country district north of New York city embracing the entire Westchester county, New York, also a portion of Connecticut, Greenwich, Stamford, New Canaan, Darien, Wilton and Ridgefield . . . 4 p. l., 17 (*i. e.* 18) col. maps. fol. Manhattan, Brooklyn, E. B. Hyde, 1908. 1477

#### HARTFORD.
**Baker & Tilden.**
 Atlas of Hartford city and county, with a map of Connecticut, from actual surveys . . . 1 p. l., 47 maps. fol. Hartford, Baker & Tilden, 1869. 1478

### LITCHFIELD.

**Beers, F. W.**
County atlas of Litchfield, Conn.  76 pp. incl. 44 maps. fol. New York, F. W. Beers & co. 1874.  1479

### MIDDLESEX.

**Beers, F. W.**
County atlas of Middlesex, Conn.  144 pp. incl. 45 maps. fol. New York, F. W. Beers & co. 1874.  1480

### NEW HAVEN.

**Beers, F. W.**
Atlas of New Haven county, Conn.  58 pp. incl. 39 maps. fol. New York, F. W. Beers, A. D. Ellis & G. G. Soule, 1868.  1481

### NEW LONDON.

**Beers, F. W.**
Atlas of New London county, Conn.  38 pp. incl. 28 maps. fol. New York, F. W. Beers [etc.] 1868.  1482

### Cities.

#### BRIDGEPORT.

**Scofield, H. G.**
Atlas of the city of Bridgeport, Conn. from actual surveys ... 1 p. l., 14 maps, 5 pl. fol. New York, J. B. Beers & co. 1876.  1483

**Hopkins, G. M.**
Atlas of the city and town of Bridgeport, Conn.  1 p. l., 25 maps. fol. Philadelphia, G. M. Hopkins, 1888.  1484

**Pidgeon, R. H.**, *& others.*
Atlas of the city of Bridgeport, Connecticut. From official records, private plans and surveys under the direction and personal supervision of Roger H. Pidgeon, c. e. assisted by Lucius E. Tenny, E. Robinson, F. Chester Hale, W. Guy Classon and Thos. Flynn. 1 p. l., 31 maps. fol. Philadelphia, D. L. Miller & co. 1896.  1485

#### DANBURY.

**Hopkins, G. M.**
Atlas of Danbury, Conn.  55 pp. incl. 13 maps. fol. Philadelphia, G. M. Hopkins, 1880.  1486

#### HARTFORD.

**Baker & Tilden.**
Atlas of Hartford city and county, with a map of Connecticut from actual surveys ...  1 p. l., 47 maps. fol. Hartford, Baker & Tilden, 1869.  1487

**Hopkins, G. M.**
    City atlas of Hartford, Conn.   115 pp. incl. 28 maps.  fol. Philadelphia, G. M. Hopkins, 1880.                 1488

### NEW BRITAIN.

**Miller, D. L.**, & *others.*
    Atlas of the town and city of New Britain, Hartford county, Conn. From official records, maps and surveys under the direction and personal supervision of D. L. Miller assisted by F. H. Oldershaw, W. H. Cadwell, F. Chester Hale.   1 p. l., 12 maps.  fol. Philadelphia, D. L. Miller & co. 1902.                 1489

### NEW HAVEN.

**Hopkins, G. M.**
    Atlas of city of New Haven, Connecticut . . . Published under contract with city of New Haven through special committe on city maps. Henry G. Lewis, chairman.   1 p. l., 48 maps.  fol. Philadelphia, G. M. Hopkins, 1888.                 1490

### WATERBURY.

**Hopkins, G. M.**
    Atlas of city of Waterbury, Conn.   89 pp. incl. 22 maps.  fol. Philadelphia, G. M. Hopkins, 1879.                 1491

## DELAWARE.

### State.

#### 1868

**Beers, D. G.**
    Atlas of the state of Delaware, from actual surveys by and under the direction of D. G. Beers.   1 p. l., 96 pp. incl. 38 maps.  fol. Philadelphia, Pomeroy & Beers, 1868.                 1492

### Cities.

#### WILMINGTON.

**Hopkins, G. M.**
    City atlas of Wilmington, Del. From official records, private plans and actual surveys . . .   81 pp. incl. 20 maps.  fol. Philadelphia, G. M. Hopkins, 1876.                 1493

**Baist, G. W.**
    Atlas of the city of Wilmington, Delaware and vicinity. From actual surveys, official records & private plans . . .   1 p. l., 19 maps.  fol. Philadelphia, G. W. Baist, 1887.                 1494

## DISTRICT OF COLUMBIA.

### WASHINGTON.

#### 1803

**King, N.**
The King plats of the city of Washington in the District of Columbia 1803. N. Peters photo. lith. 2 p. l., 21 maps. fol. Washington [1888] 1495

> NOTE.—Reproduced from original plats in war department, by the coast and geodetic survey, for use in a suit to establish the title of the government to the flats in the Potomac river, off the city of Washington.
> Contains also reproductions of L'Enfant's, Ellicott's and Dermott's maps.

#### 1856

**Forsyth, W.**
Plats of subdivisions of the city of Washington, D. C., compiled from the authentic records by William Forsyth, surveyor. 4 p. l., 62 maps. fol. Washington, R. A. Walker, 1856. 1496

#### 1873

**Martenet, S. J., Walling, H. F.,** *and* **Gray, O. W.**
New topographical atlas of the state of Maryland and the District of Columbia, with descriptions historical, scientific and statistical, together with maps of the United States and territories. 108, 8, 2, 4 pp. incl. 30 maps. fol. Baltimore, Stedman, Brown & Lyon, 1873. 1497

#### 1874

**Faehtz, E. F. M.,** *and* **Pratt, F. W.**
Real estate directory of the city of Washington, D. C. . . . Containing a separate plat of each square in the city on a scale of 50 feet to the inch; also; a statistical table for each square, containing all subdivisions of such squares recorded up to September 1, 1873 in the official numerical book, and such valuation and description of ground and improvements as fixed thereon by the assessment for the fiscal year 1873–4, and approved by the Board of appeal. Prepared at the request and under the auspices of messrs. Fitch & Fox . . . by E. F. M. Faehtz and F. W. Pratt . . . 3 v. fol. Washington, 1874. 1498

#### 1878

**Hopkins, G. M.**
Atlas of fifteen miles around Washington including the county of Prince George, Maryland. 84 pp. incl. 45 maps, 3 maps at end. fol. Philadelphia, G. M. Hopkins, 1878. 1499

### 1879

Atlas of fifteen miles around Washington, including the counties of Fairfax and Alexandria, Virginia.    87 pp., 4 l. incl. 48 maps. fol.  Philadelphia, G. M. Hopkins, 1879.    1500

### 1879

Atlas of fifteen miles around Washington including the county of Montgomery, Maryland.    84 pp. incl. 44 maps. 3 maps at end. fol.  Philadelphia, G. M. Hopkins, 1879.    1501

### 1883
**Dodge, R. P.**
Plats of the 131 squares in West Washington, Georgetown . . . 1 p. l., 131 (*i. e.* 139) maps.  fol.  [Washington] 1883.    1502

### 1887
**Hopkins, G. M.**
A complete set of surveys and plats of properties in the city of Washington, District of Columbia.  Compiled and drawn from official records and actual surveys . . .    1 p. l., 44 (*i e.* 45) maps. fol. Philadelphia, °1887.    1503

### 1892—1896

Real estate plat book of Washington, District of Columbia . . . From the original plats of squares & subdivisions, and additions upon record in the office of the surveyor of the city of Washington . . .    4 v.  fol.  Philadelphia, 1892–96.    1504

NOTE.—Title varies; v. 3, reads: Real estate plat book of Washington . . . Based upon the triangulation of the United States coast and geodetic survey topographical map of the District of Columbia.
Set is composed of 3 v. and supplement to v. 3.

CONTENTS.
v. 1. North-west section.
" 2. North-east, south-east and south-west sections.
" 3. West Washington, and balance of the county outside Florida ave.
" 3, supp. Comprising the first suburban section of the plan of the extension of permanent system of highways.

### 1903
**Baist, G. W.**
Baist's real estate atlas of surveys of Washington, District of Columbia, complete in three volumes.  Compiled and published from official records, private plans and actual surveys.    3 v.  fol. Philadelphia, G. W. Baist, 1903.    1505

CONTENTS.
v. 1. N. w. section.
v. 2. N. e., s. e. and s. w. sections.
v. 3. Suburbs.

**Baist, G. W.**—Continued.

Baist's real estate atlas of surveys of Washington, District of Columbia. Complete in four volumes. Compiled and published from official records, private plans and actual surveys.   v. 3-4. fol. Philadelphia, G. W. Baist, 1907.   1506

NOTE.—v. 1-2 not yet published.

CONTENTS.

v. 3. [Suburbs]
" 4. [Suburbs]

## GEORGIA.

### Cities.

#### ATLANTA.

**Hopkins, G. M.**

City atlas of Atlanta, Ga.   81 pp. incl. 22 maps. fol. [Philadelphia] southern and southwestern surveying and publishing co. 1878.   1507

**Latham, E. B.** *and* **Baylor, H. B.**

Atlas of Atlanta, Ga. Compiled by E. B. Latham & H. B. Baylor, civil engineers. Scale 200 feet to 1 inch.   1 p. l., 40 maps. fol. [Atlanta, the Foote & Davis co. printers] 1893.   1508

#### MACON.

**Hopkins, G. M.**

City atlas of Macon, Ga.   2 p. l., 65 pp. incl. 16 maps. fol. [Philadelphia] G. M. Hopkins, 1878.   1509

## ILLINOIS.

#### CHICAGO RIVER.

**United States.** *War department.*

Atlas containing maps of Chicago river, Illinois and its branches showing results of improvement by the U. S. government under direction of major W. L. Marshall, corps of engineers U. S. A. in 1896 to 1899. G. A. Liljencrantz, ass't engineer.   1 p. l., 29 maps. obl. fol. [Washington, 1900]   1510
[U. S. 56th Cong., 1st sess. House doc. 95, pt. 2, ser. no. 3956]

NOTE.—To accompany report of W. L. Marshall, dated november 14, 1899.

## State.

### 1870

**Campbell, R. A.,** *and* **Walling, H. F.**
Campbell's new atlas of the state of Illinois with descriptions historical, scientific and statistical. 4 p. l., 51–86 pp. incl. 2 maps. 34 maps. fol. Chicago, R. A. Campbell, 1870. 1511

### 1871

**Warner, Higgins & Beers.**
Atlas of the state of Illinois, to which is added an atlas of the United States, maps of the hemispheres, etc. 95 pp. incl. 38 maps. fol. Chicago, Warner, Higgins & Beers, 1871. 1512

### 1876

**Warner & Beers.**
Atlas of the state of Illinois, to which are added various general maps, history, statistics and illustrations. 293 pp. incl. front., 116 maps, 32 pl. fol. Chicago, Warner & Beers, 1876. 1513

### 1906

**Cram, G. F.**
Cram's superior reference atlas of Illinois and the world. 158 pp. incl. 61 maps, 17 pl. fol. New York, Chicago, G. F. Cram, 1906. 1514

## Counties.

### ADAMS.

**Ogle, G. A., & co.**
Standard atlas of Adams county, Illinois. Including a plat book of the villages, cities and townships of the county. Map of the state, United States and world. Patrons directory, reference business directory and departments devoted to general information. Analysis of the system of U. S. land surveys, digest of the system of civil government, etc., etc. . . . 2 p. l., 7–117, [1], viii, x–xxii pp. incl. 35 maps, 5 pl. (1 map in text) fol. Chicago, G. A. Ogle & co. 1901. 1515

### BOND.

**Warner & Beers.**
Atlas of Bond county and the state of Illinois to which is added an atlas of the United States, maps of the hemispheres &c. 35, 2–93 pp. incl. 35 maps, 3 pl. fol. Chicago, Warner & Beers, 1875. 1516

## BOONE.

**Page, H. R., & co.**
Illustrated atlas of Winnebago and Boone counties, Ill., containing maps of every township in counties, with village and city plats, also maps of Michigan, Indiana, Ohio, Illinois, Wisconsin, Minnesota, Iowa, Missouri, Dakota, Nebraska, Kansas, Montana, Colorado, New Mexico, Arizona, Texas and Washington territory. 3–120 pp. incl. 53 maps, 19 pl. fol. Chicago, H. R. Page & co. 1886.     1517

## BROWN.

**Ogle, G. A., & co.**
Standard atlas of Brown county, Illinois. Including a plat book of the villages, cities and townships of the county. Map of the state, United States and world. Patrons' directory, reference business directory and departments devoted to general information. Analysis of the system of U. S. land surveys, digest of the system of civil government, etc., etc. . . . 2 p. l., 7–47, [3], viii, x–xxii pp. incl. 14 maps, 1 map in text, 2 pl. fol. Chicago, G. A. Ogle & co. 1903.     1518

## BUREAU.

**Matson, Nehemiah.**
Map of Bureau county, Ill., with sketches of its early settlement. 88 pp., front., 26 maps, pl. sq. 12°. Chicago, G. H. Fergus, 1867.     1519

**Warner & Beers.**
Atlas of Bureau county and the state of Illinois, to which is added an atlas of the United States, maps of the hemispheres &c. 77, 4–93 pp. incl. 70 maps, 35 pl. fol. Chicago, Warner & Beers, 1875.     1520

## CHAMPAIGN.

**Ogle, G. A., & co.**
Plat book of Champaign county, Illinois. 3–93 pp. incl. 47 maps. fol. Chicago, G. A. Ogle & co. 1893.     1521

## CLARK.

**Ogle, G. A., & co.**
Plat book of Clark county, Illinois. 3–73 pp. incl. 26 maps. fol. Chicago, G. A. Ogle & co. 1892.     1522

## CLAY.

**Lake, D. J., & co.**
An atlas of Clay county, Illinois. From actual surveys under the direction of B. N. Griffing. 50 pp. incl. 16 maps. 3 maps. fol. Philadelphia, D. J. Lake & co. 1881.     1523

### CLINTON.

**Occidental publishing co.**
    Plat book of Clinton county, Illinois.     3–72 pp. incl. 27 maps. fol. Chicago, the Occidental pub. co. 1892.     1524

### COLES.

**American atlas co.**
    Plat book of Coles county, Illinois . . .     7 p. l., 18–80 pp. incl. 21 maps. fol. Philadelphia, the american atlas co. 1893.     1525

### COOK.

**Central map, survey and publishing co.**
    Chicago suburban maps, Cook county, Ill's.     116 maps. fol. Chicago, central map, surveying and publishing co. 1891.     1526
    NOTE.—Title on reverse map no. 1.

### DEKALB.

**Ensign, D. W., & co.**
    Plat book of De Kalb county, Illinois.     131 pp. incl. front., 47 maps. fol. [Chicago] D. W. Ensign & co. 1892.     1527

### DE WITT.

**Warner & Beers.**
    Atlas of De Witt county and the state of Illinois, to which is added an atlas of the United States, maps of the hemispheres &c. 56, 3–93 pp. incl. 56 maps, 14 pl. fol. Chicago, Warner & Beers, 1875.     1528

### DUPAGE.

**Middle-west publishing co.**
    20$^{th}$ century atlas of Du Page county, Illinois. Containing maps of villages, cities and townships of the county, of the state, United States and world. 2 p. l., 7–89, [64], viii, x–xxii pp. incl. 30 maps, 1 map in text, 21 pl. fol. Chicago, middle-west publishing co. 1904.     1529

### EDGAR.

**Warner & Higgins.**
    Atlas of Edgar county and the state of Illinois, to which is added an atlas of the United States, maps of the hemispheres &c. &c. &c. 133 pp. incl. 52 maps. fol. Philadelphia, Warner & Higgins, 1870.     1530

### FAYETTE.

**Alden, Ogle & co.**
    Plat book of Fayette county, Illinois.     3–88 pp. incl. 27 maps. fol. Chicago, Alden, Ogle & co. 1891.     1531

### FORD.

**Beers, J. H., & co.**
Historical atlas of Ford county, Illinois, containing a history of the county, its townships, towns, schools, churches, etc.; a complete set of plats of the townships and villages; portraits of early settlers and prominent men; views of residences, etc.; biographies of pioneers and leading citizens; various general maps, statistics, etc., etc.    83, [1] pp. incl. 17 maps, 15 pl., 5 maps at end. fol. Chicago, J. H. Beers & co. 1884.    1532

### FULTON.

**American atlas co.**
Plat book of Fulton county, Illinois . . .    2 p. l., 7-94, viii pp. incl. 45 maps, 8 pl.  fol.  Chicago, american atlas co. 1895.
    1533

### GREENE.

**Hammond publishing co.**
Plat book of Greene and Jersey counties, Illinois.    3-96 pp. incl. 38 maps.  fol.  [Chicago?] Hammond pub. co. 1893.    1534

### GRUNDY.

**Warner & Beers.**
Atlas of Grundy county and the state of Illinois, to which is added an atlas of the United States, maps of the hemispheres &c. 43, 2-93 pp. incl. 54 maps, 5 pl.  fol.  Chicago, Warner & Beers, 1874.    1535

### HANCOCK.

**Helms, J. C.**
Plat book of Hancock county by townships . . .    48 pp. incl. 23 maps.  sm. fol.  Carthage, Illinois, J. C. Helms, 1908.    1536

### HENRY.

**Warner & Beers.**
Atlas of Henry county and the state of Illinois, to which is added an atlas of the United States, maps of the hemispheres, &c.    75, 4-93 pp. incl. 70 maps, 37 pl.  fol.  Chicago, Warner & Beers, 1875.    1537

### JERSEY.

**Hammond publishing co.**
Plat book of Greene and Jersey counties, Illinois.    3-96 pp. incl. 38 maps. fol.  [Chicago?] Hammond publishing co. 1893.    1538

### JO DAVIESS.

**Northwest publishing co.**
Plat book of Jo Daviess county, Ill.  Drawn from actual surveys & county records.    1 p. l., 63 pp. incl. 39 maps.  fol.  [Philadelphia] the north west publishing co. 1893.    1539

## KANE.

**Ensign, D. W., & co.**
Atlas of Kane county Illinois. 86 pp. incl. front., 48 maps. fol. Chicago, D. W. Ensign & co. 1892. 1540

**Middle-west publishing co.**
20th century atlas of Kane county, Illinois. Containing maps of villages, cities and townships of the county, of the state, United States and world. 2 p. l., 8–125, [37], viii, x–xxii pp. incl. 43 maps, 8 pl., 1 map in text. fol. Chicago, middle-west publishing co. 1904. 1541

## KANKAKEE.

**Beers, J. H., & co.**
Atlas of Kankakee co. Illinois. To which is added various general maps, history, statistics, illustrations. &c. &c. &c. 116, [2], 117–170 pp. incl. 27 maps, 60 pl., 5 maps at end. fol. Chicago, J. H. Beers & co. 1883. 1542

## KNOX.

**Ogle, G. A., & co.**
Standard atlas of Knox county, Illinois. Including a plat book of the villages, cities and townships of the county. Map of the state, United States and world. Patrons directory, reference business directory and departments devoted to general information. Analysis of the system of U. S. land surveys, digest of the system of civil government, etc. etc. 2 p. l., 7–107, viii, x–xxii pp. incl. 35 maps, 3 pl., 1 map in text. fol. Chicago, G. A. Ogle & co. 1903.
1543

## La SALLE.

**Warner & Beers.**
Atlas of La Salle county and the state of Illinois, to which is added an atlas of the United States, maps of the hemispheres &c. 115, 4–93 pp. incl. 82 maps, 58 pl. fol. Chicago, Warner & Beers, 1876. 1544

## McHENRY.

**Ogle, G. A., & co.**
Plat book of McHenry county, Illinois. 3–104 pp. incl. 35 maps. fol. Chicago, G. A. Ogle & co. 1892. 1545

## McLEAN.

**Warner & Beers.**
Atlas of McLean county and the state of Illinois, to which is added an atlas of the United States, maps of the hemispheres, &c. cxxiii, 2–89 pp. incl. 75 maps, 25 pl. fol. Chicago, Warner & Beers, 1874. 1546

**Northwest publishing co.**
   Plat book of McLean county, Illinois. Drawn from actual surveys & county records . . .   1 p. l., 98 pp. incl. 62 maps.  fol. [Minneapolis] the northwest publishing co. 1895.   1547

### MACON.

**Warner & Beers.**
   Atlas of Macon county and the state of Illinois, to which is added an atlas of the United States, maps of the hemispheres &c.  67, 2-93 pp. incl. 59 maps, 16 pl.  fol.  Chicago, Warner & Beers, 1874.   1548

**Alden, Ogle & co.**
   Plat book of Macon county, Illinois.   91 pp. incl. 29 maps. fol.  Chicago, Aden, Ogle & co. 1891.   1549

### MACOUPIN.

**Warner & Beers.**
   Atlas of Macoupin county and the state of Illinois to which is added an atlas of the United States, maps of the hemispheres &c. 47, 5-93 pp. incl. 71 maps, 6 pl.  fol.  Chicago, Warner & Beers, 1875.   1550

### MADISON.

**Riniker, H., Hagnauer, R.** *and* **Dickson, G. K.**
   New atlas of Madison county, state of Illinois. Containing map of the state of Illinois, sectional map of Madison county, plat of each township, together with plats of the different cities, towns and villages of Madison county, Ill. . . .   84 pp. incl. 37 maps.  fol. St. Louis, G. D. Barnard & co. 1892.   1551

### MARION.

**Occidental publishing co.**
   Plat book of Marion county, Illinois . . .   6 p. l., 15-83 pp. incl. 29 maps.  fol.  Chicago, the occidental publishing co. 1892.   1552

### MARSHALL.

**Alden, Ogle & co.**
   Plat book of Marshall and Putnam counties, Ill.   82 pp. incl. 25 maps.  fol.  Chicago, Alden, Ogle & co. 1890.   1553

### MORGAN.

**Andreas, Lyter & co.**
   Atlas map of Morgan county, Illinois. Compiled, drawn and published from personal examinations and surveys.  1 p. l., 227 (*i. e.* 146) pp. incl. 24 maps, 47 pl.  fol.  Davenport, Ia., Andreas, Lyter & co. 1872.   1554

**American atlas co.**
Plat book of Morgan county, Illinois. 3–87 pp. incl. 31 maps. fol. [Chicago] the american atlas co. 1894. 1555

## MOULTRIE.
**Warner & Beers.**
Atlas of Moultrie county and the state of Illinois to which is added an atlas of the United States, maps of the hemisphere &c. 31, 2–93 pp. incl. 56 maps, 2 pl. fol. Chicago, Warner & Beers, 1875. 1556

## OGLE.
**Ogle, G. A., & co.**
Plat book of Ogle county, Illinois. 3–112 pp. incl. 41 maps. fol. Chicago, G. A. Ogle & co. 1893. 1557

## PEORIA.
**Ogle, G. A., & co.**
Standard atlas of Peoria city and county, Illinois, including a plat book of the villages, cities and townships of the county. 148, viii, x–xxii pp. incl. 55 maps, 24 pl. fol. Chicago, G. A. Ogle & co. 1896. 1558

## PIKE.
**Andreas, Lyter & co.**
Atlas map of Pike county, Illinois. Compiled, drawn and published from personal examinations and surveys. 1 p. l., 138 pp. incl. 27 maps, 50 pl. fol. Davenport, Iowa, Andreas, Lyter & co. 1872. 1559

NOTE.—Pagination irregular.

## PLATT.
**Warner & Beers.**
Atlas of Platt county and the state of Illinois, to which is added an atlas of the United States, maps of the hemispheres &c. 39, 2–93 pp. incl. 54 maps, 4 pl. fol. Chicago, Warner & Beers, 1875. 1560

## PUTNAM.
**Alden, Ogle & co.**
Plat book of Marshall and Putnam counties, Ill. 82 pp. incl. 25 maps. fol. Chicago, Alden, Ogle & co. 1890. 1561

## RICHLAND.
**Ogle, G. A., & co.,**
Standard atlas of Richland county, Illinois. Including a plat book of the villages, cities and townships of the county. Map of the state, United States and world. Patrons directory, reference business directory and departments devoted to general information. Analysis of the system of U. S. land surveys, digest of the system of civil government, etc. etc. 2 p. l., 7–33, [9], viii, x–xxii pp. incl. 16 maps, 1 map in text, 2 pl. fol. Chicago, G. A. Ogle & co. 1901. 1562

### ROCK ISLAND.

**Iowa publishing co.**
    Atlas of Rock Island county, Illinois, containing maps of villages, cities and townships of the county. Maps of state, United States and world. Farmers directory, business directory, general information. 184 pp. incl. 43 maps, 40 pl. fol. Davenport, Ia., the Iowa publishing co. 1905.     1563

### SANGAMON.

**Field publishing co.**
    Plat book of Sangamon county, Illinois.   3–88 pp. incl. 47 maps. fol. Chicago, Field pub. co. 1894.     1564

### SCOTT.

**Andreas, Lyter & co.**
    Atlas map of Scott county, Illinois. Compiled, drawn and published from personal examinations and surveys. 1 p. l., 52 pp. incl. 13 maps, 12 pl. fol. Davenport, Ia., Andreas, Lyter & co. 1873.     1565

### SHELBY.

**Warner & Beers.**
    Atlas of Shelby county and the state of Illinois, to which is added an atlas of the United States, maps of the hemispheres &c. 49, 2–93 pp. incl. 66 maps, 12 pl. fol. Chicago, Warner & Beers, 1875.     1566

**Ogle, G. A., & co.**
    Plat book of Shelby county, Illinois.   2 p. l., 7–56, viii pp. incl. 35 maps. fol. Chicago, G. A. Ogle & co. 1895.     1567

### STARK.

**Warner & Beers.**
    Atlas of Stark county and the state of Illinois, to which is added an atlas of the United States, maps of the hemispheres &c. xxxix, 5–93 pp. incl. 51 maps, 15 pl. fol. Chicago, Warner & Beers, 1873.     1568

### STEPHENSON.

**Thompson & Everts.**
    Combination atlas map of Stephenson county, Ill. Compiled, drawn and published from personal examinations and surveys. 66 pp., 2 l. incl. 21 maps, 34 pl. fol. Geneva, Ill., Thompson & Everts, 1871.     1569

**Northwest publishing co.**
    Plat book of Stephenson county, Ill. Drawn from actual surveys & county records. 1 p. l., 67 pp., incl. 41 maps. fol. [Minneapolis] the north west publishing co. 1894.     1570

## TAZEWELL.

**Andreas, Lyter, & co.**
Atlas map of Tazewell county, Ill. Compiled, drawn and published from personal examinations and surveys. 3 p. l., 165 pp. 1 l. incl. 27 maps, 58 pl. fol. Davenport, Ia., Andreas, Lyter & co. 1873. 1571

## UNION.

**Lake, D. J., & co.**
An atlas of Union county, Illinois. From actual surveys under the direction of B. N. Griffing. 49 pp. incl. 17 maps. 3 maps at end. fol. Philadelphia, D. J. Lake & co. 1881. 1572

## VERMILION.

**Boudinot, E. S.**
Atlas of Vermilion county, Illinois, containing maps of the county, townships, cities and villages. 1 p. l., 59 col. maps on 101 l. fol. Danville, Ill., E. S. Boudinot, 1907. 1573

## WARREN.

**Warner, Higgins & Beers.**
Atlas of Warren county and the state of Illinois, to which is added an atlas of the United States, maps of the hemispheres, &c. 4 p. l. [18], 5–95 pp. incl. 60 maps. fol. Chicago, Warner, Higgins & Beers, 1872. 1574

**Ogle, G. A., & co.**
Plat book of Warren county, Illinois. 6 p. l., 16–79 pp. incl. 28 maps. fol. Chicago, G. A. Ogle & co. 1893. 1575

## WHITESIDE.

**Warner & Beers.**
Atlas of Whiteside county and the state of Illinois, to which is added an atlas of the United States, maps of the hemispheres, &c. xxxix, 4–95 pp. incl. 62 maps, 14 pl. fol. Chicago, Warner & Beers, 1872. 1576

**Ogle, G. A., & co.**
Plat book of Whiteside county, Illinois . . . 6 p. l., 16–118 pp. incl. 37 maps. fol. Chicago, G. A. Ogle & co. 1893. 1577

## WILL.

**Ogle, G. A., & co.**
Plat book of Will county, Illinois. 3–81 pp. incl. 57 maps. fol. Chicago, G. A. Ogle & co. 1893. 1578

## WINNEBAGO.

**Page, H. R., & co.**

Illustrated atlas of Winnebago and Boone counties, Ill., containing maps of every township in counties, with village and city plats, also maps of Michigan, Indiana, Ohio, Illinois, Wisconsin, Minnesota, Iowa, Missouri, Dakota, Nebraska, Kansas, Montana, Colorado, New Mexico, Arizona, Texas and Washington territory. 3–120 pp. incl. 52 maps, 19 pl. (1 fold. map) fol. Chicago, H. R. Page & co. 1886. 1579

## WOODFORD.

**Warner & Beers.**

Atlas of Woodford county and the state of Illinois, to which is added an atlas of the United States, maps of the hemispheres &c. xxxi, 5–95 pp. incl. 60 maps, 6 pl. fol. Chicago, Warner & Beers, 1873. 1580

### Cities.

#### CHICAGO.

**Page, H. R., & co.**

Atlas of Chicago. 1 p. l., 82 pp. incl. 40 maps. fol. [Chicago] H. R. Page & co. 1879. 1581

**Greeley, Carlson & co.**

Greeley, Carlson & co's. atlas of the city of Chicago, complete in one volume. Showing all the land included within the present city limits with all subdivisions, streets, alleys, parks, boulevards, rail roads and water boundaries, upon a scale of two hundred feet to one inch, with full marginal notes. 1 p. l., 152 pp. incl. 151 maps. fol. Chicago, Greeley, Carlson & co. 1884. 1582

**Robinson, E.**

Robinson's atlas of the city of Chicago, Ill. 5 v. fol. New York, E. Robinson, 1886. 1583

**Central map, survey and publishing co.**

Union stock yards and packing houses, Chicago, Ill. 2 p. l., 30 pp. incl. 43 maps. fol. Chicago, central map, survey and publishing co. 1891. 1584

**Grosmann, C. W. F.**

Donnelley's sectional atlas of the city of Chicago. 6 p. l., 192 pp. incl. 194 maps. fol. Chicago, R. H. Donnelley, 1891. 1585

**Greeley-Carlson co.**

Greeley-Carlson company's second atlas of the city of Chicago, showing the territory bounded by Chicago avenue, Halsted street, twenty-second street and lake Michigan, being sections 9, 10, 15, 16,

21 and 22 of town 39 north, range 14 east of the third principal meridian, with all sub-divisions, railroads, docks and buildings. v. 1. 1 p. l., 40 pp. incl. 41 maps. fol. Chicago, Greeley-Carlson co. 1891. 1586

**Rascher insurance map publishing co.**
Atlas of Chicago. Scale 50 ft. to an inch. v. 1. 1 p. l., 166 maps. fol. Chicago, the Rascher insurance map publishing co. 1891. 1587

**Central map survey and publishing co.**
Insurance maps of Chicago. v. 1–2, 17. fol. Chicago, central map survey and publishing co. 1892. 1588

**Tillotson, M. D.**
Tillotson's pocket atlas and guide of Chicago, presenting in plat form the blocks, streets, alleys, street numbers, street car lines . . . and map locating all suburban towns in the county . . . World's columbian exposition buildings, etc., etc. 1 p. l., xviii, 162, [22] pp. 12°. Chicago, the city atlas & guide co. 1893. 1589

**Donnelley, R. H.**
Donnelley's sectional atlas of the city of Chicago, compiled from the public records on a scale of four hundred feet to the inch . . . Revised and corrected to the day of publication. 2 v. fol. Chicago, R. H. Donnelley, 1905. 1590

NOTE.—Copyrighted 1904.

CONTENTS.

v. 1. 1 p. l., 106 (i. e. 113) pp. incl. 107 maps, 1 inserted l. Comprising all the territory within the city limits north of thirty-ninth street.
" 2. 2 p. l., 106–209 pp. incl. 97 maps. . . . South of thirty-ninth street.

EAST MOLINE.

**Paddock, H. G.**
Plat book, Moline and East Moline. 72 l., 1 fold. map. fol. Moline, Ill., H. G. Paddock, 1904. 1591

HYDE PARK.

**Greeley & Carlson.**
Greeley and Carlson's atlas of Hyde Park. 2 v. fol. Chicago, Greeley & Carlson, 1880. 1592

CONTENTS.

v. 1. 1 p l., 69 maps. Containing the whole of town 38 north, ranges 14 and 15 east of the 3d principal meridian, showing all sub-divisions, streets, alleys and railroads.
" 2. 1 p. l., 124 maps. Showing that part of said village lying south of eighty-seventh street, comprising South Chicago, Colehour, Irondale, Pullman, Kensington and part of Riverdale, with all sub-divisions, streets, alleys, railroads and water boundaries.

## JEFFERSON.

**Real estate map publishing co.**
The real estate map publishing co.'s official atlas of the township of Jefferson and part of Norwood Park, Maine and Niles. Scale 200 ft. to 1 inch. Drawn by B. Tomassovits and H. L. McIlvain. 2 p. l., 72 (*i. e.* 76) maps. fol. Chicago, the real estate map publishing co. 1908.    1593

NOTE.—Index map on title-page.

## LAKE.

**Greeley, Carlson & co.**
Greeley, Carlson & co.'s atlas of the town of Lake . . . 2 v. fol. Chicago, Greeley, Carlson & co. 1883–1892.    1594

CONTENTS.

v. 1. 1 p. l., 73 maps. Showing that part of said town lying east of Western avenue . . .
" 2. 1 p. l., 73 maps. Being part of the city of Chicago lying east and adjoining the Chicago union transfer railway company's grounds known as the "Stickney tract".

## MOLINE.

**Paddock, H. G.**
Plat book. Moline and East Moline. 72 l., 1 fold. map. fol. Moline, H. G. Paddock, 1904.    1595

## PEORIA.

**Ogle, G. A., & co.**
Standard atlas of Peoria city and county, Illinois, including a plat book of the villages, cities and townships of the county. 148, viii, x–xxii pp. incl. 55 maps, 24 pl. fol. Chicago, G. A. Ogle & co. 1896.    1596

## ROCKFORD.

**Roe, F. B.**
Atlas of the city of Rockford, Winnebago county, Ill. and vicinity. 4 p. l., 26 maps. fol. Philadelphia, F. B. Roe, 1892.    1597

# INDIANA.

## State.

### 1870–1871

**Asher, Adams & Higgins.**
New topographical atlas and gazetteer of Indiana, comprising a topographical view of the several counties of the state, together with a railroad map of Ohio, Indiana and Illinois; an alphabetical gazetteer, giving a concise description and the location of cities,

villages, post offices, railroad stations, landings, etc., and a brief history of Indiana; including a fine copper plate railroad map of the United States and territories. 59 pp. incl. 10 maps. fol. New York, Asher, Adams & Higgins, 1870–71.     1598

### 1876
**Baskin, Forster & co.**
Illustrated historical atlas of the state of Indiana. 462 pp. incl. 149 maps, 28 pl. fol. Chicago, Baskin, Forster & co. 1876. 1599

### 1908
**Rand, McNally & co.**
Rand, McNally & co.'s new ideal state and county survey and atlas containing a large county and railway map of Indiana printed in colors, also . . . a new, complete and ready reference index to the state of Indiana . . . 104 pp. incl. 70 col. maps, 3 col. pl., 2 diagr. (2 col. fold. maps) sm. fol. Chicago, New York, Rand, McNally & co. 1908. 1600

## Counties.

### DAVIES.
**Griffing, Dixon & co.**
Atlas of Davies county, Ind. From actual surveys under the direction of B. N. Griffing. 63, 1–12 pp. incl. 24 maps. fol. Philadelphia, Griffing, Dixon & co. 1888. 1601

### DECATUR.
**Beers, J. H., & co.**
Atlas of Decatur co., Ind. To which are added various general maps, history, statistics, illustrations &c. &c. &c. 26, 37–92 pp., 7 l., incl. 18 maps, 25 pl. fol. Chicago, J. H. Beers & co. 1882.
1602
    NOTE.—Imperfect.
    Map of "City of Greensburg" inserted.

### DEKALB.
**Beers, J. H., & co.**
Atlas of De Kalb co., Indiana, to which are added various general maps, history, statistics, illustrations, &c. &c. &c. 51, [3] pp. incl. 17 maps, 14 pl. 4 maps at end. fol. Chicago, J. H. Beers & co. 1880. 1603

### ELKHART.
**Higgins, Belden & co.**
An illustrated historical atlas of Elkhart county, Ind. 109 pp. incl. 20 maps, 26 pl., 4 maps at end. fol. Chicago, Higgins, Belden & co. 1874. 1604

## FRANKLIN.

**Beers, J. H., & co.**

Atlas of Franklin co. Indiana. To which are added various general maps, history, statistics, illustrations. &c. &c. &c. 121, [9] pp. incl. 19 maps, 36 pl. fol. Chicago, J. H. Beers & co. 1882.  1605

## GIBSON.

**Lake, D. J., & co.**

An atlas of Gibson and Pike counties, Ind. From actual surveys under the direction of B. N. Griffing. 71, 1–12 pp. incl. 33 maps. fol. Philadelphia, D. J. Lake & co. 1881.  1606

## GREENE.

**Lake, D. J., & co.**

An atlas of Greene county, Ind. From actual surveys under the direction of B. N. Griffing. 54 pp. incl. 17 maps, 4 maps at end. fol. Philadelphia, D. J. Lake & co. 1879.  1607

## HANCOCK.

**Griffing, Gordon & co.**

An atlas of Hancock county, Ind. From actual surveys under the direction of B. N. Griffing. 42, 1–12 pp. incl. 19 maps. fol. Philadelphia, Griffing, Gordon & co. 1887.  1608

## HARRISON.

**Lake, D. J., & co.**

An atlas of Harrison county, Ind. From actual surveys under the direction of B. N. Griffing. 47, 1–12 pp. incl. 20 maps. fol. Philadelphia, D. J. Lake & co. 1882.  1609

**Bulleit, F. A.**

Illustrated atlas and history of Harrison county, Indiana . . . 78 pp. incl. 22 col. maps. fol. Corydon, Ind. F. A. Bulleit, 1906.  1610

## HENDRICKS.

**Ogle, G. A., & co.**

Standard atlas of Hendricks county, Indiana. Including a plat book of the villages, cities and townships of the county. Map of the state, United States and world. Patron's directory, reference business directory and departments devoted to general information. Analysis of the system of U. S. land surveys, digest of the system of civil government, etc. etc. . . . 2 p. l., 7–61, [1], viii, x–xxii pp. incl. 16 maps, 2 pl., 1 map in text. fol. Chicago, G. A. Ogle & co. 1904.  1611

## HENRY.

**Rerick brothers.**
    The county of Henry, Ind., topography, history, art folio, including chronological chart of general, national, state, and county history. 2 p. l., 7–96 pp. incl. 24 maps, 19 pl., map at end. fol. [Richmond, Ind.] Rerick brothers [1893]     1612
    NOTE.—Pagination irregular.

## HOWARD.

**Kingman brothers.**
    Combination atlas map of Howard county, Indiana. Compiled, drawn and published from personal examinations and surveys . . . 2 p. l., [9]–99 (*i. e.* 102) pp. incl. 16 maps, 37 pl. fol. [Kokomo, Ind.] Kingman brothers, 1877.     1613
    NOTE.—Pagination irregular.

## JAY.

**Griffing, Gordon & co.**
    Atlas of Jay county, Ind. From actual surveys under the direction of B. N. Griffing. 52, 1–12 pp. incl. 25 maps. fol. Philadelphia, Griffing, Gordon & co. 1887.     1614

## JENNINGS.

**Lake, D. J., & co.**
    An atlas of Jennings county, Ind. From actual surveys by J. M. Lathrop and J. H. Summers. 48, 1–20 pp. incl. 18 maps. fol. Philadelphia, D. J. Lake, & co. 1884.     1615

## LA PORTE.

**Ogle, G. A., & co.**
    Plat book of La Porte county, Indiana. 3–96 pp. incl. 33 maps. fol. Chicago, G. A. Ogle & co. 1892.     1616

## MADISON.

**American atlas co.**
    Atlas and directory of Madison county, Indiana. Including a directory of freeholders and official register of the county, with illustrations. Compiled from recent surveys, official records and personal examinations. 2 p. l., 7–119 pp. incl. 36 maps, 22 pl. fol. Cleveland, the american atlas co. 1901.     1617

## MARION.

**Fatout, H. B.**
    Atlas of Indianapolis and Marion county, Ind. Corrected and revised by Gustav Bohn . . . 96 pp. incl. 42 maps. fol. Philadelphia, Griffing, Gordon & co. 1889.     1618

## MIAMI.

**Kingman brothers.**
[A new historical atlas of Miami co. Indiana. Illustrated] 1 l., [13]–103 pp. incl. 19 maps, 47 pl., 2 maps at front. fol. [Kokomo, Ind., Kingman brothers, 1877] 1619
NOTE.—Imperfect; title-page wanting.

## OHIO.

**Lake, D. J., & co.**
An atlas of Switzerland and Ohio counties, Ind. From actual surveys under the direction of B. N. Griffing. 46, 1–12 pp. incl. 15 maps. fol. Philadelphia, D. J. Lake & co. 1883. 1620

## PIKE.

**Lake, D. J., & co.**
An atlas of Gibson and Pike counties, Ind. From actual surveys under the direction of B. N. Griffing. 71, 1–12 pp. incl. 33 maps. fol. Philadelphia, D. J. Lake & co. 1881. 1621

## POSEY.

**Keller & Fuller.**
Illustrated atlas of Posey county, Ind. 49, [26] pp. incl. 13 maps. fol. Evansville, Ind., Keller & Fuller, 1900. 1622
NOTE.—Imperfect; pp. 19–20 wanting.

## PUTNAM.

**Beers, J. H., & co.**
Atlas of Putnam co. Ind. To which are added various general maps, history, statistics, illustrations &c. &c. &c. 60 pp., 8 l., incl. 18 maps, 11 pl. fol. Chicago, J. H. Beers & co. 1879. 1623

## RANDOLPH.

**Lake, D. J., Sanford, G. P.** *and* **Gould, F. A.**
Atlas of Randolph county, Indiana. From actual surveys. To which is added a map of the state of Indiana also an outline and rail road map of the United States. 53 pp. incl. 18 maps, 2 maps at end. fol. Philadelphia, Griffing, Stevenson & co. 1874. 1624

## RIPLEY.

**Lake, D. J., & co.**
An atlas of Ripley county, Ind. From actual surveys under the direction of B. N. Griffing. 51 pp. [10] l. incl. 21 maps. fol. Philadelphia, D. J. Lake & co. 1883. 1625

## ST. JOSEPH.

**Ogle, G. A., & co.**
Standard atlas of St. Joseph county, Indiana, including a plat book of the villages, cities and townships of the county. 3–80, viii pp. incl. 23 maps. fol. Chicago, G. A. Ogle & co. 1895. 1626

### SHELBY.

**Beers, J. H., & co.**
Atlas of Shelby co. Indiana. To which are added various general maps, history, statistics, illustrations, &c. &c. &c. 108, [2] pp. incl. 16 maps, 46 pl. 4 maps at end. fol. Chicago, J. H. Beers & co. 1880. 1627

### SPENCER.

**Lake, D. J., & co.**
An illustrated historical atlas of Spencer county, Ind. From actual surveys under the direction of B. N. Griffing. 67 pp. incl. 14 maps, 12 pl. 4 maps at end. fol. Philadelphia, D. J. Lake & co. 1879. 1628

### SWITZERLAND.

**Lake, D. J., & co.**
An atlas of Switzerland and Ohio counties, Ind. From actual surveys under the direction of B. N. Griffing. 46, 1–12 pp. incl. 15 maps. fol. Philadelphia, D. J. Lake & co. 1883. 1629

### UNION.

**Beers, J. B., & co.**
Atlas of Union county, Indiana, to which are added various general maps, history, statistics, illustrations &c. &c. &c. 75, [2] pp. incl. 14 maps, 24 pl. 4 maps at end. fol. Chicago, J. H. Beers & co. 1884. 1630

### VANDERBURGH.

**Griffing, B. N.**
Griffing's atlas of Vanderburgh county, Ind. 72 pp. incl. 15 maps, 6 pl. 3 maps at end. fol. Philadelphia, D. J. Lake & co. 1880. 1631

**Tillman & Fuller publishing co.**
An illustrated plat book of Vanderburgh and Warrick counties, Ind. 4 p. l., [124] pp. incl. 33 maps, 6 pl. fol. Evansville, Ind., Tillman & Fuller publishing co. [1899?] 1632

NOTE.—Pagination irregular. Map of Indiana, p. 91, copyright 1899.

### WABASH.

**Paul, H.**
Atlas of Wabash county, Ind., to which is added a township map of the state of Indiana also an outline and railroad map of the United States. 3–65 pp. incl. 16 maps, 2 pl. 3 maps at end. fol. Philadelphia, H. Paul & co. 1875. 1633

### WARRICK.

**Lake, D. J., & co.**
An illustrated historical atlas of Warrick county, Ind. From actual surveys under the direction of B. N. Griffing. 55, 1–10 pp. incl. 16 maps, 4 pl. fol. Philadelphia, D. J. Lake & co. 1880. 1634

**Tillman & Fuller publishing co.**
   An illustrated plat book of Vanderburgh and Warrick counties, Ind.   4 p. l., [124] pp., incl. 33 maps, 6 pl.   fol.   Evansville, Ind., Tillman & Fuller publishing co. [1899?]   1635
   NOTE.—Pagination irregular. Map of Indiana, p. 91, 1899 copyright.

### WHITE.
**Ogle, G. A. & co.**
   Standard atlas of White county, Indiana, including a plat book of the villages, cities and townships of the county. Map of the state, United States and world. Farmers directory, reference business directory and departments devoted to general information. Analysis of the system of U. S. land surveys, digest of the system of civil government, etc. etc.   2 p. l., 7–69, xxii pp. incl. 20 maps.   fol.   Chicago, G. A. Ogle & co. 1896.   1636

### Cities.
#### INDIANAPOLIS.
**Fatout, H. B.**
   Atlas of Indianapolis and Marion county, Ind. Corrected and revised by Gustave Bohn . . .   96 pp. incl. 42 maps.   fol.   Philadelphia, Griffing, Gordon & co. 1889.   1637

**Baist, G. M.**
   Baist's real estate atlas of surveys of Indianapolis and vicinity, Indiana . . . Compiled and published, from official records, private plans and actual surveys . . . 1 p. l., 34 (*i. e.* 35) col. maps.   fol.   Philadelphia, G. M. Baist, 1908.   1638

## IOWA.
### State.
#### 1875
**Andreas, A. T.**
   A. T. Andreas' illustrated historical atlas of the state of Iowa. vii, [1], 7–590 (*i. e.* 550) pp. incl. front., 139 maps, 71 pl.   fol.   Chicago, Andreas atlas co. 1875.   1639
   NOTE.—Pagination irregular.

#### 1904
**Huebinger, M.**
   Atlas of the state of Iowa. Published under the direction and supervision of M. Huebinger.   1 p. l., 23, 29–360 (*i. e.* 440) pp. incl. 103 maps, 87 pl.   fol.   Davenport, Ia., the Iowa publishing co. 1904.   1640

## 1907

**Cram, G. F.**
Cram's superior reference atlas of Iowa and the world. 159 pp. incl. 68 col. maps, 21 pl. 1 fold. map. fol. New York, Chicago, G. F. Cram, 1907. 1641

### Counties.

#### ALLAMAKEE.

**Warner, G. E., *and* Foote, C. M.**
Plat book of Allamakee county, Iowa. Drawn from actual surveys and the county records. 54 pp. incl. 25 maps. fol. Minneapolis, Warner & Foote, 1886. 1642

#### APPANOOSE.

**Northwest publishing co.**
Plat book of Appanoose county, Iowa. Drawn from actual surveys & county records. 2 p. l., 2-52 pp. incl. 34 maps. fol. [Philadelphia] the north west publishing co. 1896. 1643

#### BENTON.

**Harrison & Warner.**
Atlas of Benton county, Iowa, to which is added a rail road map of the state of Iowa. 61 pp. incl. 26 maps. fol. Marshalltown, Ia., Harrison & Warner, 1872. 1644

#### BOONE.

**Northwest publishing co.**
Plat book of Boone county, Iowa. Drawn from actual surveys & county records. 6 p. l., 11-51, [4] pp. incl. 32 maps. fol. [Philadelphia] the north west publishing co. 1896. 1645

#### BREMER.

**Hoover, H. S.**
Atlas of Bremer county, Iowa. Compiled from official records and personal surveys. 56 pp. incl. 17 maps, 4 pl. 1 map at end. fol. Waverly, Iowa, H. S. Hoover & W. P. Reeves, 1875. 1646
  NOTE.—Pagination irregular.

**Union publishing co.**
Plat book of Bremer county, Iowa. 49 pp. incl. 27 maps. fol. Philadelphia, the union pub. co. 1894. 1647

#### BUCHANAN.

**Warner, G. E., *and* Foote, C. M.**
Plat book of Buchanan county, Iowa. Drawn from actual surveys and the county records. 38 pp. incl. 26 maps. fol. Minneapolis, Warner & Foote, 1886. 1648

### BUTLER.

**Union publishing co.**
Plat book of Butler county, Iowa. Drawn from actual surveys and county records. 50 pp. incl. 30 maps. fol. Philadelphia. the union publishing co. 1895. 1649

### CARROLL.

**Iowa publishing co.**
Atlas of Carroll county, Iowa, containing maps of cities, towns, villages and townships of the county. Maps of state, United States and world . . . 139, [1] pp. incl. 36 maps, 24 pl. fol. Davenport, Ia., the Iowa publishing co. 1906. 1650
NOTE.—Pagination irregular.

### CEDAR.

**Harrison & Warner.**
Atlas of Cedar county, Iowa, to which is added a rail road map of the state of Iowa. 53 pp. incl. 23 maps. fol. Marshalltown, Ia., Harrison & Warner, 1872. 1651

### CLAY.

**Inter state publishing co.**
Plat book of Clay county, Iowa. 69 pp. incl. 23 maps. fol. [Boston & Chicago] inter state pub. co. 1887. 1652

### CLAYTON.

**Warner, G. E.,** *and* **Foote, C. M.**
Plat book of Clayton county, Iowa. Drawn from actual surveys and the county records. 55 pp. incl. 35 maps. fol. Minneapolis, Warner & Foote, 1886. 1653

**Ogle, G. A., & co.**
Standard atlas of Clayton county, Iowa, including a plat book of the villages, cities and townships of the county. Map of the state, United States and world. Patrons directory, reference business directory and departments devoted to general information. Analysis of the system of U. S. land surveys, digest of the system of civil government, etc. etc. 2 p. l., 8–61, [1], xxii pp. incl. 35 maps, 2 pl. fol. Chicago, G. A. Ogle & co. 1902. 1654
NOTE.—Pagination irregular.

### CLINTON.

**Harrison & Warner.**
Atlas of Clinton county, Iowa, to which is added a rail road and sectional map of the state of Iowa. 67 pp. incl. 23 maps. 1 map at end. fol. Clinton, Ia., Harrison & Warner, 1874. 1655

### DALLAS.

**Northwest publishing co.**
Plat book of Dallas county, Iowa. Compiled from county records and actual surveys. 2 p. l., 2–36 pp., 8 l., 53–55 pp. incl. 35 maps. fol. Minneapolis, the northwest publishing co. 1901.
1656

### DUBUQUE.

**Harrison & Warner.**
Atlas of Dubuque county, Iowa, to which is added a rail road and sectional map of the state of Iowa. 53 pp. incl. 20 maps. fol. Clinton, Ia. & Philadelphia, Harrison & Warner, 1874.
1657

**Northwest publishing co.**
Plat book of Dubuque county, Iowa. Drawn from actual surveys and county records. 6 p. l., 10–59 pp. incl. 37 maps. fol. [Philadelphia] the north west publishing co. 1892.
1658

**Iowa publishing co.**
Atlas of Dubuque county, Iowa, containing maps of cities, towns, villages and townships of the county. Maps of state, United States and world. 155, 171–199 pp. incl. 45 maps, 32 pl. fol. Davenport, Ia., the Iowa publishing co. 1906.
1659

### EMMET.

**Pinkney & Brown.**
Plat book of Emmet county, Iowa. Compiled from county records and actual surveys. 2 p. l., 6–25 pp. incl. 20 maps. fol. [Philadelphia] Pinkney & Brown. 1899.
1660

### FAYETTE.

**Warner, G. E.** *and* **Foote, C. M.**
Plat book of Fayette county, Iowa. 40 pp. incl. 31 maps. fol. Philadelphia, Warner & Foote, 1879.
1661

**Union publishing co.**
Plat book of Fayette county, Iowa. Drawn from actual surveys and county records. 61 pp. incl. 38 maps. fol. Philadelphia, the union publishing co. 1896.
1662

### FLOYD.

**Union publishing co.**
Plat book of Floyd county, Iowa. Drawn from actual surveys and county records. 47 pp. incl. 24 maps. fol. Philadelphia, the union publishing co. 1895.
1663

### FREMONT.

**Northwest publishing co.**
 Plat book of Fremont county, Iowa. Drawn from actual surveys & county records. 53 pp. incl. 24 maps. fol. [Philadelphia] the north west publishing co. 1891.   1664

### GREENE.

**Northwest publishing co.**
 Plat book of Greene county, Iowa. Drawn from actual surveys & county records. 2 p. l., 47 pp. incl. 29 maps. fol. [Philadelphia] the north west publishing co. 1896.   1665

### HAMILTON.

**Northwest publishing co.**
 Plat book of Hamilton county, Iowa. Drawn from actual surveys aud county records. 2 p. l., [2]–48 pp. incl. 32 maps. fol. [Minneapolis] the north west publishing co. 1896.   1666

### HARDIN.

**Harrison & Warner.**
 Atlas of Hardin county, Iowa, to which is added a rail road and sectional map of the state of Iowa. 49 pp. incl. 21 maps. 1 map at end. fol. Philadelphia, Harrison & Warner, 1875.   1667

### HARRISON.

**Allen, C. R.**
 Illustrated atlas of Harrison county, Iowa. 92 pp. incl. 36 maps, 37 pl. fol. Logan, Ia. & Philadelphia, C. R. Allen & co. 1884.   1668

**Ogle, G. A., & co.**
 Standard atlas of Harrison county, Iowa. Including a plat book of the villages, cities and townships of the county. Map of the state, United States and world. Patrons' directory, reference business directory and departments devoted to general information. Analysis of the system of U. S. land surveys, digest of the system of civil government, etc. etc. 2 p. l., 7–101, viii, x–xxii pp. incl. 31 maps, 6 pl., 1 map in text. fol. Chicago, G. A. Ogle & co. 1902.   1669

### HENRY.

**Thompson & Everts.**
 Combination atlas of Henry county, Iowa. 34 pp. incl. 16 maps, 11 pl. fol. Geneva, Ill., Thompson & Everts, 1870.   1670

### HOWARD.

**Warner, G. E.,** *and* **Foote, C. M.**
 Plat book of Howard county, Iowa. Drawn from actual surveys and the county records. 44 pp. incl 21 maps. fol. Minneapolis, Warner & Foote, 1886.   1671

## HUMBOLDT.

**Northwest publishing co.**
 Plat book of Humboldt county, Iowa. Drawn from actual surveys and county records. 2 p. l., 44 pp. incl. 27 maps (1 map loose) fol. [Philadelphia] the north west publishing co. 1896.
1672

## IOWA.

**Harrison & Warner.**
 Atlas of Iowa county, Iowa, to which is added a rail road and sectional map of the state of Iowa. 43 pp. incl. 19 maps. 1 map at end. fol. Clinton, Ia., and Philadelphia, Harrison & Warner. 1874.
1673

**Warner, G. E.,** *and* **Foote, C. M.**
 Plat book of Iowa county, Iowa. Drawn from actual surveys and the county records. 50 pp. incl. 21 maps. fol. Minneapolis. Warner & Foote, 1886.
1674

## JACKSON.

**Northwest publishing co.**
 Plat book of Jackson co. Iowa. Drawn from actual surveys county records. 6 p. l., 11–55 pp. incl. 36 maps. fol. [Philadelphia] the north west publishing co. 1893.
1675

## JASPER.

**Huebinger survey and map publishing co.**
 Standard historical atlas of Jasper county, Iowa . . . 1 p. l., 9–69 pp. incl. 30 maps. fol. Davenport, Ia., the Huebinger survey and map publishing co. 1901.
1676
 NOTE.—Pagination irregular.

## JOHNSON.

**Thompson & Everts.**
 Combination atlas map of Johnson county, Iowa. 37 pp. incl. 18 maps, 9 pl. fol. Geneva, Ill., Thompson & Everts, 1870.
1677

## JONES.

**Northwest publishing co.**
 Plat book of Jones county, Iowa. Drawn from actual surveys & county records. 57 pp. incl. 37 maps. fol. [Minneapolis] the north west publishing co. 1893.
1678

## KEOKUK.

**Harrison & Warner.**
 Atlas of Keokuk county, Iowa, drawn from actual surveys and the county records. To which is added a rail road & sectional map of the state of Iowa. 49 pp. incl. 21 maps. fol. Clinton, Ia. & Philadelphia, Harrison & Warner, 1874.
1679

**Bishop, H. G.**
    Atlas of Keokuk county, Iowa. 1895 . . . 1 p. l., 34 l. incl. 28 maps. fol. Sigourney, Iowa, H. G. Bishop, 1895.      1680

### LINN.

**Iowa publishing co.**
    Atlas of Linn county, Iowa. Containing maps of cities. towns. villages and townships of the county. Maps of state, United States and world. Farmers' directory, historical sketches, reminiscenes of early settlers, analysis of the system of U. S. land survey, road laws, portraits of citizens of the county. 224 pp. incl. 49 col. maps. 48 pl. fol. Davenport, Ia., the Iowa publishing co. 1907.      1681

### MADISON.

**Harrison & Warner.**
    Atlas of Madison County, Iowa, to which is added a rail road map and sectional map of the state of Iowa. 41 pp. incl. 20 maps. 5 pl. fol. Philadelphia, Harrison & Warner, 1875.      1682

**Northwest publishing co.**
    Plat book of Madison county, Iowa. Compiled from county records and actual surveys. 2 p. l., 2–46, [1] pp. incl. 28 maps. fol. Minneapolis, the northwest publishing co. 1901.      1683

### MARION.

**Harrison & Warner.**
    Atlas of Marion county, Iowa, to which is added a rail road and sectional map of the state of Iowa. 45 pp. incl. 19 maps. 1 map at end. fol. Philadelphia, Harrison & Warner, 1875.      1684

### MARSHALL.

**Harrison & Warner.**
    Atlas of Marshall co., Iowa, to which is added a rail road map of the state of Iowa. 53 pp. incl. 21 maps. fol. Marshalltown. Ia., Harrison & Warner, 1871.      1685

**Warner, G. E.,** *and* **Foote, C. M.**
    Plat book of Marshall county, Iowa. Drawn from actual surveys and the county records. 56 pp. incl. 31 maps. fol. Minneapolis, Minn., Warner & Foote, 1885.      1686

### MONROE.

**Hovey & Frame.**
    Atlas of Monroe county, Iowa. Published by the Albia republican, G. C. McCormick, publisher. Drawn from the county records and actual surveys . . . 1 p. l., 27 pp. incl. 13 maps. 4°. Albia, Ia., the Albia republican [1902]      1687

## MUSCATINE.

**Harrison & Warner:**
    Atlas of Muscatine county, Iowa, to which is added a rail road and sectional map of the state of Iowa. 43 pp. incl. 18 maps. 1 map at end. fol. Clinton, Ia., and Philadelphia, Harrison & Warner, 1874.     1688

## PAGE.

**Northwest publishing co.**
    Plat book of Page county, Iowa. Compiled from county records and actual surveys. 2 p. l., 35 pp., 6 l., 51–54 pp. incl. 33 maps (1 fold. map inserted) fol. Minneapolis, the northwest publishing co. 1902.     1689

## PLYMOUTH.

**Anderson & Goodwin co.**
    Standard historical atlas of Plymouth county, Iowa, containing maps of villages, cities and townships of the county. Maps of state, United States and world. Farmer's directory, business directory and general information. 85, [17], 22, 18, 22 pp. incl. 37 maps, 22 pl. fol. Chicago, Anderson & Goodwin co. 1907.     1690

## POCAHONTAS.

**Lighter, J. H.**
    Plat book of Pocahontas county, Iowa. 34 pp. incl. 16 maps. fol. Rolfe, Ia., J. H. Lighter. 1897.     1691

## POTTAWATTAMIE.

**Allen, C. R.**
    Illustrated atlas of Pottawattamie county, Iowa. 127 pp. incl. 44 maps, 57 pl. fol. Council Bluffs, C. R. Allen & co. 1885.     1692

**Ogle, G. A., & co.**
    Standard atlas of Pottawattamie county, Iowa, including a plat book of the villages, cities and townships of the county . . . 2 p. l., 8–135, viii, x–xxii pp. incl. 41 maps, 6 pl. fol. Chicago, G. A. Ogle & co. 1902.     1693

## SCOTT.

**Iowa publishing co.**
    Atlas of Scott county, Iowa, containing maps of villages, cities and townships of the county. Maps of state, United States and world. Farmers directory, business directory, general information. 169 (*i. e.* 188) pp. incl. 37 maps, 40 pl. fol. Davenport, Ia., the Iowa publishing co. 1905.     1694

## SIOUX.

**Anderson & Goodwin co.**
    Standard historical atlas of Sioux county, Iowa. Containing maps of villages, cities and townships of the county. Maps of state, United States and world . . . 86, [16], 41 pp. incl. 39 col. maps. fol. Chicago, Anderson & Goodwin co. 1908.     1695

### STORY.

**Huebinger surveying and map publishing co.**
 Atlas of Story county, Iowa. Containing maps of cities, villages and townships of the county. Maps of state, United States and world. Farmers directory, business directory, general information ... 1 p. l., 28 maps. fol. Davenport, Ia., the Huebinger surveying and map pub'l. co. 1902.   1696
  NOTE.—Maps irregularly numbered.

### TAMA.

**Harrison & Warner.**
 Atlas of Tama county, Iowa, to which is added a rail road and sectional map of the state of Iowa. 53 pp. incl. 25 maps. 1 map at end. fol. Clinton, Ia., Harrison & Warner, 1875.   1697

**Northwest publishing co.**
 Plat book of Tama county, Iowa. Drawn from actual surveys and county records by the northwest publishing co. 1892. 60 pp. incl. 38 maps, 1 map in text. fol. [Minneapolis] the north west publishing co. 1892.   1698

### TAYLOR.

**Northwest publishing co.**
 Plat book of Taylor county, Iowa. Drawn from actual surveys and county records. 1 p. l., 50 pp. incl. 31 maps. fol. [Philadelphia] the north west publishing co. 1894.   1699

### UNION.

**Northwest publishing co.**
 Plat book of Union county, Iowa. Drawn from actual surveys. 2 p. l., 46 pp. incl. 26 maps. fol. [Minneapolis] the north west publishing co. 1894.   1700

### VAN BUREN.

**Northwest publishing co.**
 Plat book of Van Buren county, Iowa. Drawn from actual surveys and county records. 1 p. l., 51 pp., incl. 30 maps. fol. [Minneapolis] the north west publishing co. 1897.   1701

### WARREN.

**Harrison & Warner.**
 Atlas of Warren county, Iowa, to which is added a rail road map of the state of Iowa. 45 pp. incl. 20 maps. 1 map at end. fol. Marshalltown, Ia., Harrison & Warner, 1872.   1702

**Hovey & Frame.**
 Atlas of Warren county, Iowa. 1902. Drawn from the county records and official surveys ... 2 p. l., 27 pp., 22 maps. fol. Knoxville, Ia., Hovey & Frame, 1902.   1703

## WASHINGTON.

**Harrison & Warner.**
Atlas of Washington county, Iowa, to which is added a rail road and sectional map of the state of Iowa. 47 pp. incl. 21 maps. fol. Clinton, Ia. & Philadelphia, Harrison & Warner, 1874.
1704

**Northwest publishing co.**
Plat book of Washington county, Iowa. Drawn from actual surveys and county records . . . 1 p. l., 60 pp. incl. 33 maps. fol. [Minneapolis] the north west publishing co. 1894.
1705

**Iowa publishing co.**
Atlas of Washington county, Iowa, containing maps of villages, cities and townships of the county. Maps of state, United States and world. Farmers directory, business directory, general information. 129 pp. incl. 35 maps. 30 pl. fol. Davenport, the Iowa publishing co. 1906.
1706

## WINNESHIEK.

**Warner, G. E.,** *and* **Foote, C. M.**
Plat book of Winneshiek county, Iowa. Drawn from actual surveys and the county records. 46 pp. incl. 32 maps. fol. Minneapolis, Warner & Foote, 1886.
1707

**Anderson & Goodwin co.**
Standard historical atlas of Winneshiek county, Iowa, containing maps of villages, cities and townships of the county. Maps of state, United States and world. Farmer's directory, business directory, general information. [164] pp. incl. 39 maps, 30 pl. fol. Davenport, Ia., Anderson & Goodwin co. 1905.
1708
NOTE.—Various paging.

## Cities.

### DES MOINES.

**Tate, J. C. & F. C.**
Tate's atlas of Des Moines and plat directory to additions, subdivisions and official plats in Des Moines, Iowa. Giving a complete ward map of the city and the plats as shown in the county records, compiling all of the plat records in one, showing their relative position one to another, including plat index giving the correct name and date of filing of plats, giving book and page now in use in the recorder's office in Polke county, Iowa. Completed to jan., 1899. 9 p. l., 35 maps. fol. Des Moines, J. C. & F. C. Tate, 1899.
1709

## KANSAS.

### State.

#### 1887

**Everts, L. H., & co.**
The official state atlas of Kansas, compiled from government surveys, county records and personal investigations. 1 p. l., 266 l. incl. 270 maps, 25 fold. maps inserted, 145 pl. fol. Philadelphia, L. H. Everts & co. 1887. 1710

#### 1907

**Cram, G. F.**
Cram's superior reference atlas of Kansas and the world. 160 pp. incl. 68 maps, 24 pl., 1 fold. map. fol. New York, Chicago, G. F. Cram, °1907. 1711

NOTE.—pp. 136-160 relate to Kansas.

### Counties.

#### ANDERSON.

**Northwest publishing co.**
Plat book of Anderson county, Kan. Compiled from county records and actual surveys. 2 p. l., 54 pp. incl. 34 maps. fol. Minneapolis, the northwest publishing co. 1901. 1712

#### BARTON.

**Northwest publishing co.**
Plat book of Barton county, Kan., compiled from county records and actual surveys. 2 p. l., 67 pp. incl. 38 maps. fol. Minneapolis, the northwest publishing co. 1902. 1713

#### BOURBON.

**Edwards brothers.**
An illustrated, historical atlas of Bourbon county, Kan. Compiled, drawn and published from personal examinations and surveys. 58 pp., [4] l. incl. 25 maps, 7 pl. fol. Philadelphia, Edwards brothers, 1878. 1714

#### BROWN.

**Northwest publishing co.**
Plat book of Brown county, Kansas. Compiled from county records and actual surveys. 1 p. l., 58 pp. incl. 37 maps. fol. Minneapolis, the northwest publishing co. 1904. 1715

## CLOUD.

**Edwards, J. P.**
  Edwards' atlas of Cloud county, Kan. Compiled, drawn and published from personal examinations and surveys. 69 pp. incl. 26 maps. fol. Quincy, Ill., J. P. Edwards, 1885.      1716

## COFFEY.

**Edwards brothers.**
  An illustrated, historical atlas of Coffey county, Kan. Compiled, drawn and published from personal examinations and surveys. 58 pp., [4] l. incl. 24 maps, 7 pl. fol. Philadelphia, Edwards brothers, 1878.      1717

**Northwest publishing co.**
  Plat book of Coffey county, Kan. Compiled from county records and actual surveys. 2 p. l., 2-58 pp., incl. 34 maps. fol. Minneapolis, the northwest publishing co. 1901.      1718

## DOUGLAS.

**Beers, F. W.**
  Atlas of Douglas county, Kansas. 68 pp. incl. 21 maps. fol. New York, N. W. Beers & co. 1873.      1719

## FRANKLIN.

**Northwest publishing co.**
  Plat book of Franklin county, Kansas. Compiled from county records and actual surveys. 2 p. l., 51 pp. incl. 29 maps, 1 fold. map loose. fol. Minneapolis, the northwest publishing co. 1903.
      1720

## GREENWOOD.

**Northwest publishing co.**
  Plat book of Greenwood county, Kansas. Compiled from county records and actual surveys. 2 p. l., 3-75 pp. incl. 52 maps. fol. Minneapolis, the northwest publishing co. 1903.      1721

## JACKSON.

**Northwest publishing co.**
  Plat book of Jackson county, Kansas. Compiled from county records and actual surveys. 2 p. l., 2-31 pp., 8 l., 49-50 pp. incl. 33 maps. fol. Minneapolis, the northwest publishing co. 1903.
      1722

## KINGMAN.

**Northwest publishing co.**
  Plat book of Kingman county, Kansas. Compiled from county records and actual surveys. 2 p. l., 56 pp. incl. 39 maps. 1 fold. map loose. fol. Minneapolis, the northwest publishing co. 1903.
      1723

## LEAVENWORTH.

**Ogle, G. A., & co.**
Standard atlas of Leavenworth county, Kansas. Including a plat book of the villages, cities and townships of the county. Map of the state, United States and world. Patrons directory reference business directory and departments devoted to general information. Analysis of the system of U. S. land surveys, digest of the system of civil government, etc. etc. . . .   2 p. l., 7-67, [3], viii, x-xxii pp. incl. 17 maps, 1 pl., 1 map in text.  fol.  Chicago, G. A. Ogle & co. 1903.   1724

## LINCOLN.

**Northwest publishing co.**
Plat book of Lincoln county, Kansas. Compiled from county records and actual surveys.  2 p. l., 2-31 pp., 8 l., 49-51 pp. incl. 32 maps.  fol.  Minneapolis, the northwest publishing co. 1901.   1725

## LYON.

**Edwards bros.**
An historical plat book of Lyon county, Kansas.  7 p. l., 13-49 pp. incl. 32 maps.  fol.  Philadelphia, Edwards bros. 1879.   1726

## McPHERSON.

**Northwest publishing co.**
Plat book of McPherson county, Kansas. Compiled from county records and actual surveys.  2 p. l., [2]-64 pp. incl. 41 maps.  fol.  Minneapolis, the northwest publishing co. 1903.   1727

## MIAMI.

**Edwards brothers.**
An illustrated, historical atlas of Miami county, Kan. Compiled, drawn and published from personal examinations and surveys. 58 pp., [4] l. incl. 25 maps, 6 pl.  fol.  Philadelphia, Edwards brothers, 1878.   1728

## MITCHELL.

**Gillen & Davy.**
Atlas of Mitchell county, Kansas, compiled from actual surveys and the county records, to which is added maps of the state, United States and world.  83 pp. incl. 29 maps.  fol.  Chicago, Gillen & Davy, 1884.   1729

## NORTON.

**Northwest publishing co.**
Plat book of Norton county, Kansas. Compiled from county records and actual surveys.  2 p. l., 2-59 pp. incl. 39 maps.  fol. [Minneapolis] the northwest publishing co. 1900.   1730

## OSAGE.

**Edwards brothers.**
    An illustrated, historical atlas of Osage county, Kan. Compiled, drawn and published from personal examinations and surveys. 64 pp., [4] l. incl. 27 maps, 5 pl. fol. Philadelphia, Edwards brothers, 1879.     1731

## OSBORNE.

**Northwest publishing co.**
    Plat book of Osborne county, Kansas. Compiled from county records and actual surveys. 2 p. l., 2–58 pp. incl. 36 maps. fol. [Philadelphia] the northwest publishing co. 1900.     1732

## RENO.

**Northwest publishing co.**
    Plat book of Reno county, Kansas. Compiled from county records and actual surveys. 3 p. l., 3–98 pp. incl. 64 maps. fol. Minneapolis, the northwest publishing co. 1902.     1733

## REPUBLIC.

**Ogle, G. A., & co.**
    Standard atlas of Republic county, Kansas. Including a plat book of the villages, cities and townships of the county. Map of the state, United States and world. Patron's directory, reference business directory and departments devoted to general information. Analysis of the system of U. S. land surveys, digest of the system of civil government, etc. etc. 2 p. l., 7–81, [1], viii, x–xxii pp. incl. 27 maps, 4 pl., 1 map in text. fol. Chicago, G. A. Ogle & co. 1904.     1734

## RICE.

**Northwest publishing co.**
    Plat book of Rice county, Kansas. Compiled from county records and actual surveys. 2 p. l., 2–67 pp. incl. 35 maps. fol. Minneapolis, the northwest publishing co. 1902.     1735

## RUSH.

**Northwest publishing co.**
    Plat book of Rush county, Kan., compiled from county records and actual surveys. 2 p. l., 2–50 pp. incl. 26 maps. fol. Minneapolis, the northwest publishing co. 1901.     1736

## RUSSELL.

**Northwest publishing co.**
    Plat book of Russell county, Kan. Compiled from county records and actual surveys. 2 p. l., 58 pp., incl. 40 maps. fol. Minneapolis, the northwest publishing co. 1901.     1737

## SALINE.

**Northwest publishing co.**
  Plat book of Saline county, Kansas. Compiled from county records and actual surveys.  2 p. l., 2-50, [1] pp. incl. 33 maps (1 map loose) fol. [Minneapolis] the northwest publishing co. 1903.
  1738

## SHAWNEE.

**Beers, F. W.**
  Atlas of Shawnee county, Kansas.  67 pp. incl. 14 maps. fol. New York, F. W. Beers & co. 1873.  1739

**Ogle, G. A., & co.**
  Standard atlas of Shawnee county, Kansas. Including a plat book of the villages, cities and townships of the county. Map of the state, United States and world. Patrons directory, reference business directory and departments devoted to general information. Analysis of the system of U. S. land surveys, digest of the system of civil government, etc. etc. . . .  2 p. l., 7-95, [23], viii, x-xxii pp. incl. 35 maps, 4 pl., 1 map in text. fol. Chicago; G. A. Ogle & co. 1898.  1740

## SUMNER.

**Edwards, J. P.**
  [Edwards' historical atlas of Sumner co. Kan.]  [2], 5-87 pp. incl. 43 maps. fol. [Quincy, Ill., J. P. Edwards, 1883]  1741
  NOTE.—Cover title. Title page wanting.

**Ogle, G. A., & co.**
  Standard atlas of Sumner county, Kansas. Including a plat book of the villages, cities and townships of the county. Map of the state, United States and world. Patrons directory, reference business directory and departments devoted to general information. Analysis of the system of U. S. land surveys, digest of the system of civil government, etc. etc.  2 p. l., 7-85 (*i. e.* 82), viii, x-xxii pp. incl. 41 maps, 2 pl., 1 map in text. fol. Chicago, G. A. Ogle & co. 1902.  1742

## WABAUNSEE.

**Ogle, G. A., & co.**
  Standard atlas of Wabaunsee county, Kansas, including a plat book of the villages, cities and townships of the county.  2 p. l., 7-81, [1], xxii pp. incl. 21 maps, 3 pl. fol. Chicago, G. A. Ogle & co. 1902.  1743

## WYANDOTTE.

**Hopkins, G. M.**
  A complete set of surveys and plates of properties in Wyandotte county and Kansas City, Kansas.  4 p. l., 23 maps. fol. Philadelphia, G. M. Hopkins [1887]  1744

### Cities.

#### KANSAS CITY.

**Hopkins, G. M.**
A complete set of surveys and plats of properties in Wyandotte county and Kansas City, Kansas. 4 p. l., 23 maps. fol. Philadelphia, G. M. Hopkins [1887]     1745

## KENTUCKY.

### Counties.

#### BATH.

**Lake, D. J., & co.**
An atlas of Bath & Fleming counties, Ky. From actual surveys by J. M. Lathrop and J. H. Summers. 60, [12] pp. incl. 26 maps. fol. Philadelphia, D. J. Lake & co. 1884.     1746

#### BOONE.

**Lake, D. J., & co.**
An atlas of Boone, Kenton and Campbell counties, Kentucky. From actual surveys under the direction of B. N. Griffing . . . 68, [12] pp. incl. 37 maps. fol. Philadelphia, D. J. Lake & co. 1883.     1747

NOTE.—pp. 17-20 wanting.

#### BOURBON.

**Beers, D. G., & co.**
Atlas of Bourbon, Clark, Fayette, Jessamine and Woodford counties, Ky. From actual surveys aud official records . . . 77 pp. incl. 22 maps. fol. Philadelphia, D. G. Beers & co. 1877.     1748

#### BRACKEN.

**Lake, D. J., & co.**
An atlas of Bracken and Pendleton counties, Ky. From actual surveys by J. M. Lathrop and J. H. Summers. 60, [12] pp. incl. 24 maps. fol. Philadelphia, D. J. Lake & co. 1884.     1749

#### CAMPBELL.

**Lake, D. J., & co.**
An atlas of Boone, Kenton and Campbell counties, Kentucky. From actual surveys under the direction of B. N. Griffing. 68, [12] pp. incl. 37 maps. fol. Philadelphia, D. J. Lake & co. 1883.     1750

NOTE.—pp. 17-20 wanting.

### CARROLL.

**Lake, D. J., & co.**
An atlas of Carroll and Gallatin counties, Kentucky. From actual surveys under the direction of B. N. Griffing . . . 47, [21] pp. incl. 20 maps. fol. Philadelphia, D. J. Lake & co. 1883.
1751

### CLARK.

**Beers, D. G., & co.**
Atlas of Bourbon, Clark, Fayette, Jessamine and Woodford counties, Ky. From actual surveys and official records. 77 pp. incl. 22 maps. fol. Philadelphia, D. G. Beers & co. 1877. 1752

### FAYETTE.

**Beers, D. G., & co.**
Atlas of Bourbon, Clark, Fayette, Jessamine and Woodford counties, Ky. From actual surveys and official records. 77 pp. incl. 22 maps. fol. Philadelphia, D. G. Beers & co. 1877. 1753

### FLEMING.

**Lake, D. J., & co.**
An atlas of Bath & Fleming counties, Ky. From actual surveys by J. M. Lathrop and J. H. Summers . . . 60, [12] pp. incl. 26 maps. fol. Philadelphia, D. J. Lake & co. 1884. 1754

### GALLATIN.

**Lake, D. J., & co.**
An atlas of Carroll and Gallatin counties, Kentucky. From actual surveys under the direction of B. N. Griffing. 47, [21] pp. incl. 20 maps. fol. Philadelphia, D. J. Lake & co. 1883. 1755

### HENDERSON.

**Lake, D. J., & co.**
An illustrated historical atlas of Henderson and Union counties, Kentucky. From actual surveys under the direction of B. N. Griffing . . . 74, [12] pp. incl. 31 maps, 6 pl. fol. Philadelphia, D. J. Lake & co. 1880.
1756

### HENRY.

**Lake, D. J., & co.**
An atlas of Henry and Shelby cos. Kentucky. From actual surveys under the direction of B. N. Griffing. 68, [12] pp. incl. 35 maps. fol. Philadelphia, D. J. Lake & co. 1882. 1757

### JEFFERSON.

**Beers, D. G., & Lanagan.**
Atlas of Jefferson and Oldham counties, Kentucky. From new and actual surveys . . 70 pp. incl. 29 maps. fol. Philadelphia, Beers & Lanagan, 1879.
1758

### JESSAMINE.

**Beers, D. G., & co.**
    Atlas of Bourbon, Clark, Fayette, Jessamine and Woodford counties, Ky. From actual surveys and official records. 77 pp. incl. 22 maps. fol. Philadelphia, D. G. Beers & co. 1877.   1759

### KENTON.

**Lake, D. J., & co.**
    An atlas of Boone, Kenton and Campbell counties, Kentucky. From actual surveys under the direction of B. N. Griffing. 68, [12] pp. incl. 37 maps. fol. Philadelphia, D. J. Lake & co. 1883.   1760

    NOTE.—pp. 17–20 wanting.

### NELSON.

**Lake, D. J., & co.**
    An atlas of Nelson & Spencer cos., Kentucky. From actual surveys under the direction of B. N. Griffing . . . 64, [12] pp. incl. 29 maps. fol. Philadelphia, D. J. Lake & co. 1882.   1761

### OLDHAM.

**Beers, D. G., & Lanagan.**
    Atlas of Jefferson and Oldham counties, Kentucky. From new and actual surveys. 70 pp. incl. 29 maps. fol. Philadelphia, Beers & Lanagan, 1879.   1762

### OWEN.

**Lake, D. J., & co.**
    An atlas of Owen county, Kentucky. From actual surveys under the direction of B. N. Griffing. 42, [20] pp. incl. 17 maps. fol. Philadelphia, D. J. Lake & co. 1883.   1763

### PENDLETON.

**Lake, D. J., & co.**
    An atlas of Bracken and Pendleton counties, Ky. From actual surveys by J. M. Lathrop and J. H. Summers. 60, [12] pp. incl. 24 maps. fol. Philadelphia, D. J. Lake & co. 1884.   1764

### SHELBY.

**Lake, D. J., & co.**
    An atlas of Henry and Shelby cos. Kentucky. From actual surveys under the direction of B. N. Griffing. 68, [12] pp. incl. 35 maps. fol. Philadelphia, D. J. Lake & co. 1882.   1765

### SPENCER.

**Lake, D. J., & co.**
    An atlas of Nelson & Spencer cos. Kentucky. From actual surveys under the direction of B. N. Griffing . . . 64, [12] pp. incl. 29 maps. fol. Philadelphia, D. J. Lake & co. 1882.   1766

## UNION.

**Lake, D. J., & co.**
 An illustrated historical atlas of Henderson and Union counties, Kentucky. From actual surveys under the direction of B. N. Griffing . . . 74, [12] pp. incl. 31 maps, 6 pl. fol. Philadelphia, D. J. Lake & co. 1880.     1767

## WOODFORD.

**Beers, D. G., & co.**
 Atlas of Bourbon, Clark, Fayette, Jessamine and Woodford counties, Ky. From actual surveys and official records. 77 pp. incl. 22 maps. fol. Philadelphia, D. G. Beers & co. 1877.     1768

### Cities.

#### COVINGTON.

**Hopkins, G. M.**
 City atlas of Covington, Kentucky. 1 p. l., 5-63 pp. incl. 15 maps. fol. Philadelphia, G. M. Hopkins, 1877.     1769

#### LOUISVILLE.

**Hopkins, G. M.**
 Atlas of the city of Louisville and environs. 3 p. l., 30 maps. fol. Philadelphia, G. M. Hopkins, 1884.     1770

## LOUISIANA.

### Cities.

#### NEW ORLEANS.

**Robinson, E.,** *and* **Pigeon, R. H.**
 Atlas of the city of New Orleans, Louisiana, based upon surveys furnished by John F. Braun. 1 p. l., 31 maps. fol. New York, E. Robinson, 1883.     1771

## MAINE.

### State.

#### 1829

**Greenleaf, M.**
 Atlas accompanying Greenleaf's map and statistical survey of Maine . . . cover-title, 7 maps. fol. Portland, Me., Shirley & Hyde [1829]     1772

CONTENTS.

no. 1. Map of the principal rivers, mountains and highland ranges of the state of Maine. 1829. 21¼ x 13.
" 2. Sketch from Bouchette's map of Upper and Lower Canada and the district of Gaspe, exhibiting the true range of highlands dividing the waters of the St. Lawrence and the Atlantic and the imaginary ranges claimed by the british for the boundary of the state of Maine. 1829. 16 x 16½.
" 3. Sketch of the imaginary ranges of highlands reported by the british surveyors under the treaty of Ghent, as extending across the state of Maine. 1829. 11½ x 11.
" 4. Vertical sections, exhibiting the comparative altitudes of the principal highlands and rivers of the state of Maine. 20 x 29. 1828.
" 5. Map exhibiting the principal original grants and sales of lands in the state of Maine. 1829. 31½ x 23½.
" 6. Map of the inhabited part of the state of Maine, exhibiting the progress of its settlement since the year 1778, the representative districts since the year 1820 and the population and valuation of taxable property in each district at the year 1820. 1828. 19½ x 11½.
" 7. Meteorological diagrams. Monthly means and extremes of temperature at Brunswick and Williamsburgh in the state of Maine. 1829. 13 x 11½.

## 1884

**Colby, G. N., & co.**
Atlas of the state of Maine, including statistics and descriptions of its history, educational system, geology, rail roads, natural resources, summer resorts and manufacturing interests. 155 pp. incl. 48 maps. fol. Houlton, Me., G. N. Colby & co. 1884. 1773

## 1890

**Stuart, J. H., & co.**
Stuart's atlas of the state of Maine, including statistics and descriptions of its history, educational system, geology, rail roads, natural resources, summer resorts and manufacturing interests. 1st. rev. ed. 110 pp. incl. 58 maps. fol. South Paris, Me. J. H. Stuart [1890] 1774

### Counties.

#### CUMBERLAND.

**Beers, F. W.**
Atlas of Cumberland county, Maine. 62 pp. incl. 45 maps. fol. New York, F. W. Beers & co. 1871. 1775

#### PENOBSCOT.

**Sherman, W. A.**
Atlas of Penobscot county, Maine. From recent and actual surveys and records. 105 pp. incl. 48 maps. fol. New York, Comstock & Cline, 1875. 1776

## Cities.

### BAR HARBOR.

**Summer residents association.**
Atlas of Bar Harbor and vicinity, in the town of Eden, Hancock co. Maine. 1904. Published by Summer residents association, Bar Harbor, Maine. 1 p. l., 13 maps. fol. Boston, G. H. Walker & co. 1904. 1777

### MARYLAND.

#### CHESAPEAKE AND OHIO CANAL.

**Complete, A, set of maps,** drawings, and tabular statements, relating to the locations, of the canal & rail-road, from the Point of Rocks, to Harpersferry; shewing the indepent, and conjoint, locations, of all, the parts in collision, and, the coast of the independent, and conjoint, construction of each: with tables, of references and bench-marks, for retracing each line. Done under an order, of the chancellor of Maryland, by commission. Georgetown, 7th december 1830. Nathan S. Roberts, commissioner on the part of the Chesapeake & Ohio canal company. 23 l., 35 pl. obl. fol. 1830. 1778.

NOTE.—In manuscript.

CONTENTS.

no. 1. Lower Point of Rocks. 9 sheets.
" 2. Space between the Point of Rocks. 2 sheets.
" 3. Upper Point of Rocks. 8 sheets.
" 4. From the Upper Point of Rocks to Sugar-tree branch.
" 5. From Sugar tree branch to Cotoctin creek. 2 sheets.
" 6. Millers Narrows. 10 sheets.
" 7. Space between Millers Narrows and Harpers Ferry Narrows. 2 sheets.
" 8. Harpers Ferry Narrows. 8 sheets.
" [9] A set of maps & profiles of the Chesapeake & Ohio canal, independent of the Baltimore & Ohio rail road as located from the Point of Rocks to Harpers ferry, commenced 17th march & ended 3rd of july 1830 . . . Being the independent location . . . of the canal, upon which the estimates preparatory, are made by the commissioner on the part of the canal-company, previous to the conjoint location & estimates, made by the commissioners jointly. Under the order of the Chancellor of Maryland 11

[Sections 1-8] Map and profile of the Chesapeake and Ohio canal.
[Section 9] Proposed for constructing the canal independent of the basin, and, through the abutment of the bridge . . .
[Section 10] Proposed to pass the canal into the basin above the guard lock . . . 3 sheets.
[Section 11] Proposed to pass the canal into the basin, above the guard lock . . . [Shows Harpers Ferry, and the confluent of the Potomac river with the Shenandoah]

## State.

### 1866

**Martenet, S. J.**
Martenet's map of Maryland under the patronage of the legislature. Atlas ed. 93 pp. incl. 23 maps. 4°. Baltimore, S. J. Martenet [1866]    1779

### 1873

**Martenet, S. J., Walling, H. F.,** *and* **Gray, O. W.**
New topograpical atlas of the state of Maryland and the District of Columbia, with descriptions historical, scientific, and statistical, together with maps of the United States and territories. 122 pp. incl. 28 maps. fol. Baltimore, Stedman Brown & Lyon, 1873.    1780

## Counties.

### ALLEGHANY.

**Maryland.** *Geological survey.*
Physical atlas of Maryland. Alleghany county. cover-title, 2 maps on 6 l. fol. Baltimore, Johns Hopkins press, 1900.    1781

### ANNE ARUNDEL.

**Hopkins, G. M.**
Atlas of fifteen miles around Baltimore, including Anne Arundel county, Maryland. 73 pp. incl. 18 maps. 4 maps at end. fol. Philadelphia, G. M. Hopkins, 1878.    1782

### BALTIMORE.

**Hopkins, G. M.**
Atlas of Baltimore county, Maryland. 1 p. l., 11–77 pp. incl. 30 maps, 2 pl. 3 maps at end. fol. Philadelphia, G. M. Hopkins, 1877.    1783

Atlas of fifteen miles around Baltimore, including Howard county, Maryland. 1 p. l., 9–77 pp. incl. 20 maps. 4 maps at end. fol. Philadelphia, G. M. Hopkins, 1878.    1784

   NOTE.—Map of the city of Baltimore, at end.

**Bromley, G. W.,** *and* **Bromley, W. S.**
Atlas of Baltimore county, Maryland. From actual surveys and official plans. 2 p. l., 36 maps. fol. Philadelphia, G. W. Bromley & co. 1898.    1785

## CARROLL.

**Lake, Griffing & Stevenson.**
An illustrated atlas of Carroll county, Md. Compiled, drawn and published from actual surveys. 48 pp. incl. 16 maps, 2 pl. 4 maps at end. fol. Philadelphia, Lake, Griffing & Stevenson, 1877.
1786

## DORCHESTER.

**Lake, Griffing & Stevenson.**
An illustrated atlas of Talbot & Dorchester counties, Maryland. Compiled, drawn and published from actual surveys. 60 pp., [8] l. incl. 28 maps, 2 pl. fol. Philadelphia, Lake, Griffing & Stevenson, 1877.
1787

## FREDERICK.

**Lake, D. J., & others.**
Atlas of Frederick county, Maryland. From actual surveys. 73 pp. incl. 30 maps, 2 l. 2 maps at end. fol. Philadelphia, C. O. Titus & co. 1873.
1788

## HOWARD.

**Hopkins, G. M.**
Atlas of fifteen miles around Baltimore, including Howard county, Maryland. 1 p. l., 9–77 pp. incl. 20 maps. 4 maps at end. fol. Philadelphia, G. M. Hopkins, 1878.
1789

## MONTGOMERY.

**Hopkins, G. M.**
Atlas of fifteen miles around Washington including the county of Montgomery, Maryland. 84 pp. incl. 44 maps. 3 maps at end. fol. Philadelphia, G. M. Hopkins, 1879.
1790

## PRINCE GEORGE.

**Hopkins, G. M.**
Atlas of fifteen miles around Washington including the county of Prince George, Maryland. 84 pp. incl. 45 maps. 3 maps at end. fol. Philadelphia, G. M. Hopkins, 1878.
1791

## SOMERSET.

**Lake, Griffing & Stevenson.**
Atlas of Wicomico, Somerset & Worcester counties, Maryland. Compiled, drawn and published from actual surveys. 60 pp. incl. 36 maps. 5 maps at end. fol. Philadelphia, Lake, Griffing & Stevenson, 1877.
1792

## TALBOT.

**Lake, Griffing & Stevenson.**
An illustrated atlas of Talbot & Dorchester counties, Maryland. Compiled, drawn and published from actual surveys. 60 pp., [8] l. incl. 28 maps, 2 pl. fol. Philadelphia, Lake, Griffing & Stevenson, 1877.
1793

## WICOMICO.

**Lake, Griffing & Stevenson.**
 Atlas of Wicomico, Somerset & Worcester counties, Maryland. Compiled, drawn and published from actual surveys.  60 pp. incl. 36 maps. 5 maps at end. fol. Philadelphia, Lake, Griffing & Stevenson, 1877.   1794

## WORCESTER.

**Lake, Griffing & Stevenson.**
 Atlas of Wicomico, Somerset & Worcester counties, Maryland. Compiled, drawn and published from actual surveys.  60 pp. incl. 36 maps. 5 maps at end. fol. Philadelphia, Lake, Griffing & Stevenson, 1877.   1795

### Cities.

#### BALTIMORE.

**Hopkins, G. M.**
 City atlas of Baltimore, Maryland, and environs.  2 v. fol. Philadelphia, G. M. Hopkins, 1876–77.   1796

  NOTE.—Collation: 4 p. l., 5–127 pp. incl. 35 maps; 2 p. l., 9–94 pp. incl. 37 maps.

**Bromley, G. W.,** *and* **Bromley, W. S. alter S.**
 Atlas of the city of Baltimore, Maryland. From actual surveys and official plans . . .  2 p. l., 34 maps. fol. Philadelphia, G. W. Bromley & co. 1896.   1797

 Atlas of the city of Baltimore, Maryland. From actual surveys and official plans . . .  2 p. l., 34 maps. fol. Philadelphia, G. W. Bromley & co. 1906.   1798

## MASSACHUSETTS.

### ROADS.

**Scarborough co.**
 Complete road atlas, Massachusetts and Rhode Island.  6 sheets. fol. Boston, the Scarborough co. °1905.   1799

  NOTE.—In case.
  The title sheet contains a plan of "Boston showing original shore line," an index map, and an index to the cities, villages, post-offices and stations in Massachusetts and Rhode Island.

## State.

### 1871

**Walling & Gray.**
Official topographical atlas of Massachusetts from astronomical, trigonometrical and various local surveys. xxxl, 2–49 pp. incl. 15 maps. fol. Boston, Stedman, Brown & Lyon, 1871.  1800

### 1890

**Massachusetts.** *Topographical survey commission.*
Atlas of Massachusetts from topographical surveys made in co-operation by the United States geological survey and the commissioners of the commonwealth 1884–1888. United States geological survey, J. W. Powell, director. Commonwealth of Massachusetts, Francis A. Walker, Henry L. Whiting, N. S. Shaler, commissioners. Preliminary edition, subject to correction. 1 p. l., 55 maps. fol. Boston, published by the commission, 1890.  1801

NOTE.—In portfolio.

### 1891

**Walker, G. H., & co.**
Atlas of Massachusetts. Compiled under the direction of O. W. Walker . . . 231 pp. incl. 56 maps. fol. Boston, G. H. Walker & co. ᶜ1891.  1802

### 1894

**Walker, G. H., & co.**
Atlas of Massachusetts. Compiled under the direction of O. W. Walker . . . Illustrated ed. 4 p. l., 28 maps, 2 pl. fol. Boston, G. H. Walker & co. ᶜ1894.  1803

### 1900

**Walker, G. H., & co.**
Atlas of Massachusetts. Compiled under the direction of O. W. Walker . . . 1900 ed. 3 p. l., [5]–231 pp. incl. 56 maps. fol. Boston, G. H. Walker & co. 1900.  1804

### 1904

**Walker, G. H., & co.**
Atlas of Massachusetts. Compiled under the direction of O. W. Walker . . . Assistance rendered by more than one hundred prominent civil engineers and surveyors . . . 1904 ed. 231 (*i. e.* 248) pp. incl. 60 maps. fol. Boston, G. H. Walker & co. 1904.  1805

## Counties.

### BARNSTABLE.

**Walker, G. H., & co.**
    Atlas of Barnstable county, Mass.    84 pp. incl. 38 maps, 6 pl. fol. Boston, George H. Walker & co. 1880.    1806

### BERKSHIRE.

**Beers, F. W.**
    County atlas of Berkshire, Massachusetts.    116 pp. incl. 61 maps, 13 pl. fol. New York, R. T. White & co. 1876.    1807

**Miller, D. L.**
    Atlas of the towns of North Adams, Adams, Williamstown and Cheshire, Berkshire county, Mass.    80 pp. incl. 19 maps. fol. New York, D. L. Miller & co. 1894.    1808

**Barnes & Farnham.**
    Atlas of Berkshire county, Massachusetts . . . Assistance rendered by the following civil engineers, E. C. Carter, Lenox; J. W. Curtis, Gt. Barrington; H. P. Linnell, North Adams; D. L. Miller, Adams; J. M. Race, Gt. Barrington.    2 p. l., 59 maps on 118 l., 59-62 l. fol. Pittsfield, Mass., Barnes & Farnham, 1904.
   1809

### BRISTOL.

**Beers, F. W.,** *& others.*
    Atlas of Bristol county, Mass.    50 pp. incl. 32 maps. New York, F. W. Beers & co. 1871.    1810

**Everts & Richards.**
    New topographical atlas of surveys, Bristol county, Massachusetts . . . Based upon and carefully compiled from the latest national, state and local engineering sources obtainable and the personal investigations and surveys of the publishers' special corps of engineers. Accompanied by a new and original ready reference county chart . . .    181 pp. incl. 45 maps. fol. Philadelphia, Everts & Richards, 1895.    1811

### ESSEX.

**Beers, D. G. & co.**
    Atlas of Essex county, Mass.    139 pp. incl. 57 maps. fol. Philadelphia, D. G. Beers & co. 1872.    1812

**Walker, G. H. & co.**
    Atlas of Essex county, Mass.    178 pp. incl. 78 maps, 28 pl. fol. Boston, G. H. Walker & co. 1884.    1813

## FRANKLIN.

**Beers, F. W.,** & *others.*
    Atlas of Franklin co., Mass.     52 pp. incl. 36 maps.   fol.   New York, F. W. Beers & co. 1871.     1814

## HAMPDEN.

**Beers, F. W.,** & *others.*
    Atlas of Hampden county, Mass.     48 pp. incl. 36 maps, 4 pl. at end.   fol.   New York, Beers, Ellis & Soule, 1870.     1815

**Richards, L. J. & co.**
    New topographical atlas of the county of Hampden, Mass . . . 137 pp. incl. 34 maps, 1 map loose.   fol.   Springfield, Mass., L. J. Richards & co. 1894.     1816

## HAMPSHIRE.

**Beers, F. W.**
    County atlas of Hampshire, Mass.     1 p. l., 105 pp. incl. 34 maps.   fol.   New York, F. W. Beers & co. 1873.     1817

## MIDDLESEX.

**Beers, F. W.,** & *others.*
    County atlas of Middlesex, Mass.     164 pp. incl. 102 maps.   fol.   New York, J. W. Beers & co. 1875.     1818

**Walker, G. H.**
    Atlas of Middlesex county, Mass.     292 pp. incl. 136 maps.   fol.   Boston, G. H. Walker & co. 1889.     1819

**Walker, G. H., & co.**
    Atlas of Middlesex county, Massachusetts . . . from official plans and actual surveys.   v. 2–3.   fol.   Boston, G. H. Walker & co. 1906–8.     1820

    NOTE.—To be issued in 5 v.
    George W. Stadley & co. originally published v. 1, of the Atlas of Middlesex county, the stock of which was bought by Geo. H. Walker & co.

CONTENTS.

    v. 2. Cities of Melrose & Woburn, towns of Bedford, Burlington, Concord, North Reading, Stoneham, Lexington, Lincoln, Wakefield & Winchester.
    " 3. Towns of Ashland, Framingham, Holliston, Hopkinton, Natick, Sherborn, Sudbury, Wayland & Weston.

## NORFOLK.

**Sherman, W. A.**
    Atlas of Norfolk county, Mass.     138 pp. incl. 73 maps.   fol.   New York, Comstock & Cline, 1876.     1821

**Robinson, E.**
Robinson's atlas of Norfolk county, Mass. 1 p. l., 46 maps. fol. New York, E. Robinson, 1888.    1822

**Walker, G. H., & co.**
Atlas of the town of Milton, Norfolk county, Mass., from official plans and private surveys. Revised by W. W. Churchill . . . 2 p. l., 25 maps. fol. Boston, G. H. Walker & co. 1905.    1823

### PLYMOUTH.

**Walker, G. H., & co.**
Atlas of Plymouth county, Mass. 1 p. l., 97 pp. incl. 47 maps, 11 pl. fol. Boston, G. H. Walker & co. 1879.    1824

### SUFFOLK.

**Hopkins, G. M., & co.**
Atlas of the county of Suffolk, Mass. 7 v. fol. Philadelphia, G. M. Hopkins, 1874–75.    1825

CONTENTS.
v. 1. Boston proper.
" 2. Late city of Roxbury, now wards 13, 14, and 15 city of Boston.
" 3. Including South Boston and Dorchester.
" 4. Including East Boston, city of Chelsea, Revere and Winthrop.
" 5. West Roxbury, now ward 17, Boston.
" 6. The late city of Charlestown, now wards 20, 21 and 22, city of Boston.
" 7. The late town of Brighton, now ward 19 of Boston.

### WORCESTER.

**Beers, F. W.,** *& others.*
Atlas of Worcester county, Mass. 99 pp. incl. 85 maps, 1 pl. at end. fol. New York, F. W. Beers & co. 1870.    1826

**Richards, L. J., & co.**
New topographical atlas of the county of Worcester, Mass. . . . Based upon, and carefully compiled from, the latest national, state and local engineering sources obtainable and the personal investigations and surveys of the publishers' special corps of engineers. . . . 2 p. l., 55 maps, 1 pl., 43 pp. (1 map loose) fol. Philadelphia, L. J. Richards & co. 1898.    1827

### Cities.

**Massachusetts.** *Harbor and land commission.*
Atlas of the boundaries of the town of Arlington, Middlesex county. 5 p. l., 10 l. incl. 5 maps. fol. [Boston] 1901.    1828

Atlas of the boundaries of the towns of Cohasset, Weymouth, Norfolk county. Hingham, Hull, Plymouth county. 10 p. l., 15 l. incl. 5 maps. fol. [Boston] 1901.    1829

**Massachusetts.** *Harbor and land commission*—Continued.

Atlas of the boundaries of the town of Sandwich, Barnstable county . . .   5 p. l., 12 l. incl. 6 maps.  fol.  [Boston] 1901.   1830

Atlas of the boundaries of the city of Boston, Suffolk county, and town of Brookline, Norfolk county.   20 p. l., 34 l. incl. 13 maps.  fol.  [Boston] 1902.   1831

Atlas of the boundaries of the towns of Carver and Wareham, Plymouth county.   11 p. l., 20 l. incl. 8 maps.  fol.  [Boston] 1902.   1832

Atlas of the boundaries of the city of Lynn, and towns of Nahant, Saugus and Swampscot, Essex county and Wakefield, Middlesex county.   11 p. l., 19 l. incl. 8 maps.  fol.  [Boston] 1902.   1833

Atlas of the boundaries of the towns of Marshfield, Pembroke and Scituate, Plymouth county . . .   10 p. l., 23 l. incl. 9 maps.  fol.  [Boston] 1902.   1834

Atlas of the boundaries of the city of Salem, and towns of Danvers, Marblehead, and Peabody, Essex county . . .   11 p. l., 21 l. incl. 8 maps.  fol.  [Boston] 1902.   1835

Atlas of the boundaries of the cities of Cambridge, Somerville, Waltham, and towns of Belmont, Burlington, Lexington, Watertown, Middlesex county.   21 p. l., 41 l. incl. 18 maps.  fol.  [Boston] 1903.   1836

Atlas of the boundaries of the city of Quincy, and towns of Avon, Braintree, Canton, Holbrook, Hyde Park, Milton, Randolph, Stoughton, Norfolk county . . .   18 p. l., 30 l. incl. 13 maps.  fol.  [Boston] 1903.   1837

Atlas of the boundaries of the towns of Acton, Bedford, Concord, Lincoln, Maynard, Sudbury, Wayland, Weston, Middlesex county.  19 p. l., 30 l. incl. 12 maps.  fol.  [Boston] 1904.   1838

Atlas of the boundaries of the cities of Fall River, New Bedford, and towns of Acushnet, Berkley, Dartmouth, Dighton, Fairhaven, Freetown, Somerset, Swansea, Westport, Bristol county.   19 p. l., 31 pp., 2 l. incl. 14 maps.  fol.  [Boston] 1904.   1839

Atlas of the boundaries of the city of Newton, Middlesex county, and towns of Dedham, Dover, Foxborough, Medfield, Needham, Norwood, Sharon, Walpole, Wellesley, Westwood, Norfolk county . . .   15 p. l., 42 pp. incl. 18 maps.  fol.  [Boston] 1904.   1840

Atlas of the boundaries of the towns of Ashland, Framingham, Holliston, Natick, Sherborn, Middlesex county. Bellingham, Franklin, Medway, Millis, Norfolk, Plainville, Wrentham, Norfolk county. 27 p. l., 40 pp. incl. 13 maps. fol. [Boston] 1905.    1841

Atlas of the boundaries of the cities of Gloucester and Newburyport, and towns of Amesbury, Essex, Georgetown, Groveland, Hamilton, Ipswich, Manchester, Merrimac, Newbury, Rockport, Rowley, Salisbury, Topsfield, Wenham, West Newbury, Essex county . . .   26 p. l., 40 pp. incl. 14 maps. fol. [Boston] 1895.    1842

Atlas of the boundaries of the cities of Haverhill, Lawrence, and towns of Andover, Boxford, Lynnfield, Methuen, Middleton, North Andover, Essex county. North Reading, Reading, Wilmington, Middlesex county . . .   14 p. l., 32 pp. incl. 10 maps. fol. [Boston] 1906.    1843

Atlas of the boundaries of the towns of Barnstable, Brewster, Chatham, Dennis, Eastham, Falmouth, Harwich, Mashpee, Orleans, Provincetown, Truro, Wellfleet, Yarmouth, Barnstable county; Chilmark, Edgartown, Gay Head, Gosnold, Oak Bluffs, Tilsbury, West Tilsbury, Dukes county and Nantucket, Nantucket county. 12 p. l., 30 pp. incl. 9 maps. fol. [Boston] 1907.    1844

Atlas of the boundaries of the city of Lowell and the towns of Ayer, Billerica, Carlisle, Chelmsford, Dracut, Dunstable, Groton, Littleton, Pepperell, Shirley, Tewksbury, Tyngsborough, Westford, Middlesex county.   1 p. l., [30], 38 pp. incl. 13 maps. fol. [Boston] 1907.    1845

Atlas of the boundaries of the city of Marlborough and towns of Boxborough, Hudson, Stow, Middlesex county; Berlin, Bolton, Boylston, Clinton, Harvard, Holden, Hubbardston, Lancaster, Northborough, Oakham, Paxton, Princeton, Rutland, Southborough, Sterling, West Boylston, Worcester county.   1 p. l., 74 pp. incl. 13 maps. fol. [Boston] 1908.    1846

### ABINGTON.

**Sherman, W. A.,** *and* **Howland, C. W.**
   Atlas of Abington and Rockland, Mass.   42 pp. incl. 9 maps. fol.  New York, Comstock & Cline, 1874.    1847

**Massachusetts.** *Topographical survey commission.*
   Atlas of the boundaries of the town of Abington, Plymouth county.   4 p. l., 9 l. incl. 3 maps, 2 pl. fol. [Boston] 1898.    1848

## ADAMS.

**Miller, D. L.**
    Atlas of the towns of North Adams, Adams, Williamstown and Cheshire, Berkshire county, Mass.    80 pp. incl. 19 maps.  fol. New York, D. L. Miller & co. 1894.        1849

## ATTLEBORO.

**Walker, G. H., & co.**
    Atlas of Attleboro' town, Mass.    80 pp. incl. 14 maps, 10 pl. fol. Boston, G. H. Walker & co. 1880.        1850

**Massachusetts.** *Topographical survey commission.*
    Atlas of the boundaries of the town of Attleborough, Bristol county ...      5 p. l., [4], 8 l. incl. 3 maps, 1 pl. fol. [Boston] 1900.        1851

## BEVERLY.

**Hopkins, G. M.**
    Atlas of the town of Beverly, Mass.    55 pp. incl. 14 maps. fol. Philadelphia, G. M. Hopkins, 1880.        1852

**Walker, G. H.**
    Atlas of the city of Beverly, Essex county, Massachusetts. 1897 ...      2 p. l., 25 maps. fol. Boston, G. H. Walker & co. 1897.        1853

**Massachusetts.** *Topographical survey commission.*
    Atlas of the boundaries of the city of Beverly, Essex county. 5 p. l., 4, 9 l. incl. 3 maps, 1 pl. fol. [Boston] 1898.        1854

**Walker, G. H., & co.**
    Atlas of the city of Beverly, Essex county, Massachusetts. 1907. 2 p. l., 29 maps. fol. Boston, G. H. Walker & co. 1907.        1855

## BOSTON.

**Strauss, F. A.**
    Strauss' atlas of Boston & vicinity 1874–1875; a topographical and business guide of the city ...      cover-title, 24 pp. incl. 4 maps. 8°. [Boston] F. A. Strauss, 1874.        1856

**Hopkins, G. M.**
    Atlas of the county of Suffolk, Mass.    7 v. fol. Philadelphia, G. M. Hopkins, 1874–75.        1857

    City atlas of Boston, Mass.    1 p. l., 36 maps. fol. Philadelphia, G. M. Hopkins, 1882.        1858

**Bromley, G. W., & co.**
    Atlas of the city of Boston.    1 p. l., 21 maps. fol. Philadelphia, G. W. & W. S. Bromley, 1883.        1859

CONTENTS.
v. 1. City proper.

**Bromley, G. W.** *and* **Bromley, W. S.**
Atlas of the city of Boston, city proper. 2 v. 2 p. l., 33 maps; 2 p. l., 42 maps. fol. Philadelphia, G. W. Bromley & co. 1888. 1860

**Richards, L. J.**
Atlas of Dorchester, West Roxbury and Brighton, city of Boston. In 1 volume. Comprising forty-one plans compiled from official records, private plans and actual surveys, by a corps of twelve surveyors and draughtsmen. 3 p. l., 41 col. pls. fol. Boston, L. J. Richards, as. J. P. Brown & co. 1899. 1861

**Bromley, G. W.,** *and* **Bromley, W. S.**
Atlas of the city of Boston. Boston proper and Back Bay. From actual surveys and official plans . . . 2 p. l., 36 (*i. e.* 37) col. maps. fol. Philadelphia, G. W. Bromley & co. 1908. 1861a

### BOURNE.

**Massachusetts.** *Topographical survey commission.*
Atlas of the boundaries of the town of Bourne, Barnstable county . . . 4 p. l., 9 l. incl. 4 maps, 1 pl. fol. [Boston] 1899. 1862

### BRADFORD.

**Desmond, J. T.**
Atlas of Haverhill and Bradford, Mass. 88 pp. incl. 23 maps, 1 pl. fol. Boston, G. H. Walker & co. 1892. 1863

### BRIDGEWATER.

**Massachusetts.** *Topographical survey commission.*
Atlas of the boundaries of the town of Bridgewater, Plymouth county . . . 5 p. l., 11 l. incl. 4 maps, 2 pl. fol. [Boston] 1899. 1864

### BRIGHTON.

**Richards, L. J.**
Atlas of Dorchester, West Roxbury and Brighton, city of Boston. In 1 volume. Comprising forty-one plans compiled from official records, private plans and actual surveys, by a corps of twelve surveyors and draughtsmen. 3 p. l., 41 col. pls. fol. Boston, L. J. Richards, as. J. P. Brown & co. 1899. 1865

### BROCKTON.

**Hayward & Howard.**
Atlas of the city of Brockton, Mass. 2 p. l., 25 maps. fol. Brockton, Mass., Hayward & Howard, 1898. 1866

**Massachusetts.** *Topographical survey commission.*
Atlas of the boundaries of the city of Brockton, Plymouth county . . . 5 p. l., 4, 10 l. incl. 4 maps, 2 pl. fol. [Boston] 1898. 1867

## BROOKFIELD.

**Walker, G. H., & co.**
    Atlas of Brookfield, West Brookfield and North Brookfield towns, Mass.    83 pp. incl. 12 maps, 16 pl.    fol.    Boston, G. H. Walker & co. 1885.      1868

## BROOKLINE.

**Hopkins, G. M.**
    Atlas of the town of Brookline, Mass.    61 pp. incl. 15 maps. fol.    Philadelphia, G. M. Hopkins & co. 1874.      1869

    Atlas of the town of Brookline, Mass.    1 p. l., 21 maps.    fol. Philadelphia, G. M. Hopkins, 1884.      1870

## CAMBRIDGE.

**Hopkins, G. M.**
    Atlas of the city of Cambridge, Middlesex county, Mass.    69 pp. incl. 19 maps.    fol.    Philadelphia, G. M. Hopkins, 1873.      1871

    Atlas of the city of Cambridge, Mass.    1 p. l., 28 maps.    fol. Philadelphia, G. M. Hopkins, 1886.      1872

## CHELSEA.

**Massachusetts.** *Topographical survey commission.*
    Atlas of the boundaries of the city of Chelsea, Suffolk county . . .    4 p. l., 5 l. incl. 2 maps, 1 pl.    fol.    [Boston] 1898.      1873

## CHESHIRE.

**Miller, D. L.**
    Atlas of the towns of North Adams, Adams, Williamstown and Cheshire, Berkshire county, Mass.    80 pp. incl. 19 maps.    fol. New York, D. L. Miller & co. 1894.      1874

## DORCHESTER.

**Richards, L. J.**
    Atlas of Dorchester, West Roxbury and Brighton, city of Boston. In 1 volume. Comprising, forty-one plans compiled from official records, private plans and actual surveys, by a corps of twelve surveyors and draughtsmen. 3 p. l., 41 col. pls.    fol. Boston, L. J. Richards, as. J. P. Brown & co. 1899.      1875

## DUXBURY.

**Massachusetts.** *Topographical survey commission.*
    Atlas of the boundaries of the town of Duxbury, Plymouth county . . .    5 p. l., 10 l. incl. 4 maps, 2 pl.    fol.    [Boston] 1899.      1876

## EAST BRIDGEWATER.

**Massachusetts.** *Topographical survey commission.*
    Atlas of the boundaries of the town of East Bridgewater, Plymouth county . . .    4 p. l., 12 l. incl. 5 maps, 2 pl.    fol. [Boston] 1898.      1877

### EASTHAMPTON.

**Miller, D. L.**, *& others.*
    Atlas of the city of Northampton and town of Easthampton, Hampshire county, Massachusetts. From official records and surveys under the direction and personal supervision of D. L. Miller, c. e. assisted by L. E. Tenney, Roger H. Pidgeon, Thomas Flynn, F. Chester Hale, A. Y. Peck, L. E. Layman, A. B. Peck, W. H. Graves. 1 p. l., 18 maps. fol. Philadelphia, D. L. Miller & co. 1895.    1878

### EASTON.

**Massachusetts.** *Topographical survey commission.*
    Atlas of the boundaries of the town of Easton, Bristol county ... 5 p. l., 7 l. incl. 3 maps, 1 pl. fol. [Boston] 1899.    1879

### EVERETT.

**Walker, G. H., & co.**
    Atlas of the city of Everett, Middlesex county, Mass. 2 p. l., 23 maps. fol. Boston, G. H. Walker & co. 1896.    1880

**Massachusetts.** *Topographical survey commission.*
    Atlas of the boundaries of the city of Everett, Middlesex county ... 5 p. l., 11 l. incl. 4 maps, 2 pl. fol. [Boston] 1898.    1881

### FALL RIVER.

**Walker, G. H., & co.**
    Atlas of Fall River city, Mass. 1 p. l., 91 pp. incl. 19 maps, 10 pl. fol. Boston, G. H. Walker & co. 1883.    1882

### FITCHBURG.

**Miller, D. L.**, *& others.*
    Atlas of the city of Fitchburg, Worcester county, Massachusetts. From official records and surveys under the direction and personal supervision of D. L. Miller, c. e. assisted by L. E. Tenney, F. A. Tolman, H. W. Bowen, A. Y. Peck, W. H. Graves, L. E. Layman. 1 p. l., 11 maps. fol. New York, D. L. Miller & co. 1895.    1883

### GARDNER.

**Walker, O. W.**
    Atlas of Gardner town, Mass. 31 pp. incl. 7 maps, 6 pl. fol. Boston, O. W. Walker & co. 1886.    1884

### GLOUCESTER.

**Hopkins, G. M.**
    Atlas of the city of Gloucester and the town of Rockport, Mass. 1 p. l., 24 maps. fol. Philadelphia, G. M. Hopkins, 1884.    1885

### GREENFIELD.

**Walker, G. H., & co.**
    Atlas of Greenfield town, Mass. 29 pp. incl. 7 maps. fol. Boston, G. H. Walker & co. 1884.    1886

### HALIFAX.

**Massachusetts.** *Topographical survey commission.*
    Atlas of the boundaries of the town of Halifax, Plymouth county
. . .     5 p. l., 11 l. incl. 5 maps, 2 pl.   fol.   [Boston] 1899.    1887

### HANOVER.

**Massachusetts.** *Topographical survey commission.*
    Atlas of the boundaries of the town of Hanover, Plymouth county . . .     4 p. l., 8 l. incl. 3 maps, 1 pl.   fol.   [Boston] 1898.
    1888

### HANSON.

**Massachusetts.** *Topographical survey commission.*
    Atlas of the boundaries of the town of Hanson, Plymouth county
. . .     5 p. l., 14 l. incl. 5 maps, 2 pl.   fol.   [Boston] 1898.    1889

### HAVERHILL.
**Hopkins, G. M.**
    City atlas of Haverhill, Mass.    61 pp. incl. 15 maps.   fol.
Philadelphia, G. M. Hopkins, 1881.    1890

**Desmond, J. T.**
    Atlas of Haverhill and Bradford, Mass.    88 pp. incl. 23 maps, 1 pl.   fol.   Boston, G. H. Walker & co. 1892.    1891

### HOLYOKE.
**Walker, G. H., & co.**
    Atlas of Holyoke city, Mass.    45 pp. incl. 10 maps, 3 pl.   fol.
Philadelphia, G. H. Walker & co. 1884.    1892

### HULL.
**Walker, G. H., & co.**
    Atlas of the town of Hull, Plymouth county and part of the Jerusalem Road, Norfolk county, Massachusetts. From actual surveys and official plans.    1 p. l., 17 maps.   fol.   Boston, G. H. Walker & co. °1895.    1893

### KINGSTON.

**Massachusetts.** *Topographical survey commission.*
    Atlas of the boundaries of the town of Kingston, Plymouth county . . .     5 p. l., 11 l. incl. 4 maps, 2 pl.   fol.   [Boston] 1899.    1894

### LAKEVILLE.

**Massachusetts.** *Topographical survey commission.*
    Atlas of the boundaries of the town of Lakeville, Plymouth county . . .     5 p. l., 12 l. incl. 4 maps, 2 pl.   fol.   [Boston] 1899.    1895

## LAWRENCE.

**Hopkins, G. M.**
 City atlas of Lawrence, Mass. 75 pp. incl. 18 maps. fol. Philadelphia, G. M. Hopkins, 1875.    1896

## LEOMINSTER.

**Miller, D. L.**
 Atlas of the town of Leominster, Worcester county, Massachusetts. From official records and surveys under the direction and personal supervision of D. L. Miller, assisted by L. E. Tenney, Thomas Flynn, F. Chester Hale, C. A. Potts, A. Y. Peck, W. H. Graves, L. E. Layman, A. B. Peck. 1 p. l., 8 maps, 1 l. fol. New York, D. L. Miller & co. 1895.    1897

## LYNN.

**Hopkins, G. M.**
 City atlas of Lynn, Mass. 1 p. l., 20 maps. fol. Philadelphia, G. H. Hopkins, 1880.    1898

## MALDEN.

**Walker, G. H., & co.**
 Atlas of Malden city, Mass. 1 p. l., 151 pp. incl. 37 maps, 1 pl. fol. Boston, G. H. Walker & co. 1885.    1899

 Atlas of the city of Malden, Middlesex county, Mass. 2 p. l., 45 maps. fol. Boston, G. H. Walker & co. 1897.    1900

**Massachusetts.** *Topographical survey commission.*
 Atlas of the boundaries of the city of Malden, Middlesex county. 4 p. l., 10 l. incl. 4 maps 2 pl. fol. [Boston] 1898.    1901

## MANSFIELD.

**Massachusetts.** *Topographical survey commission.*
 Atlas of the boundaries of the town of Mansfield, Bristol county . . . 4 p. l., 8 l. incl. 3 maps, 1 pl. fol. [Boston] 1899.    1902

## MARBLEHEAD.

**Hopkins, G. M.**
 Atlas of Marblehead, Mass. 63 pp. incl. 15 maps. fol. Philadelphia, G. M. Hopkins, 1881.    1903

## MARION.

**Massachusetts.** *Topographical survey commission.*
 Atlas of the boundaries of the town of Marion, Plymouth county . . . 5 p. l., 11 l. incl. 4 maps, 2 pl. fol. [Boston] 1899.    1904

## MATTAPOISETT.

**Massachusetts.** *Topographical survey commission.*
 Atlas of the boundaries of the town of Mattapoisett, Plymouth county . . . 4 p. l., 8 l. incl. 3 maps, 1 pl. fol. [Boston] 1899.    1905

## MEDFORD.

**Massachusetts.** *Topographical survey commission.*
... Atlas of the boundaries of the city of Medford, Middlesex county ... 5 p. l., 14 l. incl. 6 map, 2 pl. fol. [Boston] 1898. 1906

## MELROSE.

**Massachusetts.** *Topographical survey commission.*
... Atlas of the boundaries of the city of Melrose, Middlesex county ... 4 p. l., 7 l. incl. 3 maps, 1 pl. fol. [Boston] 1898. 1907

**Walker, G. H., & co.**
Atlas of the town of Melrose, Middlesex county, Mass. 2 p. l., 14 maps. fol. Boston, G. H. Walker & co. 1899. 1908

## MIDDLEBOROUGH.

**Massachusetts.** *Topographical survey commission.*
Atlas of the boundaries of the town of Middleborough, Plymouth county ... 6 p. l., 17 l. incl. 6 maps, 2 pl. fol. [Boston] 1899. 1909

## MILTON.

**Walker, G. H., & co.**
Atlas of the town of Milton, Norfolk county, Mass. 1896. 2 p. l., 21 maps. fol. Boston, G. H. Walker & co. 1896. 1910

## NAHANT.

**Hopkins, G. M.**
Atlas of the town of Nahant, Mass. 1 p. l., 14 maps. fol. Philadelphia, G. M. Hopkins, 1880. 1911

## NEW BEDFORD.

**Walker, G. H., & co.**
Atlas of New Bedford city, Mass. 79 pp. incl. 16 maps, 12 pl. fol. Boston, G. H. Walker & co. 1881. 1912

## NEWTON.

**Beers, F. W.**
Atlas of the city of Newton, Mass. 119 pp. incl. 29 maps. fol. New York, F. W. Beers & co. 1874. 1913

**Hopkins, G. M.**
Atlas of the city of Newton, Middlesex county, Mass. 85 pp. incl. 23 maps. fol. Philadelphia, G. M. Hopkins & co. 1874. 1914

**Beers, J. B., & co.**
Atlas of the city of Newton, Mass. 2 p. l., 23 maps. fol. New York, J. B. Beers & co. 1886. **1915**

### NORTH ADAMS.

**Miller, D. L.**
    Atlas of the towns of North Adams, Adams, Williamstown and Cheshire, Berkshire county, Mass.   80 pp. incl 19 maps.  fol. New York, D. L. Miller & co. 1894.                          1916

### NORTHAMPTON.

**Walker, G. H,. & co.**
    Atlas of Northampton city, Mass.   45 pp. incl. 12 maps.  fol. Boston, G. H. Walker & co. 1884.                            1917

**Miller, D. L.**, *& others.*
    Atlas of the city of Northampton and town of Easthampton, Hampshire county, Massachusetts. From official records and surveys, under the direction and personal supervision of D. L. Miller, c. e. assisted by L. E. Tenney, Roger H. Pidgeon, Thomas Flynn, F. Chester Hale, A. Y. Peck, L. E. Layman, A. B. Peck, W. H. Graves.   1 p. l., 18 maps. fol. Philadelphia, D. L. Miller & co. 1895.                                                         1918

### NORTH ATTLEBOROUGH.

**Massachusetts.** *Topographical survey commission.*
    Atlas of the boundaries of the town of North Attleborough, Bristol county . . .   4 p. l., 6 l. incl. 2 maps, 1 pl.  fol. [Boston] 1900.                                                    1919

### NORTH BROOKFIELD.

**Walker, G. H., & co.**
    Atlas of Brookfield, West Brookfield and North Brookfield towns, Mass.   83 pp. incl. 12 maps, 16 pl.  fol. Boston, G. H. Walker & co. 1885.                                                    1920

### NORTON.

**Massachusetts.** *Topographical survey commission.*
    Atlas of the boundaries of the town of Norton, Bristol county . . . 5 p. l., 8 l. incl. 3 maps, 1 pl.  fol. [Boston] 1900.      1921

### NORWELL.

**Massachusetts.** *Topographical survey commission.*
    Atlas of the boundaries of the town of Norwell, Plymouth county . . .   4 p l., 8 l. incl. 3 maps, 1 pl.  fol. [Boston] 1899.                                                                 1922

### PITTSFIELD.

**Miller, D. L.**
    Atlas of the city of Pittsfield, Berkshire county, Massachusetts, including the village of Dalton, from official records and surveys under the direction and personal supervision of D. L. Miller.  1 p. l., 12 maps, 1 l.  fol.  New York, D. L. Miller & co. 1893.                                                                         1923

## PLYMOUTH.

**Massachusetts.** *Topographical survey commission.*
    Atlas of the boundaries of the town of Plymouth, Plymouth county . . . 5 p. l., 9 l. incl. 3 maps, 2 pl. fol. [Boston] 1899.
    1924

## PLYMPTON.

**Massachusetts.** *Topographical survey commission.*
    Atlas of the boundaries of the town of Plympton, Plymouth county . . . 4 p. l., 10 l. incl. 4 maps, 1 pl. fol. [Boston] 1899.
    1925

## QUINCY.

**Branch, E. W.**
    Atlas of the city of Quincy, Norfolk county, Massachusetts. Compiled from the latest official plans and original surveys . . . 2 p. l., 30 (*i. e.* 34) col. maps. fol. Quincy, Boston, E. W. Branch, 1907.
    1926

## RAYNHAM.

**Massachusetts.** *Topographical survey commission.*
    Atlas of the boundaries of the town of Raynham, Bristol county . . . 5 p. l., 17 l. incl. 7 maps, 3 pl. fol. [Boston] 1900. 1927

## REHOBOTH.

**Massachusetts.** *Topographical survey commission.*
    Atlas of the boundaries of the town of Rehoboth, Bristol county. 4 p. l., 8 l. incl. 3 maps, 1 pl. fol. [Boston] 1900. 1928

## REVERE.

**Massachusetts.** *Topographical survey commission.*
    Atlas of the boundaries of the town of Revere, Suffolk county . . . 4 p. l., 8 l. incl. 3 maps, 1 pl. fol. [Boston] 1898. 1929

**Whitman & Howard.**
    Atlas of the towns of Revere and Winthrop, Suffolk county, Massachusetts . . . 2 p. l., 27 maps. fol. Boston, Whitman & Howard, 1906.
    1930

## ROCHESTER.

**Massachusetts.** *Topographical survey commission.*
    Atlas of the boundaries of the town of Rochester, Plymouth county . . . 7 p. l., 22 l. incl. 7 maps, 5 pl. fol. [Boston] 1899.
    1931

## ROCKLAND.

**Sherman, W. A.,** *and* **Howland, C. W.**
    Atlas of Abington and Rockland. Mass. 42 pp. incl. 9 maps. fol. New York, Comstock & Cline, 1874.
    1932

**Massachusetts.** *Topographical survey commission.*
    Atlas of the boundaries of the town of Rockland, Plymouth county . . . 4 p. l., 8 l. incl. 3 maps, 1 pl. fol. [Boston] 1898.
    1933

### ROCKPORT.
**Hopkins, G. M.**
    Atlas of the city of Gloucester and the town of Rockport, Mass. 1 p. l., 24 maps. fol. Philadelphia, G. M. Hopkins, 1884.   1934

### SALEM.
**Hopkins, G. M., & co.**
    Atlas of the city of Salem, Mass. 82 pp. incl. 19 maps. fol. Philadelphia, G. M. Hopkins & co. 1874.   1935

### SEEKONK.
**Massachusetts.** *Topographical survey commission.*
    Atlas of the boundaries of the town of Seekonk, Bristol county . . . 5 p. l., 8 l. incl. 3 maps, 1 pl. fol. [Boston] 1900.
    1936

### SOMERVILLE.
**Hopkins, G. M., & co.**
    Atlas of the city of Somerville, Mass. 55 pp. incl. 13 maps. fol. Philadelphia, G. M. Hopkins & co. 1874.   1937

**Hopkins, G. M.**
    Atlas of the city of Somerville, Mass. 1 p. l., 16 maps. fol. Philadelphia, G. M. Hopkins, 1884.   1938

### SPENCER.
**Craig, G. A.**
    Atlas of Spencer town, Mass. 2 p. l., 11 maps, 3 pl. fol. Boston, G. H. Walker & co. 1884.   1939

### SPRINGFIELD.
**Walker, G. H.**
    Atlas of Springfield city, Mass. 65 pp. incl. 17 maps. fol. Boston, G. H. Walker & co. 1882.   1940

**Massachusetts.** *Topographical survey commission.*
    Atlas of the boundaries of the city of Springfield, Hampden county . . . 5 p. l., 8 l. incl. 3 maps, 1 pl. fol. [Boston] 1900.   1941

### STONEHAM.
**Massachusetts.** *Topographical survey commission.*
    Atlas of the boundaries of the town of Stoneham, Middlesex county . . . 5 p. l., 11 l. incl. 4 maps, 2 pl. fol. [Boston] 1899.   1942

## SWAMPSCOTT.

**Hopkins, G. M.**
    Atlas of the town of Swampscott, Mass.    2 p. l., 9 maps.   fol.
    Philadelphia, G. M. Hopkins, 1880.                              1943

## TAUNTON.

**Walker, G. H.**
    Atlas of Taunton city, Mass.    1 p. l., 66 pp. incl. 18 maps, 7 pl.   fol.   Boston, G. H. Walker & co. 1881.          1944

**Massachusetts.** *Topographical survey commission.*
    Atlas of the boundaries of the city of Taunton, Bristol county . . .    7 p. l., 23 l. incl. 9 maps, 3 pl.   fol.   [Boston] 1900.    1945

## WEST BRIDGEWATER.

**Massachusetts.** *Topographical survey commission.*
    Atlas of the boundaries of the town of West Bridgewater, Plymouth county . . .    4 p. l., 8 l. incl. 3 maps, 1 pl.   fol.   [Boston] 1898.                                                      1946

## WEST BROOKFIELD.

**Walker, G. H.**
    Atlas of Brookfield, West Brookfield and North Brookfield towns, Mass.    83 pp. incl. 12 maps, 16 pl.   fol.   Boston, G. H. Walker & co. 1885.                                                 1947

## WESTFIELD.

**Walker, G. H., & co.**
    Atlas of Westfield town, Mass.    45 pp. incl. 11 maps.   fol. Boston, G. H. Walker & co. 1884.                                               1948

## WEST ROXBURY.

**Richards, L. J.**
    Atlas of Dorchester, West Roxbury and Brighton, city of Boston. In 1 volume. Comprising, forty-one plans compiled from official records, private plans and actual surveys, by a corps of twelve surveyors and draughtsmen.    3 p. l., 41 col. pl.   fol.   Boston, L. J. Richards, as. J. P. Brown & co. 1899.              1949

## WHITMAN.

**Massachusetts.** *Topographical survey commission.*
    Atlas of the boundaries of the town of Whitman, Plymouth county . . .    4 p. l., 8 l. incl. 3 maps, 1 pl.   fol.   [Boston] 1898.      1950

## WILLIAMSTOWN.

**Miller, D. L.**
Atlas of the towns of North Adams, Adams, Williamstown and Cheshire, Berkshire county, Mass.   80 pp. incl. 19 maps.  fol. New York, D. L. Miller & co. 1894.   1951

## WINCHENDON.

**Walker, O. W., & co.**
Atlas of Winchendon town, Mass.   63 pp. incl. 10 maps, 12 pl. fol. Boston, O. W. Walker & co. 1886.   1952

## WINCHESTER.

**Massachusetts.** *Topographical survey commission.*
Atlas of the boundaries of the town of Winchester, Middlesex county . . . 4 p. l., 11 l. incl. 4 maps, 2 pl. fol. [Boston] 1899.
1953

## WINTHROP.

**Massachusetts.** *Topographical survey commission.*
Atlas of the boundaries of the town of Winthrop, Suffolk county . . .   3 p. l., 4 l. incl. 2 maps.  fol.  [Boston] 1898.   1954

**Whitman & Howard.**
Atlas of the towns of Revere and Winthrop, Suffolk county, Massachusetts . . .   2 p. l., 27 maps.  fol.  Boston, Whitman & Howard 1906.   1955

## WOBURN.

**Hopkins, G. M.**
Atlas of the town of Woburn, Mass.   67 pp. incl. 17 maps, 1 map at end.  fol.  Philadelphia, G. M. Hopkins & co. 1875.   1956

**Massachusetts.** *Topographical survey commission.*
Atlas of the boundaries of the city of Woburn, Middlesex county . . . 5 p. l., 13 l. incl. 4 maps, 2 pl. fol. [Boston] 1899.
1957

## WORCESTER.

**Beers, F. W., & *others*.**
Atlas of the city of Worcester, Worcester county, Mass.   33 pp. incl. 19 maps.  fol.  New York, F. W. Beers & co. 1870.
1958

**Hopkins, G. M.**
Atlas of the city of Worcester, Mass.   1 p. l., 29 maps.  fol. Philadelphia, G. M. Hopkins, 1886.   1959

## MICHIGAN.

### State.

#### 1873

**Walling, H. F.**
Atlas of the state of Michigan; including statistics and descriptions of its topography, hydrography, climate, natural and civil history, railways, educational institutions, material resources, etc. by Alexander Winchel, C. I. Walker, Oramel Hosford, Henry M. Utley and Ray Haddock. 162 pp. incl. 84 maps. fol. Detroit, R. M. & S. T. Tackabury [1873] 1960

#### 1908

**Cram, G. F.**
Cram's superior reference atlas of Michigan and the world. 160 pp incl. 68 col. maps, 3 pl., illus. fol. New York, Chicago, G. F. Cram, ᶜ1908. 1960a

### Counties.

#### ALLEGAN.

**Lake, D. J., & others.**
Atlas of Allegan county, Mich. From actual surveys. 81 pp. incl. 33 maps, 2 maps at end. fol. Philadelphia, C. O. Titus, 1873. 1961

#### ANTRIM.

**Pond, S. E.**
The official atlas and directory of Antrim county, Mich. Drawings by Charles M. Beers. 88 pp. incl. 29 maps. fol. Philadelphia, S. E. Pond & co. 1897. 1962

#### BARRY.

**Ogle, G. A., & co.**
Standard atlas of Barry county, Michigan, including a plat book of the villages, cities and townships of the county. 3–90, viii pp. incl. 29 maps, 8 pl. fol. Chicago, G. A. Ogle & co. 1895. 1963

#### BRANCH.

**Lake, D. J., & others.**
Atlas of Branch county, Mich. From actual surveys. 65 pp. incl. 28 maps, 2 maps at end. fol. Philadelphia, C. O. Titus, 1872. 1964

#### CALHOUN.

**Beers, F. W.**
Atlas of Calhoun county, Mich. 91 pp. incl. 37 maps. fol. New York, F. W. Beers & co. 1873. 1965

## CASS.

**Lake, D. J.,** & others.
    Atlas of Cass county, Mich. From actual surveys. 54 pp. incl. 20 maps, 2 maps at end. fol. Philadelphia, C. O. Titus, 1872.
    1966

**Ogle, G. A., & co.**
    Standard atlas of Cass county, Michigan, including a plat book of the villages, cities and townships of the county. 3–75, viii pp. incl. 29 maps. fol. Chicago, G. A. Ogle & co. 1896.
    1967
    NOTE.—pp. 76–77: Reference directory of Cass county, wanting.

## GENESEE.

**Beers, F. W.**
    Atlas of Genesee county, Mich. 119 pp. incl. 42 maps. fol. New York, F. W. Beers & co. 1873.
    1968

## GRAND TRAVERSE.

**Hayes, E. L.**
    Atlas of Grand Traverse county, Mich., to which is added a township map of Michigan, a railroad map of the United States and map of the world. 50, i–viii pp. incl. 19 maps. fol. Philadelphia, C. O. Titus, 1881.
    1969

**Pond, S. E., & co.**
    New Atlas and directory of Grand Traverse county, Michigan. Drawings, descriptive text &c. by hon. George E. Steele, assisted by . . . Chas. M. Beers . . . 108 pp. incl. 24 maps. fol. Traverse City, Mich., S. E. Pond & co. 1895.
    1970

## GRATIOT.

**National publishing co.**
    Imperial atlas of Gratiot county, Mich. Drawn from original surveys and field notes, official county records and other authentic sources. 66, 32 pp. incl. 29 maps, 1 map in pocket. fol. Boston, national publishing co. 1901.
    1971

## HILLSDALE.

**American atlas co.**
    Plat book of Hillsdale county, Michigan. 3–90 pp. incl. 33 maps. fol. Chicago, the american atlas co. 1894.
    1972

## INGHAM.

**Beers, F. W.**
    County atlas of Ingham, Mich. 104 pp. incl. 40 maps. fol. New York, F. W. Beers & co. 1874.
    1973

## IONIA.

**Beers, F. W.**
    Atlas of Ionia county, Mich. 108 pp. incl. 37 maps. fol. New York, F. W. Beers & co. 1875.
    1974

**Crawford, D. C.**
    Atlas of Ionia county, Mich.    103 pp. incl. 36 maps. fol. New York, J. B. Beers & co. 1891.    1975

### ISABELLA.
**Hayes, E. L.**
    Atlas of Isabella county, Mich., to which is added a township map of Michigan, a railroad map of the United States and map of the world.    50 i–viii pp. incl. 25 maps, 1 pl. fol. Philadelphia, C. O. Titus, 1879.    1976

### JACKSON.
**Everts & Stewart.**
    Combination atlas map of Jackson county, Michigan.    144 pp. incl. maps, illus. fol. Chicago, Everts & Stewart, 1874.    1977
    NOTE.—Pagination irregular.

### KALAMAZOO.
**Beers, F. W.**
    Atlas of Kalamazoo county, Mich.    95 pp. incl. 36 maps. fol. New York, F. W. Beers & co. 1873.    1978

### KENT.
**Belden, H., & co.**
    Illustrated historical atlas of the county of Kent, Michigan.    92 pp. incl. maps, illus. fol. Chicago, H. Belden & co. 1876.    1979

**Polk, R. L., & co.**
    R. L. Polk & co.'s illustrated historical atlas of Kent county, Mich.    56 pp. incl. 34 maps. fol. Grand Rapids, R. L. Polk & co. 1894.    1980

    R. L. Polk & co's illustrated historical atlas of Grand Rapids and Kent county, Mich.    86 pp. incl. 61 maps. fol. Grand Rapids, R. L. Polk & co. 1894.    1981

### LAPEER.
**Beers, F. W.**
    Atlas of Lapeer county, Mich.    77 pp. incl. 38 maps. fol. New York, F. W. Beers & co. 1874.    1982

### LEELANAU.
**Hayes, E. L.**
    Atlas of Leelanau county, Mich.    37 pp. incl. 14 maps. 4 maps at end. fol. Philadelphia, C. O. Titus, 1881.    1983

### LENAWEE.
**Everts & Stewart.**
    Combination atlas map of Lenawee county, Mich. Compiled, drawn and published from personal examinations and surveys. 1 p. l., 113 pp. incl. 22 maps, 82 pl. fol. Chicago, Everts & Stewart, 1874.    1984
    NOTE.—Pagination includes fractional numbers.

**Treat bros.**
    Pocket atlas of Lenawee county, 1906.    cover-title, 24 maps. nar. 4°.  Adrian, Mich., Treat bros. °1906.    1985

## LIVINGSTON.
**Beers, F. W.**
    Atlas of Livingston county, Mich.    86 pp. incl. 30 maps.  fol. New York, F. W. Beers & co. 1875.    1986

## MECOSTA.
**Hayes, E. L.**
    Atlas of Mecosta county, Mich. . . . to which is added a township map of Michigan, a railroad map of the United States & map of the world.  62, i–viii pp. incl. 28 maps.  fol.  Philadelphia, C. O. Titus, 1879.    1987

## MONROE.
**Bartlett, S. M.**
    County atlas of Monroe, Mich.    130 pp. incl. 33 maps, 21 pl. fol.  New York, F. W. Beers & co. 1876.    1988

**Ogle, G. A., & co.**
    Standard atlas of Monroe county, Michigan. Including a plat book of the villages, cities and townships of the county. Map of the state, United States and world. Farmers directory, reference business directory and departments devoted to general information. Analysis of the system of U. S. land surveys, digest of the system of civil government etc. etc.  2 p. l., 7–82, viii, x–xxii pp. incl. 24 maps, 1 map in text.  fol.  Chicago, G. A. Ogle & co. 1896.    1989

## MUSKEGON.
**Beers, F. W.**
    County atlas of Muskegon, Mich.    114 pp. incl. 38 maps.  fol. New York, F. W. Beers & co. 1877.    1990

**Ogle, G. A., & co.**
    Standard atlas of Muskegon county, Mich., including a plat book of the villages, cities and townships of the county, map of the state, United States and world, etc. etc.  2 p. l., 7–103, xxii pp. incl. 33 maps, 4 pl.  fol.  Chicago, G. A. Ogle & co. 1900.    1991

## NEWAYGO.
**Hayes, E. L.**
    Atlas of Newaygo county, Mich., to which is added to township map of Michigan, a railroad map of the United States and map of the world.  71, i–viii pp. incl. 33 maps.  fol.  Philadelphia, C. O. Titus, 1880.    1992

**Ogle, G. A., & co.**

    Standard atlas of Newaygo county, Michigan. Including a plat book of the villages, cities and townships of the county. Map of the state, United States and world. Patrons directory, reference business directory and departments devoted to general information. Analysis of the system of U. S. land surveys, digest of the system of civil government, etc. etc.    2 p. l., 8–75, [21], viii, x–xxii pp. incl. 31 maps, 3 pl., 1 map in text.    fol.    Chicago, G. A. Ogle & co. 1900.    1993

## OAKLAND.

**Beers, F. W.**

    Atlas of Oakland county, Mich.    141 pp. incl. 55 maps.    New York, F. W. Beers & co. 1872.    1994

## OSCEOLA.

**Hayes, E. L.**

    Atlas of Osceola county, Mich., to which is added a township map of Michigan, a railroad map of the United States and map of the world.    60, i–viii pp. incl. 27 maps.    fol.    Philadelphia, C. O. Titus, 1878.    1995

## ST. CLAIR.

**Ogle, G. A., & co.**

    Standard atlas of St. Clair county, Michigan. Including a plat book of the villages, cities and townships of the county. Map of the state, United States and world. Farmers directory, reference business directory and departments devoted to general information. Analysis of the system of U. S. land surveys, digest of the system of civil government, etc. etc.    2 p. l., 7–115, [1], viii, x–xxii pp. incl. 34 maps, 5 pl. 1 map in text.    fol.    Chicago, G. A. Ogle & co. 1897.    1996

## ST. JOSEPH.

**Noll, E. P., & co.**

    Property atlas of St. Joseph county, Michigan.    1 p. l., 44 pp. incl. 31 maps.    fol.    Philadelphia, E. P. Noll & co. 1893.    1997

## SANILAC.

**Cookingham, E. R.**

    Atlas of Sanilac county, Michigan, containing maps of every township in the county, with village and city plats and outline map of the county, also maps of Michigan, United States and the world. Compiled from late and authentic sources, together with other valuable information . . .    117, [11] pp. incl. 44 maps.    fol.    Philadelphia, J. L. Smith, 1894.    1998

    Note.—Pagination irregular.

## SHIAWASSEE.

**Beers, F. W.**

    County atlas of Shiawassee county, Mich.    102 pp. incl. 37 maps.    fol.    New York, F. W. Beers & co. 1875.    1999

## WASHTENAW.

**Everts & Stewart.**
Combination atlas map of Washtenaw county, Mich. Compiled, drawn and published from personal examinations and surveys. 6 p. l., 15–124, [2] pp. incl. 30 maps, 57 pl. fol. Chicago, Everts & Stewart, 1874. 2000
NOTE.—Imperfect, pp. 65–66, 79–80 wanting.

## WAYNE.

**Belden, H., & co.**
Illustrated historical atlas of the county of Wayne, Mich. 79 pp. incl. 24 maps, 25 pl. fol. Chicago, H. Belden & co. [187–] 2001

**Sauer, W. C.**
Detailed official atlas of Wayne county, Michigan. Containing general maps of Wayne county and city of Detroit, general township maps on a scale of two and a half inches to one mile, showing areas of lands and owners' names, rail roads, electric car lines, wagon roads, streams, drains, location of school houses, churches, cemeteries, etc., and detail plats of the city of Wyandotte and all interior villages on a scale as shown on each map; also sundry details showing all subdivisions outside the incorporated villages and an alphabetically arranged index for reference to locating subdivisions. Compiled and drawn from authentic records and private surveys . . . 2 p. l., 44 maps. fol. [Detroit] W. C. Sauer [1905] 2002

### Cities.

#### DETROIT.

**Robinson, E., *and* Pidgeon, R. H.**
Atlas of the city of Detroit and suburbs, embracing portions of Hamtramck, Springwells and Greenfield townships, Wayne county, Mich. 1 p. l., 30 maps. fol. New York, E. Robinson, 1885. 2003

**Baist, G. W.**
Baist's real estate atlas of surveys of Detroit, Mich. . . . Compiled and published from official records, private plans and actual surveys . . . 1 p. l., 33 maps. fol. Philadelphia, G. W. Baist, 1906. 2004

#### GRAND RAPIDS.

**Polk, R. L., & co.**
R. L. Polk & co's illustrated historical atlas of Grand Rapids and Kent county, Mich. 86 pp. incl. 61 maps. fol. Grand Rapids, Mich., R. L. Polk & co. 1894. 2005

## MINNESOTA.

### GEOLOGICAL.

**United States.** *Department of the Interior. Geological survey.*
Atlas to accompany monograph XLV on the Vermilion iron-bearing district of Minnesota, by J. Morgan Clements. 3 p. l., 23 maps. fol. Washington, 1903.
[57th Cong., 2d sess. House. Doc. no. 433] 2006

NOTE.—At head of title: Department of the interior, United States geological survey, Charles D. Walcott, director.

### GEOLOGICAL.

### LAKES.

**Woodman, P. M.**
Woodman's Minnetonka map-directory 1908 . . . 5 p. l., 63 pp. incl. 15 maps. 1 fold. map. 8°. Minneapolis, Woodman publishing co. 1908. 2006a

NOTE—Folded map in pocket.

### State.

#### 1874

**Andreas, A. T.**
An illustrated historical atlas of the state of Minnesota. 272, [27] pp. incl. 76 maps, 107 pl. fol. Chicago, A. T. Andreas, 1874.
2007

NOTE.—Pagination irregular.

#### 1875

**Wheeler, E. A.**
Minnesota: its geography, history, and resources. A text book for schools, with a manual of methods in general geography, for the use of teachers. 4 p. l., 78 pp. incl. 3 maps. 8°. St. Paul, D. D. Merrill [1875] 2008

#### 1907

**Cram, G. F.**
Cram's superior reference atlas of Minnesota and the world. 160, [2] pp., front., incl. 68 maps, 31 pl. fol. New York, Chicago, G. F. Cram, ᶜ1907. 2009

NOTE.—pp. 136–160 relate to Minnesota.

#### 1907

**Rand, McNally & co.**
New atlas of the state of Minnesota. 100 pp. incl. 42 maps, 3 pl., 3 tab., 1 fac-sim., 2 fold. maps. fol. Chicago–New York, Rand, McNally & co. 1907. 2010

NOTE.—Copyright 1906.
pp. 53–59 relate to Minnesota.

## Counties.

### BROWN.

**Polk, R. L., & co.**
The county of Brown, Minnesota, 1905. Topographical, historical, pictorial, miscellaneous. 1 p. l., 7–[52], [55]–112, viii, x–xxii pp. incl. 28 maps, 21 pl., 1 map in text. fol. St. Paul, R. L. Polk & co. 1905. 2011

### CHIPPEWA.

**Northwest publishing co.**
Plat book of Chippewa county, Minnesota. Compiled from county records and actual surveys. 45 pp. incl. 24 maps. fol. [Minneapolis] the northwest publishing co. 1900. 2012

### CHISAGO.

**Foote, C. M., *and* Hood, E. C.**
Plat book of Chisago county. Minn. Drawn from actual surveys and the county records. 38 pp. incl. 21 maps. fol. Minneapolis, C. M. Foote & co. 1888. 2013

### COTTONWOOD.

**Gibson, A.**
Plat book of Cottonwood county, Minnesota. Compiled and published by Arthur Gibson. 82 pp. incl. 24 maps, 11 pl. fol. St. Paul, Minn., the pioneer press co. 1896. 2014
   NOTE.—Pagination irregular.

### DAKOTA.

**Pinkney, B. F.**
Plat book of Dakota county, Minnesota. Drawn from actual surveys and county records . . . 1 p. l., 55 pp. incl. 34 maps. fol. Philadelphia, the union publishing co. 1896. 2015

### DODGE.

**Polk, R. L., & co.**
The county of Dodge, Minnesota, 1905. Topographical, historical, pictorial, miscellaneous. 129 pp. incl. 22 maps, 28 pl. fol. St. Paul, R. L. Polk & co. 1905. 2016

### FREEBORN.

**Union publishing co.**
Plat book of Freeborn county, Minnesota. Drawn from actual surveys and county records. 55 pp. incl. 32 maps. fol. Philadelphia, the union publishing co. 1895. 2017

### GOODHUE.

**Foote, C. M., *and* Henion, J. W.**
Plat book of Goodhue county, Minn. Drawn from actual surveys and the county records. 58 pp. incl. 33 maps. fol. Minneapolis, Minn., C. M. Foote & co. 1894. 2018

## GRANT.

**Ogle, G. A. & co.**
 Standard atlas of Grant county, Minnesota. Including a plat book of the villages, cities and townships of the county. Map of the state, United States and world. Patrons directory, reference business directory and departments devoted to general information. Analysis of the system of U. S. land surveys, digest of the system of civil government, etc. etc.   2 p. l., 7–47, [19], viii, x–xxii pp. incl. 23 maps, 1 map in text, 2 pl.   fol.   Chicago, G. A. Ogle & co. 1900.    2019

## HENNEPIN.

**Dahl, P. M.**
 Plat book of Hennepin county, Minn. Compiled and drawn from official records and actual surveys.   2 p. l., 77 pp. incl. 62 maps. fol.   Minneapolis, the northwestern map publishing co. 1898.
   2020

## HOUSTON.

**Warner, G. E.,** *and* **Foote, C. M.**
 Plat book of Houston county, Minn. Drawn from actual surveys and the county records.   46 pp. incl. 23 maps. fol.   Philadelphia, Warner & Foote, 1878.    2021

**Ogle, G. A., & co.**
 Standard atlas of Houston county, Minnesota, including a plat book of the villages, cities and townships of the county.   3–86, viii, x–xxii pp. incl. 26 maps. fol.   Chicago, G. A. Ogle & co. 1896.    2022

## KANDIYOHI.

**Northwest publishing co.**
 Plat book of Kandiyohi county, Minnesota. Compiled by Brown & Wright.   29, 33–73, 77–84 pp. incl. 29 maps. fol.   [Philadelphia] northwest publishing co. 1886.    2023
  Note.—Pagination irregular.

## LE SUEUR.

**Northwest publishing co.**
 Plat book of Le Sueur county, Minn. Drawn from actual surveys and county records.   51 pp. incl. 26 maps, 1 map loose. fol.   [Philadelphia?] the northwest publishing co. 1898.   2024

## LYON.

**Northwest publishing co.**
 Plat book of Lyon county, Minn., compiled from county records and actual surveys.   2 p. l., 4–54 pp. incl. 35 maps. fol.   Minneapolis, the northwest publishing co. 1902.    2025

## McLEOD.

**Ogle, G. A., & co.**
Standard atlas of McLeod county, Minnesota. Including a plat book of the villages, cities and townships of the county. Map of the state, United States and world. Patrons directory, reference business directory and departments devoted to general information. Analysis of the system of U. S. land surveys, digest of the sytem of civil government, etc. etc. 2 p. l., 7–49, [19], viii, x–xxii pp. incl. 22 maps, 2 pl., 1 map in text. fol. Chicago, G. A. Ogle & co. 1898. 2026

## MEEKER.

**Pinkney & Brown.**
Plat book of Meeker county, Minn. Compiled from official records and actual surveys. 50 pp. incl. 29 maps. fol. [Philadelphia] Pinkney & Brown, 1897. 2027

## MOWER.

**Ogle, G. A., & co.**
Standard atlas of Mower county, Minnesota, including a plat book of the villages, cities and townships of the county. 3–95, viii, x–xxii pp. incl. 35 maps, 3 pl. fol. Chicago, G. A. Ogle & co. 1896. 2028

## NICOLLET.

**Northwest publishing co.**
Plat book of Nicollet county, Minnesota. Compiled from county records and actual surveys. 45 pp. incl. 22 maps. fol. [Minneapolis] the northwest publishing co. 1899. 2029

## NORMAN.

**Hintze, L.**
Atlas of Norman county, Minnesota. 2 p. l., 28 maps. fol. Winona [Minn.] Jos. Leicht press [c1907] 2030

## OLMSTED.

**Warner, G. E.** *and* **Foote, C. M.**
Plat book of Olmsted county, Minn. Drawn from actual surveys and the county records. 42 pp. incl. 28 maps. fol. Philadelphia, Warner & Foote, 1878. 2031

**Ogle, G. A., & co.**
Standard atlas of Olmstead county, Minnesota, including a plat book of the villages, cities and townships of the county. 3–87, viii, x–xxii pp. incl. 33 maps. fol. Chicago, G. A. Ogle & co. 1896. 2032

## OTTERTAIL.

**Warner, G. E.** *and* **Foote, C. M.**
    Plat book of Otter Tail county, Minn. Drawn from actual surveys and the county records. 76 pp. incl. 64 maps. fol. Minneapolis, Warner & Foote, 1884.     2033

## POLK.

**Northwest publishing co.**
    Plat book of Polk county, Minnesota. Showing boundary of the proposed new county. 105 pp. incl. 81 maps. fol. Minneapolis, the Northwest publishing co. 1902.     2034

## RAMSEY.

**Hopkins, G. M.**
    Atlas of the environs of St. Paul, including the whole of Ramsey county, Minn. 1 p. l., 23 maps. fol. Philadelphia, G. M. Hopkins, 1886.     2035

**Dahl, P. M.**
    Plat book of Ramsey county, Minn. Compiled and drawn from official records and actual surveys. 2 p. l., 25 pp. incl. 16 maps. fol. Minneapolis, the Northwestern map publishing co. 1898.
[*With his* Plat book of Hennepin county, Minn. fol. Minneapolis, the northwestern map publishing co. 1898]     2036

## RENVILLE.

**Haynes, M. B.**
    Atlas of Renville county, Minn. Compiled from public and private records and personal examinations and surveys, to which are added maps of the state, United States and world. 3 p. l., 5–75 pp. 3 l., incl. 36 maps. fol. Mankato, Minn., M. B. Haynes. 1888.     2037

**Northwest publishing co.**
    Plat book of Renville county, Minnesota. Compiled from county records and actual surveys. 59 pp. incl. 41 maps. fol. [Minneapolis] the northwest publishing co. 1900.     2038

## RICE.

**Northwest publishing co.**
    Plat book of Rice county, Minn. Compiled from county records and actual surveys. 2 p. l., 6–46 pp. incl. 27 maps, 1 map loose. fol. [Philadelphia] the north west publishing co. 1900.     2039

## ROCK.

**Interstate publishing co.**
    Plat book of Rock county, Minnesota. 61 pp. incl. 16 maps. fol. [Boston & Chicago] interstate pub. co. 1886.     2040

## SHERBURNE.

**Northwest publishing co.**
Plat book of Sherburne county, Minnesota. Compiled from county records and actual surveys. 30, [12] pp. incl. 19 maps. fol. Minneapolis, the northwest publishing co. 1903. 2041

NOTE.—Accompanied by their Plat book of Benton county, Minnesota. Minneapolis, 1903.

## STEARNS.

**Foote, C. M., & co.**
Plat book of Stearns county, Minn. Compiled from official records and actual surveys. 90 pp. incl. 62 maps (1 map loose) fol. [Minneapolis?] Pinkney & Brown, 1896. 2042

## WABASHA.

**Ogle, G. A., & co.**
Standard atlas of Wabasha county, Minnesota, including a plat book of the villages, cities and townships of the county. 3–78, viii, x–xxii pp. incl. 31 maps, 4 pl. fol. Chicago, G. A. Ogle & co. 1896. 2043

## WASECA.

**Ogle, G. A., & co.**
Standard atlas of Waseca county, Minnesota, including a plat book of the villages, cities and townships of the county. 3–60, viii, x–xxii pp. incl. 22 maps. fol. Chicago, G. A. Ogle & co. 1896. 2044

## WILKIN.

**Northwest publishing co.**
Plat book of Wilkin county, Minnesota. Compiled from county records and actual surveys. 2 p. l., 52 pp. incl. 34 maps. fol. Minneapolis, the northwest publishing co. 1903. 2045

## WINONA.

**Bennett, L. G.,** *and* **Smith, A. C.**
Map of Winona county, Minn. 1867. 1 p. l., front., 21 maps, 17 pl. 4°. Chicago, lith. by C. Shober & co. 1867. 2046

**Foote, C. M.,** *and* **Henion, J. W.**
Plat book of Winona county, Minn. Drawn from actual surveys and county records. 60 pp. incl. 38 maps. fol. Minneapolis, Minn., C. M. Foote & co. 1894. 2047

## WRIGHT.

**Central publishing co.**
The standard township map and gazetteer of Wright county, Minn., showing all carriage roads, railroads, the legal description of every farm, the owner's name of every piece of land outside the

**Central publishing co.**—Continued.

village limits, with its assessed value, also value of the improvements, the boundaries of every school district, and the location of every school house and church; also a description of the business interests of every village in each township. The description of each piece of land has been carefully compared with the records, and this publication is absolutely correct.   2-44 pp. incl. 20 maps, 1 map at end.   sm.fol.   Minneapolis, the central publishing co. 1894.   2048

**Northwest publishing co.**

Plat book of Wright county, Minnesota. Compiled from county records and actual surveys.   56 pp. incl. 34 maps.   fol.   Minneapolis, the northwest publishing co. 1901.   2049

### YELLOW MEDICINE.

**Northwest publishing co.**

Plat book of Yellow Medicine county, Minn. Compiled from county records and actual surveys.   56 pp. incl. 36 maps.   fol.   [Philadelphia?] the northwest publishing co. 1900.   2050

### Cities.
### DULUTH.

**Roe, F. B.**

Atlas of the city of Duluth, St. Louis county, Minn., and vicinity. Embracing the corporations of West Duluth and Lakeside and the platted lands adjoining; also acreage maps of the territory in the state of Minnesota within a radius of about twelve miles, showing the property of the different land and improvement companies, etc., etc.   127 pp. incl. 31 maps.   fol.   Philadelphia, F. Roe, 1890.   2051

**Frank, C. P.**

C. P. Frank's atlas of the city of Duluth, Minn., complete in one volume. Compiled and drawn from official records, private plans and actual surveys.   3 p. l., 51 maps.   fol.   Duluth, C. P. Frank, 1902.   2052

### MINNEAPOLIS.

**Hopkins, G. M.**

A complete set of surveys and plats of properties in the city of Minneapolis, Minn.   1 p. l., 35 maps.   fol.   Philadelphia, G. M. Hopkins [1885]   2053

**Davidson, C. W.**

Davidson's atlas of the city of Minneapolis, Hennepin county, Minn.   1 p. l., 72 maps.   fol.   Minneapolis, C. W. Davidson, 1887.   2054

## ST. PAUL.

**Hopkins, G. M.**
Atlas of the city of St. Paul, Minn. 1 p. l., 31 maps. fol. Philadelphia, G. M. Hopkins [1884] 2055

Atlas of the environs of St. Paul, including the whole of Ramsey county, Minn. 1 p. l., 23 maps. fol. Philadelphia, G. M. Hopkins, 1886. 2056

**Curtice, D. L.**
Curtice's standard atlas of the city of St. Paul. This work containing 40 plates, each plate covering one and one-half congressional sections of land; embraces all the territory covered by the last edition of "Curtices standard map of the city of St. Paul," and also a large part of the city of south St. Paul, showing the location of recent improvements along the line of the Minnesota & Northwestern railway, and showing the location in colors of buildings, etc. 2 p. l., 41 maps. fol. St. Paul, D. L. Curtice [1887] 2057

**Donnelley, R. H.**
Donnelley's atlas of the city of St. Paul, Minn. Compiled from public records and surveys, by Roger H. Pidgeon, George E. Ryan, James P. Brown and Thomas F. Parry. Complete in two volumes. v. 2. 1 p. l., 26 maps. fol. Chicago, R. H. Donnelley, 1892.
2058

CONTENTS.

v. 2. Comprises all of the city, west of Rice street and Delaware avenue, and contains sections 20, 22, 23, 24, 25, 26, 27, 28, 29, 32, 33, 34, 35 and 36, all in town 29, range 23. Also sections 1, 2, 3, 4, 9, 10, 11, 12, 15, 16, and part of sections 5, 8, 14, 17, 20, 21, 22 and 23, all in town 28, range 23.

**Curtice, D. L.**
Curtice's revised atlas of the city of St. Paul. Published by the H. M. Smyth printing co. 1908, under the direction and supervision of C. L. Annan . . . 1 p. l., 40 (*i. e.* 41) maps. fol. [St. Paul] H. M. Smyth printing co. 1908. 2058a

NOTE.—First edition published by D. L. Curtice, 1887. This edition copyrighted by Mrs. D. L. Curtice.

## MISSOURI.

### GEOLOGICAL.

**Missouri.** *Geological survey.*
Report on the iron ores and coal fields, from the field work of 1872 . . . Atlas. 1 p. l., 10 maps, 4 diagr. obl. fol. New York, J. Bien, 1873. 2059

NOTE.—Printed by authority of the legislature of Missouri under the direction of the bureau of geology and mines. Atlas has title: . . . Atlas accompanying report on iron ores and coal fields.

**Broadhead, G. C.**
  Atlas accompanying reports of Missouri geological survey, 1874. C. C. Broadhead, state geologist.  cover-title, 12 maps, 3 pl.  fol. Jefferson City, Regan & Carter, 1874.  2060

### State.

#### 1873
**Campbell, R. A.**
  Campbell's new atlas of Missouri, with descriptions historical, scientific, and statistical.  Maps constructed and drawn on the polyconic projection.  Letter press articles by G. Engelmann, G. H. Swallow, J. P. Cadman, C. V. Riley, J. Monteith, William T. Harris, J. F. Wielandy, N. H. Parker and others.  2–116, [4], 27, [20] pp. incl. 32 maps. fol. St. Louis, R. A. Campbell, 1873. 2061

#### 1874
**Whipple, A.**
  A. Whipple & co's insurance maps, 2d series, special risks.  C. T. Anbin, civil engineer.  Rev. ed.  [v. 3]  196 pp. incl. 49 maps. obl. fol.  St. Louis, Mo., A. Whipple & co. [1874] 2062

#### 1876
  A. Whipple's insurance maps, 2d series, special risks.  Rev. ed. 196 pp. incl. 99 maps.  [v. 4]  obl. fol.  St. Louis, Mo., A. Whipple [1876] 2063

#### 1876
**Harrison & Warner.**
  Illustrated historical atlas of Adair county, Missouri, in connection with a general atlas of the United States and the state of Missouri.  2 p. l., [3]–54, 57–89 pp. incl. 35 maps.  fol. Philadelphia, Harrison & Warner, 1876. 2064

#### 1908
**Cram, G. F.**
  Cram's superior reference atlas of Missouri and the world.  160 pp. incl. 67 col. maps, 3 col. pl. (1 fold. map)  sm. fol.  New York, Chicago, G. F. Cram, ᶜ1908. 2065

### Counties.

#### ADAIR.
**Harrison & Warner.**
  Illustrated historical atlas of Adair county, Missouri, in connection with a general atlas of the United States and the state of Missouri.  2 p. l., [3]–54, 57–89 pp. incl. 35 maps. fol. Philadelphia, Harrison & Warner, 1876. 2066

**Ogle, G. A., & co.**
Standard atlas of Adair county, Missouri, including a plat book of the villages, cities and townships of the county. Map of the state, United States and world. Patrons directory, reference business directory and departments devoted to general information. Analysis of the system of U. S. land surveys, digest of the system of civil government, etc. etc. 2 p. l., 7–78, viii, x–xxii pp. incl. 27 maps, 4 pl. fol. Chicago, G. A. Ogle & co. 1898. 2067

### AUDRAIN.
**Northwest publishing co.**
Plat book of Audrain county, Missouri. Drawn from actual surveys & county records. 2 p. l., 2–49 pp. incl. 32 maps. fol. [Philadelphia] the northwest publishing co. 1898. 2068

### BARTON.
**Missouri publishing co.**
Plat book of Barton county, Missouri. Compiled from county records and actual surveys. 2 p. l., 2–47 pp. incl. 27 maps. fol. [Philadelphia] the Missouri publishing co. 1903. 2069

### BATES.
**Northwest publishing co.**
Plat book of Bates county, Missouri. Drawn from actual surveys and county records. 1 p. l., 67 pp. incl. 43 maps. fol. [Philadelphia?] the northwest publishing co. 1895. 2070

### BOONE.
**Northwest publishing co.**
Plat book of Boone county, Missouri. Compiled from county records and actual surveys. 2 p. l., 3–53 pp. incl. 29 maps. fol. [Philadelphia] the northwest publishing co. 1898. 2071

### CARROLL.
**Brink, McDonough & co.**
An illustrated historical atlas map of Carroll county, Mo. Carefully compiled from personal examinations and surveys. 5 p. l., 12–99 pp. incl. 27 maps, 19 pl. 2 maps at end. fol. [n. p.] Brink, McDonough & co. 1876. 2072

**Ogle, G. A., & co.**
Standard atlas of Carroll county, Missouri, including a plat book of the villages, cities and townships of the county. 3–98, viii, x–xxii pp. incl. 29 maps, 5 pl. fol. Chicago, G. A. Ogle & co. 1896. 2073

### CASS.
**Northwest publishing co.**
Plat book of Cass county, Missouri. Drawn from actual surveys & county records. 66 pp. incl. 35 maps. fol. [Philadelphia] the northwest publishing co. 1895. 2074

## CHARITON.

**Northwest publishing co.**
Plat book of Chariton county, Missouri. Drawn from actual surveys & county records by the Northwest publishing co. 1 p. l., 47, [13] pp. incl. 40 maps. fol. [Minneapolis] the northwest publishing co. 1897. 2075

## CLARK.

**Edwards brothers.**
An illustrated historical atlas of Clark county, Missouri. 52 pp. incl. 20 maps, 6 pl., 2 maps at end. fol. Philadelphia, Edwards bros. 1878. 2076

## DEKALB.

**Northwest publishing co.**
Plat book of De Kalb county, Missouri. Drawn from actual surveys & county records. 2 p. l., 2–42 pp. incl. 26 maps. fol. [Philadelphia] the northwest publishing co. 1897. 2077

## HENRY.

**Northwest publishing co.**
Plat book of Henry county, Missouri. Drawn from actual surveys & county records . . . 1 p. l., 63 pp. incl. 36 maps. fol. [Minneapolis] the northwest publishing co. 1895. 2078

## JASPER.

**Northwest publishing co.**
Plat book of Jasper county, Missouri. Drawn from actual surveys & county records. 61 pp. incl. 35 maps (3 folded maps) fol. Philadelphia, by F. Bourquin, 1895. 2079

## LAFAYETTE.

**Northwest publishing co.**
Plat book of Lafayette county, Missouri. Drawn from actual surveys & county records. 1 p. l., 56 pp. incl. 36 maps (1 map folded) fol. [Philadelphia] the northwest publishing co. 1897.
2080

## LAWRENCE.

**Edwards brothers.**
An illustrated historical atlas of Lawrence county, Missouri. 59 pp. incl. maps, illus. fol. Philadelphia, Edwards brothers, 1879. 2081

**Hovey, A. M.**
Atlas of Lawrence county, Missouri. Drawn from the county records and personal inspections. 1 p. l., 23 maps. fol. Chicago, Rand, McNally & co. 1900. 2082

## LEWIS.

**Edwards brothers.**
An illustrated historical atlas of Lewis county, Missouri. 52 pp. incl. 22 maps, 7 pl. fol. Philadelphia, Edwards bros. 1878.
2083

**Western atlas co.**
Atlas of Lewis county, Missouri. 1 p. l., i–xxii, 34 pp. incl. 19 maps. fol. Keokuk, Iowa, western atlas co. 1897. 2084

## LINCOLN.

**Ogle, G. A., & co.**
Standard atlas of Lincoln county, Missouri. Including a plat book of the villages, cities and townships of the county. Map of the state, United States and world. Patrons directory, reference business directory and departments devoted to general information. Analysis of the system of U. S. land surveys, digest of the system of civil government, etc. etc. 2 p. l., 7–76, viii, x–xxii pp. incl. 26 maps, 1 map in text, 2 pl. fol. Chicago, G. A. Ogle & co. 1899.
2085

## NODAWAY.

**Northwest publishing co.**
Plat book of Nodaway county, Missouri. Drawn from actual surveys & county records. 2 p. l., 87 pp. incl. 38 maps. fol. [Philadelphia] the northwest publishing co. 1893. 2086

## PETTIS.

**Northwest publishing co.**
Plat book of Pettis county, Missouri. Drawn from actual surveys & county records. 2 p. l., 2–55 pp. incl. 32 maps. fol. [Philadelphia] the northwest publishing co. 1896. 2087

## PIKE.

**Ogle, G. A., & co.**
Standard atlas of Pike county, Missouri, including a plat book of the villages, cities and townships of the county. Map of the state, United States and world. Patrons directory, reference business directory and departments devoted to general information. Analysis of the system of U. S. land surveys, digest of the system of civil government, etc. etc. . . . 2 p. l., 7–88, viii, x–xxii pp. incl. 27 maps, 2 pl. fol. Chicago, G. A. Ogle & co. 1899. 2088

## PLATTE.

**Ogle, G. A. & co.**
Standard atlas of Platte county, Missouri. Including a plat book of the villages, cities and townships of the county, map of the state, United States and world . . . 2 p. l., 78, viii, x–xxii pp. incl. 20 maps, 9 pl. fol. Chicago, G. A. Ogle & co. 1907. 2089

## RALLS.

**Edwards brothers.**
An illustrated historical atlas of Ralls county, Missouri. Compiled, drawn and published from personal examinations and surveys . . . 52, [4] pp. incl. 20 maps, 8 pl. fol. Philadelphia, Edwards brothers, 1878. 2090

**Carroll, S. S., & co.**
Atlas of Ralls county, Missouri. Compiled and drawn from personal examinations and surveys by S. S. Carroll & company, New London, Mo. 1904. 63 pp., 23 maps. fol. Des Moines, the Kenyon printing & manufacturing co. 1904. 2091
NOTE.—Copyrighted december 1903.

## RAY.

**Ogle, G. A., & co.**
Standard atlas of Ray county, Missouri, including a plat book of the villages, cities and townships of the county. 3–79, viii, x–xxii pp. incl. 24 maps, 3 pl. fol. Chicago, G. A. Ogle & co. 1897. 2092

## SALINE.

**Northwest publishing co.**
Plat book of Saline county, Missouri. Drawn from actual surveys & county records . . . 2 p. l., 2–63, [4] pp. incl. 49 maps. fol. [Minneapolis] the northwest publishing co. 1896. 2093

## SCHUYLER.

**Edwards brothers.**
An illustrated historical atlas of Schuyler county, Missouri. 47 pp. incl. 14 maps, 5 pl., 2 maps at end. fol. Philadelphia, Edwards bros. 1878. 2094

**Northwest publishing co.**
Plat book of Schuyler county, Missouri. Compiled from county records and actual surveys. 2 p. l., 3–21 pp., 7 l., 35–36 pp. incl. 19 maps. fol. [Philadelphia] the northwest publishing co. 1898. 2095

## SCOTLAND.

**Northwest publishing co.**
Plat book of Scotland county, Missouri. Compiled from county records and actual surveys. 2 p. l., 4–39 (*i. e.* 41) pp. incl. 20 maps. fol. [Minneapolis] the northwest publishing co. 1898. 2096

## SHELBY.

**Edwards bros.**
An illustrated historical atlas of Shelby county, Missouri. 2 p. l., 5–50 pp. incl. 18 maps, 7 pl. 1 map at end. fol. Philadelphia, Edwards bros. 1878. 2097

## Cities.

### EAST ST. LOUIS.

**Elliot, W. H. H.**
Official plat book. The city of East St. Louis and environs. Scale 100 ft. = 1 in. . . . 3 p. l., 49 maps. fol. [East St. Louis, W. H. H. Elliot] 1904.    2098
NOTE.—Blue print.

### KANSAS CITY.

**Hopkins, G. M.**
Atlas of the environs of Kansas City, in Jackson county, Missouri. 1 p. l., 15 maps. fol. Philadelphia, G. M. Hopkins, 1886.    2099

A complete set of surveys and plats of properties in the city of Kansas, Missouri. 1 p. l., 38 maps. fol. Philadelphia, G. M. Hopkins [1886]    2100

A complete set of surveys and plats of properties in the city of Kansas, Missouri. 2d. ed. 1 p, l., 37 maps. fol. Philadelphia, G. M. Hopkins [1887]    2101

A complete set of surveys and plats of properties of Kansas City, Missouri. 3d. ed. 1 p. l., 44 maps. Philadelphia, G. M. Hopkins [1891]    2102

**Tuttle, F. W.** *and* **Pike, D. W.**
Tuttle and Pike's atlas of Kansas City and vicinity. Edition of 1907. 2 p. l., 90 (*i. e.* 91) col. maps. fol. Kansas City, Mo., Tuttle & Pike, ᶜ1908.    2103

### SAINT JOSEPH.

**Floyd, W. H. jr., & co.**
Atlas of the city of Saint Joseph, Buchanan county, Missouri . . . 68 pp. incl. 17 maps. fol. St. Joseph, Mo., W. H. Floyd, jr. & co. 1884.    2104

### ST. LOUIS.

**Hopkins, G. M.**
Atlas of the city of St. Louis, Missouri. 1 p. l., 45 maps. fol. Philadelphia, G. M. Hopkins, 1883.    2105

**St. Louis plat and record co.**
Atlas of the city of St. Louis. 8 v. fol. St Louis, plat and record co. ᶜ1905.    2106

## NEBRASKA.

### State.

**1885**

**Everts & Kirk.**
 The official state atlas of Nebraska. 1 p. l., 207 pp. incl. 162 maps, 26 pl. fol. Philadelphia, Everts & Kirk, 1885. 2107

**1908**

**Cram, G. F.**
 Cram's superior reference atlas of Nebraska and the world. 162 pp. incl. 77 col. maps, 3 pl., illus. fol. New York, Chicago, G. F. Cram, ᶜ1908. 2107a

### Counties.

#### ANTELOPE.

**Ogle, G. A., & co.**
 Standard atlas of Antelope county, Nebraska, including a plat book of the villages, cities and townships of the county. Map of the state, United States and world. Patron's directory, reference business directory and departments devoted to general information, analysis of the system of U. S. land surveys, digest of the system of civil government, etc. etc. 2 p. l., 7–85, [1], viii, x–xxii pp. incl. 32 maps, 3 pl. fol. Chicago, G. A. Ogle & co. 1904. 2108

#### BOONE.

**Northwest publishing co.**
 Plat book of Boone county, Nebraska. Compiled from county records and actual surveys. 2 p. l., 2–51 pp. incl. 32 maps. fol. [Philadelphia] the northwest publishing co. 1899. 2109

#### FILLMORE.

**Alden publishing co.**
 Standard atlas of Fillmore county, Nebraska, including a plat book of the villages, cities and townships of the county, map of the state, United States and world, patrons directory, reference business directory and departments devoted to general information. Analysis of the system of U. S. land surveys, digest of the system of civil government, etc. etc. 2 p. l., 7–69, [3], viii, x–xxii pp., incl. 25 maps, 1 pl., 1 map in text. fol. Chicago, Alden publishing co. 1905. 2110

#### GREELEY.

**Ogle, G. A., & co.**
 Standard atlas of Greeley county, Nebraska, including a plat book of the villages, cities and townships of the county. Map of the state, United States and world. Patron's directory, reference business directory and departments devoted to general information.

Analysis of the system of U. S. land surveys, digest of the system of civil government etc. etc. . . . 1 p. l., 7–45, [9], vi, xii–xxii pp. incl. 21 maps. fol. Chicago, G. A. Ogle & co. 1904.  2111

## HAMILTON.
**Dunham, J. R.**
An atlas of Hamilton county, Nebraska. 64, [12] pp. incl. 24 maps, 2 pl. fol. Philadelphia, Griffing, Dixon & co. 1888.  2112

## HOLT.
**Ogle, G. A., & co.**
Standard atlas of Holt county, Nebraska, including a plat book of the villages, cities and townships of the county. Map of the state, United States and world. Patrons directory, reference business directory and departments devoted to general information. Analysis of the system of U. S. land surveys, digest of the system of civil government, etc. etc. 2 p. l., 7–85, [1], viii, x–xxii pp. incl. 20 maps, 2 pl. fol. Chicago, G. A. Ogle & co. 1904.  2113

## HOWARD.
**Northwest publishing co.**
Plat book of Howard county, Nebraska. Compiled from county records and actual surveys. 2 p. l., 2–46 pp. incl. 29 maps. fol. [Philadelphia] the northwest publishing co. 1900.  2114

## JEFFERSON.
**Northwest publishing co.**
Plat book of Jefferson county, Neb. Compiled from county records and actual surveys. 2 p. l., 2–54 pp. incl. 34 maps. fol. [Philadelphia] the northwest publishing co. 1900.  2115

## JOHNSON.
**Ogle, G. A., & co.**
Standard atlas of Johnson county, Nebraska. Including a plat book of the villages, cities and precincts of the county. Map of the state, United States and world. Patron's directory, reference business directory and departments devoted to general information. Analysis of the system of U. S. land surveys, digest of the system of civil government, etc. etc. Compiled by Geo. A. Ogle & co., assisted by W. L. Dunlap, county surveyor of Johnson county, Neb. 2 p. l., 8–64, [8], viii, x–xxii pp. incl. 15 maps, 1 map in text, 3 pl. fol. Chicago, G. A. Ogle & co. 1900.  ·2116

## KEARNEY.
**Sears, J. H.**
Historical atlas of Kearney county, Neb., with index to township maps. Compiled and drawn from official records and actual surveys. 91 pp. incl. 25 maps, 1 pl. fol. Minden, Neb., J. H. Sears, 1894.  2117

## MADISON.

**Northwest publishing co.**
Plat book of Madison county, Neb. Compiled from county records and actual surveys. 1 p. l., 46 pp. incl. 27 maps. (1 map loose) fol. [Philadelphia] the northwest publishing co. 1899.
2118

## MERRICK.

**Northwest publishing co.**
Plat book of Merrick county, Nebraska. Compiled from county records and actual surveys. 1 p. l., 48 pp. incl. 27 maps. fol. [Philadelphia] the northwest publishing co. 1899. 2119

## NANCE.

**Northwest publishing co.**
Plat book of Nance county, Nebraska. Compiled from county records and actual surveys. 2 p. l., 3–42 pp. incl. 23 maps. fol. [Philadelphia] the northwest publishing co. 1899. 2120

## NUCKOLLS.

**Northwest publishing co.**
Plat book of Nuckolls county, Neb. Compiled from county records and actual surveys. 2 p. l., 2–49 pp. incl. 31 maps. fol. [Philadelphia] the northwest publishing co. 1900. 2121

## OTOE.

**Munn, A. M.**
Munn's atlas of Otoe county, Neb. 2 p. l., 30 l. incl. 27 maps. fol. Chicago, Rand, McNally & co. 1902. 2122

## PLATTE.

**Northwest publishing co.**
Plat book of Platte county, Nebraska. Compiled from county records and actual surveys. 2 p. l., [2]–52 pp. incl. 32 maps. (1 fold. map loose.) fol. [Minneapolis] the northwest publishing co. 1899. 2123

## SALINE.

**Northwest publishing co.**
Plat book of Saline county, Neb. Compiled from county records and actual surveys. 2 p. l., 2–53 pp. incl. 32 maps. fol. [Minneapolis] the northwest publishing co. 1900. 2124

## STANTON.

**Northwest publishing co.**
Plat book of Stanton county, Nebraska. Compiled from county records and actual surveys. 1 p. l., 35 pp. incl. 19 maps. fol. [Minneapolis] the northwest publishing co. 1899. 2125

### THAYER.

**Northwest publishing co.**
Plat book of Thayer county, Nebraska. Compiled from county records and actual surveys. 2 p. l., 2–48, [1] pp. incl. 31 maps. fol. [Minneapolis] the northwest publishing co. 1900. 2126

### WAYNE.

**Northwest publishing co.**
Plat book of Wayne county, Nebraska. Compiled from county records and actual surveys. 1 p. l., 60 pp. incl. 26 maps. fol. [Minneapolis] the northwest publishing co. 1898. 2127

### WEBSTER.

**Northwest publishing co.**
Plat book of Webster county, Neb. Compiled from county records and actual surveys. 2 p. l., 2–49 pp. incl. 29 maps. fol. [Minneapolis] the north west publishing co. 1900. 2128

## Cities.

### OMAHA.

**Gibson, G. E.,** *and* **W.**
Map of Omaha and South Omaha, with additions thereto. 1 p. l., 31 maps. fol. Omaha, Neb., G. E. & W. Gibson [1887]
2129

**Hopkins, G. M.**
A complete set of surveys and plats of properties in the city of Omaha and environs, Neb. 1 p. l., 19 maps. fol. Philadelphia, G. M. Hopkins [1887] 2130

## NEVADA.

### GEOLOGICAL.

**Hague A.**
Atlas to accompany the monograph on the geology of the Eureka district, Nevada. 2 p. l., 11 maps. fol. Washington, J. Bien & co. 1883. 2131
[United States. Department of the interior. Geological survey]
NOTE.—House miscellaneous documents. 1st. sess., 52d cong. 1901–'92.

**United States.** *Department of the interior. Geological survey.*
Atlas to accompany the monograph of the geology of the Comstock lode and the Washoe district. By George F. Becker. 2 p. l., 19 col. maps. fol. Washington, J. Bien & co. New York, 1882. 2132

**Shearer, The W. H., publishing co.**
Atlas of the Goldfield, Tonopah and Bullfrog mining districts of Nevada. 3 p. l., 11–93 pp., 4 fold. maps. 8°. Chicago, Rand, McNally & co. 1905. 2133

### State.

#### 1908

**Cram, G. F.**
Cram's superior reference atlas of California, Nevada and the world. 164 pp., incl. 68 col. maps, 3 col. pl. 1 fold. map. fol. Chicago, New York, for E. A. Davis by G. F. Cram, ᶜ1908. 2134

## NEW HAMPSHIRE.

### GEOLOGICAL.

**New Hampshire.** *Geological survey.*
The geology of New Hampshire. A report comprising the results of explorations ordered by the legislature. C. H. Hitchcock, state geologist. . . . Atlas. 1 p. l., 9 maps, 2 pl., diagr. fol. Concord, E. A. Jenks, state printer, 1874–1878. 2135

> NOTE.—Atlas entitled: Atlas accompanying the report on the geology of New Hampshire. C. H. Hitchcock, state geologist. New York, J. Bien, 1878. Contains two important fac-similes:
> no. 1. A topographical map of the state of New Hampshire surveyed under the direction of Samuel Holland . . . 1784.
> " 2. Map of New Hampshire, by Philip Carrigan. 1816.

### State.

#### 1877

**Walling, H. F.,** *and* **Hitchcock, C. H.**
Atlas of the state of New Hampshire including statistics and descriptions of its topography, geology . . . 86 pp., 1 l. incl. 23 maps. fol. New York, Comstock & Cline [1877] 2136

#### 1892

**Hurd, D. H., & co.**
Town and city atlas of the state of New Hampshire. 2 p. l., 337 pp., front. incl. 260 maps, 35 pl. fol. Boston, D. H. Hurd & co. 1892. 2137

### Counties.

#### CHESHIRE.

**Rockwood, C. H.**
Atlas of Cheshire county, N. H. 2 p. l., 7–49 pp., 3 l. incl. 12 maps. fol. New York, Comstock & Cline, 1877. 2138

#### STRAFFORD.

**Sanford & Everts.**
Atlas of Strafford county, New Hampshire. From actual surveys . . . 74 pp. incl. 23 maps, 1 pl. fol. Philadelphia, Sanford & Everts, 1871. 2139

## Cities.

### MANCHESTER.

**Flynn, T.**
Atlas of the city of Manchester, New Hampshire. From official records, private plans and surveys . . .   1 p. l., 18 maps. fol. Philadelphia, D. L. Miller & co. 1886.   2140

## NEW JERSEY.

### COAST.

**Rose, T. F., Woolman, H. C.,** *and* **Price, T. T.**
Historical and biographical atlas of the New Jersey coast. Proposed, arranged and illustrated by T. F. Rose, surveys by H. C. Woolman, history and statistics by T. T. Price.   1 p. l., 372 pp. incl. 45 maps, 72 pl. fol. Philadelphia, Woolman & Rose, 1878.
2141

**Scarlett & Scarlett.**
Scarlett & Scarlett's fire map of the coast resorts of New Jersey. Monmouth county—Deal to Manasquan. v. 2.  1 p. l., 66 maps. fol. Newark, N. J., Scarlett & Scarlett, 1890.   2142

### State.

#### 1776–1782

**Hills, J.**
A collection of plan's &c. &c. &c. in the province of New Jersey. . . .  2 p. l., 20 maps on 15 l. fol. 1776–1782]   2143

> NOTE.—In manuscript. Maps showing sir Henry Clinton's operations in the Jerseys; by various draftsmen including John Hills, A. Dunham, J. Rue, J. Fisher, James Grant, T. Milliadge, B. Morgan, A. Sutherland, J. Williams, A. Dennis.
> Twelve of this collection are by John Hills. Some are signed, "Lieut. J. Hills, 23$^d$ reg$^t$" In the british army lists of 1781–84 is the following: "—— Hill, 23$^d$ reg$^t$ foot. America. 5 oct. 1781. Second lieut." Records of the 23$^d$ regt. after 1784 do not contain his name. It is probable that he settled in Philadelphia at the close of the revolution. "John Hills, surveyor and draftsman" appears in the Philadelphia directory from 1795 to 1817. The same John Hills made plans of the city of Philadelphia in 1796 and 1801–1807; that of 1796 being signed, "John Hills, surveyor and draughtsman."
> no. 14, a map of Monmouth county . . . is dedicated "To his excellency sir Henry Clinton . . . general and commander of his majesty's forces &c. &c. &c. in North America . . . by . . . Iohn Hills, afs$^t$ engineer."

CONTENTS.

no. 1. Plan of Perth Amboy from an Actual Survey [By James Grant]   9 x 8.
" 2. Sketch of Bonham Town [showing] Redoubts for its Defence in the Winter. 1776. 77. [By A. Sutherland]   7½ x 12.
" 3. Sketch of Brunswick [By A. Sutherland]   8½ x 10½.

**Hills, J.**—Continued.

  no. 4. Sketch of the Ground near M$^r$ Low's at Rariton Landing [By John Hills] 8½ x 10¼.
  "  5. Sketch of Haddonfield    March. 1778 [By John Hills] Scale 400 paces to an inch  6½ x 8½.
  "  6. Sketch of the Roads from Penny Hill to Black Horse through Mount Holly.  By I Hills June 1778  Scale 400 paces to an inch  19 x 27.
  "  7. Sketch of the Road from Black Horse to Crosswick.  By I Hills June 1778  Scale 400 paces to an inch  19 x 21½.
  "  8. Sketch of Allens Town June. 1778 [By John Hills] Scale 400 paces to an inch  8 x 7.
  "  9. Sketch of Part of the Road from Freehold to Middle Town shewing the Skirmish between the Rear of the British Army under the Command of his Excellency Gen! Sir Henry Clinton and the advanced Corps of the Rebel Army June 28. 1778.  By I Hills  Scale 400 paces to an inch  17¼ x 22¾.
  " 10. Sketch of Middle Town    June  [By John Hills]  Scale 400 paces to an inch  8 x 7½.
  " 11. A Map of Part of the Province of Jersey  [By Morgan, Williams, Dennis, Rue, Dunham, Taylor, Skinner, &c.]  Compiled from the Original Surveys.  By I. Hills Afs! Engineer 1781  N. B. The Doted [!] Red Line is the Line of March of the Royal Army under the Command of His Excellency Gen! Sir Henry Clinton K. B. &c &c &c 1778  20 x 27.
  " 12. A Map Somerset County [By B. Morgan] Reduced from the Original Survey  By I. Hills, Afs! Engineer  1781  19 x 26½.
  " 13. A Map Middlesex County [By A. Dunham and J. Rue] Reduced from the Original Survey.  By I Hills Afs! Engineer.  1781  24 x 27.
  " 14. A Map of Monmouth County [By I. Williams and A. Dennis]  Reduced from the Original Survey By I. Hills Afs! Engineer 1781 . . . 28½ x 53¼.
  " 15. A Sketch of the Northern Parts of New Jersey [By T. Milliadge] Copied from the Original By Lieu! I Hills 23$^d$ Reg! 1781  Scale 2 miles to an inch  38½ x 33.
  " 16. A Chart of Delaware Bay and River, from the Cape's to Philadelphia, being Part of the Province of New Jersey & Pennsylvania. [By Joshua Fisher] Copied from the Original By I. Hills 1777.  24 x 56
  " 17. Sketch of the Road from Paulus Hook and Hoboken to New Bridge  By I. Hills 1778  Scale 800 paces to an inch  28 x 23½.
  " 18. A Plan of Paulus Hook with the Road to Bergen and Parts adjacent in the Province of New Jersey.  Survey'd by I Hills Afs! Engineer 1781  Inset: A Plan of Paulus Hook shewing the Works erected for its Defence 1781-2  26¾ x 27½.
  " 19. Plan of Paulus Hook shewing the Works erected for its Defence 1781-2  Surveyd [!] By I Hills Lieu! in the 23$^d$ Reg! Scale 200 feet to an inch  18½ x 14.
  " 20. Plan of the Road from Elizabeth Town Point to Elizabeth Town Shewing the Rebel Works Raised for its Defence  Survey'd By I Hills Afsistant Eng! 1780  Scale 400 feet to an inch  17¼ x 27¼.

### 1872
**Beers, F. W.**

  State atlas of New Jersey.    122 pp. incl. 43 maps.  fol.  New York, Beers, Comstock & Cline, 1872                                     2144

## 1873

**Hopkins, G. M.**
Combined atlas of the state of New Jersey and the city of Newark. 120 pp. incl. 34 maps. fol. Philadelphia, G. M. Hopkins & co. 1873. 2145

## 1873

Combined atlas of the state of New Jersey and the county of Hudson. 1 p. l., 65 pp. incl. 51 maps. 2 maps at end. fol. Philadelphia, G. M. Hopkins, 1873. 2146

## 1884

**Meleney, C. E., and Griffin, W. M.**
Primary geography of the state of New Jersey, with a proposed course of study for primary and grammar schools. Teacher's ed. 28 pp. incl. 1 map. fol. Newark, N. J., advertiser printing house, 1884. 2147

## 1885

**Hopkins, G. M.**
Atlas of properties near the Philadelphia and Trenton railroad. Frankfort to Trenton. (New York div. Penn$^a$ r. r.) 1 p. l., 22 maps. fol. Philadelphia, G. M. Hopkins, 1885. 2148

## 1889

**New Jersey.** *Geological survey.*
Atlas of New Jersey. 2 p. l., 21 maps. fol. [New York] J. Bien & co. [1889] 2149

## 1891

**Bien, J. R., and Vermeule, C. C.**
Atlas of the metropolitan district and adjacent country comprising the counties of New York, Kings, Richmond, Westchester and part of Queens in the state of New York, the county of Hudson and parts of the counties of Bergen, Passaic, Essex and Union in the state of New Jersey; showing in a series of maps the relative geographical position, the topography, hydrography and economic features of this area. 2 p. l., 13 maps. fol. New York, J. Bien & co. 1891. 2150

## 1905

**Survey map company.**
Atlas of the state of New Jersey carefully compiled from official and private sources by Survey map company . . . A. L. Westgard, chief engineer. 1 p. l., 42 l. incl. 45 maps. fol. [New York] survey map co.$^c$ 1905. 2151

## Counties.

### BERGEN.

**Walker, A. H.**
Atlas of Bergen county, N. J.  167 pp. incl. 61 maps, 27 pl. fol. Reading, Pa. C. C. Pease [1876]  2152

### BURLINGTON.

**Scott, J. D.**
Combination atlas map of Burlington county, New Jersey. Compiled, drawn and published from personal examinations and surveys. 9 p. l., xiii–xxvii, 28–lxxxviii pp. incl. 35 maps, 22 pl. fol. Philadelphia, J. D. Scott, 1876.  2153

### ESSEX.

**Pidgeon, R. H.**
Atlas of Essex county, N. J.  169 pp. incl. 45 maps. fol. New York, E. Robinson, 1881.  2154

**Robinson, E.**
Robinson's atlas of Essex county, N. J.  1 p. l., 41 maps. fol. New York, E. Robinson, 1890.  2155

**Scarlett & Scarlett.**
Scarlett & Scarlett's fire map of Essex county, N. J. v. 5. fol. Newark, N. J., Scarlett & Scarlett, 1891.  2156

CONTENTS.

v. 5. Belleview, Bloomfield, Montclair, Caldwell.

**Mueller, A. H., & co.**
Atlas of Essex county, New Jersey . . . 3 v. fol. Philadelphia, A. H. Mueller & co. [1901]–1906.  2157

NOTE.—Title varies: [v. 1] Atlas of the city of Newark . . . comp. by E. Robinson and L. E. Tenney. 1901; [v. 2] Atlas of the Oranges . . . [by] E. Robinson. 1904; v. 3 Atlas of Essex county . . . comp. . . . [by] Ellis Kiser. 1906.

**Kiser, E.**
Atlas of Essex county, New Jersey . . . Compiled from actual surveys, official records and private plans under the direct management and supervision of Ellis Kizer . . . 2 p. l., 36 maps. fol. Philadelphia, A. H. Mueller & co. 1906.  2158

NOTE.—[v.] 3 of, Mueller, A. H., & co. Atlas of Essex county, New Jersey, 1901-6.

### GLOUCESTER.

**Everts & Stewart.**
Combination atlas map of Salem & Gloucester counties, New Jersey. Compiled, drawn and published from personal examinations and surveys. 86, [6] pp. incl. 32 maps, 23 pl. fol. Philadelphia, Everts & Stewart, 1876.  2159

## HUDSON.

**Hopkins, G. M.**
Combined atlas of the state of New Jersey and the county of Hudson, from actual survey, official records & private plans. 1 p. l., 169 pp incl. 53 maps. fol. Philadelphia, G. M. Hopkins & co. 1873. 2160

**Spielmann & Brush.**
Sanitary & topographical map of Hudson county, N. J. Prepared for the national board of health Washington, D. C. 1880. 1 p. l., 1 map on 8 sheets. fol. New York, Snyder & Black, 1880. 2161

Certified copies of original maps of Hudson county, New Jersey, filed in the register's office and elsewhere, together with certified copy of general index of all maps on file in register's office, previous to april 25th, 1881, and important notes and information regarding the same. v. 1. 34, 76 pp. incl. 47 maps. fol. Hoboken, N. J., Spielmann & Brush, 1882. 2162

**Hopkins, G. M., co.**
Atlas of Hudson county, New Jersey . . . volume one comprising Jersey City, volume two including balance of county. From official records, private plans and actual surveys . . . v. 1. fol. Philadelphia, G. M. Hopkins co. 1908. 2162a
  NOTE.—Collation: v. 1, 2 p. l., 33 (*i. e.* 34) col. maps.

## HUNTERDON.

**Beers, F. W.**
Atlas of Hunterdon county, N. J. 77 pp. incl. 26 maps. fol. New York, Beers, Comstock & Cline, 1873. 2163

## MERCER.

**Scarlett & Scarlett.**
Scarlett & Scarlett's fire map of Mercer county, N. J., including Trenton and suburbs. 2 p. l., 111 maps. fol. Scarlett & Scarlett, Newark, N. J., 1890. 2164

## MIDDLESEX.

**Everts & Stewart.**
Combination atlas map of Middlesex county, New Jersey. Compiled, drawn and published from personal examinations and surveys. 82 pp. incl. 23 maps, 18 pl. fol. Philadelphia, Everts & Stewart, 1876. 2165

## MONMOUTH.

**Beers, F. W.**
Atlas of Monmouth county, N. J. 121 pp. incl. 41 maps. fol. New York, Beers, Comstock & Cline, 1873. 2166

## MORRIS.

**Beers, F. W., Prindle, A. B.** & *others*.
    Atlas of Morris county, N. J.    31 pp. incl. 21 maps. 2 pl. at end.  fol.  New York, F. W. Beers, A. D. Ellis & G. G. Soule, 1868.    2167

**Robinson, E.**
    Robinson's atlas of Morris county, N. J.    2 p. l., 34 maps. fol.  New York, E. Robinson, 1887.    2168

## SALEM.

**Everts & Stewart.**
    Combination atlas map of Salem & Gloucester counties, New Jersey. Compiled, drawn and published from personal examinations and surveys.    86, [6] pp. incl. 32 maps, 23 pl.  fol.  Philadelphia, Everts & Stewart, 1876.    2169

## SOMERSET.

**Beers, F. W.**
    Atlas of Somerset county, N. J.    62 pp. incl. 19 maps.  fol. New York, Beers, Comstock & Cline, 1873.    2170

## WARREN.

**Beers, F. W.**
    County atlas of Warren, N. J.    92 pp. incl. 33 maps.  fol. New York, F. W. Beers & co. 1874.    2171

### Cities.

#### ATLANTIC CITY.

**Kiser, E.** *and* **Barthel, O.**
    Atlas of Atlantic City, New Jersey. Including South Atlantic City, Chelsea, Ventnor, Oberon and Longport. Compiled and drawn from official plans and actual surveys . . .    1 p. l., [3] pp., 20 maps.  fol.  Philadelphia, A. H. Mueller & co. 1896.    2172

**Lathrop, J. M.** *and* **Kiser, E.**
    Atlas of Atlantic City, city of Ventnor, South Atlantic city and borough of Longport, New Jersey. Compiled from actual surveys, official records and private plans . . .    2 p. l., 23 (*i. e.* 24) col. maps.  fol.  Philadelphia, A. H. Mueller, 1908.    2172a

#### BERGEN.

**Fowler, L. D.**
    Title and assessment map of that part of Jersey City which constituted the city of Bergen, prior to consolidation in 1870. From the records and verified by surveys 1882. Scale: 200 ft. = 1 inch. 6 sheets.  fol.  New York, L. D. Fowler [1883]    2173

## CAMDEN.

**Hopkins, G. M.**
 City atlas of Camden, N. J.   77 pp. incl. 19 maps. fol. Philadelphia, G. M. Hopkins, 1877.   2174

**Baist, G. W.**
 Atlas of the city of Camden, N. J.   1 p. l., 22 maps. fol. Philadelphia, G. W. Baist, 1886.   2175

 Baist's property atlas of the city of Camden, New Jersey, complete in one volume. Compiled and published from official records, private plans and actual surveys.   1 p. l., 19 maps. fol. Philadelphia, G. W. Baist, 1902.   2176

**Hopkins, G. M. co.**
 Atlas of the vicinity of Camden, New Jersey. From official records, private plans and actual surveys . . .   3 p. l., 34 (*i. e.* 35) col. maps. fol. Philadelphia, G. M. Hopkins co. 1907.   2177

## EAST NEWARK.

**Miller, D. L.**
 Atlas of the towns of Harrison and Kearny and the borough of East Newark, Hudson county, N. J. From official records, maps and surveys.   1 p. l., 8 maps. fol. Philadelphia, D. L. Miller & co. 1903.   2178

## EAST ORANGE.

**Hopkins, G. M.**
 Atlas of the town of East Orange, N. J.   81 pp. incl. 21 maps. fol. Philadelphia, G. M. Hopkins, 1879.   2179

**Robinson, E.**
 Atlas of the Oranges, Essex county, N. J. Comprising the cities of Orange and East Orange, town of West Orange, village and township of South Orange and the borough of Vailsburgh. Compiled under the direct management and supervision of E. Robinson.   2 p. l., 27 maps. fol. Philadelphia, A. H. Mueller, 1904.   2180

## HARRISON.

**Miller, D. L.**
 Atlas of the towns of Harrison and Kearny and the borough of East Newark, Hudson county, N. J. From official records, maps and surveys.   1 p. l., 8 maps. fol. Philadelphia, D. L. Miller & co. 1903.   2181

## JERSEY CITY.

**Fowler, L. D.**
 Title and assessment map of that part of Jersey City which constituted the city of Bergen, prior to consolidation in 1870. From the records and verified by surveys 1882. Scale: 200 ft. = 1 inch. 6 sheets. fol. New York, L. D. Fowler [1883]   2182

**Fowler, L. D.** & *others.*
Official assessment map of Jersey City, N. J.   1 p. l., 64 maps. fol. New York, R. A. Welcke, 1894.   2183

**Hopkins, G. M., co.**
Atlas of Hudson county, New Jersey . . . volume one comprising Jersey City, volume two including balance of county. From official records, private plans and actual surveys . . . v. 1. 2 p. l., 33 (*i. e.* 34) col. maps. fol. Philadelphia, G. M. Hopkins co. 1908.   2183a

### KEARNEY.
**Miller, D. L.**
Atlas of the towns of Harrison and Kearny and the borough of East Newark, Hudson county, N. J. From official records, maps and surveys.   1 p. l., 8 maps. fol. Philadelphia, D. L. Miller & co. 1903.   2184

### LONG BRANCH.
**Seaman, J. W.**
Map of city of Long Branch, New Jersey, adopted by the city council. august 6th 1906 . . . Scale 1″–200′. 2 p. l., 19 fold. maps. obl. fol. [Long Branch] 1906.   2185

**Baist, G. W.**
Atlas of Long Branch, N. J.   1 p. l., 19 maps. fol. Philadelphia, J. L. Smith, 1886.   2186

### NEWARK.
**Hopkins, G. M.**
Combined atlas of the state of New Jersey and the city of Newark. 120 pp. incl. 34 maps. fol. Philadelphia, G. M. Hopkins & co. 1873.   2187

**Scarlett & Scarlett.**
Atlas of the city of Newark, N. J.   1 p. l., 37 maps. fol. Newark, N. J. Scarlett & Scarlett, 1889.   2188

**Robinson, E.,** *and* **Tenny, L. E.**
Atlas of the city of Newark, New Jersey. From official records, private plans and actual surveys.   1 p. l., 37 maps. fol. New York, E. Robinson & co. 1901.   2189

NOTE.—[v. 1] of Mueller, A. H. & co. Atlas of Essex county, New Jersey, 1901–06.

### ORANGE.
**Hopkins, G. M.**
City atlas of Orange and township of West Orange, N. J.   111 pp. incl. 29 maps. fol. Philadelphia, G. M. Hopkins, 1878.   2190

**Robinson, E.**
Atlas of the Oranges, Essex county, N. J. Comprising the cities of Orange and East Orange, town of West Orange, village and

township of South Orange and the borough of Vailsburgh. Compiled under the direct management and supervision of E. Robinson. 2 p. l., 27 maps. fol. Philadelphia, A. H. Mueller, 1904. 2191

NOTE.—[v. 2] of Mueller, A. H. & co. Atlas of Essex county, New Jersey, 1901–06.

## PASSAIC.

**Robinson, E.**, *& others*.

Atlas of the city of Passaic and Acquackanonk township, Passaic county, New Jersey. Compiled from surveys furnished by Messrs. Wise & Watson, civil and consulting engineers, Passaic, N. J., official records, private plans and actual surveys by L. E. Tenney and P. R. Stickney, surveyors under the supervision of E. Robinson. 1 p. l., 21 maps. fol. New York, E. Robinson & co. 1901. 2192

## PATERSON.

**Robinson, E.**, *and* **Pidgeon, R. H.**

Atlas of the city of Paterson, N. J. 1 p l., 24 maps. fol. New York, E. Robinson, 1884. 2193

## PLAINFIELD.

**Dunham, F. A.**

Atlas of the city of Plainfield, Union county, and borough of North Plainfield, Somerset county, N. J. 1 p. l., 13 maps. fol. Plainfield, N. J., F. A. Dunham, 1894. 2194

## PRINCETON.

**Lathrop, J. M.**

Atlas of the city of Trenton and borough of Princeton, Mercer county, New Jersey. Compiled and drawn from official records, private plans and actual surveys . . . 1 p. l., [1] l., 25 maps. fol. Philadelphia, A. H. Mueller & co. 1905. 2195

## SOUTH ORANGE.

**Robinson, E.**

Atlas of the Oranges, Essex county, N. J. Comprising the cities of Orange and East Orange, town of West Orange, village and township of South Orange and the borough of Vailsburgh . . . 2 p. l., 27 maps. fol. Philadelphia, A. H. Mueller, 1904. 2196

## SUMMIT.

**Robinson, E.**, *& others*.

Atlas of the city of Summit, N. J., including Baltusrol, and the Brantwood club property. Compiled from surveys furnished by Carl J. Seiler . . . Mead & Taylor . . . official records and actual surveys by Paul R. Stickney and L. E. Tenny under the supervision of E. Robinson. 1 p. l., 14 maps. fol. New York, E. Robinson & co. 1900. 2197

### TRENTON.

**Scarlett & Scarlett.**
 Scarlett & Scarlett's fire map of Mercer county, N. J., including Trenton and suburbs.  2 p. l., 111 maps.  fol.  Newark, N. J., Scarlett & Scarlett, 1890.   2198

**Lathrop, J. M.**
 Atlas of the city of Trenton and borough of Princeton, Mercer county, New Jersey.  Compiled and drawn from official records, private plans and actual surveys . . .   1 p. i., 25 maps, 1 l. unp.  fol.  Philadelphia, A. H. Mueller & co. 1905.   2199

### WEST ORANGE.

**Robinson, E.**
 Atlas of the Oranges, Essex county, N. J.  Comprising the cities of Orange and East Orange, town of West Orange, village and township of South Orange and the borough of Vailsburgh . . . 2 p. l., 27 maps.  fol.  Philadelphia, A. H. Mueller, 1904.   2200

## NEW YORK.

### Miscellaneous.

#### HUDSON RIVER VALLEY.

**Beers, F. W.**
 Atlas of the Hudson river valley from New York city to Troy, including a section of about 8 miles in width.   1 p. l., 72 maps. fol.  New York, Watson & co. 1891.   2201

#### LONG ISLAND.

**Beers, F. W.**
 Atlas of Long Island, N. Y.   192 pp. incl. 99 maps.  fol. New York, Beers, Comstock & Cline, 1873.   2202

#### STATEN ISLAND.

**Beers, F. W.**
 Atlas of Staten Island, Richmond county, N. Y.   1 p. l., 36 maps.  fol.  New York, J. B. Beers & co. 1874.   2203

**Beers, J. B., & co.**
 Atlas of Staten Island, Richmond county, N. Y.   2 p. l., 12 maps.  fol.  New York, J. B. Beers & co. 1887.   2204

**Lefèvre, I. A.**
 Atlas of Staten Island, Richmond county, New York.  v. 1.   1 p. l., 31 maps, 1 pl.  fol.  New York, I. A. Lefèvre, 1894.   2205

CONTENTS.
 v. 1. Castleton.

### State.

#### 1829

**Burr, D. H.**
An atlas of the state of New York, containing a map of the state and of the several counties. Projected and drawn under the superintendence and direction of Simon De Witt, pursuant to an act of the legislature. And also the physical geography of the state and of the several counties and statistical tables of the same. 2 p. l., 7–29, 120 pp. incl. 52 maps. fol. New York, D. H. Burr, 1829.
2206

#### 1838

**Burr, D. H.**
Atlas of New York. [anon.] 98 (*i. e.* 158) pp., front. (fold. map) incl. 58 maps. 8°. New York, for sale by the principal booksellers, 1838.
2207

> NOTE.—Author furnished by G. W. Colton, june 1894. Pagination irregular. Folded map of New York state contains insets of "Niagara river," "From Albany to lake Champlain & l. George," "Environs of Utica," "City of New York," "Environs of New York."

#### 1869

**Asher & Adams.**
Asher & Adams' new topographical map of the state of New York, made from official records and actual surveys. 2 p. l., 28 pp., 11 l. incl. 16 maps. fol. New York, Asher & Adams [1869]
2208

#### 1870

**Asher & Adams.**
Asher & Adams' new topographical atlas and gazetteer of New York, comprising a topographical view of the several counties of the state, together with a railroad map, geological and meteorological maps; an alphabetical gazetteer, giving a concise description and the location of cities, villages, post offices, railroad stations, landings, &c., including a fine copper plate railroad map of the United States and territories, drawn on the polyconic projection, expressly for this work . . . 2 p. l., 7–79 pp. incl. 15 maps. fol. New York, Asher & Adams [1870]
2209

#### 1891

**Bien, J. R.,** *and* **Vermeule, C. C.**
Atlas of the metropolitan district and adjacent country comprising the counties of New York, Kings, Richmond, Westchester and part of Queens in the state of New York, the county of Hudson and parts of the counties of Bergen, Passaic, Essex and Union, in the state of New Jersey; showing in a series of maps the relative geographical position, the topography, hydrography and economic features of this area. 2 p. l., 13 maps. fol. New York, J. Bien & co. 1891.
2210

## 1895

**Bien, J. R.**
  Atlas of the state of New York, from original surveys and various local surveys revised and corrected based on the triangulations of of the U. S. coast and geodetic survey, U. S. geological survey, U. S. lake survey and the N. Y. state survey.  6 p. l., 37 maps. fol.  New York, J. Bien & co. 1895.  2211

## Counties.

### ALBANY.

**Beers, S. N.,** *and* **Beers, D. G.**
  New topographical atlas of the counties of Albany and Schenectady, N. Y.  From actual surveys.  63 pp. incl. 24 maps, 1 pl. fol.  Philadelphia, Stone & Stewart, 1866.  2212

### ALLEGANY.

**Beers, D. G., & co.**
  Atlas of Allegany county, N. Y.  1 p. l., 4–98 pp. incl. 43 maps. fol.  New York, D. G. Beers & co. 1869.  2213

### CATTARAUGUS.

**Beers, G. D., & co.**
  Atlas of Cattaraugus county, N. Y.  1 p. l., 3–98 pp. incl. 41 maps. fol.  New York, D. G. Beers & co. 1869.  2214

### CAYUGA.

**Beers, F. W.**
  County atlas of Cayuga, N. Y.  1 p. l., 4–147 pp. incl. 38 maps, 17 pl.  fol.  New York, Walker & Jewett, 1875.  2215
  NOTE.—Pagination irregular.

**Century map co.**
  The new century atlas of Cayuga county, New York.  With farm records.  By the company's corps of expert engineers and draughtsmen.  Otto Barthel, chief engineer.  1 p. l., 112, [25] pp. incl. 51 col. maps.  fol.  Philadelphia, century map co. 1904.  2216

### CHAUTAUQUA.

**Beers, F. W., & co.**
  Illustrated historical atlas of the county of Chautauqua, N. Y.  2 p. l., 6–204 pp. incl. 64 maps, 39 pl.  fol.  New York, F. W. Beers & co. 1881.  2217

### CHEMUNG.

**Beers, F. W., Sandford, G. P.** *& others.*
  Atlas of Chemung county, N. Y.  1 p. l., 3–29 pp. incl. 8 maps, 4 pl.  fol.  New York, F. W. Beers, A. D. Ellis & G. G. Soule, 1869.  2218

## CLINTON.

**Beers, F. W., Sanford, G. P.,** & others.
 Atlas of Clinton county, N. Y.  1 p. l., 20 maps, 2 pl. fol. New York, F. W. Beers, A. D. Ellis & G. G. Soule, 1869.  2219

**Averill & Hagar.**
 A new and concise geographical and historical description of Clinton county, accompanying Averill & Hagar's new map of the county. 17 pp. incl. 1 map. sm. fol. [Plattsburgh, N. Y.] Averill & Hagar, 1879.  2220

## COLUMBIA.

**Beers, D. G., & co.**
 Atlas of Columbia county, New York.  From actual surveys and official records . . .  89 pp. incl. 35 maps. fol. Philadelphia, D. G. Beers & co. 1873.  2221

**Beers, Ellis & co.**
 Atlas of Columbia county, N. Y.  2 p. l., 6–120 pp., 3 l. incl. 33 maps. fol. New York, Beers, Ellis & co. 1888.  2222

## DELAWARE.

**Beers, F. W.,** & others.
 Atlas of Delaware county, N. Y.  1 p. l., 3–38 pp. incl. 24 maps, 1 pl. fol. New York, F. W. Beers, A. D. Ellis & G. G. Soule, 1869.  2223

## DUTCHESS.

**Gray, O. W., & son.**
 New illustrated atlas of Dutchess county, New York.  71, [2]–37, iv pp., incl. 48 maps, 5 pl. fol. Reading, Pa., Reading publishing house, 1876.  2224

## ERIE.

**Stone & Stewart.**
 New topographical atlas of Erie county, N. Y.  From actual surveys especially for this atlas.  [93] pp. incl. 40 maps, 2 pl. fol. Philadelphia, Stone & Stewart, 1866.  2225

  NOTE.—Pagination irregular.

**Beers, F. W., & co.**
 Illustrated historical atlas of Erie county, N. Y.  1 p. l., 201 pp. incl. 50 maps, 46 pl. fol. New York, F. W. Beers & co. 1880.
 2226

## ESSEX.

**Gray, O. W., & son.**
 New topographical atlas of Essex county, N. Y., with a supplement comprising a map of the state of New York and general maps of the United States and the world with descriptions.  4 p. l., 10–79 pp., 1 l., 6–37 pp., 2 l. incl. 32 maps, 6 pl. fol. Philadelphia, O. W. Gray & son, 1876.  2227

## FULTON.

**Nichols, Beach** & *others.*
    Atlas of Montgomery and Fulton counties, N. Y.   2 p. l., 28 maps. fol. New York, J. J. Stranahan & B. Nichols, 1868.   2228

## GREENE.

**Beers, F. W., Warner, G. E.** & *others.*
    Atlas of Greene county, N. Y.   2 p. l., 18 maps, 2 pl. fol. New York, F. W. Beers, A. D. Ellis & G. G. Soule, 1867.   2229

## HERKIMER.

**Nichols, Beach** & *others.*
    Atlas of Herkimer county, N. Y.   1 p. l., 27 maps. fol. New York, J. J. Stranahan & B. Nichols, 1868.   2230

## JEFFERSON.

**Beers, S. N., Beers, D. G.** & *others.*
    New topographical atlas of Jefferson county, N. Y. From actual surveys. 1 p. l., [84] pp. incl. 37 maps, 1 pl. fol. Philadelphia, C. K. Stone, 1864.   2231

**Robinson, E.**
    Robinson's atlas of Jefferson county, N. Y.   1 p. l., 34 maps. fol. New York, E. Robinson, 1888.   2232

## KINGS.

**Robinson, E.**
    Robinson's atlas of Kings county, N. Y.   1 p. l., 33 maps. fol. New York, E. Robinson, 1890.   2233

**Kenna, T. J.**
    The land map of the county of Kings, state of New York, compiled by the register of the county of Kings under and in pursuance of the provisions of chapter 365 of the laws of New York, 1894. M. E. Finnigan, superintendent of records. v. 1–2.   2 v. in 1. 1 p. l., 58 maps. fol. New York, Sanborn-Perris map co. limited, 1894.   2234

## LIVINGSTON.

**Beers, F. W.**
    Atlas of Livingston county, N. Y.   2 p. l., 31 maps. fol. New York, F. W. Beers & co. 1872.   2235

**Century map co.**
    New century atlas of Livingston county, New York, with farm records . . . A. L. Westgard, chief engineer. 1 p. l., 71 pp. incl. 39 maps, 1 pl. fol. Philadelphia, century map co. 1902.   2236

## MONROE.

**Beers, F. W.**
    Atlas of Monroe county, N. Y.     3 p. l., 38 maps. fol. New York, F. W. Beers & co. 1872.      2237
    NOTE.—Pagination irregular.

**Lathrop, J. M., & co.**
    Plat book of Monroe county, New York. Compiled from deed descriptions and plats furnished by the title and guarantee company of Rochester, also from records and surveys . . . 1 p. l., 32 maps. fol. Philadelphia, J. M. Lathrop & co. [1902]     2238

## MONTGOMERY.

**Nichols, Beach,** *& others.*
    Atlas of Montgomery and Fulton counties, N. Y.    2 p. l., 28 maps. fol. New York, J. J. Stranahan & B. Nichols, 1868.
    2239

## NASSAU.

**Belcher-Hyde, E.**
    Atlas of Nassau county, Long Island, N. Y. . . . Based on maps on file at the county seat in Mineola and upon private plans and surveys furnished by surveyors and individual owners . . . 2 p. l., 37 maps. fol. Brooklyn, N. Y., E. Belcher-Hyde, 1906.
    2240

## ONEIDA.

**Beers, D. G., & co.**
    Atlas of Oneida county, N. Y.     139 pp. incl. 50 maps. fol. Philadelphia, D. G. Beers & co. 1874.      2241

**Century map company.**
    New century atlas, Oneida county, New York. From government surveys, official records, and general compilations and notations, by the company's corps of expert engineers and draughtsmen. 180 pp. incl. 103 col. maps, fold. map. fol. Philadelphia, century map company, 1907.      2242

## ONONDAGA.

**Sweet, H. D. L.**
    Sweet's new atlas of Onondaga county, N. Y.    2 p. l., 5 l., 43 maps. fol. New York, Walker bros. & co. 1874.     2243
    NOTE.—Pagination irregular.

## ORANGE.

**Beers, F. W.**
    County atlas of Orange, N. Y.    2 p. l., 160 pp. incl. 35 maps, 32 pl. fol. Chicago, A. Baskin & Burr, 1875.      2244
    NOTE.—Pagination irregular.

**Lathrop, J. M.**, & *others*.

    Atlas of Orange county, New York. Compiled and drawn from official records, public and private plans and actual surveys by J. M. Lathrop, assisted by Roger H. Pidgeon, Paul R. Stickney, H. E. Halfpenny, W. C. Fronk, Thomas W. Hassan, Gilbert M. Monroe and E. Robinson.   2 p. l., 47 maps. fol. Philadelphia, A. H. Mueller & co. 1903.     2245

### OSWEGO.

**Stone, C. K.**

    New topographical atlas of Oswego county, N. Y. From actual surveys especially for this atlas.   86 pp. incl. 35 maps, 4 pl. fol. Philadelphia, C. K. Stone, 1867.     2246

### OTSEGO.

**Beers, F. W.**

    Atlas of Otsego county, N. Y.   2 p. l., 36 maps, 3 pl. fol. New York, F. W. Beers, A. D. Ellis & G. G. Soule, 1868.     2247

**Century map co.**

    New century atlas of Otsego county, New York, with farm records. By the company's corps of expert engineers and draughtsmen. Otto Barthel, chief engineer.   1 p. l., 94 pp. incl. 50 maps. fol. Philadelphia, century map co. 1903.     2248

    NOTE.—Contains one loose map.

### RENSSELAER.

**Beers, F. W.**

    County atlas of Rensselaer, N. Y.   2 p. l., 3 l., 39 maps, 7 pl. fol. New York, F. W. Beers & co. 1876.     2249

### ROCKLAND.

**Beers, F. W.**

    County atlas of Rockland, N. Y.   2 p. l., 33 maps. fol. New York, Walker & Jewett, 1875.     2250

    NOTE.—Pagination irregular.

**Davis, F. A., & co.**

    Combination atlas map of Rockland county, N. Y. Compiled, drawn and published from personal examinations and surveys. 79, 30 pp., incl. 27 maps, 26 pl. fol. Philadelphia, F. A. Davis & co. 1876.     2251

### ST. LAWRENCE.

**Beers, S. N., Beers, D. G.**, & *others*.

    New topographical atlas of St. Lawrence county, N. Y. From actual surveys.   3 p. l., 94 pp. incl. 41 maps, 2 pl. fol. Philadelphia, Stone & Stewart, 1865.     2252

### SCHENECTADY.

**Beers, S. N., Beers, D. G.,** & *others.*
    New topographical atlas of the counties of Albany and Schenectady, N. Y. From actual surveys. 63 pp. incl. 24 maps, 1 pl. fol. Philadelphia, Stone & Stewart, 1866.    2253

### SCHOHARIE.

**Beers, S. N., Beers, D. G.,** & *others.*
    New topographical atlas of Schoharie co. New York. From actual surveys. 3 p. 1., 9–63 pp. incl. 26 maps, 1 pl. fol. Philadelphia, Stone & Stewart, 1866.    2254

### SUFFOLK.

**Ullitz, H.**
    Atlas of Suffolk county, Long Island, New York. Based upon actual measurements by our own corps of engineers, maps on file at county offices also maps from actual surveys furnished by individual owners. v. 1. 1 p. 1., 29 maps on 56 l. fol. Brooklyn, N. Y., E. B. Hyde, 1902.    2255

CONTENTS.
    v. 1. Ocean shore.

### SULLIVAN.

**Beers, F. W.**
    County atlas of Sullivan, N. Y. 2 p. 1., 3 l., 36 maps. fol. New York, Walker & Jewett, 1875.    2256
    NOTE.—Pagination irregular.

### TIOGA.

**Beers, F. W., Sanford, G. P.,** & *others.*
    Atlas of Tioga county, N. Y. 3 p. 1., 20 maps, 4 pl. fol. New York, F. W. Beers, A. D. Ellis & G. G. Soule, 1869.    2257

### TOMPKINS.

**Stone & Stewart.**
    New topographical atlas of Tompkins county, New York. From actual surveys especially for this atlas. 1 p. 1., 17 pp., 17 maps. fol. Philadelphia, Stone & Stewart, 1866.    2258

### ULSTER.

**Beers, F. W.**
    County atlas of Ulster, N. Y. 1 p. 1., 4–140 pp. incl. 51 maps, 29 pl. fol. New York, Walker & Jewett, 1875.    2259
    NOTE.—Pagination irregular and pages missing.

### WARREN.

**Beers, F. W.**
    County atlas of Warren, N.Y. 2 p. 1., 2 l., 24 maps, 1 pl. fol. New York, F. W. Beers & co. 1876.    2260
    NOTE.—Pagination irregular.

## WESTCHESTER.

**Beers, J. B., & co.**
 County atlas of Westchester, N. Y.   2 p. l., 44 maps. fol. New York, J. B. Beers & co. 1872.   2261
  Note.—Pagination irregular.

**Bien, J. R.**
 Atlas of Westchester county, N. Y.   2 p. l., 32 maps. fol. New York, J. Bien & co. 1893.   2262

**Bromley, G. W.** *and* **Bromley, W. S.**
 Atlas of Westchester county, N. Y. From actual surveys and official plans.   2 p. l., 55 maps. fol. Philadelphia, G. W. Bromley & co. 1901.   2263

**Hyde, E. B.**
 Atlas of the rural country district north of New York city embracing the entire Westchester county, New York, also a portion of Connecticut, Greenwich, Stamford, New Canaan, Darien, Wilton and Ridgefield . . .   4 p. l., 17 (*i. e.* 18) col. maps. fol. Manhattan, Brooklyn, E. B. Hyde, 1908.   2264

## WYOMING.

**Century map co.**
 New century atlas of Wyoming county, New York, with farm records. By the company's corps of expert engineers and draughtsmen. A. L. Westgard, chief engineer. J. O. McClure, Warsaw, consulting engineer.   1 p. l., 78, [1] pp., incl. 36 maps. fol. Philadelphia, century map co. 1902.   2265
  Note.—Large folded map of Wyoming county. 1802–1902.

### Cities.

#### ALBANY.

**Hopkins, G. M.**
 City atlas of Albany, N. Y.   2 p. l., 6–98 pp., 2 l. incl. 24 maps. fol. Philadelphia, G. M. Hopkins, 1876.   2266

**Scarlett & Van Wagoner.**
 Scarlett & Van Wagoner's fire map of Albany, N. Y.   2 v. fol. Albany, N. Y. Scarlett & Van Wagoner, 1892.   2267
  Note.—Collection: v. 1, 1 p. l., 64 maps; v. 2, 1 p. l., 57 maps.

CONTENTS.

  v. 1. Including Albany city north of state street and western avenue.
  " 2. Including Albany city south of state street and western avenue.

#### AUBURN.

**Hopkins, G. M.**
 City atlas of Auburn, N. Y.   1 p. l., 17 maps. fol. Philadelphia, G. M. Hopkins, 1882.   2268

## BABYLON.

**Wendelken & co.**
  Atlas of the towns Babylon, Islip, and south part of Brookhaven in Suffolk county, N. Y.   2 p. l., 18 maps.   fol.   New York, Wendelken & co. 1888.    2269
  NOTE.—Copyrighted by F. W. Beers & co.

## BALLSTON.

**Beers, F. W.** *and* **Cramer, L. H.**
  Combination atlas of Saratoga and Ballston.   1 p. l., 18 maps, 8 pl.   fol.   New York, J. B. Beers & co. 1876.    2270

## BINGHAMTON.

**Hopkins, G. M.**
  Atlas of the city of Binghamton, N. Y.   1 p. l., 20 maps.   fol.   Philadelphia, G. M. Hopkins, 1885.    2271

## BROOKHAVEN.

**Wendelken & co.**
  Atlas of the towns of Babylon, Islip and south part of Brookhaven in Suffolk county, N. Y.   2 p. l., 18 maps.   fol.   New York, Wendelken & co. 1888.    2272
  NOTE.—Copyrighted by F. W. Beers & co.

## BROOKLYN.

**Dripps, M.**
  Map of the city of Brooklyn (being the former cities of Brooklyn & Williamsburgh) and the town of Bushwick as consolidated january 1st 1855 by an act of the legislature of the state of New York passed april 17th 1854 showing the same as laid out by commissioners and corrected as altered by different acts of the legislature up to date, showing also a part of the city of New York.   1 p. l., 9 maps, incl. front.   fol.   New York, M. Dripps, 1869.    2273

**Bromley, G. W., & co.**
  Atlas of the entire city of Brooklyn, complete in one volume. From actual surveys and official records by G. W. Bromley & co. 1 p. l., 36 maps.   fol.   New York, G. W. Bromley & E. Robinson, 1880.    2274

**Hopkins, G. M.**
  Detailed estate and old farm line atlas of the city of Brooklyn. 6 v.   fol.   Philadelphia, G. M. Hopkins, 1880.    2275

CONTENTS.

  v. 1. Comprising wards 23–25.
  " 2.      "         "    18.
  " 3.      "         "    7, 9, 20–21.
  " 4.      "         "    8 and 22.
  " 5.      "         "    1–6, 10–12.
  " 6.      "         "    13–17, 19.

**Robinson, E.** *and* **Pidgeon, R. H.**
  Robinson's atlas of the city of Brooklyn, N. Y., embracing all territory within its corporate limits. 3 p. l., 41 maps. fol. New York, E. Robinson, 1886. 2276

**Robinson, E.**
  Certified copies of important maps of wards 8, 17, 18, 22, 23, 24, and 25, city of Brooklyn, filed in the office of register Kings county, New York. 2 p. l., 43 maps. fol. New York, E. Robinson, 1889. 2277

  Atlas of the 29th, 30th, 31st and 32d wards (formerly towns of Flatbush, New Utrecht, Gravesend and Flatlands, Kings co., New York) borough of Brooklyn, city of New York. From official records, private plans and actual surveys. Compiled by and under the supervision of E. Robinson. 1 p. l., 35 maps. fol. New York, E. Robinson, 1898. 2278

### BUFFALO.

**Hopkins, G. M., & co.**
  Atlas of the city of Buffalo, Erie county, N. Y. 5 p. l., 30 maps. fol. Philadelphia, G. M. Hopkins & co. 1872. 2279

**Hopkins, G. M.**
  Atlas of the city of Buffalo, N. Y. 1 p. l., 36 maps. fol. Philadelphia, G. M. Hopkins, 1884. 2280

  Atlas of the city of Buffalo, N. Y. 1 p. l., 38 maps. fol. Philadelphia, G. M. Hopkins, 1891. 2281

  Atlas of the vicinities of the cities of Niagara Falls, North Tonawanda and Buffalo, N. Y. 2 p. l., 34 maps. fol. Philadelphia, G. M. Hopkins, 1893. 2282

### ELMIRA.

**Converse, M. S.**
  City atlas of Elmira, N. Y. 2 p. l., 1 l., 24 maps. fol. Philadelphia, M. S. Converse & co. 1876. 2283

**Pidgeon, R. H.,** *& others.*
  Atlas of the city of Elmira, N. Y. 1 p. l., 18 maps. fol. Philadelphia, D. L. Miller & co. 1896. 2284

### GREEN ISLAND.

**Barton, W.**
  Map of the city of Troy, West Troy and Green Island, N. Y., from actual surveys. 3 p. l., 1 map on 11 sheets. fol. Troy, 1869. 2285

  NOTE.—Date 1869 on title page; sheet no. 11 has title of map with date 1858.

## ISLIP.

**Wendelken & co.**
Atlas of the town of Babylon, Islip, and south part of Brookhaven in Suffolk county, N. Y. 2 p. l., 18 maps. fol. New York, Wendelken & co. 1888. 2286

NOTE.—Copyrighted by F. W. Beers & co.

## JAMESTOWN.

**Beers, F. W., & others.**
Atlas of Jamestown, N. Y. 1 p. l., 1 l., 17 maps. fol. New York, J. W. Vose & co. 1888. 2287

## MOUNT VERNON.

**Fairchild, J. F.**
Atlas of the city of Mount Vernon and the town of Pelham. 3 p. l., 24 maps. fol. Mount Vernon, N. Y., J. F. Fairchild, 1899. 2288

Atlas of the city of Mount Vernon and the town of Pelham ... 2d ed. 3 p. l., 38 (i. e. 39) col. maps. fol. Mount Vernon, N. Y., J. F. Fairchild, 1908. 2288a

NOTE.—Thaddeus S. Strange, chief draftsman. Copyrighted 1907.

## NEW ROCHELLE.

**New Rochelle, N. Y.** *Assessors.*
City of New Rochelle, New York. The assessors maps. Chap. 236 laws of N. Y. 1905. Uniform scale, except where otherwise stated, is 80 feet to one inch. Made by Horace Crosby ... 1906 ... 8 v. fol. [New Rochelle] ᶜ1907. 2289

CONTENTS.

v. 1. Section 1, blocks 1–400.
" 2.   "   2,   "   401–800.
" 3.   "   3,   "   801–1200.
" 4.   "   4,   "   1201–1400.
" 5.   "   5,   "   1401–2000.
" 6.   "   6,   "   2001–2600.
" 7.   "   7,   "   2601–3200.
" 8.   "   8,   "   3201–3500.

## NEW YORK.

**Beers, F. W., Warner, G. E., & others.**
Atlas of New York and vicinity from actual surveys ... 2 p. l., 61 maps, 5 pl. fol. New York, F. W. Beers, A. D. Ellis & G. G. Soule, 1867. 2290

**Dripps, M.**
Plan of New York city from the battery to Spuyten Duyvil creek. Showing every lot and building thereon; old farm lines, street num-

**Dripps, M.**—Continued.
bers at the corners of blocks, railroads, steamboat landings, bulkhead and pier lines, etc. Based on the surveys made by messrs. Randall & Blackwell, and on the special survey by J. F. Harrison. 1 p. l., 19 maps. fol. New York, M. Dripps, 1867. 2291

**Beers, F. W., Prindle, A. B.,** & *others*.
Atlas of New York and vicinity. 1 p. l., 72 pp. incl. 50 maps, 3 pl. fol. New York, F. W. Beers, A. D. Ellis & G. G. Soule, 1868. 2292

**Devlin & co.**
The metropolis explained and illustrated in familiar form. 61 pp., 1 l., front., 1 map. 16°. New York, Devlin & co. 1871. 2293

**Croes & Van Winkle.**
The west side of the city of New York between eighth avenue and Hudson river, from fifty ninth street to one hundred and fifty-fifth street. Showing graphically the existing condition of all real estate as regards all public improvements, with an appendix giving the dates of the confirmation of the assessment for each improvement. 2 p. l., 13 pp., 12 maps. fol. New York, Croes & Van Winkle [1873] 2294

**Wallace, J. B., *and* Shillington, T.**
The empire city lot book, being a complete atlas of Manhattan island north of forty-second street. 1 p. l., 71 maps. fol. New York, J. B. Wallace & T. Shillington [1873] 2295

**Beers, F. W.**
New York city from official records and surveys. 5 v. fol. New York, J. B. Beers & co. 1876–[85] 2296

CONTENTS.

v. 1. Map of 23d ward.
" 2. Southern half of map of the 24th ward.
" 3. Northern half of map of the 24th ward.
" 4. Map of southern part of 12th ward.
" 5. Map of northern part of 12th ward.

**Croes, J. J. R.**
Additions to, and revisions of the West Side atlas, to october 1st, 1879. [New York] J. J. R. Croes [1879] 2297

**Bromley, G. W., & co.**
Atlas of the 19th & 22nd wards, city of New York. 1 p. l., 27 maps. fol. Philadelphia, G. W. & W. S. Bromley, 1880. 2298

**Pidgeon, R. H.**
Atlas of the twelfth ward, city of New York.   1 p. l., 37 maps. fol. New York, E. Robinson, 1880.   2299

Atlas of the 16th, 18th, 20th & 21st wards, city of New York. 1 p. l., 18 maps.  fol.  New York, E. Robinson, 1880.   2300

**Spielmann & Brush.**
Certified copies of original maps of property in New York city, filed in the register's office and elsewhere, together with the register's index to maps and important notes regarding the same.   6 p. l., 372, 16 pp. incl. 101 maps.  fol.  Hoboken, N. J., Spielmann & Brush, 1881.   2301

**Robinson, E.,** *and* **Pidgeon, R. H.**
Atlas of the city of New York.   2d ed.   v. 1, 3-6.   fol.   New York, E. Robinson, 1883-87.   2302

CONTENTS.

v. 1. Embracing the 19th and 22nd wards.
" 3. Embracing the 16th, 18th, 20th and 21st wards.
" 4. Lying south of fourteenth street.
" 5. Embracing the 23d ward.
" 6. Embracing the 24th ward.

Atlas of the city of New York, embracing the twelfth ward. 2d ed.  v. 2.   1 p. l., 36 maps.  fol.  New York, E. Robinson, 1884.   2303

Robinson's atlas of the city of New York, embracing all territory within its corporate limits.   1 p. l., 43 maps.   fol.   New York, E. Robinson, 1885.   2304

**Robinson, E.**
Certified copies of important maps appertaining to the 23rd and 24th wards, city of New York, filed in the register's office at White Plains, county of Westchester, N. Y.  2 v.  fol.  New York, E. Robinson, 1888-90.   2305

NOTE.—Collection: v. 1, 2 p. l., 39 maps; v. 2, 3 p. l., 27 maps.

**Robinson, E.,** *and* **Pidgeon, R. H.**
Robinson's real estate atlas of the city of New York, embracing Manhattan island.   In nine volumes.   v. 5-7.   fol.   New York, E. Robinson, 1889-90.   2306

CONTENTS.

v. 5. 22nd ward.
" 6. 12th ward between 86th and 114th streets.
" 7. 12th ward between 114th and 138 streets.

**New York, City of.** *Board of taxes and assessments.*
The land map of the city of New York prepared by the board of taxes and assessments under authority of chapter 349 of the laws of 1889 and chapter 166 of the laws of 1890. v. 1–2, 2 v. in 1. 1 p. l., 46 maps. obl. fol. [New York, 1890] 2307

    Note.—Copyright 1890 by Michael Coleman, Thos. F. Feiter, and Edward L. Parris, commissioners of taxes and assessments.

**Robinson, E.,** *and* **Pidgeon, R. H.**
Atlas of the city of New York. 3d ed. 4 v. fol. New York, E. Robinson, 1890–93. 2308

    CONTENTS.

    v. 1. Embracing the 19th and 22nd wards.
    " 2. Embracing the 12th ward.
    " 3. Embracing the 16th, 18th, 20th and 21st wards.
    " 4. South of fourteenth street.

**Bromley, G. W.,** *and* **Bromley, W. S.**
Atlas of the city of New York, Manhattan island. From actual surveys and official plans. 2 p. l., 46 maps. fol. Philadelphia, G. W. Bromley & co. 1891. 2309

**Colton, G. W. & co.**
Complete ward atlas of New York city with key locating wards. cover-title, 31 maps. 4°. New York, New York city record publishing co. [°1892] 2310

    Note.—Copyrighted by G. W. Colton & co.

**Lefèvre, I. A.**
Atlas of Manhattan island, New York . . . Scale 50 ft. to 1 inch. v. 1–2, 5–6. fol. [New York] I. A. Lefèvre, 1895–96. 2311

    Note.—v. 2 dated 1896.

Index to atlas of Manhattan island, N. Y. Blocks 1593 to 1819. Comprising from 96th street to the Harlem river and from 6th ave. to East River. v. 6. 109 pp. sm. fol. New York, I. A. Lefèvre, 1896. 2312

    Note.—This index is corrected up to dec. 3d 1896.

Yearly index to atlas of Manhattan island, N. Y. Blocks 1257 to 1592. Comprising from 40th to 96th streets and from 6th ave. to East River. v. 5. 109 pp. sm. fol. New York, I. A. Lefèvre, 1896. 2313

    Note.—Entirely newly revised and corrected up to march 26th, 1896.

**Robinson, E., & co.**
Certified copies of maps of the annexed district, annexed to the city of New York under authority of chapter 934 of the laws of

1895, filed in the register's office at White Plains, county of Westchester, N. Y. v. 3.    1 p. l., 30 maps. fol. New York, E. Robinson & co. 1897.    2314

**Hammond, C. S., & co.**
Hammond's atlas of New York city and the metropolitan district. Contains new maps of each borough on large scale . . . Also road maps of the country around New York, showing all roads, with automobile routes, etc.    cover-title, 13 maps on 16 pp., inside covers. fol. New York, C. S. Hammond & co. 1907.    2315

**Robinson, E.,** *and* **Pidgeon, R. H.**
Atlas of the borough of Richmond, city of New York . . . From official records, private plans and actual surveys compiled by and under the supervision of E. Robinson and R. H. Pidgeon. 2d and rev. ed.    2 p. l., 34 col. maps. fol. New York, E. Robinson, 1907.    2316

**Hammond, C. S., & co.**
Hammond's atlas of New York city and the metropolitan district. Contains new maps of each borough on large scale . . . Also road maps of the country around New York showing all roads, with automobile routes, etc. cover-title, 13 col. maps. sm. fol. New York, C. S. Hammond & co. 1908.    2316a

**Hyde, E. B.**
Atlas of the rural country district north of New York city embracing the entire Westchester county, New York, also a portion of Connecticut; Greenwich, Stamford, New Caanan, Darien, Wilton, and Ridgefield . . .    4 p. l., 17 (*i. e.* 18) col. maps. fol. Manhattan, Brooklyn, E. B. Hyde, 1908.    2317

### NIAGARA FALLS.
**Hopkins, G. M.**
Atlas of the vicinities of the cities of Niagara Falls, North Tonawanda and Buffalo, N. Y.    2 p. l., 34 maps. fol. Philadelphia, G. M. Hopkins, 1893.    2318

### NORTH TONAWANDA.
**Hopkins, G. M.**
Atlas of the vicinities of the cities of Niagara Falls, North Tonawanda and Buffalo, N. Y.    2 p. l., 34 maps. fol. Philadelphia, G. M. Hopkins, 1893.    2319

### OSWEGO.
**Hopkins, G. M.**
City atlas of Oswego, N. Y.    1 p. l., 21 maps. fol. Philadelphia, G. M. Hopkins, 1880.    2320

35799—08——58

## PELHAM.

**Fairchild, J. F.**
Atlas of the city of Mount Vernon and the town of Pelham. 3 p. l., 24 maps. fol. Mount Vernon, N. Y., J. F. Fairchild, 1899.
2321

Atlas of the city of Mount Vernon and the town of Pelham ... 2d ed. 3 p. l., 38 (*i. e.* 39) col. maps. fol. Mouut Vernon, N. Y., J. F. Fairchild, 1908.
2321a

NOTE.—Thaddeus S. Strange, chief draftsman. Copyrighted 1907.

## ROCHESTER.

**Hopkins, G. M.**
City atlas of Rochester, N. Y. 1 p. l., 38 maps. fol. Philadelphia, G. M. Hopkins, 1875.
2322

**Robinson, E.**
Robinson's atlas of the city of Rochester, Monroe county, N. Y. 2 p. l., 35 maps. fol. New York, E. Robinson, 1888.
2323

## SARATOGA.

**Beers, F. W.**, *and* **Cramer, L. H.**
Combination atlas of Saratoga and Ballston. 1 p. l., 18 maps, 8 pl. fol. New York, J. B. Beers & co. 1876.
2324

## SCHENECTADY.

**Hopkins, G. M.**
City atlas of Schenectady, N. Y. 1 p. l., 19 maps. fol. Philadelphia, G. M. Hopkins, 1880.
2325

**Cunningham, R. S., & co.**
Atlas of Schenectady, N. Y. 2 p. l., 20 maps. fol. [New York] R. S. Cunningham & co. 1892.
2326

**Miller, D. L.**
Atlas of the city of Schenectady, New York, embracing maps of the village of Scotia. From official records, private plans and surveys under the direction and personal supervision of D. L. Miller, c. e., assisted by Harry E. Haff ... 1 p. l., 16 fold. maps. fol. Philadelphia, D. L. Miller & A. H. Mueller, 1905.
2327

## SCOTIA.

**Miller, D. L.**
Atlas of the city of Schenectady, New York, embracing maps of the village of Scotia. From official records, private plans and surveys under the direction and personal supervision of D. L. Miller, c. e., assisted by Harry E. Haff ... 1 p. l., 16 fold. maps. fol. Philadelphia, D. L. Miller & A. H. Mueller, 1905.
2328

## SYRACUSE.

**Vose, J. W., & co.**
    Atlas of the city of Syracuse, Onondago county, N. Y.   2 p. l., 25 maps.  fol.  New York, J. W. Vose & co. 1892.     2329

**Hopkins, G. M., co.**
    Atlas of . . . Syracuse . . .   2 p. l., 36 (*i. e.* 37) col. maps. fol.  Philadelphia, G. M. Hopkins co. 1908.     2329a

## TROY.

**Barton, W.**
    Map of the city of Troy, West Troy and Green Island, N. Y., from actual surveys.   3 p. l., 1 map on 11 sheets.  fol.  Troy, 1869.     2330

    NOTE.—Date 1869 on title page; sheet no. 11 has title of map with date 1858.

**Hopkins, G. M.**
    City atlas of Troy, N. Y.   1 p. l., 21 maps.  fol.  Philadelphia, G. M. Hopkins, 1881.     2331

## UTICA.

**Hopkins, G. M.**
    Atlas of the city of Utica, N. Y.   1 p. l., 20 maps.  fol.  Philadelphia, G. M. Hopkins, 1883.     2332

**Miller, D. L.**
    Atlas of the city of Utica, New York. From official records, private plans and surveys under the direction and personal supervision of D. L. Miller, assisted by Roger H. Pidgeon, L. E. Tenne, Thomas Flynn, F. Chester Hale, W. H. Graves, L. E. Layman, A. Y. Peck, A. B. Peck, A. R. Whipple, E. Robinson.   1 p. l., 26 maps.  fol.  Philadelphia, D. L. Miller & co. 1896.     2333

## WEST TROY.

**Barton, W.**
    Map of the city of Troy, West Troy and Green Island, N. Y., from actual surveys.   3 p. l., 1 map on 11 sheets.  fol.  Troy, 1869.     2334

    NOTE.—Date 1869 on title page; sheet no. 11 has title of map with date 1858.

## YONKERS.

**Pidgeon, R. H.**
    Atlas of the city of Yonkers, N. Y.   1 p. l., 26 maps.  fol.  New York, E. Robinson, 1889.     2335

**Pidgeon, R. H.,** *& others.*
    Atlas of the city of Yonkers, New York. From official records, private plans and surveys, under the direction and personal supervision of Roger H. Pidgeon, c. e. assisted by Lucius E. Tenny, Charles J. Bord . . .   2 p. l., 25 maps.  fol.  Philadelphia, D. L. Miller & co. 1896.     2336

**Mueller, A. H.**

Atlas of the city of Yonkers, Westchester county, New York. Also embracing north-west section of the borough of Bronx. Compiled from official records, private plans and actual surveys, by Ellis Kiser, c. e.   2 p. l., 26 maps.   fol.   Philadelphia, A. A. Mueller, 1907.
2337

## NORTH DAKOTA.

### State.

### 1880

**United States.**   *Geographical and geological survey of the Rocky mountain region.*

Report on the geology and resources of the Black Hills of Dakota with atlas by Henry Newton . . . and Walter P. Jenney . . .   1 p. l., 2 maps, pl.   fol.   Washington, gov't print. off., 1880.
2338

NOTE.—Atlas has title: . . . Topographical and geological atlas of the Black Hills of Dakota to accompany the report of Henry Newton . . . New York, J. Bien, 1879.

### 1884

**Andreas, A. T.**

Andreas' historical atlas of Dakota.   2 p. l., 13–210, [2], 211–255 pp. incl. 69 maps, 1 fold. map inserted.   fol.   Chicago, R. R. Donnelley & sons, the Lakeside press, 1884.
2339

### 1894

**Graves & Hardy.**

Eureka pocket atlas of the Red River valley.   1 p. l., 45 pp. incl. 20 maps.   4°.   Fargo, N. Dak., Graves & Hardy, 1894.
2340

### 1908

**Cram, G. F.**

Cram's superior reference atlas of No. and So. Dakota and the world.   170 pp. incl. 79 col. maps, 2 col. pl., illus.   fol.   New York, Chicago, G. F. Cram, ᶜ1908.
2340a

### Counties.

#### CASS.

**Ensign, D. W., & co.**

Plat book of Cass county, North Dakota. Drawn and compiled from personal observations, actual surveys and county records. 138 pp. incl. front., 60 maps, 27 pl. (1 map loose)   fol.   [Philadelphia] D. W. Ensign & co. 1893.
2341

**Polk, R. L., & co.**
The county of Cass, North Dakota, 1906. Topographical, historical, pictorical, miscellaneous.  2 p. l., 5-159 (*i. e.* 162) pp. incl. 62 maps, 11 pl.  fol.  St. Paul, Minn., R. L. Polk & co. 1906.
2342

### GRAND FORKS.
**Ensign, D. W., & co.**
Plat book of Grand Forks, Walsh and Pembina counties, North Dakota. Drawn and compiled from personal observations, actual surveys and county records.  122 pp. incl. front., 78 maps, 17 pl. (folded map loose)  fol.  [Philadelphia?] D. W. Ensign & co. 1893.
2343

### PEMBINA.
**Ensign, D. W., & co.**
Plat book of Grand Forks, Walsh and Pembina counties, North Dakota. Drawn and compiled from personal observations, actual surveys and county records.  122 pp. incl. front., 78 maps, 17 pl. (folded map loose)  fol.  [Philadelphia?] D. W. Ensign & co. 1893.
2344

### WALSH.
**Ensign, D. W., & co.**
Plat book of Grand Forks, Walsh and Pembina counties, North Dakota. Drawn and compiled from personal observations, actual surveys and county records.  122 pp. incl. front., 76 maps, 17 pl. (folded map loose)  fol.  [Philadelphia?] D. W. Ensign & co. 1893.
2345

## OHIO.
### State.
#### 1868
**Walling, H. F.**
Atlas of the state of Ohio, to which is added an atlas of the United States.  2 p. l., 6-101 pp., 2 l. incl. 35 maps.  fol.  New York, H. H. Lloyd & co. 1868.
2346

#### 1872
**Walling, H. F.** *and* **Gray, O. W.**
New topographical atlas of the state of Ohio, with descriptions historical, scientific and statistical together with maps of the United States and territories.  2 p. l., 6-89 pp., 3 l. incl. 34 maps.  fol.  Cincinnati, Stedman, Brown & Lyon, 1872.
2347

#### 1877
**Hayes, E. L.**
Illustrated atlas of the upper Ohio river and valley from Pittsburgh, Pa. to Cincinnati, Ohio.  2 p. l., 5-231 pp. incl. 67 maps, 73 pl.  fol.  Philadelphia, Titus, Simmons & Titus, 1877.
2348

## 1878
**Ohio.** *Geological survey.*
Report of the geological survey of Ohio . . . Atlas.   2 p. l., 6 maps.   fol.   Columbus, Nevins & Myers, 1873–1878.   2349

> Note.—Atlas has title: . . . Geological atlas of the state of Ohio prepared by J. S. Newberry, chief geologist . . . Published by authority of the legislature of Ohio. 1879.

## 1883
**Hardesty, H. H.**
Hardesty's historical and geographical encyclopedia, illustrated . . . Special history of northwestern Ohio, and the geological history of the state. Outline map and history of Meigs county, Ohio, containing a condensed history of the county; biographical sketches; general statistics; miscellaneous matters, &c.   xxiv, [1], 16–294, 40 pp., front., 58 col. maps, 32 pl.   fol.   Chicago and Toledo, H. H. Hardesty & co. 1883.   2350

## 1884
**Hardesty, H. H.**
Hardesty's historical and geographical encyclopedia, illustrated . . . Special military history of Ohio, giving its part in the Indian wars, border annals, the war of 1812, the mexican war, the war of the rebellion . . .   454, [1] pp., front., 82 col. maps, 58 pl.   fol. New York [etc.] H. H. Hardesty & co. 1884.   2351

### Counties.

#### ADAMS.
**Arms, W. F.,** *& others.*
Caldwell's illustrated historical atlas of Adams county, Ohio. 1797–1880. Compiled from actual surveys by professional engineers, by order of county commissioners. Walter F. Arms, manager, Jacob Leamon, historian, F. R. Robjohns, artist.   184 pp. incl. 29 maps, 37 pl.   fol.   Newark, O., J. A. Caldwell [1880?]
2352

#### ASHTABULA.
**Lake, D. J.,** *& others.*
Atlas of Ashtabula county, Ohio. From actual surveys.   93 pp. incl. 38 maps.   fol.   Philadelphia, Titus, Simmons & Titus, 1874.   2353

**Sill, Tucker & co.**
Ashtabula county atlas.   [164] pp. incl. 43 maps, 1 pl.   fol. Ashtabula, O., Sill, Tucker & co. 1905.   2354

> Note.—Various paging.

## ATHENS.

**Lake, D. J.**
 Atlas of Athens county, Ohio, to which is added a township map of the state of Ohio, also an outline and railroad map of the United States. 88 pp. incl. 26 maps, 32 pl. 2 fold. maps at end. fol. Philadelphia, Titus, Simmons & Titus, 1875. 2355

### BROWN.

**Lake, D. J.,** *and* **Griffing, B. N.**
 Atlas of Brown county, Ohio. From actual surveys. To which is added a map of the state of Ohio, also an outline and railroad map of the United States and the hemispheres. 78 pp. incl. 19 maps, 29 pl. 4 maps at end. fol. Philadelphia, Lake, Griffing & Stevenson, 1876. 2356

### BUTLER.

**Everts, L. H.**
 [New historical atlas of Butler county, Ohio, illustrated] cover-title, 10–24, 30–46, 51–104, 107–140 pp. incl. 22 maps, 83 pl. fol. [Philadelphia, L. H. Everts, 1875] 2357
  NOTE.—Imperfect. Title-page and many pages wanting.

### CLARK.

**Lake, D. J.,** *& others.*
 Atlas of Clarke county, Ohio. From actual surveys by and under the direction of D. J. Lake, assisted by B. N. Griffing, J. E. Sherman & J. W. Drew. 57 pp. incl. 22 maps. fol. Philadelphia, C. O. Titus, 1870. 2358

**Rerick brothers.**
 The county of Clark, Ohio, an imperial atlas and art folio, including chronological chart, statistical tables, and description of surveys. 118 pp., 9 l. incl. 23 maps, 18 pl., 4 charts. fol. [Richmond, Ind.] Rerick brothers, 1894. 2359

### CLERMONT.

**Lake, D. J.,** *& others.*
 Atlas of Clermont county, Ohio. From actual surveys. 59 pp. incl. 29 maps. fol. Philadelphia, C. O. Titus, 1870. 2360

 Atlas of Clermont county, Ohio. From actual surveys by D. J. Lake, assisted by J. M. Lathrop, H. L. Kramer and G. P. Sanford. 73, [1] pp., [6] l. incl. 31 maps. fol. Philadelphia, Lake & Gordon, 1891. 2361

### CLINTON.

**Lake, Griffing & Stevenson.**
 An illustrated historical atlas of Clinton county, Ohio. Compiled, drawn and published from actual surveys. 64 pp., [6] l. incl. 20 maps, 13 pl. fol. Philadelphia, Lake, Griffing & Stevenson, 1876. 2362

**Mitchell, Thirey & Hahn.**
    Historical-directory and atlas, Clinton county, Ohio . . . 95, [1] pp., 11 maps, illus. fol. Cincinnati [printed by] S. Rosenthal & co. 1903. 2363

## COLUMBIANA.

**Lake, D. J.**
    Atlas of Columbiana county, Ohio. From actual surveys. 69 pp. incl. 29 maps, 1 pl. fol. Philadelphia, C. O. Titus, 1870.
2364

## COSHOCTON.

**Lake, D. J.**, *& others.*
    Atlas of Coshocton county, Ohio. From actual surveys. 60 pp. incl. 29 maps. fol. Philadelphia, C. O. Titus, 1872. 2365

## CRAWFORD.

**Weber, H. L.** *&* **Swingley, C. D.**
    The 1894 atlas of Crawford county, Ohio. 20 l. incl. 14 maps. fol. Bucyrus, O., H. L. Weber & C. D. Swingley, 1894. 2366
    NOTE.—Pagination irregular; pp. 13–14, 17–21, 23–24, 27–28, 35–38, 41–42, 45–46, 49–52, 57–58, 63–64 wanting.

## CUYAHOGA.

**Lake, D. J.**
    Atlas of Cuyahoga county, Ohio. From actual surveys . . . 205 pp. incl. 52 maps, 48 pl. fol. Philadelphia, Titus, Simmons & Titus, 1874. 2367

**Cram, G. F.**, *& others.*
    Atlas of Cuyahoga county and the city of Cleveland, Ohio. 1 p. l., 4–134 pp. incl. 110 maps. fol. Chicago, G. F. Cram & co. 1892.
2368

**Stranahan, H. B., & co.**
    Maps of Cuyahoga county outside of Cleveland. 1903. 2 p. l., 3–160 pp. incl. 41 maps. fol. Cleveland, H. B. Stranahan & co. 1903. 2369

## DARKE.

**Griffing, B. N.**
    Atlas of Darke county, Ohio. 2 p. l., 5–88 pp. incl. 36 maps. fol. Philadelphia, Griffing, Gordon & co. 1888. 2370

## DEFIANCE.

**Griffing, B. N.**
    Atlas of Defiance county, Ohio. 2 p. l., 5–70 pp., 6 l. incl. 29 maps. fol. Philadelphia, Griffing, Gordon & co. 1890. 2371

## DELAWARE.

**Beers, F. W., Leavenworth, A.**, *and* **Warner, G. E.**, *& others.*
    Atlas of Delaware county, Ohio. From actual surveys. 58 pp. incl. 24 maps, 4 pl. fol. New York, Beers, Ellis & Soule, 1866.
2372

## ERIE.

**Stewart & Page.**
Combination atlas map of Erie county, Ohio. Compiled, drawn and published from personal examinations and surveys. 4 p. l., xix, 4–72 pp. incl. 19 maps, 41 pl. fol. Philadelphia, Stewart & Page, 1874. 2373

**Atlas publishing co.**
Illustrated atlas and directory of Erie county, Ohio. Including a directory of the freeholders of the county, compiled and published from official records and personal examination. 75 pp., 8 l. incl. 24 maps, 3 pl. fol. Battle Creek, Mich., the atlas publishing co. 1896. 2374

## FAIRFIELD.

**Everts, L. H.**
Combination atlas map of Fairfield county, Ohio. Compiled, drawn and published from personal examinations and surveys. 108 pp. incl. 23 maps, 64 pl. fol. Philadelphia, L. H. Everts, 1875. 2375

## FRANKLIN.

**Caldwell, J. A., Gould, H. T.**, & others.
Caldwell's atlas of Franklin county and of the city of Columbus, Ohio. From actual surveys. 3 p. l., 8–96 pp. incl. 37 maps, 8 pl. fol. Columbus, O., J. A. Caldwell & H. T. Gould, 1872. 2376

## FULTON.

**Griffing, B. N.**
Atlas of Fulton County, Ohio. 2 p. l., 5–51 pp., 6 l. incl. 21 maps. fol. Philadelphia, Griffing, Gordon & co. 1888. 2377

## GALLIA.

**Griffith, W.**, *jr.*
Illustrated atlas of Gallia county, Ohio. 52 pp. incl. 23 maps, 11 pl. fol. Cincinnati, the county commissioners, 1874. 2378

## GEAUGA.

**Lake, D. J.**
Atlas of Lake and Geauga counties, Ohio. From actual surveys. 95 pp. incl. 32 maps, 5 pl. 2 fold. maps. fol. Philadelphia, Titus, Simmons & Titus, 1874. 2379

## GUERNSEY.

**Lake, D. J.**
Atlas of Guernsey county, Ohio. From actual surveys. 59 pp. incl. 29 maps. fol. Philadelphia, C. O. Titus, 1870. 2380

## HAMILTON.

**Harrison, R. H.**, & others.
Titus' atlas of Hamilton co., Ohio. From actual surveys by R. H. Harrison, assisted by Geo. E. Warner, A. Leavenworth,

**Harrison, R. H.**, & others—Continued.
   J. E. Sherman, L. C. Warner & R. T. Higgins, to which is added a township map of the state of Ohio, also an outline & railroad map of the United States.   117 pp. incl. 39 maps.   fol.   Philadelphia, C. O. Titus, 1869.   2381
   NOTE.—Imperfect: pp. 6–7, 111–112, 2 maps, wanting.

## HARDIN.

**Howland, H. G.**
   Atlas of Hardin co., Ohio, from records & original surveys drawn & compiled by H. G. Howland, illustrations by H. G. Howland, Chas. Gasche, & Wm. Engel.   130 pp. incl. 22 maps, 29 pl.   fol.   Philadelphia, R. Sutton & co. 1879.   2382
   NOTE.—pp. 119–120 wanting.

## HARRISON.

**Caldwell, J. A.**
   Caldwell's atlas of Harrison county, Ohio. From actual surveys by and under the direction of J. A. Caldwell, c. e., assisted by C. T. Arms, sr., c. e., J. A. Underwood, c. e., C. T. Arms, jr., H. Cring, c. e. . . .   2 p. l., [1], 5–107 pp., 1 l., incl. 27 maps, 33 pl.   fol.   Condit, Ohio, J. A. Caldwell, 1875.   2383
   NOTE.—Pagination irregular.

## HIGHLAND.

**Lake, D. J.**, & others.
   Atlas of Highland county, Ohio.   From actual surveys.   64 pp. incl. 26 maps.   fol.   Philadelphia, C. O. Titus, 1871.   2384

**Lathrop, J. M.** and **Penny, H. C.**
   Atlas of Highland county, Ohio.   2 p. l., 82 pp. incl. 27 maps.   fol.   Philadelphia, H. C. Mead & co. 1887.   2385

## HOCKING.

**Lake, D. J.**
   Atlas of Hocking county, Ohio, to which is added a township map of the state of Ohio, also an outline and railroad map of the United States.   2 p. l., 17 maps, 1 pl.   fol.   Philadelphia, Titus, Simmons & Titus, 1876.   2386

## HURON.

**Mesnard, H. W.** and **Perrin, W. N.**
   Atlas of Huron county, Ohio.   2 p. l., 5–104 pp. incl. 36 maps, 2 pl.   fol.   Cleveland, L. B. Mesnard, son & co. 1891.   2387

## JACKSON.

**Lake, D. J.**
   Atlas of Jackson county, Ohio, to which is added a township map of the state of Ohio, also an outline and railroad map of the United States.   2 p. l., 5–45 pp. incl. 18 maps, 6 pl.   fol.   Philadelphia, Titus, Simmons & Titus, 1875.   2388

## JEFFERSON.

**Beers, F. W., Warner, G. E.** & *others.*
Atlas of Jefferson county, Ohio. 1 p. l., 29 maps. fol. New York, F. W. Beers & co. 1871. 2389

## KNOX.

**Caldwell, J. A., Starr, J. W.,** & *others.*
Atlas of Knox county, Ohio. From actual surveys. 89 pp. ncl. 31 maps, 9 pl. fol. Granville. O., J. A. Caldwell & J. W. Starr, 1871. 2390

**Caldwell, J. A.**
Atlas of Knox county, Ohio. 3 p. l., 10–140 pp. incl. 40 maps, 1 pl. fol. Philadelphia, E. R. Caldwell, 1896. 2391
NOTE.—Pagination irregular.

## LAKE.

**Lake, D. J.**
Atlas of Lake and Geauga counties, Ohio. From actual surveys. 95 pp. incl. 32 maps, 5 pl. 2 fold. maps. fol. Philadelphia, Titus, Simmons & Titus, 1874. 2392

## LICKING.

**Beers, F. W., Nichols, B.,** & *others.*
Atlas of Licking county, Ohio. 2 p. l., 33 maps, 8 pl. fol. New York, Beers, Soule & co. 1866. 2393

**Everts, L. H.**
Combination atlas map of Licking county, Ohio. Compiled, drawn and published from personal examinations and surveys. 159 pp. incl. 37 maps, 73 pl. 1 folded map. fol. [Philadelphia] L. H. Everts, 1875. 2394

## LORAIN.

**Lake, D. J.**
Atlas of Lorain county, Ohio. From actual surveys by and under the direction of D. J. Lake, c. e., assisted by B. N. Griffing, E. L. Hayes, C. H. Edwards, J. P. Edwards, A. C. Ferry. 73 pp. incl. 29 maps. fol. Philadelphia, Titus Simmons & Titus, 1874. 2395

## LUCAS.

**Uhl, J. B.**
The official atlas of Lucas county, Ohio. v. 1. 69 pp. incl. 17 maps. fol. Toledo, Ohio, Uhl bros. co. 1900. 2396
CONTENTS.
v. 1. Townships & villages.

## MAHONING.

**Mueller, A. H., co.**
Atlas of surveys of Manoning county, Ohio. Compiled and published under the personal supervision and management of the Mahoning county abstract co. Youngstown, Ohio. 2 p. l., 1 l., 30 maps. fol. Philadelphia, A. H. Mueller co. 1899–1900. 2397

## MARION.

**Harrison, Sutton & Hare.**
Atlas of Marion county, Ohio, from records and original surveys, to which is added a map of the United States & a railroad map of Ohio. Illustrations by H. G. Howland. 128 pp. incl. 25 maps, 24 pl. fol. Philadelphia, Harrison, Sutton & Hare, 1878. 2398
NOTE.—pp. 17–18, 25–26, 99–100 wanting.

## MERCER.

**Griffing, B. N.**
Atlas of Mercer county, Ohio. 2 p. l., 5–60 pp. incl. 28 maps. fol. Philadelphia, Griffing, Gordon & co. 1888. 2399

## MIAMI.

**Furnas, B. E.**
A combined atlas-directory of Miami county, Ohio . . . Comp. and arranged by B. E. Furnas. Pub. by F. M. Sterrett and B. E. Furnas. 2 p. l., 44, 140, 187 pp., 14 maps. sm. 4°. [Springfield, O., republic printing co.] 1883. 2400

**Rerick brothers.**
The county of Miami, Ohio, an imperial atlas and art folio, including chronological chart, statistical tables and description of surveys. 95 pp., 9 l. incl. 27 maps, 12 pl., 4 charts. fol. [Richmond, Ind.] Rerick brothers, 1894. 2401

## MONROE.

**Caldwell, J. A.**
Caldwell's atlas of Monroe county, Ohio. 3 p. l., 8–139 pp. incl. 25 maps. fol. Mount Vernon, O., atlas publishing co. 1898. 2402

## MORROW.

**Lake, D. J., & *others*.**
Atlas of Morrow county, Ohio. From actual surveys. 51 pp. incl. 23 maps. fol. Philadelphia, C. O. Titus, 1871. 2403

**Buck, T. E.**
Atlas of Morrow county, Ohio, from actual surveys and official records, 75 pp. incl. 27 maps. fol. Mt. Gilead, O., T. E. Buck, 1901. 2404

## MUSKINGUM.

**Beers, F. W., Nichols, B., & *others*.**
Atlas of Muskingum county, Ohio. From actual surveys. 2 p. l., 4–37 pp. incl. 31 maps, 3 pl. fol. New York, Beers, Soule & co. 1866. 2405

## NOBLE.

**Wall, Mann & Hall.**
 Illustrated atlas of Noble county, Ohio. 2 p. l., 4–95 pp. incl. 27 maps, 13 pl. fol. Philadelphia, Wall, Mann & Hall, 1879.
                                                                                                      2406

## OTTAWA.

**Goodman, H. J.**
 Illustrated historical atlas of Ottawa county, Ohio . . . Compiled from the most reliable records and from actual surveys. 1 p. l., [106] pp. incl. 29 col. maps. fol. Port Clinton, Ohio, H. J. Goodman, 1900.                                                    2406a
   NOTE.—Pagination irregular.

## PAULDING.

**Morrow, O.**
 Atlas and directory of Paulding county, Ohio. Containing maps of Paulding county, townships and incorporated villages, also maps of the United States and state of Ohio, together with an outline map of Paulding county, showing location of townships, villages, roads, railroads, pikes, principal streams, etc., etc., etc. 55 pp. incl. 26 maps. fol. [Paulding, O.] F. Miller & W. N. Shaffer [°1906]                                                                                2407

## PICKAWAY.

**Lake, D. J.,** & others.
 Atlas of Pickaway county, Ohio. From actual surveys. 57 pp., incl. 26 maps. fol. Philadelphia, C. O. Titus, 1871.  2408

## PORTAGE.

**Stranahan, H. B., & co.**
 Atlas of Portage county, Ohio. 81 pp. incl. 27 maps (2 maps in text), 10 pl. fol. Cleveland, H. B. Stranahan & co. 1900.
                                                                                                      2409

## PREBLE.

**Lake, D. J.,** & others.
 Atlas of Preble county, Ohio. From actual surveys. 49 pp. incl. 24 maps. fol. Philadelphia, C. O. Titus, 1871.  2410

## RICHLAND.

**Andreas, A. T.**
 Atlas map of Richland county, Ohio. Compiled, drawn & published from personal examinations & surveys. [79] pp. incl. 17 maps, 15 pl. fol. Chicago, A. T. Andreas, 1873.     2411

**Rerick brothers.**
 The county of Richland, Ohio. An imperial atlas and art folio, including chronological chart, statistical tables and description of surveys. 98 pp., 6 l. incl. 29 maps, 24 pl., 4 charts. fol. Richmond, Ind., Rerick brothers, 1896.                                  2412

## ROSS.

**Gould, H. T.,** *& others.*
Illustrated atlas of Ross county and Chillicothe, Ohio. From surveys and official records. 83 pp. incl. 20 maps, 15 pl. fol. Columbus, O., H. T. Gould & co. 1875. 2413

## SENECA.

**Rerick brothers.**
The county of Seneca, Ohio, an imperial atlas and art folio, including chronological chart, statistical tables, and description of surveys. 1896. 84 pp. incl. 31 maps, 10 pl., 4 charts. fol. Richmond, Ind., Rerick brothers, 1896. 2414

## STARK.

**Beers, F. W., Sanford, G. P.,** *& others.*
Atlas of Stark county, Ohio. Scale 300 feet to the inch. 2 p. l., 4 l., 30 maps. fol. New York, F. W. Beers & co. 1870. 2415

**Kauffman, W. J.,** *and* **Kauffman, O. F.**
Atlas of Stark county, Ohio. 2 p. l., 8-92 pp. incl. 78 maps, 23 pl. fol. Canton, O., the Ohio map and atlas co. 1896. 2416

## SUMMIT.

**Akron map and atlas co.**
Illustrated Summit county, Ohio, representing her manufacturing interests, commercial houses, public institutions, farms, homes and people, with history, statistics and general information, maps of United States, Ohio, Summit county townships, towns, villages and city of Akron. 180 pp. incl. 99 maps, 4 pl. fol. Akron, O. Akron map and atlas co. 1891. 2417

## TUSCARAWAS.

**Rhodes, E. S.**
The first centennial history and atlas of Tuscarawas county, Ohio ... 1 p. l., 36, 236 pp. incl. 32 maps, illus. fol. New Philadelphia, O. E. S. Rhodes, 1908. 2418

## VINTON.

**Lake, D. J.**
Atlas of Vinton county, Ohio, to which is added a township map of the state of Ohio, also an outline and railroad map of the United States. 2 p. l., 15 maps, 3 pl. fol. Philadelphia, Titus, Simmons & Titus, 1876. 2419

## WASHINGTON.

**Lake, D. J.,** *& others.*
Atlas of Washington county, Ohio. From actual surveys. To which is added a township map of the state of Ohio, also an outline & railroad map of the United States. 96 pp. incl. 24 maps, 20 pl. fol. Philadelphia, Titus, Simmons & Titus, 1875. 2420

## Cities.

### CHILLICOTHE.

**Gould, H. T.,** & *others.*
Illustrated atlas of Ross county and Chillicothe, Ohio. From surveys and official records. 83 pp. incl. 20 maps, 15 pl. fol. Columbus, H. T. Gould & co. 1875. 2421

### CINCINNATI.

**Harrison, R. H.,** & *others.*
Titus' atlas of Hamilton county, Ohio, to which is added a township map of the state of Ohio also an outline and railroad map of the United States. 117 pp. incl. 38 maps. fol. Philadelphia, C. O. Titus, 1869. 2422

NOTE.—Cover-title : Atlas of Cincinnati and Hamilton co.

**Robinson, E.,** & **Pidgeon, R. H.**
Atlas of the city of Cincinnati, Ohio. 1 p. l., 29 maps. fol. New York, E. Robinson, 1883–1884. 2423

### CLEVELAND.

**Hopkins, G. M.**
City atlas of Cleveland, Ohio. 1 p. l., 42 maps. fol. Philadelphia, G. M. Hopkins, 1881. 2424

**Cram, G. F.,** & *others.*
Atlas of Cuyahoga county and city of Cleveland, Ohio. 1 p. l., 4–134 pp. incl. 110 maps. fol. Chicago, G. F. Cram & co. 1892. 2425

**Schake, W., co.**
Ward directory of the city of Cleveland. Published bi-monthly. The 42 wards of the city, each separate with boundary and streets, with ward numbers and arranged with alphabetic index . . . 1 p. l., [33] pp., 42 maps. 24º. Cleveland, W. Schake co. [1894] 2426

**Stranahan, H. B., & co.**
Official atlas of Cleveland, Ohio, showing wards and precincts, 1894–95. 3 p. l., 23 maps. obl. 8º. [Cleveland] H. B. Stranahan & co. [1894] 2427

NOTE.—"This atlas was issued by the authority of the board of elections, and adopted by them as the only official publication showing the new wards and precincts."

**Flynn, T.,** & *others.*
Atlas of the suburbs of Cleveland, Ohio . . . 2 p. l., 29 maps. fol. Philadelphia, A. H. Mueller & co. 1898. 2428

**Krause, F. L.,** & *others.*
Atlas of the city of Cleveland, Ohio. 3 p. l., 45 maps. fol. Philadelphia, A. H. Mueller & co. 1898. 2429

**Mohr, J.**
 Atlas of Cleveland, O., showing wards and precincts. Compiled from original drawings . . . 1 p. l., 32 maps. obl. 8°. Cleveland, Mohr & co. [1906]  2430

### COLUMBUS.

**Caldwell, J. A., Gould, H. T.,** & *others.*
 Caldwell's atlas of Franklin county and of the city of Columbus, Ohio. From actual surveys. 3 p. l., 8–96 pp. incl. 37 maps, 8 pl. fol. Columbus, J. A. Caldwell & H. T. Gould, 1872.  2431

### DAYTON.

**Cellarius, F. J.**
 Atlas of the city of Dayton, Ohio and adjoining territory. Compiled from original surveys and official records . . . 4 p. l., 34 maps (1 fold. map) obl. fol. [Dayton] 1907.  2432

### MANSFIELD.

**Robinson, E.,** *and* **Pidgeon, R. H.**
 Atlas of the city of Mansfield, Ohio. 1 p. l., 13 maps. fol. New York, E. Robinson, 1882.  2433

### MARIETTA.

**Roe, F. B.**
 Atlas of the city of Marietta, Washington co., Ohio, and vicinity; iucluding Williamstown, Wood co., W. Va. Drawn from recent surveys and official records . . . 2 p. l., 18 maps. fol. Chicago-New York, G. F. Cram & co. 1902.  2434

### SPRINGFIELD.

**Robinson, E.,** *and* **Pidgeon, R. H.**
 Atlas of the city of Springfield, Ohio. 1 p. l., 21 maps. fol. New York, E. Robinson, 1882.  2435

### TOLEDO.

**Hopkins, G. M.**
 City atlas of Toledo, Ohio. 1 p. l., 36 maps. fol. Philadelphia, G. M. Hopkins, 1881.  2436

# OKLAHOMA.

### State.

#### 1908

**Cram, G. F.**
 Cram's superior reference atlas of Oklahoma and the world. 160 pp. incl. 68 col. maps, 3 pl., illus. fol. New York, Chicago, G. F. Cram, ᶜ1908.  2436a

## OREGON.

### State.

#### 1840-1842

**Duflot de Mofras, E.**
Exploration du territoire de l'Orégon, des Californies et de la mer Vermeille exécutée pendant les années 1840, 1841 et 1842 . . . Atlas. 2 p. l., front., 22 maps on 15 l., 2 pl., diagr. fol. Paris, A. Bertrand, 1844. 2437

NOTE.—Atlas accompanying this work has same title. pl. 23 is bound in as frontispiece.

CONTENTS.

no. 1. Carte de la côte de l'Amérique sur l'océan Pacifique septentrionale comprenant le territoire de l'Orégon, les Californies, la mer Vermeille, partie des territoires de la compagnie de la baie d'Hudson et de l'Amérique russe. 1844.
" 2. Carte de l'océan Pacifique au nord de l'équateur.
" 3. Isthme de Tehuantepec.
" 4. Plan du port d'Acapulco sur la côte occidentale du Mexique.
" 5. Plan du port del Manzanillo . . .
" 6. Plan de San Blas.
" 7. Plan de Mazatlan.
" 8. Plan de la baie de la Paz et du port de Pichilingue.
" 9. Plan du port de Guaymas sur la mer Vermeille.
" 10. Plan de l'embouchure du rio Colorado . . .
" 11. Plan du port de S. Diego . . .
" 12. Mouillage de San Pedro.
" 13. Mouillage de la mission de Sta. Bárbara.
" 14. Plan du port et de la baie de Monte-Rey . . .
" 15. Baie de la Trinidad.
" 16. Port de San Francisco . . .— Entrée du port de San Francisco . . .
" 17. Carte détaillée du mouillage du fort Ross et du port de la Bodega ou Romanzoff . . .
" 18. Carte du rio Colombia . . .
" 19. Port de Quadra ou de la découverte.
" 20. Plan du port de Nutka . . .
" 21. Plan du port de la nouvelle Archangel dans l'île de Sitka . . .
" 22. Plan du port Mulgrave.

#### 1894

**Eitel, E. E.**
County atlas of Oregon and Washington, showing all towns, posts offices, railroads, county roads, stage lines carrying passengers, mail and express, and distances between points. Drawn expressly for Fireman's fund insurance co. 4 p. l., 19 maps. obl. 16°. San Francisco, D. S. Stanley & co. [1894] 2438

NOTE.—Copyright by Fireman's fund insurance co. 1894.

## PENNSYLVANIA.

### FORTS.

**Pennsylvania.** *Indian forts commission.*
Report of the commission to locate the site of the frontier forts of Pennsylvania. 2 v. 8°. [Harrisburg] C. M. Busch, state printer, 1896.     2439

CONTENTS.

*Maps and views.*

v. 1, opp. p. 1. Site of frontier forts between the Delaware and Susquehanna.
"   "   "   5. Log house of John Harris.—1720.
"   "   "   9. Site of fort Hunter.
"   "   "   27. Site of forts Manada, Brown, and Swatara.
" bet. pp. 32–33. Site of Robinson's fort.
"   "   "   34–35. " " Harper's and Reed's block houses.
"   "   "   46–47. " " fort Swatara.
"   "   "   48–49. " " line of forts along Blue Mountains.
"   "   "   52–53. " " fort Swatara and Hess' block house.
" opp. p. 59. Site of Ulrich fort or block house.
"   "   "   61. " " Moravian church stockade, Lebanon county.
"   "   "   62. " " Gloninger block house, 1895.
"   "   "   63. " " Gloninger fort or block house.
"   "   "   65. " " Zeller fort block house.
"   "   "   " Zeller block house. 1895.
"   "   "   69. Brietenbach block house, 1895.
" bet. pp. 70–71. Site of fort Henry, Berks county.
" opp. p. 99. Present site of fort Northkill.
"   "   "   121. " " " fort Lebanon.
"   "   "   135. " " " fort Franklin.
"   "   "   141. " " " fort Everett.
"   "   "   157. Site of fort Lehigh.
" bet. pp. 160–161. Site of Kern's block house [Tucker's fort]
" opp. p. 175. Front view of Deshler's fort. 1895.
" bet. pp. 176–177. Site of Deshler's fort or block house.
" opp. p. 177. Deshler fort or block house, built 1760.
"   "   "   179. Ralston and Brown stockade.—"Irish settlement."
"   "   "   181. Ralston and Brown stockade, in the "Irish settlement."
" bet. pp. 182–183. Site of Ralston's fort or block house.
" opp. p. 185. Plan of fort Allen.—1756.
"   "   "   186. Present site of fort Allen.
"   "   "   225. " " " " Norris.
"   "   "   237. Fort or block house near Wind Gap.
"   "   "   245. Site of Doll's block house.
"   "   "   251. Old Whitefield house at Nazareth.
" bet. pp. 256–257. Historical map of the barony of Nazareth, in Northampton county Pennsylvania comprising its five moravian settlements, 1758. From surveys by C. G. Reuter and others. Drawn by Spencer Bonsall, jany. 1878.—Inset: Town of Nazareth.
"   "   "   258–259. Friedensthal . . . 1758.
" opp. p. 267. Christians' spring.—Stockade.
"   "   "   269. The Rose tavern.—Stockade.
"   "   "   277. Stroudsburg—Showing site of fort Hamilton.

v. 1, opp. p. 281. View of Stroudsburg in 1842, showing site of fort Hamilton.
" " " 301. Site of fort Hyndshaw.
" " " 323. Fort or block house at Depui's.
" " " 326. Old Shawnee church, site of fort Dupui.
" bet. pp. 328-329. Site of fort Penn at Stroudsburg.
" " " 348-349. Plan of fort Augusta.
" opp. p. 354. " " " "
" " " 356. Headquarters of commandant, fort Augusta, 1757.
" " " 360. Remains of the old magazine of fort Augusta.
" " " 363. Site of fort Jenkins, southwest view, showing North branch.
" " " 367. Site of fort Jenkins, southeast view, showing old well.
" " " 373. Site of fort McClure, town of Bloomsburg.
" " " 375. Fort Rice, at Montgomery's, Northumberland county.
" " " 377. Scene of the Sugarloaf massacre, 1780.
" " " 381. Site of fort Freeland, showing spring and old kitchen.
" bet. pp. 418-419. Position of the Wyoming forts.
" opp. p. 439. Forty fort, Wyoming, in 1778.
" " " 446. Pittston fort on Susquehanna at Pittston.
" " " 450. Stewart's block house.
" bet. pp. 466-467. Disposition of the Pennsylvania troops in the western district for the winter season 1764.
" " " 476-477. Original plan of fort Bedford.
" opp. p. 505. Site of fort Potter.
" " " 509. Site of fort Lowther.
" " " 511. Plan of fort Lowther, Carlisle.
" bet. pp. 512-513. Shippensburg, Pa.
" bet. pp. 604-605. Site of fort Granville, Mifflin co., near Lewistown.
" opp. p. 618. Remains of Hendrick's block house, Snyder county.
v. 2, front. Carte d'un voyage fait dans la belle rivière en la Nouvelle France 1749. Par révérend père Bonnecamps.
" bet. pp. 32-33. Site of fort Necessity and the Great Meadows.
" " " 38-39. Fort Du Quesne 1754.
" opp. p. 49. Braddock's route. 1755.
" " " 53. Braddock's battle field, july 9, 1755. 1.
" " " 59. " " " " " " 2.
" bet. pp. 64-65. Historical map of southwestern Pennsylvania showing sites of principal old forts, block-houses, military roads and trails . . . By G. D. Albert and L. W. Fogg.
" " " 80-81. West Pennsylvania and Virginia. 1755. From mr. Darlington's fort Pitt.
" " " 98-99. The first fort Pitt, 1758.
" opp. p. 101. Fort Pitt and its environs. January, 1759.
" bet. pp. 106-107. Bouquet's redoubt at fort Pitt.
" opp. p. 113. Plan of Fort Pitt, 1761.
" bet. pp. 120-121. The old redoubt at fort Pitt.
" " " 154-155. Fort Pitt in 1795.
" " " 208-209. Plan of fort Ligonier with part of the retranchment.
" " " 224-225. Copy made from official map of the borough of Erie made in 1837.
" " " 288-289. Plan of fort Ligonier with part of the retranchment.
" " " 320-321. Hannastown with line of the Forbes road and route of the Indians at the time of destruction july 13th, 1782. John B. Street. 15 jany 1895.
" " " 358-359. Map of Fairfield twp. & part of Ligonier valley, Westmoreland co. Pa. Showing the location of fort Palmer.

**Pennsylvania.** *Indian forts commission*—Continued.

  v. 2, bet. pp. 358–359. Plan of fort Palmer.
  " opp. p. 382. Fort Burd or Redstone. Brownsville, Pa.
  " " " 485. Fort McIntosh.—Site of town of Beaver.
  " " " 496. Site of fort McIntosh, Beaver. From a sketch made by hon. Daniel Agnew.
  " bet. pp. 512–513. Sketch of col. Bouquet's engagement with 400 Indians near Bushy run aug. 6–1763.
  " opp. p. 537. Site of old fort Presque Isle.
  " " " 544. Plan of Presque Isle and harbor of Erie, 1763.
  " " " 566. Sketch of the site of fort Le Bœuf, Waterford, Erie co. Pa.
  " " " 576. Fort Le Bœuf (1796) at Waterford, Erie county, Pa.
  " bet. pp. 584–585. French fort Machault. 1753–9.
  " opp. p. 591. English fort Venango. 1760–1763.

## GEOLOGICAL.

**Pennsylvania.** *2ᵈ geological survey.*

Grand atlas. Division i–v. 6 v. fol. Harrisburg, L. S. Hart, 1884–5. 2440

  NOTE.—This atlas contains "Maps and sections printed on heavy paper (sheets 26 inches by 32 inches) of similar maps and sections printed on light paper sheets contained in the octavo atlases" [accompanying Annual reports of the geological survey of Pennsylvania for 1885–7] *cf.* Ingham's "List . . . of publications of the Pennsylvania geological survey, 1874–1891. [Harrisburg] C. M. Busch, 1896."

CONTENTS.

  Div. I. County geological maps. pt. I. Contains fifty six county maps on forty nine sheets. title, 49 sheets.
  " II. Anthracite coal fields. pt. 1. Contains twenty six sheets relating to the eastern ends of the western, middle and southern fields in Carbon, Schuylkill, Columbia and Northumberland counties. 1884. title, 26 sheets.
  " II. pt. 2. Contains twenty two sheets relating to portions of the northern and eastern middle fields in Luzerne county. 1885. title, 22 sheets.
  " III. Petroleum and bituminous coal fields. pt. I. Contains thirty-two sheets relating to . . . petroleum and bituminous coal fields and three sheets relating to the quaternary period. 1885. title, 35 sheets.
  " IV. South mountain and Great valley topographical maps. pt. I. Contains thirty sheets relating to the Durham and Reading Hills and Bordering valleys in Northampton, Lehigh, Bucks and Berks counties, and thirteen sheets relating to the South mountains in Adams, Franklin, Cumberland and York counties. 1885. title, 34 sheets. "Sheets XXXV to XLIII (inclusive) of this atlas are now (june 1, 1885) being printed. These sheets, printed on light paper, will be published in octavo atlas D⁶, and those on heavy paper will be issued for subsequent insertion in this portfolio."
  " V. Central and south-eastern Pennsylvania. pt. 1. Contains thirty-five sheets. Twenty-nine sheets relate to the topography and geology of the paleozoic strata in parts of Cambria, Blair, Bedford, Huntington, Mifflin, Centre and Union counties. Five sheets contain a map and geological cross section along the east bank of the Susquehanna river . . . one sheet contains cross-section of the Philadelphia belt of Azoic rocks. 1885. title, 35 sheets.

**Beers, F. W.,** & *others.*
  Atlas of the oil region of Pennsylvania.   4 p. l., 7 l., 38 maps. obl. fol.   New York, F. W. Beers, A. D. Ellis & G. G. Soule [1865]   2441

### OHIO RIVER.
**Hayes, E. L.**
  Illustrated atlas of the upper Ohio river and valley from Pittsburgh, Penn. to Cincinnati, Ohio.   2 p. l., 5-231 pp. incl. 67 maps, 73 pl.   fol.   Philadelphia, Titus, Simmons & Titus, 1877.   2442

### RAILROADS.
**Hopkins, G. M.**
  Atlas of Bryn Mawr and vicinity, or of property along the Pennsylvania r. r., including 1½ miles each side of the road and from city line to Malvern station.   1 p. l., 29 maps.   fol.   Philadelphia, G. M. Hopkins, 1881.   2443

  Atlas of properties along the Philadelphia, Wilmington and Baltimore railroad and the Philadelphia & Westchester rail road, from Philadelphia to Chester.   1 p. l., 28 maps.   fol.   Philadelphia, G. M. Hopkins, 1882.   2444

  Atlas of properties near the north Pennsylvania rail road from Wayne junct. to Penllyn stan.   1 p. l., 23 maps.   fol.   Philadelphia, G. M. Hopkins, 1883.   2445

  Atlas of properties near the Philadelphia and Trenton railroad, Frankfort to Trenton. (New York div. Penna. r. r.)   1 p. l., 22 maps.   fol.   G. M. Hopkins, Philadelphia, 1885.   2446

**Baist, G. W.**
  Atlas of properties along the Schuylkill valley from Philadelphia to Norristown, including 1½ miles each side of the Schuylkill river northwest from School Lane and Fairmount Park.   1 p. l., 25 maps.   fol.   Philadelphia, J. L. Smith, 1886.   2447

**Smith, J. L.**
  Atlas of properties along the Philadelphia, Wilmington and Baltimore r. r., Baltimore & Ohio r. r., Phila. & West Chester r. r. and part of Philada. & Reading r. r. Philadelphia to Chester and Elwyn sta., from official surveys, private plans and records.   1 p. l., 32 maps.   fol.   Philadelphia, J. L. Smith, 1889.   2448

**Mueller, A. H.**
  Atlas of properties on line of Pennsylvania r. r. from Rosemont to Westchester. Compiled and drawn from official plans and actual surveys by Ellis Kiser, Otto Barthel & St. J. Ogier . . .   1 p. l., 20 maps.   fol.   Philadelphia, A. H. Mueller & co. 1897.   2449

Atlas of properties on main line Pennsylvania railroad from Overbrook to Paoli. Compiled from actual surveys, official records and private plans, by Ellis Kiser . . .   1 p. l., 30 maps.   fol.   Philadelphia, A. H. Mueller, 1908.   2450

## State.

### 1871
**Hopkins, G. M., & co.**
Atlas of the county of Montgomery and the state of Pennsylvania. 2 p. l., 36 maps.   fol.   Philadelphia, G. M. Hopkins & co. 1871.
2451

### 1872
**Hopkins, G. M., & co.**
Atlas of the county of Fayette and the state of Pennsylvania. 3 p. l., 34 maps.   fol.   Philadelphia, G. M. Hopkins & co. 1872.
2452
NOTE.—Pagination irregular.

### 1872
**Walling, H. F.,** *and* **Gray, O. W.**
New topographical atlas of the state of Pennsylvania, with descriptions historical, scientific and statistical, together with a map of the United States and territories.   2 p. l., 6-110, [120] pp. incl. 25 maps.   fol.   Philadelphia, Stedman, Brown & Lyon, 1872.   2453

### 1873
**Hopkins, G. M., & co.**
Combination atlas of the county of Mercer and the state of Pennsylvania, from actual surveys & official records.   2 p. l., 111 pp. incl. 40 maps.   fol.   Philadelphia, G. M. Hopkins & co. 1873.
2454
NOTE.—Imperfect: pp. 67-72, 85-86, 93-94, 109-110 wanting.

### 1874
**Hopkins, G. M., & co.**
Combination atlas of the county of Butler and the state of Pennsylvania.   2 p. l., 32 maps.   fol.   Philadelphia, G. M. Hopkins & co. 1874.   2455
NOTE.—Pagination irregular.

### 1900
**Bien, J. R.**
Atlas of the state of Pennsylvania, prepared from original surveys and various local surveys revised and corrected. Based on the triangulations and surveys of the U. S. geological survey, U. S. coast and geodetic survey, U. S. lake survey and the second geological survey of Pennsylvania.   2 p. l., ii-xx pp., 47 maps, 1 chart.   fol.   New York, J. Bien & co. 1900.   2456

## 1901
**Bien, J. R.**
Atlas of the state of Pennsylvania, prepared under the direction of Joseph R. Bien from original surveys and various local surveys revised and corrcted, based on the triangulations and surveys of the U. S. geological survey, U. S. coast and geodetic survey, U. S. lake survey and the second geological survey of Pennsylvania. 2 p. l., xx pp., 47 maps, 1 chart. fol. New York, J. Bien & co. 1901. 2457

## 1901
**Miller, H. P.**
Outline maps of the counties of Allegheny, Berks, Bucks, Cambria, Dauphin, Fayette, Lackawanna, Lancaster, Luzerne, Montgomery, Philadelphia, Schuylkill, Westmoreland and York, and cities of Philadelphia, Pittsburg, Allegheny and Scranton, with population of 1900, vote for president, 1900, and vote for governor, 1898, by minor civil divisions, as ordered by resolution of the legislature. 1 p. l., 52 pp. incl. 16 maps. obl. fol. [Harrisburg?] 1901. 2458

### Counties.
#### ALLEGHENY.
**Hopkins, G. M.**
Atlas of the county of Allegheny, Penn. 2 p. l., 2 l., 60 maps. fol. Philadelphia, G. M. Hopkins, 1876. 2459

#### BEDFORD.
**Beers, F. W.**
County atlas of Bedford, Penn. 2 p. l., 2 l., 33 maps. fol. New York, F. W. Beers & co. 1877. 2460

#### BERKS.
**Davis, F. A.**
Illustrated historical atlas of Berks county, Penn. Compiled & drawn from personal examinations, surveys &c. 7 p. l., 19–106, ii–xii pp. incl. 47 maps, 20 pl. fol. Reading, Pa., Reading publishing house, 1876. 2461

#### BLAIR.
**Nichols, B.**
Atlas of Blair and Huntingdon counties, Penn., from actual surveys. 161 pp. incl. 55 maps. fol. Philadelphia, A. Pomeroy & co. 1873. 2462

#### BRADFORD.
**Beers, F. W., Sanford, G. P.,** *& others.*
Atlas of Bradford county, Penn. 3 p. l., 40 maps, 4 pl. fol. New York, F. W. Beers, A. D. Ellis & G. G. Soule, 1869. 2463
NOTE.—Pagination irregular.

## BUCKS.

**Scott, J. D.**
  Combination atlas map of Bucks county, Penn. Compiled, drawn and published from personal examinations and surveys. 96 pp. incl. 42 maps, 31 pl. fol. Philadelphia, J. D. Scott, 1876.     2464

## BUTLER.

**Hopkins, G. M., & co.**
  Combination atlas of the county of Butler and the state of Pennsylvania. 2 p. l., 32 maps. fol. Philadelphia, G. M. Hopkins & co. 1874.     2465
  NOTE.—Pagination irregular.

## CAMBRIA.

**Caldwell, J. A.**
  Illustrated historical combination atlas of Cambria county, Penn. 3 p. l., 8–194 pp. incl. front., 53 maps, 51 pl. fol. Philadelphia, atlas publishing co. 1890.     2466
  NOTE.—Pagination irregular.

## CARBON.

**Beers, F. W.**
  County atlas of Carbon, Penn. 2 p. l., 4–82 pp. incl. 25 maps. fol. New York, F. W. Beers & co. 1875.     2467

## CHESTER.

**Bridgens, H. F., Witmer, A. R.,** & *others.*
  Atlas of Chester county, Penn. 2 p. l., 1 l., 58 maps. fol. Safe Harbor, Pa., A. R. Witmer, 1873.     2468

**Kirk, W. H., & co.**
  Chester county, Pennsylvania. 265 pp. incl. 80 maps. fol. Philadelphia, W. H. Kirk & co. 1883.     2469
  [Breou's official series of farm maps]

## CLEARFIELD.

**Newton, J. H.**
  Caldwell's illustrated historical, combination atlas of Clearfield county, Penn. From actual surveys by & under the direction of J. H. Newton, assisted by C. O. Mann & J. A. Underwood. Artists, J. D. McKissen and E. Franks. 2 p. l., 219 pp. incl. 38 maps, 91 pl. (1 map loose) fol. Condit, Ohio, J. A. Caldwell, 1878.     2470
  NOTE.—Pagination irregular.

## COLUMBIA.

**Walker, G. H.,** *and* **Jewett, C. F.**
  Columbia and Montour counties, Penn. 2 p. l., 3 l, 43 maps, 10 pl. fol. New York, F. W. Beers & co. 1876.     2471
  NOTE.—Pagination irregular.

## CUMBERLAND.

**Beers, F. W.**
  Atlas of Cumberland county, Penn.   3 p. l., 33 maps, 2 pl. fol.  New York, F. W. Beers & co. 1872.   2472
  NOTE.—Pagination irregular.

## DAUPHIN.

**Everts & Stewart.**
  Combination atlas map of Dauphin county, Penn. Compiled, drawn and published from personal examinations and surveys. 6 p. l., xii pp., 1 l., 50 pp. incl. 29 maps, 13 pl. (2 fold. maps) fol. Philadelphia, Everts & Stewart, 1875.   2473

## DELAWARE.

**Hopkins, G. M.**
  Atlas of Delaware county, Penn. Comprehending 26 maps. Drawn from official records, private plans and deeds . . . by Henry W. Hopkins. Surveyed, compiled, drawn and published under the direction of G. M. Hopkins.   6 p. l., 50 pp. incl. 29 maps, 15 pl. fol. Philadelphia, G. M. Hopkins, 1870.   2474
  NOTE.—Manuscript alterations on title page credit authorship to Everts & Stewart.

## ERIE.

**Beers, F. W., & others.**
  Atlas of Erie county, Penn.   2 p. l., 2 l., 35 maps. fol. New York, F. W. Beers, A. D. Ellis & G. G. Soule, 1865.   2475

## FAYETTE.

**Hopkins, G. M., & co.**
  Atlas of the county of Fayette and the state of Pennsylvania. 3 p. l., 34 maps. fol. Philadelphia, G. M. Hopkins & co. 1872.
  2476
  NOTE.—Pagination irregular.

## HUNTINGDON.

**Nichols, B.**
  Atlas of Blair and Huntingdon counties, Penn., from actual surveys.   161 pp. incl. 55 maps. fol. Philadelphia, A. Pomeroy & co. 1873.   2477

## INDIANA.

**Beers, F. W.**
  Atlas of Indiana county, Penn.   3 p. l., 34 maps, 1 pl. fol. New York, F. W. Beers & co. 1871.   2478

## JUNIATA.

**Nichols, B.**
  Atlas of Perry, Juniata and Mifflin counties, Penn. From actual surveys.   70 pp. incl. 50 maps. fol. Philadelphia, Pomeroy, Whitman & co. 1877.   2479

## LEBANON.

**Beers, F. W.**
County atlas of Lebanon, Penn. 1 p. l., 4–81 pp. incl. 33 maps. fol. Philadelphia, F. A. Davis, 1875. 2480

## LEHIGH.

**Davis, F. A.**
New illustrated atlas of Lehigh county, Penn. 2 p. l., 7–72, i–vi, [3–37] pp. incl. 47 maps, 8 pl. fol. Reading, Pa., Reading publishing house, 1876. 2481

## LUZERNE.

**Beers, D. G.**
Atlas of Luzerne county, Penn. 1 p. l., 4–183 pp. incl. 71 maps. fol. Philadelphia, A. Pomeroy & co. 1873. 2482

## LYCOMING.

**Nichols, B.**
Atlas of Lycoming county, Penn. From actual surveys by and under the direction of Beach Nichols. 3 p. l., 5–48 pp. [1] l. incl. 36 maps. fol. Philadelphia, A. Pomeroy & co. 1873. 2483
NOTE.—Extra leaf numb. 42 inserted at end.

## MERCER.

**Hopkins, G. M., & co**
Combination atlas of the county of Mercer and the state of Pennsylvania, from actual surveys & official records. 2 p. l., 111 pp. incl. 40 maps. fol. Philadelphia, G. M. Hopkins & co. 1873. 2484
NOTE.—Imperfect: pp. 67–72, 85–86, 93–94, 109–110 wanting.

## MIFFLIN.

**Nichols, B.**
Atlas of Perry, Juniata and Mifflin counties, Penn. From actual surveys. 70 pp. incl. 50 maps. fol. Philadelphia, Pomeroy, Whitman & co. 1877. 2485

## MONROE.

**Beers, F. W.**
County atlas of Monroe, Penn. 2 p. l., 1 l., 28 maps, 18 pl. fol. New York, F. W. Beers & co. 1875. 2486

## MONTGOMERY.

**Hopkins, G. M., & co.**
Atlas of the county of Montgomery and the state of Pennsylvania. 2 p. l., 36 maps. fol. Philadelphia, G. M. Hopkins & co. 1871. 2487

**Scott, J. D.**
Combination atlas map of Montgomery county, Penn. Compiled, drawn and published from personal examinations and surveys. 106 pp. incl. 39 maps, 12 pl. fol. Philadelphia, J. D. Scott, 1877. 2488

**Naeff, M. A.**
    Property atlas of Montgomery county, Pennsylvania. Compiled by M. A. Naeff . . . from private plans, official records, actual surveys.   2 p. l., 44 col. maps.  fol.  Philadelphia, J. L. Smith, 1893.     2489

**Mueller, A. H., & co.**
    Atlas of Cheltenham, Abington and Springfield townships and vicinity of Montgomery county, Penna. Compiled and drawn from official plans and actual surveys by Ellis Kiser, Otto Barthels, & B. A. Skeels.   1 p. l., 19 maps.  fol.  Philadelphia, A. H. Mueller & co. 1897.     2490

### MONTOUR.

**Walker, G. H.,** *and* **Jewett, C. F.**
    Columbia and Montour counties, Penn.   2 p. l., 3 l., 43 maps, 10 pl.  fol.  New York, F. W. Beers & co. 1876.     2491
    NOTE.—Pagination irregular.

### NORTHAMPTON.

**Beers, D. G.**
    Atlas of Northampton county, Penn. From actual surveys. 2 p. l., 6–91 pp. incl. 33 maps.  fol.  Philadelphia, A. Pomeroy & co. 1874.     2492
    NOTE.—Pagination irregular.

### PERRY.

**Nichols, B.**
    Atlas of Perry, Juniata and Mifflin counties, Penn. From actual surveys.   70 pp. incl. 50 maps.  fol.  Philadelphia, Pomeroy, Whitman & co. 1877.     2493

### SCHUYLKILL.

**Beers, F. W.,** *and* **Cochran, A. B.**
    County atlas of Schuylkill, Penn.   2 p. l., 4 l., 69 maps, 23 pl. fol.  New York, F. W. Beers & co. 1875.     2494

### SOMERSET.

**Beers, F. W.**
    County atlas of Somerset, Penn.   2 p. l., 4–110 pp. incl. 38 maps.  fol.  New York, F. W. Beers & co. 1876.     2495

### SUSQUEHANNA.

**Beers, F. W.**
    Atlas of Susquehanna county, Penn.   3 p. l., 35 maps.  fol. New York, A. Pomeroy & co. 1872.     2496

### TIOGA.

**Walker, G. H.,** *and* **Jewett, C. F.**
    County atlas of Tioga, Penn.   109 pp. incl. 44 maps, 2 pl.  fol. New York, F. W. Beers & co. 1875.     2497
    NOTE.—Pagination irregular.

### WARREN.

**Howden, J. A., & Odbert, A.**
Howden & Odbert's atlas of Warren county, Penn. From actual surveys & records. 68 l. incl. 33 maps, 43 pl. 1 map loose. fol. Washington, Pa., J. A. Howden & A. Odbert, 1878.    2498

### WAYNE.

**Beers, F. W.**
Atlas of Wayne county, Penn. 4 p. l., 27 maps. fol. New York, A. Pomeroy & co. 1872.    2499

### YORK.

**Nichols, B.**
Atlas of York county, Penn. Illustrated. From actual surveys. 81 pp. incl. 41 maps, 11 pl. fol. Philadelphia, Pomeroy. Whitman & co. 1876.    2500

### Cities.

#### ABINGTON.

**Mueller, A. H. & co.**
Atlas of Cheltenham, Abington and Springfield townships and vicinity of Montgomery county, Penna. Compiled and drawn from official plans and actual surveys by Ellis Kizer, Otto Barthels & B. A. Skeels. 1 p. l., 19 maps. fol. Philadelphia, A. H. Mueller & co. 1897.    2501

#### ALLEGHENY.

**Hopkins, G. M., & co.**
Atlas of the cities of Pittsburgh, Allegheny, and the adjoining boroughs. 4 p. l., 36 maps. fol. Philadelphia, G. M. Hopkins & co. 1872.    2502

NOTE.—Pagination irregular.

**Hopkins, G. M.**
Atlas of the cities of Pittsburgh & Al'egheny. 1 p. l., 39 maps. fol. Philadelphia, G. M. Hopkins, 1882.    2503

Atlas of the vicinity of the cities Pittsburgh and Allegheny, Penn. 1 p. l., 33 maps. fol. Philadelphia, G. M. Hopkins, 1886.    2504

Atlas of the city of Allegheny. v. 1–2. fol. Philadelphia, G. M. Hopkins, 1890–1.    2505

CONTENTS.

v. 1. 1st, 2nd, 5th, 6th, 9th, & 11th wards.
" 2. 3rd, 4th, 7th, 8th, 10th, 12th & 13th wards.

**Hopkins, H. W.**
  Real estate plat book of the city of Allegheny; from official records, private plans and actual surveys. v. 1-2. fol. Philadelphia, H. W. Hopkins, 1901-[1902]     2506
  NOTE.—Collation: v. 1, 1 p. l., 28 maps; v. 2, 1 p. l., 34 maps.

CONTENTS.

  v. 1. 1-8, 12, 13th wards.
  " 2. 9-11, 14 & 15th wards.

**Hopkins, G. M., co.**
  Real estate plat-book of the city of Allegheny . . . From official records, private plans and actual surveys . . . v. 1. 1 p. l., 32 (*i. e.* 33) col. maps. fol. Philadelphia, G. M. Hopkins co. 1907.     2507

CONTENTS.

  v. 1. 1st to 8th inc. 12th & 13th wards.

## BRYN MAWR.

**Hopkins, G. M.**
  Atlas of Bryn Mawr and vicinity, or of property along the Pennsylvania r. r., including 1½ miles each side of the road and from city line to Malvern station. 1 p. l., 29 maps. fol. Philadelphia, G. M. Hopkins, 1881.     2508

## CHELTENHAM.

**Mueller, A. H., & co.**
  Atlas of Cheltenham, Abington and Springfield townships and vicinity of Montgomery county, Penna. Compiled and drawn from official plans and actual surveys by Ellis Kiser, Otto Barthels & B. A. Skeels. 1 p. l., 19 maps. fol. Philadelphia, A. H. Mueller & co. 1897.     2509

## ERIE.

**Lathrop, J. M.,** *& others.*
  Atlas of the city of Erie, Penn. Compiled and drawn from official records, private plans and actual surveys. 3 p. l., 1 l., 21 maps. fol. Philadelphia, A. H. Mueller, 1900.     2510

## HARRISBURG.

**Roe, F. B.**
  Atlas of the city of Harrisburg, Dauphin county, Penn. 1 p. l., 23 maps. fol. Philadelphia, F. B. Roe, 1889.     2511

**Harrisburg title co.**
  Atlas of the city of Harrisburg, Dauphin county, Penn. Made from plans, deeds and surveys. 1 p. l., 22 maps. fol. Harrisburg, Harrisburg title co. 1901.     2512

## LEBANON.

**Roe, F. B.**

Atlas of the city of Lebanon, Lebanon county, Penn'a. Compiled, drawn and published from official plans and actual surveys. 75 pp., incl. 19 maps. fol. Philadelphia, F. B. Roe, 1888. 2513

## LOWER MERION.

**Mueller, A. H.**

Atlas of Lower Merion, Montgomery co. including part of Delaware co. and Overbrook Farms, Wynnefield & Overbrook impr. co. Philadelphia. Compiled and drawn from official plans and actual surveys by Ellis Kiser and C. A. Potts . . . 1 p. l., 19 maps. fol. Philadelphia, A. H. Mueller, 1896. 2514

## OIL CITY.

**Beers, Ellis & co.**

Atlas of Oil City, Penn. 1 p. l., 4–69 pp. incl. 14 maps. fol. New York, Beers, Ellis & co. 1887. 2515

## PHILADELPHIA.

**Birch, W. & son.**

The city of Philadelphia, in the state of Pennsylvania, North America; as it appeared in the year 1800 consisting of twenty-eight plates. Drawn and engraved by W. Birch & son. 3 l., 1 map, 29 col. pl. obl. fol. Springland Cot, near Neshaminy Bridge on the Bristol road, Pa., 1800. 2516

NOTE.—Engraved title, by William Barker. The following biographical note is taken from Stauffer's American engravers. New York, the Grolier club, 1907, pt. 1. p. 22: "Birch, William. Born in Warwickshire, England, april 9, 1755; died in Philadelphia, aug. 7, 1834. Birch was an enamel painter and engraver; for a time he was working in Bristol, and in 1788–91 he was engraving prints and publishing them at Hampstead Heath, near London . . . In 1794 he came to Philadelphia . . . and in that city he painted landscape in water-colors and miniatures in enamel; among the latter were several portraits of Washington done after the Stuart head. The earlier engraved work of Birch was executed in stipple and was much more finished than that published in this country . . . In 1791 he published in London a quarto volume entitled 'Délices de la Grande Bretagne,' a collection of views of places in the neighborhood of London, and well done in stipple. His reputation as an american engraver is founded upon his 'Views of Philadelphia,' drawn and engraved in 1798–1800 in connection with his son Thomas Birch, later well known as a landscape and marine painter. In 1808 he also issued a smaller series of plates showing the country seats of the United States. These views are now chiefly valued for their historical interest. His 'Views of Philadelphia' were republished by him in 1802, and again republished by Robert Desilver in 1841." In pt. 2 of the same work is given a check list of his engravings.

CONTENTS.

no. [1] Frontispiece. The city & port of Philadelphia, on the river Delaware from Kensington. 1800.
" [2] Plan of the city of Philadelphia. W. Barker sculp.
" [3] Arch street ferry, Philadelphia. 1800.
" [4] Arch street, with the second Presbyterian church, Philadelphia. 1799.
" [5] New Lutheran church, in Fourth street, Philadelphia. 1799.
" [6] Old Lutheran church, in Fifth street, Philadelphia. 1800.
" [7] South east corner of Third and Market streets, Philadelphia. 1799.
" [8] High street, with the first Presbyterian church, Philadelphia. 1799.
" [9] High street market, Philadelphia. 1799.
" [10] High street, from the country market-place. Philadelphia. 1798.
" [11] High street, from the country market-place. Philadelphia, with the procession in commemoration of the death of general George Washington, december 26th. 1799. Philad$^a$. 1800.
" [12] High street, from Ninth street, Philadelphia. 1799.
" [13] The house intended for the President of the United States, in Ninth street, Philadelphia. 1799.
" [14] An unfinished house, in Chestnut street, Philadelphia. 1800.
" [15] Second street, north from Market s$^t$ $\underset{w}{\text{ch}}$ Christ church. Philadelphia. 1799.
" [16] New Market, in South second street, Philadelphia. 1799.
" [17] Bank of the United States, in Third street, Philadelphia. 1799.
" [18] Bank of the United States, with a view of Third street, Philadelphia. 1798.
" [19] View in Third street, from Spruce street, Philadelphia.
" [20] Library and surgeons hall, in Fifth street, Philadelphia. 1799.
" [21] Congress Hall and new theatre, in Chestnut street, Philadelphia. 1800.
" [22] State-house, with a view of Chestnut street, Philadelphia. 1798.
" [23] Back of the State house, Philadelphia. 1799.
" [24] State-house garden, Philadelphia. 1798.
" [25] Gaol, in Walnut street, Philadelphia. 1799.
" [26] Alms house in Spruce street, Philadelphia. 1799.
" [27] Pennsylvania hospital, in Pine street, Philadelphia. 1799.
" [28] Bank of Pennsylvania, South second street, Philadelphia.
" [29] The water works, in Centre square, Philadelphia.
" [30] Preparation for war to defend commerce. The swedish church Southwark with the building of the frigate Philadelphia. 1800.

—— Eleven of the principal views of Birch's Philadelphia, North America. cover-title, 11 pl. obl. fol. [Philadelphia, 1800–1827]
2517

NOTE.—Most of these views are from the same plates as those of the preceding collection, although the titles and dates have been altered.

CONTENTS.

no. [1] Penn's tree, with the city & port of Philadelphia, on the river Delaware from Kensington. Decayed & blow'd down in 1810.
" [2] High street, with the First Presbyterian church. Taken down in 1820. Philadelphia.

**Birch, W. & son**—Continued.

no. [3] Second street north from Market s$^{\text{th}}_{\text{w}}$ Christ church, Philadelphia. 1800.
" [4] Girard's bank, late the Bank of the United States, in Third street, Philadelphia. 1800.
" [5] The water works, in Centre square, Philadelphia. Taken down in 1827.
" [6] The late theatre in Chestnut street, Philadelphia. Destroy'd by fire in 1820.
" [7] The new theatre in Chestnut street, Philadelphia. 1823.
" [8] Bank of Pennsylvania, South second street, Philadelphia. 1804.
" [9] Philadelphia bank, in Fourth street, Philadelphia.
" [10] Bank of the United States, Chestnut street, Philadelphia. 1827.
" [11] Back of the State House, Philadelphia. 1800.

**Hexamer, E.,** *and* **Locher, W.**

Maps of the city of Philadelphia, comprising the 13th, 14th, and part of 20th ward. v. 5. 1 p. l., 15 maps. fol. [Philadelphia] E. Hexamer & W. Locher, 1859. 2518

**Smedley, S. L.**

Smedley's atlas of the city of Philadelphia. 4 p. l., 25 maps. fol. Philadelphia, J. B. Lippincott & co. 1862. 2519

NOTE.—Illustrated title has date of 1860, Joseph H. Bonsall & Samuel L. Smedley, surveyors & draftsmen.

**Hopkins, G. M.**

Atlas of (the late borough of) Germantown, twenty-second ward, city of Philadelphia, drawn from official records, private plans, deeds and actual surveys by H. W. Hopkins. Based upon plans of streets, authorized by the city councils and deposited in the department of surveys. Surveyed, compiled, drawn and published under the direction of G. M. Hopkins. 57 pp. incl. 14 maps. fol. Philadelphia, G. M. Hopkins, 1871. 2520

Atlas of West Philadelphia, including the 24th & 27th wards of the city of Philadelphia. From actual surveys & official records. 2 p. l., 3-60 pp. incl. 16 maps. fol. Philadelphia, G. M. Hopkins & co. 1872. 2521

**Jones, G. H., & co.**

Atlas of Philadelphia. In 15 v. v. 1-4. fol. Philadelphia, G. H. Jones & co. 1874-5. 2522

CONTENTS

v. 1. 5th, 7th, & 8th wards.
" 2. 19th ward.
" 3. 6th, 9th, & 10th wards.
" 4. 20th ward.

**Hopkins, G. M.**
City atlas of Philadelphia by wards. Complete in 7 vols. v. 1-6. fol. Philadelphia, G. M. Hopkins, 1875-6. 2523

CONTENTS.
v. 1. 22nd ward.
" 2. 21st & 28th wards.
" 3. 23rd ward.
" 4. 25th ward.
" 5. 1st, 26th & 30th wards.
" 6. 2nd to 20th inclusive & 29th and 31st wards.

Atlas of Philadelphia and environs. 2 p. l., 48 maps, 2 pl. fol. Philadelphia, G. M. Hopkins, 1877. 2524

**Scott, J. D.**
Atlas of the 24th & 27th wards, West Philadelphia. From official records and actual surveys based upon plans deposited in the department of surveys. 2 p. l., 88 pp. incl. 30 maps. fol. Philadelphia, J. D. Scott, 1878. 2525

NOTE.—Pagination irregular.

**Hopkins, G. M.**
Atlas of properties along the Philadelphia, Wilmington and Baltimore railroad and the Philadelphia & Westchester rail road from Philadelphia to Chester. 1 p. l., 28 maps. fol. Philadelphia, G. M. Hopkins, 1882. 2526

City atlas. Philadelphia. 29th ward. **1 p. l.,** 18 maps. fol. Philadelphia, G. M. Hopkins, 1882. 2527

Atlas of the city of Philadelphia. 21st & 28th wards. 1 p. l., 20 maps. fol. Philadelphia, G. M. Hopkins, 1884. 2528

Atlas of the city of Philadelphia. 1st, 26th, and 30th wards. 1 p. l., 18 maps. fol. Philadelphia, G. M. Hopkins, 1885. 2529

Atlas of the city of Philadelphia. 11th, 12th & 14th wards. 1 p. l., 15 maps. fol. Philadelphia, G. M. Hopkins, 1885. 2530

Atlas of the city of Philadelphia. 15th ward. 1 p. l., 14 maps. fol. Philadelphia, G. M. Hopkins, 1885. 2531

Atlas of the city of Philadelphia. 22nd ward. Properties near Philadelphia, Germantown and Chestnut Hill rail road. 1 p. l., 29 maps. fol. Philadelphia, G. M. Hopkins, 1885. 2532

Atlas of the city of Philadelphia. 25th ward. 1 p. l., 20 maps. fol. Philadelphia, G. M. Hopkins, 1886. 2533

Atlas of the city of Philadelphia. 23rd ward. 1 p. l., 17 maps. fol. Philadelphia, G. M. Hopkins [1887] 2534

**Baist, G. W.**
Baist's atlas of the city of Philadelphia, Penn. Complete in one volume. Compiled and published from official records, private plans and actual surveys. 3 p. l., 45 maps. fol. Philadelphia, G. W. Baist, 1888. 2535

**Bromley, G. W. & W. S.**
Atlas of the city of Philadelphia. From actual surveys and official plans of the survey department. v. 7. 2 p. l., 31 maps. fol. Philadelphia, G. W. Bromley & co. 1889. 2536
NOTE.—Contains 22nd. ward.

**Schiedt, J. E.**
Schiedt's atlas of the city of Philadelphia, by wards. Containing all streets, and boundary lines of each election division. Complete in one volume. 1 p. l., 33 maps. fol. Philadelphia, J. E. Schiedt, 1892. 2537
NOTE.—Blue prints.

**Kaufmann, C. D.**
Street atlas of Philadelphia by wards, 1895. 2 p. l., 38 maps (1 map loose) fol. [Philadelphia] C. D. Kaufmann, 1895. 2538
NOTE.—Contains a reproduction of Varle's map of Philadelphia in 1796.

### PITTSBURGH.

**Hopkins, G. M., & co.**
Atlas of the cities of Pittsburgh, Allegheny, and the adjoining boroughs. 4 p. l., 36 maps. fol. Philadelphia, G. M. Hopkins & co. 1872. 2539
NOTE.—Pagination irregular.

**Hopkins, G. M.**
Atlas of the cities of Pittsburgh & Allegheny. 1 p. l., 39 maps. fol. Philadelphia, G. M. Hopkins, 1882. 2540

Atlas of the vicinity of the cities Pittsburgh and Allegheny, Penn. 1 p. l., 33 maps. fol. Philadelphia, G. M. Hopkins, 1886. 2541

Atlas of the city of Pittsburgh. Comprising the 1st to the 11th wards. v. 1. 1 p. l., 23 maps. fol. Philadelphia, G. M. Hopkins, 1889. 2542

Atlas of the city of Pittsburgh. v. 3–5. fol. Philadelphia, G. M. Hopkins, 1890. 2543
CONTENTS.
v. 3. 15th, 17th, 18th, 19th & 21st wards.
" 4. 16th, 20th, 22nd & 23rd wards.
" 5. 24th, to 36th ward inclusive.

Real estate plat book of the eastern vicinity of Pittsburgh, Penna. From official records, private plans and actual surveys. 1 p. l., 34 maps. fol. Philadelphia, G. M. Hopkins, 1895. 2544

Real estate plat-book of the southern vicinity of Pittsburgh, Penna. From official records, private plans and actual surveys . . . 1 p. l., 31 maps. fol. Philadelphia, G. M. Hopkins, 1896. 2545

Real estate plat-book of the northern vicinity of Pittsburgh, Penn. 1 p. l., 32 maps. fol. Philadelphia, G. M. Hopkins, 1897. 2546

Real estate plat-book of the city of Pittsburgh. v. 2–4. fol. Philadelphia, G. M. Hopkins, 1899–1900. 2547

CONTENTS.

v. 2. East end, comprising the 18th, 19th, 20th, & 21st wards.
" 3. Comprising the 1st to the 12th wards, and 15th, 16th, and 17th wards.
" 4. Comprising the 24th to the 31st wards.

Real estate plat book of the south-eastern vicinity of Pittsburgh, Penn. From official records, private plans and actual surveys. 1 p. l., 30 maps. fol. Philadelphia, G. M. Hopkins, 1900. 2548

**Hopkins, G. M., co.**

Real estate plat-book of the eastern vicinity of Pittsburgh, Penna. From official records, private plans and actual surveys. 1 p. l., 35 maps. fol. Philadelphia, G. M. Hopkins co. 1903. 2549

Real estate plat book of the city of Pittsburgh, supplement to vol. 3 comprising the 1st, 2nd, 3rd, 4th, 5th, & 7th wards and parts of 6th, 8th, & 9th wards. From official records, private plans and actual surveys . . . 1 p. l., 23 maps. fol. Philadelphia, G. M. Hopkins co. 1903. 2550

Real estate plat book of the city of Pittsburgh. From official records, private plans and actual surveys . . . v. 1, 3. fol. Philadelphia, G. M. Hopkins co. 1904–1906. 2551

CONTENTS.

v. 1. Comprising the 13th, 14th, 22nd, & 23rd wards.
" 3. Comprising the wards, 6 to 12, 15, 16 & 17.

Real estate plat book of the southern vicinity of Pittsburgh, Penna. From official records, private plans and actual surveys . . . 2 p. l., 41 maps. fol. Philadelphia, G. M. Hopkins co. 1905. 2552

Real estate plat-book of the northern vicinity of Pittsburgh, Penn. From official records, private plans and actual surveys . . . 2 p. l., 40 maps. fol. Philadelphia, G. M. Hopkins co. 1906. 2553

### READING.

**Breou, F., & co.**
　　Property and insurance atlas of the city of Reading, Berks county, Penn.　　1 p. l., 4 l., 47 maps.　fol.　Philadelphia, F. Breou & co. 1884.　　2554

### ROSEMONT.

**Mueller, A. H., & co.**
　　Atlas of properties on line of Pennsylvania r. r. from Rosemont to Westchester.　Compiled and drawn from official plans and actual surveys by Ellis Kiser, Otto Barthel, & St. J. Ogier.　　1 p. l., 20 maps.　fol.　Philadelphia, A. H. Mueller & co. 1897.　　2555

### SCRANTON.

**Hopkins, G. M.**
　　City atlas of Scranton, Penn.　　2 p. l., 1 l., 22 maps, 3 pl.　fol. Philadelphia, G. M. Hopkins, 1877.　　2556

### SPRINGFIELD.

**Mueller, A. H., & co.**
　　Atlas of Cheltenham, Abington and Springfield townships and vicinity of Montgomery county, Penna.　Compiled and drawn from official plans and actual surveys by Ellis Kiser, Otto Barthel, & B. A. Skeels.　　1 p. l., 19 maps.　fol.　Philadelphia, A. B. Mueller & co. 1897.　　2557

### WESTCHESTER.

　　Atlas of properties on line of Pennsylvania r. r. from Rosemont to Westchester.　Compiled and drawn from official plans and actual surveys by Ellis Kiser, Otto Barthel, & St. J. Ogier.　　1 p. l., 20 maps.　fol.　Philadelphia, A. H. Mueller & co. 1897.　　2558

### WILKESBARRE.

**Sturdevant, W. H.**
　　Atlas of the city of Wilkes-Barre, Pennsylvania.　Compiled from actual surveys, official maps and records . . . 1894.　　3 p. l., 19 maps.　fol.　Philadelphia, J. L. Smith, 1894.　　2559

### WILLIAMSPORT.

**Hunter, C. M.**
　　Atlas of the city of Williamsport, Penna.　　1 p. l., 13 maps. fol.　Philadelphia, C. M. Hunter, 1888.　　2560

### YORK.

**Roe, F. B.**
　　Atlas of the city of York, York county, Pennsylvania.　From official records, railroad surveys and recent surveys by the author . . . 1 p. l., 22 maps.　fol.　Philadelphia, F. B. Roe, 1903.　　2561

# RHODE ISLAND.

## State.

### 1905

**Scarborough co.**
  Complete road atlas, Massachusetts and Rhode Island. 6 sheets. fol. Boston, the Scarborough co. ᶜ1905.  2562
   NOTE.—In case.
   The title sheet contains a plan of "Boston showing original shore line," an index map, and an index to the cities, villages, post-offices and stations in Massachusetts and Rhode Island.

## Counties.

### PROVIDENCE.

**Everts & Richards.**
  New topographical atlas of surveys, Providence county, Rhode Island . . . Based upon and carefully compiled from the latest national, state and local engineering sources obtainable and the personal investigations and surveys of the publishers' special corps of engineers. Accompanied by a new and original ready reference county chart . . . 4 p. l., 12–214 pp. incl. 47 maps. fol. Philadelphia, Everts & Richards, 1895.  2563

## Cities.

### NEWPORT.

**Hopkins, G. M.**
  City atlas of Newport, Rhode Island. From official records, private plans and actual surveys, based upon plans deposited in the department of surveys. 101 pp. incl. 25 maps. fol. Philadelphia, G. M. Hopkins, 1876.  2564

  Atlas of the city of Newport, Rhode Island. From official records, private plans and actual surveys. 1 p. l., 25 maps. fol. Philadelphia, G. M. Hopkins, 1883.  2565

**Elliott, C. L.,** *and* **Flynn, T.**
  Atlas of the city of Newport, Rhode Island, from official records and actual surveys. 1 p. l., 23 maps. fol. Springfield, Mass., L. J. Richards & co. 1893.  2566

### PAWTUCKET.

**Hopkins, G. M.**
  Atlas of the town of Pawtucket, R. I. From actual surveys and records. 99 pp. incl. 25 maps. fol. Philadelphia, G. M. Hopkins, 1880.  2567

## PROVIDENCE.

**Hopkins, G. M.**
City atlas of Providence, Rhode Island, by wards. 3 v. Philadelphia, G. M. Hopkins, 1875. 2568

CONTENTS.

v. 1. 1st, 2nd & 3rd wards, and part of East Providence.
" 2. 5th, 6th, 8th & 9th wards, and parts of Johnston & Cranston.
" 3. 4th, 7th & 10th wards.

Atlas of the city of Providence, R. I. and environs. From official records, private plans and actual surveys. 1 p. l., 45 maps. fol. Philadelphia, G. M. Hopkins, 1882. 2569

## SOUTH CAROLINA.

### State.

### 1825

**Mills, R.**
Atlas of the state of South Carolina, made under the authority of the legislature; prefaced with a geographical, statistical and historical map of the state . . . 1 p. l., 25 maps. fol. Baltimore, F. Lucas, jr. [1825] 2570

## SOUTH DAKOTA.

### State.

### 1880

**United States.** *Geographical and geological survey of the Rocky mountain region.*
Report on the geology and resources of the Black Hills of Dakota with atlas by Henry Newton . . . and Walter P. Jenney . . . 1 p. l., 2 maps, pl. fol. Washington, government printing office, 1880. 2571

NOTE.—Atlas has title: . . . Topographical and geological atlas of the Black Hills of Dakota to accompany the report of Henry Newton. New York, J. Bien, 1879.

### 1884

**Andreas, A. T.**
Andreas' historical atlas of Dakota. 2 p. l., 13–210, [2], 211–255 pp. incl. 69 maps, 1 fold. map inserted. fol. Chicago, R. R. Donnelley & sons, the Lakeside press, 1884. 2572

## 1904

**Peterson, E. F.**
Historical atlas of South Dakota, containing state and county maps, geologic maps, statistical charts, geography, geology, history, descriptive notes, tables, etc. Illustrated. 215 pp., front. incl. 82 maps, 12 pl., [30] pl. fol. Vermilion, E. F. Peterson, 1904. 2573

## 1908

**Cram, G. F.**
Cram's superior reference atlas of North and South Dakota and the world. 170 pp. incl. 79 col. maps, 2 col. pl., illus. fol. New York, Chicago, G. F. Cram, °1908. 2573a

### Counties.

#### BEADLE.

**Peterson, E. F.**
Atlas of Beadle county, South Dakota, compiled and drawn from official records and a special survey. 106, [2], 8 pp. incl. 43 maps, 3 pl. fol. Lake Andes, E. F. Peterson, 1906. 2574

#### BON HOMME.

**Peterson, E. F.**
Atlas of Bon Homme county, South Dakota. Compiled and drawn from a special survey and official records. 2 pts. in 1 v.; 48, 8 pp., incl. 23 maps, 6 pl. fol. Lake Andes, E. F. Peterson, 1906. 2575

NOTE.—Text of pt. 1 contains: Bon Homme county, descriptive.—History of Bon Homme county, by J. C. Young . . . pt. 2, Analysis of the system of rectangular surveys of the public lands of the United States.

#### BROWN.

**Peterson, E. F.**
Atlas of Brown county, South Dakota, compiled and drawn from a special survey and official records by E. Frank Peterson. 138, [6], 2–8 pp., front., incl. 62 maps (4 maps in text) 4 pl. fol. Vermilion, 1905. 2576

#### CHARLES MIX.

**Peterson, E. F.**
Atlas of Charles Mix county, South Dakota. Compiled and drawn from a special survey and official records. 68, 8 pp. incl. 38 maps, 9 pl. fol. Lake Andes, E. F. Peterson, 1906. 2577

## CLAY.

**Peterson, E. F.**

Illustrated historical atlas of Clay county, South Dakota. Including a brief history of Clay county, by F. Belle Conrow. Published under contract for R. M. Tackabury. 72 pp. incl. 22 maps, 14 pl. fol. [Vermilion, E. F. Peterson] 1901. 2578

## DAVISON.

**Peterson, E. F.**

Twentieth century atlas of Davison county, South Dakota. With maps compiled and drawn from official records and a special survey, also including brief historical and descriptive sketches. 47 pp. incl. 19 maps, 11 pl. fol. Vermilion, E. F. Peterson, 1901.
2579

## EDMUNDS.

**Peterson, E. F.**

Atlas of Edmunds county, South Dakota, compiled and drawn from official records and special survey. 90, 8, [2] pp. incl. 40 maps, 4 pl. fol. Lake Andes, 1905. 2580

## HANSON.

**Peterson, E. F.**

Twentieth century atlas of Hanson county, South Dakota. Compiled and drawn from a special survey and official records. 62, 8, [1] pp. incl. 20 maps, 5 pl. fol. Vermilion, E. F. Peterson, 1902.
2581

## SANBORN.

**Peterson, E. F.**

Atlas of Sanborn county, South Dakota. Compiled and drawn from a special survey and official records. 55 pp. incl. 22 maps. fol. Vermilion, E. P. Peterson, 1900. 2582

## TURNER.

**Peterson, E. F.**

Atlas of Turner county, South Dakota. Compiled and drawn from a special survey and from official records. 57 pp. incl. 21 maps. fol. Vermilion, Rowley & Peterson, 1893. 2583

**Peterson, E. F.**

Twentieth century atlas of Turner county, South Dakota, compiled and drawn from a special survey and official records. 87, 8, [1] pp. incl. 34 maps, 9 pl. fol. Vermilion, E. F. Peterson, 1901. 2584

## TENNESSEE.
### Cities.
#### CHATTANOOGA.

**Hopkins, G. M.**
Atlas of the city of Chattanooga, Tennessee. From official records, private plans and actual surveys. . 1 p. l., 17 maps. fol. Philadelphia, G. M. Hopkins, 1889. 2585

**Hopkins, G. M., co.**
Real estate plat-book of the city of Chattanooga and vicinity. From official records, private plans and actual surveys . . . 2 p. l., 36 maps. fol. Philadelphia, G. M. Hopkins co. 1904. 2586

#### NASHVILLE.

**Hopkins, G. M.**
Atlas of the city of Nashville, Tennessee. From official records, private plans and actual surveys. 1 p. l., 20 maps. fol. Philadelphia, G. M. Hopkins, 1889. 2587

**Andrews, J. D., & son.**
Atlas of the suburbs of greater Nashville, Tennessee. Compiled from the plan books and other official records in the register's office of Davidson county. Showing recent additions and subdivisions. 1 p. l., 11 maps. fol. [Nashville] J. D. Andrews & son, c1906.
2588

**Hopkins, G. M., co.**
Atlas of the city of Nashville, Tennessee. From official records, private plans and actual surveys . . . 1 p. l., 34 (i. e. 35) col. maps, 1 pl. fol. Philadelphia, G. M. Hopkins co. 1908. 2589


## UTAH.
### GEOLOGICAL.

**United States.** *Geological and geographical survey of the territories.*
Report on the geology of the eastern portion of the Uinta mountains and a region of country adjacent thereto. With atlas. By J. W. Powell. Atlas. 1 p. l., 2 maps, 3 pl., 3 diagr. fol. Washington, government printing office, 1876. 2590

> NOTE.—Atlas has title: Atlas accompanying the report on the geology of a portion of the Uinta mountains . . .

**United States.** *Geographical and geological survey of the Rocky mountain region.*
Report on the geology of the high plateaus of Utah with atlas. By C. E. Dutton. Atlas. 1 p. l., 5 maps, 2 pl., diagr. fol. Washington, government printing office, 1880. 2591

> NOTE.—Atlas has title: . . . Topographical and geological atlas of the district of the high plateaus of Utah to accompany the report of capt. C. E. Dutton . . . New York, J. Bien, 1879.

## VERMONT

### State.

**1808**

**Dean, J.**
An alphabetical atlas, or, gazetteer of Vermont; affording a summary description of the state, its several counties, towns and rivers. Calculated to supply, in some measure, the place of a map; and designed for the use of offices, travellers, men of business, etc. 43, [1] pp. 8°. Montpelier, S. Goss, for the author, 1808. 2592

**1876**

**Burgett, H. W., & co.**
Illustrated topographical and historical atlas of the state of Vermont. 163 pp. incl. 24 maps, 54 pl. fol. New York, H. W. Burgett, & co. 1876. 2593
NOTE.—Pagination irregular.

### Counties.

#### ADDISON.

**Beers, F. W., Peet, W. S., & others.**
Atlas of Addison co., Vermont. From actual surveys by and under the direction of F. W. Beers, assisted by W. S. Peet and others. 1 p. l., 48 pp. incl. 33 maps. fol. New York, F. W. Beers & co. 1871. 2594

#### BENNINGTON.

**Beers, F. W., Sanford, G. P., & others.**
Atlas of Bennington co., Vermont. From actual surveys by and under the direction of F. W. Beers, assisted by Geo. P. Sanford & others. 1 p. l., 30 pp. incl. 23 maps, 4 pl. fol. New York, F. W. Beers, A. D. Ellis & G. G. Soule, 1869. 2595

#### CALEDONIA.

**Beers, F. W.**
County atlas of Caledonia, Vermont. From actual surveys by and under the direction of F. W. Beers. 99 pp. incl. 35 maps, 14 pl. fol. New York, F. W. Beers & co. 1875. 2596

#### CHITTENDEN.

**Beers, F. W., Sanford, G. P., & others.**
Atlas of Chittenden co., Vermont. From actual surveys by and under the direction of F. W. Beers, assisted by Geo. P. Sanford &

others.　　1 p. l., 32 pp. incl. 21 maps, 4 pl.　　fol.　New York, F. W. Beers, A. D. Ellis & G. G. Soule, 1869.　　　　　　　　　　　　2597

NOTE.—Pagination irregular.

### FRANKLIN.

**Beers, F. W.**

Atlas of Franklin and Grand Isle cos., Vermont. From actual surveys by and under the direction of F. W. Beers. 1 p. l., 46 pp. incl. 29 maps. fol. New York, F. W. Beers & co. 1871.　　2598

### GRAND ISLE.

**Beers, F. W.**

Atlas of Franklin and Grand Isle cos., Vermont. From actual surveys by and under the direction of F. W. Beers. 1 p. l., 46 pp. incl. 29 maps. fol. New York, F. W. Beers & co. 1871.　　2599

### ORANGE.

**Beers, F. W.**

Atlas of the county of Orange, Vermont.　90 pp. incl. 33 maps. fol. New York, F. W. Beers & co. 1877.　　　　　　　　　　　　2600

### RUTLAND.

**Beers, F. W., Fulmer, F. S.,** *& others.*

Atlas of Rutland co., Vermont. From actual surveys by and under the direction of F. W. Beers, assisted by F. S. Fulmer & others. 1 p. l., 37 pp. incl. 30 maps, 4 pl. fol. New York, F. W. Beers, A. D. Ellis & G. G. Soule, 1869.　　　　　　　　　　　　2601

### WASHINGTON.

**Beers, F W.**

County atlas of Washington, Vermont. From actual surveys by and under the direction of F. W. Beers. 1 p. l., 65 pp. incl. 32 maps. fol. New York, F. W. Beers & co. 1873.　　　　　　2602

### WINDHAM.

Atlas of Windham co., Vermont. From actual surveys . . . 1 p. l., 39 pp. incl. 30 maps, 4 pl. fol. New York, F. W. Beers, A. D. Ellis & G. G. Soule, 1869.　　　　　　　　　　　　　　2603

### WINDSOR.

**Beers, F. W., Sanford, G. P.,** *& others.*

Atlas of Windsor co., Vermont. From actual surveys . . . 1 p. l., 47 pp. incl. 36 maps, 5 pl. fol. New York, F. W. Beers, A. D. Ellis & G. G. Soule, 1869.　　　　　　　　　　　　　　2604

## VIRGINIA.
### CIVIL WAR.

**Whitney, W. H.**

Union and Confederate campaigns in the lower Shenandoah valley illustrated. Twenty years after—at the first reunion of Sheridan's veterans on the fields and in the camps of the valley. 1 p. l., 66 pp. incl. 25 maps. fol. Boston, W. H. Whitney, 1883.

2605

NOTE.—Blueprints.

**Bechler, G. R.**

Atlas showing battles, engagements, and important localities connected with the campaigns in Virginia, completing the Campaign map . . . 4 p. l., 16 pl. obl. 12°. Philadelphia, G. R. Bechler, 1864.

2606

NOTE.—L. C. has also his Campaign map, 1864.

CONTENTS.

no. 1. [Washington and its forts]
" 2. Harper's ferry and the main features of Bolivar, Loudon & Maryland heights.
" 3. Battlefield of Manassas plains or Bull Run, july 21″, 1861.
" 4. F! Monroe, Norfolk and vicinity.
" 5. Defensive positions of the Confederates near Yorktown. Peninsula campaign.
" 6. Main features of the country between Williamsburg, West Point, Charles city & White House relative to the peninsula campaign.
" 7. Richmond and eastern environs relative to the peninsula campaign.
" 8. Entrenchments of the Union army after the battle of Malvern Hill's. Peninsula campaign.
" 9. Plan of Cedar mountain and north east vicinity with reference to gen! Pope's campaign.
" 10. Map of Rappahannock and Brandy station in connection with Beverly's, Freeman's, Lee's, & Fox's Ford in reference to gen! Pope's campaign in Va.
" 11. Vicinity of Sulphur springs and Waterloo bridge with reference to gen! Pope's campaign.
" 12. Plan of the battle of Groveton near Bull Run, fought on the 30th of August 1862. Gen! Pope's campaign.
" 13. Plan of the battlefield of Antietam fought on the 16 & 17 september 1862.
" 14. Principal features of the battle of Fredericksburg, december 13, 1862. Burnside's campaign.
" 15. Topographical features near Ely's Bank's & U. S. ford on the Rappahannock river, including the main positions of the U. S. army at the battle of Chancellorsville, Va., gen! Hooker's campaign.
" 16. The battle of Gettysburg before the final assault.

## Counties.

### ALEXANDRIA.

**Hopkins, G. M.**
Atlas of fifteen miles around Washington, including the county of Prince George, Maryland. 84 pp. incl. 48 maps. fol. Philadelphia, G. M. Hopkins, 1878. 2607
> NOTE.—Contains map: Alexandria county, Va. Scale 2 inches to the mile. pp. 66–67.

Atlas of fifteen miles around Washington, including the counties of Fairfax and Alexandria, Virginia. 87 pp., 4 l. incl. 48 maps. fol. Philadelphia, G. M. Hopkins, 1879. 2608

### FAIRFAX.

**Hopkins, G. M.**
Atlas of fifteen miles around Washington including the county of Prince George, Maryland. 84 pp. incl. 48 maps. fol. Philadelphia, G. M. Hopkins, 1878. 2609
> NOTE.—pp. 69–76 include Fairfax county.

Atlas of fifteen miles around Washington, including the counties of Fairfax and Alexandria, Virginia. 87 pp., 4 l. incl. 48 maps. fol. Philadelphia, G. M. Hopkins, 1879. 2610

Atlas of fifteen miles around Washington including the county of Montgomery, Maryland. 84 pp. incl. 48 maps. fol. Philadelphia, G. M. Hopkins, 1879. 2611
> NOTE.—pp. 69–76 include Fairfax county.

### FREDERICK.

**Lathrop, J. M.**, *and* **Dayton, A. W.**
An atlas of Frederick county, Virginia. From actual surveys. 62 pp. incl. 13 maps. fol. Philadelphia, D. J. Lake & co. 1885. 2612

### HENRICO.

**Redd, T. C., & brother.**
Sectional map of that portion of Henrico county, Virginia, adjacent to the city of Richmond. cover-title, 10 maps. fol. Richmond, T. C. Redd & brother, 1901. 2613

### ROCKINGHAM.

**Lake, D. J., & co.**
An atlas of Rockingham county, Virginia. From actual surveys by J. M. Lathrop and B. N. Griffing. 58 pp., [6] l. incl. 18 maps. fol. Philadelphia, D. J. Lake & co. 1885. 2614

## Cities.

### ALEXANDRIA.

**Hopkins, G. M.**
City atlas of Alexandria, Va. From official records, private plans and surveys, based upon plans deposited in the department of surveys. 51 pp., 1 l. incl. 12 maps. fol. Philadelphia, G. M. Hopkins, 1877.    2615

### BERKLEY.

**Bowman, S. W.**
Atlas of Norfolk, Portsmouth, and Berkley, Va. Including Lambert's Point, Norfolk on the Roads, South Norfolk, Pinner's Point, West Norfolk, town of Hampton Roads, etc. etc. From actual surveys, official records & private plans approved by Walter H. Taylor jr., ass't city engineer. 1 p. l., 32 maps. fol. Norfolk, Va., S. W. Bowman, 1900.    2616

### NORFOLK.

**Hopkins, G. M.**
Atlas of the city of Norfolk, Va. and vicinity, including the city of Portsmouth. From official records, private plans and actual surveys. 1 p. l., 17 maps. fol. Philadelphia, G. M. Hopkins, 1889.    2617

**Bowman, S. W.**
Atlas of Norfolk, Portsmouth, and Berkley, Va. Including Lambert's Point, Norfolk on the Roads, South Norfolk, Pinner's Point, West Norfolk, town of Hampton Roads, etc. etc. From actual surveys, official records & private plans approved by Walter H. Taylor jr., ass't city engineer. 1 p. l., 32 maps. fol. Norfolk, Va., S. W. Bowman, 1900.    2618

### PORTSMOUTH.

**Hopkins, G. M.**
Atlas of the city of Norfolk, Va., and vicinity, including the city of Portsmouth. From official records, private plans and actual surveys. 1 p. l., 17 maps. fol. Philadelphia, G. M. Hopkins, 1889.    2619

**Bowman, S. W.**
Atlas of Norfolk, Portsmouth, and Berkley, Va. Including Lambert's Point, Norfolk on the Roads, South Norfolk, Pinner's Point, West Norfolk, town of Hampton Roads etc. etc. From actual surveys, official records & private plans approved by Walter H. Taylor jr., ass't city engineer. 1 p. l., 32 maps. fol. Norfolk, Va., S. W. Bowman, 1900.    2620

### RICHMOND.

**Beers, F. W.**
　Illustrated atlas of the city of Richmond. Published for the southern and southwestern surveying and pub. co. 　108 pp., 4 l. incl. 21 maps, 7 pl. 　fol. 　[Richmond] F. W. Beers [1877] 　2621
　　Note.—Pagination irregular.

## WASHINGTON.

### State.

#### 1894

**Eitel, E. E.**
　County atlas of Oregon and Washington, showing all towns, post offices, railroads, county roads, stage lines carrying passengers, mail and express, and distances between points. Drawn expressly for fireman's fund insurance co. 　4 p. l., 19 maps. obl. 16°. San Francisco, D. S. Stanley & co. [1894] 　2622
　　Note.—Copyright by Fireman's fund insurance co. 1894.

### Counties.

#### PIERCE.

**Plummer, F. G.**
　Plummer's complete atlas of the county of Pierce, Washington. 3 p. l., 57 maps. fol. Tacoma, F. G. Plummer, 1889. 　2623
　　Note.—Blue-prints.

#### SPOKANE.

**Fidelity abstract co.**
　Township maps of Spokane county, Washington. Showing ownerships of acreage property september 1, 1905. Compiled from the official records of the county auditor of Spokane county, United States land office at Spokane, state land commissioner at Olympia and other authentic sources by the Fidelity abstract co. . . . under the direction of A. T. Hastings, manager. 　1 p. l., 49 maps. fol. 　Spokane, Wash., quick print, 1905. 　2624

#### WHITMAN.

**Roberts, W. J.,** *and* **Fuller, J. F.**
　Atlas of Whitman county, Washington. Compiled by W. J. Roberts, civil engineer, Jno. F. Fuller, draughtsman. 　2 p. l., 62 maps. fol. Philadelphia, J. L. Smith, 1895. 　2625

### Cities.

#### SEATTLE.

**Baist, G. W.**
　Baist's real estate atlas of surveys of Seattle, Wash. Complete in one volume. Compiled and published from official records, private plans and actual surveys . . . 　1 p. l., 24 maps. fol. Philadelphia, G. W. Baist, 1905. 　2626

Baist's real estate atlas of surveys of Seattle, Wash. . . . Compiled and published from official records, private plans and actual surveys . . .   2 p. l., 33 (*i. e.* 34) col. maps.  fol.  Philadelphia, G. W. Baist, 1908. 2626a

## WEST VIRGINIA.

### State.

### 1873

**White, M. W.**

White's new county and district atlas of the state of West Virginia, comprising fifty-four counties; from the most recent surveys and authentic sources. Maps drawn by William H. Gamble, Philadelphia, Penna. Examined and corrected by M. A. Miller, top. eng., Staunton, Virginia.   1 p. l., 4–74, 28, pp., 5 l. incl. 29 maps, 1 pl.  fol.  Grafton, W. Va., M. W. White, 1873. 2627

### Cities.

#### PARKERSBURG.

**Roe, F. B.**

Atlas of the city of Parkersburg, Wood county, West Virginia, and vicinity. Drawn from recent surveys and official records. 2 p. l., 18 maps. fol. Chicago & New York, G. F. Cram & co. 1901.
2628

#### WHEELING.

**Richards, L. J., & co.**

Atlas of the city of Wheeling, West Virginia, from official records and surveys.  C. M. Hunter, c. e.   1 p. l., 12 maps.  fol.  Philadelphia, L. J. Richards & co. 1889. 2629

**Barthel, O., Halfpenny, H. E., Hasson, T. W.,** *and* **Doyle, J. B.**

Atlas of the city of Wheeling, West Virginia. Compiled and drawn from official records, private plans and actual surveys. 2 p. l., 1 l., 16 maps. fol. Philadelphia, A. H. Mueller, 1901.
2630

#### WILLIAMSTOWN.

**Roe, F. B.**

Atlas of the city of Marietta, Washington co., Ohio, and vicinity; including Williamstown, Wood co. W. Va. Drawn from recent surveys and official records . . . 2 p. l., 18 maps. fol. Chicago, New York, G. F. Cram & co. 1902. 2631

## WISCONSIN.

### LAKE REGION.

**Lawler, F.**

Plat book of Wisconsin lake region.  57 maps.  $8^o$.  Milwaukee, Foust & Junblut, 1908. 2632

NOTE—Title on map no. 1.

### State.

#### 1876

**Walling, H. F.**
Atlas of the state of Wisconsin, including statistics and descriptions of its history, educational institutions, geology, railroads, natural resources and manufacturing interests by col. C. D. Robinson, hon. Edward Searing, I. A. Lapham, A. M. Thomson, and John W. Cary . . .   130 pp., [20] l. incl. 69 maps. fol. Boston and Detroit, Walling, Tackabury & co. [1876]   2633

NOTE—pp. 101–112 wanting. Map of the United States, pp. 104–105, and Europe, pp. 138–139, inserted after p. 100.

#### 1878

**Snyder, Van Vechten & co.**
Historical atlas of Wisconsin, embracing complete state and county maps, city & village plats, together with separate state and county histories; also special articles on the geology, education, agriculture, and other important interests of the states. 322 pp. incl. front., 108 maps, 34 pl. fol. Milwaukee, Snyder, Van Vechten & co. 1878.   2634

#### 1908

**Cram, G. F.**
Cram's superior reference atlas of Wisconsin and the world. 2 p. l., 160 pp. incl. 66 col. maps, 3 pl., illus. fol. New York, Chicago, G. F. Cram, ᶜ1908.   2634a

### Counties.

#### BARRON.

**Foote, C. M.,** *and* **Hood, E. C.**
Plat book of Barron county, Wisconsin. Drawn from actual surveys and the county records.   73 pp. incl. 24 maps. fol. Minneapolis, C. M. Foote & co. 1888.   2635

#### BROWN.

**Foote, C. M.,** *and* **Brown, W. S.**
Plat book of Brown county, Wis. Drawn from actual surveys and the county records.   53 pp. incl. 30 maps. fol. Minneapolis, C. M. Foote & co. 1889.   2636

#### CALUMET.

**Foote, C. M.,** *and* **Henion, J. W.**
Plat book of Manitowoc and Calumet counties, Wis. Drawn from actual surveys and the county records.   84 pp. incl. 44 maps. fol. Minneapolis, C. M. Foote & co. 1893.   2637

## COLUMBIA.

**Harrison & Warner.**
    Atlas of Columbia county, Wisconsin. Drawn from actual surveys and the county records. To which is added a rail road & sectional map of the state of Wisconsin. 68 pp. incl. 26 maps. fol. Madison, Harrison & Warner, 1873.     2638

**Foote, C. M.,** *and* **Henion, J. W.**
    Plat book of Columbia county, Wis. Drawn from actual surveys and the county records. 50 pp. incl. 32 maps. fol. Minneapolis, C. M. Foote & co. 1890.     2639

## CRAWFORD.

**Ogle, G. A., & co.**
    Standard atlas of Crawford county, Wisconsin. Including a plat book of the villages, cities and townships of the county. Map of the state, United States and world. Patron's directory, reference business directory and departments devoted to general information. Analysis of the system of U. S. land surveys, digest of the system of civil government, etc. etc. . . . 2 p. l., 7–83, [1], viii, x–xxii pp. incl. 20 maps, 1 map in text, 5 pl. fol. Chicago, G. A. Ogle & co. 1901–1902.     2640

## DANE.

**Harrison & Warner.**
    Atlas of Dane county, Wisconsin. Drawn from actual surveys and the county records. To which is added a rail road & sectional map of the state of Wisconsin. 104 pp. incl. 42 maps. fol. Madison, Harrison & Warner, 1873.     2641

    NOTE.—Rail road & sectional map of Wisconsin wanting. See title 2647 for copy of this map.

## DODGE.

**Harrison & Warner.**
    Atlas of Dodge county, Wisconsin, drawn from actual surveys and the county records. To which is added a rail road & sectional map of the state of Wisconsin. 88 pp. incl. 32 maps. fol. Madison, Harrison & Warner, 1873.     2642

**Foote, C. M.,** *and* **Henion, J. W.**
    Plat book of Dodge county, Wisconsin. Drawn from actual surveys and the county records. 65 pp. incl. 43 maps. fol. Minneapolis, C. M. Foote & co. 1890.     2643

## DUNN.

**Foote, C. M.,** *and* **Brown, W. S.**
    Plat book of Dunn county, Wis. Drawn from actual surveys and the county records. 53 pp. incl. 32 maps. fol. Minneapolis, C. M. Foote & co. 1888.     2644

### FOND DU LAC.

**Foote, C. M.,** *and* **Henion, J. W.**
Plat book of Fond du Lac county, Wis. Drawn from actual surveys and the county records. 60 pp. incl. 38 maps. fol. Minneapolis, C. M. Foote & co. 1893. 2645

### GRANT.

**Warner & Foote.**
Atlas of Grant county, Wisconsin. Drawn from personal observations & the county records. To which is added official statistics and business references. 76 pp. incl. 38 maps. fol. Red Wing, Minn., and Philadelphia, Warner & Foote, 1877. 2646

### GREEN.

**Harrison & Warner.**
Atlas of Green county, Wisconsin, drawn from actual surveys and the county records. To which is added a rail road & sectional map of the state of Wisconsin. 54 pp. incl. 22 maps. fol. Madison, Harrison & Warner, 1873. 2647

### JEFFERSON.

**Foote, C. M.,** *and* **Hood, E. C.**
Plat book of Jefferson county, Wisconsin. Drawn from actual surveys and the county records. 58 pp. incl. 32 maps. fol. Minneapolis, C. M. Foote pub. co. 1899. 2648

### JUNEAU.

**Foote, C. M.,** *and* **Hood, E. C.**
Plat book of Juneau county, Wis. Drawn from actual surveys and the county records. 72 pp. incl. 30 maps. fol. Minneapolis, C. M. Foote pub. co. 1898. 2649

### KENOSHA.

**Hixson, W. W. & co.**
Plat book of Racine & Kenosha counties, Wis. 1 p. l., 6–41 pp. incl. 17 maps. fol. Rockford, Ill., W. W. Hixson & co. 1899. 2650

### LAFAYETTE.

**Foote, C. M.,** *and* **Henion, J. W.**
Plat book of Lafayette county, Wis. Drawn from actual surveys and the county records. 55 pp. incl. 29 maps. fol. Minneapolis, C. M. Foote & co. 1895. 2651

### MANITOWOC.

**Foote, C. M.,** *and* **Henion, J. W.**
Plat book of Manitowoc and Calumet counties, Wis. Drawn from actual surveys and the county records. 84 pp. incl. 44 maps. fol. Minneapolis, C. M. Foote & co. 1893. 2652

## MARATHON.

**Northwest publishing co.**
 Plat book of Marathon county, Wis. Compiled from county records and actual surveys.   2 p. l., 4–88 pp. incl. 65 maps.   fol. Minneapolis, the northwest publishing co. 1901.   2653

### OZAUKEE.

**Foote, C. M.,** *and* **Henion, J. W.**
 Plat book of Washington and Ozaukee counties, Wis. Drawn from actual surveys and the county records.   63 pp. incl. 37 maps. fol.   Minneapolis, C. M. Foote & co. 1892.   2654

### PIERCE.

**Nash, G. V.,** *and* **Morgan, F. B.**
 Atlas of Pierce county, Wisconsin. Drawn and compiled from personal surveys.   53 pp., 1 l. incl. 22 maps, 1 pl. fol.  Milwaukee, Wis., G. V. Nash & F. B. Morgan, 1877–1878.   2655
 NOTE.—Pagination irregular.

### POLK.

**Foote, C. M.,** *and* **Hood, E. C.**
 Plat book of Polk county, Wis. Drawn from actual surveys and the county records.   59 pp. incl. 27 maps.   fol.   Minneapolis, C. M. Foote & co. 1887.   2656

### PORTAGE.

**Northwest publishing co.**
 Plat book of Portage county, Wisconsin. Drawn from actual surveys and county records by the Northwest publishing co. 1895. 1 p. l., 58 pp., 31 maps (1 map loose)  fol.  [Minneapolis] the northwest publishing co. 1895.   2657

### RACINE.

**Hixson, W. W., & co.**
 Plat book of Racine & Kenosha counties, Wis.   1 p. l., 6–41 pp. incl. 17 maps.   fol.   Rockford, Ill., W. W. Hixson & co. 1899.   2658

### RICHLAND.

**Hood, E. C.**
 Plat book of Richland county, Wis. Drawn from actual surveys and the county records.   44 pp. incl. 24 maps.   fol.  Minneapolis, C. M. Foote & co. 1895.   2659

### ROCK.

**Everts, Baskin and Stewart.**
 Combination atlas map of Rock county, Wisconsin. Compiled, drawn and published from personal examinations and surveys. 105 (*i. e.* 182) pp. incl. 23 maps, 61 pl.  fol.  Chicago, Everts, Baskin and Stewart, 1873.   2660

**Foote, C. M.,** *and* **Henion, J. W.**

    Plat book of Rock county, Wis. Drawn from actual surveys and the county records. 54 pp. incl. 35 maps. fol. Minneapolis, C. M. Foote & co. 1891.     2661

### SAINT CROIX.

**Pinkney & Brown.**

    Plat book of Saint Croix county, Wisconsin. Compiled from official records and actual surveys. 57 pp. incl. 33 maps. fol. Philadelphia, F. Bourquin, 1897.     2662

### SHEBOYGAN.

**Joerns brothers.**

    Illustrated historical atlas of Sheboygan county, Wis. 1 p. l., 62 pp., 29 maps. fol. Sheboygan, Wis., Joerns brothers, 1902.     2663

### VERNON.

**Hood, E. C.**

    Plat book of Vernon county, Wisconsin. Drawn from actual surveys and the county records. 62 pp. incl. 36 maps. fol. Minneapolis, C. M. Foote & co. 1896.     2664

### WALWORTH.

**Everts, Baskin & Stewart.**

    Combination atlas map of Walworth county, Wisconsin. Compiled, drawn and published from personal examinations and surveys by Everts, Baskin and Stewart. 1 p. l., 78 pp. incl. 23 maps, 37 pl. fol. Chicago, Everts, Baskin & Stewart, 1873.     2665

    NOTE.—Pagination irregular.

**Northwest publishing co.**

    Plat book of Walworth county, Wisconsin. Drawn from actual surveys & county records by the northwest publishing co. 66 pp. incl. 37 maps (1 map in text). fol. [Minneapolis] the northwest publishing co. 1891.     2666

### WASHINGTON.

**Foote, C. M.,** *and* **Henion, J. W.**

    Plat book of Washington and Ozaukee counties, Wis. Drawn from actual surveys and the county records. 63 pp. incl. 37 maps. fol. Minneapolis, C. M. Foote & co. 1892.     2667

### WAUKESHA.

**Harrison & Warner.**

    Atlas of Waukesha co., Wis., drawn from actual surveys and the county records, to which is added a rail road & sectional map of the state of Wisconsin. 49, [3] pp. incl. 21 maps. fol. Madison, Harrison & Warner, 1873.     2668

    NOTE.—Manuscript map on p. 32.

**Foote, C. M.** *and* **Henion, J. W,**
  Plat book of Waukesha county, Wisconsin. Drawn from actual surveys and the county records . . . 52 pp. incl. 32 maps. fol. Minneapolis, C. M. Foote & co. 1891.    2669

### WAUPACA.

**Foote, C. M.** *and* **Brown, W. S.**
  Plat book of Waupaca county, Wis. Drawn from actual surveys and the county records. 56 pp. incl. 37 maps. fol. Minneapolis, C. M. Foote & co. 1889.    2670

**Hixson map co.**
  Township plats of Waupaca county, Wis. 2–23 pp. incl. 22 maps. fol. [Rockford, Ill., Hixson map co. 1901?]    2671

### Cities.

#### EAU CLAIRE.

**Bussell, C. E.**
  Bussell's atlas of the city of Eau Claire, Wisconsin. 1 p. l., 14 maps. fol. [Eau Claire, C. E. Bussell] 1888.    2672

#### MILWAUKEE.

**Dupré, J. V.**
  Quarter-sectional atlas of the city of Milwaukee. Drawn and compiled from the records of Milwaukee co. 1879–1881. 3 p. l., 63 maps. fol. Milwaukee, J. V. Dupré, 1881.    2673

  Quarter-sectional atlas of the city of Milwaukee. Drawn and compiled from the records of Milwaukee co. 2d & rev. ed. 1884. 3 p. l., 63 maps. fol. Milwaukee, J. V. Dupré abstract co. 1884.    2674

  Quarter-sectional atlas of the city of Milwaukee. Drawn and compiled from the records of Milwaukee co. 3d rev. ed. 1889. 4 p. l., 70 maps. fol. Milwaukee, J. V. Dupré abstract co. 1889.    2675

**Baist, G. W.**
  Baist's property atlas of the city of Milwaukee and vicinity, Wis. Compiled and published from official records, private plans and actual surveys, by G. Wm. Baist. 2 p. l., 32 maps. fol. Philadelphia, G. W. Baist, 1898.    2676

**Poetsch, C. J.,** *and* **Leidel, E. F.**
  Official quarter sectional atlas of the city of Milwaukee. According to the records of the register of deeds at the court house and at the office of the city engineer, city hall . . . 7 p. l., 101 col. maps. fol. Milwaukee, C. N. Casper co. 1907.    2677

### OSHKOSH.

**Leach, H. W.**
Atlas of the city of Oshkosh, Wisconsin, 1895 . . . 2 p. l., 20 l. incl. 10 maps. fol. Philadelphia, E. P. Noll & co. 1895. 2678

### SUPERIOR.

**Roe, F. B.**
Atlas of the city of Superior, Douglas county, Wisconsin, and vicinity. Embracing West Superior, South Superior and St. Louis; also acreage maps of northern Douglas county, showing the platted portions and locations of the different town sites, &c. Compiled and drawn from official records and actual surveys and published by Fred'k B. Roe. 2 p. l., 29 maps. fol. Philadelphia, F. B. Roe, 1891. 2679

# MEXICO.

## BOUNDARY.

**International boundary commission.**
Boundary between the United States and Mexico, as surveyed and marked by the international boundary commission, under the convention of july 29th, 1882. Revived february 18th, 1889. 1 p. l., 26 maps. fol. [Washington, 1899] 2680

NOTE.—Published to accompany the "Report of the boundary commission," 1898, by the Norris Peters co. litho., Washington, D. C.
Published also as U. S. 55th cong., 2d sess. Senate doc. no. 247 (v. 25)

### CONTENTS.

A and B.—Index map of the boundary.
no. 1–4. California line.
" 5. Colorado line.
" 6–11. Arizona-Sonora line.
" 12–16. Parallel 31° 30' north latitude.
" 16–17. Meridian section.
" 17–19. Parallel 31° 47' north latitude.
" 20–24. Profile of the boundary.

Línea divisoria entre México y los Estados Unidos al oeste del Río Grande leventada y marcada, bajo la dirección por parte de México del ingeniero Jacobo Blanco, por la comisión internacional de límites creada por la convención de julio 29 de 1882, renovada por la de febrero 18 de 1889. 1 p. l., 19 maps. fol. [Nueva York, J. Polhemus y co. 1901?] 2681

NOTE.—Lettered "Planos. vol. II."
Atlas to accompany "Memoria de la Sección mexicana de la Comisión internacional de límites entre México y los Estados Unidos."

**International boundary commission**—Continued.

CONTENTS.

no. 1–3. Paralelo 31° 47'.
" 3–4. Sección meridiana.
" 4–8. Paralelo 31° 20'.
" 9–14. Línea azimutal entre Sonora y Arizona.
" 15–18. Línea azimutal entre la baja y Alta Californias.
" 19. Rio Colorado (en dos colores)

## GENERAL.

(Arranged chronologically)

### 1812

**Humboldt, F. W. H. A.**, *freiherr von*.
Atlas géographique et physique du royaume de la Nouvelle-Espagne ... 1 p. l., 4 pp., 15 maps on 16 sheets, 3 pl. fol. Paris, G. Dufour & cie. 1812. 2682

CONTENTS.

no. 1–2. Carte générale du royaume de la Nouvelle Espagne. 1804–9.
" 3. Carte du Mexique et des pays limitrophes situés au nord et à l'est. 1811.
" 4. Carte de la vallée de Mexico et des montagnes voisines esquissée sur les lieux en 1804, par don Louis Martin rédigée et corrigée en 1807.
" 5. Points de partage et communications projettées entre le Grand océan et l'océan Atlantique.
" 6. Carte réduite de la route d'Acapulco à Mexico.
" 7. Carte de la route qui mène depuis la capitale de la Nouvelle Espagne jusqu'à S. Fe du Nouveau Mexique. Dressée sur les journaux de don Pedro de Rivera ... 1807.
" 8. Carte réduite de la partie orientale de la Nouvelle Espagne depuis le plateau de la ville de Mexico jusqu'au port de la Veracruz. Dressée sur les opérations géodesiques de don Miguel Costanzo et de dn. Garcia Conde. 1807.
" 9. Carte des fausses positions de Mexico, Acapulco, Veracruz et du Pic d'Orizaba. 1804.
" 10. Plan du Port de Veracruz, dressé par don Bernardo de Orta.
" 11. Tableau physique de la pente orientale du plateau de la Nouvelle Espagne. 1804.
" 12. Tableau physique de la pente occidentale du plateau de la Nouvelle Espagne.
" 13. Tableau du plateau central des montagnes du Mexique, entre les 19 et 21° de latitude boréale. 1803.
" 14. Profil du canal de Huehuetoca. 1808.
" 15. Volcans de la Puebla vus depuis la ville de Mexico. 1805.
" 16. Pic d'Orizaba, vu depuis la forêt de Xalapa. 1805.
" 17. Plan du port d'Acapulco. 1791.
" 18. Carte des diverses routes par lesquelles les richesses métalliques refluent d'un continent à l'autre.
" 19. Tableau comparatif de l'étendue territoriale des jntendances de la Nouvelle-Espagne—Étendue territoriale et population des métropoles et des colonies en 1804.

## 1858
**Garcia Cubas, A.**
Atlas geográfico, estadístico é histórico de la república Mexicana ... 3 p. l., 4 pp., 1 l., 18 pp., 31 (*i. e.* 30) fold. maps, 2 fold. pl. fol. México, J. M. Fernandez de Lara, 1858.    2683

CONTENTS.

no. 1. Carta general de la república Mexicana ...
" 2. Sonora.
" 3. Chihuahua.
" 4. Coahuila.
" 5. Nuevo Leon.
" 6. Tamaulipas.
" 7. San Luis Potosí.
" 8. Zacatecas.
" 9. Aguascalientes.
" 10. Durango.
" 11. Sinaloa.
" 12. Jalisco.
" 13. Guanajuato.
" 14. Michoacán.
" 15. Querétaro.
" 16. México.
" 17. Valle de México.
" 18. Puebla.
" 19. Veracruz.
" 20. Guerrero.
" 21. Oaxaca.
" 22. Chiapas.
" 23. Tabasco.
" 24. Yucatán.
" 25. Baja California.
" 26. Sierra Gorda.
" 27. Colima.
" 28. Tlaxcala.
" 29. Tehauntepec.
" 30. Territorios de Sierragorda é isla del Cármen.
" 31. Carta general de la república Mexicana.
Cuadro 1. Cuadro histórico-geroglífico de la peregrinación de las tribus Aztecas.
" 2. Cuadro historico-geroglifico de la peregrinación de las tribus Aztecas que poblaron el valle de México.

## 1874
**García Cubas, A.**
Atlas metodico para la enseñanza de la geografia de la republica Mexicana formado y dedicado a la sociedad Mexicana de geografia y estadistica ... 54 pp., front. (port.) 33 maps. 4°. Mexico, Sandoval y Valquez, 1874.    2684

## 1884–1886
**García Cubas, A.**
[Atlas Mexicano]    31 col. maps.    fol.    [Mexico, Debray suc's, 1884–1886]    2685

NOTE.—Title-page wanting.
Maps have running title as given above. Each map separately copyrighted; dated 1884–1886.

**García Cubas, A.**—Continued.
Scale of maps generally varies. Two sheets numbered "xxviii."
no. [29] Plano de la cuidad de Mexico.—Mexico regia . . .

CONTENTS.

Carta general de los estados unidos Mexicanos, formada por el ingeniero, Antonio García Cubas. Escala 1/4.400.000.
no  1. Sonora. 1:2.000.000.
"   2. Chihuahua. Escala 1/2.000.000.
"   3. Coahuila. Escala 1:1.200.000.
"   4. Nuevo Leon. Escala 1/1.200.000.
"   5. Tamaulipas. Escala 1/1.500.000.
"   6. Veracruz. Escala 1 1.200.000.
"   7. Tabasco. Escala 1/1.200.000.
"   8. Campeche. Escala 1/1.200.000.
"   9. Yucatan. Escala 1/1.200.000.
" 10. Sinaloa. Escala 1/1.500.000.
" 11. Jalisco. 1:1.500.000.
" 12. Colima. 1:500.000.
" 13. Michoacan. Escala 1/1.000.000.
" 14. Guerrero. Escala 1:1.000.000.
" 15. Oaxaca. Escala 1.100.000.
" 16. Chiapas. Escala 1:1.200.000.
" 17. Durango. 1:1.200.000.
" 18. Zacatacas. Escala 1:1.200.000.
" 19. Aguascalientes. Escala 1:300.000.
" 20. San Luis Potosi. Escala 1:1.325.000.
" 21. Guanajuato. Escala 1:600.000.
" 22. Querétaro. Escala 1/480.000.
" 23. Hidalgo. 1:600.000.
" 24. Mexico. 1/500.000.
" 25. Morelos. 1:250.000.
" 26. Puebla. 1:900.000.
" 27. Tlaxcala. Escala 1:230.000.
" 28. Baja California. Escala 1:3.000.000.
" 29. Distrito Federal. Escala 1.245.000.
" 30. Territorio de Tepic.

**1885**

**García Cubas, A.**
Atlas pintoresco é historico de los estados unidos mexicanos . . . 1 p. l., 13 maps. obl. fol. Mexico, Debray sucesores, 1885.
2686

NOTE.—The maps have border illustrations of buildings, churches, costumes, railway bridges, mountains, plants, antiquities, and portraits of prominent men.

**1886**

**García Cubas, A.**
Atlas geográfico y estadístico de los estados unidos mexicanos . . . 3 p. l., [124] pp., 31 col. maps. obl. fol. Mexico, Debray sucesores, 1886.
2687

NOTE.—The text accompanying the maps is printed in spanish, french and english, and gives, besides general information, a detailed topographical description of every state.

CONTENTS.

no. 1. Sonora.
" 2. Chihuahua.
" 3. Coahuila.
" 4. Nuevo Leon.
" 5. Tamaulipas.
" 6. Vera Cruz.
" 7. Tabasco.
" 8. Campeche.
" 9. Yucatan.
" 10. Sinaloa.
" 11. Jalisco.
" 12. Colima.
" 13. Michoacan.
" 14. Guerrero.
" 15. Oaxaca.
" 16. Chiapas.
" 17. Durango.
" 18. Zacatecas.
" 19. Aguascalientes.
" 20. San Luis Potosi.
" 21. Guanajuato.
" 22. Queretaro.
" 23. Hidalgo.
" 24. Mexico.
" 25. Morelos.
" 26. Puebla.
" 27. Tlaxcala.
" 28. Baja California.
" 29. Distrito federal, city of Mexico, plans, etc.
" 30. Territorio de Tepic.
" 31. Carta general de los Estados Unidos mexicanos.

## 1887

**Memoria** presentada al congreso de la unión por el secretario de estado y del despacho de fomento, colonización, industria y comercio de la república Mexicana, general Cárlos Pacheco. Corresponde á los años trascurridos de enero de 1883 de 1885. v. 6. Atlas. 2 p. l., 48 maps. fol. México, oficina tipográfica de la secretaría de fomento, 1887.   2688

CONTENTS.

Carta general. Telegráfica de los estados unidos Mexicanos, comprendiendo lo construido y en explotación en las diversas líneas hasta junio de 1885 . . .
no. [1] Diagrama que manifiesta el estado de las hojas de publicación á la 100,000ª en junio 30 de 1885. Región del norte.
" [2] Canevás de las operaciones topográficas ejecutadas hasta junio 30 de 1885. Región del norte. Fracción superior.
" [3] Canevás de las operaciones topográficas ejecutadas hasta junio 30 de 1885. Región del norte. Fracción inferior.
" [4] Diagrama que manifiesta el estado de las hojas de publicación á la 100,000ª en junio 30 de 1885. Región central y de oriente.

**Memoria, etc.—Continued.**

no. [5] Canevás de las operaciones topográficas ejecutadas hasta junio 30 de 1885. Región central y de oriente. Fracción superior.
" [6] Canevás de las operaciones topográficas ejecutadas hasta junio 30 de 1885. Región central y de oriente. Fracción inferior.
" [7] Territorio de la Baja California. Carta de la 1ª fracción de la zona . . .
" [8] Territorio de la Baja California. Carta de la porción 1ª de la 2ª fracción de la zona . . .
" [9] Territorio de la Baja California. Carta de la porción 2ª de la 2ª fracción de la zona . . .
" [10] Territorio de la Baja California. Carta de la porción 1ª de la 3ª fracción de la zona . . .
" [11] Territorio de la Baja California. Carta de la porción 2ª de la 3ª fracción de la zona . . .
" [12] Plano de la triangulación practicada entre Campo Astronómico y Cabo Haro, en el puerto de Guaymas . . . 1884.
" [13] Plano del puerto de Guaymas, con un proyecto para el mejoramiento de sus condiciones sanitarias . . . 1885.
" [14] Mapa del cantón Meoqui. Estado de Chihuahua . . . 1884.
" [15] Mapa del cantón Balleza. Estado de Chihuahua . . .
" [16] Mapa del cantón Jiménez. Estado de Chihuahua . . . 1883.
" [17] Mapa del cantón Camargo. Estado de Chihuahua . . . 1883.
" [18] Puente para el rio Atoyac. Dirección del camino de Tehuacán á Puerto Ángel por Oaxaca. Plano núm. 1.
" [19] Ferrocarril Hidalgo. Proyecto para el ensanche de la estación de Pachuca y alineamiento del camino que conduce á México . . . 1883.
" [20] Ferrocarril de Mérida á Calkiní. Proyecto de estación en Umán . . . 1883.
" [21] Ferrocarril de Puebla á Izúcar de Matamoros. Sección 1ª de Puebla á Cholula. Proyecto del Puente de la Unión sobre el rio Atoyac . . . 1881.
" [22] Ferrocarril de Puebla á Izúcar de Matamoros. Sección 2ª de Cholula á Atlixco. 2º tramo. Puente de Teyecatl . . . 1883.
" [23] Ferrocarril de Puebla á Izúcar de Matamoros. 2ª sección de Cholula á Atlixco. Puente de Tejaluca en el kº 43 . . . 1883.
" [24] Plano topográfico del rio Chubiscar en una zona de dos kilómetros á cada lado de la línea del puente del ferrocarril Central Mejicano . . .
" [25] Ferrocarril Central Mexicano. Plano de una de las trabas del puente sobre el rio Grande del Norte . . . 1885.
" 26 Ferrocarril central Mexicano. Plano de la fundación estacada y de los apoyos del puente sobre el rio Grande del Norte . . . 1885.
" 27 Plano topográfico del rio Conchos en una zona de dos kilómetros á cada lado de la línea del puente del ferrocarril central Mexicano . . . 1883.
" 28 Plano general del puente sobre el rio Conchos.
" 29 Puente sobre el rio Salto. Ferro-carril central. División de San Luis Potosí á Tampico . . . 1884.
" 30 Ferrocarril central Mexicano. Detalles del puente sobre el rio Salto . . .
" 31 Ferro-carril central. División de San Luis Potosí á Tampico. Pilares del centro y del este del puente sobre el rio Salto, en Santa Rosa . . . 1886.
" 32 Ferro-carril central. División de San Luis Potosí á Tampico. Estribo oeste del puente sobre el rio Salto, en Santa Rosa . . . 1886.

no. 33 Ferro-carril central. División de San Luis Potosí á Tampico. Plano y detalles del puente provisional, sobre un agujero en el kil. 118.
" [34] Ferro-carril central. División de San Luis Potosí á Tampico. Plano y detalles del puente de Palastro proyectado sobre un agujero en la est. 4,715 kil. 118 . . . 1884.
" [35] Ferro-carril central. Mampostería y cimientos para el puente sobre el rio Tamasopo . . . 1883.
" [36] Puente sobre el rio Choy. Tampico división. F. c. c. M.
" [37] 1883. F. c. c. M. Línea del Pacífico. División oriental. Líneas y reconocimientos entre Guadalajara y Lagos . . .
" [38] F. c. de Puebla á S. Márcos y Villa de Libres. Puente en la barranca de Xalacatl. Tercera sección . . . 1884.
" [39] Rada de Salina Cruz . . . 1883.
" [40] Proyecto de muelle para el puerto de Salina Cruz . . . 1883.
" [41] Canal n. del Chijol. Proyecto de trazo final para someterlo á la aprobación del supremo gobierno . . . 1886.
" [42] Faro y torre para el puerto de Guaymas, México. Establecidos por la Compañía del ferro carril de Sonora . . . 1884.
" [43] Plano de una parte del estado de Colima. Proyecto de saneamiento para el puerto del Manzanillo . . . 1884.
" [44–46] Muelle para el puerto de Manzanillo . . . 1883. 3 sheets.
" [47] Proyecto de monumento á la memoria de Sor. Juana Inéz de la Cruz . . . 1884. Provinces.

States.

## SAN LUIS POTOSI.

**Mexico.** *Comisión geográfico-exploradora.*
Carta general del estado de S. Luis Potosi, levantada por iniciativa de su actual gobernador gral. Carlos Diez Gutierrez; por la comisión geográfico-exploradora. Escala de 1:250 000. 2 p. l., 10 maps. obl. fol. [Xalapa] comisión geográfico-exploradora, 1904. 2689

## TEHUANTEPEC.

**Williams, J. J.**
Maps illustrating the isthmus of Tehuantepec. 2 p. l., 8 fold. maps. 8°. New York, D. Appleton & co. 1852. 2690

NOTE.—Copyrighted by "B. Fallon, secretary of the Tehuantepec railroad company of New Orleans."
To accompany work entitied: The isthmus of Tehuantepec; being the results of a survey for a railroad to connect the Atlantic and Pacific oceans made by the scientific commission under the direction of major J. G. Barnard . . . Arranged and prepared for the Tehuantepec railroad company of New Orleans, by J. J. Williams. New York, D. Appleton & co. 1852.

CONTENTS.

no. 1. Map of the isthmus of Tehuantepec. 1851.
" 2. Plan of that part of the isthmus of Tehuantepec between Jaltepec river and the Pacific plains. 1851.
" 3. Mouth of the Coatzacoalcos river, surveyed jan. 1848.
" 4. Sketch from the mouth of the Coatzacoalcos river to the town of Mina-Titlan. 1847.

**Williams, J. J.**—Continued.
- no. 5. Map of the Coatzacoalcos river, from Mina-Titlan to the isla del Suchil, and of the Jaltepec river, from its junction to the railroad crossing. 1851.
- " 6. Map of the river Uspanapa to the Playa del Tigre. Made in may 1851 by J. McL. Murphy.—Insets: Map of the Tancochapa river. 1851.—Map of the village of Mina-Titlan . . . by Chas. C. Smith. 1851.
- " 7. Chart of the ports of Laventosa & Salina Cruz. By . . . P. E. Trastour. 1851.
- " 8. Chart of the entrance and channel of the Boca-Barra. By . . . P. E. Trastour. 1850.—Inset: Isthmus of Tehuantepec.

# CENTRAL AMERICA.
## COSTA RICA.
### BOUNDARY.

**Peralta, M. M. de.**

Límites de Costa-Rica y Colombia. Nuevos documentos para la historia de su jurisdicción territorial con notos, comentarios y un examen de la cartografía de Costa-Rica y Veragua. . . Atlas. cover-title, 26 maps. fol. Madrid, 1890. 2691

NOTE.—"Examen de la cartografía de Costa-Rica." pp. 584–637.

Atlas accompanying this work of 778 pp., entitled: Atlas histórico-geográfico de la república de Costa-Rica, Veragua y Costa de Mosquitos para servir al arbitraje de la cuestion de límites entre Costa-Rica y Colombia ordenado por d. Manuel M. de Peralta . . .

A collection of maps, for the most part reproductions, dated 1597–1864.

#### CONTENTS.

- A. Mapa de Costa Rica segun sus límites legales durante la dominación española (1540 á 1821) . . . Madrid, 1890.
- B. Mapa de Costa Rica, istmo de Panamá, Veragua y Costa de Mosquitos . . . Madrid, 1890.
- no. 1. Ivcatana regio et Fondvra. Cornelio Wytfliet . . . 1597.
- " 2. Descripción del avdiencia de Gvatimala. Antonio de Herrera. 1601.
- " 3. Descripción del avdiencia de Panama. A. de Herrera. 1601.
- " 4. Veragua y parte de Costa-Rica Lorenzo del Salto. Ms. Remedios. 1620.
- " 5. Insulæ Americanæ in oceano septentrionali, cum terris adiacentibus—Islas Antillas y costas de Tierra Firme—Anónimo. Amsterdam 1610 (?).
- " 6. Terra Firma et novum regnum Granatense et Popayan. Juan Jansson, 1640.
- " 7. Pascaerte vande Caribische eylanden vande Barbados tot dende bocht van Mexico. Hendrick Doncker. 1642.
- " 8. Audiencia de Guatimala, con la demarcacion de Costa-Rica y Veragua. Sanson d'Abbeville. 1657.
- " 9. Las islas y Tierra-Firme de las Indias Occidentales del Mar del Norte. Jacob Colom. 1660–1669.
- " 10. Indiarum occidentalium. Tractus littorales cum insulis Caribicis. Frederick de Witt. 1680.

no. 11. Honduras, Costa-Rica, Veragua é Islas Antillas. Oexmelin, 1688.
" 12. Islas Antillas, Honduras, Nicaragua, Costa-Rica, Tierra-Firme etc. Juan van Keulen. 1695.
" 13. Las costas de la América—Honduras, Nicaragua, Costa-Rica etc. Gerard van Keulen-Jean Sikkena. 1698-1715.
" 14. Carte des isles de l'Amérique et de plusieurs pays de Terre Ferme . . . d'Anville . . . 1731.
" 15. A map of the british empire in America with the french and spanish settlements adjacent thereto by Henry Popple.
" 16. Amérique Septentrionale. d'Anville. 1746.
" 17. Carte des provinces de Nicaragua et Costa Rica. Bellin 1754(?)
" 18. Mapa maritimo del golfo de México é islas de la América. Tomas Lopez y Juan de la Cruz (copistas de d'Anville, no. 16) 1755.
" 19. Amérique Septentrionale et Méridionale. Robert de Vaugondy (copistas de d'Anville, no. 16) 1785(?)
" 20. Nuevo mapa de la América Septentrional: Costa-Rica y Veragua (copistas d'Anville, no. 16) Lóndres, 1785.
" 21. Costa-Rica y Veragua. Thomas Jefferys. 1792.
" 22. Carta esférica del mar de las Antillas y de las costas de Tierra Firme. 1805-1809.
" 23. Colombia—from Humboldt and other recent authorities. 1822.
" 24. Carta corográfica del estado de Panama . . . Manuel Ponce de Leon y Manuel Maria Paz. 1864.

# PANAMA.

## 1899

**Compagnie nouvelle du canal de Panama.**

Notes techniques concernant l'exposé des dispositions adoptées pour la solution de divers problèmes particuliers de l'exécution du canal. 1 p. l., 123 pp. 4°. Atlas of 17 pl. fol. Paris, société anonyme de publications périodiques, 1899. 2692

CONTENTS.

no. 1. Plan général du canal.
" 2. Profils en long.
" 3. Profils en travers types du canal.
" 4. Plan général de la région de Bohio.
" 5. Écluses de Bohio.
" 6. Barrage de Bohio.
" 7. Déversoirs de Bohio.
" 8. Écluse de Paraiso.
" 9. Barrage & déversoir d'Alhajuela.
" 10. Plan général du haut Chagres avec indications des tracés de la rigole d'alimentation et du chemin de fer.
" 11. Rigole d'alimentation. Profil en long schématique.
" 12. id. id. Profils en travers types et ouvrages d'art principaux.
" 13. Chemin de fer de Gamboa à Alhajuela. Profil en long schématique.
" 14. id. id. id. Profils en travers type et pont métallique sur le Chilibre.
" 15. Plan général figurant la situation des voies à un moment donné des travaux.—Plan détaillé des chantiers d'attaque à une phase donnée de l'exécution.

**Compagnie nouvelle du canal de Panama**—Continued.

no. 16. Schema figuratif des phases successives d'exécution.
" 17. I. Graphique figuratif des nombres journaliers d'ouvriers ordinaires et d'ouvriers maçons nécessaires pour l'exécution des travaux.
II. Graphique figuratif de la répartition des dépenses sur un délai total de dix ans.

### 1907

**Hammond, C. S., & co.**

Hammond's descriptive atlas of Panama and the Isthmian canal; contains new maps, plans, illustrations and complete descriptive text.   cover-title, 7, [1] pp. incl. 4 maps.   fol.   New York, C. S. Hammond & co. [°1907] 2693

---

# WEST INDIES.

## GENERAL.

(Arranged chronologically)

### 1675

**Roggeveen, A.**

Het eerste deel van het brandende veen, verlichtende alle de vafte kuften ende eylanden van geheel West-Indien ofte rio Amasones . . .   6 p. l., 62, [1] pp., 33 col. maps.   fol.   t'Amsteldam, P. Goos [1675] 2694

NOTE.—The date 1675 at end of dedication. Engraved title-page, colored, containing portrait of Roggeveen. Few copies of this work were published, of which there was no continuation.

CONTENTS.

Generaele kaert van Westindien . . .
no. 1. De zeekufsten van Westindien . . .
" 2. Paskaert vande cust van Westindien, streckende van rio Wia tot rio Soronama.
" 3. Paskaert vande cust van Westindien tufschen rio Soronama en rio Demerary . . .
" 4. De cuft van Westindien, tufschen rio Demerary, en rio d'Oronoque . . .
" 5. Paskaerte vande rivier Oronoque van Moco moco tot St. Thome, en een gedeelte van golfo de Paria . . .
" 6. Paskaerte van 't eylandt Trinidad en de eÿlanden daer ontrent gelegen, mitsgaders de vaste cuft van cabo Salines tot Commonagod bay.
" 7. Pascaert vande cust van Westindien tufschen Baÿa Commonagod en golfo de Venecuela . . .
" 8. De cuft van Westindien tufschen golfo Venecuela en St. Martha . . .
" 9. Paskaerte vande cust van West-Indien tufschen St. Martha en ilha Cares . . .
" 10. De cuft van Westindien, tufschen i. Cares, en c. de Tÿburon . . .
" 11. De cuft van Westindien, van cabo de Tÿburon, tot punta St. Blaes . . .
" 12. De cuft van Westindien, tufschen punta St. blaes, en punta d Naes . . .

no. 13. Paskaert vande cust van Westindien, van punta de Naes, tot rio Defaguadera . . .
" 14. Paskaerte vande cust van Westindien van r. Defaguadera tot c. de Honduras . . .
" 15. De cuft van Westindien, van c. Honduras, tot c. Serra . . .
" 16. De cuft van Westindien, van la Defconofcida, tot c. Efcondido . . .
" 17. Pascaert van 't canael de Bahama, en de eÿlanden gelegen benoorden Cuba . . .
" 18. Pascaert vande Caribes eÿlanden van 't eÿlant Granadillos, tot 't eÿlant Anguilla . . .
" 19. Pascaert van 't eÿlant St. Juan de Puerto Rico en de andere refterende Caribes eÿlanden van Anguilla tot Spagnola . . .
" 20. Pascaerte van 't eÿlant Spagnola en alle de andere eÿlanden daer aen gelegen . . .
" 21. Pascaerte van de noordcuft van Spagnola tufschen de bäy van Manfaniella tot de reede van 't eÿlandt Tortugas . . .
" 22. Pascaert van de weft cuft van Spagnola, tufschen cabo St. Nicolaes, en ilha de Vaca . . .
" 23. Pascaert van de eÿlanden Cuba en Jamaica en de andere eÿlanden daer ontrent gelegen . . .
" 24. Paskaert vande noord cust van Cuba, ftreckende van bahia de Matancas tot bahia Honda . . .
" [24½] Paskaarte van 't eÿlant Sta. Catalina . . .
" 25. Caert vande cuft van Florida tot de Verginis streckende van cabo de Canaveral tot baya de la Madalena.
" 26. Pascaert vande Virginies van baÿa de la Madelena tot de Zuÿdt revier.
" 27. Pascaert van Nieu Nederland streckende vande Zuÿdt revier tot de Noordt revier en 't Lange Eÿland.
" 28. Pascaerte van Nieu Nederland streckende vande Noordt revier tot Hendrick Chriftiaens eÿlandt.
" 29. Pascaert van Nieu Nederland van Hendrick Chriftiaens eÿland tot Staten hoeck of Cabo Cod.
" 30. Pascaert van 't eÿland la Bermuda of Sommer iflandssen de andere eÿlanden daer bÿ geleeghen.
" 31. Pascaert van Terra Nova, Nova Francia, Nievw Engeland en de groote revier van Canada.

## 1680

La primera parte del monte de turba ardiente allumbrando con la claridad de fu fuego todas las coftas firmes, y yslas de toda la India-Occidental . . .  2 p. l., 68 pp., 33 maps. fol. Amsterdam, P. Goos, 1680. 2695

NOTE.—Engraved title.
Same maps as in the dutch edition. See contents, title 2694. Text in spanish. maps in dutch. Engraved title, uncolored, containing portrait of Roggeveen.

## 1766

**Speer, J. S.**

The West-India pilot . . . the whole illustrated with a number of copper plates, finished by the best hands, describing the ports and bays . . . with the true soundings, laid down with the utmost

**Speer, J. S.**—Continued.

exactness, by an officer who has served upwards of twenty years in the West Indies. 3 p. l., 52 pp., 1 l., 13 maps. fol. London, for the author, 1766.     2696

    Note.—See also title 2698.

CONTENTS.

    no. [ 1] A plan of the harbour of Port Royal, in the island of Jamaica.
     "  [ 2] Plan of Blewfield's harbour, in the island of Jamaica.
     "  [ 3] Plan of Lucia harbour on the north side of Jamaica in lat$^d$ 18° 23″.
     "  [ 4] Plan of Mantica bay on the north side of Jamaica.
     "  [ 5] A plan of Cape Nichola Mole, at the n. w. end of the island of Hispaniola.
     "  [ 6] Plan du Cap François et de ses environs.
     "  [ 7] [Bay of Honduras]
     "  [ 8] A plan of Port S$^t$ Fernando de Omoa near Honduras.
     "  [ 9] A plan of Port Royal harbour Rattan.
     "  [10] A plan of Blewfields harbour, on the Musquito shore.
     "  [11] Plan du Cul de Sac de Leogane, ou le Port Au Prince.
     "  [12] Plan de la rade du Port Paix, à la côte septentrionale de Saint Domingue.
     "  [13] Plan of the entrance into Cape Fear harbour, North Carolina.

1768

**Jefferys, T.**

A general topography of North America and the West Indies. Being a collection of all the maps, charts, plans, and particular surveys, that have been published of that part of the world, either in Europe or America . . . 4, 4 pp., 100 maps on 109 sheets. fol. London, for R. Sayer & T. Jefferys, 1768.     2697

    Note.—Title and contents also in french.
    Maps no. 102, "Plan of the french attacks upon the island of Grenada . . . 1779," and no. 109, "Attack of the rebels upon fort Penobscot in the province of New England . . . 1779," inserted.
    For complete contents, see title 1196.

1771

**Speer, J. S.**

The West-India pilot: containing piloting directions for Port Royal and Kingston harbours in Jamaica, in and out through the kays, &c. . . . the whole illuftrated with a number of maps and plans engraved by the best artists, describing the ports and bays above-mentioned: with the true soundings, laid down with the utmost exactness. 4 p. l., 67 pp., 26 maps. fol. London, for the author, & sold by S. Hooper, 1771.     2698

    Note.—See also title 2696.

CONTENTS.

    no. [1] A plan of the harbour of Port Royal, in the island of Jamaica.
     "  [2] Plan of Blewfield's harbour, in the island of Jamaica.
     "  [3] Plan of Lucia harbour on the north side of Jamaica . . .

no. [ 4] Plan of Mantica bay on the north side of Jamaica.
" [ 5] A plan of Cape Nichola mole, on the n. w. end of the island of Hispaniola.
" [ 6] Plan du Cap François et de ses environs.
" [ 7] A plan of Port Antonio, on the north-east side of Jamaica.
" [ 8] A chart of the bay of Honduras . . . 1771.
" [ 9] A plan of port St. Fernando de Omoa near Honduras.
" [10] Plan of the fortification now finishing in the port of St. Fernando de Omoa . . . 1765.
" [11] A plan of Port Royal harbour Rattan.
" [12] A plan of Blewfields harbour on the Mosquito shore.
" [13] Plan of the harbour of St. Juan de Port O Rico. [!]
" [14] Aiguiade de Port O Rico . . . [!]
" [15] Plan de la rade du Port Paix, à la côte septentrionale de Saint Domingue.
" [16] Plan of the entrance into Cape Fear harbour, North Carolina.
" [17] Plan of the town, and harbour of Puerto Vello.
" [18] Plan of Carthagena harbour and city . . . 1771.
" [19] References [and plan] for the plan of the city and suburbs of Carthagena.
" [20] Plan of the harbour and city of Havanah . . . Cuba. 1771.
" [21] The bay of Ocoa on the south side of the island of St. Domingo.
" [22] Plan du port de Gouadaquini now called Jekil sound in the province of Georgia . . .
" [23] [Island of Old Providence]
" [24] Plan du Cul de Sac de Leogane, ou le Port au Prince.
" [25] Plan of Vera Crux lying in the gulph of Mexico.
" [26] Plan of the bay of Matanzas lying on the north side of Cuba.

## 1775

**Jefferys, T.**
 The West-India atlas: or, a compendious description of the West-Indies: illustrated with forty correct charts and maps, taken from actual surveys. Together with an historical account of the several countries and islands which compose that part of the world . . . 3 p. l., 28 pp., 39 maps. fol. London, for R. Sayer & J. Bennett, 1775. 2699

NOTE.—Engraved title. See also titles 2701, 2702, 2703, 2705 and 2708.

### CONTENTS.

no. 1. A chart of British channel . . .
" 2. A chart of the Atlantic ocean.
" 3. Chart of the Acores (Hawks) islands, called also Flemish and Western islands from mr. d'Anville with several additions.
" 4. A chart of the Maderas and Canary islands. From draughts . . . of capt. G. Clas . . .
" 5. The Cape Verd islands. By d'Après de Mannevillette . . . A view of Praya bay . . .
" 6. The Bermudas or Summer's islands from a survey by C. Lempriere . . .
" 7. An index map to the following sixteen sheets, being a compleat chart of the West Indies . . .
" 8. The western coast of Louisiana and the coast of New Leon . . .

**Jefferys, T.**—Continued.
- no. 9. The coast of West Florida and Louisiana . . .
- " 10. The peninsula and gulf of Florida or channel of Bahama . . .
- " 11. The coast of Mexico from Laguna de Esmotes to Punta Brava . . .
- " 12. The coast of Yucatan from Campeche to Bahia del Ascension . . .
- " 13. The island of Cuba . . .
- " 14. The Windward passage . . .
- " 15. The coast of New Spain from Neuva Vera Cruz to Triste island . . .
- " 16. The bay of Honduras . . .
- " 17. The island of Jamaica . . .
- " 18. South part of St. Domingo, or Hispaniola . . .
- " 19. The Caribbee islands, the Virgin islands . . .
- " 20. Part of the provinces of Costa Rica and Nicaragua . . .
- " 21. The isthmus of Panama . . .
- " 22. The coast of Tierra Firma from Cartagena to golfo Triste . . .
- " 23. The coast of Caracas, Cumana, Parla and the mouths of rio Orinoco . . .
- " 24. Jamaica from the latest surveys . . .
- " 25. Ruatan or Rattan, surveyed by lieutenant Henry Barnsley with improvements by Thomas Jefferys . . .
- " 26. The Virgin islands from english and danish surveys . . .
- " 27. St. Christophers or St. Kitts, surveyed by Anthony Ravell . . .
- " 28. Antigua surveyed by Robert Baker . . .
- " 29. Guadaloupe, done from actual surveys and observations of the english . . .
- " 30. Dominica from an actual survey compleated in the year 1773 . . .
- " 31. Martinico done from actual surveys and observations, made by english engineers . . .
- " 32. St. Lucia, done from surveys and observations, made by the english . . .
- " 33. Barbadoes, surveyed by William Mayo . . .
- " 34. St. Vincent, from an actual survey made in the year 1773, after the treaty with the Caribs . . .
- " 35. Bequia or Becouya the northernmost of the Granadilles. Surveyed in 1763 . . .
- " 36. Grenada divided into its parishes, surveyed by order of his excellency governor Scott . . .
- " 37. Tobago from actual surveys and observations . . .
- " 38. Turks islands from a survey made in 1753, by the sloops L'Aigle and L'Emeraude . . . with improvements from observations made in 1770 . . .
- " 39. Curacao from the dutch originals of Gerard van Keulen . . .

**1784**

**Matthews, J.**
Twenty-one plans, with explanations, of different actions in the West Indies, during the late war: by an officer of the royal navy, who was present. 24 pp., 21 fold. col. plans. 8°. Chester [Eng.] by J. Fletcher, for the author, 1784. 2700

NOTE.—Dedication signed: John Matthews.
Battles of Grenada, july 6, 1779; Martinique, april 29, 1781; St. Christopher, january 25-26, 1782; and Dominica, april 9 and 12, 1782.

## 1787

**Jefferys, T.**

The West-India atlas: or, a compendious description of the West-Indies: illustrated with forty-one correct charts and maps, taken from actual surveys. Together with an historical account of the several countries and islands which compose that part of the world. . . .   3 p. l., 28 pp., 40 maps.   fol.   London, for R. Sayer & J. Bennett, 1783–[1787]                                                2701

   NOTE.—Engraved title dated 1775; descriptive title 1783; latest date on maps is 1787 which is on map no. 1, A chart of the British channel . . .
   Maps no. 6–40 dated 1775 are the same as the corresponding maps in the edition of 1775. See also titles 2699, 2702, 2703 and 2708.
   The following bear later dates:
   no. 1. A chart of the British Channel . . .   1787.
   "   2. A chart of the Atlantic ocean . . .   1786.
   "   3. Chart of the Açores (Hawks) islands . . .   1782.
   "   4. A chart of the Maderas and Canary islands.   1781.
   "   5. The Cape Verd islands . . .   1782—A view of Praya bay . . .   1782.

## 1794

The West-India atlas or, a compendious description of the West-Indies: consisting of a complete collection of accurate charts, with plans of the harbours, roads, bays—and maps of the separate islands, taken from actual surveys. Together with an historical account of the several countries and islands which compose that part of the world . . .   4 p. l., 28 pp., 60 maps on 61 sheets.   fol.   London, for R. Sayer, 1794.                                               2702

   NOTE.—Engraved title inserted after p. 28. See also titles 2699, 2701, 2703 and 2708.

                           CONTENTS.

   no. 1. A new chart of the British channel . . .   Corrected and improved by John Stephenson . . .   1788.
   "   2–3. A new general chart of the Atlantic or Western ocean and adjacent seas . . . mr. de Fleurieu . . .   1768–1769.
   "   4. Chart of the Açores (Hawks) islands . . .   [1794]
   "   5. A chart of the Maderas and Canary islands . . .   Thomas Lopés . . .   1780.
   "   6. The Cape Verd islands . . .   d'Après de Mannevillette . . . 1788.— A view of Praya bay in the island of St. Jago . . .   1788.
   "   7. The Bermudas, or Summer's islands. From a survey by C. Lempriere . . .   1787.
   "   8. Index to the following sixteen sheets, being a compleat chart of the West Indies . . .   1792.
   "   9. The western coast of Louisiana and the coast of New Leon . . .   1792 . . .
   "   10. The coast of West Florida and Louisiana . . .   1792 . . .
   "   11. The peninsula and gulf of Florida, or New Bahama channel . . .   1792 . . .
   "   12. The coast of Mexico from Laguna de Esmontes to Punta Brava . . .   1792.

**Jefferys, T.**—Continued.
- no. 13. The coast of Yucatan from Campeche to Ascension bay . . . 1792.
- " 14. The island of Cuba with part of the Bahama banks . . . 1792.
- " 15. The Windward passage, with the several passages from the east end of Cuba . . . 1792.
- " 16. The coast of New Spain . . . 1792.
- " 17. The bay of Honduras . . . 1792.
- " 18. The island of Jamaica . . . 1792.
- " 19. South part of St. Domingo, or Hispaniola . . . 1792.
- " 20. The Caribbee or Leeward islands . . . 1792.
- " 21. Part of the provinces of Costa-Rica and Nicaragua . . . 1792.
- " 22. The isthmus of Panama with the coast from Great river on the Moskito shore to Cartagena . . . 1792.
- " 23. The coast of Tierra Firma from Cartagena to golfo Triste . . . 1792.
- " 24. The coast of Caracas Cumana Paria . . . 1792.
- " 25. A new chart of the coast of Guayana . . . 1787.
- " 26. Plan of the road and town of La Guayra. 1788.—Plan of Puerto Cavello on the coast of the Caracas by lt. Jones in 1741.
- " 27. Plan of the bay and town of St. Martha on the coast of Terra Firma. 1788.—Plan of the harbour of Carthagena, by don Juan de Herrera. 1788.
- " 28. Plan of Zispata bay. 1788.—A plan of Portobelo harbour 1767 . . . 1788.
- " 29. Plan of the road and harbour of Chagre with the town and castle. 1788.—A draught of the Bahias del Almirante named by the buccaniers Bocatoro. 1788.
- " 30. A draught of Blewfields lagoon on the Moskito shore. 1788.—A plan of Truxillo bay, called also St. Giles bay . . . 1788.
- " 31. A draught of the harbour of San Fernando de Omoa . . . 1759 & 1767. London, 1788.—Plan of the road and port of La Vera Cruz surveyed in 1740 . . . 1788.
- " 32. The entrance of the river Missisipi at Fort Balise. 1764 . . . 1788.—A draught of the entrance of Mobile. 1764 . . . 1788.
- " 33. A plan of Mobile bar, surveyed by B. Romans, 1771 . . . 1788.—Plan of the harbour of Pensacola. By B. Romans, 1771 . . . 1788.
- " 34. A plan of the entrances of Tampa bay . . . 1788.—Plan of Lucia harbour and Mantega bay in Jamaica. 1788.
- " 35. The harbours of Port Antonio, in Jamaica. 1788.—Plan of Bahia Honda on the north side of Cuba. 1788.
- " 36. Plan of Port Cavanas, on the north side of Cuba. 1788.—Plan of Port Mariel, on the north side of Cuba. 1788.
- " 37. Plan of the city and harbour of Havanna. 1788.—Plan of the bay of Matanzas, on the north side of Cuba. 1788.
- " 38. A plan of Nuevitas harbour in the island of Cuba. 1788.—Plan of Great bay of Nipe on the north side of Cuba. 1788.
- " 39. Plan of Barracoa in the island of Cuba. 1788.—Plan of Bahia Xagua on the south side of Cuba. 1788.
- " 40. Plan of Guantanimo on the south side of Cuba . . . 1740. By admiral Durell.—The harbour of St. Yago in the island of Cuba. 1788.
- " 41. A plan of Fort St. Louis harbour . . . 1788.—Petit Guave in the island of Hispaniola. 1788.
- " 42. Leogane and Port au Prince . . . 1788.—A plan of Cape Nicola mole . . . 1788.

no. 43. A plan of the road of Port Paix . . . 1788.—A plan of the town and harbour of Cap François in the island of St. Domingo. 1788.
" 44. Plan of the bay and town of Bayaha or Port Dauphin in the island of Hispaniola. 1788.—A plan of Monte-Christe bay . . . 1788.
" 45. A survey of the West road of Portorico named by the spaniards Aguada Nueva. 1740. London, 1788.—A plan of the forts and harbour of San Juan de Portorico. 1788.
" 46. Jamaica from the latest surveys; improved and engraved by Thomas Jefferys . . . 1775.
" 47. Ruatan or Rattan, surveyed by lieut. Henry Barnsley. 1775.
" 48. The Virgin islands from english and danish surveys, by Thomas Jefferys . . . 1775.
" 49. St. Christophers, or St. Kitts, surveyed by Anthony Ravell . . . 1775.
" 50. Antigua surveyed by Robert Baker . . . [n. d.]
" 51. Guadaloupe, done from actual surveys and observations of the english . . . by Thomas Jefferys. 1775.
" 52. Dominica from an actual survey compleated in the year 1773 . . . 1775.
" 53. Martinico, done from actual surveys and observations, made by english engineers . . . 1794.
" 54. St. Lucia; done from surveys and observations made by the english. 1775.
" 55. Tobago from actual surveys and observations . . . 1775.
" 56. Barbadoes, surveyed by William Mayo . . . 1775.
" 57. St. Vincent, from an actual survey made in the year 1773, after the treaty with the Caribs . . . 1775.
" 58. Bequia or Becouya . . . Surveyed in 1763 . . . 1775.
" 59. Grenada divided into its parishes, surveyed by order of gov. Scott, and engraved by Thomas Jefferys. 1775.
" 60. Turks islands, from a survey made in 1753 . . . 1775.
" 61. Curaçao, from the dutch originals of Gerard van Keulen. 1775.

**1794–1796**

The West-India atlas: or, a compendious description of the West-Indies: consisting of a complete collection of accurate charts with plans of the harbours, roads, bays—and maps of the separate islands, taken from actual surveys. Together with an historical account of the several countries and islands which compose that part of the world . . . and improved from the latest discoveries, the whole neatly engraved on eighty-four plates which comprises sixty charts . . . 3 p. l., 28 pp., 60 maps on 61 sheets. fol. London, for R. Sayer, 1794–[1796] 2703

NOTE.—Same title-page as the R. Sayer edition of 1794, see title 2702, but has Laurie & Whittle names pasted on slip over the original imprint and later maps inserted. Engraved title-page wanting. The latest date in this edition is 1796 on map no. 25½, "A new chart of the coast of Guayana, from the river Berbice to Cape North" . . .
See also titles 2699, 2701, 2702, 2705 and 2708.

CONTENTS.

no. 1. A new chart of the British channel . . . By John Stephenson . . . 1794.
" 2–3. A new general chart of the Atlantic or Western ocean and adjacent seas . . . 1794. 2 sheets.

**Jefferys, T.**—Continued.
- no. 4. Chart of the Açores (Hawks) islands . . . 1794.
- " 5. A chart of the Maderas and Canary islands . . . By don Thomas Lopés. 1780.
- " 6. The Cape Verd islands . . . 1794.—A view of Praya bay . . . 1794.
- " 7. The Bermudas, or Summer's islands. From a survey by C. Lempriere . . . 1794.
- " 8. Index to the following sixteen sheets, being a complete chart of the West Indies . . . 1794.
- " 9. The western coast of Louisiana and the coast of New Leon . . . 1794.
- " 10. The coast of West Florida and Louisiana . . . 1794.
- " 11. The peninsula and gulf of Florida . . . 1794.
- " 12. The coast of Mexico . . . 1794.
- " 13. The coast of Yucatan . . . 1794.
- " 14. The island of Cuba . . . 1794.
- " 15. The Windward Passage . . . 1794.
- " 16. The coast of New Spain . . . 1794.
- " 17. The bay of Honduras . . . 1792.
- " 18. The island of Jamaica . . . 1794.
- " 19. South part of St. Domingo . . . 1794.
- " 20. The Caribbee or Leeward islands . . . 1794.
- " 21. Part of the province of Costa-Rica . . . 1794.
- " 22. The isthmus of Panama . . . 1794.
- " 23. The coast of Tierra Firma . . . 1794.
- " 24. The coast of Caracas, Cumana, Paria . . . 1794.
- " 25. A new chart of the coast of Guayana . . . 1795.
- " 25½. A new chart of the coast of Guayana, from river Berbice to Cape North . . . 1796.
- " 26. Plan of the road and town of La Guayra.—Plan of Puerto Cavello . . . 1794.
- " 27. Plan of the bay and town of St. Martha.—Plan of the harbour of Carthagena.
- " 28. Plan of Zispata bay.—A plan of Portobelo.
- " 29. A plan of the road and harbour of Chagre.—A draught of the Bahias del Almirante . . .
- " 30. A draught of Blewfields lagoon.—A plan of Truxillo bay . . .
- " 31. A draught of the harbour of San Fernando de Omoa . . .—Plan of the road and port of La Vera Cruz, surveyed in 1740.
- " 32. The entrance of the river Mississipi at Fort Balise. 1764.—A draught of the entrance of Mobile . . . 1764.
- " 33. A plan of Mobile bar. B. Romans, 1771.—Plan of the harbour of Pensacola. B. Romans, 1771.
- " 34. A plan of the entrances of Tampa bay.—Plan of Lucia harbour . . .
- " 35. The harbours of Port Antonio, in Jamaica.—Plan of Bahia Honda . . .
- " 36. Plan of Port Cavanas.—Plan of Port Mariel.
- " 37. Plan of the city and harbour of Havanna.—Plan of the bay of Matanzas.
- " 38. A plan of Nuevitas harbour.—Plan of great bay Nipe . . .
- " 39. Plan of Barracoa.—Plan of Bahia Xagua.
- " 40. Plan of Guantanimo.—The harbour of St. Yago.
- " 41. A plan of Fort St. Louis harbour.—Petit Guave in the island of Hispaniola.
- " 42. Leogane and Port Au Prince.—A plan of Cape Nicola mole.
- " 43. A plan of the road of Port Paix.—A plan of the town and harbour of Cap François.

no. 44. Plan of the bay and town of Bayaha or Port Dauphin.—A plan of Monte-Christe bay.
" 45. A survey of the west road of Portorico.—A plan of the forts and harbour of San Juan de Portorico.
" 46. Jamaica from the latest surveys . . . 1794.
" 47. Ruatan or Rattan, surveyed by lieut. Henry Barnsley . . . improvements by Thomas Jefferys . . . 1794.
" 48. The Virgin islands . . . 1794.
" 49. St. Christophers, or St. Kitts, surveyed by Anthony Ravell . . . 1794.
" 50. Antigua surveyed by Robert Baker . . . 1794.
" 51. Guadaloupe . . . with material improvements added since the conquest 1794 . . . 1795.
" 52. Dominica from an actual survey compleated in the year 1773.
" 53. Martinico . . . 1794.
" 54. St. Lucia . . . 1794.
" 55. Tobago from actual surveys and observations . . . 1794.
" 56. Barbadoes, surveyed by William Mayo . . . 1794.
" 57. St. Vincent from an actual survey . . . 1773.
" 58. Bequia or Becouya . . . surveyed in 1763.
" 59. Grenada divided into its parishes . . . 1794.
" 60. Turks islands, from a survey made in 1753.
" 61. Curaçao, from the dutch originals of Gerard van Keulen . . . 1794.

## 1810

**Edwards, B.**

A new atlas of the British West Indies, with a whole sheet general map of the West India islands, and a whole sheet map of the island of Hispaniola, or St. Domingo. Engraved to accompany the Philadelphia edition of Edwards's History of the West Indies. 2 p. l., 11 maps. 4°. Charleston, E. Norford, Willington & co. 1810. 2704

CONTENTS.

no. [1] A new map of the West Indies. Reduced by S. Louis. Engraved by J. H. Seymour.
" [2] Jamaica, divided into counties & parishes.
" [3] Barbadoes. Tanner sc.
" [4] Grenada. Tanner sc.
" [5] St. Vincent. Tanner sc.
" [6] Map of the island of Dominica . . . J. H. Seymour sc.
" [7] Island of St. Christopher's. Marſhall sc.
" [8] Island of Antigua. Marſhall sc.
" [9] Virgin Islands . . . Tanner sc.
" [10] Island of Tobago . . . Tanner sc.
" [11] St. Domingo. Scale of 30 british statute miles.

## 1810

**Jefferys, T.**

The West-India islands, Spanish Main, and northern parts of South America, including the gulf of Mexico; from the best surveys and observations, in twenty-two correct maps: with plans of most of the distinguished harbours . . . Compiled, originally, by

**Jefferys, T.**—Continued.
Thomas Jefferys . . . and now enlarged, and improved throughout, by the spanish and other recent surveys. 1 p. l., 20 col. maps on 42 l. fol. London, R. Laurie & J. Whittle, 1810. 2705
> NOTE.—The following note is beneath the imprint, "Accompanied by a book of descriptive directions," which is wanting. See also titles 2699, 2701, 2702, 2703 and 2708.

CONTENTS.

no. 1-2. New chart of the West Indies, gulf of Mexico, and northern provinces of South America; compiled from the most recent spanish and other surveys, by Joseph Dessiou.
" 3. Jamaica from the latest surveys . . .—Inset: The harbours of Kingston and Port Royal.
" 4. The Windward passage, with the several passages from the east end of Cuba & from the north part of St. Domingo . . .
" 5-6. . . . Chart of the Caribbee or West India islands, from Porto Rico to Trinidad . . . from the chart . . . by don Cosme Churruca and don Joaquin Franc? Fidalgo.
" 7. Plan of the island of St. Croix from an actual survey made in 1794-1799 by P. L. Oxholm.
" 8. St. Christophers, or St. Kitts, surveyed by Anthony Ravell . . .
" 9. Antigua surveyed by Robert Baker . . .
" 10. Guadaloupe . . .
" 11. Dominica . . .
" 12. Martinico . . .
" 13. St. Lucia . . .
" 14. Barbadoes, surveyed by William Mayo . . .
" 15. St. Vincent, from . . . survey made in . . . 1773 . . .
" 16. Bequia or Becouya, the northernmost of the Granadilles.
" 17. Granada, divided into its parishes . . .
" 18. Tobago . . .
" 19. Plan of the isle of Trinidad, from . . . surveys made . . . 1797.
" 20. Curaçao from the dutch originals of Gerard van Keulen . . .
" 21. Ruatan or Rattan, surveyed by lieut. Henry Barnsley . . .—Inset: New Port Royal harbour.
" 22. Turks islands . . .

**1818**

**Edwards, B.**
History of the British West Indies . . . v. 5. Maps & plates. 1 p. l., 11 maps, 9 pl., 1 l. at end. 4°. London, for the proprietors, 1818. 2706
> NOTE.—Engraved title.

CONTENTS.

*Maps.*

no. [ 1] A new map of the West Indies . . . 2 sheets.
" [ 2] A map of the island of Jamaica . . . Divided into its counties & parishes . . . 1794.
" [ 3] Map of the island of Barbadoes . . . G. Allen sculpt.
" [ 4] " " " " " Grenada . . . J. Cooke sc.
" [ 5] " " " " " St. Vincent . . .
" [ 6] " " " " " Dominica . . . J. Cooke sc.

no. [ 7] Map of the island of St. Christophers . . .
" [ 8] "    "    "    "    " Antigua . . .
" [ 9] "    "    " Virgin Islands . . .
" [10] "    "    " island of St. Domingo.  Scale of 50 british statute miles.
" [11] "    "    "    "    " Tobago . . .

### 1818

A new altas of the West-India islands . . .   cover-title, 11 maps.  4°.  Philadelphia, I. Riley, 1818.   2707

NOTE.—Atlas to accompany Edwards' History of the West Indies.

#### CONTENTS.

no. [ 1] A new map of the West Indies.  Reduced by S. Lewis.  Engraved by J. H. Seymour.
" [ 2] St. Domingo.  Scale of 50 british statute miles.
" [ 3] Jamaica, divided into counties & parishes . . .
" [ 4] Map of the island of Dominica.  J. H. Seymour sc.
" [ 5] St. Vincent.  Tanner sc.
" [ 6] Virgin Islands.  Tanner sc.
" [ 7] Barbadoes.  Tanner sc.
" [ 8] Island of S! Christophers.  Marſhall sculpt.
" [ 9] Island of Antigua.  Marſhall sculpt.
" [10] Island of Tobago.  Tanner sc.
" [11] Grenada.  Tanner sc.

### 1818

**Jefferys, T.**

The West-India atlas: comprehending a complete collection of accurate charts, of the navigation of the West-Indies and gulf of Mexico; with plans of the harbours, roads, bays, &c. and distinct maps of the different islands; from actual surveys, adjusted by the latest astronomic observations.  The whole newly arranged, and including the large chart of the Atlantic ocean, by John Purdy; the new general chart of the West-Indies, by Joseph Dessiou; and the improved editions of the maps, by the late Thomas Jefferys, geographer to the king; with several others recently published. 2 p. l., 52 maps on 57 sheets.  fol.  London, J. Whittle & R. H. Laurie, 1818.   2708

NOTE:—See also titles 2699, 2701, 2702, 2703 and 2705.

#### CONTENTS.

no. 1-2. General chart of the Atlantic ocean.  By John Purdy.  1812.
"   3. Laurie and Whittle's new chart of the Azores, or Western islands . . . 1807.  2d ed., with additions, 1811.
"   4. Laurie and Whittle's new chart of the Cape Verde islands.  2d ed., improved, 1812.
"   5. The Bermudas, or Summer's islands.  From a survey by C. Lempriere.  1810.  New ed.
"   6. Turks islands.  1810.
"   7-8. A new chart of the West Indies.  By Joseph Dessiou.  Improved edition with additions to 1818

**Jefferys, T.**—Continued.

no. 9-10. Laurie and Whittle's new chart of the Caribee or West India islands . . . 3d ed. 1817.
" 11-13. Laurie and Whittle's new chart of the Windward passages . . . 1811. Third edition improved 1818.
" 14. The bay of Honduras . . . Corrected and improved in 1800.
" 15. Ruatan or Rattan, surveyed by lieut. Henry Barnsley. 1794. Improved edition 1810.
" 16. Jamaica . . . A new ed. 1810.
" 17. Plan of the island of St. Croix, from an actual survey made in 1794-1799 . . . 1804.
" 18. The Virgin islands. 1816.
" 19. Chart of the islands and channels of St. Bartholomew, St. Martin, Anguilla . . . from the surveys and observations of mr. Samuel Fahlberg.
" 20. St. Christophers, or St. Kitts, surveyed by Anthony Ravell. Improved edition, 1810.
" 21. Antigua surveyed by Robert Baker, improved edition 1810.
" 22. Guadaloupe . . . improved edition, 1817.
" 23. Dominica . . . improved edition, 1810.
" 24. Martinico . . . Lately improved by an officer, 1810.
" 25. St. Lucia . . . New edition, 1810.
" 26. Barbadoes . . . Improved edition 1810.
" 27. St. Vincent, from an actual survey made in . . . 1773. New edition, 1810.
" 28. Bequia or Becouya. New edition, 1810.
" 29. Granada . . . New edition, 1810.
" 30. Tobago from actual surveys and observations . . . New edition, 1810.
" 31. Plan of the isle of Trinidad, from surveys made in the year 1797 . . 1809.
" 32. Curaçao from the dutch originals of Gerard van Keulen. New edition 1810.
" 33. A new chart of the coast of Guayana, from rio Orinoco to river Berbice . . . 1795.
" 34. A new chart of the coast of Guayana from river Berbice to Cape North . . . 1796.
" 35. A new chart of Surinam river . . . 1801.
" 36. Plan of the road and town of La Guayra. 1794.—Plan of Puerto Cavello, by lt. Jones, 1741.
" 37. Plan of the bay and town of St. Martha.—Plan of the harbour of Carthagena.
" 38. Plan of Zispata bay.—A plan of Portobelo harbour. 1767.
" 39. Plan of the road and harbour of Chagre . . .—A draught of the Bahias del Almirante.
" 40. A draught of the Blewfields lagoon.—A plan of Truxillo bay. 1766.
" 41. A draught of the harbour of San Fernando de Omoa. 1759 & 1767.
" 42. The coast of Mexico . . . 1816.
" 43. The coast of West Florida . . .
" 44. The entrance of the river Missisipi at Fort Balise. 1764.—A draught of the entrance of Mobile. 1764.
" 45. A plan of Mobile bar. Surveyed by B. Romans, 1771.—Plan of the harbour of Pensacola, by B. Romans, 1771.
" 46. A plan of the entrance of Tampa bay.—Plan of Lucia harbour and Mantega bay.

no. 47. The harbours of Port Antonio in Jamaica.—Plan of bahia Hondia on the north side of Cuba.
" 48. Plan of Port Cavanas.—Plan of Port Mariel.
" 49. Plan of the city and harbour of Havanna.—Plan of the bay of Matanzas.
" 50. A plan of Nuevitas harbour.—Plan of great bay of Nipe.
" 51. Plan of Barracoa.—Plan of Bahia Xagua.
" 52. Plan of Guantanamo 1740.—The harbour of St. Yago . . . 1816.
" 53. A plan of Fort St. Louis harbour.—Petit Guave in the islands of Hispaniola.
" 54. Leogane and Port au Prince.—A plan of Cape Nicola mole . . . from a french survey.
" 55. A plan of the road of Port Paix . . .—A plan of the town and harbour of Cap François.
" 56. Plan of the bay and town of Bayaha or Port Dauphin.—A plan of Monte-Christe bay with the Seven Brothers.
" 57. A survey of the West Road of Portorico . . . 1740.—A plan of the forts and harbour of San Juan de Portorico.

### 1824?

**Lucas, F.**

A new general atlas of the West India islands comprehended in twenty-one maps from the best authorities.  2 p. l., 21 col. maps. fol.  Baltimore, F. Lucas, jr. [1824?]   2709

NOTE.—Engraved title-page and maps.  Maps are like those in his "General atlas" of 1823, see title 742, excepting no. 1, "West Indies" which gives more information and is probably a later map.  Hence 1824 has been assigned to this atlas.

CONTENTS.

no. [ 1] West Indies.
" [ 2] Bahama's.
" [ 3] Bermudas.
" [ 4] Cuba.
" [ 5] Jamaica.
" [ 6] Hayti or Saint Domingo.
" [ 7] Porto Rico.
" [ 8] Virgin islands.
" [ 9] S! Christophers.
" [10] Nevis.
" [11] Antigua.
" [12] Guadaloupe &c.
" [13] Dominca.
" [14] Martinico.
" [15] S! Lucia.
" [16] S! Vincent.
" [17] Barbadoes.
" [18] Grenada.
" [19] Tobago.
" [20] Trinidad.
" [21] Curaçao.—Inset: Fort Amsterdam.

## 1854

**Kerhallet, C. M. P. de.**
Manuel de la navigation dans la mer des Antilles et dans le golfe du Mexique . . . Vues de côtes. 3 p. l., 48 pl. sm. fol. Paris, dépôt général de la marine, 1854. 2710

> NOTE.—To accompany work of the same title.
>
> CONTENTS.
>
> Les Petites Antilles.—Les Grandes Antilles.—Iles de Bahama.—La côte de Venezuela.—La côte de la Nouvelle-Grenade.—La côte de Guatemala.—La côte du Mexique.—La côte des États-Unis.

## 1856?

**France.** *Ministère de la marine et des colonies. Dépôt des cartes et plans de la marine.*
[Portulan général. Mer des Antilles et golfe du Mexique] 2 v. sm. fol. [Paris, dépôt général de la marine, 1856?] 2711

> NOTE.—Collation: v. 1, 96 maps; v. 2, 79 maps.
> Title-pages wanting.
> Maps have a serial number. In catalogue no. 515 of the dépôt des cartes et plans de la marine, the maps of the portulan général are arranged according to the number. In this copy the maps are not so arranged.
>
> CONTENTS.
>
> v. 1, no. [1] Les Saintes [French West Indies] 1858.
> " " [2] Ile Antigoa. 1856.
> " " [3] Port Anglais et Port Falmouth (Ile Antigoa) 1858.
> " " [4] Baie Cade ou de Carlisle, —— 1857.
> " " [5] Port des Cinq Iles, —— 1857.
> " " [6] Port S! Jean, —— 1857.
> " " [7] Port de Parham, —— 1857.
> " " [8] Baie Nonsuch, —— 1857.
> " " [9] Baie Willoughby, —— 1856.
> " " [10] La Barbuda (Petites Antilles) . . . 1856.
> " " [11] Baie du Marigot (Ile Saint-Martin) 1858.—La Grande baie, ——.
> " " [12] Lac des Huîtres (Ile de Saint Martin) ——.—Port de Gustavia (Ile de Saint-Barthélémy) 1858.
> " " [13] L'Anguille, S! Martin, & S! Barthélémy (Petites Antilles) 1855.
> " " [14] Baies Crocus et Road (Ile de l'Anguille) 1858.
> " " [15] Ile Anegada (Iles Vierges) 1856.
> " " [16] Ile de Virgin-Gorda. 1856.
> " " [17] Gorda sound (Ile de Virgin-Gorda) 1856.
> " " [18] Canal de François Drake (Iles Vierges) 1856.
> " " [19] Baie de Road (Ile Tortola) 1856.
> " " [20] Iles Saint Jean et Saint Thomas, d'après la carte danoise des Iles Vierges. 1856.—Croquis de la baie Lynster (Ile Saint Jean)—Croquis de la baie de Coral, ——.—Croquis de la baie de Kruyts, ——.
> " " [21] Iles Culebra et de Vièques. 1856.—Porto Mula (Ile de Vieques)—Port Culebra (Ile Celebra)
> " " [22] Ile de Vièques. 1856.
> " " [23] Ile de Saint-Croix. 1856.—Mouillage de Fredricksted (Ile de Sainte Croix)—Mouillage de Christiansted, —.

v. 1, no. [24] Baie de Mayagues (Porto-Rico) 1856.
" " [25] Mouillage à l'entrée de la Baie de Samana (Ile Haïte ou S$^t$ Domingue) . . . 1849.
" " [26] Port du Cap Haïti, —— 1849.
" " [27] Mole de S$^t$ Nicolas, —— 1856.
" " [28] Baie des Gonaïves, —— 1858.
" " [29] Golfe de Port au Prince, —— 1856.
" " [30] Rade de Port-au-Prince, —— 1849.
" " [31] Jaquemel, —— 1856.
" " [32] Navaza (Canal du Vent) 1856.
" " [33] Cayes Morant (Jamaïque) 1856
" " [34] Ile de la Jamaique. 1856.
" " [35] Port Morant (Jamaïque) 1856.
" " [36] Baie de Morant, —— 1856.
" " [37] Port de Kingston, —— 1856.
" " [38] Baie de Old Harbour, —— 1856.
" " [39] Port Bluefields, —— 1856.
" " [40] Savana de la Mar, —— 1856.
" " [41] Port de Ile Verte, —— 1856.
" " [42] Port de Lucea, —— 1856.
" " [43] Port de Mosquito, —— 1856.
" " [44] Baie Montego, —— 1856.
" " [45] Port de Falmouth, —— 1856.
" " [46] Baie de S$^{te}$ Anne, —— 1856.
" " [47] Baie d'Anota, —— 1856.
" " [48] Port d'Antonio, —— 1856.
" " [49] Port de Guantanamo (Ile de Cuba) 1857.
" " [50] Port de Santiago de Cuba, —— 1857.
" " [51] Port de Jagua, —— 1856.
" " [52] Ile de Pinos, —— 1857.
" " [53] Le Grande Caïman. 1856.
" " [54] Récifs des Colorados (Ile de Cuba) 1856.
" " [55] Port du Bahia-Hondia, —— 1856.
" " [56] Entrée de Cabañas, —— 1856.
" " [57] Port de Mariel, —— 1856.
" " [58] Port de Mata, —— 1856.
" " [59] Port de Baracoa, —— 1856.
" " [60] Mouillage de la Caye Confites, —— 1857.
" " [61] Port de Matanzas, —— 1856.
" " [62] Cardenas. 1858.
" " [63] Mouillages Mathew et Molasses (Grand Inague) 1858.
" " [64] Mouillage d'Alfred, —— 1858.
" " [65] Cayes Turques. 1858.
" " [66] Mouillage de l'Ile de Crooked (Iles de Bahama) 1856.
" " [67] Port de Clarence (Ile Longue, G$^d$ Banc de Bahama) 1856.
" " [68] Mouillage de la Pointe du Trou dans le mur (Ile Abaco . . .)— Caye Gun (Grand Banc de Bahama)—Canal de la Providence, —— 1857.
" " [69] Canal du Nurse, —— 1856.
" " [70] Passe de Racoon, —— 1856.
" " [71] Mouillage des Iles Ragged, —— 1856.
" " [72] Port de l'Ile Ragged, —— 1856.
" " [73] Le Grand Stirrup, —— 1856.
" " [74] Nouvelle-Providence, —— 1856.
" " [75] Port de Nassau (Nouvelle-Providence) 1856.
" " [76] Baies de l'Ouest et du Sud-Ouest, —— 1856.

**France**—Continued.
  v. 1, no. [77] Le Nid du Faucon (G$^{de}$ Caye Turque) 1857.
  "  " [78] Cayes du Boulet Ramé (Banc de la Caye de Sel)—Banc de la Caye de Sel (Iles de Bahama) 1856.
  "  " [79] Rade de Douglas (Grand Banc de Bahama) 1856.
  "  " [80] Canal de Fleeming, —— 1856.
  "  " [81] Ile Royale, —— 1856.
  "  " [82] Port de l'Ile Royale, —— 1856.
  "  " [83] Canal du Navire, —— 1856.
  "  " [84] Canal du Highborn, —— 1856.
  "  " [85] Passe de la Caye de Wax, —— 1856.
  "  " [86] Canal de Wide-Opening, —— 1856.
  "  " [87] Grande Exuma (Iles de Bamama [!]) 1856.
  "  " [88] Ports de la Grande Exuma, —— 1856.
  "  " [89] Le Petit-port et le Port du Pélican (Petit Banc de Bahama) 1856.
  "  " [90] Mouillage—Man of War, —— 1856.
  "  " [91] Mouillage de la Tortue-Verte, —— 1856.
  "  " [92–93] Banc de la Floride, P$^{ie}$ O. (États-Unis) Par E. et W. Blunt. 1846–1856.
  "  " [94] Les Tortugas (côte des États-Unis) Par Edmund et W. Blunt. 1858.
  "  " [95] Caye de l'Ouest, —— 1856.
  "  " [96] Mouillage du Cap Canaveral (Floride, côte est) 1856.
  v. 2, no. [1] Golfe de Paria (côte est de Venezuela) 1856.
  "  " [2] Baie de Chaguaramas (Ile de la Trinité) Baie de Toco, —— 1856.
  "  " [3] Bouches du Serpent, —— 1856. Baies de Salibia et du Manzanillo, ——.
  "  " [4] Port d'Espagne, —— 1856.
  "  " [5] Bouches du Dragon, —— 1855.
  "  " [6] Ile de Margarita et Golfe de Cariaco (côte n. de Venezuela) 1856.
  "  " [7] Baie de San-Juan-Griego (Ile de Margarita) 1856.—Baie de Pampatar, —— 1856.
  "  " [8] Port de Barcelona (côte n. de Venezuela) 1856.
  "  " [9] Mouillage de la Guayra, —— 1856.
  "  " [10] Puerto-Cabello, —— 1856.
  "  " [11] San Juan de Nicaragua. 1849.
  "  " [12] Les Roques (côte n. de Venezuela) 1858.—Bassin est des Roques.
  "  " [13] Baie de Santa Anna (Ile de Curazao) Curazao et Buen Ayre (côte n. de Venezuela) 1856.
  "  " [14] Plan de la Baie de S$^{te}$ Marthe (côte ferme d'Amerique) 1858.
  "  " [15] Port de Sabanilla (côte de la Nouv. Grenade) 1856.
  "  " [16] Port de Carthagène, —— 1856.
  "  " [17] Isthme de Panama, Port de Naos. 1850.
  "  " [18] "  "  " Port de Chagres. 1850.
  "  " [19] Lagune de Chiriqui (côte de la Nouvelle-Grenade) 1856.
  "  " [20] Canal du Tigre (Lagune de Chiriqui) 1856.
  "  " [21] Bouche du Toro, —— 1856.
  "  " [22] Bouche du Dragon, —— 1856.
  "  " [23] Canal de Crawl, —— 1856.
  "  " [24] Port de Shepherd, —— 1856.
  "  " [25] Port de Greytown (côte de Mosquitos) 1856.
  "  " [26] Lagune de Blewfield, —— 1856.
  "  " [27] Entrée de la lagune des Perles, —— 1856.
  "  " [28] Cayes des Perles, —— 1856.

v. 2, no. [29] Petite ile de Corn, ——. Grande Ile de Corn, —— 1856.
" " [30] Port de Gracias á Dios, —— 1856.
" " [31] Cayes d'Albuquerque, —— 1856.—Cayes Courtown, —— 1856.
" " [32] Ile de Saint André, —— 1856.
" " [33] Anse du Sud-ouest (Ile Saint-André) 1856.
" " [34] La Vieille Providence (côte des Mosquitos) —— 1856.—Baie de S$^{ta}$ Catalina (Vieille Providence)
" " [35] Banc de Serrana (côte des Mosquitos) 1856.—Canal de la Caye du Sud.—Banc du Roncador (côte de Mosquitos) 1856.
" " [36] Banc Serranilla, —— 1856.
" " [37] Trou de Coxen (Ile Roatan)—Atterrages de la Baie de Truxillo (côte de Honduras). 1856.—Port Royal (Ile Roatan)
" " [38] Ile Bonacca (golfe de Honduras) 1856.
" " [39] Mouillage de Dunbar (Ile de Bonacca) 1856.
" " [40] Ile Utila (golfe de Honduras) . . . 1855.—Port de l'est.
" " [41] Omoa (côte de Honduras) 1856.—Baie de l'hôpital, ——.
" " [42] Port de Honduras (côte du Honduras anglais) 1855.
" " [43] Port de Belize, —— 1856.
" " [44] Baies de l'Ascension et d'Espiritu, —— 1856.
" " [45] Port de Mugeres (côte du Yucatan) 1856.
" " [46] Cap Catoche, —— 1856.
" " [47] Banc de Chinchorro (golfe de Honduras) 1856.—Mouillages de Chinchorro.
" " [48] Ile Cozumel (côte du Yucatan) 1856.
" " [49] Plan de Sisal (côte n. o. du Yucatan) 1856.—Mouillage de Sisal.—Banc n. o. Sisal.—Banc s. e. de Sisal.
" " [50] Cayes Arcas (côte du Yucatan) 1856.
" " [51] Lagune de Terminos, —— 1856.
" " [52] Banc d'Alacran (golfe du Yucatan) . . . 1856.—Port Alacran.
" " [53] Caye d'Arenas (côte du Yucatan) 1856.
" " [54] Triangle du S. E., —— 1856.—Banc de l'Obispo, ——.
" " [55] Rivière de Tampico (côte du Mexique) 1856.
" " [56] Passe Caballo (côte des États-Unis) 1856.
" " [57] Port de Saint-Louis, —— 1856.
" " [58] Embouchure de la rivière Sabine, —— 1856.
" " [59] Iles Cat et Ship, —— 1858.
" " [60] Pensacola (États Unis) 1858.
" " [61] Rivière de Savannah, —— 1855.
" " [62] Port de Charleston, —— 1855.
" " [63] Entrée de la rivière du Cap Fear, —— 1856.
" " [64] Mouillage du Cap Hatteras, —— 1856.
" " [65] Canal d'Hatteras, —— 1856.
" " [66] Entrée de la Delaware, —— 1856.
" " [67] Rivière de la Delaware, —— 1856.
" " [68] Port de Refuge de Little Egg, —— 1856.
" " [69] New York, —— 1856.
" " [70] Baie Oyster, —— 1858.
" " [71] Port de New Haven, —— 1856.
" " [72] Détroit de l'Ile des Pêcheurs, —— 1856.
" " [73] Port de New Bedford, —— 1856.
" " [74] Port de New London, —— 1856.
" " [75] Baie Narraganset, —— 1858.
" " [76] Port de Nantucket. — Ile de Nantucket (États Unis) 1856.
" " [77] Port Edgartown, —— 1856.
" " [78] Port Hyannis, —— 1856.
" " [79] Port du Cap Cod, ——1855.

# SEPARATE ISLANDS.
## CUBA.
### 1842

**Cuba.** *Gobierno y capitanía general.*

Planos de bolsillo de la isla de Cuba, la ciudad de la Habana y sus barrios estramuros, tabla de distancias de unos pueblos á otros, y el plan de señales del Morro.  3 p. l., 3 maps, 3 pl., 1 tab.  16°. Habana, gobierno y capitanía general, 1842.   2712

### 1884
**Quintana, S. A.**

Planos de comunicaciones de las provincias de la isla de Cuba, con otros datos relativos al ramo de correos, por el sub inspector d$^n$ Sebastian Acosta Quintana.  1 p. l., 6 maps, 5 tab. sq. 18°. Habana, J. Menéndez & brother, 1884.   2713

### 1898
**United States.** *War department. Adjutant general's office.*

Atlas of ports, cities and localities of the island of Cuba. Containing reproductions of maps, charts and plans obtained from the United States congressional library, coast and geodetic survey, hydrographic office, engineer dept. U. S. army; also Pichard's map of the island of Cuba, and other sources.  2 p. l., 7 l., 61 maps.  obl. fol.  Washington, 1898.   2714

## DUTCH WEST INDIES.
### 1901
**Dornseiffen, I.**

Atlas van Nederlandsch Oost- en West-Indië ... 5. druk. Uitgave in 26 kaarten.  2 p. l., 26 maps. fol. Amsterdam, Seyffardt [1901]   2715

NOTE.—Map no. 2 contains inset plan: Batavia met de havenwerken.

#### CONTENTS.
- no. 1. Overzichtskaart.
- " 2–5. Java. 1:950.000. 1901.
- " 6–17. Soematra, Bangka en de Riouw-Lingga archipel. 1:1.000.000. 1896–1900.
- " 18. Borneo. 1:3.000.000. 1900.
- " 19–21. Borneo en bělitoeng. 1:1.000.000. 1899–1900.
- " 22. Celebes, de kleine Soenda-eilanden ... 1:4.200.000. 1899.
- " 23. De Moluksche eilanden en Nieuw-Guinea. 1:4.200.000. 1899.
- " 24. Amboina, de Oeliassers en de Banda-eilanden.
- " 25. De West-Indische eilanden. 1892.
- " 26. Suriname. 1:1.250.000. 1900. De omstreken van Paramaribo. 1:400.000.

# HAITI.

## 1788

**France.** *Dépôt de la marine.*

Le pilote de l'isle de Saint-Domingue et des débouquemens de cette isle, comprenant une carte de l'isle de Saint-Domingue et une carte des débouquemens depuis la Caye d'Argent jusqu'à la partie ouest du placet des isles Lucayes . . . 1 p. l., 18 pp., 5 maps, 2 pl. fol. Paris, imprimerie royale, 1787–[1788]    2716

    NOTE.—Imperfect; map no. 1 wanting.
    Published after the surveys made by the comte de Chastenet-Puységur.

## 1795

**Ponce, N.**

Recueil de vues des lieux principaux de la colonie française de Saint-Domingue, gravées par les soins de m. Ponce. Accompagnées de cartes et plans de la même colonie, gravés par les soins de m. Phelipeau, ingénieur géographe. Le tout exécuté aux frais de m. [Mederic Louis Élié] Moreau de Saint-Méry; auxquels on a joint le plan de la partie française de Saint-Domingue, où sont désignés les endroits incendiés de cette colonie.    1 p. l., 14 maps, 31 pl., 2 diagr. fol. Paris, chez Moreau de St. Méry, Ponce, Phelipeau, 1795.    2717

    NOTE.—Atlas to accompany Moreau de St. Méry's work entitled "Description topographique, physique, civile, etc., de la partie française de l'île de Saint-Domingue. 1797–1798." Quérard in his "La France littéraire," mentions in connection with the work only 31 plates and not the maps. The maps with two exceptions are by Phelipeau; the plates by Ponce. The two exceptions are, "Carte de l'isle S.t Domingue dressée pour l'ouvrage de M. L. E. Moreau de St. Méry. Dessinée par I. Sonis 1796. Gravée par Vallance," and, "Carte de la partie françoise de St. Domingue faite par Bellin . . . et depuis augmentée par P. C. Varlé et autres.—A map of the french part of St. Domingo. J. T. Scott sculp. Philad.ª"

# MARTINIQUE.

## 1827–1831

**Monnier, P.**

[Atlas de la Martinique]    10 maps. fol. [Paris, dépôt général de la marine, 1827–31]    2718

    NOTE.—No title-page. Binder's title.
    Maps dated 1827–31.

        CONTENTS.

    no. 1. Plan des triangles de la Martinique, observés dans les années 1824 et 1825.
    " 2. Carte générale de la Martinique. 1831.
    ' 3. Carte particulière des côtes de la Martinique. (Partie orientale de l'île . . .) 1828.
    " 4. Carte particulière des côtes de la Martinique. (Partie méridionale de l'île . . .) 1829.

**Monnier, P.**—Continued.

    no.  5. Carte particulière des côtes de la Martinique. (Partie séptentrionale . . .) 1829.
    "  6. Plan de la baie du Fort-Royal (île de la Martinique) 1827.
    "  7. Plan de la rade et de la ville de S! Pierre (île de la Martinique) 1827.
    "  8. Plan du havre de la Trinité (île de la Martinique) 1827.
    "  9. Plan des havres du Robert et du François (île de la Martinique) 1828.
    " 10. Plan du cul-de-sac Marin (île de la Martinique) 1828.

## SOUTH AMERICA.

### REPRODUCTIONS.

**Brazil.** *Treaties, etc., 1894–1898.*

Frontières entre le Brésil et la Guyane Française. Mémoire présenté par les états unis du Brésil au gouvernement de la confédération Suisse arbitre choisi selon les stipulations du traité conclu à Rio-de-Janeiro, le 10 avril 1897, entre le Brésil et la France. Atlas. 1 p. l., [2] pp., 1 l., 104 maps. fol. Paris, A. Lahure, 1899–1900.

    2719

    Note.—Atlas to accompany the "Premier mémoire présenté par le Brésil" . . . Title of atlas reads: . . . Atlas contenant un choix de cartes antérieures au traité conclu à Utrecht le 11 avril 1713 entre le Portugal et la France.—Annexe au mémoire présenté par les états-unis du Brésil . . . Paris, A. Lahure, 1899. A collection of reproductions from various sources; dated 1500–1707.
    Another edition, with imprint date 1900, is like this one, except that the maps are smaller and folded.
    A number of maps are highly colored and embellished by various designs. no. 75 has border text.

### CONTENTS.

    "  1. Mappemonde manuscrite sur parchemin . . . au musée naval de Madrid. Juan de la Cosa. 1500.
    " 1a. Carte de Vesconte de Maiollo. 1515. [The Antilles and coast of Honduras]
    "  2. Mappemonde manuscrite sur parchemin. À la bibliothèque royale de Turin. Sans nom d'auteur, ni date; vers 1523.
    "  3. Carte de Vesconte de Maiollo. 1527. [South America]
    "  4. Carte de Diego Ribero (Diogo Ribeiro) 1529. [South America]
    "  5. Carte de Nicolas Desliens 1543 ou 1544. [North and South America]
    "  6. Carte de Sebastiano Cabotto (Sébastien Cabott) 1544. [South America and part of North America]
    "  7. Americae sive qvartae orbis partis nova et exactissima descriptio. Diego Gutierrez. 1562.
    "  8. Carte manuscrite sur parchemin, datée de Séville, 1550. Diego Gutierrez.
    "  9. Amérique. Pierre Desceliers. 1550.
    " 10a–b. Mappemonde . . . attribuée à Jacopo Gastaldi.

no. 11. Carte de Diogo Homen. 1558. [South America] Manuscrite. British Museum.
" 12. Carte de Diogo Homen, 1558(?) Bibliothèque Nationale de Paris.
" 13. Mapa de los Rios Amazonas, Esequivo ò Dulce y Orinoco y de las comarcas adyacentes. Carte espagnole vers 1560.
" 14. Carte de Bartholomeu Velho. 1561. [South America]
" 15. Carte de Bartolomeo Olives, de Mallorca, 1562. [Coast of South America and the Greater Antilles]
" 16a-b. Carte de Lazaro Luis, 1563. [South America, Cuba, Porto Rico, etc.]
" 17a-b. Cartes de Diogo Homen. 1568. [South America]
" 18a-b. Cartes de Fernão Vaz Dourado 1568. [Part of coasts of North and South America]
" 19. Carte de Gerardus Mercator [Gerard Cremer] 1569. [East coasts of North and South America]
" 20. Typvs orbis terrarvm. Abrahanus Ortelius (Abraham Ortelz) 1570-1575, 1579, 1581 et 1584.
" 21. Americae sive novi orbis, nova descriptio. Abr. Ortelius . . . 1570-1575, 1579, 1581 et 1584.
" 22a. Carte de Fernão Vaz Dourado. 1571. [Part of coasts of North and South America]
" 22b. Carte de Fernão Vaz Dourado. 1571. [South America]
" 23. Le novveav monde descovvert et illvstre de nostre temps. André Thevet. 1575.
" 24. Typvs orbis terrarvm. François de Belleforest. 1575.
" 25. Carte de Jacques de Vaudeclaye. 1579.
" 26a. Carte de Fernão Vaz Dourado. 1580. [Coasts of North and South America]
" 26b. Carte de Fernão Vaz Dourado. 1580. [South America]
" 27. [Map of the world] Joan Martines. 1582.
" 28. [South America] Joan Martines. 1582.
" 29. Americae et proximar regionumoræ descriptio. Giovanni Battista Mazzo. 1584.
" 30. Meridionalis Americæ . . . Jan van Doet. 1585.
" 31. Typvs orbis terrarvm. Abr. Ortelius (Abraham Ortelz) 1587-1589, 1592, 1593, 1595, 1596, 1598, 1601, 1602, 1603, 1606, 1608, 1609, 1612 et 1624.
" 32. Americae sive novi orbis, nova descriptio. Abr. Ortelius (Abraham Ortelz) 1587-1589, 1592, 1593, 1595, 1596, 1598, 1601-1603, 1606, 1608 1609, 1612 et 1624.
" 33. Orbis terrae compendiosa descriptio. Rumoldus Mercator. 1587, 1595, 1602, 1606, 1607.
" 34. Americæ pars magis cognita. Théodore De Bry 1592, 1593, 1605, 1630.
" 35. Hemispheriv ab æqvinoctiali linea, ad circvlv poli Arctici.—Hemispheriv ab æqvinoctiali linea, ad circvlv poli Atarctici. Cornelis de Jode (Cornelius de Judœis) 1593.
" 36. Brasilia et Pervvia . . . Cornelis de Jode . . . 1593.
" 37. Orbis terrarvm typvs de integro multis in locis emendatus . . . Petrus Plancius. 1592, 1594, 1596, 1599, 1605, 1610, 1614, 1623, 1638 et 1645.
" 38. Occidentalis Americæ partis . . . Théodore De Bry. 1594, 1613 et 1644.
" 39. America siue India Nova . . . Michael Mercator, 1595.
" 40. America . . . Théodore De Bry, 1596, 1597, 1617, 1619, 1623 et 1624.

**Brazil**—Continued.

no. 41. Carte de Arnold Florentin van Langeren, 1596, 1598, 1599, 1605, 1610, 1614, 1619, 1623, 1638 et 1645. [South America]
" 42. Residvvm continentis cvm adiacentibvs insvlis. Cornelis Wytfliet, 1597, 1598, 1603, 1607 et 1611.
" 43. Typus totius orbis terrarum . . . Jodocus Hondius (Josse Hond) 1597.
" 43a. Pervvia id est Noui orbis pars meridionalis . . . Matthias Quaden. 1598, 1600 et 1608.
" 43b. [South America] B. Langenes 1598.
" 44. [West Indies] Carte anglaise (anonyme) vers 1598.
" 45. Nieuwe caerte van het wonderbaer ende goudrijcke landt Guiana . . . Jodocus Hondius (Josse Hond) 1598.
" 46. Nova et exacta delineatio Americæ partis Avstralis . . . Levinus Hulsius, 1599, 1603, 1612, 1663.
" 47. Niewe landtaffel in welcher eigentlich und warhafftiglich furgestelt wirdt das gewaltige und goldtreiche kunigreich Guiana . . . Théodore De Bry, 1599 et 1624.
" 48. Orbis terraræ compendiosa descriptio ex peritissimorum totius orbis gæographorum operibus desumta. J. B. Vrient, d'après P. Plancius, 1599.
" 49. [Map of the world] Richard Hakluyt. 1599.
" 50. [Guiana] Gabriel Tatton. 1602.
" 51. Orbis terrae novissima descriptio. Jodocus Hondius (Josse Hond) 1602 et 1633.
" 52. Americæ novissima descriptio. Jodocus Hondius (Josse Hond) 1602 et 1633.
" 53. America Meridionalis. Jodocus Hondius . . . 1606.
" 54. Carte de Gabriel Tatton, 1608. [Guiana]
" 55. America Meridionalis. Harmen Janss et Marten Jans. 1610.
" 56. Americæ nova descriptio. Petrus Kœrius (P. Keer) 1614.
" 57–59. Carte de Cornelis Claeszon 1605 et 1617.—America. P. Bertius. 1616.—America Meridionalis. P. Bertius. 1616.
" 60. Gvaiana siue provinciæ intra rio de las Amazonas atque rio de Yviapari siue Orinoqve. Joannes de Laet, 1625, 1630, 1633, et 1640.
" 61–61b. Carton dans le globe de van Langeren.—La Guyane dans le globe de van Langaren.—Globe, gravé. Arnold Florentin van Langerin. 1630.
" 62. Gviana siue Amazonvm regio. G. Blaeuw (Willem Janson Blaeuw) 1631.
" 63. Orbis terrae novissima descriptio Jodocus Hondius (Josse Hond) 1633.
" 64. Die landschafft Gvaiana . . . Mathieu Merian. 1634.
" 65. L'Amérique. Clemendt de Jonghe. Vers 1640.
" 66. Carte manuscrite du Brésil. João Teixeira. 1640.
" 67. Provinsia de Santa Cruz aqve vulgarmente chamão Brazil. João Teixeira. 1642.
" 68. Carte manuscrite de la côte de Pará et de la Guyane portugaise . . . João Teixeira. 1640.
" 69. Carta prima générale d'Affrica è par$^e$ d'America. Robert Dudley. 1646 et 1661.
" 70. America. Robert Dudley. 1646 et 1661.

no. 71. Carta particolare dell' rio d'Amazone con la costa sin al' fiume Maranhan . . . Robert Dudley. 1646 et 1661.
" 72. Amérique Meridionale. Nicolas Sanson. 1650.
" 73. Partie de Terre Ferme ou sont Gviane et Caribane . . . Nicolas Sanson. 1656.
" 74. Nova totius terrarum orbis tabula auctore D. D. Dancker Danckerts. 1660.
" 75. L'Amérique autrement le Nouveau monde et Indes occidentales. Pierre Du Val, 1655, 1664 et 1665.
" 76. Carte nouvelle de la France eqvinoctiale.—Inset: Description particvlière de l'isle de Cayenne. Le Febvre de la Barre. 1666.
" 77. Coste de Gvayane . . .—Inset: Isle Cayenne. Pierre Du Val. 1664, 1667, 1677.
" 78. Amérique Méridionale. Guillaume Sanson. 1679.
" 79. La mer de Nort où sont lan^le France, la Floride, lan^le Espagne les isles et la Terre-Ferme d'Amérique. Par P. Du-val . . . 1679.
" 80. Le cours de la rivière des Amazones . . . Guillaume Sanson. 1680.
" 81a. Pas-kaart van de zee-kusten, van Brazilia, tusschen cabo Noord, en cabo de Cuma. Claes J. Vooght. 1680, 1684, 1687, 1699, 1714, 1715, 1730.
" 81b. Pas-kaart van de zee-kusten van Guiana tusschen cabo Noord en rio Amano. Claes J. Vooght, 1680, 1684, 1687, 1699, 1714, 1715, 1730.
" 82. America Meridionale. Le père M. Coronelli. 1688.
" 83–85. Magni Amazoni flvvii in America Meridionali . . . Comte de Pagan.—Pays des Caribes de Gviane. Manesson Mallet. 1688.—Carte du gouvernement de Cayenne, ou France æquinoctiale. Froger. 1698 et 1699.
" 86a-b. Mapa geographica del rio Maranon o Amazonas . . . Le père Samuel Fritz. 1691.
" 87. Globe terrestre . . . Guillaume De l'Isle. 1700.
" 88. L'Amérique Méridionale . . . Guillaume De l'Isle. 1700.
" 89. Carte de la Terre Ferme du Pérou, du Brésil et du pays des Amazones. Guillaume De l'Isle. 1703.
" 90. La Terre Ferme et le Pérou avec le pays des Amazones et le Brésil . . . Nicolas de Fer. 1705.
" 91. El gran rio Maranon, o Amazonas . . . por el p^e. Samuel Fritz. 1707.

——— Frontières entre le Brésil et la Guyane française. Second mémoire présenté par les états unis du Brésil au gouvernement de la confédération Suisse arbitre choisi selon les stipulations du traité conclu à Rio-de-Janeiro, le 10 avril 1897, entre le Brésil et la France. Atlas. 2 pts. in 1 v.; 4 p. l., 88 maps. fol. Berne, Stæmpfli & cie. 1899. 2720

NOTE.—"Cet atlas se compose de deux parties. La première, comprenant quatorze cartes antérieures au traité d'Utrecht, est un supplément à l'Atlas annexé au 1^er mémoire du Brésil . . . La seconde partie de l'atlas renferme soixante-quinze cartes postérieures au traité d'Utrecht" . . . See preface of atlas.
A collection of reproductions from various sources; dated 1536–1860.
Atlas is "tome VI" of the "Second mémoire," imprint: Paris, A. Lahure, 1899.

**Brazil**—Continued.

Imperfect: map no. 46 wanting.

A number of maps, including nos. 3, 4 and 6, are colored.

Maps no. 62, 68, 69 and 71 have border text; no. 62 is a sheet from the "Atlas historique et géographique" de Le Sage, pseud. of Marie Joseph Auguste Emmanuel Dieudonné, comte de Las Cases, 1815.

CONTENTS.

no. 1. Reconstruction schématique de la carte d'Alonzo de Chaves (1536) depuis le cap St. Augustin jusqu'au Huyapari (Orénoque) d'après le texte d'Oviedo.
" 2. Andreas Homo. Cosmographvs Lvzitanvs me faciebat antverpiæ Anno millessimo, qvingentessimo, qvinqvagessimo, nono. André Homen. 1559.
" 3. Costa da Nova Espanha. Fernão Vaz Dourado. 1564.
" 4. Nova Espanha. Fernão Vaz Dourado, vers 1570.
" 5. Partie du globe de Philippe Apian. 1576.
" 6. Rio de las . . . Amesones. Bartolomeo Olives. 1580.
" 7. [Partie d'une mappemonde] . . . Christianus Sgrothenus. 1588.
" 7bis. [Partie de l'Amérique du Sud] Christianus Sgrothenus. 1588.
" 8. Partie du globe de Zurick. 1595(?)
" 9–9bis. Carta de navegacion of Gualtero Rale (Walter Raleigh) 1618. (2 feuilles)
" 10. Lucas de Quiros. 1618. [Partie de sa carte manuscrite de l'Amérique du Sud]
" 11. Coste de Gviane despvis le cap dv. Nord ivsqves à la rivière d'Eziqvebe. Carte hollandaise anonyme. 1625.
" 12. Partie d'une carte intitulée "Universale descritione di tutto il mondo." Giuseppe Rosaccio. 1657.
" 13. Carte générale du royaume de France . . . Nicolas Sanson. 1658.
" 14. [Carta nautica del mar, costas, y islas de las Yndias Occidentales, emendada por Sebastien de Ruesta . . . vers 1660]
" 15. A new and correct map of the world . . . C. Price, 1774.
" 16. Cours du fleuve Maragnon autrement dit des Amazones . . . Samuel Fritz. 1717.
" 17. Carte française de l'Amazone. vers 1719.
" 18. La partie méridionale de l'Amérique appelée Terre Ferme . . . Nicolas de Fer. 1719.
" 19. Carte de la Guïane françoise . . . Par le sr. d'Anville. 1729.
" 20. Horizon de Paris. Carte française par S., 1739.
" 21. Copie d'une carte manuscrite de la Guiane. Carte des jésuites français de la Guyane. 1741.
" 22. Carte réduite de l'océan occidental comprenant les côtes d'Europe et d'Afrique, depuis le 52° de latitude septent.[le] jusqu'à l'equateur et les côtes d'Amérique opposées. . . . Carte du dépôt de la marine 1742.
" 23. Carte depuis l'Amazone jusqu'à la rivière de Marony aux hollandois. Pierre Barrère. 1743.
" 24. Carte du cours du Maragnon ou de la grande rivière des Amazones . . . La Condamine. 1745.
" 24bis. [La même carte comparée avec nos cartes modernes]
" 25. L'Amérique . . . Par le sr. Le Rouge, 1746.

no. 26. [Le Brésil de la carte marine manuscrite]  João de Abreu Gorjão. 1747.
" 27. Amérique Méridionale . . . Par le sr. d'Anville. 1748.
" 28. Amérique Méridionale . . . Par le sr. Robert de Vaugondy. 1750.
" 29. Mapa dos confins do Brazil comas terras da Corva de Espana America Meridion! Carte portugaise de 1751.
" 30. La même carte comparée avec les cartes marines modernes.
" 31. Globe terrestre . . . par L. C. Desnos et J. B. Nolin . . . 1754.
" 32. Carte réduite des costes de la Guyane depuis la rivière d'Orénoque jusqu'au cap de Nord à l'entrée de la rivière des Amazones . . . Par le s. Bellin. 1760.
" 33. Carte géographique de l'isle de Cayenne et de ses environs . . . L[ouis] C[harles] Buache et de Préfontaine. 1762.
" 34. L'Amérique Méridionale . . . par le sr. Janvier, 1762.
" 35. Carte des costes de la Guyane françoise par le sr Bellin . . . 1762.
" 36. Carte de la Guyane françoise et l'isle de Cayenne . . . par le sr. Bellin 1763.
" 37. Carte réduite pour la navigation de Cayenne à la Martinique.—Inset: Carte de l'entrée de Cayenne. Bellin. 1764.
" 38. Esquisse inédite de la Guyane, par Philippe Buache. 1766.
" 39. Carte de la Terre Ferme de la Guyane et du pays des Amazones . . . par m. Bonne . . . 1771.
" 40. Carte de l'Amérique Méridionale . . . Bourgoin. 1774.
" 41. Mapa geográfico de America Meridional . . . por Juan la Cruz Cano y Olmedilla . . . 1775.
" 42. [Part of the coast of Brazil.—Partie d'une carte marine manuscrite, sur parchemin] Titre et date illisibles. Jose Monteiro Salazar.
" 43. [Partie d'une carte marine manuscrite, sur parchemin] Planta da America Austral do Mar do Sul e parte da America do Mar do Norte . . . Jose Monteiro Salazar, 1777.
" 44. Carte du nouv. r$^{me}$ de Grenade, de la nou$^{le}$ Andalouse, et de la Guyane . . . Par m. Bonne, 1780.
" 44bis. La Guyane françoise avec partie de la Guyane hollandoise . . . Par m. Bonne. 1780.
" 45. Carte de la partie septentrionale du Brésil. Par m. Bonne 1780.
" 46. Nouvelle Andalousie et Guyane. Par m. Bonne. 1781.
" 47. Carte générale de l'Amérique Méridionale. Par m. Bonne, 1781.
" 48. Carte de la Guyane françoise ou France équinoxiale . . . par m$^r$ Biteow, vers 1781.—Insets: Carte de l'isle S$^{te}$ Lucie l'une des Antilles.—Plan de la ville de Cayenne.
" 49. L'Amérique Méridionale . . . par le sr. Janvier, 1782.
" 50. L'Amérique divisée en ses principaux états . . . par le s$^r$ Janvier. 1784.
" 51. Carte de la Terre Ferme, de la Guyane et du pays des Amazones . . . par m. Bonne, 1785.
" 52. Kaart van het Nordlyk gedeelte van Bresil. W. A. Bachiene. 1785.
" 52bis. Kaart van het Nieuw Koningrijk Grenada, Nieuw Andalusie en Guyane . . . W. A. Bachiene. 1785.
" 53. Carte d'Amérique . . . par Dezauche, 1790.
" 54. Carte d'Amérique . . . par J. B. Nolin, 1791.
" 55. Carte de la Guiane française . . . Daniel Lescallier, 1797.
" 56. Carte des parties connues de la Guyane française et batave . . . V. P. Malouet, 1802.

**Brazil**—Continued.
- no. 57. Carte des colonies française et hollandaise de la Guyane . . . Edme Mentelle et P. G. Chanlaire, 1805.
- " 58. Carte d'Amérique . . . Par Dezauche, 1808.
- " 59. Carte géographo-géologique de la Guyane française . . . Poirson d'après Leblond, 1814.
- " 60. A map of South America.—Carte de l'Amérique Méridionale . . . par P. I. Lapie, 1814.
- " 61. [Partie de la carte du Brésil] Adolphe de Beauchamp, 1815.
- " 62. [Feuille de l'Amérique de l'Atlas historique et géographique de Le Sage] 1815.
- " 63. Carte encyprotype de l'Amérique Méridionale . . . par H. Brué, 1816.
- " 64. Amérique Méridionale, par Brion de la Tour et Poirson, 1806.
- " 65. Amérique Septentrionale et Méridionale . . . Lapie, 1820.
- " 66. Carte physique et politique de l'Amérique Méridionale par A. H. Brué, 1821–1825.
- " 67. Carte de l'Amérique Méridionale par L. Vivien, 1825.
- " 68. Carte géographique, statistique et historique du Brésil. Buchon, 1825.
- " 69. Carte géographique, historique et politique de l'Amérique Méridionale. Darmet, 1825.
- " 70. Carte générale de l'Amérique . . . par F$^r$ Delamarche, 1825.
- " 71. Carte géographique, statistique et historique de la Guyane. Buchon, 1825.
- " 72. Carte de la Guiane française par A. M. Perrot, 1826.
- " 73. Carte générale de l'Amérique Méridionale et des îles qui en dependent. Dressée par A. Brué, 1826.
- " 74. Carte du Brésil et d'une partie des pays adjacents. Redigée par A. Brué, 1826.
- " 75. Carte générale de l'empire du Brésil; par L. Vivien . . . 1826.
- " 76. Carte de la Colombie et des Guyanes. Dressée par m. Lapie . . . 1828.
- " 77. Carte du Brésil . . . m. Lapie, 1829.
- " 78. Nouvelle carte de l'Amérique Méridionale et des îles qui en dépendent . . . Par A. H. Brué . . . 1834.
- " 79. Carte du Brésil, dressée par m. Lapie . . . 1838.
- " 80. Nouvelle carte de l'Amérique Méridionale et des îles qui en dépendent . . . Par A. Brué . . . 1839.
- " 81. Carta corographica do imperio do Brazil . . . Conrado Jacob de Niemeyer, 1846.
- " 82. Colonies françaises (en Amérique) . . . V. Levasseur . . . 1849.
- " 83. Carta topographica da provincia de Oyapockia, 1853 [Carte anonyme brésilienne]
- " 84. . . . no. 1. Carta hydrografica e descriptiva da parte comprehendida entre o rio Conani e o rio Oyapock . . . José da Costa Azevedo, 1860.
- " 85. . . . no. 2. Carta hydrografica e descriptiva da parte comprehendida entre o rio Araguary e o rio Calsoene . . . José da Costa Azevedo, 1860.
- " 86. Carte des côtes de la Guyane depuis Cayenne jusqu'à l'embouchure de l'Amazone . . . m. F. Mouchez . . . 1868.

—— [Frontières du Brésil et de la Guyane anglaise] Premier mémoire. Le droit du Brésil présenté à Rome le 27 février, 1903 par Joaquim Nabuco . . . Atlas. 2 p. l., 85 maps, 5 pl. fol. Paris, A. Lahure [1903] 2721

NOTE.—Atlas accompanying this work entitled: Question des limites du Brésil et de la Guyane anglaise soumise à l'arbitrage de s. m. le roi d'Italie. Atlas accompagnant le premier mémoire du Brésil. Paris, Ducourtioux & Huillard, 1903.
Cover-title: Limites entre le Brésil et la Guyane Anglaise. Atlas démonstratif des droits du Brésil au territoire contesté par la Grande-Bretagne. 1903.
A collection of maps by various cartographers from the 16th to the 20th century. pp. 402–417, "Premier mémoire" contain explanatory notes to the maps

CONTENTS.

no. 1. Carte de la Guyane et des territoires limitrophes . . . dressée par Henri Tropé, 1903.
" 2–3. Carte du territoire contesté entre les états-unis du Brésil et la Guyane-Britannique . . . par Henri Tropé, 1903.
" 4. Carte Espagnole anonyme du xvi$^e$ siècle vers 1560.
" 5. Americae sive novi orbis, nova descriptio. Ortelius, 1587.
" 6. Nieuwe caerte van het wonderbaer ende goudrÿcke landt Guiana, gelegen onder de linie æquinoctiael, tusschen Brasilien ende Peru . . . Hondius, 1598.
" 7. [Les forts pris aux Hollandais] João Teixeira, 1640.
" 8. Amérique Méridionale par N. Sanson d'Abbeville . . . 1650.
" 9. Carte de la Terre Ferme du Pérou du Brésil et du pays des Amazones . . . par Guillaume De l'Isle . . . 1703.
" 10. El gran Rio Maranon, o Amazonas . . . por el p? Samuel Fritz . . . 1707.
" 11. Carte de la route de m. Nicolas Horstman de Rio Esquibe a Rio Negro . . . 1743.
" 16. Carte du cours du Maragnon ou de la grande rivière des Amazones . . . par m de la Condamine . . . 1745.
" 17. Amérique Méridionale . . . par le sr. d'Anville. 1748.
" 18. Carte ayant servi aux plénipotentiaires du traité des limites entre le Portugal et l'Espagne. 1749.
" 19. Légende au verso de la carte précédente.
" 20. Caart van volkplantinge in Esseqebo en Demerary . . . Storm van's Gravesande . . . 1749.
" 21. Rios Essequebo et Demeray. Storm van's Gravesande. 1750 (?)
" 22. Amérique Méridionale . . . par le sr. Robert de Vaugondy . . . 1750.
" 23. Carte de la province de Maranhão de la compagnie de Jésus. 1753.
" 24. [Guayana] Van Bercheyck, 1759.
" 25. Carte française manuscrite vers 1755.
" 26. [Rio Orinoco] D'Anville vers 1760.
" 27. Amérique Méridionale . . . par le sr. d'Anville, 1748.
" 28. Carte générale de la Guyane. 1763.
" 29. Guyane portugaise et partie du cours de la rivière des Amazones . . 1763.

**Brazil**—Continued.

no. 30. Kaart van geheel Guajana of de Wilden-kust en die der Spaansche Westindien . . . Isaac Tirion, 1767.
" 31. Caart van Guiana. Hartsinck, 1770.
" 32. Carte de la Terre Ferme de la Guyane et du pays des Amazones . . . par m. Bonne . . . 1771.
" 33. Ribeiro de Sampaio. 1775.
" 34. Carte des établissements portugais du rio Negro, vers 1775.
" 35–36. Mappa do rio Branco. Felippe Sturm. 1775.
" 37. Continuaçao do mappa do rio Branco . . . Gronfeld. 1776.
" 38. Schets kaart van de limite tusschen het koningl. spaansch en neederlansch-Guiana . . . door Heneman vers 1776.
" 39. Schets kaart van de colonien van rio Demerary en rio Essequebo . . . Heneman, 1776.
" 40. Carta da região do rio Branco da America portugueza. Ribeiro de Sampaio. 1778.
" 41. Mapa coro-grafico de la Nueva Andalucia . . . por Luis de Surville. 1778.
" 42. Borrador topographico vers 1779.
" 43. The coast of Guyana from the Oroonoko to the river of Amazons . . . Thompson. 1781.
" 44–45. Carte des explorations portugaises de 1781 dans le contesté actuel Silva Pontes et Ricardo Franco d'Almeida Serra.
" 46–48. Carte des explorations portugaises dans le contesté actuel, 1787. Gama Lobo de Almada.
" 49. Carta do rio Branco . . . J. Simões de Carvalho. 1787.
" 50. Carta geografica das viages feitas nas capitanias do r. Negro e Mato-Grosso . . . J. Joaquim Victorio da Costa. 1789.
" 51. South America with its several divisions according to the possessions of the european powers; by Thomas Kitchen . . . 1794.
" 52. Map of South America . . . By Thos. Kitchin sen! . . . 1795.
" 53. Mapa geográfico de la mayor parte de la América Meridional que contiene los paises por donde debe trazarse la linea divisoria que divida los dominios de Espana y Portugal . . . D$^{n}$ Francisco Requeña, 1796.
" 54. Carta geografica das viages feitas nas capitanias do r. Negro e Mato Grosso . . . J. Joaquim Victoria da Costa. 1797.
" 55. Carte générale & particulière de la colonie d'Essequebe & Demerarie . . . Par . . . F. von Bouchenroeder. 1798.
" 56–57. Nova Lusitania. 1798 (1804?) Silva Pontes.
" 58. Chart o fGuyana &c. shewing the connections between the two great rivers Amazon & Orronocco . . . Commandant Hislop. 1802.
" 59–60. Carta topographica das provincias do Pará e rio Negro vers 1804.
" 61. Carta corografica de la republica de Colombia. 1810.
" 62. Outlines of the physical and political divisions of South America . . . A. Arrowsmith . . . 1811.
" 63. [Guiana hespanhola, Guiana Portugeza] Seraphim José Lopes. 1813.
" 64. Map of Brazil and Paraguay with adjoining countries. A. Arrowsmith. 1817.
" 65. A map of the united and independant provinces of Venezuela and New Granada . . . Sidney Hall. 1820.
" 66. Carte physique et politique de l'Amérique Méridionale par A. H. Brué . . . 1821.
" 67. Map of Columbia . . . Humboldt. 1826.

no. 68. " " British Guiana by William Hillhouse . . . 1827.
" 69. Carte du Brésil dressée par m. Lapie . . . 1829.
" 70. Tracing of part of a map of Colombia dedicated to colonel B. H. Wilson . . . J. Arrowsmith. 1832.
" 71. Nouvelle carte de l'Amérique Méridionale . . . A. H. Brué . . . 1834.
" 72. West India islands and adjacent coast. Montgomery Martin, 1834.
" 73. Guayana. Montgomery Martin, 1834.
" 74. Karte von Amerika . . . von H. Mahlman, 1837.
" 75. Amérique Méridionale dressée par Th. Duvotenay, 1839.
" 76. South America from original documents . . . John Arrowsmith, 1839.
" 77. Mapa fisico y politico de la república de Venezuela . . . Agustin Codazzi . . . 1840.
" 78. Map of British Guiana . . . Hadfield. 1842.
" 79. [Venezuela and Spanish Guiana] Gardner.
" 80. Carta geographica dos terrenos contestados . . . Commission Brésilienne de 1843.
" 81. Süd America . . . Kiepert, 1849.
" 82. Tabula geographica Brasiliae et terrarum adjacentium . . . von Martius vers 1853.
" 83. Colombia Prima. De la Rochette. 1857.
" 84. Brasil. Millet de Saint-Adolphe, 1863.
" 85. Provincia do Amazonas . . . Candido Mendes de Almeida. 1868.
" 86. Carte des sources des rivières Takuta, Mapouerre Trombetta, Essequibo &. Levée par H. A. Coudreau, 1884.
" 87. Carte des fazendas du rio Branco supérieur . . . par H. A. Coudreau en 1885.
" 88. Rio Branco levé à la boussole par H. A. Coudreau. 1884–1885.
" 89. Commission brésilienne de démarcation des limites du Brésil avec le Venezuela. 1884.
" 90. Carte de l'état de l'Amazone . . . Sant' Anna Nery et Bern, Ramos. 1901.

**Great Britain and Brazil.**

Atlas annexé au mémoire présenté par le gouvernement de sa majesté britannique à sa majesté le roi d'Italie dans sa qualité d'arbitre entre la Grande Bretagne et les états-unis du Brésil selon les articles d'un traité ratifié à Rio de Janeiro, le 28 janvier, 1902. Dressé par major E. H. Hills . . . 2 p. l., 25 maps on 37 l. fol. [London, 1903] 2722

NOTE.—1er mémoire, 1 v.; 2e mémoire, 2 v.; 2e mémoire annexés, 2 v. [Paris, 1903]
Reproductions of maps dated 1691–1846.
Maps nos. 1–5, and 18–24 have english text.

CONTENTS.

Cartes spécialement dressées pour le mémoire.
no. 1. Cartes des pays septentrionaux de l'Amérique du Sud, montrant la position du territoire contesté, et les limites des divers états qui occupent le bassin de l'Amazone.
" 2. Carte de la zone soumise à l'arbitre, et des territoires limitrophes de Guyane anglaise et du Brésil.

**Great Britain and Brazil**—Continued.
- no. 3. La même carte, montrant les diverses lignes proposées dans le cours des négociations.
- " 4. Carte du pays autrefois portugais situé au sud et à l'ouest de la zone soumise à l'arbitrage, pour servir d'explication aux documents annexés au mémoire.
- " 5. La même carte, avec des routes marquées en couleur, pour servir d'explication à de certains documents spéciaux.
- " 6. Fritz, padre Samuel. Mapa geographica del rio Maranon o Amazonas. 1691.
- " 7. Fritz, padre Samuel. El gran rio Maranon o Amazonas. 1707.
- " 8 (a) Horstman, Nicholas. Carte de la route de m. Nicholas Horstman de rio Esquibe à rio Negro. 1740 (?)
-   8 (b) Horstman, Nicholas. Carte de la route de m. Nicholas Horstman de rio Esquibe à rio Negro. Copie de l'ébauche originale travaillée à l'usage de la Condamine. 1740.
- " 9. D'Anville, J. A. B. Amérique Méridionale. 1$^{re}$ édition. 1748.
- " 10. The spanish-portuguese treaty map. Carta geographica de que se serviu o ministro plenipotenciario de s. magestade fidelissima para ajustar o tratado de limites na America Meridional assignado em 13, janeiro de 1750. 1749–50.
- " 11. Storm van's Gravezande, Laurens. Rio Essequebe et Demerary. 1750.
- " 12. Robert de Vaugondy, Didier. Amérique Méridionale. 1750.
- " 13. Hartsinck, Jacob Jan. Caart van Guiana. 1770.
- " 14. Ribeiro de Sampaio, Francisco Xavier. Carta geographica das Capitanias do Gram Para e rio Negro. 1774–75.
- " 15. De la Cruz Caño y Olmedilla, Juan. Mapa geográfico de America Meridional. 1775.
- " 16. Ribeiro de Sampaio, Francisco Xavier. Mappa da America Meridional para fazer comprehender a verdadeira cituacão do rio Branco. 1778.
- " 17. Van Heneman, J. C. Schets kaart van de limite tusschen het koningl. spaansch en neederlandsch Gujana. 1801 (?)
- " 18. Colonel Hislop. Chart of Guyana, etc., showing the connections between the two great rivers, Amazon and Orronocco. 1802.
- " 19. Hancock, John (Dr.) Chart of the interior of British Guiana. 1811.
- " 20. Arrowsmith, John. Colombia. 1832.
- " 21. Schomburgk, Robert Hermann. Sketch map of British Guiana to explain a memoir on its boundaries. 1839.
- " 22. Schomburgk, Robert H. Map of Guayana to illustrate the route of R. H. Schomburgk, esq. 1840.
- " 23. Schomburgk, Robert H. Sketch map of the river Takutu. 1842.
- " 24. Schomburgk, Robert H. Map of British Guiana, compiled from the surveys executed under her majesty's commission from 1841–44. 2 feuilles (Réproduction de la feuille méridionale seulement) 1844.
- " 25. Schomburgk, Richard. (Gravé par Mahlmann) Karte von Britisch Guyana nebst dem Quelllande des Parima (rio Branco) und Orinoco. 1846.

**Bravo, F. J.**

Atlas de cartas geográficas de los países de la América Meridional, en que estuvieron situadas las más importantes misiones de los jesuitas; como tambien de los territorios sobre cuya posesion versaron allí las principales cuestiones entre España y Portugal; acompañado de varios documentos sobre estas últimas, y precedido de una introducción histórica . . . xxiii, 51 pp., 6 fold. maps. fol. Madrid, M. Rivadeneyra, 1872. 2723

> NOTE.—"Catálogo de los documentos relativos á las cuestiones entre Españoles y Portugueses en el Rio de la Plata y Amazonas, y que forman parte de mi coleccion", p. [33]–40.
> "Catálogo de los documentos relativos á los tratados ajustados entre España y Portugal sobre límites de los territorios que poseian en América ambas naciones (De mi coleccion)", p. [41]–51.
> "Noticia de los mapas que forman este atlas", pp. xix–xxiii.
>
> CONTENTS.
>
> MAPS.
>
> no. 1. [Carta esférica de las provincias septentrionales del rio de la Plata, desde la capital, Buenos Ayres, hasta el Paraguay y costa del mar Oceano correspondiente. Construida segun las mejores noticias . . . en los años 1784 á 96. El señalado con el núm. 1 es la mitad proximamente del original, que se conserva en el depósito hidrográfico de Madrid . . . Fué construida y delineada por d. Andres Oyarvide.
> " 2. Cróquis del Rio Paraguay y alto Paraná . . . donde se puso el marco de los límites entre España y Portugal el 14 de enero de 1753.
> " 3. Cróquis del alto Paraguay y rio Jaurú comprediendo la linea divisoria entre los dominios de España y Portugal . . . 1750 y cuyo marco se colocó en el punto señalado el dia 14 de enero de 1753.
> " 5. Descripcion de las provincias del Chaco . . . segun las relaciones modernas, y noticias adquiridas por diversas entradas de los missioneros de la compania de Jesus . . . 1700.
> " 6. Plano general de las montañas orientales del reino del Perú . . . formado sobre los reconocimientos que verificó el rdo. p. Fr. Joaquin Soler. Hecho.—por d. Andres Baleatc. 1795.

## Great Britain and Brazil.

Atlas annexé au contre-mémoir présenté par le gouvernement de sa majesté britannique à sa majesté le roi d'Italie dans sa qualité d'arbitre entre la Grande Bretagne et les états-unis du Brésil selon les articles d'un traité ratifié à Rio de Janeiro, le 28 janvier, 1902. Dressé par major E. H. Hills . . . 2 p. l., 37 maps on 25 l. fol. [London, 1903] 2724

> NOTE.—Reproductions of maps dated 1832–1894.
> Maps no. 1–6, 8, 9, 12, 13, 21 have english text.
>
> CONTENTS.
>
> Cartes spécialement dressées pour le contre-mémoire.
> no. 1. Carte de la zone soumise à l'arbitre, et des territoires limitrophes de la Guyane anglaise et du Brésil, montrant les localités habitées par les Indiens avant les Descimentos portugaises.
> " 2. La même carte, montrant les localités habitées par les Indiens après les Decimentos portugaises.

**Great Britain and Brazil**—Continued.

no. 3. La même carte, avec des routes marquées en couleur, pour servir d'explication à de certains documents spéciaux.
" 4. La même carte, avec les routes de sir R. Schomburgk marquées en couleur.
" 5. La même carte, avec les routes de m. Barrington Brown marquées en couleur. Cartes réproduites.
" 6. Alexander. A sketch map of British Guiana, South America. 1832.
" 7. Stieler. Extrait d'une carte de "Süd-America." 1846.
" 8. Martin. Carte de la Guyane Britannique. 1849.
" 9. Petermann. Extrait de la carte de "Colombia." 1851.—Black. Extrait d'une carte de "Brazil, Uruguay, Paraguay, and Guayana." 1854. Black. Extrait d'une carte l'Amérique Méridionale. 1854.
" 10. Colton. Extrait d'une carte du Brésil et de la Guyane. 1855.—Kiepert. Extrait d'une carte Mittel-America und West indien. 1857.—Stanford. Extrait d'une carte de l'Amérique Méridionale. 1857.
" 11. Kiepert. Extrait d'une carte nouvelle de l'Amérique tropique au nord de la ligne équinoctiale. 1858.
" 12. Blackie. Extrait d'une carte intitulée "British, Dutch and French Guiana." 1860.
" 13. Keith Johnston. Extrait d'une carte de l'Amérique Méridionale (Feuille du nord) 1861.—Stein. Extrait d'une carte de "Süd Amerika." 1862.
" 14. Philip. Extrait d'une carte de l'Amérique Méridionale, dressée par Augustus Petermann . . . 1864.—Johnson. Extrait d'une carte de l'Amérique Méridionale. 1865.—Meyer. Extrait d'une carte de "Süd America, Nördl Theil." 1866.
" 15. Vuillemin. Extrait d'une carte intitulée "Física y política de la América del Sur." 1867.
" 16. Andriveau-Goujon. Extrait d'une carte de la Colombie, Guyane, Venezuela, Equateur. 1868.—Keith Johnston. Extrait d'une carte de l'Amérique Méridionale. (Feuille du nord) 1868.
" 17. Brué. Extrait d'une nouvelle carte de l'Amérique Méridionale. 1869.
" 18. Sohr-Berghaus. Extrait d'une carte de "Süd-America" no. 1, von F. Handtke. 1872.—Frijlink. Extrait d'une carte "Zuid-Amerika." 1872.—Brué. Extrait des cartes des républiques de l'Equateur, de la Colombie, de Venezuela, et des Guyanes. 1875.
" 19. Hungarian commission. Extrait d'une carte intitulée "Del Amerika Fali Abrosza a magyar királyi közoktatásügyi minister megrend eleséböl." Kiadja Justus Perthes gothaban. 1877.
" 20. Keith Johnston. Extrait d'une carte de l'Amérique Mérdionale (Feuille du nord) 1879.—Kiepert. Extrait d'une carte intitulée Mapa general de la America Meridional, por Enrique Kiepert, 1882.—Lorsignol. Extrait d'une carte intitulée America Meridional. 1884.
" 21. Bradley. Extrait d'une carte de l'Amérique Méridionale. (Feuille du nord) 1887.
" 22. Loth. Extrait d'une carte intitulée Kaart van Guiana, engelsch, nederlandsch en fransch. 1889.
" 23. Kiepert. Extrait d'une carte intitulée Mapa del América del Sur por Ricardo Kiepert. 1890.—Hoepli. Extrait d'une carte intitulée Venezuela e Guiana. 1894.
" 24. Schrader. Extrait d'une carte de l'Amérique du Sud en 5 feuilles. Feuille 2. 1894.

### RIVERS.

**Crevaux, J. N.**
Fleuves de l'Amérique du Sud, 1877–1879 . . . Missions du ministère de l'instruction publique. Publié par la Société de géographie. 1 p. l., iv pp., 1 l., 40 fold. maps. obl. 4°. Paris, société de géographie, 1883. 2725

Note.—pp. i–iv contain biography of author.

### GENERAL.

(Arranged chronologically)

#### 1805–1834

**Humboldt, F. W. H. A.**, *freiherr von*.
Voyage de Humboldt et Bonpland. v. 2. Atlas géographique et physique. 8 p. l., front., vi, 3, 72 pp., 2 l., 22 maps, 7 pl. fol. Paris, F. Schoell [etc.] 1805–1834. 2726

Note.—Maps dated 1814–1833. Imperfect: map no. 28 and part of "l'Examen critique," wanting. Atlas accompanying pt. 1 of "Voyage de Humboldt et Bonpland," entitled: Voyage aux régions équinoxiales du nouveau continent, fait en 1799, 1800, 1801, 1802, 1803 et 1804, par Al. de Humboldt et A. Bonpland; rédigé par Alexandre de Humboldt. Avec deux atlas qui renferment, l'un les vues de Cordillères et les monumens des peuples indigènes de l'Amérique, et l'autre des cartes géographique et physique.

The entire work is often cited by the title of pt. 1, since the general title varies or is frequently wanting.

Atlas has various title-pages, because of the relation it bears to the entire work and its closer relation to pt. 1. Considered in the latter case, its title reads: Atlas géographique et physique des régions équinoxiales du nouveau continent, fondé sur des observations astronomiques, des mesures trigonométriques et des nivellemens barométriques; par Al. de Humboldt. Paris, F. Schoell [etc.] 1814–1834.

A complete copy of the text is in his Histoire de la géographie du nouveau continent.—Examen critique . . . 5 v. 8°. Paris, 1836.

In atlas v. 2, preface p. 5, is the following reference to the text: Des deux atlas qui accompagnent la "Relation historique," le premier, l' "Atlas pittoresque," offre un texte explicatif des planches qui a paru sous les titres de "Vues des Cordillères et monumens des peuples indigènes de l'Amérique." "L'ouvrage que je publie en ce moment, offre le texte du second atlas, de celui des "Cartes géographiques et physique." Il renferme l' "Examen critique de l'histoire de la géographie du nouveau continent" et l' "Analyse raisonnée" . . .

CONTENTS.

v. 1. "Atlas pittoresque," plates only.
  2, no. 1. Limite inférieure des neiges perpétuelles à différentes latitudes.
  "  " 2. Tableau physique des îles Canaries . . . 1817.
  "  " 3. Profil de la peninsule Espagnole . . .
  "  " 4. Chemin de La Guayra à Caracas . . .

**Humboldt, F. W. H. A.**—Continued.

v. 2, no. 5. Esquisse hypsométrique des nœuds de montagnes et des ramifications de la Cordillère des Andes depuis le cap de Horn jusqu'à l'isthme de Panama et à la chaine littorale du Venezuela . . . 1827–1831.
" " 6. Profil du chemin de Carthagene des Indes au plateau de Santa Fé de Bogota . . . 1820.
" " 7. Esquisse géognostique des formations entre la vallée de Mexico, Moran et Totonilco. 1833.
" " 8. Carte itinéraire de la route de Zacatecas à Bolaños tracée en 1825 . . .
" " 9. Voyage vers la cime du Chimborazo, tenté le 23 juin 1802 . . . 1824.
" " 10. Carte de la province de Quixos . . .
" " 11. Esquisse d'uue carte de la province d'Avila . . . 1833.
" " 12. Plan du port et des environs de Tampico . . . 1833.
" " 13. . . . Bifurcations et . . . deltas d'affluens pour l'éclaircissement aux discussions d'hydrographie comparée . . .—Bifurcation de la rivière de Torneo.—Haase et Else . . .—Bifurcation de la rivière de Vaucluse.—Carpathes . . .—Bifurcation du rio Cababuri . . .—Ancienne bifurcation de l'Arno.—Rio Yapura—Delta d'affluent . . .
" " 14. Histoire de la géographie de l'Orénoque, Lac Parime, Dorado, bifurcation. [Cartes tracées d'après:] Jodocus Hondius, 1599. Sanson, 1656 [et] 1680.—p. Samuel Fritz, 1690.—Gumilla, 1741 d'Anville (1º. éd.) 1748 . . . p. Caulin, 1759.—La Cruz Olmedilla, 1775.—d'Anville (3º éd.) 1760.—Buache, 1798.—Surville pour l'ouvrage du p. Caulin, 1778.
" " 15. Carte du cours de l'Orénoque, depuis l'embouchure du Rio Sinaruco jusqu'à l'Angostura . . .
" " 16. Carte itinéraire du cours de l'Orénoque, de l'Atabapo, du Casiquiare, et du Rio Negro offrant la bifurcation de l'Orénoque et sa communication avec la rivière des Amazones . . . 1814.
" " 17. Carte du cours du Rio Apure et d'une partie de la chaine des montagnes de la Nouvelle Grenade . . .
" " 18. Carte de la partie orientale de la province de Varinas comprise entre l'Orénoque, l'Apure et le Rio Meta . . . 1812.
" " 19. Carte du cours de Rio Meta et d'une partie de la chaine orientale des montagnes de la Nouvelle Grenade . . . 1817.
" " 20. Carte du Rio Caura . . . 1816.
" " 21. Carte spéciale de la partie du Rio Apure . . .—Cours du Rio Guaviare . . . 1814.
" " 22. Carte générale de Colombia dressée par A. H. Brué . . . 1825.
" " 23. Carte de l'ile de Cuba . . .—Inset: Plan du port et de la ville de la Havane. 1826.
" " 24. Carte du Rio Grande de la Magdalena . . .—Insets: Plan topographique de l'Angostura de Carare . . .—Carte du Rio Grande de la Magdalena depuis ses sources jusqu'aux 4° de latitude, par F. J. de Caldas.
" " 25. Carte hydrographique de la province du Choco esquissée d'après le plan de don Juan Donoso et les matériaux communiques par le gouvernement de la république de Colombia.—Inset: Partie de la côte occidentale d'après les combinaisons de don Felipe Bauza.

v. 2, no. 26. Carte géologique du Nevado de Antisana . . .
" " 27. Plan hypsométrique du volcan de Pichincha . . . 1827
" " 28. [Wanting]
" " 29. Plan du volcan de Jorullo . . .
" " 30. Esquisse géologique des environs de Guanaxuato . . . 1817.

## 1822–1825

**Duperrey, L. I.**
Voyage autour du monde, exécuté par ordre du roi, sur la corvette de sa majesté, la Coquille, pendant les années 1822, 1823, 1824 et 1825 . . . Atlas. 2 p. l., 21 pp., 49 maps, 4 pl. fol. Paris, A. Bertrand, 1826–1830. 2727

NOTE.—Atlas to accompany v. 5, "Hydrographie et physique" of his "Voyage autour du monde."
A collection of maps by various hydrographers, many of whom were officers in the french navy: m. m. Bérard, de Blois, de Blossville, Givry and Lottin.
Engraved title by Abel Malo.
Imprint date is 1827. Map no. 33 bears date 1828.
pp. 5–21, "Tableaux des positions géographiques des stations principales . . ."
Routes of various french and english navigators are indicated on maps no. 3 bis., 8, 8 bis., and 33.
The following maps relate to America:
no. 1. Carte et plan des ilots de Martin-Vaz et de la Trinité levés par m. Bérard.
" 2. Carte de la baye de Payta levée par m. Bérard . . .—Inset: Carte de l'entrée de l'anse de Séchura . . .
" 41. Carte d'une partie de la côte du Brésil comprise entre le rio Guaratuba et la laguna de Gurupaba . . .—Plan de l'île Santa Catharina . . .
" 41 bis. Plan du port de Valparaiso . . .
" 42. Carte des îles Gallapagos . . .—Plan de la baie Albany . . .—Plan du mouillage de l'île Hood . . .—Plan de la baie Salango . . .—Plan du mouillage de Tacames (Colombie) . . .—Plan du banc de la Perle . . .

## 1827

**Carey, H. C., *and* Lea, I.**
A complete historical, chronological, and geographical american atlas, being a guide to the history of North and South America, and the West Indies: exhibiting an accurate account of the discovery, settlement, and progress, of their various kingdoms, states, provinces &c., together with the wars, celebrated battles, and remarkable events, to the year 1826. According to the plan of Le Sage's [pseud. of M. J. A. E. D., comte de Las Cases] atlas, and intended as a companion to Lavoisne's improvement of that celebrated work. 3d ed. cor. and impr. 3 p. l., [109] l. incl. 46 maps, 2 pl. fol. Philadelphia, H. C. Carey & I. Lea, 1827. 2728

NOTE.—First edition published in 1822. See title 1175, for description of this edition.
Maps have border text.

**Carey, H. C.**, *and* **Lea, I.**—Continued.

CONTENTS.

no. 1. N. America.—S. America. Drawn by J. Finlayson.
" 3. North America. Drawn by J. Finlayson.
" 4. British possessions in North America. Drawn by F. Lucas jr.
" 5. United States of America. Engraved by B. Tanner.
" 10. Maine. J. Yeager sculp.
" 11. New Hampshire. Engrav'd by Young & Delleker.
" 12. Massachusetts. Drawn by F. Lucas.
" 13. Rhode Island. Drawn by F. Lucas, jr.
" 14. Connecticut. Engrav'd by Young & Delleker.
" 15. Vermont. Drawn by F. Lucas jr.
" 16. New York. Drawn by F. Lucas jr.
" 17. New Jersey. Kneass sc.
" 18. Pennsylvania. Engr'd by J. Yeager.
" 19. Delaware. Drawn by F. Lucas jr.
" 20. Maryland. Drawn by F. Lucas, jr.
" 21. District of Columbia. Engraved by Young & Delleker.
" 22. Virginia. Engrav'd by Young & Delleker.
" 23. North Carolina. Drawn by F. Lucas jr.
" 24. South Carolina. Reduced by J. Drayton from the state map by J. Wilson.
" 25. Georgia. Drawn by F. Lucas jr.
" 26. Ohio. Drawn by F. Lucas jr.
" 27. Kentucky. Drawn by F. Lucas jr.
" 28. Tennessee. Drawn by F. Lucas jr.
" 29. Mississippi. Drawn by F. Lucas jr.
" 30. Alabama. J. Drayton del.
" 31. Louisiana. Kneass sc.
" 32. Indiana. Drawn by F. Lucas jr.
" 33. Illinois. J. Yeager sculp.
" 34. Missouri. Engraved by Young & Delleker.
" 35. Map of Arkansas and other territories of the United States . . . by S. H. Long . . .
" 36. Michigan territory. Drawn by J. Finlayson.
" 37. Florida. Drawn by J. Drayton.
" 38. Mexico and internal provinces. Prepared from Humbolt's map & other documents by J. Finlayson.
" 39. West Indies. Drawn by F. Lucas jr.
" 40. Cuba and the Bahama islands. B. Tanner sc.
" 41. Jamaica. Drawn by J. Finlayson.
" 42. Hayti . . . Drawn by F. Lucas jr.
" 43. Porto Rico and Virgin islands. Drawn by F. Lucas.
" 44. Windward islands. Drawn by F. Lucas.
" 45. Leeward islands. J. Yeager sculp.
" 46. South America. Drawn by E. Paguenaud.
" 47. Colombia. Drawn by J. Finlayson.
" 48. Brazil. Drawn by J. Finlayson.
" 49. United provinces of South America. Drawn by J. Finlayson.
" 50. Peru. Drawn by J. Finlayson.
" 51. Chili. Drawn by J. Finlayson.

### 1836–1839

**Du Petit-Thouars, A. A.**
Voyage autours du monde sur la frégate la Vénus pendant les années 1836–1839, publié par ordre du roi sous les auspices du ministre de la marine ... Atlas.   1 p.l., 17 maps. fol. Paris, Gide, 1840–1855.   2729

>   NOTE.—Atlas hydrographique to accompany v. 6–10, "Physique, par. U. de Tessan."
>   Title of atlas varies: ... Atlas hydrographique.   Rédigé par U. de Tessan, ingénieur hydrograph ... Dépôt-général de la marine, 1845.
>   Maps dated 1837–1845.
>   For contents see title no. 205.

# ARGENTINA.

### BOUNDARY.

**Argentine-Chilian boundary.** Report presented to the tribunal appointed by her britannic majesty's government "to consider and report upon the differences which have arisen with regard to the frontier between the Argentine and Chilian republics" to justify the Argentine claims for the boundary in the summit of the cordillera de los Andes, according to the treaties of 1881 & 1893. Printed in compliance with the request of the tribunal, dated december 21, 1899.   4 v. and atlas in portfolio.   fol. London, printed for the gov't of the Argentine republic, by W. Clowes & sons, limited, 1900.   2730

#### CONTENTS.

> no. 1. North-western region of the argentine republic.
> "  2. The proposed argentine boundary line ... and the proposed chilian boundary line ... Between 38° 50′ and 41° 10′.
> "  3. Ipela ridge and lakes Huechu-Lafquen, Lolog and Lacar. Between 39° 40′ and 40° 30′.
> "  4. The proposed argentine boundary line ... and the proposed chilian boundary line ... Between 41° 0′ and 43° 40′.
> "  5. The proposed argentine boundary line ... and the proposed chilian boundary line ... Between 43° 0′ and 45° 20′.
> "  6. Continental divide in the tertiary table-land to the east of the Cordillera de los Andes ... Between 43° 30′ and 44° 45′.
> "  7. The proposed argentine boundary line ... and the proposed chilian boundary line ... Between 45° 0′ and 47° 20′.
> "  8. Headwaters of rivers Aisen and Mayo. Between 45° 14′ and 46° 10′.
> "  9. Valley of lake Buenos Aires and rivers Fenix and Deseado. Between 46° 5′ and 46° 56′.

**Argentine-Chilian boundary**—Continued.

   no. 10. The proposed argentine boundary line . . . and the proposed chilian boundary line . . . Between 47° 0′ and 49° 30′.
   " 11. The proposed argentine boundary line . . . and the proposed chilian boundary line . . . Between 49° 30′ and 52° 30′.
   " 12. Orographical preliminary map of the south-western region of the argentine republic showing the different sections represented in chap. xxviii of the "argentine evidence."
   " 13. Preliminary map of the south-western region of the argentine republic, showing the different points from which photographs reproduced in "argentine evidence" have been taken.
   " 14. Preliminary map of the southern region of the argentine republic.
   " 15. The continental divide in the table-land and the transversal depressions of Vizcachas and rio Gallegos. Between 50° 40′ and 52°.
   " 16. The proposed argentine boundary line along the crest of the cordillera de los Andes, showing its deviation according to article II of protocol of 1893. Between 50° 40′ and 52°.

## GENERAL

(Arranged chronologically)

### 1873

**Martin de Moussy, J. A. V.**
   Description géographique et statistique de la confédération Argentine. 3 p. l., 20 pp., 29 maps. 2e éd. fol. Paris, Firmin Didot frères, fils & cie. 1873.    2731

   Note.—The work of the author having been interrupted by illness, the atlas was completed by L. Bouvet.
   This atlas accompanies "Description géographique et statistique de la confédération Argentine, par V. Martin de Moussy . . . 3 v. Paris, Firmin Didot frères, fils & cie. 1860–73."

   CONTENTS.

   no. 1. Frontispice orné. [Engraved title page]
   " 2. Carte de l'empire espagnol dans les deux Amériques en 1776 à l'époque de la fondation de la vice royauté de La Plata. 1867.
   " 3. Carte de l'Amérique du Sud divisée en ses différents états. 1867.
   " 4. Fac-simile d'une carte du bassin de La Plata. Dressé par les missionnaires de la compagnie de Jésus de la province du Paraguay. Publiée à Rome en 1732.
   " 5. Carte de la Confédération Argentine divisée en ses différentes provinces et territoires.
   " 6. Carte historique de la province des missions et des établissements des jésuites sur le Parana et l'Uruguay de 1575 à 1768.
   " 7. Carte de la province de Corrientes du territoire des missions et des pays adjacents.
   " 8. Carte des provinces d'Entre-Rios de Santa-Fé et de la Bande Orientale. 1863.

no. 9. Carte de la province de Buenos-Ayres et des régions voisines. 1866.
" 10. Carte du territoire Indien du Sud et de la région des Pampas. 1865.
" 11. Carte de la Patagonie et des archipels de la Terre de Feu. 1865.
" 12. Carte des provinces de Cordova de San Luis et des régions voisines. 1865.
" 13. Carte de la province de Mendoza de l'Araucanie et de la plus grande partie du Chili. 1865.
" 14. Carte des provinces de La Rioja de San Juan. 1865.
" 15. Carte des provinces de Catamarca de Tucuman et des régions voisines. 1866.
" 16. Carte des provinces de Salta et de Jujuy et d'une partie de la Bolivie. 1866.
" 17. Carte de la province de Santiago del estero. 1866.
" 18. Carte du grand Chaco . . . pour servir à l'histoire du bassin de la Plata de 1520 à 1865.
" 19. Carte physique de l'Amérique du Sud. 1868.
" 20. Carte physique de la confédération Argentine. 1869.
" 21. Coup géologique des puits artésiens de la piedad et de Barracas à Buenos-Ayres.
" 22. Coupes géologiques diverses—Altitudes.
" 23. Coupes orographiques des parties centrales du territoire Argentin de 26° a 33° l. s.
" 24. Coupe du continent Sud Américain entre les océans Atlantique et Pacifique.
" 25. Coupe de la route de Buenos-Ayres a Lima par les Pampas et les Andes.
" 26. Coupe de divers passages de la Cordillère des Andes.
" 27. Carte du cours du Haut Uruguay. 1866. 1 sheet.
" 28. Carte du cours du Haut Uruguay. 1866. 2 sheets.
" 29. Cours inférieur et bouches du rio Paraguay. 1853.
" 30. Carte des voyages du dr. V. Martin de Moussy.

## 1886

**Instituto geográfico Argentino.** *Buenos Aires.*
Atlas de la república Argentina construido y publicado por resolucion del "Instituto geografico Argentino" bajo los auspicios del exmo. gobierno nacional y redactado por el dr. Arturo Seelstrang . . . Primera entrega.    cover-title, 1 p. l., 26 pp., 27 maps. fol. Buenos Aires, G. Kraft, 1886.    2732

## 1887

**Paz Soldan, M. F.**
Atlas geográfico de la república Argentina conteniendo: el mapa general los de cada provincia, y los del Uruguay del Paraguay compuesto en vista de los últimos documentos y trabajos científicos.    2 p. l., 28 maps. fol.   Buenos Aires, F. Lajouane, 1887.    2733

NOTE.—pl. 17, plan of the city of Buenos Aires.

## 1893

**Martinez, B. T.**
Cartografiá histórica de la república Argentina; curso gradual de historia para los colegios y escuelas argentinas. 1ª pte. 11, [62] pp. incl. 23 maps. fol. [Buenos Aires] museo de la Plata, 1893.
2734

NOTE.—21 full page maps and 2 maps in text.
Imperfect: pp. 3-4 wanting.
Besides maps illustrating the history of Argentine republic, this atlas contains fac-similes of part of La Cosa's map, of: "Paraqvariæ provinciae soc. jesu cum adiacentib<sup>q</sup> novissima descriptio . . . 1732," and engravings of views, public buildings and portraits of Columbus, A. Vespucci, Magellan, S. Cabot, "Francisco Pisarro de Truxillo."
Contains facsimile maps of Buenos-Ayres, "Facsimile de un grabado antiguo. (Ulderico Schmidt)" and of "Monte Vidio." 1748.
Reviewed by Helio Guzman in Instituto geografico Argentino. Bulletin. Buenos Aires, 1894. v. 14, pt. 9-12, pp. 609-611.

## 1898

**Instituto geográfico Argentino.** *Buenos Aires.*
Atlas de la república Argentina, construido y publicado por el "Instituto geográfico Argentino" bajo los auspicios del excmo. gobierno nacional. 2 p. l., 26 pp., 29 maps. fol. Buenos Aires, J. Ruland, 1898.
2735

### Provinces.

#### BUENOS AIRES.

**Delachaux, E. A. S.**
Atlas meteorológico de la república Argentina. Primera parte. Provincia de Buenos Aires. cover-title, 24 maps. fol. Buenos Aires, compañia Sud-Americana de billetes de banco, 1901.
2736

NOTE.—Text printed on verso of maps.
". . . Cuando sea suficiente el número de datos meteorológicos reunidos sobre las otras regiones, proseguiremos la publicación del "Atlas meteorologico" provincia por provincia y territorio por territorio según el mismo plan que el presente trabajo . . . "

#### CÓRDOBA.

**Río, M. E.** *and* **Achával, L.**
Geografía de la provincia de Córdoba por Manuel E. Río y Luis Achával . . . (escrita por encargo del excmo. gobierno de la provincia) Publicación oficial. Atlas. 1 p. l., 7 col. maps, 5 pl. fol. Buenos Aires, companía Sud-Americana de billetes de banco, 1905.
2737

NOTE.—To accompany work by same authors, entitled, "Geografía de la provincia de Córdoba." 2 v. Buenos Aires, 1904-05.

# BOLIVIA.

**BOUNDARY.**

**Peru.** Juicio de límites entre el Perú y Bolivia. Prueba. Peruana presentada al gobierno de la república Argentina por Victor M. Maurtua . . . 12 v. Atlas. 2 v. 4º (v. 2, fol.) Barcelona, Henrich & co. 1906. **2738**

> NOTE.—Collation: v. 1, portfolio, 34 fold. maps; v. 2, 1 p. l., [4] pp., 58 maps. Reproductions from various sources.
> Atlas to accompany a collection of documents for the most part previously unpublished.
> Title of atlas varies: v. 1 . . . Cartas geográfica sprimera serie. Cartera de mapas. v. 2 . . . Cartas geograficas (segunda serie)
> A few maps have accompanying text: v. 1, no. 25, text: "Plano general de las montañas orientales al reyno del Perú" . . . v. 1, no. 14, v. 2, nos. 18 and 57 have border text; a full-page text, faces no. 35, v. 2: "Los fundamentos de este trabajo geografico se indican . . . Notas al mapa."
> Most of the maps are colored.
> For contents, see title 2767.

# BRAZIL.

**BOUNDARY.**

**Brazil.** *Treaties, etc., 1894–1898.*
Frontières entre le Brésil et la Guyane française. Mémoire présenté par les états unis du Brésil au gouvernement de la confédération Suisse arbitre choisi selon les stipulations du traité conclu à Rio-de-Janeiro, le 10 avril 1897, entre le Brésil et la France. Atlas. 1 p. l., [2] pp., 1 l., 104 maps. fol. Paris. A. Lahure, 1899–1900.
**2739**

> NOTE.—Atlas to accompany the "1er mémoire présenté par le Bresil" . . .
> Title of atlas reads: . . . Atlas contenant un choix de cartes antérieures au traité conclu à Utrecht le 11 avril 1713 entre le Portugal et la France—Annexe au mémoire présenté par les états-unis du Brésil . . . Paris, 1899.
> A collection of reproductions from various sources; dated 1500–1707.
> Another edition with imprint date 1900, is like this one, except that the maps are smaller or folded.
> A number of maps are highly colored and embellished by various designs and no. 75 has border text.
> Imperfect: no. 46 wanting.
> Maps no. 62, 68, 69 and 71 have border text; no. 62 is a sheet from the "Atlas historique et géographique" de Le Sage, pseud. of M. J. A. E. D. comte de Las Cases 1815.
> For contents, see title 2719.

**Brazil.** [Frontières du Brésil et de la Guyane anglaise] Premier mémoire. Le droit du Brésil présenté à Rome le 27 février, 1903 par Joaquim Nabuco ... Atlas.   2 p. l., 85 maps, 5 pl.   fol. Paris, A. Lahure [1903]   2740

    Note.—Accompanying atlas entitled: Question des limites du Brésil et de la Guyane anglaise soumise à l'arbitrage de s. m. le roi d'Italie. Atlas accompagnant le premier mémoire du Brésil. Paris, Ducourtioux & Huillard, 1903.
    Cover-title: Limites entre le Brésil et la Guyane anglaise. Atlas démonstratif des droits du Brésil au territoire contesté par la Grande-Bretagne. 1903.
    A collection of maps by various cartographers from the 16th to the 20th century.
    "Premier mémoire," pp. 402–417, contains explanatory notes to the maps.
    For contents, see title 2721.

———— Frontières entre le Brésil et la Guyane Française. Second mémoire présenté par les états unis du Brésil au gouvernement de la confédération Suisse arbitre choisi selon les stipulations du traité conlu à Rio-de-Janeiro, le 10 avril 1897, entre le Brésil et la France. Atlas.   2 pts. in 1 v.; 4 p. l., 88 maps.   fol.   Berne, Stæmpfli & cie. 1899.   2741

    Note.—"Cet atlas se compose de deux parties. La première, comprenant quatorze cartes antérieures au traité d'Utrecht, est un supplément à l'atlas annexé au 1er Mémoire du Brésil ... La seconde partie de l'atlas renferme soixante-quinze cartes postérieures au traité d'Utrecht" ... See preface of atlas.
    A collection of reproductions from various sources; dated 1536–1860.
    Atlas is "tome vi" of the "Second mémoire," imprint: Paris, A. Lahure, 1899.
    For contents, see title 2720.

———— Atlas annexé au mémoire présenté par le gouvernement de sa majesté britannique à sa majesté le roi d'Italie dans sa qualité d'arbitre entre la Grande Bretagne et les états-unis du Brésil selon les articles d'un traité ratifié à Rio de Janeiro, le 28 janvier 1902. Dressé par major E. H. Hills ...   2 p. l., 25 maps on 37 l.   fol. [London, 1903]   2742

    Note.—1er mémoire 1 v.; 2e mémoire, 2 v.; 2e mémoire annexés, 2 v. [Paris, 1903]
    Reproductions of maps dated 1691–1846.
    Maps no. 1–5, and 18–24 have english text.
    For contents, see title 2722.

———— Atlas annexé au contre-mémoire présenté par le gouvernement de sa majesté Britannique à sa majesté le roi d'Italie dans sa qualité d'arbitre entre la Grande Bretagne et les états-unis du Brésil selon les articles d'un traité ratifié à Rio de Janeiro, le 28 janvier 1902. Dressé par major E. H. Hills ...   2 p. l., 37 maps on 25 l.   fol.   [London, 1903]   2743

    Note.—Reproductions of maps dated 1832–1894.
    Maps no. 1–6, 8, 9, 12, 13, 21 have english text.
    For contents, see title 2724.

## EXPLORATIONS.

**Cruls, L.**
Commissão exploradora do planalto central do Brazil. Atlas dos itinerarios, perfis, longitudinaes e da zona demarcada . . . 1 p. l., 7 pp., 74 maps. fol. Rio de Janeiro, H. Lombaerts & cie. 1894.
2744

## RIVERS.

**Halfeld, H. G. F.**
Atlas e relatorio concernente a exploração do rio de S. Francisco desde Cachoéira da Pirapóra até ao oceano Atlantico. Levantado por ordem do governo de s. m. i. o. senhor dom Pedro II . . . em 1852, 1853 e 1854. 1 p. l., 57 pp., 1 l., 48 maps. fol. Rio de Janeiro, E. Rensburg, 1860. 2745

**Liais, E.**
Hydrographie du haut San-Francisco et du rio das Velhas ou résultats au point de vue hydrographique d'un voyage effectué dans la province de Minas-Geraes par Emm. Liais. Ouvrage publié par ordre du gouvernement impérial du Brésil, et accompagné de cartes levées par l'auteur avec la collaboration de mm. Eduardo José de Moraes et Ladislao de Souza Mello Netto. 2 p. l., 26 pp., 1 l., 20 maps. fol. Paris, Rio de Janeiro, B. L. Garnier, 1865. 2746

NOTE.—At head of title: Explorations scientifiques au Brésil.

**Sampaio, T. F.**
Exploração dos rios Itapetininga e Paranapanema . . . Relatorio apresentado ao illm. e exm. sr. dr. Pedro Vicente de Azevedo, sobre os estudos effectuados em 1886 por ordem do illm. e exm. sr. conselheiro João Alfredo Corrêa de Oliveira, pelos engenheiros Theodoro Fernandes Sampaio, Francisco de Paula Oliveira, J. F. Washington de Aguiar.   cover-title, 2 p. l., 14 pp., 26 maps. obl. fol. Rio de Janeiro, imprenta nacional, 1889. 2747
[Brazil. São Paulo (Province of) Commissão geographica e geologica]

## GENERAL.

(Arranged chronologically)

### 1809

**Pimentel, M.**
The Brazil pilot; or, a description of the coast of Brazil. Translated from the portuguese of Manoel Pimentel, principal hydrographer to his majesty John the fifth, of Portugal. To which are added, charts, of some of its most considerable ports. From mss.

**Pimentel, M.**—Continued.
never before published. 2 p. l., iv, 78 pp., front. (map), 14 maps. 4°. London, for Longman, Hurst, Rees & Orme, & A. Arrowsmith, 1809. 2748

> NOTE.—His most important work is entitled, "Arte práctica de navegar e roteiro dos viagues e costas maritimas do Brasil, Guinea, Angola, Indias, etc. Lisboa, 1699. en fol. y 1712." *cf.* Diccionario enciclopedico Hispano-Americano.

### 1868
**Mendes de Almeida, C.**
Atlas do imperio do Brazil comprehendendo as respectivas divisões administrativas, ecclesiasticas, eleitoraes e judiciarias, dedicado á sua magestade o imperador o senhor d. Pedro II, destinado á instrucção publica no imperio com especialidade á dos alumnos do imperial collegio de Pedro II, organisado por Candido Mendes de Almeida. 37 pp., 27 maps. fol. Rio de Janeiro, lithographia do instituto philomathico, 1868. 2749

> NOTE.—A bibliography of maps of Brasil, "Material e outros auxilios consultados e aproveitados nos mappas e plantas do Atlas do imperio do Brazil," pp. 9-35, precedes atlas proper.

CONTENTS.

no. 1. Mappa-mundi.
" 2. Idem do imperio do Brazil (com divisões administrativas)
    A. Idem do imperio do Brazil (com divisões ecclesiasticas)
    B. Idem do imperio do Brazil (com divisões eleitoraes)
    C. Idem do imperio do Brazil (mundo)
" 3. Mappa da provincia do Amazonas.
" 4. " " " " Grão-Pará.
" 5. " " " " Maranhão.
" 6. " " " " Piauhy.
" 7. " " " " Ceará.
" 8. " " " " Rio-Grande do Norte.
" 9. " " " da Parahyba.
" 10. " " " de Pernambuco.
" 11. " " " das Alagôas.
" 12. " " " de Sergipe.
" 13. " " " da Bahia.
" 14. " " " do Espirito-Santo.
" 15. Mappa do municipio Neutro.
" 16. Mappa da provincia do Rio de Janeiro.
" 17. " " " de S. Paulo.
" 18. " " " do Paraná.
" 19. " " " de Santa Catharina.
" 20. " " " " S. Pedro.
" 21. " " " " Minas-Geraes.
" 22. " " " " Goyaz.
" 23. " " " " Matto-Grosso.
" 24. " " " " Pinsonia (projecto)

Provinces.

### ESPIRITO SANTO.

**Brazil.** *Ministerio da agricultura, commercio e obras publicas.*
Inspectoria geral das terras e colonisação. Mappa topographico da provincia do Espirito Santo, organisado na inspectoria geral das terras e colonisação com elementos fornecidos pelas commissões technicas e precedido de uma breve noticia sobre a mesma provincia. cover-title, 1 p. l., [32] pp., 2 maps. 4°. Rio de Janeiro, 1878. 2750

NOTE.—Text in portuguese, italian, french and german.

### PARANÁ.

**Brazil.** *Ministerio da agricultura, commercio e obras publicas.*
Mappa topographico da provincia do Paraná, organisada na inspectoria geral de terras e colonisação pelo engenheiro C. Rivièrre, segundo os trabalhos dos engenheiros Mouchez, Ochs, Keller, Black e Rebouças. Acompanhado de uma breve descripção noticiando as principaes riquezas . . .    cover-title, 1 p. l., [30] pp., 3 maps, 2 tab. 4°. Rio de Janeiro, S. A. Sisson, 1877.     2751

NOTE.—Text in portuguese, italian and german.

### SANTA CATHARINA.

**Brazil.** *Ministerio da agricultura, commercio e obras publicas.*
Descripção topographica do mappa da provincia de Santa Catharina, organisada na commissão do registro geral e estatistica das terras publicas e possuidas sob a presidencia do conselheiro Bernado Augusto Nascentes de Azambuja. Lithographado e publicado por ordem do governo imperial.    26 pp., 1 fold. map.    8°.    Rio de Ganeiro, typographia franco-americana, 1873.     2752

NOTE.—Text in portuguese, french and german.

# BRITISH GUIANA.

#### BOUNDARY.

**Maps** of the Orinoco-Essequibo region. South America. Compiled for the commission appointed by the president of the United States "to investigate and report upon the true divisional line between the republic of Venezuela and British Guiana . . ."    3 p. l., 76 maps. fol.    Washington, 1897.     2753

NOTE.—Volume four of the report.
For contents, see title 2776.

**Case, The,** of the United States of Venezuela before the tribunal of arbitration to convene at Paris, under the provisions of the treaty between the united states of Venezuela and her britannic majesty signed at Washington, feb. 2, 1897. v. 4. Appendix atlas. 2 p. l., 91 maps. fol. Baltimore, A. Hoen & co. 1898.    2754

NOTE.—For contents, see title 2777.

**Counter-case, The,** of the United States of Venezuela before the tribunal of arbitration to convene at Paris, under the provisions of the treaty between the united states of Venezuela and her britannic majesty signed at Washington, february 2, 1897. v. 4. Appendix atlas. 2 p. l., 91 maps. fol. Baltimore, A. Hoen & co. 1898.    2755

NOTE.—For contents, see title 2778.

**Atlas** to accompany the case presented on the part of her britannic majesty to the arbitral tribunal between Great Britain and the united states of Venezuela constituted under the provisions of a treaty ratified at Washington on june 14th, 1897. Compiled under the supervision of major S. C. N. Grant . . . in the intelligence division of the war office. Major-gen. sir John Ardagh . . . director of military intelligence. 3 p. l., [1] l., 51 (*i. e.* 46) maps. fol. London, printed for her majesty's stationery office by E. Stanford, 1898.    2756

NOTE.—For contents, see title 2779.

# CHILI

### BOUNDARY.

Esposicion que por parte de Chile i en respuesta a la esposicion arjentina se somete al tribunal que constituyó el gobierno de su majestad británica en su carácter de árbitro nombrada por el acuerdo de 17 de abril de 1896. 6 v. illus., plates (partly fold.) fold. maps and portfolio of maps. 8°. Paris [imprimerie Chaix] 1902.    2756a

NOTE.—On back of covers: Arbitrage de limites entre Chile i la República Arjentina.

Text and atlas printed also in english. London, 1901.

#### CONTENTS.

no. 1. J. de la Cruz Cano i Olmedilla. "Mapa geográfico de América Meridional," 1775. 4 sheets.
" 2. Del instituto jeografico arjentino. "Plano demonstrativo de la cordillera de los Andes i de la linea divisoria de aguas entre las latitudes 42° i 46° sud," Buenos Aires, 1895.

no. 3. Del museo de la plata. "Mapa preliminar y parcial de los territorios del Neuquen, rio Negro, Chubut y Santa Cruz," 1896 . . .
Mapas de demarcacion.
no. 1. Desde 25° 20′ á 28° 6′ lat. s.
" 2. " 27° 40′ " 30° 57′ " "
" 3. " 30° 38′ " 34° 3′ " "
" 4. " 34° " 37° 20′ " "
" 5. " 37° 20′ " 40° 20′ " "
" 6. " 40° 20′ " 43° " "
" 7. " 43° . " 46° " "
" 8. " 46° " 49° " "
" 9. " 49° " 52° " "

## GENERAL.

(Arranged chronologically)

### 1895

**Türke, J.**
Atlas de Chile, correjido segun los ultimos datos . . . 1 p. l., 20 col. maps. fol. Santiago, E. Cadot, 1895. 2757

### 1897

**Espinoza, E.**
Atlas de Chile arreglado para la jeografia descriptiva de la republica de Chile. 1 p. l., 39 maps. 4°. [Paris, Erhard hermanos, 1897] 2758

### 1904

**Boloña, N.**
Nuevo mapa de Chile. Construido segun los datos oficiales mas recientes por Nicanor Boloña. Revisado i correjido por el sr. Alejandro Bertrand . . . i el sr. Cárlos Sage . . . Publicado por Cárlos Tornero para la obra "Chile." cover-title, 6 col. maps. sm. fol. Santiago, a venta en la libreria "C. Tornero i ca." de Tornero i Torres, 1904. 2758a

## COLOMBIA.

### BOUNDARY.

**Peralta, M. M. de.**
Límites de Costa Rica y Colombia nuevos documentos para la historia de su jurisdicción territorial con notas, comentarios y un examen de la cartografia de Costa-Rica y Veragua. 778 pp. Atlas. cover-title, 26 maps in portfolio. fol. Madrid, 1890. 2759

NOTE.—"Examen de la cartografia de Costa Rica," pp. 584–637. Atlas accompanying this work entitled: Atlas histórico-geográfico de la republica de

**Peralta, M. M. de**—Continued.
Costa-Rica, Veragua y Costa de Mosquitos para servir al arbitraje de la cuestion de limites entre Costa-Rica y Colombia ordenado por d. Manuel M. de Peralta. A collection of maps for the most part reproductions dated 1597-1864.

CONTENTS.

A. Mapa de Costa-Rica segun sus límites legales durante la dominacion española (1540 á 1821) . . . Madrid, 1890.
B. Mapa de Costa-Rica, Istmo de Panamá, Veragua y Costa de Mosquitos . . . Madrid, 1890.
no. 1. Ivcatana regio et Fondvra. Cornelio Wytfliet . . . 1597.
" 2. Descripcion del avdiencia de Gvatimala. Antonio de Herrera. 1601.
" 3. Descripcion del avdiencia de Panama. A. de Herrera, 1601.
" 4. Veragua y parte de Costa-Rica Lorenzo del Salto. Ms. Remedios, 1620.
" 5. Insulæ Americanæ in oceano septentrionali, cum terris adiacentibus.— Islas Antillas y costas de Tierra Firme.—Anónimo. Amsterdam 1610(?)
" 6. Terra Firma et novum regnum Granatense et Popayan. Juan Jansson, 1640.
" 7 Pascaerte vande Carbische eylanden vande Barbados tot dende bocht van Mexico. Hendrick Doncker. 1642.
" 8. Audiencia de Guatimala, con la demarcacion de Costa-Rica y Veragua. Sanson d'Abbeville, 1657.
" 9. Las islas y Tierra-Firme de las Indias Occidentales del Mar del Norte. Jacob Colom. 1660-1669.
" 10. Indiarum occidentalium. Tractus littorales cum insulis Caribicis. Frederick de Witt. 1680.
" 11. Honduras, Costa-Rica, Veragua é Islas Antillas. Oexmelin, 1688.
" 12. Islas Antillas, Honduras, Nicaragua, Costa-Rica, Tierra-Firme etc. Juan van Keulen. 1695.
" 13. Las costas de la América—Honduras, Nicaragua, Costa-Rica etc. Gerard van Keulen-Jean Sikkena. 1698-1715.
" 14. Carte des isles de l'Amérique et de plusieurs pays de Terre Ferme . . . d'Anville . . . 1731.
" 15. A map of the british empire in America with the french and spanish settlements adjacent thereto, by Henry Popple.
" 16. Amérique Septentrionale. D'Anville. 1746.
" 17. Carte des provinces de Nicaragua et Costa Rica. Bellin 1754(?)
" 18. Mapa maritimo del golfo de México é islas de la América. Tomas Lopez y Juan de la Cruz (copistas de d'Anville no. 16) 1755.
" 19. Amérique Septentrionale et Méridionale. Robert de Vaugondy (copistas de d'Anville no. 16) 1785(?)
" 20. Nuevo mapa de la América Septentrional: Costa-Rica y Veragua (copistas d'Anville no. 16) Lóndres 1785.
" 21. Costa-Rica y Veragua. Thomas Jefferys. 1792.
" 22. Carta esférica del mar de las Antillas y de las costas de Tierra Firme. 1805-1809.
" 23. Colombia—from Humboldt and other recent authorities. 1822.
" 24. Carta corográfica del estado de Panama . . . Manuel Ponce de Leon y Manuel Maria Paz. 1864.

## GENERAL.

(Arranged chronologically)

### 1827

**Restrepo, J. M.**
Historia de la revolucion de la república de Colombia . . . Atlas.
7 pp., 13 maps. 8°. Paris, libreria americana, 1827.  2760

NOTE.—To accompany his work of the same title.

CONTENTS.

no. [A] Carta de la republica de Colombia.
" 1. " del departamento del Ismo . . .
" 2. " " " de la Magdalena . . .
" 3. " " " del Zulia . . .
" 4. " " " de Venezuela . . .
" 5. " " " del Orinoco ó de Maturin . . .
" 6. " " " del Cauca . . .
" 7. " " " de Cundinamarca . . .
" 8. " " " de Boyaca . . .
" 9. " " " de Apure . . .
" 10. " " " del Equador . . .
" 11. " " " de Guayaquil . . .
" 12. " " " del Asuay . . .

### 1889-1890

**Codazzi, G. B. A.**
Atlas geográfico é histórico de la república de Colombia (antiqua Nueva Grenada) el cual comprende las repúblicas de Venezuela y Ecuador con arreglo á los trabajos geográficos del general de ingenieros Agustin Codazzi ejecutados en Venezuela y Nueva Grenada. Construida la parte cartográfica por Manuel M. Paz . . . y redactado el texto explicativo por el doctor Felipe Perez . . .  4 p. l., 25 pp., 1 l., 21 maps on 20 sheets, 1 pl., 1 por. fol. Paris, A. Lahure, 1889-[1890]  2761

NOTE.—Map no. 21 is a plan of the city of Bogota, with border illustrations of public buildings: Plano de Bogotá, levantado por . . . Agustin Codazzi. 1852. Arreglado . . . por M. M. Paz. Paris, 1890.

### 1906-1908

**Vergara y Velasco, F. J.**
Atlas completo de geografia Colombiana. 90 planchas, texto explicativo é indice . . . 1-5 entrega. fol. Bogota, imprenta electrica, 1906-1908.  2762

NOTE.—All published to date.

# ECUADOR.

## GENERAL.

(Arranged chronologically)

**1907**

**López, F.**
Atlas geográfico del Ecuador, arreglado según la carta del dr. Teodoro Wolf.   1 p. l., 21 l. incl. 17 col. maps.   1 fold. map.   4°. [New York, american bank note co.] 1907.

2763

---

# FRENCH GUIANA.

## BOUNDARY.

**France.** *Treaties, etc., 1895–99.*
Mémoire contenant l'exposé des droits de la France dans la question des frontières de la Guyane française et du Brésil soumise à l'arbitrage du gouvernement de la confédération Suisse. Atlas. 3 p. l., 87 l., incl. 39 maps, 5 p. l. fol.   Paris, Berthaud frères [1899]

2764

NOTE.—To accompany work in 1 v. (4°) with same title.

Collection of reproductions of maps found in the Bibliothèque Nationale, Archives scientifiques du service hydrographique de la marine, dépôt géog. du ministère des affaires étrangères, of Paris, in the British Museum of London, and the royal library at Lisbon.

CONTENTS.

no. 1. Partie de l'Amérique tirée du seul exemplaire qui existe de la mappemonde que Sébastien Cabot a publiée en 1544.
" 2. Partie de l'Amérique du Sud extraite d'une carte marine manuscrite de l'Océan Occidental . . . "Diego Gutierrez . . . me fizo en Seuilla, ano de 1550."
" 3. Partie de l'Amérique du Sud tirée . . . d'un portulan en 9 feuilles . . . "Diego Homem cosmographus fecit hoc anno salutis 1558."
" 4. Partie de l'Amérique du Sud empruntée à la célèbre mappemonde de G. Mercator (1569)
" 5. Reproduction d'un globe anonyme de la fin du xvi$^e$ siècle qui se trouve au "Schweizerisches landes-museum de Zurich."
" 5bis. Partie de l'Amérique tirée du globe de Zürich reproduit au no. 5.
" 6. Reproduction de la carte . . . "Delineatio omnium orarum totius Australis partis Americæ &c. &c. Arnoldus Florentius à Langren, author & scalptor" (sic) 1578.
" 7. Partie de l'Amérique tirée de la mappemonde de R. Hakluyt . . . Cette mappemonde a été insérée dans l'ouvrage de R. Hakluyt "Principal navigations" 2$^e$ edition, 1598.
" 8. Partie de l'Amérique du Sud extraite d'une carte de l'Océan Occidental . . . où se trouve inscrite cette mention: "Domingo Sanchez a fes em Lisboa anno 1618."

no. 9. Partie de l'Amérique tirée de la mappemonde manuscrite . . . "Nouvelle description hydrographique de tout le monde. Carte faite en Dieppe, par Jean Guérard, l'an 1625."

" 10, 11. Reproduction en 2 feuilles . . . de la carte générale du Brésil, inscrite sous le no. 5 dans le portulan en 46 feuilles dont le titre set: "Livro emq se mostra a descripçao de toda a costa do Estado do Brasil e seus portos, barras e sondas delas (sic) Feito por Joao Teixeira Albernas moço da camara de sua mag$^{de}$ e seu cosmographo. Em Lixboa, anno de 1627."

" 12. Reproduction de la carte générale du Brésil (feuille no. 1 de l'atlas de Teixeira, 1640)

" 12bis. Reproduction de la carte des bouches de l'Amazone (feuille no. 32 de l'Atlas de Teixeira, 1640)

" 13. Partie extraite de la carte "Imperio di Guiana" qui est insérée, sous le n°. xiv, dans le livre vi "Dell' Arcano del mare" de Robert Dudley. 1647.

" 13bis. Réduction extraite de la " Carta particulare dell' Rio d'Amazona" qui est insérée, sous le no. xv dans le livre vi "Dell' Arcano del mare" de Robert Dudley. 1647.

" 14. Réduction de la carte de N. Sanson dont le titre est: "Partie de Terre Ferme où sont Gviane et Caribane . . . 1656."

" 15. "De Zeekuíten van Westindien" . . . "tirée de la primera parte del monte de la Turba Ardiente Alumbrando con la claridad de su fuego toda la India occidental, espeçando desde el rio Amazonas y Fenesciendo al norte de Tierra Nueva descrita por Arnoldo Roggeven. Amsterdam, por Pedro Goos, 1680."

" 16. Carte de bouches de l'Amazone. extraite du "Livro das praças de Portugal" de Joao Nunes Tinoco (1663)

" 17. Partie inférieure du cours de l'Amazone réduite d'après la . . . "Carte de la rivière des Amazones." Original de la main du père Fritz . . . levée (sic) par lui en 1689 et 1691.

" 18. Partie de la côte de la Guyane comprise entre la r. Cawo et lec abo Noord . . . reproduite d'après la feuille no. 124 de l'Atlas de J. van Keulen: "De groote nieuwe vermeerderde zee-atlas oste water werelt." Amsterdam, 1695.

" 18bis. Partie de la côte de la Guyane, comprise entre le Cabo Noord et l'embouchure de la r. de Para . . . d'après la feuille n° 126 de l'atlas de J. van Keulen.

" 19. Reproduction de la plus grande partie de la "Carte de la Terre ferme, du Pérou, du Brésil, et du pays des Amazones . . ." par Guillaume De l'Isle. 1703.

" 20. Carte du "Cours du Maragnon . . ." du père Samuel Fritz, telle qu'elle a été reproduite à Paris, dans le 12$^{me}$ recueil des "Lettres édifiantes et curieuses" . . . 1717.

" 21. Reproduction d'une partie de la "Carte d'Amérique" de Guillaume De l'Isle. 1722.

" 22. Réduction de la "carte de la Guïane françoise . . ." par d'Anville . . . 1729.

" 23. Reproduction de la "Carte du cours du Maragnon . . ." de m. de la Condamine, qui accompagne la "Relation abrégée d'un voyage fait dans l'intérieur de l'Amérique méridionale . . . Paris, veuve Pissot, 1745.

" 24. Réduction . . . d'un dessin manuscrit de d'Anville . . . 1745.

" 25. Titre de la carte . . . no. 25$^{bis}$.

**France**—Continued.

- no. 25bis. "Amérique méridionale publiée sous les auspices de monseigneur le duc d'Orleans . . . par . . . d'Anville. 1748."
- " 26. Réduction d'une carte manuscrite qui porte pour titre: "Mapa dos confins do Brazil com as terras da Coroa de Esp$^a$ na America Merid $^{n1}$ Feito no anno de 1749.
- " 26bis. Reproduction de l'explication placée au dos de la carte manuscrite qui porte le no. 26.
- " 27. Reproduction de la "Mapa dos confins do Brazil com as terras da Coroa de Esp$^a$ na America meridion! Feito no anno de 1751."
- " 28. Réduction de la carte qui porte ce titre: "Borrador topografico de la linea divisoria, que cita el articulo 12° del tratado preliminar y ajustadas distancias hasta su punto final. (Tirado do mss. pertencente ao archivo da secretaria d'estado dos negocios estrangeiros)
- " 29. Réduction de la "carte de l'Amérique du Sud . . ." 1753, par T. Jefferys.
- " 30. Titre et échelles de la carte dont une partie est reproduite au no. 30bis.
- " 30bis. Partie septentrionale de l'évêché du Para, tirée d'une grande carte [manuscrite] de cet évêché qui a été dressée en 1759.
- " 31. Titre de la carte . . . no. 31bis: A new and compleat map of all America, also of the West India & other islands depending thereon . . . by John Gibson [1763]
- " 31bis. Partie de l'Amérique tirée de la carte . . . dont le titre est donné au no. 31.
- " 32. Partie de la Guyane tirée de la "Caart van Guiana" qui accompagne . . . "Beschryving van Guiana . . . door m. Jan Jacob Hartsinck. Amsterdam, 1770."
- " 33. Réduction de la carte de E. Thompson (1783) qui est insérée dans le mémoire intitulé: "Question de frontière entre la Guyane Britannique et le Venezuela." Map is entitled: The coast of Guyana from the Oroonoko to the river of Amazons and the inland parts . . . from the observations of captain Edward Thompson . . . by L. S. de la Rochette. 1783.
- " 34. Réduction d'une " Carte de la Guiane française" . . . par Simon Mentelle, 1778 & 1788.
- " 35. Reproduction d'une partie de la 13$^e$ feuille d'un atlas dont le titre est: "Trabalhos hydrographicos ao Norte do Brazil dirigidos pelo . . . José da Costa Azevedo. Primeiros traços geraes da carta particular do rio Amazonas no curso brazileiro. Levantada pelo sr. Joao Soares Pinto. 1862-64."

---

# PARAGUAY.

### GENERAL.

(Arranged chronologically)

#### 1862

**Van der Maelen, P. M. G.**

Carte générale et vues de la république du Paraguay. cover-title, 6 maps, 1 fold. map, 14 pl. obl. 12°. Bruxelles, P. van der Maelen, 1862. 2765

CONTENTS.

no. [1] Arsenal de construction et port de l'Assomption.
" 2. Fort Olympo (Fleuve Paraguay)
" 3. Église cathédrale (Assomption)
" 4. Palais du gouvernement (Assomption)
" [5] Marché de la capitale (Assomption)
" 6. Église de l'Incarnation (Vue prise de la hauteur de l'Assomption)
" 7. Église cathédrale (Vue prise de la hauteur de l'Assomption)
" 8. Le fort Borbon actuellement Olympo . . .
" 9. Ville de Conception et son port.
" 10. Las Siete Puntas (Fleuve Paraguay)
" 11. Les Salines . . .
" 12. Embouchure du rio Negro . . .
" 13. Place du gouvernement (Assomption)
" 14. Tracé de la première section du chemin de fer de l'Assomption à Villa-Rica . . .
" [15] La ville de San Pedro et ses environs.
" 16. Cacique des Indiens Payaguas.
" 17. Palais du gouvernement (Vue prise de la hauteur de l'Assomption)
" 18. Pan de Azucar (Fleuve Paraguay)
" 19. Cerro de la Margarita (Rive droite de la rivière Apa)
" 20. Marché de l'Assomption (Vue prise des hauteurs)
" 21. Carte de la république du Paraguay . . . 1861 . . .

**1871**

**Jourdan, E. C.**

Atlas historico da guerra do Paraguay . . . 2 p. l., 13 maps on 16 sheets, 1 pl. fol. Rio de Janeiro, E. Rensburg, 1871. 2766

NOTE.—To accompany his "Guerra do Paraguay. 1871."

# PERU.

## BOUNDARY.

**Peru.** Juicio de límites entre el Perú y Bolivia. Prueba Peruana presentada al gobierno de la república Argentina por Victor M. Maurtua . . . 12 v. Atlas. 2 v. 4°. (v. 2. fol.) Barcelona, Henrich comp. 1906. 2767

NOTE.—Collation: v. 1, portfolio, 34 fold. maps; v. 2, 1 p. l., [4] pp., 58 maps. Reproductions from various sources.
Atlas to accompany a collection of documents for the most part previously unpublished.
Title of atlas varies: v. 1 . . . Cartas geográficas primera serie. Cartera de mapas. v. 2 . . . Cartas geográficas (segunda serie)
A few maps have accompanying text: v. 1, no. 25, text: "Plano general de las montañas orientales al reyno del Perú" . . . v. 1, no. 14, v. 2, nos. 18 and 57 have border text; a full page text, faces no. 35, v. 2: "Los fundamentos de este trabajo geografico se indican . . . Notas al mapa."
Most of the maps are colored.

**Peru**—Continued.

CONTENTS.

v. 1, no. 1. Pervvia id est Novi orbis pars meridionalis . . . Johan Bussemecher, 1598.
" " 2. Le Pérou et le cours de la rivière Amazone . . . N. Sanson d'Abbeville . . . 1656.
" " 3. L'Amérique Méridionale . . . G. de l'Isle . . . 1700.
" " 4. L'Amérique Méridionale ou la partie méridionale des Indes Occidentales . . . I. B. Nolin, 1704.
" " 5. Tabula Americæ specialis geographica regni Peru . . . Homañianos heredes, 1725.
" " 6. L'Amérique Méridionale . . . P. vander Aa [1700?]
" " 7. Totius Americæ Septentrionalis et Méridionalis . . . Johannes Baptista Homann [1732?]
" " 8. Le pays de Pérou et Chili . . . Math. Seutter [1734?]
" " 9. . . . South America . . . Herman Moll [1709]
" " 10. . . . Carte du Pérou pour servir à l'histoire des incas . . . Philippe Buache . . . 1739.
" " 11. Amérique Méridionale . . . le sr Robert de Vaugondy. 1750.
" " 12. Mapa anexo á un oficio dirigido por d. Pedro de Cevallos al ministro de estado . . . 1759.
" " 13. L'Amérique Méridionale . . . le sr Janvier . . . 1762.
" " 14. Nuevo mapa del Obispado de Santa Cruz de la Sierra . . . [1766] Antonio Monesterio de Asuá . . .
" " 15. Mapa que comprehende las missiones de Moxos y Chiquitos . . . Miguel Blanco y Crespo, 1770.
" " 16. Del mapa de Sud-América de mr. d'Anville. 1775.
" " 17. Mapa qᵉ comprehende las missiones de la compañía de Tho [Jesús] en el territorio de Moxos y Chiquitos . . . Del British Museum . . . Ms.
" " 18. Mapa del obispado de La Paz, dividido en todas sus provincias . . . Del British Museum . . . Ms.
" " 19. Plano del obispado del Cuzco . . . José Ramos de Figueroa . . . 1781.
" " 20. Carte du Pérou où se trouvent les audiences de Quito, Lima et la Plata . . . m. Bonne [1788?]
" " 21. Mapa de las montañas y fronteras del rº del Perú . . . Fr. Manuel Sobreviela, 1788.
" " 22. Partidos de la nueva intendencia de Stª Cruz de la Sierra . . . Tadeo Haënke. B. M. ms.
" " 23. Provincia Moxos . . . Xav. Eder, 1791.
" " 24. Descripcion geografyca de la provincya de Moxos. 1792. Lázaro de Ribera.
" " 25. Plano general de las montaños orientales al reyno del Perú . . . Balcato, Joaquin Soler. 1795?
" " 26. Plano corográfico de la provincia de Puno. 1802. (De la Mapoteca de la Sociedad geográfica de Lima)
" " 27. Charte von Süd America . . . Conrad Mannert, 1803.
" " 28. Plana de la intendª de Puno . . . P. Fr. Benito Valencia. 1809.
" " 29. Carte générale du Pérou . . . A. Brué . . . 1843.

v. 1, no. 30. Del mapa geográfico y corográfico de la república de Bolivia . . .
Leigue Moreno (1894)
" " 31. Del mapa elemental de Bolivia . . . Eduardo Ydiáquez (1894)
" " 32. Mapa de las exploraciones y estudios verificados . . . en el norte de Bolivia. 1896.
" " 33. Del mapa de la república de Bolivia, mandado organizar y publicar por el presidente d. José Manuel Pando (La Paz, 1901)
" " 34. Del mapa general de Bolivia . . . Luis García Mesa (1904)
v. 2, no. 1. Americae sive qvartae orbis partis nova et exactissima descriptio. Diego Gutiero. 1562.
" " 2. Venetiis. Ioan. Francisci Camotii . . . 1562.
" " 3. Pervviae avriferæ regionis typvs. Didaco Mendezio auctore. Theatrum orbis terrarum, de Abraham Ortelius [1584]
" " 4. Nova totius terrarum orbis geographica ac hydrographica tabula . . . N. I. Piscator [1639]
" " 5. Jan van Doet. 1585.
" " 6. Pervani regni descriptio . . . Cornely Wytfliet. 1597.
" " 7. Delineatio omnium orarum totius Australis partis Americæ . . . Iohn Hvighen van Linschoten. 1598.
" " 8. Nova et exacta delineatio Americæ . . . Leiunum Hülsium. 1599.
" " 9. Pervani regni descriptio . . . Natalius Metellus, 1602.
" " 10. Americæ nova descriptio. Petrus Kærius . . . 1614.
" " 11. Description corographic de las provincias del Piru [!] Chile . . . Lucas de Quirós, 1618.
" " 12. Globus cœlestis . . . Tychonis Brahe. 1630. (De la biblioteca de Grenoble)
" " 13. Novissima et accuratissima totius Americae descriptio. F. de Wit. [1660 ?]
" " 14. Anexo á una carta del conde de Castellar . . . 1678.
" " 15. South America . . . William Berry. 1680.
" " 16. De la carta "Recentissima novi orbis sive Americae Septentrionalis et Meridionalis tabula" . . . Caroli Allard, 1684.
" " 17. A new map of South America . . . Dedicated to William, duke of Gloucester [1722]
" " 18. Mission de Mojos de la compañia de Jesús de el Perú, 1713?
" " 19. Le Pérou dans l'Amérique Méridionale . . . N. de Fer. 1719.
" " 20. Americæ tam Septentrionalis quam Meridionalis . . . A. F. Zürneri [1735 ?]
" " 21. De la "Carta nouvelle de la mer du Sud . . . And. et Henry de Leth [1720 ?]
" " 22. Del mapa "America laid down from the observations of the royal academy of sciences and compared with the maps of Sanson, Nolin, de Fer, de l'Isle. London" . . . (Popples y Moll) [1733?]
" " 23. De la carte très curieuse de la mer du Sud . . . Zaccharie Chatelain, 1732 . . .
" " 24. Kaart van Zuid America . . . Thom.ͤ Kitchin . . . [1775]
" " 25. Del "Mapa geográfico de América Meridional dispuesto y grabado por d. Juan de la Cruz Cano y Olmedilla . . . 1775."
" " 26. Tableau géneral de l'Amérique . . . m. Brion . . . 1775.
" " 27. Descripcion geografica del rio Mamore ò Madera . . . Carlos Hirschko . . . 1782.

**Peru**—Continued.

v. 2, no. 28. Mapa en que se manifiestan los sitios en que se hallan situados el colegio de propaganda Fide de Santa Rosa de Ocopa . . . Fr. Pedro Gonzáles Agüeros. 1784.
" " 29. Demostración de las provincias interiores del Perú que componen parte del virreinato de Buenos Aires . . . Del British museum. Ms.
" " 30. El Obispado de La Paz . . .
" " 31. Demostración geográfica de las provincias que abraza cada intendencia de las establecidas en la parte del Perú . . . Joachin Alos.
" " 32. Plano de la intendencia de Lima . . . Andres Baleato. 1792.
" " 33. Plano de la intendencia del Cuzco . . . Andres Baleato. 1792.
" " 34. Mapa geografico de America Meridional . . . Francisco Fernandez.
" " 35. Carta corografica del Virreynato de las provincias del rio de la Plata . . .
" " 36. South America . . . E. Baker, 1806.
" " 37. Del mapa "Outlines of the physical and political divisions of South America . . . A. Arrowsmith . . . 1810."
" " 38. De la "Carte de l'Amérique Méridionale dressée d'après les cartes de La Cruz, Jefferys . . . P. Lapie . . . 1814."
" " 39. Carte encyprotype de l'Amérique Méridionale . . . H. Brué, 1816.
" " 40. Misiones del Ucayali, y verdadero curso de este rio . . . p. Pablo Alonso Carvallo. 1819.
" " 41. Map of Spanish America . . . W. Ebden. 1820.
" " 42. Amérique Méridionale. De la Biblioteca del Congreso . . . 182? . . .
" " 43. South America. Del atlas de H. C. Carey & J. Lea . . . 1823.
" " 44. De la carta "Colombia prima or South America . . . Louis Stanislas d'Arcy Delarochette." 1824.
" " 45. New map of America . . . Mackenzie, Langara, Vancouvert, Ellicott, Falconer . . . 1824.
" " 46. Carte générale de l'Amérique Méridionale . . . Lapie. 1829.
" " 47. Sud Amerika . . . Schlieben. 1830.
" " 48. Plan del curso de los ríos Huallaga y Ucayali y de la Pampa del Sacramento. P. Fr. Manuel Sobreviela (1790) y Amadeo Chaumette-des-Fosses. 1836.
" " 49. Perú and Bolivia . . . 1834. J. Arrowsmith.
" " 50. Carte générale d'une partie de l'Amérique du Sud . . . L. Vivien. 1839.
" " 51. Karte von Amerika . . . H. Mahlmann. 1837.
" " 52. Carte de l'Amérique Méridionale . . . Alcide d'Orbigny. 1838.
" " 53. Peru and Bolivia . . . Greenleaf. 1842.
" " 54. America . . . J. Arrowsmith. 1844.
" " 55. Amérique du Sud . . . A. H. Dufour. 1849.
" " 56. Milliet de Saint Adolphe. 1863.
" " 57. República del Perú. Cuenca del Madre de Dios. Croquis Catastral.
" " 58. Mapa de la región controvertida entre el Perú y Bolivia . . . 1906.

## GENERAL.

(Arranged chronologically)

**1797**

**Gonzales, A.**

Atlas maritimo del reyno de el Perù, Chile, costa Patagonica oriental, y occidental costruìdas sobre las melores, y mas modernas noticias de este continente. Para uso del capitan, y piloto de la carrera de Indias d.n Alexandro Gonzales. 1 p. l., 16 col. maps. obl. fol. Montevideo, 1797. 2768

NOTE.—Manuscript atlas. Maps colored and elaborately executed. Some have border index.

Maps dated 1787-1796.

CONTENTS.

no. [ 1] Carta reducida que comrehende desde el cavo de S.ta Maria en el rio de la Plata hasta la bahia de San Julian en la costa Patagonica . . . 1796.
" [ 2] Carta reducida del extremo de la America Meridíonal, ó costas Patagonícas . . .
" [ 3] Carta reducida que contiene la costa de Chile desde los 32° de latitud meridíonal para el S. y parte de la occidental Patagonica . . .
" [ 4] Carta reducida, que contiene las costas del Peru, y Chile comprehendid? entre 12 y 35 grados de lat. meridional . . .
" 5 Plano del fondeadero de Arica.—Diseño de la costa de varlovento del puerto de Valparaiso.
" [ 6] Carta reducida que contiene la navegacion de Lima à Guayaquil . . .
" [ 7] Plana del p.to del callao de Lima . . .
" [ 8] Plano del puerto de Valparaiso . . .
" [ 9] Plano de la bahia de la Concepsion de Chile . . .
" [10] Plano del rio de Valdivia, y surgidero del corral . . .
" [11] Plano del canal del n. de la isla de Chiloè y puerto de S.n Carlos . . .
" [12] Carta reducida que comprehende desde la bahia de Iodos los Santos, hasta Caro Trio en la costa del Brasil . . .
" [13] Plano del rio Geneiro . . .
" [14] Plano del puerto de Maldonado . . . 1796.
" [15] Carta reducida que comprehende desde Caro Trio en la costa del Brasil hasta el Caro de Santa Maria en la embocadura del rio de la Plata . . .
" [16] Plano de la costa del n. del rio de la Plata desde Castillos hasta el rio Pabon . . .

**1865**

**Paz Soldan, M. F.**

Atlas geográfico del Perú . . . 1 p. l., 81 pp., 45 maps, 27 pl. fol. Paris, Fermin Didot hermanos, hijos & ca. 1865. 2769

NOTE:—"Bibliografia," pp. 76-81.

CONTENTS.

no. 1. Mapa general del Perú.
" 2. Departamento de Amazónas.
" 3. Plano que manifiesta los reconocimientos de caminos hechos en el departamento dé Amazónas, por el ingeniero del estado D. A. Montferrier.

**Paz Soldan, M. F.**—Continued.
  no. 4. Plano de la ciudad de Chachapóyas.
  " 5. Departamento de Piura.
  " 6. Plano de la ciudad de Piura.—Plano de la ciudad de Huaraz.
  " 7. Departamento de Cajamarca.
  " 8. Plano de la ciudad de Cajamarca.
  " 9. Santa Catalina iglesia matriz de Cajamarca.—Baños termales de Cajamarca.
  " 10. Mineral de Hualgayoc.
  " 11. Departamento de La-Libertad.
  " 12. Plano de la ciudad de Trujillo.
  " 13. Plano de la ciudad de Lambayeque.
  " 14. Puerto de Huanchaco.
  " 15. Departamento de Ancachs.
  " 16. Vista de la plaza mayor de Huánuco.—Vista de la plaza mayor de Huari.
  " 17. Departamento de Junin.
  " 17bis. Mapa de la exploracion de cuatro vias entre Lima, Jauja y Pasco.
  " 18. Plano de la ciudad del Cerro de Pasco.
  " 18bis. Plano de la ciudad de Tarma.
  " 19. Departamento de Lima.
  " 20. Plano de la ciudad de Lima.
  " 21. Plano de la ciudad de Chorríllos.
  " 22. Vista general de Lima.
  " 23. Vista de la plaza mayor.
  " 24. Plano de la Penitenciaria.
  " 24bis. Vista de la Penitenciaria de Lima.—Primer claustro del convento de San Francisco.
  " 25. La Catedral.—Iglesia de San Pedro.
  " 26. Iglesia de San Francisco.—Iglesia de San Pedro.
  " 27. Calle de Mercaderes.—Alameda de los Descaloz.
  " 28. Vista de la torre de Santo Domingo.
  " 29. Departamento de Huancavelica.
  " 30. Departamento de Ayacucho.
  " 31. Plano de la ciudad de Ayacucho.
  " 32. Departamento del Cuzco.
  " 33. Plano de la ciudad del Cuzco.
  " 34. Plano de Sacsahuaman.—Plano del Cuzco segun un grabado antiguo.
  " 35. Un Indio.
  " 35bis. Un grupo de Indios.
  " 35ter. Una India y su hija.
  " 36. Departamento de Puno.
  " 37. Plano de la ciudad de Puno.
  " 38. Vista general de Puno.
  " 39. Departamento de Arequipa.
  " 40. Cróquis del trazo probable del ferro-carril entre Arequipa y la costa.
  " 41. Plano de la ciudad de Arequipa.
  " 42. Vista panorámica de la ciudad de Arequipa.
  " 43. Catedral de la ciudad de Arequipa.
  " 44. Vista de Arequipa tomada de Santo Domingo.
  " 45. Tambo de la Joya (en la pampa de Islay)—Disierto de Isláy.
  " 46. Vista de Islay.
  " 47. Departamento de Moquegua.
  " 48. Plano de la ciudad de Tacna.

no. 49. Plano de la ciudad de Iquique.
" 50. Panorama de la ciudad de Arica.
" 51. Panorama de la ciudad de Moquegua.
" 52. Vista de Iquique.
" 53. Provincia litoral de Loreto.
" 54. "  "  "
" 55. Plano de la ciudad de Moyobamba.
" 56. Plano de la ciudad de Tarapoto.
" 57. Provincia litoral de Ica.
" 58. Plano de la ciudad de Ica.
" 59. Plano de Islay.—Plano de Pisco.
" 60. Plano de las islas de Chincha.—Vista de las islas de Chincha.
" 61. Pla o de la ciudad del Callao.
" 62. Mapa mineralógico del Perú.
" 63. Cuadro general de alturas comparativas del Perú.
" 64. Línea que representa los temblores sentidos en Arequipa desde 1811 hasta 1845.—Corte vertical del camino del Pacífico al Huallaga.—Corte vertical del camino de Arica al Cuzco.—Plano del pongo de Manseriche.
" 65. Lecho del rio Amazónas segun los sondeos de Lister Maw.—Corte vertical del camino de Lima al Cerro de Pasco.
" 66. Fondeaderos de algunos puertos del Perú.
" 67–68. Corte geológico de la parte Sur del Perú que comprende los departamentos de Puna, Arequipa, Ica y Lima.

### 1867
**Jouanny, L. A.**

Atlas del Perú. Editor, P. V. Jouanny. Comisionados, E. Niemeyer & Inghiramt. 4 p. l., xvi pp., 2 l., 13 maps. sm.fol. Lima, 1867–[1871]  2770

NOTE.—Gravado en el instituto geografico de J. Perthes en Gotha.
"Prologo" dated deciembre de 1871.

### 1902
**Peru.** *Estado mayor.*

Estado mayor general del ejército. Viaje de estado mayor. 18 de marzo–25 de junio 1902. Anexo a la Memoria del coronel P. Clément . . . con la colaboracion del teniente coronel L. Bailly-Maitre . . . Atlas de los trabajos topográficos del $2^d$ grupo de la comision . . . 1 p. l., 14 maps. fol. [Chorrillos, 1902]  2771

NOTE.—Table of contents on title-page. To accompany text, entitled: Memoria. fol. Chorrillos, 1902.
At bottom of title-page, the following, "Maestro litógrafo de la Escuela militar de Chorrillos: Juvenal Garcia Rossell. Maestro de la imprenta, Escuela militar de Chorrillos: Federico Talledo y Robles."
"Extracto de la memoria (pagina 352)" on verso of title-page.

### 1903
**Cisneros, C. B.**

Atlas del Perú, político, minero, agrícola, industrial y comercial (con las ultimas demarcaciones territoriales) y texto descriptivo de cada departamento. Ilustrado con 123 vistas. 2 p. l., 57 pp., 20 maps. fol. Lima, libreria é imprenta Gil [1903]  2772

# URUGUAY.

## GENERAL.

(Arranged chronologically)

### 1891

**Sureda, J.**
Atlas geográfico de la republica oriental del Uruguay. Este atlas puede servir de complemento á los textos de geografía usados en los liceos, seminarios, institutos ... cover-title, 20 col. maps. obl. 4°. Montevideo [imp.ª y litog.ª oriental] 1891. 2773

NOTE.—Excepting the first, all maps have the following, "Es propiedad de d. Eugenio Ruis Zorilla."

CONTENTS.

- no. 1. Mapa de la república oriental del Uruguay.
- " 2. Plano del departamento de Artigas.
- " 3. " " " " Canelones.
- " 4. " " " " Cerro Largo.
- " 5. " " " " Calonia.
- " 6. " " " " Durazno.
- " 7. " " " " Flores.
- " 8. " " " " Florida.
- " 9. " " " " Maldonado.
- " 10. " " " " Minas.
- " 11. " " " " Montevideo.
- " 12. " " " " Paysandú.
- " 13. " " " " Rio Negro.
- " 14. " " " " Rivera.
- " 15. " " " " Rocha.
- " 16. " " " " San José.
- " 17. " " " del Salto.
- " 18. " " " de Soriano.
- " 19. " " " " Tacuarembó.
- " 20. " " " " Treinta y tres.

### 1896

**Bollo, L. C.**
Atlas geográfico y descripción geográfica y estadística de la república oriental del Uruguay ... noticia histórica, por Santiago Bollo ... 2 p. l., 96 pp. incl. 6 fold. maps, tab. 4°. Montevideo, A. Barreiro y Ramos, 1896. 2774

NOTE.—"Autores consultados," p. [iv]

---

# VENEZUELA.

## GENERAL.

(Arranged chronologically)

### 1840

**Codazzi, G. B. A.**
Atlas físico y político de la república de Venezuela dedicado por su autor, el coronel de ingenieros Agustin Codazzi al congreso cons-

tituyente de 1830.   1 p. l., 8 pp., 18 col. maps, 1 pl.   fol.   Paris, Thierry frères, Caracas, 1840.   2775

NOTE.—Engraved title.

CONTENTS.

no. 1. Mapa-mundi histórico.
" 2. América histórica, física y política actual. 1840.
" 3. Mapa de las costas de Tierra-Firme, desde el Orinoco hasta Yucatan, de las islas Antillas y la mayor parte de las Lucayas con las derrotas que siguió dn. Cristobal Colon.
" 4. Mapa político de Venezuela antes de la revolución de 1810.—Mapa político de la república de Venezuela en 1840.
" 5. Mapa físico de Venezuela dividida en hoyas hidrográficas.—Mapa físico de Venezuela dividido en tres zonas.
" 6. Mapa de Venezuela para servir á la historia de las campañas de la guerra de independencia en los años de 1812, 1813, y 1814.—Mapa de Venezuela para servir á la historia de las campañas de la guerra de independencia en los años 1816, 1817 y 1818. Mapa de Venezuela y parte de la Nueva-Granada para servir á la historia de las campañas de la guerra de independencia en los años 1818 y parte de 1819.
" 7. Mapa de Venezuela, Nueva Granada y Quito, para servir á la historia de las campañas de la guerra de independencia en los años 1819 y 1820.
" 8. Mapa de los tres departamentos Venezuela, Cundinamarca y Ecuador que formaron la república de Colombia para servir á la historia de las campañas de la guerra de independencia en los años de 1821, 1822 y 1823.
" 9. Mapa que contiene una parte de las repúblicas del Ecuador, Perú y Bolivia para servir á la historia de las compañas del ejército colombiano en el alto y bajo Perú sacado de otro publicado en 1826 y corregido según las observaciones é itinerarios de los oficiales facultativos que acompañaron los ejércitos en sus diferentes operaciones.
" 10. Carta de la república de Colombia dividida por departamentes.
" 11. Provincia de Caracas.
" 12. Islas y provincia de Margarita.—Provincia de Barcelona.—Provincia de Cumana.—Canton de Piacoa de la provincia de Guayana.
" 13. Provincia de Maracaibo.—Provincia de Coro.—Provincia de.Mérida.
" 14. Provincia de Carabobo.—Provincia de Barquisimeto.—Provincia de Trujillo.—Provincia de Barinas.
" 15. Provincia de Apure.—Carta del canton de Cayara de la provincia de Guayana.
" 16. Carta del canton de Upata de la provincia de Guayana.
" 17. Carta del canton de Angostura de la provincia de Guayana.
" 18. Carta del canton de rio Negro de la provincia de Guayana.

**BOUNDARY.**

**Maps** of the Orinoco-Essequibo region. South America. Compiled for the commission appointed by the president of the United States to "investigate and report upon the true divisional line between the republic of Venezuela and British Guiana."   3 p. l., 76 maps. fol.   Washington, 1897.   2776

NOTE.—Vol. 4 of the Report.

**Maps**—Continued.

CONTENTS.

no. 1. Boundaries claimed or proposed.
" 2. Forests and savannas.
" 3. Drainage basins.
" 4. Geology.
" 5. European occupation in 1597.
" 6. " " " 1626.
" 7. " " " 1648.
" 8. " " " 1674.
" 9. " " " 1703.
" 10. " " " 1724.
" 11. " " " 1756.
" 12. " " " 1773.
" 13. " " " 1796.
" 14. " " " 1803 [1814]
" 15. General view of european occupation, 1597-1803 [1814]
" 16. Mercator. Map of the world, 1538.
" 17. Orontius Finæus. Map of the world, 1566.
" 18. Martyr. Map of America, 1534.
" 19. Martyr. Map of the New World, 1587.
" 20. Ortelius. Map of America, 1587.
" 21. Raleigh. Chart of Guiana [1595?]
" 22. Speed. Map of America, 1626.
" 23. De Bry. Map of Guiana, 1599.
" 24. De Laet. Map of Guiana, 1630.
" 25. Blaeuw. Map of Guiana, 1635.
" 26. Blaeuw. Map of Guiana, 1667.
" 27. Blaeuw. Map of Guiana, 1640.
" 28. Blaeuw. Map of Guiana. No date.
" 29. Sanson. Part of his map of South America, 1650.
" 30. Sanson. Map of Guiana and Caribana, 1656.
" 31. Robert de Vaugondy. Part of his South America 1750.
" 32. Delamarche. Part of his map of South America [1767?]
" 33. Popple. Map of Surinam, 1733.
" 34. Popple. Map of the british empire in America, 1733.
" 35. Popple. Part of above, enlarged, 1733.
" 36. Delisle. Part of his map of South America, 1700.
" 37. Delisle. Part of northern portion of South America, 1703.
" 38. Delisle. Part of his map of America, 1722.
" 39. D'Anville. Map of South America, 1748.
" 40. D'Anville. Part of above, enlarged, 1748.
" 41. Jefferys. Part of his chart of the Guiana coast, 1775.
" 42. Jefferys. Part of his chart of the Guiana coast, 1781.
" 43. Thompson. Part of his chart of the Guiana coast, 1783.
" 44. Jefferys. Part of northern coast of South America, 1792
" 45. Jefferys. Part of his chart of the Guiana coast, 1795.
" 46. Bouchenroeder. Map of a part of Guiana, 1798.
" 47. Arrowsmith. Map of part of Colombia, 1832.
" 48. Arrowsmith. Part of his map of South America, 1840.
" 49. Schomburgk. Part of the great colonial map, 1875.
" 50. Cruz Cano y Olmedilla. Part of his South America, 1775.
" 51. Bonne. Map of South America, 1781.

no. 52. Bellin. Map of Guiana, 1763.
" 53. Güssefeldt. Part of his map of America, 1796.
" 54. Hartsinck. Map of Guiana, 1770.
" 55. Mannert. Part of his map of South America, 1803.
" 56. Gumila. Map of the jesuit missions of New Granada, 1741.
" 57. Van Petten? Cayenne [1598?]
" 58. Van Petten. The Gulf of Paria, 1598.
" 59. Maas. Essequibo, 1706.
" 60. Storm van's Gravesande. Essequibo, 1748.
" 61. Storm van's Gravesande. Orinoco-Essequibo region, 1750.
" 62. D'Anville inset in Bercheyck. Guiana [1761?]
" 63. Heneman. The mouth of the Cuyuni, 1772.
" 64. Heneman. Essequibo and Demerara, 1775.
" 65. Heneman. Boundary-line of Spanish and Dutch Guiana [1776?]
" 66. Siraut-Destouches. Essequibo 1779.
" 67. Siraut-Destouches? Essequibo [1780?]
" 68. Chollet. Coast region of the Essequibo colony, 1791 or earlier.
" 69. Chollet. The Pomeroon coast region, 1794.
" 70. Bouchenroeder. Essequibo and Demerara, 1795.
" 71. Surville. Nueva Andalucia, 1778.
" 72. Anonymous. Capuchin missions of Guayana [1735?]
" 73. Fr. Carlos De Barcelona. Capuchin missions of Guayana, 1771.
" 74. Fr. Carlos De Barcelona. Capuchin missions of Guayana, 1779.
" 75. Anonymous. Capuchin missions of Guayana [1789?]
" 76. Early spanish map of Guiana [15—] [This map, evidently made not long after the middle of the sixteenth century, is the earliest known special map of this region]

**Case, The,** of the United States of Venezuela before the tribunal of arbitration to convene at Paris, under the provisions of the treaty between the united states of Venezuela and her britannic majesty signed at Washington, feb. 2, 1897. v. 4. Appendix atlas. 2 p. l., 91 maps. fol. Baltimore, A. Hoen & co. 1898.  2777

NOTE.—Atlas contains 78 maps not numbered consecutively; the numbers 2, 3, 5–15, being omitted. This omission was made in order that those maps which appear in both the U. S. commission atlas and in this atlas might bear same numbers. Thirteen maps in the U. S. commission atlas (numbers 2, 3, 5–15) do not appear in this atlas. Fifteen other maps, here numbered 77 to 91, inclusive, appear here, but not in the U. S. commission atlas.

CONTENTS.

no. 1. Boundaries claimed or proposed, 1897; from U. S. commission atlas.
" 4. Geological map, 1897; from U. S. commission atlas.
" 16. Mercator. Map of the world, 1538; from U. S. commission atlas.
" 17. Orontius Finaeus. Map of the world, 1566; from U. S. commission atlas.
" 18. Martyr. Map of America, 1534; from U. S. commission atlas.
" 19. Martyr. Map of the New World, 1587; from U. S. commission atlas.
" 20. Ortelius. Map of America, 1587; from U. S. commission atlas.
" 21. Raleigh. Chart of Guiana [1595?] from U. S. commission atlas.
" 22. Speed. Map of America, 1626; from U. S. commission atlas.
" 23. De Bry. Map of Guiana, 1599; from U. S. commission atlas.
" 24. De Laet. Map of Guiana, 1630; from U. S. commission atlas.

**Case, The**—Continued

no. 25. Blaeuw. Map of Guiana, 1635; from U. S. commission atlas.
" 26. Blaeuw. Map of Guiana, 1667; from U. S. commission atlas.
" 27. Blaeuw. Map of Guiana, 1640; from U. S. commission atlas.
" 28. Blaeuw. Map of Guiana, no date; from U. S. commission atlas.
" 29. Sanson. Part of his map of South America, 1650; from U. S. commission atlas.
" 30. Sanson. Map of Guiana and Caribana, 1656; from U. S. commission atlas.
" 31. Robert de Vaugondy. Part of his South America, 1750; from U. S. commission atlas.
" 32. Delamarche. Part of his map of South America [1767?] from U. S. commission atlas.
" 33. Popple. Map of Surinam, 1733; from U. S. commission atlas.
" 34. Popple. Map of the British Empire in America, 1733; from U. S. commission atlas.
" 35. Popple. Part of the above, enlarged, 1733; from U. S. commission atlas.
" 36. Delisle. Part of his map of South America, 1700; from U. S. commission atlas.
" 37. Delisle. Part of northern portion of South America, 1703; U. S. commission atlas.
" 38. Delisle. Part of his map of America, 1722; from U. S. commission atlas.
" 39. D'Anville. Map of South America, 1748; from U. S. commission atlas.
" 40. D'Anville. Part of above, enlarged, 1748; from U. S. commission atlas.
" 41. Jefferys. Part of his chart of the Guiana coast, 1775; from U. S. commission Atlas.
" 42. Jefferys. Part of his chart of the Guiana coast, 1781; from U. S. commission atlas.
" 43. Thompson. Part of his chart of the Guiana coast, 1783; from U. S. commission atlas.
" 44. Jefferys. Part of northern coast of South America, 1792; from U. S. commission atlas.
" 45. Jefferys. Part of his chart of the Guiana coast, 1795; from U. S. commission atlas.
" 46. Bouchenroeder. Map of a part of Guiana, 1798; from U. S. commission atlas.
" 47. Arrowsmith. Map of a part of Colombia, 1832; from U. S. commission atlas.
" 48. Arrowsmith. Part of his map of South America, 1840; from U. S. commission atlas.
" 49. Schomburgk. Part of the great colonial map, 1875; from U. S. commission atlas.
" 50. Cruz Cano y Olmedilla. Part of his South America, 1775; from U. S. commission atlas.
" 51. Bonne. Map of South America, 1781; from U. S. commission atlas.
" 52. Bellin. Map of Guiana, 1763; from U. S. commission atlas.
" 53. Güssefeldt. Part of his map of America, 1796; from U. S. commission atlas.

no. 54. Hartsinck. Map of Guiana, 1770; from U. S. commission atlas.
" 55. Mannert. Part of his map of South America, 1803; from U. S. commission atlas.
" 56. Gumilla. Map of the jesuit missions of New Granada, 1741; from U. S. commission atlas.
" 57. Van Petten. Cayenne [1598?] from U. S. commission atlas.
" 58. Van Petten. The gulf of Paria, 1598; from U. S. commission atlas.
" 59. Maas. Essequibo, 1706; from U. S. commission atlas.
" 60. Storm van, s Gravesande. Essequibo, 1748; from U. S. commission atlas.
" 61. Storm van, s Gravesande. Orinoco-Essequibo Region, 1750; from U. S. commission atlas.
" 62. D'Anville inset in Bercheyck. Guiana [1761?]
" 63. Heneman. The mouth of the Cuyuni, 1772; from U. S. commission atlas.
" 64. Heneman. Essequibo and Demerara, 1775; from U. S. commission atlas.
" 65. Heneman. Boundary-line of Spanish and Dutch Guiana [1776?]
" 66. Siraut-Destouches. Essequibo, 1779; from U. S. commission atlas.
" 67. Siraut-Destouches. Essequibo [1780?] from U. S. commission atlas.
" 68. Chollet. Coast region of the Essequibo colony, 1791 or earlier; from U. S. commission atlas.
" 69. Chollett. The Pomeroon coast region, 1794; from U. S. commission atlas.
" 70. Bouchenroeder. Essequibo and Demerara, 1796; from U. S. commission atlas.
" 71. Surville. Nueva Andalucia, 1778; from U. S. commission atlas.
" 72. Anonymous. Capuchin mission of Guayana [1735?]; from U.S. commission atlas.
" 73. Fr. Carlos de Barcelona. Capuchin missions of Guayana, 1771; from U. S. commission atlas.
" 74. Fr. Carlos de Barcelona. Capuchin mission of Guayana [1779?]; from U. S. commission atlas.
" 75. Anonymous. Capuchin missions of Guayana [1789?]; from U. S. commission atlas.
" 76. Anonymous. Early spanish map of Guiana [15—?] from U. S. commission atlas.
" 77. Manuel Antonio Flores. Spanish Guayana, 1777; from copy of an unpublished manuscript in archives at Seville.
" 78. B. D'Urban. Settlements in British Guiana, 1828; from Parliamentary papers, 1828. v. 23.
" 79. J. Hadfield. British Guiana, 1838; from Parliamentary papers, 1839. v. 35.
" 80. A. Codazzi. Canton of Upata in Guayana, 1840; from his atlas of Venezuela, Caracas, 1840.
" 81. West India Islands, etc. showing lighthouses, 1850; from Parliamentary papers, 1850. v. 53 (sometimes bound up in v. 55)
" 82. R. H. Schomburgk. British Guiana, 1840; from Parliamentary papers [may 11,] 1840. v. 34.
" 83. R. H. Schomburgk. British Guiana, 1840; from his description of British Guiana, London, 1840.

**Case, The**—Continued.
>   no. 84. R. H. Schomburgk. Karte von Guyana, 1841; from his Reisen in Guiana und am Orinoco, Leipzig, 1841.
>   " 85. R. H. Schomburgk. Part of Guiana, 1841; from Journal Royal geographical society London, 1842. v. 12.
>   " 86. A. British Guiana from Colonial list, march, 1886.
>   B. British Guiana from Colonial list, december, 1886.
>   C. Mündungsland des Essequibo, Demerara und Berbice, 1847; from Schomburgk (Richard) Reisen in British Guiana, Leipzig, 1847. v. 1.
>   " 87. R. H. Schomburgk. Karte von British Guyana, 1847; from same.
>   " 88. R. H. Schomburgk. Part of British Guiana, 1875; from great colonial map, by E. Stanford, London. First edition [Left page]
>   Same, second edition. No. 49 repeated [Right page]
>   " 89. R. H. Schomburgk. British Guiana, 1867; from exposition universelle de Paris, 1867—Catalogue des produits exposés par la Guyane Anglaise; London, 1867.
>   " 90. C. Barrington Brown. British Guiana, 1876; from his Canoe and camp life in British Guiana, London, 1876.
>   " 91. H. I. Perkins. British Guiana, 1895; from his Notes on British Guiana and its gold industry, London, 1895.

**Counter-case, The**, of the united states of Venezuela, before the tribunal of arbitration to convene at Paris, under the provisions of the treaty between the united states of Venezuela and her britannic majesty signed at Washington, february 2, 1897. v. 4. Appendix. Atlas. 2 p. l., 91 maps. fol. Baltimore, A. Hoen & co. 1898.

2778

CONTENTS.

>   pt. 1, no. 1. Boundary claimed by Venezuela, 1898.
>   " 2. Sucre. Part of Guiana, 1732.
>   " 3. Lara. Lower Orinoco and mission region, 1747.
>   " 4. Centurion. Guiana, 1770.
>   " 5. Russell. Part of his map of South America, 1794.
>   " 6. Poirson. French and Dutch Guiana, 1802.
>   " 7. De Pons. Captain-generalcy of Caracas, 1805.
>   " 8. Mentelle and Chanlaire. French and Dutch Guiana [1806]
>   " 9. Pinkerton. Part of his map of South America, 1811.
>   " 10. Delarochette. Part of his map of South America, 1823.
>   " 11. Vivien. South America, 1825.
>   " 12. Brué. Part of his map of South America, 1827.
>   " 13. Restrepo. Department of the Orinoco, 1827.
>   " 14. Weimar geographic Institute. Guiana, 1828.
>   " 15. Lapie. Colombia and the Guianas, 1828.
>   " 16. Wyld. Part of his map of South America, 1829.
>   " 17. Bauza. Part of his map of Colombia, 1830.
>   " 18. Duvotenay. Colombia and Guiana, 1838.
>   " 19. Codazzi. Drainage basins of Venezuela, 1840.
>   " 20. Codazzi. Map of the republic of Colombia, 1840.
>   " 21. Frijlink. Part of his map of South America, 1854.

pt. 2, Reprints of eleven maps, prepared for the United States commission on boundary between Venezuela and British Guiana by professor George L. Burr, to show european occupation at various dates. Copied from maps, numbered 5 to 15 inclusive, in the atlas accompanying the report of that commission.
no. 22. European occupation in 1757.
" 23. " " " 1626.
" 24. " " " 1648.
" 25. " " " 1674.
" 26. " " " 1703.
" 27. " " " 1724.
" 28. " " " 1756.
" 29. " " " 1772.
" 30. " " " 1796.
" 31. " " " 1803 (1814)
" 32. General view of european occupation, 1597-1803 (1814)

**Atlas** to accompany the case presented on the part of her britannic majesty to the arbitral tribunal between Great Britain and the united states of Venezuela constituted under the provisions of a treaty ratified at Washington on june 14th, 1897. Compiled under the supervision of major S. C. N. Grant ... in the intelligence division of the war office. Major-gen. sir John Ardagh ... director of military intelligence. 3 p. l., [1] l., 51 (*i. e.* 46) maps. fol. London, printed for her majesty's stationary office by E. Stanford, 1898. 2779

CONTENTS.

no. 1-2. British Guiana. Geographical map. Sheet 1-2.
" 3. " " Shewing Savannah, forest, and river basins.
" 4. " " Shewing boundaries to illustrate diplomatic correspondence.
" 5. Hondius, Jodocus. Nieuwe caerte van het landt Guiana. 1599.
" 6. De Laet, Joannes. Gvaiana, ofte de provincien tusschen rio de las Amazonas ende rio Yviapari, ofte Orinoqve. 1625.
" 7. Blaew, Guiljelmus. Gviana, siue Amazonvm regio. 1640.
" 8. Jansson, Joannes. Gviana, siue Amazonum regio. 1647.
" 9. Du Val d'Abbeville, Pierre. La Gvaiane, ou Coste Sauuage, autrément El Dorado et Pais des Amazones. 1654.
" 10. Sanson d'Abbeville, Nicholas. Partie de Terre Ferme, ou sont Gviane et Caribane. 1656.
" 11. Visscher, Nicholas. Insulæ Americanæ. 1690.
" 12. Delisle, Guillaume. Carte d'Amérique. 1722.
" 13. Popple, Henry. The british empire in America. 1733.
" 14. Buache, Philippe. Carte d'une partie de l'Amérique pour la navigation des isles et du golfe du Mexique. 1740.
" 15. Gumilla, padre Joseph. Mapa de la provincia, y missiones de la compañia de IHS del nuevo reyno de Granada. 1741.
" 16. D'Anville, Jean Baptiste. Amérique Méridionale. 1748.
" 17. Storm van's Gravesande, Laurens. Caart van de volkplantinge in Essequebo en Demarary. 1748.

**Atlas**—Continued.

no. 18. Storm van's Gravesande, Laurens. Lists of plantations and owners. 1748.
" 19. Storm van's Gravesande, Laurens. Nievwe caart van Essequebo en Demarary. 1749.
" 20. Storm van's Gravesande, Laurens. Rios Essequebe et Demarary. 1749.
" 21. Robert de Vaugondy, Didier. Amérique Méridionale. 1750.
" 22. Cigni, Julius Caesar. [Jesuit map] Provincia Quitensis societatis Jesu in America. 1751.
" 23. D'Anville, Jean Baptiste. Amérique Méridionale. 1760.
" 24. Centurion, don Manuel. Plano general de la provincia de Guaiana. 1770.
" 25. Hartsinck, Jan Jacob. Caart van Guiana. 1770.
" 26. Bonne, R. Carte de la Terre Ferme, de la Guyane et du pays des Amazones. 1771.
" 27. Cruz Cano y Olmedilla, Juan de la. Mapa geografico de America Meridional. 1775.
" 28. Valdes, Juan . . . 1776.
" 29. Surville, Luis de. Mapa-corografico de la Nueva Andalucia, provincias de Cumaná, y Guyana, &c. 1778.
" 30. Rochette, L. S. de la. [Thompson, Edward] The coast of Guyana from the Oroonoko to the river of Amazons, &c. 1783.
31. Janvier, Jean. L'Amérique, divisée en ses principaux états. 1790.
" 32. Laurie & Whittle. Map of South America, containing Tierra Firma, Guayana, &c. 1794.
" 33. Laurie & Whittle. New map of the whole continent of America. 1794.
" 34. Walker, captain Thomas. Chart of the coast of Guyana. 1798.
" 35. Bouchenroeder, F. von. Carte générale & particulière de la colonie d'Essequebe & Demerarie. 1798.—Carte générale.—[Inset map in preceding on a smaller scale] 1798.
" 36. Hislop, commandant. Chart of Guyana, &c$^a$. 1802.
" 37. Arrowsmith, John. Colombia. 1832.
" 38. Hebert, L. J. Map of British Guiana. Sheet 1. 1842.
" 39. Hebert, L. J. Map of British Guiana. Sheet 2. 1842.
" 40. Mahlmann, H. [For Richard Schomburgk] Karte von Britisch-Guyana. 1846.
" 41. Stanford, Edward. Map of British Guiana. 1875.
" 42. Stanford, Edward. Map of British Guiana. Re-issue of the edition of 1875. 1886.
" 43. Schomburgk, sir Robert Herman. Sketch map of British Guiana. 1839.
" 44. Schomburgk, sir Robert Herman. First map of the limits of British Guiana, 1841. Western sheet.
" 45. Same. Eastern sheet.
" 46. Schomburgk, sir Robert Herman. Second map of the limits between British Guiana and Venezuela, 1841.
" 47. Schomburgk, sir Robert Herman. Third map, physical features. North sheet.
" 48. Same. South sheet.
" 49. Schomburgk, sir Robert Herman. Entrance to the river Barima, 1841.
" 50. Schomburgk, sir Robert Herman. Entrance to the river Waini or Guainia. 1841.
" 51. Schomburgk, sir Robert Herman. Sketch map of the river Takutu, 1842.

# EUROPE.

### CITIES.

**DuSauzet, H.**
Profils ou vues des principales villes de l'Europe, &c.　2 p. l., 33 pl.　nar. 8°.　Amsterdam, H. du Sauzet, 1739.　　2779a

NOTE.—Bound with his "Atlas de poche, à l'usage des voyageurs et des officiers." Amsterdam, 1734. See title 584a.
The following map relates to America:
no. 30. [City of] Mexico.

### CONTENTS.

no. 1. Paris.
" 2. Londres.
" 3. Anvers.
" 4. Amsterdam.
" 5. La maison de ville d'Amsterdam.
" 6. Batavia.
" 7. Genève.
" 8. Basle.
" 9. Straetsbourg.
" 10. Heydelberg ou le Mont Payen.
" 11. Trèves.
" 12. Maience.
" 13. Cologne.
" 14. Mvnster.
" 15. Francfort sur le Main.
" 16. Nurenberg.
" 17. Augsbourg.
" 18. Dresde.
" 19. Berlin.
" 20. Koningsberg.
" 21. Dantzig.
" 22. Koppenhague.
" 23. Stockholme.
" 24. Vienne.
" 25. Prague.
" 26. Constantinople.
" 27. Alger.
" 28. Madrid.
" 29. L'Escurial.
" 30. Mexico.
" 31. Vue de Lisbonne du côté du Tage. W. Jongman sculp.
" 32. Rome.
" 33. Venise.

**Fer, N. de.**
Les forces de l'Europe, ou description des principales villes, avec leurs fortifications. Deffignées par les meilleurs ingénieurs, par-

**Fer, N. de**—Continued.

ticulièrement celles qui font fous la domination de la France, dont les plans ont efté levez par monfieur de Vauban . . . [204] 1. incl. 168 maps, 18 pl., 1 tab. obl. 4°. Paris, chez l'auteur, 1696-[1697]
2780

> Note.—See also title 2781a. Composed of 8 parts, each having separate title-page.
> Collation: pt. 1, 4 p. l., 4 l., 9 maps, 9 pl; pt. 2, 2 p. l., 21 maps, 3 pl.; pt. 3, 1 p. l., 22 maps, 2 pl.; pt. 4, 1 p. l., 20 maps; pt. 5, 1 p. l., 21 maps, 2 pl.; pt. 6, 1 p. l., 26 maps; pt. 7, 1 p. l., 25 maps; pt. 8, 1 p. l., 24 maps, 2 pl., tab.
> "This very rare work [1726 ed.] to be found in no catalogue and published in 1726 according to the sale catal. of v. d. Aa's books, p. 339, no. 1025, is properly a collection of plans and views of the most remarkable cities and fortresses in Europe. In this last edition 16 plates on America are added, mostly published before in other works or separately and afterwards reproduced anew (but with large borders and cartouches) in the: Galerie agréable du monde (no. 1) This is a work similar to that but on a smaller scale and of a more topographical character.—The present book was originally published by N. de Fer at Paris in 8 vol. containing 176 plates; these were copied by P. Mortier at Amsterd. and augmented to 319 pl. in 14 vol.; these copies were bought by van der Aa, who re-issued them with other pl. augmented to the number of 509 in this edition." *cf.* Muller, Frederik. Catalogue of books, maps, plates on America. Amsterdam, 1872. p. 2, no. 2.
> Plates i-viii relate to fortifications and have special title-page, "Introduction à la fortification, dédiée à monseigneur le duc de Bourgogne par . . . de Fer. A Paris, chez l'auteur . . . 1693." Each plate is accompanied by explanatory text.
> Maps, pt. 6, nos. 6 & 7, "Belgrade" and "Veue de Constantinople," are indexed as nos. 20 & 21; pt. 8, maps, "L'isle de Wight . . . 1692," and "Plan de la bataille de Fleurus . . ." nos. 176 & 177, are not in the index, and have been inserted at a later date.
> The following map relates to America:
> pt. 5, no. 23. [Quebec]

**Le Masson du Parc, —.**

Vües, plans et perspectiues de diuers lieux et places considérables. 6 p. l., 11 maps, 5 pl. fol. [n. p., 1713]
2781

> Note.—Collection of miscellaneous maps and views, by various authors including Baillieux, Gournay, Jollain, Aveline, de Fer, Beaulieu and Blaeu, brought together by Le Masson du Parc.
> The following maps are manuscript:
> no. 1. [Without title]
> " 8. Phillipsbourg.
> " 10. Plan de la ville et citadelle de Turin.
> "Tables des sciences" dated 1713.
> Imperfect: index calls for 42 maps and plans.
> Manuscript title in red, within colored, engraved ornamental border, followed by five manuscript leaves comprising, "Table des sciences", "Table des plans", "Dessin et explication du cartouche des fortifications", and half title, "Les plans, veües et éléuations de différentes places fortes et lieux considérables, de divers auteurs et receuillies par le s.r le Masson du Parc."

**Mortier, P.**

Les forces de l'Europe, Asie, Afrique et Amérique ou description des principales villes, avec leurs fortifications. Deffignées par les meilleurs ingénieurs, particulièrement celles qui sont sous la domination de la France, dont les plans ont efté levez par monfieur de Vauban, avec la defcription de tous les inftrumens fervans à la fortification, à l'attaque & deffenfe des places, enfemble ceux qui fervent pour l'artillerie, des magafins; la manière de dresser un camp devant une ville assiegée, &c. Et ornées de plufieurs fuperbes èdifices. Ouvrage necessaire pour toutes sortes de personnes. 2 v. obl. fol. Amsterdam, P. Mortier [1702?] 2781a

    NOTE.—Collation: v. 1, title, [2] pp., 6 l., 132 maps, 26 pl.; v. 2, title, 6 l., 124 maps, 23 pl.

    Date 1702 on no. 34, v. 1, and no. 274, v. 2.

    Originally published by Nicolas de Fer at Paris in 1696-1697. See title 2780. The plates were copied by Pieter Mortier at Amsterdam for the present edition. Mortier's plates were bought by van der Aa who reissued them with many others in an edition published at Paris and Leide, 1726.

    The following maps relate to America:

    v. 1, no. 160. Québec.
    "  " 161. Bay et chateav de Porto Bello.
    "  " 162. Baye et ville de Havana ou S. Christoval.
    "  " 163. Cartegène avec ses ports, et fortresses.

**Werner, F. B.**

[Views of the cities of Europe]     [91] pp., 90 pl. obl. 8°. [Augsburg, 1700-1754]     2782

    NOTE.—Without title-page.

    Colored views engraved by Iohann Christian Leopold; without dates.

    Latin and german border text contains dates 1700-1754. Manuscript text p. 57, contains date 1755.

    Descriptive manuscript text in dutch from Werner's "Historische geographische en ondheids-kundige aanteekingen."

    B. M. catalogue mentions many of Werner's views dated 1700-1740 but these dates are questioned.

## COLONIES.

**Supan, A. G.**

Die territoriale entwicklung der europäischen kolonien. Mit einem kolonialgeschichtlichen atlas von 12 karten und 40 kärtchen im text. xi, 344 pp. illus. (maps) 12 fold. maps. 4°. Gotha, J. Perthes, 1906.     2782a

    NOTE.—Bibliographical foot-notes.

    Reviewed by L. Perruchat in La Géographie, aug. 15, 1906, v. 14, pp. 123-124; also by M. K. Genthe in Bulletin of the American geographical society, nov., 1908. pp. 699-702.

    CONTENTS.

    Einleitung.—Die ersten anfänge der überseeischen kolonisation.—Die spanisch-portugiesische periode 1492-1598.—Die holländische periode 1598-1670.—Die

**Supan, A. G.**—Continued.

französisch-britische periode 1670–1783.—Die britisch-amerikanische periode 1783–1786.—Die europäisch-amerikanische periode, seit 1876.—Die hauptergebnisse der kolonisation.—Register.

## COMMERCIAL.

**Koch, W.**

Verkehrs-atlas von Europa, mit einer in sechs farben ausgeführten weltverkehrs-karte nebst einer übersichts-karte der Transsibirischen eisenbahn. Hrsg. von C. Opitz. Enthaltend 80 sektionen in vier- bis achtfachem farbendruck, 6 übersichtskarten, 34 nebenkarten, mit einem alphabetischen stationsverzeichnis von Europa, nebst einer alphabetischen übersicht selbständiger eisenbahnen und bahnbetriebe Europas und einem verkehrshandbuch enthaltend: kilometertabelle—frachtentarif—einrichtung und anwendung der eisenbahn-gütertarife in Deutschland und Österreich-Ungarn—ortsregister des deutschen reiches. 2 v. fol. Leipzig, J. J. Arnd, 1906.

2783

NOTE.—Collation: v. 1, xi, 144 pp., 79 maps; v. 2, 1 p. l., 163 pp.

"Die einrichtung und anwendung der eisenbahn-gütertarife in Deutschland und in Österreich-Ungarn. Bearb. von Alexander Klinger" v. 1, p. [96]

Title of v. 2 varies: Verkehrs-handbuch zu dr. Koch's Atlas von Europa inhalt: kilometertabelle, ortsverzeichnis, gütertarif . . .

Inset plans of the environs of: Dresden, Leipzig, Berlin, Breslau, Hamburg, Cologne, Frankfurt, Strassburg, Stuttgart, München, Paris, St. Petersburg, Moscow, Zurich, Lucerne.

## ECCLESIASTICAL.

**Heussi, K.,** *and* **Mulert, H.**

Atlas zur kirchengeschichte. 66 karten auf 12 blättern. 18 pp., 1 l., 12 maps. 4°. Tübingen, J. C. B. Mohr, 1905.

2784

### CONTENTS.

no. 1. Zur geschichte der alten kirche.
" 2. Einzelkarten zur geschichte der alten kirche.
" 3. Zur kirchengeschichte von Asien bis zum xiv. jahrhundert.
" 4. Zur kirchengeschichte Osteuropas.
" 5. Zur abendlandischen kirchengeschichte vom v. bis zum ix. jahrhundert.
" 6. Romanische länder im mittelalter.
" 7. Germanische länder im mittelalter, 1.
" 8. Germanische länder im mittelalter, 2.
" 9. Zur geschichte des papsttums.
" 10. Zur geschichte der deutschen reformation und gegenreformation.
" 11. Zur neueren westeuropäischen kirchengeschichte.
" 12. Zur verbreitung der religionen und konfessionen um 1900.

**Wiltsch, J. E. T.**
Kirchenhistorischer atlas von den ersten zeiten der ausbreitung des christenthums bis zum anfang des XVI jahrh.—Atlas sacer sive ecclesiasticus.   cover-title, 5 col. maps.   fol.   Gotha, J. Perthes, 1843. 2785

NOTE.—Accompanied by explanatory text entitled: Atlas sacer sive ecclesiasticus inde ab antiquissimis religionis christianae propagatae temporibus usque ad primordia saeculi decimi sexti.  3 p. l., 22 pp.  4°.  Gothae, J. Perthes, 1843.

## ETHNOGRAPHICAL.

**Erckert, R. von.**
Wanderungen und siedelungen der germanischen stämme in Mittel-Europa, von der ältesten zeit bis auf Karl den grossen . . .   4 p. l., 12 maps.   fol.   Berlin, E. S. Mittler & sohn, 1901. 2786

CONTENTS.

no. 1. Die zweite [grösste] und dritte eiszeit in Mittel-Europa.
" 2. Indo-Germanische völker in Europa zu anfang des 6. jahrhunderts v. Chr.
" 3. Ungefähre ausbreitung der Germanen und Kelten in Mittel-Europa vom 6. bis 2. jahrhundert v. Chr.
" 4. Germanen in Mittel-Europa und ihre nachbarvölker um das jahr 60 v. Chr.
" 5. Germanen in Mittel-Europa und ihre nachbarvölker um das jahr 150 n. Chr.
" 6. Ptolemaeische karte von Gross-Germanien nach dem text der Müllerschen ausgabe (Paris 1883)
" 7. Wander- und kriegszüge germanischer völker.  4 sheets.
" 8. Germanen in Mittel-Europa und ihre nachbarvölker nach dem jahre 300 n. Chr.
" 9. Germanen in Mittel-Europa und ihre nachbarvölker nach dem jahre 400 n. Chr.
" 10. Germanen in Mittel-Europa und ihre nachbarvölker nach dem jahre 500 n. Chr.
" 11. Germanen in Mittel-Europa und ihre nachbarvölker nach dem jahre 600 n. Chr.
" 12. Germanen in Mittel-Europa und ihre nachbarvölker um das jahr 814 n. Chr.

## HISTORICAL.

**Bretschneider, C. A.**
Historisch-geographischer wand-atlas nach Karl von Spruner. 10 maps in 2 pts.   fol.   Gotha, J. Perthes, 1856. 2786a

CONTENTS.

pt. 1, no. 1. Europa um 350 nach Christo.
" 2. Europa im anfange des sechsten jahrhunderts.
" 3. Europa zur zeit Carls des grossen.
" 4. Europa in der zweiten hälfte des zehnten jahrhunderts.
" 5. Europa zur zeit der kreuzüge.

**Bretschneider, C. A.**—Continued.
  pt. 2, no. 6. Europa zur zeit des vierzehnten jahrhunderts.
  " 7. Europa zur zeit der reformation.
  " 8. Europa zur zeit des 30 jährigen krieges und bis 1700.
  " 9. Europa im achtzehnten jahrhundert von 1700 bis 1789.
  " 10. Europa im zeitalter Napoleons, 1789 bis 1815.

**Bury, J. B.**
  Atlas to the historical geography of Europe, by Edward A. Freeman. 3d ed.  viii pp., 65 maps on 58 l. 8°. London, New York, Longmans, Green & co. 1903. 2787

**Dow, E. W.**
  Atlas of european history . . .  v, 46 pp., 32 (*i. e.* 50) maps. 4°. New York, H. Holt & co. 1907. 2788

**Fischer, W.,** *and* **Streit, F. W.**
  Historischer und geographischer atlas von Europa . . .  2 v. in 3. 12°. Berlin, W. Natorff & co. 1834–1837. 2789
  NOTE.—v. 1 has added engraved title-page.
  Without maps.

**Hannak, E.,** *and* **Umlauft, F.**
  Historischer schulatlas in dreiszig karten.  Zur geschichte des altertums, des mittelalters und der neuzeit für gymnasien, realschulen und diesen verwandte anstalten . . .  2 v.  2 p. l., 12 col. maps; 2 p. l., 18 col. maps. 4°. Wien, A. Hölder, 1908. 2789a
  CONTENTS.
  v. 1. Das altertum.
  " 2. Das mittelalter und die neuzeit.

**Hildebrand, E.,** *and* **Selander, N.**
  Atlas till allmänna och Svenska historien. 4 pts. in 1 v.  cover-titles, 29 col. maps. obl. 4°. Stockholm, P. A. Norstedt & söners [1883] 2790

**Koch, C. G.**
  Maps, and tables of chronology and genealogy; selected and translated from monsieur Koch's "Tableau des révolutions de l'Europe." For the use of Harrow school.  2 p. l., 26 pp., 7 maps. 4°. London, Baldwin & Cradock, 1831. 2791
  NOTE.—Edited and translated by Charles Thomas Longley, archbishop of Canterbury. *cf.* Dictionary of national biography.

**Kruse, C.**
  Atlas zur übersicht der geschichte aller europäischen länder und staaten von ihrer ersten bevölkerung an bis zu den neuesten zeiten . . .  3$^{te}$ ausg.  1 p. l., 41 l., 12 maps. fol. Leipzig, verfasser [1822?] 2792

Tabellen und charten zur allgemeinen geschichte der drey letzten jahrhunderte . . .  1 p. l., 20 l., 5 maps. fol. Leipzig, verfasser, 1821. 2793
[ *With his* Atlas zur übersicht der geschichte aller europäischen länder und staaten von ihrer ersten bevölkerung an bis zu den neuesten zeiten . . . 3^te ausg. fol. Leipzig, verfasser [1822?] Title] 2792

**Poole, R. L.**
Historical atlas of modern Europe from the decline of the roman empire, comprising also maps of parts of Asia, Africa and the new world connected with european history . . .  30 pts. in 1 v. 4 p. l., [164] l., 90 maps. fol. Oxford, the Clarendon press [1896]–1902. 2794

    NOTE.—Map no. 90 shows "South Africa previous to the suppression of the Boer republics."
    The following maps relate to America:
    no. 85. Explorations & colonies of the 15th, 16th, & 17th centuries.—Insets: North American colonies.—West India islands.
    " 86. European colonies & dependencies after the peace of Utrecht, 1713.—Insets: Map to illustrate struggle between France & Britain in America between 1713 & seven years' war.—West India is
    " 87. European colonies & dependencies. 1763.
    " 88. The french proposals of 1782.—The two lines of frontier agreed to in . . . 1782.—The United States after the treaty of Paris, 1783.—The boundary established by treaty of Washington . . . 1842.
    " 89. European colonies & dependencies and states independent of european powers from 1815 to 1897.—Inset: West India Is

    CONTENTS.

no. 1. The roman empire, 285-395. By professor J. B. Bury.
" 2. Europe, 395-527. By professor Bury.
" 3. Europe, 527-750. By professor Bury.
" 4. Europe in the time of Charles the great.
" 5. Europe in the time of Otto the great, 962.
" 6. Europe at the time of the third crusade, 1190.
" 7. Europe in 1360. By professor C. Oman.
" 8. Europe at the accession of emperor Charles V., 1519. By professor Oman.
" 9. Europe after the peace of Westphalia, 1648. By professor Oman.
" 10. Europe in the eighteenth century prior to the french revolution. By W. E. Rhodes.
" 11.⎫ Europe in the time of the french revolution and empire, 1789-1809.
" 12.⎭ By H. A. L. Fisher.
" 13. Europe, 1814-1863. By G. W. Prothero.
" 14. Europe, 1863-1897. By G. W. Prothero.
" 15. Roman Britain. By F. Haverfield.
" 16. England and Wales before the norman conquest. By W. H. Stevenson.
" 17. England and Wales in 1086. By professor James Tait.
" 18. England and Wales under Edward I. By professor T. F. Tout.
" 19. Anglia sacra, showing the ecclesiastical geography in the time of Edward I. By professor Oman.

**Poole, R. L.**—Continued.
- no. 20. England and Wales under the house of Lancaster. By professor Tait.
- " 21. Anglia monastica. By miss A. M. Cooke.
- " 22. England and Wales after the accession of the house of Tudor.
- " 23. England, showing the parliamentary representation down to 1832. By G. W. Prothero.
- " 24. England and Wales, showing the parliamentary representation according to the reform act of 1832.
- " 25. Scotland, c. 1300. By G. Gregory Smith.
- " 26. Scotland, showing the ecclesiastical organization in the middle ages. By G. Gregory Smith.
- " 27. Scotland, c. 1600. By G. Gregory Smith.
- " 28. Scotland, showing the principal clans and families, and also the parliamentary representation down to 1832. By Robert S. Rait.
- " 29. Early Ireland. By Goddard H. Orpen.
- " 30. Ireland under the early Tudors. By Robert Dunlop.
- " 31. Ireland, from 1541 to 1653. By Robert Dunlop.
- " 32. The frankish dominions in merovingian times, 486–768.
- " 33. The frankish dominions in carolingian times, 768–900.
- " 34. Germany under the saxon and salian dynasties, 919–1137.
- " 35. Germany under the house of Hohenstaufen, 1138–1254.
- " 36. Germany in the later middle ages, 1273–1492.
- " 37. Germania sacra, illustrating the ecclesiastical divisions in the middle ages.
- " 38.) Germany during the period of the reformation and the thirty years'
- " 39.) war. By the rev. J. P. Whitney, M. A.
- " 40. Germany at the peace of Westphalia, 1648. By the rev. J. P. Whitney.
- " 41. Germany, 1648–1795. By C. Grant Robertson.
- " 42. The growth of Prussia. By C. Grant Robertson.
- " 43. The formation of the modern German empire. By C. Grant Robertson.
- " 44. The Swiss Confederation. By the rev. W. A. B. Coolidge.
- " 45. Hungary, 997–1382. By R. Nisbet Bain.
- " 46. Hungary, 1382–1739. By R. Nisbet Bain.
- " 47. Poland and Lithuania before the union of Lublin, 1569. By R. Nisbet Bain.
- " 48. Poland from the union of Lublin to the third partition, 1569–1795. By R. Nisbet Bain.
- " 49. Russia, 1613–1878. By R. Nisbet Bain.
- " 50. Scandanavia in the thirteenth century. By W. A. Craigie.
- " 51. Scandanavia, 1521–1815. By R. Nisbet Bain.
- " 52. The Netherlands. By the late Julius Frederichs.
- " 53. France, Lotharingia, and Burgundy in the eleventh and twelfth centuries. By W. E. Rhodes.
- " 54. Northern France in 1066. By professor Tait.
- " 55. France in the thirteenth century. By W. E. Rhodes.
- " 56. France during the hundred years' war. By professor Tait.
- " 57. Gallia sacra. By W. E. Rhodes.
- " 58. France under the ancien regime, 1600–1790. By W. E. Rhodes.
- " 59. The french empire in 1810. By H. A. L. Fisher.
- " 60. The spanish peninsula, 1263–1492. By the late Ulick R. Burke.
- " 61. The ecclesiastical organization of the Spanish peninsula.
- " 62. The Spanish kingdoms since 1513. By the late Ulick R. Burke.
- " 63. Italy in the Lombard period, 568–774. By professor Bury.

no. 64. Italy, c. 850–1067. By miss Lina Eckenstein.
" 65. Italy, c. 1060–1167. By miss Lina Eckenstein.
" 66. Italy, 1167–1250. By miss Lina Eckenstein.
" 67. Northern Italy in the fourteenth and fifteenth centuries. By miss K. Dorothea Ewart (mrs. H. M. Vernon)
" 68. Italy after the peace of Lodi, 1454. By miss K. Dorothea Ewart.
" 69. Italia sacra, illustrating the ecclesiastical divisions in the middle ages. By miss K. Dorothea Ewart.
" 70. The house of Savoy in Italy. By miss K. Dorothea Ewart.
" 71.}
" 72.} The eastern roman empire in the tenth century. By professor Bury.
" 73. The eastern roman empire, 1025–1472. By professor Bury.
" 74. South-eastern Europe and Asia minor, c. 1210. By professor Bury.
" 75. The four eastern patriarchates, c. 750. By E. W. Brooks.
" 76. Syria during the period of the crusades, 1096–1291. By T. Archer.
" 77. Western Asia under the Abbasid caliphs, 780. By professor Stanley Lane-Poole.
" 78. Western Asia under the mohammedan dynasties, c. 970 and c. 1070. By professor Lane-Poole.
" 79. Western Asia at the time of Saladin, 1190. By professor Lane-Poole.
" 80. Western Asia under the mongols, 1330. By professor Lane-Poole.
" 81. Western Asia under the turks and persians. By professor Lane-Poole.
" 82. The ottoman empire in Europe, 1356–1897. By W. Miller.
" 83. India under mohammedan rule. By professor Lane-Poole.
" 84. India in 1792 and 1845. By professor Oman.
" 85. European explorations and colonies ftom the fifteenth to the seventeenth century. By Hugh E. Egerton.
" 86. European colonies and dependencies after the peace of Utrecht, 1713. By Hugh E. Egerton.
" 87. European colonies and dependencies, 1763. By Hugh E. Egerton.
" 88. The United States of America after the treaty of 1783. By Hugh E. Egerton.
" 89. European colonies and dependencies, and states independent of european powers. 1815–1897. By Hugh E. Egerton.
" 90. South Africa previous to the suppression of the boer republics. By G. Geoffrey Robinson.
For the maps to which no contributor's name is assigned the editor is himself responsible.

**Reich, E.**
Atlas antiquus. In forty-eight original, graphic maps, with elaborate text to each map, and full index . . .   4 p. l., [90], 10 pp., 48 (*i. e.* 33) col. maps. 4°. London, Macmillan & co. limited, 1908. 2794a

**Spruner von Mertz, K.**
Historisch-geographischer hand-atlas zur geschichte der staaten Europa's vom anfang des mittelalters bis auf die neueste zeit. 1 p. l., 52 pp., 73 maps. fol. Gotha, J. Perthes, 1846. 2795

**Wolff, C.**
Historischer atlas. Neunzehn karten zur mittleren und neueren geschichte. Mit erläuterndem text.   iv, 7 pp., 19 maps. fol. Berlin, D. Reimer, 1877. 2796

## RAILROADS.

**Nietmann, W.**
Eisenbahn-atlas für deutsches reich, Luxemburg, Schweiz, Oesterreichish-Ungarische monarchie und angrenzende gebiete. Dargestellt in 30 nach einzelnen ländern und provinzen getrennten specialkarten, 2 übersichtskarten und vollständigen stationsverzeichnissen. Schweiz und Oesterreich-Ungarn ausserdem genauestens durchgesehen und verbessert von Karl Schönfelder und Emanuel Schütze. 18$^{te}$ aufl. 3 p. l., 52, 33 pp., 32 fold. maps. fol. Leipzig, W. Nietmann, 1902. 2797

**Stülpnagel, F. von,** *and* **Bär, J. C.**
Eisenbahn-atlas von Deutschland, Belgien, Elsass und dem nördlichsten theile von Italien in 16 specialkarten auf 13 blättern, nebst einer uebersichtskarte. In kupferstich ausgeführt. 10. verm. aufl. 2 p. l., 17 maps. 8°. Gotha, J. Perthes, 1856. 2798

## REPRODUCTIONS.

**Bjørnbo, A. A.,** *and* **Petersen, C. S.**
Anecdota cartographica septentrionalia. 2 p. l., 32 pp., 11 maps. fol. Hauniae, sumpt. societatis regiae scientiarum danicae, 1908. 2798a

> NOTE.—Letterpress and titles of maps in danish and english. The english translation by Sophia Bertelsen.
> "A chronologically arranged series of ·cartographical sources concerning the north from the 14th to the 17th century."—Introduction.
> Table of names, p. [14]–32.
> The following map relates to America:
> no. 11. Joris Carolus: map of Iceland, Greenland and the northeastern part of America, 1626.
>
> CONTENTS.
>
> no. 1. Anonymous catalanian sea-chart, 14th c. (Biblioteca nazionale, Museo Borbonico, Napoli)
> " 2. Henricus Martellus germanus: map of the north, ca. 1490. (Universiteitsbibliotheek, Leiden)
> " 3. Henricus Martellus germanus: map of Scandinavia, ca. 1490. (British Museum, London)
> " 4. Anonymous chart of the Atlantic ocean, ca. 1504. (Kgl. Bayerische armee-bibliothek, München)
> " 5. Cornelis Anthonisz: map of Denmark and adjacent countries, ca. 1550–1565. (Ehemal Universitätsbibliothek, Helmstedt)
> " 6. Marcus Jorden: map of Schleswig and Holstein, 1559. (Universiteitsbibliotheek, Leiden)
> " 7. Anonymous map of the inner Baltic, 1550–1600. (Universiteitsbibliotheek, Leiden)

no. 8. Anonymous map of North Fjord, 1594. (K. K. Hofbibliothek, Wien)
" 9. Anonymous sketch for a map of the southern part of the west coast of Norway, 1586–1600. (K. K. Hofbibliothek, Wien)
" 10. Simon van Salinghen: map of the northernmost parts of Europe, 1601. (Riksarkivet, Stockholm)
" 11. Joris Carolus: map of Iceland, Greenland and the northeastern part of America, 1626. (Algemeene rijksarchief, 's Gravenhage)

**Ruelens, C. L.**
Les monuments de la géographie des bibliothèques de Belgique. Carte de l'Europe 1480–1485 . . . Texte explicatif par Ch. Ruelens. 3 p. l., 1 col. map on 8 l. fol. Bruxelles, institut national de géographie [1888] 2799

NOTE.—Reproduction of copies of the prototype edition of Nicolas Denis' maps. Dedicated to J. van Raemdonck "dont les consciencieux travaux sur Gérard Mercator forment une page éclatante de l'histoire de la géographie en Belgique."
The text gives the following explanation in regard to the original source of the maps, "Il est évident qu'avant de confier à la gravure ces cartes modernes, l'habile géographe [N. Denis] en avait exécuté d'abord des dessins manuscrits. M. Le baron von Nordenskiöld pense qu' elles doivent être antérieures à 1471. Le fait n'est pas impossible; nous ne connaissons cependant aucun exemplaire portant cette date . . . Les cartes reproduites dans cette première série de nos monuments géographiques appartiennent à l'un de ces exemplaires, que nous regardons comme des copies de l'édition prototype . . . Elles font partie d'un magnifique manuscrit portant le no. 14887 à l'inventaire de la Bibliothèque royale de Bruxelles, et contenant la cosmographie de Ptolémée dans la traduction latine de Jacobus Angelus."

## RIVERS.

**Commission européenne du Danube.**
Cartes du delta du Danube et plans comparatifs de l'embouchure et des sections fluviales du bras de Soulina. Indiquant les derniers travaux qui y ont été exécutés par la commission européenne d'après les projets de sir Ch. A. Hartley, son ingénieur consultant, sous la direction de monsieur C. Kühl, son ingénieur résidant, faisant suite au recueil de plans comparatifs publié par la commission en 1874. 6 p. l., 5 maps, 73 pl. fol. Leipzig, F. A. Brockhaus, 1887. 2800

## SCHOOL.

**Letoschek, E.**
Geographischer repetitions- und zeichen-atlas. I. Europa. 18 tafeln mit 80 kartenskizzen und begleitendem text . . . 3 p. l., 18 l. incl. maps. 4°. Wien, E. Hölzel, 1888. 2801

## SEAS.

### ADRIATIC.

**Austria.** *I. r. istituto geografico militare di Milano.*
Carta di cabottaggio del mare Adriatico disegnata ed incisa sotto la direzione dell' i. r. stato maggiore generale nell' i. r. istituto geografico militare di Milano pubblicata negli anni 1822 e 1824. 2 p. l., 20 maps, 7 pl. fol. [Milano, i. r. istituto geografico militare, 1822–24]  2802

>   NOTE.—"La presente earta è stata costrutta alla scala di 1 : 175.000 del naturale ... "

### MEDITERRANEAN.

**Levanto, F. M.**
Prima parte dello specchio del mare, nel qvale si descrivono tvtti li porti, spiaggie, baye, isole, scogli, e seccagni del Mediterraneo ... 3 p. l., 152 pp., 25 maps. fol. Genova, G. Marino & B. Celle, 1664.  2803

>   NOTE.—Engraved title-page.

**Erskine, R.**
To the right honourable sr. Charles Wager, admiral of the whit squadron, first lord commiſsioner of the admiralty and one of his majestie's moſt honble privy-council, these views, plans and remarks are moſt humbly inscribed by sir, your moſt dutiful & most humble servant R: Erſkine. 1 p. l., 15 maps, 16 views. fol. [1727–1734]  2804

>   NOTE.—In manuscript; illustrated title.
>   Maps dated from 1727–1734.
>   Robert Erskine mentioned by Charnock, Biografia navalis, v. 5, p. 170, has not been identified as the author of this work as the account does not begin until his appointment in 1742 as captain of the Fox frigate. Previous to that date he may have served in the spanish expedition under sir Charles Wager, to whom the work is dedicated, but of this no account has been found. Charnock states that Robert Erskine died in 1766.

#### CONTENTS.

no. 1. A plan of the coast of Portugal from Cape Roxent to C: Spitchel.  1732.
"   2. A view of Cadiz.*
"   3. A plan of Lagos bay as in 1727.
"   4. A plan of Tangier bay as in 1727.
"   5. A view of St Jerom's bay on the coast of Barbary.  1730.
"   6. A plan of the streights of Gibraltar.  1734.
"   7. A north prospect of Gibraltar hill ...
"   8. A plan of the hill and bay of G[i]braltar ...  1734.
"   9. Fangerole bay.

no. 10. A view of Malago bay in 1732.
" 11. A view of Malago.
" 12. [Views of parts of the coast of Spain]
" 13. A plan of Cala Figuira bay 1734.
" 14. A plan of Cartagena harbour in the year 1732.
" 15. A prospect of Alicant in the year 1733.
" 16. A plan of Altea bay in the year 1731.
" 17. [Cape S! Martine—Cape S! Anthony]
" 18. A plan of Salo bay in the year 1732.
" 19. A view of Taragona from the sea in the year 1733.—A view of Barcelona.
" 20. [Views of the coast of Spain north of Barcelona]
" 21. A view of Merseille as in 1733.
" 22. A plan of the port and bay of Toulon as in the year 1733.
" 23. A view of Genoa lanthorn.
" 24. A plan of the port of Genoa.
" 25. A view of Leghorn in 1733.
" 26. Part of the island of Corsico.
" 27. A view of S! Phillip's castle as in 1734.
" 28. A plan of the town and harb! of Mahon w!ʰ the town & castle of S! Phillips. 1732.
" 29. A view of Palma as in 1732.
" 30. A plan of Palma bay on the island Maiorca. 1732.
" 31. A plan of the island of Fermentera with part of the island of Ivica.

**English, The, pilot.**

Part III. Describing the sea coafts, capes, head-lands, bays, roads, harbours, rivers and ports, together with the soundings, sands, rocks and dangers in the whole Mediterranean sea. Likewise the courfes and diftances from one place to another. The setting of the tides and currents. The ebbing and flowing of the sea. The bearing, diftance, and profpects of the land, and how they fhew themfelves at sea. Carefully corrected, with new editions of feveral ports, harbours, bays and profpects of land, never before made publick. 1 p. l., 86 pp., 16 sheet maps, 36 maps in text. fol. London, for W. Mount & T. Page, 1736. 2805

**Alagna, J. G.**

A compleat set of new charts on thirty-eight large plates, containing an accurate survey of the coast of Portugal and the Mediterranean sea in which are included seventy-five charts, of the principal harbours in the straits, shewing the rocks, shoals, soundings & anchoring places, with their true latitude. The whole being accurately surveyed by J. Giacomo Alagna of Mefsina . . . J. Larken del. et sculp! 93 maps on 53 l. fol. London, for J. Mount & T. Page [1767?] 2806

NOTE.—Engraved title, elaborately ornamented with figures, on map no. 1. Published in or about 1767. The British Museum gives this atlas the date 1760?, but this is without doubt erroneous. The name of the publishing firm

**Alagna, J. G.**—Continued.

under-went a number of changes, the form being for several years before and after 1760, W. and J. Mount, T. Page and son. During the period which followed this form of the name, and in which this atlas was published, the firm name was J. Mount and T. Page. A little later the name was J. Mount, T. Page, W. Mount and T. Page. The next change being simply to Mount and Page.

**Olivier, J.**

Livre de plufieurs plans des ports & rades de la mer Méditerranée auec les villes & les forts auec les sondes marquées par braffes de cinz pieds. le tout exactement tires par obferuation. Prefenté à monfieur le conte Marquefy. Par fon seruiteur Jean Oliuier pilotte. 1 p. l., 115 col. maps, 1 eng. map, 1 l. fol. [1796?]   2807

NOTE.—In manuscript. Title in red and black within ornamental border with Neptune on one side and a mermaid on the other. Both uphold the drapery forming the background for the arms of France. Three cupids surmount the whole.
Maps dated 1707, 1725, 1731; dates in text, 1704, 1716, 1796.
Maps no. 65–66, wanting.
Engraved map no. [100] inserted.
Maps no. 1—96, similar in drawing and coloring, appear to have been made by the same person. Those with different style and without numbers are of superior workmanship to the others and are not included in the "Table du nom des plans qui font dans ce livre."
Verso of maps contain descriptive text.
The following maps relate to America:
no. 97. Plan de la baye du cap François . . . & St Dominque . . .
" 98. Islle Martinique.
" 103. Fort Royal en lille dé lá Martinique.
" 115. Carte de terre neuue[!] . . . fait en l'ennee 1731.
" 118. Plan de la cote de la Louizianne ou du Missippi[!]

CONTENTS.

no. 1. Plan du port & rade de Marfeille . . .
" 2. Plan du port de Caffis . . .
" 3. Plan du port & rade de la Ciotat.
" 4. Plan de la rade du Brusq, Senary & Bandol . . .
" 5. Plan de la rade et ville de Toulon . . .
" 6. Plan de la baye des isles d'Hyeres et les isles de Porcairole & Porte Cros . . .
" 7. Plan de la rade d'Araiffe auec les sondes et du mouillage de l isle d Arbengue.
" 8. Plan de la rade & mouillage de Dian . . .
" 9. Plan de la rade, du mole & de la d arce de Ligourne . . .
" 10. Plan du port & de la rade de porte Ferrare à l isle de l'Elbe . . .
" 11. Plan du gouf Ian & les isles S$t$ Margueritte & l isle St. Honnorat . . .
" 12. Plan du port & rade de Ville Franche . . .
" 13. Plan de la rade de Galipoly . . .
" 13½. [Plan du golfe de l Efpecy & de port Vendré auec les forts qui font dans le golfe]   Uncolored.

no. 14. Plan du golfe de l Eſpecy & de port Vendré auec les forts qui ſont dans le golfe.
" 15. Plan de la rade de S.t Eſteué [!] & de la rade des Caniers . . .
" 16. Plan de du port & de la rade de baye & de Pouſſole . . .
" 17. Plan de la ville et de la rade de Tarante . . .
" 18. Plan de l isle Rouſſe . . .
" 19. Plan de la rade de Cailiry . . .
" 20. Plan de l isle Tolare à l'eſt de l isle de Sardaigne & l isle Boſqude . . .
" 21. Plan du mouillage de l isle de S.t Pierre au sud oueſt de la Sardaigne . . .
" 22. Plan de la baye du gouf de Palme . . .
" 23. Plan du mouillage de la Faueillane . . .
" 24. Plan de la ville, port & mole de Naples . . .
" 25. Plan du port de Meſſine . . .
" 26. Plan du port de Malte.
" 27. Plan de la ville & rade de l'Auguſte . . .   1707.
" 28. Plan de la rade de Saragouze . . .
" 29. Plan de la ville & rade de Barrj . . . [!]
" 30. Plan de la ville & rade de Brundiſi . . .
" 31. Plan du mouillage d'Anconne . . .
" 32. Plan des mouillages de Rouignes . . .
" 33. Plan du golfe & mouillages de Catero . . .
" 34. Plan de la rade de l isle du Zante . . .
" 35. Plan de la rade de S. George . . .
" 36. Plan des isles de Sapience & les mouillages . . .
" 37. Plan du port du Serigue . . .
" 38. Plan du port qui eſt à l isle d'Eſquire appelé S. George . . .
" 39. Plan du port qui eſt à l isle de Lemnos . . .
" 40. Plan du port de Porte Sidre . . .
" 41. Plan du port de André . . .
" 42. Plan du port & de la rade de tantien Athene . . .
" 43. Plan des Caſtelis neuf à l entrée de Constantinople . . .
" 44. Plan des Dardaneles qui eſt du coſté de l Eurepe . . .
" 45. Plan du port and rade de Fogia Noua . . .
" 46. Plan de rade de Sire à l archipelle . . . [Verso dated 1716]
" 47. Plan du port Toron . . .
" 48. Plan du port de lipſe [!] à larchipelle . . .
" 49. Plan du port de Niou a l archipelle . . .
" 50. Plan du golfe d'Smirne . . .
" 51. Plan de l isle Solidrony . . .
" 52. Plan du mouillage de Treo à l isle de Paris . . .
" 53. Plan du port de Paris . . .
" 54. Plan des mouillages de S.t Jean de Patinos
" 55. Plan du mouillage du Caze à l archipelle . . .
" 56. Plan de l isle Carabuza . . .
" 57. Plan du golfe de la Sude à l isle de Candie . . .
" 58. Plan de la rade de Spine Longue à l isle de Candie . . .
" 59. Plan du moüillage de Larniqua à l isle de Chipre . . .
" 60. Plan du golfe d' Alezandrette . . .
" 61. Plan de la rade de Tripoli de Sirie . . .
" 62. Plan de la ville de Seide . . .
" 63. Plan des Ruines de Sour ou Tir . . .
" 64. Plan de la rade S Iean d Acre de Caiſſe & du mont Carmel.
" 67. Plan du port & rade de Tripoly de Barbarie . . .
" 68. Plan de la rade de la Goulette qui eſt la rade de Tunis . . .

**Olivier, J.**—Continued.

no. 69. Plan de la rade de porte Farine . . .
" 70. Plan de la rade de Bizerti . . .
" 71. Plan du moüillage de bonne à la coſte de Barbarie . . .
" 72. Plan du moüillage Deſtore [!] à la coſte de Barbarie . . .
" 73. Plan de la rade de Bougie à la coſte de Barbarie . . .
" 74. Plan de la rade & port d'Alger . . .
" 75. Plan des isles de Chafarine à la coſte de Barbarie . . .
" 76. Plan du moüillage de la marce d'Oram . . .
" 77. Plan de la rade de Roſe . . . [Verso dated 1796]
" 78. Plan de la rade de Palamos à la coſte d'Eſpaigne . . .
" 79. Plan du port Maon . . .
" 80. Plan de la rade de Larcudy & du port de Poüillence . . .
" 81. Plan de la rade de Mailorque . . .
" 82. Plan de la rade des Formentieres & du port d'Iuice . . .
" 83. Plan de la rade d'Ampoule . . .
" 84. Plan de la rade d'Aliquant . . .
" 85. Plan de la rade d Altea . . .
" 86. Plan du port & rade Cartagene à la coſte d'Eſpaigne . . .
" 87. Plan du Cap de Pales . . .
" 88. Plan de la rade de la Carboniere . . .
" 89. Plan du moüillage d'Almerie . . .
" 90. Plan du moüillage d'Estoponne . . . [Verso dated 1704]
" 91. Plan de la rade de Gilbatar [!] . . .
" 92. Plan du mouillage de Seute au coſté de Barbarie . . .
" 93. Plan du mouillage de Tetouan a la coſte de Barbarie . . .
" 94. Plan de la ville & rade de Tanger . . .
" 95. Plan de la baye de Cadix . . .
" 96. Plan de l entrée de la riuiere de Lisbonne . . .
" 97. Plan de la baye du cap Francois . . . & St. Domingue . . .
" 98. Islle Martinique.
" 99. Plan de Blanne.—Plan de la rade de Madére.
" [100a] Carte du golfe de Lyon . . . Par Guillaume Delile [Delisle] . . . 1725.
" 100. Archo.—Naxie du cote du nord.
" 101. [Carte des Indes Orientalles]
" 102. V. d alcudia [!]—Escolles ou port é de dilles [!]
" 103. Fort Royal en lille dé lá Martinique.
" 104. Plan de Mallagua.—Cap de' Moullin.
" [105] Plan de la rade et ville de Lhernica.
" [106] Plan du port d'aguſtà.—Plan de Saǧvsa.
" [107] Plan de la coste et seches de Barbarie . . .
" [108] Plan de l'isle de Scicile et partie de calabry [!]
" [109] Plan de la radhe de Trapani . . .
" [110] Plan du golphe de la hiacio [!]—Du golphe de Valincou.
" [111] Plan du port boniffacio.—Plan du golphe S$^{ta}$ Manza.
" [112] Plan du golphe Saint Florents.—Plan de la bayée de Calui.
" [113] Plan du mille et de Largentiere.
" [114] Brindisi.
" [115] Carte de terre neuue [!] . . . fait en l'ennee 1731.
" [116] Carte de la côte depuis Biserte jusqu'au Cap bon [!]
" [117] Carte de la coste de France.
" [118] Plan de la cote de la Louizianne ou du Missippi [!]

## STATISTICAL.

**Block, M.**
Puissance comparée des divers états de l'Europe. Ed. française. 13 maps. fol. Gotha, J. Perthes, 1862. 2808
NOTE.—Title-page wanting.
Atlas to accompany work of the same title.

## TRAVELS.

**Langlois, H.**
Atlas portatif et itinéraire de l'Europe, pour servir d'intelligence au guide des voyageurs dans cette partie du monde; composé de treize cartes et vues. 2 p. l., 8 fold. maps. 8°. Paris, H. Langlois, 1817. 2809
NOTE.—Imperfect: maps no. 5-9 wanting.

**Reichard, H. A. O.**
Atlas portatif et itinéraire de l'Europe, pour servir d'intelligence au guide des voyageurs . . . Composé de neuf grandes cartes itinéraires. 8. éd. 2 p. l., [8] fold. maps. 16°. Weimar, bureau d'industrie, 1818-[1821] 2810

CONTENTS.

no. 1. Carte itinéraire de l'Espagne et du Portugal. 1820.
" 2. Carte routière de l'Angleterre. 1820.
" 3. Post-charte von Frankreich. 1818.
" 4. Post charte von Italien. 1819.
" 5. General charte von der Schweiz . . . von C. F. Weiland. 1821.
" 6. Neueste post charte von Teutschland . . . von C. F. Weiland. 1821.
" 7. Carte itinéraire du Dañemark et d'une partie de la Suède. 1820.
" 8. Carte de la route de Leipzic à St. Pétersbourg.

**Bartholomew, J. G.**
The tourist's atlas-guide to the continent of Europe; a series of section maps & plans with notes for travellers. viii, 168 pp. incl. 107 maps. 12°. London, G. Philip & son [1896] 2811

## WARS.

**Austria.** *K. k. reichs-kriegs ministerium.*
Feldzüge des prinzen Eugen von Savoyen. (Geschichte der kämpfe Österreichs) Graphische beilagen, I–XIV, XVI, XVII. obl. fol. Wien, k. k. generalstab [1876–1892] 2812
NOTE.—"Beilage XV" wanting.

**Beaurain, J. de.**

Carte d'Allemagne pour servir à l'intelligence de l'histoire de la guerre entre les roys de France et d'Angleterre; entre le roy de Prusse et l'impératrice reine, l'électeur de Saxe, l'empire, la Suède, et la Russie. Dans laquelle on a marqué les batailles, combats, prises de villes, et camps qu'on a puy faire entrer. On y a tracé les routes publiques et joint une histoire abrégé des principaux faits militaires arrivés tant sur terre que sur mer, jusqu'aux traités de paix. Enrichie et entourée de 74 plans représentant les événements les plus mémorables arrivés pendant le cours de la guerre, com$^{c6}$ en 1755, finie en 1763. Dédiée et presentée au roi . . . 8°. Paris, 1765. 2813

> NOTE.—One large map of central Europe, cut in four parts, each folded; 67 small plans of battles, forts, etc., of the seven years war, each pasted on one leaf.
> The following maps relate to America:
> no. [ 2] Bataille sous Quebec . . . 1762.—Attaques des f$^{ts}$ de Chouaguen . . . 1756.—Attaques du f$^t$ Villiam-Henri . . . 1757.—Attaques des retranchements en avant du f$^t$ Carillon . . . 1758.
> " [11] Plan de Louisbourg . . . dans l'isle royale, au Canada . . .
> " [16] L'isle de la Guadeloupe . . . l'une des Antilles, en Amérique . . .
> " [19] Plan de Quebec . . . dans le Canada . . .
> " [27] L'isle de la Martinique . . .
> " [29] Plan du siége du fort Moro . . .

**Bodenehr, G.**

Curioses staats und kriegs theatrvm dermahliger begebenheiten durch unterschiedliche geographische, hydrographische, topographische, chronologische, genealogische, historische &c. carten abrisse und tabellen erlæutert und zu bequæmen gebrauch ausgefertiget. 11 pts. in 3 v. obl. 8°. Avgspvrg, G. Bodenehr [1710–1730?] 2814

> NOTE.—Maps relate to the wars in Germany and Europe during the 17$^{th}$ and 18$^{th}$ centuries.
> Each part has an engraved title-page.
> Maps engraved by J. G. Bodenehr, Aug. Vind and Johan Stridbeck, jun.
> The following map relates to America:
> v. 3, pt. 3, no. 26. Carte générale de l'Amérique Septentrionale et principalement des colonies françoises qui s'y trouvent avec les armes de la compagnie francoise des Indes orientales et occidentales. Gabriel Bodenehr sculps. et excudit Aug. Vind. [Contains an engraved portrait of "m$^r$ de Laws . . . controlleur général des finances du royaume de France," which would bring the date of the map to 1717]
>
> CONTENTS.
>
> v. 1. Seven maps of the world, in hemispheres, and on Mercator's projection: "Europæ compendiosa representatio," with index sheet, "Das mittellændische meer." 10 l.
> " pt. 1. Curioses staats . . . theatrvm und kriegs in Holstein Pomern und Mecklenburg. eng. title, 19 l. incl. 11 maps, 8 views.

v. 1, pt. 2. Curioses staats und kriegs theatrvm . . . [in Francken] eng. title, 102 l. incl. 59 maps, 43 views.
v. 2, " 1. Curioses staats und kriegs theatrvm . . . [in französisch. Niederl.] title, 67 l. incl. 54 maps, 12 views.
" " 2. Curioses staats und kriegs theatrvm . . . [in spanisch. Niederland] eng. title, 28 l. incl. 27 maps, 1 view.
" " 3. Curioses staats und kriegs theatrvm . . . in Hispanien und Italien. eng. title, 35 l. incl. 21 maps, 14 views.
v. 3, " 1. Curioses staats und kriegs theatrvm . . . [in Bayern] eng. title, 37 l. incl. 12 maps, 24 views.
" " 2. Curioses staats und kriegs theatrvm . . . [in Schwaben] eng. title, 37 l. incl. 16 maps, 21 views.
" " 3. Theatrum einiger der vornehmsten stædte und örther in Franckreich. eng. title, 25 l. incl. 21 maps, 4 views.
" " 4. Curioses staats und kriegs theatrvm . . . [in Savoyen] eng. title, 13 l. incl. 8 maps, 4 views.
" " 5. Curioses staats und kriegs theatrvm . . . in Lothringen, Elsas der Undern Pfaltz am Mayn, mitt einig anderen, &c. eng. title, 36 l. incl. 22 maps, 14 views.

**Camocio, G. F.**
Isole famose porti, fortezze, e terre maritime sottoposte alla ser.$^{ma}$ sig.$^{ria}$ di Venetia, ad altri principi christiani, et al sig.$^{or}$ Turco, nouamēte poste in luce. 1 p. l., [79] maps, 1 pl. obl. 12°. In Venetia, alla libraria del segno di S. Marco [1571–1572]    2815

NOTE.—Engraved title.
Maps no. 1–3, 49–52, 65, 67, 72, wanting.
The engraving at the top of the title-page represents attributes of war, cannon, shields, armor, drums, swords, etc.; at the left is Mars, at the right Neptune; at the foot are two smaller engravings, one representing a battle, the other a sea-fight, between these two are the initials N. B.
A collection of maps to illustrate the war between Turkey and Venice, 1570–73, comprising maps of the coasts and of the most important ports of Austria, Turkey, Greece, and of the principal islands of the Mediterranean sea; also of Italy, England, Ireland, Iceland.
Map no. 38 is a plan of the battle of Lepanto; no. 66 is a plan of Constantinople.

**Corréard, J.**
Atlas du guide maritime et stratégique dans la mer Noire, la mer d'Azof et sur le théatre de la guerre en Orient.   2 p. l., 40 maps. fol.  Paris, J. Corréard, 1854.    2816

NOTE.—To accompany work entitled: Guide maritime et stratégique dans la mer Noire, la mer d'Azof, et sur le théâtre de la guerre on Orient. 8°. Paris, J. Corréard, 1854.

**Dubail, A. Y. E.**
Atlas de l'Europe militaire.  2 p. l., 11 col. maps.  fol.  Paris, J. Dumaine, 1880.    2817

**Dubail, A. Y. E.**—Continued.

Cartes-croquis de géographie militaire avec un exposé sommaire des principales campagnes depuis Louis xiv jusqu'à nos jours . . . 6. éd.   1 p. l., [32] pp. incl. 14 maps.   fol.   Paris, J. Dumaine, 1880–[1881]   2818

Note.—Cover-title dated 1881.

CONTENTS.

no. 1. Frontière nord-est.—Campagnes de 1712–1793–1815.—Opérations de l'armée du Nord (1870–1871)
" 2. Frontière du Jura et des Alpes.—Campagnes de Berwick (1709 et 1711)—Opérations de 1814.—Campagne de l'Est (1870–1871)
" 3. Frontière des Pyrénées.—Campagnes de 1793–1814.
" 4. Seine.—Campagnes de 1792–1814.
" 5. France centrale.—Opérations des armées de la Loire (1870–1871)
" 6. Algérie.—Résumé de la conquête.—Considérations générales.—Statistique.
" 7. Rhin (rive gauche)—Campagnes de 1674–1799—Metz et Sedan (1870–1871)—Rhin (rive droite)—Campagne de 1796.
" 8. Elbe (Allemagne septentrionale)—Campagnes de 1806–1813–1866.
" 9. Danube moyen (Autriche)—Campagnes de 1800–1805–1809.
" 10. Roumanie et Bulgarie, Arménie.—Guerre d'Orient (1877–1878)
" 11. Russie occidentale.—Campagnes de 1807–1812.
" 12. Espagne.—Campagnes de 1808–1810.
" 13. Italie septentrionale.—Campagnes de 1796–1797–1800–1859.
" 14. États-Unis, Mexique.—Guerre de la sécession (1861–1864)—Guerre du Mexique (1862–1867)

**Dumas, M.** *i. e.* **G. M.**

Précis des événemens militaires . . . Recueil de plans et de cartes, pour servir à l'intelligence des opérations militaires décrites dans le texte . . .   1 p. l., [6] l., 90 maps, 4 pl.   fol.   [Paris, Strasbourg, Londres, Treuttel & Würtz, etc., etc., 1816–1826]   2819

Note.—To accompany his: Précis des événemens militaires, ou, essais historiques sur les campagnes de 1799 à 1814 . . .   19 v.   1816–26.
Maps by Ambroise Tardieu.

**La Feuille, D. de.**

Atlas portatif, ou le nouveau théâtre de la guerre en Europe; contenant les cartes géographiques, avec les plans des villes & forteresses les plus exposées aux révolutions présentes. Accompagné d'une nouvelle méthode pour apprendre facilement la géographie & la chronologie des potentats.   1 p. l., 14 pp., 115 maps, 8 pl.   obl. 8°.   Amsterdam, D. de La Feuille, 1706–[1708]   2820

Note.—Title-page dated 1706; date 1708 on maps no. [49] and [59]
Maps no. [20, 43] and [59], by Paul de La Feuille; no. [47] by N. Sanson d'Abbeville; no. [101], Frisia occidentalis, mutilated.
The following maps relate to America:
no. [1] Mappemonde planisphère.
" [5] L'Amérique Méridionale.
" [6] L'Amérique Septentrionale.

**Leer, G. A.**
Карты къ стратегіи (тактикѣ театра военныхъ дѣйствій) 2 pts. obl. 4°. С.-Петербургъ, П. Я. Иванова, 1885-1887. 2821

> NOTE.—Translated title: Strategical maps (military tactics in the field) by lieutenant-general Leer. St. Petersburg, lithography P. I. Ivanov, 1885–1887. Part 1 refers mainly to Napoleon's campaigns in Germany, Austria, and Italy; pt. 2, to the Franco-German war of 1870-71.
> To accompany the following work: Записки стратегіи Леера. Вып. 1-2; 1880.
> Maps and plans numbered continuously; pt. 1: I-XXXIV; pt. 2: XXXV-XLIII, XLIII[b], XLIX-LX, LX²-LX[14].
>
> CONTENTS.
>
> pt. I. Cover-title, 21 l. incl. 33 maps, 1 pl. 1885.
> " II. Cover-title, 27 l. incl. 33 maps, 7 pl. 1887.

**Marga, A.**
Géographie militaire. Atlas. 2 v. 4°. Paris, Berger-Levrault & cie. 1884–1885. 2822

> NOTE.—v. 1, 4. ed. viii pp., 129 maps. 1885; v. 2, 3. ed. viii pp., 149 maps. 1884.
> To accompany work of same title.
> The following maps relate to America:
> v. 1, no. 121. Carte du monde avec indications des colonies françaises.
> "   " 127. Colonies françaises en Amérique.
> "   " 128. La Martinique. Baie de fort de France.
> "   " 129. Rade de la Pointe-à-Pitre.
>
> CONTENTS.
>
> v. 1. Généralités et France.
> " 2. Principaux états de l'Europe.

**Mortier, P.**
Atlas nouveau des cartes géographiques choisies, ou le grand théâtre de la guerre en Brabant, Flandres . . . sur le Rhin, Mofelle, Mayn . . . dans la Bavière, Souabe . . . le théâtre de la guerre du Nord, &c. et toutes les cartes géographiques tant générales que particulières d'Italie, le Véronois, Vicence . . . auquel on a joint les cartes d'Efpagne, Portugal, de la France &c. le théâtre de la guerre en Amérique . . . 4 p. l., 32, 4 pp., 1 l., 61 maps. fol. Amsterdam, P. Mortier, 1703. 2823

> NOTE.—Title printed in red and black. Engraved. colored title, "Atlas minor ad usum serenissimi Burgundiæ ducis. Atlas françois à l'usage de monseigneur le duc de Bourgogne . . ."
> Sanson's "Introduction à la géographie, où sont la géographie astronomique . . . la géographie naturelle . . . la géographie historique . . . Par le sieur Sanson d'Abbeville. Amsterdam, P. Mortier" [n. d.] 2 p. l., 31, [1] pp. no. [5–6], "Table géographique pour savoir combien il y a de lieues entre les principales villes de l'Europe."
> 2 l. between maps no. 46–47, "L'état présent de toute l'Italie"; 2 l. between maps no. 47–48 contain maps of the cities of Milan, Pavie, Crema, Mantoue, Brescia & Bergamo.

**Mortier, P.**—Continued.
  Maps no. 45-46 have border illustrations.
  Maps by Jaillot, Vaultier, Sanson, Schenk, Blaeu and Mortier.
  The following maps relate to America:
   no. [1] Carte générale de toutes les costes du monde, et les pays nouvellement découvert.
    " [2] Théâtre de la guerre en Amérique telle qu'elle est à présent possédée par les espagnols, anglois, françois, et hollandois.  2 sheets.

**Pramberger, E.**
  Atlas zum studium der militar-geographie von Mittel-Europe.
  . . .   1 p. l., 10 (*i. e.* 11) maps.  fol.  Wien, E. Hölzel [1907]
  2824

**Raspe, G. N.**
  Schauplatz des gegenwærtigen kriegs, durch accurate plans von den wichtigften bataillen, belagerungen und feldlægern.   1 p. l., 15 l., 160 maps.  obl. 8°.  Nurnberg, G. N. Raspe [1757-1764]  2825

  Note.—10 pts. in 1 v.
  Engraved colored title.
  The title-pages of pts. 1-4 within ornamental borders; pt. 6 lacks title-page. Titles vary. Simultaneously with pts. 6-10 appeared an anonymous sketch of the seven years' war, published by G. N. Raspe in 6 pts. under title: Entwurf einer geschichte des gegenwårtigen krieges . . . Frankfurt und Leipzig (pts. 3-6: Nůrnberg) 1762-64.
  Imperfect: map no. 108, pt. 6, Insel Aix, wanting.
  The following maps relate to America:
   no. 97. L'Amérique Septentrionale.
    " 109. Plan des hafens und festung Louisburg.
    " 113. Grund riss der americanischen insuln Cape Breton, St. Jean, und Anticosti . . .
    " 126. Plan der stadt Quebec . . .
    " 127. Plan der insuln Guadeloupe und Marie Galante.
    " 135. Karte von der insel Montreal.  1760.
    " 141. Plan der insul Martinique.
    " 142. Karte von der insel Grenada und den Grenadillen in Nord America.
    " 143. Karte von der insel St. Lucia.
    " 147. Carte von der insel Terre-Neuve.
    " 152. Plan der insul Cuba.
    " 156. Isles Philippines.

**Schenk, P.**
  Le théâtre de Mars contenant XLVIII nouvelles cartes géographiques de la haute et basse Allemagne, partie de la France, d'Italie et autres païs adjacents où l'on fait aprésent la guerre contre les couronnes de France et d'Espagne . . .   8 p. l., 29 pp., 48 maps on 96 l.   12°. Amfterdam, P. Schenk & A. Braakman, 1706.   2826

  Note.—Engraved title-page preceded by two printed title-pages in red and black entitled: [1] Schouw-tonneel des oorlogs verbeeld in 50 nieuwe geographische land-caarten der spaanfche, en vereenigde Nederlanden, hoog en neder Duytfland, de aan den Rhyn gelegen Keur- en vorften dommen op en neder Elſas, groot Lotheringe, Bourgondien, Switſerland, Savoyen en Piemont, nevens een gedeelten van Frankryk, Italien en andere aangrenſende landſchappen, waartegenwoordig den oorlog gevoerd word op een nieuwe manier tot nut en gemak geſchikt voor alle officiers en ryzigers . . . by gevoegt, een regiſter der voornaamſte steden, forten, en andere voorname plaatzen en rivieren . . . Amsterdam, A. Braakman en P. Schenk, 1706.—[2] Le théâtre de Bellone contenant 50 nouvelles cartes géographiques des Païs-bas eſpagnols-unies . . .

### Visscher, N.

Variæ tabulæ geographicæ in quibus loca in orbe bello flagrantia conspiciuntur.   2 p. l., 36 maps, 1 pl. fol.   Amstelodami, â Nicolas Visscher [1709?]   2827

> NOTE.—Visscher began this atlas which was probably finished or published by his widow in 1709 or later, as the title of map no. 16 contains the following: "Mise au jour chez la veve de Nicolaus Visscher."
> Engraved title, "Atlas minor sive totius orbis terrarumcontracta delinea[ta] ex conatibus Nico. Visscher" . . . Signed "Ger: de Lairesse delin: & sculp."— Titles in latin, french and dutch on p. l. 2.
> The maps generally relate to the countries in which were fought the wars between 1667 and 1697 and the war of the spanish succession beginning in 1701. Several maps have indexes on the reverse.
> The following map relates to America:
> no. 1. Orbis terrarum nova et accuratissima tabula.

## GENERAL.

(Arranged chronologically)

### 1594

### Quad, M.

Europæ totivs orbis terrarvm partis praestantissimae, vniversalis et particvlaris descriptio . . .   5 p. l., 50 maps on 100 l., 1 l. 4°.   Coloniæ, ex officina typographica J. Buſsemechers, 1594.   2828

> NOTE.—Engraved title-page. Several maps adorned with vignette portraits of sovereigns and with the arms of the countries represented by the maps. Title-page and maps colored.
> Imperfect: map no. 12, Franconia, lacks first leaf, i. e., one half of the map including the description on recto, the same map from another edition where it is numbered 23 and not colored is inserted.
> Many of the maps are reduced copies of those in Ortelius' Theatrum orbis terrarum.

### 1620

### Blaeu, W. J.

Le flambeav de la navigation, monſtrant la deſcription & délineation de toutes les coſtes & havres de la mer occidentale, septentrionale & orientale. Selon les inſtructions des plus entendus autheurs des eſcrits de marine, & déclarations des plus expérimentez pilotes: illuſtrè de diverſes cartes marines, & comprins en deux livres. A quoy est adjouſtée une inſtruction de l'art de marine, avec tables de

**Blaeu, W. J.**—Continued.

la déclination du soleil fuivant les observations de Tycho Brahé, dreffées sur le méridian d'Amfterdam: enfemble nouvelles tables & repréfentation du droit ufage de l'eftoile du nord & autres eftoiles fixes . . . 2 pts. in 1 v. obl. 4°. Amsterdam, Iean Ieanffon, 1620. 2829

NOTE.—Collation: pt. 1, 4 p. l., [52], 119 pp., 20 maps; pt, 2, 127, [1] pp., 22 maps. The french title is pasted over part of the original dutch title which reads: Licht der zee-vaert daerinne claerlijck beschreven ende afghebeeldet werden alle de custen ende havenen vande westersche, noordsche, oostersche, ende middelandsche zeën . . . Amst. . . . 1620. *cf.* Tiele, Nederlandsche bibliographie, pp. 31–32.

Engraved frontispiece. Titles on maps in french and dutch.

Each part has a special title-page: pt. 1. Le premier livre dv phalot de la mer dans leqvel sont descriptes et representeez tovtes les costes et havres de la mer occidentale: nommément de Hollande, Zeelande, Flandres, France, Efpaigne & Barbarie jufques au Cap de Geer. En oultre des ifles de Canarie. Madère & des ifles Flamandes: enfemble les coftes occidentales & méridionales d'Yrlande & d'Angleterre.—pt. 2. Devxiesme livre dv phalot de mer, la ov sont descrites tovtes les costes, havres, & ifles de la mer septentrionale & orientale: comme de Frife, Iutlandt, Danemarck, Pomeranie, Pruffe, Livonie, Suède, Norwège, Lapponie, & Mofcovie. Item les coftes septentrionales & orientales d'Efcoffe & Angleterre. Nouvellement traduict de flameng en françois.

### 1680?

**Visscher, N.**

N: Visscheri Germania inferior sivè xvii provinciarum geographicæ generales ut et particulares tabulæ.—Kaert-boeck van de xvii nederlandtsche provincien. 1 p. l., 52 col. maps. fol. [Amsterdam, 1680?] 2830

NOTE.—Engraved title signed, "G. Lairesse in[venit] sculp."

Map no. 6, "Novissima et accuratissima xvii provinciarum Germaniæ inferioris delineatio", dedicated to Joh. Munter, burgomaster of Amsterdam from 1670 to 1680. *cf.* Tiele, Nederlandsche bibliographie. Amsterdam, 1884.

The following maps are dated:

no. 35. Ducatus Brunsvicensis . . . descriptio geographica. 1650.

" 48. Tabula Russiæ. 1651.

Several maps have vignettes engraved by Rom. de Hooghe.

Maps by the following cartographers: B. Schotanus, J. Janssonius, Fred de Wit, Justus Danckers, J. Laurenberg.

Includes maps of the Netherlands, the world, Asia, America, Africa, the several countries of Europe, and plans and views of Antverp, Moscow and Candia.

The following maps relate to America:

no. 1. Orbis terrarum nova et accuratissima tabula.

" 5. Novissima et accuratissima totius Americæ descriptio.

### 1680–1683

**English, The,** atlas . . . 4 v. fol. Oxford, for Moses Pitt, 1680–1682. 2831

NOTE.—"In 1680 appeared the first volume of the magnificent publication for which Pitt is chiefly known, 'The English atlas,' a work formerly held in great estimation. Bishop William Nicolson [q. v.] and Richard Peers [q. v.] were generally responsible for the geographical and historical descriptions, and their names appear on some of the title-pages, but Thomas Lane, Obadiah Walker, and dr. Todd had compiled the first volume; the maps are mainly based on Janssen's 'Atlas.' It was to extend to eleven volumes, but only four volumes, and the text of a fifth, large folio, appeared . . ." *cf.* Dictionary of national biography, under M. Pitt.

The following maps relate to America:

vol. 1, no. 1. Orbis terrarum nova et accuratissima tabula. Auctore Ioanne à Loon.
" " 2. Nova totius terrarum orbis geographica ac hydrographica tabula.
" " 3. A map of the North Pole, and the parts adjoining.

CONTENTS.

v. 1. Pitt, Moses (fl. 1654–1696) Description of the places next the North Pole; as also of Muscovy, Poland, Sweden, Denmark and their severa dependances. 1680.
" 2. Nicolson, William (1655–1727) Description of part of the empire of Germany, viz, The Upper and Lower Saxony; the dukedoms of Mecklenburg, Bremen, Magdeburg, &c. the marquisates of Brandenburg and Misnia, with the territories adjoining. The palatinate of the Rhine: and the Kingdom of Bohemia. 1681.
" 3. —— Description of the remaining part of the empire of Germany, viz, Schwaben, the palatinate of Bavaria, arch-dukedom of Austria, kingdom of Hungary, principality of Transylvania, the circle of Westphalia; with the neighbouring provinces. 1683.
" 4. Peers, Richard (1645–1690) Description of the seventeen provinces of the Low Countries, or Netherlands. 1682.

## 1689–1692

**Jacobsz, T., Doncker, H.,** *and* **Goos, H.**

The lightning columne, or, sea-mirrour, containing the sea-coafts of the northern, eaftern and weftern navigation: setting forth in divers neceffaire sea-cards, all the ports, rivers, bayes, roads, depths and sands; very curioufly placed on its due polus heigt furnifhed. With the difcoveries of the chief countries, and on what cours and diftance they lay one from another. Never theretofore fo clearly laid open, and here and there very deligently bettered and augmented for the ufe of all seamen. As alsoo the situation of the northernly countries, as iflands, the strate Davids, the ifle of Jan Mayen, Bears ifland, old Greenland, Spitzbergen, and Nova Zembla: adorneth with many sea-cards and difcoveries. Gathered out ôf the experience and practice of divers pilots and lovers of the famous art of navigation. Where unto is added a brief inftruction of the art of navigation, together with new tables of the suns declination, wit an new almanach. 3 parts in 1 v. 2 p. l., 29, [3], 96, 90 pp.; 1 p. l., 4 l., 3–104 pp., 84 maps. fol. Amsterdam, printed by C. Loots-Man, 1689–[1692] 2832

**Jacobsz, T., Doncker, H.,** *and* **Goos, H.**—Continued.

NOTE.—"With previledge for fiftheen iears." See also title 2833.

In the "priviledge" on p. l. 2, granted to Henry Doncker, Caspar Loots-man and Henry Goos, this work is described as, "A sea-book, containing the eaſtern, weſtern and straits navigation, entitled The mariners sea-mirrour and the new great sea-mirrour, being one book, yet bearing a threefold name and title, with the third part annexed to the end thereof, called The straits book" . . .

The "Lighting colom of the Midland-sea . . . 1692", bound at the end, is considered the third part of the work.

The following names appear on the maps: Theunis Iacobſz; Casparus Loots-Man; Iacob Theuniſz, Iacobus en Casparus Loots-man.

In pt. 3, map no. 1, is by Theunis Iacobſz; map no. 2 by Anthoni Iacobſz, the others are not credited.

CONTENTS.

Priviledge. 1 l.—A short introduction in the art of navigation. pp. 1-29.— Almanach, to the yeare 1695. pp. [30-31]—A table . . . of the eastern-water . . . p. [32]

pt. I, book I. Easterne navigation, contaigning the diſcription of the North-Sea, the coaſt of Holland, Freeſland, Holſteyn, Jutland, Meklenburgh and Denemark to Valſterboen, in the iſland of Rugen, and with all the coaſt of Norway to Dronten: as alſo de eaſt-ſide of England and Scotland. pp. 1-52, 17 maps.

" " II. Eastern navigation, contaigning the deſcription of the sea-coaſts of Norway, Finmarck, Lapand and the whole White Sea. pp. 53-66, 9 maps.

" " III. Easterne and northerne navigation, contaigning the deſcription of Yceland, Greenland, or the Strait of Davids: likewiſe the situation of John Mayens iſland and Spitzbergen: alſo situation of Candenoes eaſtward, throug Weygats, to the Tartariſh or Yce-sea. pp. 67-76, 3 maps.

" " IV. Easterne navigation, contaigning the diſcription of the whole Eaſt-sea. pp. 77-96, 7 maps.

pt. II, book I. Westerne navigation, containing the deſcription of the sea-coaſts of Holland, Zealand, and Flanders, from Teſſel to the heads of Dover and Calice. pp. 1-15, 5 maps.

" " II. Western navigation, containing the deſcription of the sea-coaſts of France, from Blackeneſſe to Uſhand and the coaſt of Englant, from Dover weſt-wards, tho the Lands-end the channel of Briſtow, with al the sea-coaſts of Ireland. pp. 16-50, 8 maps.

" " III. Western navigation, containing the deſcription of France, Biſcay, Galiſſia, Portugall and Algarve, from Heyſſant to the straight of Gibralter. pp. 51-80, 11 maps.

" " IV. Western navigation, containing the deſcription of the sea-coaſts, from Barbarie, Gualata, Arguyn, Genehoe and the Flemiſh and Canary iſlands together, from the straigt of Gibralter to Cabo Verde. pp. 81-90, 5 maps.

pt. III. Lighting colom of the Midland-sea containing a deſcription of all the knowne coasts, iſlands, sands, depthes and roads: begining from the naroweſt of the streat unto Alexandrette in the Levant. Amsterdam, printed by C. Loots-Man, 1692. 4 p. l., 3-104 pp., 19 maps.

## 1690

**Seller, J.**

The english pilot. First book, first part. Describing the sea-coafts, capes, head-lands, bays, roads, harbours, rivers and ports together with the soundings, sands, rocks and dangers in the southern navigation upon the coafts of England, Holland, France, Ireland, Spain, Portugal, to the straits-mouth, and fo off to the western iflands. Shewing the courfes and diftances from one place to another: the setting of the tydes and currents: the ebbing and flowing of the sea. Cum privilegio regis majeftatis . . . 1 p. l., 24, 21–52, [2], 53–82 pp., 24 maps. fol. London, G. Larkin, 1690.

[*With* Jacobsz, T., *or* A., *called* Loots-Man. The lightningh columne, or sea-mirrour. fol. Amsterdam, C. Loots-Man, 1692. Title 2834]     2833

> NOTE.—Maps made and sold by John Seller, John Colson, William Fisher, James Atkinson, John Thornton, R. Mount.
> The "Atlas maritimus, or, the sea atlas of the world," by John Thornton, 1703, is copied almost verbatum from the above.
>
> CONTENTS.
>
> pt. I, book I. [General title] 4 maps.
> " " II. A defcription of the south-coafts of England, with the coafts of Ireland, Holland, Flanders, France, Bifcay, Portugal, Spain, part of Barbary, with the Canary and Madera-iflands. 24, 21–52, [2], 53–82 pp., 20 maps.

## 1692

**Jacobsz, T.,** *or* **A.,** *called* **Loots-Man, C.**

The lightningh columne, or sea-mirrour, contaigning the sea-coafts of the northern and eaftern navigation, setting forth in divers neceffaire sea-cards, all the ports, rivers, bayes, roads, depths and sands, very curioufly placed on its due polus height furnished. With the difcoveris of the chief countries, and on what cours and diftance they lay one from another. Never theretofore fo clearly laid open and here and there very diligently bettered and augmented for the ufe of all seamen. As alsoo the situation of the northernly countries, as iflands, the strate Davids, the ifle of Jan Mayen, Bears Ifland, old Greenland, Spitzbergen and Nova Zembla: adorneth with many sea-cards and difcoveries. Where unto is added a brief inftruction of the art of navigation, together with new tables of the suns declination, with an new almanach. Gathered out of the experience and practice of divers pilots and lovers of the famous art of navigation. 1 p. l., 10, 15–24, 27–29, [3], 96 pp., 35 maps. fol. Amsterdam, C. Loots-Man, 1692.     2834

> NOTE.—"With previlege for fifteen jears."
> This copy does not contain pts. 2 and 3, found in the 1689 ed. See title 2832. "The English pilot", by John Seller, London, 1690, is bound with this. See title 2833.

**Jacobsz, T.**, *or* **A**, *called* **Loots-Man, C.**—Continued.

pp. 11-14, 25-26, wanting.
The following names appear on the maps: Theunis Iacobsz; Casparus Lootsman; Iacob Theunisz; Jacobus en Casparus Loots man.
The family of Jacobsz, map makers and printers of Amsterdam, were called Loots-Man, meaning sea pilot. Theunis or Anthonie Iacobsz made the maps. Caspar is mentioned as the printer or publisher although his name appears on some of the maps. Jacob Theunis was the son of Theunis Anthonic. The name appears in various forms and spelling.—*cf.* Tiele, Nederlandsche bibliographie. Amsterdam, 1884.

CONTENTS.

A short instruction in the art of navigation. pp. 1-29.—Almanach, to the year 1695. pp. [30-31]—A table . . . of the eastern-water . . . p. [32]
pt. I. book I. Easterne navigation, contaigning the discription of the North-Sea, the coaft of Holland, Freefland, Holsteyn, Jutland, Meklenburgh and Denemark to Valfterboen, in the ifland of Rugen, and with all the coaft of Norway to Dronten: as alfo de eaft-fide of England and Scotland. pp. 1-52, 17 maps.
" " II. Easterne navigation, contaigning the defcription of the seacoafts of Norway, Finmarck, Lapland and the whole White sea. pp. 53-66, 8 maps.
" " III. Eafterne and northerne navigation, contaigning the defcription of Yceland, Greenland, or the Strait of Davids: likewife the situation of John Mayens ifland and Spitzbergen: alfo situation of Candenoes eaftward, throug Weygats, to the Tartarifh or Yce-sea. pp. 67-76, 3 maps.
" " VI. Easterne navigation, contaigning the difcription of the whole Eaft-sea. pp. 77-96, 7 maps.

**1694**

**Hooghe, R.**

Zee atlas tot het gebruik van de vlooten des konings van Groot Britanje, gemaakt volgens de nieuwste memorien der ervarenste ingenieurs en stuurlieden, en verrykt met de porfilen van de vermaardste zeehavenen en zeesteden van Europa . . .   1 p. l., front., 9 maps. fol. Amsterdam, P. Mortier, 1694.   2835

NOTE.—With De fransche neptunus. Amsterdam, 1693-1700. See title 517.
Colored, engraved title contains a latin quotation and the following: Atlas maritime. Tom. 2. Romanus de Hooghe J. U. D. et Com. Reg. tab: hanc suis. D. dedit. auct. et inv. 1693. Amsterdam, P. Mortier.
The small engraving on the second title-page, by J. van Vianen, is a dupli.cate of that on the second title page of De fransche neptunus.
Maps are colored and embellished by 63 views of cities, harbors, fortresses, etc. Titles on maps are in french; the following titles are given on the title-page:

CONTENTS.

no. 1. De kaart van Holland, Zeeland, Vlaanderen, Picardyen, en Normandyen.
" 2. De kaart der omleggende oorden van Dieppe.
" 3. De kaart van Normandyen en Bretagne.
" 4. De kaart van Bretagne, van St Malo af tot aan den mond der rivier de Loire.

no. 5. De kaart van de rivier van Bourdeaux af tot aan St Sebastiaan.
" 6. De kaart der omleggend oorden van het eiland Oleron.
" 7. De kaart der kusten van Engeland, van de Teems af tot aan Portland.
" 8. De kaart der kusten van Engeland, van de Sorlings af tot aan Portland.
" 9. De kaart van de Middellandsche zee.

## 1716

**English, The, pilot.** The second part. Defcribing the sea-coafts, capes, head-lands, soundings, sands, shoals, rocks and dangers. The bays, roads, harbours, rivers and ports in the whole northern navigation. Shewing the courfes and diftances from one place to another: the setting of the tides and currents; the ebbing and flowing the sea. With many other things belonging to the art of navigation. Being furnifhed with new and exact draughts, charts and descriptions; gathered from the experience and practice of divers able and expert navigators of our own and other nations. Defcribing the north coaft of England and Scotland, with the iflands of Orkney, Shetland, Lewis, Farre, Iceland, &c. The sea-coaft of Flanders, Zealand, Holland, Germany, Denmark, Norway, Finland, Lapland, Russia, the ifland of Vaigts and Nova Zembla as far as the Tartarian-sea. Alfo Greenland, Trinity-Ifland, Cherry-Ifland, Hope-Ifland, &c. The sea coafts of Sweden, east Finland, Lyfland, Prussia, Pomeren, &c. With all the iflands belonging to the faid countries in the Baltick-sea. 1 p. l., 22, 58 pp., 34 maps. fol. London, for R. & W. Mount & T. Page, 1716. 2836

## 1718

**English, The, pilot.** Part I. Describing the sea-coafts, capes, head-lands, bays, roads, harbours, rivers, and ports, together with the soundings, sands, rocks, and dangers in the southern navigation upon the coafts of England, Scotland, Ireland, Holland, Flanders, Spain, Portugal, to the straights-mouth, with the coafts of Barbary, and off to the Canary, Madera, Cape de Verd, and Weftern Iflands. Shewing the courfes and diftances from one place to another. The setting of the tides and currents. The ebbing and flowing of the sea, &c. 1 p. l., 16, [3], 28–88, 93–100 pp., 24 maps (2 maps in text) fol. London, for R. & W. Mount & T. Page, 1718. 2837

NOTE.—Pagination irregular.

## 1723

**English, The, pilot.** The second part. Describing the sea-coafts, capes, head-lands, soundings, sands, shoals, rocks and dangers. The bays, roads, harbours, rivers and ports in the whole northern navigation. Shewing the courfes and diftances from one place to another; the fetting of the tides and currents; the ebbing and flowing of the sea.

**English, The, pilot.**—Continued.

With many other things belonging to the art of navigation. Being furnifhed with new and exact draughts, charts and defcriptions; gathered from the experience and practice of divers able and expert navigators of our own and other nations. Defcribing the north coaft of England and Scotland, with the iflands of Orkney, Shetland, Lewis, Farre, Iceland, &c. The sea coaft of Flanders, Zealand, Holland, Germany, Denmark, Norway, Finland, Lapland, Ruffia, the ifland of Vaigats, and Nova Zembla, as far as the Tartarian sea. Alfo Greenland, Trinity-Ifland, Cherry-Ifland, Hope-Ifland, &c. Sea coafts of Sweden, eaft-Finland, Lyfland, Pruffia, Pomerina, &c. With all the iflands belonging to the faid countries in the Balticksea. 1 p. l., 20, 58 pp., 31 maps. fol. London, for T. Page & W. Mount & F. Mount, 1723. 2838

### 1723
**Norris, J.**

A compleat sett of new charts, containing the North-sea, Cattegatt, and Baltick; wherein the head-lands, iflands, soundings, banks, shoals and dangers are laid down in their proper places, and the errors of the former charts corrected, by the obfervations of the britifh officers, belonging to the squadron employ'd in thofe seas. Also draughts, of feveral particular parts of the coaft, which contain roads, bays, harbours, fuers, and paffages at large, being preferable to any one of this kind heretofore publifhed . . . 2 p. l., 20 maps. fol. London, for T. Page, & W. & F. Mount, 1723. 2839

### 1735
**Ratelband, J.**

Kleyne en beknopte atlas, of tooneel des oorlogs in Europa. [anon.] 2 p. l., 16 pp., 216 maps, pls. obl. fol. t' Amsterdam, J. Ratelband & co. 1735. 2840*

NOTE.—Imperfect: pls. no. 162, 163–164, wanting.
Manuscript index, 1 leaf.

### 1752
**Bougard, R.**

Le petit flambeau de la mer; ou, le véritable guide des pilotes côtiers; où il est clairement enseigné la maniére de naviguer le long de toutes les côtes de France, d'Angleterre, d'Irlande, d'Espagne, de Portugal, d'Italie, de Sicile, de Malte, de Corse & de Sardaigne, & autres isles du détroit; & des côtes de Barbarie, depuis le cap Bon jusqu'au cap Verd . . . Dernière éd. Par le feu sieur Bougard . . . cor. & augm. 3 p. l., 415, [19] pp. incl. charts, diagrs. 12°. Havre de Grace, chez la veuve de G. Gruchet & P. Faure, 1752. 2841

NOTE.—First edition published in 1684. For bibliographical information, see title 2852.

### 1758

**English, The, pilot.** For the southern navigation: describing the sea-coasts, capes, headlands, bays, roads, harbours, rivers and ports: together with the soundings, sands, rocks and dangers on the coast of England, Scotland, Ireland, Holland, Flanders, Spain, Portugal, to the streight's mouth; with the coasts of Barbary, and off to the Canary, Madeira, Cape de Verde and Western-Islands. Shewing the courses and distances from one place to another: the setting of the tides and currents; the ebbing and flowing of the sea, &c. 1 p. l., 92 pp., 18 maps, 1 map in text. fol. London, for W. & J. Mount, T. Page & son, 1758. 2842

### 1764

**English, The, pilot.** For the southern navigation: describing the sea-coasts, capes, headlands, bays, roads, harbours, rivers and ports: together with the soundings, sands, rocks and dangers on the coast of England, Scotland, Ireland, Holland, Flanders, Spain, Portugal, to the streight's mouth; with the coasts of Barbary and off to the Canary, Madeira, Cape de Verde and Western Islands. Shewing the courses and distances from one place to another; the setting of the tides and currents; the ebbing and flowing of the sea, &c. 1 p. l., 92 pp., 21 maps, 3 maps in text. fol. London, for J. Mount & T. Page, 1764. 2843

### 1775

**English, The, pilot.** Describing the sea-coasts, capes, headlands, soundings, sands, shoals, rocks and dangers. The bays, roads, harbours, rivers and ports in the whole northern navigation: shewing the courses and distances from one place to another; the setting of the tides and currents; the ebbing and flowing of the sea, with many other things belonging to the art of navigation. Being furnished with new and exact draughts, charts, and descriptions; gathered from the experience and practice of divers able and expert navigators of our own and other nations. Describing the north coast of England and Scotland, with the islands of Orkney, Shetland, Lewits, Farro, Ireland, &c. The sea-coast of Flanders, Zealand, Holland, Germany, Denmark, Norway, Finland, Lapland, Russia, the islands of Waigats, and Nova Zembla, as far as the Tartarian sea. Also Greenland, Trinity-Island, Cherry-Island, Hope-Island, &c. The sea coast of Sweden, east-Findland, Lyfland, Prussia, Pomerania, &c. With all the islands belonging to the said countries in the Baltic-sea. 1 p. l., 78 pp., 31 maps. fol. London, for J. Mount, T. Page & W. Mount, 1775. 2844

## 1789–1791

**Reilly, F. J. J. von.**
[Schauplaz der welt . . .—Atlas oder schauplaz der 5 teile der welt . . .] v. 1 in 3 pts. obl. 8°. [Wien, 1789–1791]  2845
   Note.—Without title-page.
   Imperfect: v. 2–3 wanting.
   Maps engraved by Ign. Albrecht.
   Woltersdorf's "Repertorium" gives the following collation: [v. 1] enthält ausser 3 einleitungskarten, die karten 1–91, Ost- und N. Europa.—[v. 2, pt. 1] Deutschland und Helvezien, (92–427) und eine uebersichtskarte; [pt. 2] Italien, Spanien, Portugall, Niederland; [pt. 3] Frankreich.—[v. 3] Asien, Afrika, Amerika, (428–700) ferner sind 48 wappentafeln bei dem werke.

## 1790

**English, The, pilot,** for the southern navigation: describing the sea-coafts, capes, headlands, bays, roads, harbours, rivers and ports: together with the soundings, sands, rocks and dangers, on the coafts of England, Scotland, Ireland, Holland, Flanders, Spain, Portugal, to the streight's-mouth; with the coafts of Barbary, and off to the Canary, Madeira, Cape de Verde and Weftern-iflands. Shewing the courfes and diftances from one place to another; the setting of the tides and currents; the ebbing and flowing of the sea, &c. 1 p. l., 84 pp., 18 maps, 4 maps in text. fol. London, for Mount & Davidson, 1790.  2846

## 1792

**English, The, pilot,** for the southern navigation: describing the sea-coafts, capes, headlands, bays, roads, harbours, rivers and ports: Together with the soundings, sands, rocks and dangers on the coaft of England, Scotland, Ireland, Holland, Flanders, Spain, Portugal, to the streight's mouth; with the coafts of Barbary, and off to the Canary, Madeira, Cape de Verde, and Wefstern iflands, shewing the courses and distances from one place to another . . . 1 p. l., 92 pp., 20 sheet maps, 1 map in text. fol. London, for Mount & Davidson, 1792.  2847

## 1792–1803

**Neptune, Le, françois,** ou [recueil des cartes marines, levées et gravées par ordre du roy. Premier volume, contenant les côtes de l'Europe sur l'océan . . .] 2 p. l., [8], 49 maps on 96 l., pl. fol. [Paris, imprimerie royale, 1792–1803]  2848
   Note.—Engraved title.
   pp. [1–8] of the introduction contain "Remarques sur les cartes."
   According to p. [7], the first edition was published at Paris, in 1693. M. Sauveur, de l'académie royale des sciences, and m. de Chazelles, ingénieur de la marine, were considered the authors.

Maps are similar to those of De fransche neptunus, of nieuwe atlas van de zeekarten ... Amsterdam, 1693. See title 517.

Brunet, Graesse, Quérard and la Bibliothèque Nationale mention a 1753 edition, and attribute it to m. Bellin.

"Neptune (Le) français; ou, receuil des cartes marines (par Ch. Pene) avec un mémoire sur les cartes ... Ce volume se joint à l'hydrographie française. Les nouveaux tirages de ces trois volumes, sont plus estimés que les anciens, parceque les cartes ont été rectifiées et qu'ensuite on en a ajouté de nouvelles." cf. Quérard.

The table of contents for v. 3 is the same as that for v. 1, given on p. [6]
The following maps are not in the table:

no. $8^2$-$8^4$. Reconnoissance du cours du Hont, ou Wester Schelde (Escaut occidental) depuis Antwerpen (Anvers) jusqu'à l'embouchure ...
" $9^2$-$9^3$. Côte orientale d'Angleterre, depuis South Foreland jusques et compris l'embouchure de l'Humber ... l'an vi de la république.
" $11^2$. Carte particulière de la mer d'Irlande appellée communement, canal St Georges ... l'an vi de la république.
" $11^3$. Carte particulière du canal de Bristol ... l'an vi de la république.
" 13. Carte de l'ile de Wight et de la côte adjacente de Hampshire ... en l'an xii.
" $13^2$. Carte réduite de l'entrée de la mer d'Irlande et du canal de Bristol ... l'an vi de la république.
" $18^2$. Reconnoissance hydrographique de la côte nord de France ...
" $13^3$-$18^9$. Côtes de France ... 1792.
" $32^2$. Plan des havres de Ferrol, Betanze et la Corogne, d'après les plans levés par D. vic. Tofino, en 1787. Publié par ordre du ministre ... 1792.

## 1792–1831

**France.** *Ministère de la marine et des colonies.*

[A collection of charts by various hydrographers, including don Vincente Tofino, St. Jacques-Sylvabelle, Verguin, Beautemps-Beaupré, Bernard, Garnier, Thulis, and m. Hell, capitaine de frégate] 101 maps on 74 l., 2 pl. fol. [Paris, depôt général de la marine, 1792–1831]     2849

NOTE.—Without title-page and text.
Maps dated 1792–1831.

CONTENTS.

no. 208. Anse de la Herradura.—Mouillage de Almunecar.—Anse des Berengueles.—Anse de Belilla.
" 209. Plage de Salobrena.—Mouillage du château de Ferro.—Plan de Cala-Honda.—Mouillage d'Adra.
" 210. Côte méridionale d'Espagne ...—Mouillage d'Almeria.—Mouillage de Roquetas.—Mouillage de St Francisco de Paula ...
" 211. Plan de l'anse St Joseph et du port Genois.—Port de San Pedro.—Anse de los Escullos ...—Mouillage de la Carbonera.
" 212. Plan du port et village de las Aguilas.—Anses d'Almazarron et de la Subida.—Mouillage du mont de Cope.—Anse de Portus.
" 213. Plan de la ville, du port et de l'arsenal de Carthagene ...
" 214. Port de Por Man.—Anse de Torre Vieja.—Mouillage de l'île Grosa.—Mouillage de Lugar Nuevo.

**France**—Continued.

no. 215. Côte orientale d'Espagne . . . 1793.
" 216. Baie d'Alicante.—Rade de Benidorme.—Mouillage d'Altea.
" 217. Anse de Calpe.—Rade d'Almorayra.—Anse de Calpe.—Mouillage de Xavia.
" 218. Plan de la ville et du port de Denia. —Mouillage du cap Cullera.— Môle et grao de Valence.
" 219. Port des Alfaques.—Mouillage de Peniscola.—Port de Fangal.
" 220. Ville et port de Tarragone.—Ville, port et rade de Barcelone.
" 221. Mouillage de Salou.—Port de Blanes.—Plage et mouillage de Mataro.— Mouillage de Lloret.
" 222. Mouillage de Palamos.—Îles Medas.—Mouillage de Tosa.—Port de San Feliu de Quixols.
" 223. Port de Cadaqués.—Mouillage de Roses.—Port de Santa Cruz . . .
" 224. Baie de Palme . . . 1793.—Insets: Port-Pi . . . 1786.—Port de Andrache . . .—Port de Soller . . .—Port de l'île Cabrera . . .— Port Petra.—Cala-Longa . . . 1786.
" 225. Carte réduite des côtes de France sur la Méditerranée . . .
" 226. Côtes de France . . . 1792.
" 227. Carte de la côte et des îles des environs de Marseille . . . 1792.
" 228. Côtes de France . . . 1792.
" 230. " " " département du Var . . . 1792.
" 232. Carte générale de l'île de Corse . . . 1831.
" 233. Carte des bouches de Bonifacio . . . 1823.
" 234. Plan des passages de la Plantarella . . . 1827.
" 235. Plan des ports de Porto Liscia, Porto Puzzo et Porto Polio . . . 1823.
" 236. Plan de Porto Palma . . . 1823.—Plan de la rade d'Agincourt . . . 1823.
" 237. Plan de la rade d'Arsachena . . . 1824.
" 238. Carte de la côte occidentale de l'île de Corse . . . 1825.
" 239. Plan du port de Figari . . . 1825.—Plan de la Calanque de Conca . . . 1825.—Plan du port de Bonifacio . . . 1825.
" 240. Plan des Moines ou Monachi . . . 1825.
" 241. Plan du mouillage de Porto-Pollo.—Plan du mouillage de Campo-Moro.—Plan du mouillage de Propriano . . . 1821.
" 242. Plan des mouillages situés au fond du golfe d'Ajaccio . . . 1825.
" 243. Plan des îles Sanguinaires . . . 1826.
" 244. Carte de la côte occidentale de l'île de Corse . . . 1829.
" 245. Plan du mouillage de Sagone . . . 1829.
" 246. Plan du golfe de Lava et du port Provençal . . . 1830.—Plan du golfe et du porte de Girolata . . . 1830.
" 247. Plan du golfe et du porte de Galéria . . . 1829.
" 248. Carte de la côte n. o. de l'île de Corse . . . 1829.
" 249. Plan des golfes de Calvi et de Revellata . . . 1829.
" 250. Plan du port de Malfalco . . .—Plan du port et de la côte de Centuri.—Plan du danger de l'Algajola . . . 1829.
" 251. Plan du mouillage de l'île Rousse . . . 1829.
" 252. Carte de la côte septentrionale de l'île de Corse . . . 1828.
" 253. Plan du golfe de St Florent . . . 1828.
" 254. Plan des mouillages situés à la côte septentrionale de l'île de Corse . . . 1828.—Inset: Plan du port et de la rade du Macinaggio . . .
" 255. Plan de la côte de Bastia . . . 1830.
" 256. Plan du port de Bastia . . . 1831.

no. 257-258. Carte de la côte orientale de l'île de Corse . . . 1827-1831.
" 259. Plan du porte de Favone . . .—Plan de Porto Nuovo . . .— Plan du golfe de Pinarello . . . 1828.
" 260. Plan du golfe de Porto Vecchio . . . 1828.
" 261. Plan des îles Cerbicale . . . 1827.
" 262. Vue de la côte de Corse depuis la pte. de Latoniccia jusques au cap Pertusato.
" 263. Vues servant de reconnaissance aux bouches de Bonifacio.
" 264. Plan du golfe de Palerme et des environs . . . 1826.
" 265. Plan du port de Syracuse . . . 1827.
" 266. Plan des îles Écueils et mouillages des environs de Trapani . . . 1826.
" 267. Plan des îles de Lipari . . . 1826.
" 269. Plan de la rade de Pirano . . . 1821.
" 270. Plan du Porto-Quieto . . . 1821.
" 271. Plan du port de Parenzo . . .—Plan du port d'Umago . . . 1806.—Plan de l'entrée du Lemo . . . 1806.
" 272. Plan des environs de Pola . . . 1821.
" 273. Plan du port de Pola . . . 1821.

## 1794-1807
**Heather, W.**
[The North sea and Baltic pilot] 15 maps. fol. [London, 1807]
2850

NOTE.—A collection of charts, without title-page.
Maps dated 1794-1807.
Maps no. [14] and [15] published by Laurie & Whittle; remainder published by W. Heather, at the navigation warehouse, 1801-1807.

### CONTENTS.

no. [ 1] A new and improved chart of the North sea or the German ocean constructed on Mercator's projection . . . 1807.
" [ 2] Sous's chart of the Cattegat, improved by W. Heather . . . [1801]
" [ 3] . . . Chart of the Sound and grounds . . . 1801.
" [ 4] A new chart of the Cattegat and Baltic . . . 1801.
" [ 5] A new chart of the Gulf of Finland . . . 1802.
" [ 6] A new and improved chart of the . . . Elbe and Weser to Hamburg and Bremen . . . 1795.
" [ 7] . . . New chart of the coasts of England and Holland . . . 1805.
" [ 8] A new chart of Holland with the entrances to the Scheld . . . 1802.
" [ 9] . . . Chart of the entrances to the river Thames . . . [1801]
" [10] . . . Chart of the east coast of England . . . 1802.
" [11] . . . Chart of the east coast of England and Scotland from the Humber to Aberdeen . . . 1798.
" [12] A new and accurate chart of the coast of Norway including the White sea . . . 1801.
" [13] A new chart of the White sea . . . . . . 1801.
" [14] A new chart of the Skager Rak, or Skaw Reach between the east coast of Norway and the north coast of Jutland . . . 1794.
" [15] A chart of the northern coast of Norway, from Halten islands to Christiansund . . . 1797.

In Heather's The marine atlas . . . [1804], title 700, the following maps relating to America were inadvertently omitted in the contents:

**Heather, W.**—Continued.

no. [1] A new chart of the world . . . 1803 . . . Drawn by J. Norie. Engraved by J. Stephenson.
" [2–3] A new chart of the Atlantic or Western ocean . . . 1799 . . . 2 sheets. Drawn by J. Norie. Engraved by J. Stephenson.
" [35] . . . Chart of the China seas . . . 1799 . . . [Philippine archipelago] Engraved by J. Stephenſon.
" [41] To the officers in the India company's service this outline chart intended for their use to pick off a ship's track is most respectfully dedicated . . . Engraved by J. Stephenson.
" [42] A new chart of Guayana with the colonies of Cayenne, Surinam, & Trinidad . . . 1797 . . . Drawn by J. Norie. Engraved by J. Stephenſon. Insets: Essequebo.—Berbice river.—The river Surinam.—Cayenne.—Chaguaramas.
" [43] [The island of Trinidad] . . . 1802 . . . W. Heather fecit. J. Stephenſon ſculpſit.
" [44] A new and improved chart of the West India or Carribbee islands . . . 1795 . . . Stephenſon ſculpſit.
" [45] A new and correct general chart of the West Indies . . . 1801 . . . Drawn by J. Norie.
" [46] A new chart of the West Indies including the Florida gulf and stream . . . 1797 . . . Drawn by J. Norie . . . Engraved by J. Stephenſon.
" [47] A new chart of America with the harbors of Port Royal, Savannah, &c. . . . 1799. Engraved by J. Stephenſon. Insets: Savannah river.—Port Royal.—Charleston.—Cape Fear river.
" [48] A new chart of America with the harbors of New-York, Boston &c. . . . 1799 . . . Drawn by J. Norie. Stephenſon ſculp. Insets: New York [harbor]—Boston bay.—Delaware bay.
" [49] A new and improved chart of the gulf and river Sᵗ Laurence . . . 1801 . . . Drawn by J. Norie. Engraved by J. Stephenſon.

**1799**

**Rèilly, F. J. J. von.**

Atlas universae rei veredariae bilinguis, omnes cursus publicos, quatenus pertotum terrarum orbem patent, ex quadraginta tabulis geographicis latine ac germanice docens, secundum novissimas rei cursoriæ dispositiones et institutiones curatissime compositus, et pleno indice instructus, qui singula stationum nomina situsque locorum puncto temporis quasi digito monstrat. Viennæ, Austriæ, MDCCXCIX. Venalis in officina chalco-geographica editoris.— Allgemeiner post-atlas von der ganzen welt, in so ferne posten darauf bestehen, aus vierzig lateinisch und deutsch beschriebenen landkarten zusammen gesetzt, nach den neuesten in den verschiedenen staaten im postwesen gemachten verordnungen und einrichtungen ausgearbeitet, und mit einem vollständigen register versehen, wodurch man auf was immer für einer karte jeden ort in wenig augenblicken auffindet . . .    4 p. l., 11 fold. l., 40 maps.    fol. Wien, 1799.    2851

Nᴏᴛᴇ.—Contains maps of Europe only.

## 1801
**Bougard, R.**
The little sea torch: or, true guide for coasting pilots: by which they are clearly instructed how to navigate along the coasts of England, Ireland, France, Spain, Portugal, Italy, and Sicily; the isles of Malta, Corsica, Sardinia and others in the straits; and of the coasts of Barbary, from Cape Bon to Cape De Verd. Enriched with upwards of one hundred appearances of head-lands and light-houses. Together with plans of the principal harbours . . . Translated from the french with corrections and additions, by J. T. Serres . . . vi, 144, [5] pp., 12 l. incl. 24 col. maps, 20 col. pl. fol. London, for the author, by J. Debrett, 1801. 2852

> NOTE.—Collation: title, dedication, list of subscribers, 6 pp.; "The little sea torch, &c, &c.," pp. 1–130; "Appearances from drawings by J. T. Serres, engraved by J. Stadler" pp. 131–134; 20 pl.; "Charts" pp. 135, 136; 24 maps on 12 l.; "Soundings" pp. 137–142; "A short treatise of variations", pp. 143–144; "Index", 3 l.
>
> A translation by John Thomas Serres (1759–1825) of the work entitled, "Le petit flambeau de la mer ou le véritable guide des pilotes côtiers" by Bougard; published at Havre, by G. Gruchet, in 1684. See also title 2841, for french edition, 1752. A new french edition was published at Saint Malo by Hovius in 1817.
>
> Besides the minute description of the coasts of the countries and islands indicated by the title, this work contains a "Description of the principal harbours and bays, where ships touch at, both going to and coming from the East Indies, with a table of variations met with in that voyage," pp. 126–130.
>
> The "Appearances" comprise a series of beautifully drawn and colored views of the principal headlands, harbors, lighthouses, ports, etc., mentioned in the descriptive text. These views have been added to the original french edition by Serres.
>
> Maps, each measuring 5 x 6½ inches and engraved by J. Luffman, as follows: Dieppe, Havre, Brest, Port Louis, Belle isle, Ferrol and Corunna, Vigo, Oporto, Lisbon, Cadiz, Gibraltar, Corsica, Marseilles, Toulon, Genoa, Leghorn, Elba, Porto Ferajo, Naples, Malta, Messina, Palermo, Porto Vecchio, Corfu.

## 1829–1830
**Schlieben, W. E. A.**
Atlas von Europa, nebst den kolonien . . . 6 pts. obl. 4°. G. J. Göschen, 1829–1830. 2853

> NOTE—Published in 15 pts., of which the Library of Congress has 6, namely: pt. 2, Türkei in Europa; pt. 3, Portugal; pt. 4, Spanien; pt. 5, Niederlande, Dänemark, Schweden mit Norwegen; pt. 13, Russland; pt. 15, Das britische reich.
>
> Text, containing a brief account of the geography and topography of each country, precedes maps.
>
> The following maps relate to America:
> pt. 4, no. [20] Die asiatischen kolonien die Philippinen.
> " " " [21] . . . Cuba mit Pinos und dem general kapitanate Puerto Rico.
> " 5, " [12] Das niederlændische, dænische und schwedische Westindien.— Die kolonie Surinam in Süd Amerika.

**Schlieben, W. E. A.**—Continued.
 pt. 5, no. [13] Die niederlændischen und dænischen besitzungen auf der Guinea küste.
 "   "   " [18] Island und die Færöer gruppe.
 "   "   " [19] Groenland.
 " 13, " [25] Das russische Amerika.
 " 15, " [24] Das britische Westindien.
 "   "   " [26] Das britische Nord Amerika.
 "   "   " [27] Das britische Süd Amerika.

### 1832–1845

**Klint, G.**
 Sveriges sjö-atlas.   1 p. l., 61 maps.   fol.   [Stockholm, 1832–1845]    2854
  Note.—Maps dated 1832—1845.
  Swedish hydrographic charts of the coasts of Europe.

### 1853

**Stieler, A.**
 Atlas von Deutschland, Niederland, Belgien und Schweiz, xxv blätter. Maasstab: 1:750000. Neue aufl.   1 p. l., 1 map on 20 sheets.   obl. fol.   Gotha, J. Perthes [1853]    2855

### 1900

**Taylor, W. R.**
 Synthetical atlas of Europe . . .   2 p. l., 12 fold. maps.   12°. London, A. & C. Black, 1900.    2856

### 1905

**Dubois, E. M.,** *and* **Sieurin, E.**
 Cartes d'étude pour servir à l'enseignement de la géographie . . . 7. éd. . . .   2 p. l., 33 maps.   4°.   Paris, Masson & cie. 1905.    2857

---

# AUSTRIA-HUNGARY.

#### FORESTRY.

**Austria-Hungary.** *K. k. ackerbau-ministerium.*
 Die forste der in verwaltung des k. k. ackerbau-ministeriums stehenden staats- und fondsgüter . . . Dargestellt vom k. k. forstrath Karl Schindler. 41 übersichts-karten. Hrsg. vom k. k. ackerbau-ministerium.   2 p. l., 42 maps.   fol.   Wien, k. k. hof- und staatsdruckerei, 1885.    2858

## HISTORICAL.

**K. Akademie der wissenschaften,** *Vienna.*
Historischer atlas österreichen Alpenländer . . . 1. Abteilung: Die landgerichtskarte bearbeitet unter leitung von weil. Edward Richter. 1. Lieferung: Salzburg, von Edward Richter, Oberösterreich, von Julius Strnadt, Steiermark, von Anton Mell und Hans Pirchegger. cover-title, 12 col. maps. obl. fol. Wien, A. Holzhausen, 1906.     2858a

> NOTE.—Accompanied by text entitled: Erläuterungen zum historischen atlas der österreichen Alpenländer . . . cover-title, 49 pp. fol.

## LAKES.

**Penk, A.,** *and* **Richter, E.**
Atlas der österreichischen Alpenseen, mit unterstützuug des hohen k. k. ministeriums für cultus und unterricht, herausgegeben von . . . Albrecht Penk und . . . Eduard Richter. 2 pts. in 1 v. obl. fol. Wien, E. Hölzel, 1895-1896.     2859

### CONTENTS.

pt. 1. Müllner, J. Die seen des Salzkammergutes . . . nach den lothungen von . . . Friederich Simony. 1 p. l., 18 maps on 12 l. 1895. [Geographische abhandlungen. Hrsg. von . . . Albrecht Penck . . . bd. I, heft I]

> NOTE.—Accompanied by explanatory text entitled: Die seen des Salzkammergutes und die österreichische Traun. Erläuterung zur ersten lieferung des österreichischen seenatlasses. Von . . . J. Müllner. Wien, E. Hölzel, 1896.

" 2. Richter, E. Seen von Kärnthen, Krain und Südtirol. 1 p. l., 9 pl. 1896. [Geographische abhandlungen. Hrsg. von . . . Albrecht Penck . . . bd. I, heft II]

> NOTE.—Accompanied by explanatory text entitled: Seestudien. Erläuterungen zur zweiten lieferung des atlas der österreichischen alpenseen. Von E. Richter. Wien, E. Hölzel, 1897.

## MINING.

**Austria-Hungary.** *K. k. ackerbau-ministerium.*
Atlas der urproduction Oesterreichs . . . Die bergwerksproduction Oesterreichs in x karten. Redigirt von A. Schauenstein. 4 pp., 18 maps, 4 diagr. fol. Wien, R. v. Waldheim [1877]     2860

## SCHOOL.

**Berghaus, H.**
Schul-atlas der österreichischen monarchie nach der neuesten politischen und gerichtlichen eintheilung. 2. umgearbeitete aufl. . . . 1 p. l., 7 col. maps. obl. 4°. Gotha, J. Perthes, 1855.     2861

#### STATISTICAL.

**Austria-Hungary.** *K. k. ackerbau-ministerium.*
Atlas der urproduction Oesterreichs in 35 blättern mit erläuterndem texte . . . Redigirt von d. Jos. R. ritter Lorenz von Liburnau. 13 pp., 86 maps, 4 diagr. fol. Wien, R. v. Waldheim [1877] 2862

#### WARS.

**Austria.** *K. k. reichs kriegs ministerium.*
Oesterreichischer erbfolge-krieg, 1740-1748. (Die kriege unter der regierung der kaiserin-königin Maria-Theresia) Graphische beilagen I–VII. obl. fol. [Wien] L. W. Seidel & sohn [1896–1905]
2863
NOTE.—In progress.

### GENERAL.

(Arranged chronologically)

#### 1683

**Nicolson, W.**
The description of the remaining part of the empire of Germany, viz. Schwaben, the palatinate of Bavaria, arch-dukedom of Austria, kingdom of Hungary, principality of Transylvania, the circle of Westphalia; with the neighbouring provinces. fol. Oxford, for M. Pitt, 1683. 2864
[English, The, atlas. v. 3]
NOTE.—See title 2831 for bibliographical notice.

**Erödi, B., Berecz, A.,** *and* **Brózik, K.**
Nagy magyar atlasz 158 szines fötérkép és kétszázöt-venhét melléktérképpel és névmutatóval a magyar földrajzi tarsaság. 4 p. l., 158 l. incl. 114 col. maps, 3 pl., 52 pp. fol. Budapest, Lampel R. könyvkereskedése, 1906. 2865
NOTE.—Received too late to enter under general atlases of the world.

#### PROVINCES

#### BOHEMIA

**Homann heirs.**
Atlas regni Bohemiae consistens in quindecim mappis edentibus Homannianis heredibus . . . 1 p. l., 15 maps. fol. Norimbergæ, 1776. 2866

## HUNGARY.

**Marsigli, L. F.**
La Hongrie et le Danube . . . en XXXI cartes très fidèlement gravées d'après les desseins originaux & les plans levez sur les lieux par l'auteur même. Ouvrage où l'on voit la Hongrie, par rapport à ses rivières, à ses antiquitez romaines, & à ses mines; & les sources & le cours du Danube, &c. Avec une préface sur l'excellence & l'usage de ces cartes, par mr. [Antoine Augustin] Bruzen de la Martinière. 5 p. l., 30 maps. fol. La Haye, 1741. 2867

NOTE.—Frontispiece signed, "F. Ottens delineavit et fecit 1725."

### JOACHIMSTHAL.

**Austria.** *K. k. ackerbau-ministerium.*
Geologisch-bergmännische karte mit profilen von Joachimsthal nebst bildern von den erzgängen in Joachimsthal und von den kupferkies-lagerstätten bei Kitzbühel. Aufgenommen von den k. k. bergbeamten. Redigirt von . . . F. M. ritter von Friese, und . . . Wilhelm Göbl, hrsg. auf befehl seiner excellenz des herrn k. k. akerbau-ministers Julius grafen Falkenhayn. Atlas. cover-title, 1 map, 5 pl. fol. Wien, k. k. hof- und staats-druckerei, 1891.
2868

NOTE.—To accompany work with same title.

---

# BELGIUM.

### AGRICULTURAL.

**Belgium.** *Ministère de l'agriculture.*
Statistique de la Belgique. Agriculture. Recensement général de 1895 publié par le ministre de l'agriculture. Atlas. cover-title, 34 pl. fol. Bruxelles, 1899. 2869

### CITIES.

**Deventer, J. R.**
Atlas des villes de la Belgique au XVI$^e$ siècle. Cent plans du géographe Jacques de Deventer exécutés sur les ordres de Charlesquint et de Philippe II reproduits en fac-simile chromographique par l'institut national de géographie, à Bruxelles. Texte par mm. Alvin . . . Bormans . . . sous la direction de m. Ch. Ruelens. liv. 1–15. fol. Bruxelles, institut national de géographie [1884–1895] 2870

NOTE.—No more published.

"L'atlas des villes de la Belgique au XVI$^e$ siècle sera publié en 20 fascicules in-folio, renfermant chacun 5 planches chromographiques, avec texte descriptif sur beau papier vélin."

**Deventer, J. R.**—Continued.
    See also article by C. Ruelens, giving the history of this atlas, in the Bulletin of the Société royale belge de géographie. 1884. v. 8, pp. 5–25.
    Liv. 7 contains "Notice sur Jacques de Deventer, par m. Ch. Ruelens."
    "La moitié environ des minutes originales de ce travail est dispersée dans les Pays-Bas, une autre moitié à la Bibl. roy. à Bruxelles; deux tomes de l'atlas exécutés d'après ces minutes sont conservés à la Bibliothèque royale de Madrid. Ces collections qui servent de complément l'une à l'autre, fournissent le tracé topographique de plus de 200 villes des Pays-Bas espagnols." *cf.* Nijhoff's Livres anciens et modernes. 8°. La Haye, 1906. no. 349, p. 35.

## TRANSPORTATION.

**Belgium.** *Ministère des travaux publics. Administrations des ponts et chaussées et des chemins de fer.*
    Album du développement progressif du réseau des routes, des voies navigables et des chemins de fer de 1830 à 1880. Annexe au compte-rendu des opérations du département des travaux publics pendant l'année 1880. 3 pts. in 1 v. cover-title, 3 l., 18 maps, 2 tab. obl. fol. [Bruxelles, 1881]     2871

————— ————— *Direction des travaux hydrauliques.*
    Service des voies navigables. Album des dépenses et des recettes faites par l'état sur le réseau des voies navigables de 1830 à 1880 4 p. l., 1 map, 23 diagr. obl. fol. Bruxelles, J. Fuytynck-Bajart [1881]     2872

## WARS.

**Ropes, J. C.**
    An atlas of the campaign of Waterloo . . . Designed to accompany the author's "Campaign of Waterloo—a military history". 2 p. l., 14 fold. maps. fol. New York, C. Scribner's sons, 1893.
    2873

## GENERAL.

(Arranged chronologically)

### 1667

**Du Val, P.**, *d'Abbeville.*
    Cartes et tables de géographie, des provinces efchûës à la reine très-chrétiēne, par le décez de la reine Eliſabeth ſa mère, du prince dom Balthazar ſon frère, et du roy catholique Philippe IV son père. . . . 1 p. l., 48 l. incl. 14 maps. 24°. Paris, l'auteur, 1667.
    2874

### 1899

**Belgium.** *Institut cartographique militaire.*
    Carte topographique de la Belgique [publiée en 427 planchettes en couleurs] à l'échelle du 20 000°. Nouvelle éd. 2 v. fol. [Bruxelles, 1899]     2875
    Note.—Collation: v. 1, 1 p. l., 202 maps; v. 2, 1 p. l., 227 maps

**1899**

Carte topographique de la Belgique. [Publiée en 72 feuilles en noir] gravée à l'échelle de 1 pour 40 000 ... 2 p. l., 72 maps. fol. [Bruxelles, 1899] 2876

Note.—Engraved maps. Cover dated 1899.

**1899**

Carte topographique de la Belgique, publiée en couleurs à l'échelle de 1 pour 40 000 (1895–1896) 2 p. l., 72 col. maps. fol. [Bruxelles, 1899] 2877

Note.—Maps of later editions than those in the engraved copy with same cover date.

---

## BRITISH ISLES.

### CITIES.

**Rocque, J.**, *and* **Bellin, J. N.**
Recueil des villes ports d'Angleterre. Tiré des grands plans de Rocque et du portuland de l'Angleterre du s$^r$ Belin [!] 3 p. l., 12 maps, 2 pl. 4°. Paris, Desnos, 1766. 2878
[*With* Desnos, L. C. Nouvel atlas d'Angleterre. 4°. Paris, Desnos, 1767. Title 2918]

Note.—Engraved title.

CONTENTS.

no. [1] [Plan of London] 1766.
" [2] Bouche de la Tamise.
" [3] Yarmouth.—Douvres.
" [4] Carnarvan.—Veue de Portsmouth.
" [5] Plymouth.—Fanal de Plymouth.
" [6] Shrewsbury.
" [7] Yorck.
" [8] New-Castel.—Barwick.—Veuë de Lastiff.
" [9] Plan de Chester.
" [10] Veue de Carrick-Fergus.—Chateau de Chester.
" [11] Waterford.—Oxford.
" [12] Leith.—Harwick.
" [13] Plan d' Edinbourgh. Inset: Chateau d' Edimbourg.
" [14] Chateau d' Edinburgh.
" [15] Dublin.
" [16] Gallway.—Havre de Kinsale.—Kinsale.
" [17] Limerick.
" [18] Environs de Limerick.—Inset: Veües des montagnes de Dundram à l' entrée de Carlingfort, côte orientale d' Irlande.

## GEOLOGICAL.

**Woodward, H. B.**
Stanford's geological atlas of Great Britain <based on [James] Reynolds's geological atlas> with plates of characteristic fossils preceded by a description of the geological structure of Great Britain and its counties; and of the features observable along the principal lines of railway . . .   x, 139 pp., 34 col. maps, 16 pl., tab.  12°.  London, E. Stanford, 1904.   2879

**Woodward, H. B.**
Stanford's geological atlas of Great Britain and Ireland <based on [James] Reynolds's geological atlas> with plates of characteristic fossils preceded by descriptions of the geological structure of Great Britain and Ireland and their counties; and of the features observable along the principal lines of railway . . .   2d ed.   x, 189, [1] pp., 34 col. maps, 16 pl., tab.  12°.  London, E. Stanford, 1907.
2880

NOTE.—Map no. 1, frontispiece.

## HISTORICAL.

**Benians, E. A.** *and* **Knight, T. H.**
Historical atlas with chronological notes. Intended to provide suitable material for a general knowledge of english history and more especially for use as a supplementary work in examination preparation.   1 p. l., 88, [1] pp. incl. 39 col. maps, 1 col. pl.  12°. London, G. Gill & sons, 1908.   2880a

**Gardiner, S. R.**
A school atlas of english history: a companion atlas to 'The students history of England.'   New ed.   23 pp., 72 maps.  8°. London and New York, Longmans, Green, & co. 1895.   2881

NOTE.—The following maps relate to America:
no. 46. Eastern and Central America. 1755.—Eastern & Central America. 1763.
" 47. The world (1772)
" 48. United States of America.  1783.
" 65. The world.  1892.

**Labberton, R. H.**
Chautauqua atlas of english history; selected from "The new historical atlas and general history" . . .   [8] l. incl. 15 maps.  8°. [New York, 1886]   2882

**Pearson, C. H.**
Historical maps of England, during the first thirteen centuries. With explanatory essays and indices . . .   3d ed. rev.   xii, 70 pp., 5 maps.  fol.  London, G. Bell & sons, 1883.   2883

**Reich, E.**
   A new student's atlas of english history . . .   vi, 15 pp., [34] l.,
55 maps.   4°.   London, New York, Macmillan & co. 1903.   2884
   NOTE.—"This atlas . . . attempts to be a cartographic complement to John Richard Green's History of the english people."

**Robertson, C. G.,** *and* **Bartholomew, J. G.**
   Historical and modern atlas of the british empire specially prepared for students . . .   15, 64 pp. incl. maps, plans and diagrs. 4°.   London, Methuen & co. 1905.   2885
   NOTE.—The following maps relate to America:
   p. 47.   North America.—Orographical.
   " 48.   North American colonies, 1755–1763.
   " 49.   North America, 1783.
   " 50.   British North America, 1791–1841.
   " 51.   Dominion of Canada, 1905.
   " 52.   Lower Canada & Newfoundland, 1905.
   " 53.   The West Indies, 1660–1763.
   " 54.   West Indies, British Guiana & Honduras, 1905.
   " 55.   Leading explorers of the Pacific.

**Tindal, N.**
   [Maps and plans of Tindal's continuation of Rapin's history of England]   71 maps.   fol.   [London, Harrison, 1785–1789?]
   2886
   NOTE.—Title-page wanting.
   Contains maps of France, Italy, Netherlands, Germany, Spain, America and plans of the principal fortified towns of these countries, which relate to the history of England.
   The following maps relate to America:
   no. 30.   A map of South America with all the european settlements & whatever else is remarkable from the latest & best observations. R. W. Seale delin. et sculp.
   " 31.   A map of North America with the european settlements & whatever else is remarkable in ỹ West Indies, from the latest and best observations. R. W. Seale delin. et sculp.

### ROADS.

**Bacon, G. W.**
   Bacon's cycling and touring pocket atlas of the British Isles . . .
6 p. l., 60 pp., 32 fold. maps.   16°.   London, G. W. Bacon & co. 1898.   2887

**Bartholomew, J. G.**
   The handy touring atlas of the British Isles specially prepared for cyclists, motorists and travellers . . . Reduced . . . from the ordinance survey.   viii, 120, 20 pp. incl. 62 maps, 2 diagrs.   24°. London, G. Newness [1903]   2888
   NOTE.—"100 cycling routes," 16 pp. at end.

### ST. GEORGE'S CHANNEL.

**Morris, L.**
Plans of the principal harbours, bays, & roads, in St. George's and the Bristol channels from surveys made under the direction of the lords of the admiralty . . . New ed. . . . xii, 21 pp., 32 maps. 4°. Shrewsbury, for the author, by Sandford & Maddocks, 1801. 2889

### STATISTICAL.

**Bevan, G. P.**
The statistical atlas of England, Scotland and Ireland . . . 4 p. l., 75 pp., 1 l., 45 maps. fol. Edinburgh and London, W. & A. K. Johnston, 1882. 2890

NOTE.—Maps and statistics illustrating religions, education, industries, crime, pauperism, marine commerce, agriculture, military and naval conditions, civil courts, railways, health, minerals, water supply, political parties, population.

### WARS.

**Palmer,** *Sir* **T.,** *and* **Covert, W.**
A survey of the coast of Sussex, made in 1587, with a view to its defence against foreign invasion, and especially against the spanish armada. Edited, with notes, by Mark Antony Lower. 7 l., 6 pp. (5 l.), 5 maps. obl. 4°. Lewes, W. E. Baxter, 1870. 2891

NOTE.—Caption title: A survey made by sr. Thomas Palmere, knight, and mr. Waltar Couerte, esquire, deputie lieutennts of her maties countie of Sussex, of all the places of descente alongste the sea coaste of the said shire.

**Pine, J.**
The spanish armada, 1588. The tapestry hangings of the house of lords, representing the several engagements between the english and spanish fleets. Reproduced in heliotype from an original copy in the collection of Charles Hervey Townshend. 4 p. l., 24, 8 pp., 11 maps, 10 pl. fol. Boston, Houghton, Osgood & co. 1878.
2892

NOTE.—Facsimile title-page, p. l. 2, entitled, "The tapestry hangings of the house of lords . . . with the portraits of the lord high-admiral . . . to which are added from a book entitled, Expeditionis Hispanorum in Angliam vera descriptio, A. D. 1588, done as is supposed, for the said tapestry to be work'd after, ten charts of the sea-coasts of England, and a general one of England, Scotland, Ireland, France, Holland . . . By John Pine, engraver. London, 1739." For life of Pine, *cf.*-Dictionary of national biography.
"Le même m. Pine travaille actuellement à graver les tapisseries de la chambre des pairs, qui représentent la défaite de la flotte espagnole en 1588, il y ajoutera les cartes géographiques des côtes de la mer . . . Le tout doit faire 19 ou 20 feuilles, extrêment ornées dans les bordures de tout ce qui pourra avoir quelque rapport au sujet: elles se vendront par souscription deux guinées & demie, sçavoir une guinée en souscrivant & une guinée & demie en recevant l'ouvrage entier qui est déjà fort avancé." *cf.* Journal des sçavans. Janvier 1739. v. 117. p. 135.

**Wyld, J.**

Maps & plans, showing the principal movements, battles & sieges, in which the british army was engaged during the war from 1808 to 1814 in the spanish peninsula and the south of France. 3 p. l., 37 maps and views on 51 sheets. fol. London, J. Wyld [1840]
2893

NOTE.—Map no. 35, wanting.

Accompanied by, "Memoir annexed to an atlas containing plans of the principal battles, sieges, and affairs, in which the british troops were engaged during the war in the spanish peninsula and the south of France, from 1808 to 1814." 4°. London, J. Wyld, 1841. This memoir chiefly consists of letters and orders of major-general sir George Murray, during and after the war in the spanish peninsula from 1808 to 1814, and of the description of the battles and the movement of the troops, as illustrated on the maps made by sir Thomas Livingstone Mitchell, and contained in this atlas. "Prospectus" in Kritischer wegweiser, feb. 28, 1835. v. 7, pp. 72-79.

CONTENTS.

no. 1. Operations from Mondego bay to Lisbon, 1808.
" 2. Action near Rolica, 1808.
" 3. Battle of Vimiero, 1808.
" " Passage of the river Douro, 1809.
" 4. Battle of Corunna, 1809.
" 5. Battle of Talavera de la Reyna, 1809.
" 6. General map of part of Portugal and Spain.
" 7. Affair of Almeica, 1810.
" " Position of Santarem, 1801 [1810]
" 8. Plan of movements before and after the battle of Busaco [1810]
" 9. Battle of Busaco, 1810.
" 10. Plan of the lines constructed to cover Lisbon.
" 11. Views of the lines.
" 12-17. Retreat of marshal Massena, 1810.
" 18-19. Battle of Fuentes d'Onoro, 1811.
" 20. Action near the Vigia de la Barrosa [1811]
" " Battle of Albuera, 1811.
" 21. Town and island of Tarifa.
" " Affair near El-Bodon, 1811.
" " Affair at Arroyo Molinos, 1811.
" 22. Plan of ciudad Rodrigo, 1812.
" " " " Badajoz, 1812.
" 23. Battle of Salamanca, 1812.
" 24. Salamanca with the french forts, 1812.
" " Castle of Burgos, 1812.
" 25. Battle of Vittoria, 1813.
" 26. Plan of St. Sebastian, 1813.
" " Action at Castalla, 1813.
" 27-28. Battle of Pamplona, 1813.
" 29. Battle of San Marcial, 1813.
" 30. Passage of the Bidassoa, 1813.
" 31. Attack of Nivelle, 1813.
" 32. Actions in the vicinity of Bayonne, 1813.
" 33. Battle of Orthès, 1814.
" 34. Map of a part of the Pyrenees.
" 35. [Wanting]
" 36. Battle of Toulouse, 1814.
" 37. Island of Leon, and bay of Cadiz.

## GENERAL.

(Arranged chronologically)

### 1646

**Jansson, J.**

Ioannis Ianssonii novus atlas, sive theatrum orbis terrarum: in quo Magna Britannia, seu Angliæ & Scotiæ nec non Hiberniæ, regna exhibentur. 1 p. l., 266 l. incl. 56 maps. fol. Amstelodami, apud Ioannem Ianssonium, 1646. 2894

NOTE.—Engraved title.
v. 4 of Jansson's "Novus atlas," Amstelodami, 1646–49.

### 1756

**Collins, G.**

Great Britain's coasting pilot. In two parts. Being a new and exact survey of the sea-coaft of England and Scotland, from the river of Thames to the weftward and northward. With the islands of Scilly, and from thence to Carlisle. Likewise the islands of Orkney and Shetland, describing all the harbours, rivers, bays, rocks, sands, buoys, beacons, sea-marks, depths of water, latitude, bearings and diftances from place to place; the setting and flowing of tides; with directions for the knowing of any place, and how to harbour a ship in the fame with safety. With directions for coming into the channel between England and France . . . 3 p. l., 26 pp., 49 maps. fol. London, for W. & J. Mount, T. Page & son, 1756. 2895

NOTE.—Engraved title.
The following views on the maps:
no. [6] King William landing. Novemb$^r$ 5, 1688.
" [14] At Sherehampton, near King road landed his maj$^{tie}$ on the 6$^t$ of sept$^r$ 1690.
" [23] Peel castle.
" [24] A prospect of Carreck-Fergus, being the place where king William landed in Ireland.
" [4] Prospect of Leith from the east.

### 1767

Great-Britain's coasting pilot: in two parts. Being a new and exact survey of the sea-coast of England and Scotland, from the river of Thames to the weftward and northward; with the islands of Scilly, and from thence to Carlisle: likewise the islands of Orkney and Shetland, describing all the harbours, rivers, bays, rocks, sands, buoys, beacons, sea-marks, depths of water, latitude, bearings and diftances from place to place; the setting and flowing of the tides; with directions for the knowing of any place, and how to harbour a ship in the fame with safety. With directions for coming into the channel between England and France . . . 3 p. l., 26 pp., 49 maps. fol. London, for J. Mount & T. Page, 1767. 2896

NOTE.—Engraved title.
See note, title 2895.

### 1785

**Collins, G.**

Great-Britain's coasting pilot: being a new and exact survey of the sea-coast of England and Scotland from the river of Thames to the weftward and northward; with the islands of Scilly and from thence to Carlisle, likewise the islands of Orkney and Shetland, describing all the harbours, rivers, bays, roads, rocks, sands, buoys, beacons, seamarks, depths of water, latitude, bearings and diftances from place to place; the setting and flowing of the tides, with directions for the knowing of any place and how to harbour a ship in the fame with safety. With directions for coming into the channel between England and France . . . 1 p. l., 30 pp., front, 50 maps. fol. London, for Mount & Page, 1785. 2897

NOTE.—See note title 2895.

### 1835

**Teesdale, H., & co.**

Improved edition of the new british atlas, containing a complete set of county maps on which are delineated the mail, turnpike and principal cross roads, cities, towns and most considerable villages, parks, rivers, navigable canals & railways, preceded by general maps of England, Ireland, Scotland, north and south Wales, the whole carefully revised & corrected to the year 1835. 1 p. l., 49 maps. fol. London, H. Teesdale & co. [1835] 2898

NOTE.—Bound with "A new general atlas of the world," by John Dower. See title 772.

### 1884

**Bacon, G. W.**

New large scale ordnance atlas of the British Isles with plans of towns, copious letterpress descriptions, alphabetical indexes and census tables. 1 p. l., lix pp., 104 col. maps. fol. London, G. W. Bacon [1884] 2899

### 1897

**Lucas,** *Sir* **C. P.**

Our empire atlas showing british possessions at home and abroad. 3 p. l., vi, 60, 36 pp. incl. 59 col. maps. 4°. Edinburgh and London, W. & K. Johnston, 1897. 2900

NOTE.—The following maps relate to America:
no. 49. North America.
" 50. British North America.
" 51. "    "    "    (New Brunswick, Nova Scotia, and Newfoundland)

**Lucas, C. P.**—Continued.
    no. 52. Ontario.
    " 53. Quebec.
    " 54. Manitoba.
    " 55. Saskatchewan and Assiniboia.
    " 56. British Columbia.
    " 57. Alberta and Athabasca.
    " 58. Jamaica.—Bahamas islands.—Bermuda islands.—Trinidad.
    " 59. British Guina.—British Honduras.—Lesser Antilles.
    ' 60. South America.

## 1901–1902
**Taylor, W. R.**
    Synthetical atlas . . .    3 pts.   12°.   London, A. & C. Black, 1901–1902.      2901

    NOTE.—Collation: pt. 1, 2 p. l., 8 fold. col. maps; pt. 2, 2 p. l., 5 fold. col. maps; pt. 3, 2 p. l., 4 fold. col. maps.

CONTENTS.
    pt. 1. England and Wales.
    " 2. Scotland.
    " 3. Ireland.

## 1904
**Bartholomew, J. G.**
    The handy atlas of the british empire . . .    xxxii pp., front., (port.) 120 (*i. e.* 98) maps, 3 tab.   24°.   London, G. Newness [1904]      2902

## ENGLAND.

### HUNTING.

**Hobson, W. C.**
    Hobson's fox-hunting atlas; containing separate maps of every county in England, and the three ridings of Yorkshire . . . showing the roads, railways, canals, parks, etc., etc. Compiled from the maps of the board of ordnance and other surveys, by J. and C. Walker . . .    2 p. l., 42 maps.   fol.   London, J. & C. Walker [1848?]      2903

    NOTE.—Published by: J. & C. Walker; Longman, Rees, Orme, Brown & co.; Longman, Orme, Rees & Co.; Longman, Rees, Orme & Co.; Longman, Hurst, Rees, Orme & co.; Longman & co.

### ROADS.
**Bowles, C.**
    Bowles's poſt-chaife companion; or, travellers directory through England and Wales, being an actual survey of all the direct and

principal cross roads with the mile stones expreſſed as they ſtand at preſent, exhibiting the ſeveral towns, villages, post-stages &c., on or near the roads; together with the circuits of judges and an exact alphabetical list of all the fairs as ſettled since the alteration of the style. 2d ed. corr. ... 2 v. 16°. London, for the proprietor, C. Bowles, 1782. 2904

 Note.—Collation: v. 1, xv, [1] pp., 100 l. incl. 50 maps, [5] pp. front. (map); v. 2, 1 p. l., 101–200 l. incl. 50 maps, 191–243, [2] pp.

### Cary, J.

Cary's traveller's companion, or, a delineation of the turnpike roads of England and Wales: shewing the immediate route to every market and borough town throughout the kingdom, laid down from the best authorities, on a new set of county maps, to which is added an alphabetical list of all the market towns with the days on which they are held. 3 p. l., 16 pp., 43 maps. 16°. London, for J. Cary, 1814. 2905

### Inglis, H. R. G.

The "contour" road book of England. A series of elevation plans of the roads, with measurements and descriptive letterpress ... With 1500 maps and plans. 1 p. l., vii–x, [18], 848, 24 pp., front., 42 maps. 16°. London [etc.] Gall & Inglis, 1901. 2906

 Note.—Map of England and Wales at end.

### Ogilby, J.

Britannia: volume the firſt; or, an illustration of the kingdom of England and dominion of Wales: by a geographical and hiſtorical description of the principal roads thereof. Actually admeaſured and delineated in a century of whole-sheet copper sculps. Accomodated with the ichnography of the ſeveral cities and capital towns; and compleated by an accurate account of the more remarkable paſſages of antiquity, together with a novel diſcourſe of the preſent state ... 1 p. l., [28] 200 pp., 100 maps. fol. London, by the author, 1675. 2907

Britannia depicta or Ogilby improv'd; being a correct coppy of mr. Ogilby's actual survey of all ye direct & principal croſs roads in England and Wales: wherein are exactly delineated & engraven, all ye cities, towns, villages, churches, seats, &c. ſcituate on or near the roads, with their reſpective diſtances in measured and computed miles ... Eman: Bowen, engraver. 4th ed. 1 p. l., 5, [3], 273 pp. incl. 254 maps, 2 pl. 12°. London, T. Bowles, 1736. 2908

 Note.—Border text to each map.

**Ogilby, J.**
　Britannia depicta or Ogilby improv'd; being a correct coppy of m.^r Ogilby's actual survey of all y̌ direct ... roads in England and Wales ... By In.° Owen ... Lastly particular & correct maps of all y̌ counties of South Britain ... by Eman: Bowen, engraver. 4th ed.　3 p. l., 273 pp. incl. maps.　8°.　London, T. Bowles, 1751.　　　　　　　　　　　　　　　　　　　　　2909
　　NOTE.—Border text to each map.

　Britannia depicta: or, Ogilby improved. Being an actual survey of all the direct and principal cross roads of England and Wales ... with distances laid down in measured miles, through each road. Engraved by Emanuel Bowen ... To which is added, an accurate historical and topographical description of all the cities, boroughs, towns corporate ... compiled from the best authorities by John Owen ...　12, 273 pp. incl. 54 maps.　12°.　London, for C. Bowles, 1764.　　　　　　　　　　　　　　　　　2910
　　NOTE.—Ogilby's work first published in 1675, under title "Itinerarium Angliæ"; abridged as "The traveller's guide" 1699; an "improved edition" by John Senex in 1719, as "An actual survey". Other editions, with descriptions of towns by John Owen, and engraved maps by Nathaniel Bowen, appeared in 1720, 1724, 1731, 1736, 1753 and 1764, entitled, "Britannia depicta" ...
　　Marginal text contains historical facts. Maps and text embellished by arms of counties, nobility, and the colleges of Oxford and Cambridge.

**Senex, J.**
　Itinéraire de toutes les routes de l'Angleterre, revuës, corrigées, augmentées & réduites par Senex en 101 cartes ... Bowles a ajouté en 1757 plusieurs nouvelles routes à cet ouvrage, plusieurs renvois et corrections nécessaires ... Ouvrage traduit de l'anglois ...—The roads through England or, Ogilby's survey revised, improved and reduced by Senex ...　1 p. l., [8] pp., 102 maps. 4°.　Paris, chez Desnos, 1766.　　　　　　　　　　　　　　2911
[*With* Desnos, L. C.　Nouvel atlas d'Angleterre.　4°.　Paris, Desnos, 1767.　Title 2918]

　　　　　　　　　　　　　　　TRAVELS.
**Taylor, T.**
　England exactly described or a guide to travellers, in a compleat sett of mapps of all the county's of England being a map; for each county where every town & village in each county is perticulerly exprefsed with the names and limits of every hundred &c. Very usefull for all gentlemen & travellers being made fitt for thē pockett; printed coloured and sold by Tho: Taylor at ye golden lyon in Fleet street where are sold all sorts of mapps and fine french dutch and italian prints.　1 p. l., 41 fold. maps; 6 maps, 8 táb. on 24. fold. l.　8°.　[London] T. Taylor [1715]　　　　　　　　2912

NOTE.—Maps same as those in [1715] B. M. copy with the following exceptions: two maps are numbered 17; no. 27, 34, have same patrons as those in Blome's "Speed's maps epitomiz'd. 1681;" no. 36 dated 1667. B. M. list gives 1680.
Maps of Scotland dated 1715; nos. 2, 15, 23, 32, 34 dated 1671; nos. 24, 1667; no. 26, 1670.
Maps engraved by W. Hollar, Richard Blome and Richard Palmer.
"Richard Blome used other people's plates as the addition of his name is evident on some of the plates and Thomas Taylor was not behind him in the same acts of appropriation and in finding new patrons as subscribers." *cf.* B. M. letter.
The following maps are inserted:
A new mapp of North Britain or Scotland ... 3 sheets.
A new mapp of the kingdom of Ireland ... 3 sheets. By Will$^m$ Knight ... 3 sheets.
S. imperium Romano-Germanicum ... 2 sheets.
A new mapp of France ... 3 sheets.
A correct mapp of Spain and Portugal ... 3 sheets.
Totius Italiæ tabula per Nicolaum Vifscher ... 2 sheets.

## GENERAL.

(Arranged chronologically)

### 1574-1579

**Saxton, C.**
[Saxton's maps of England and Wales]     front., 35 col. maps, 2 tab. fol. [London, 1574–1579]     2913

NOTE.—Maps dated 1574–1578. The earliest survey maps of England and Wales. This collection has been referred to as the Elizabethan atlas. Thomas Seckford, master of requests and of the court of wards, became the author's patron and secured for him the authority of the queen to survey and draw the maps and a license to sell them for a term of ten years. *cf.* Acts of the privy council, 1575-77; also, Ames, History of printing. London, 1749. pp. 542–544, and Dictionary of national biography. London, 1897, v. 50.
Complete sets of Saxton's maps are very scarce. This copy is complete and is bound in dark blue morocco, with raised bands, gilt edges and tooling, by Lloyd, Wallis & Lloyd.
Engraved frontispiece, illuminated in color and gold, the central figure of which is queen Elizabeth, holding the scepter and globe, seated on a throne, under an elaborate canopy surmounted by the royal arms and two cupids holding laurel crowns; at her right and left, two figures of men with globes and compasses; beneath the pediment two latin verses and a tablet containing six latin verses dated 1579. Recto of following leaf, a table in three divisions with marginal notes at the right; title beginning "Indicem huic operi tripartitum adiecimus" ... verso blank; followed by a folded plate of arms of the peers, in colors and gold (recto blank) facing "Catalogvs vrbiu, epifco" ... (verso blank)
Each map a work of art; hand colored, and embellished by ornamental corners, the royal arms, and arms of the patron, Thomas Seckford.
Maps by various engravers including: Augustine Ryther, Remigius Hogenberg, Leonard Terwoort, Nicholas Reynold, Cornelius Hogius and Francis Scatter. There is no evidence on the maps that Saxton engraved any of them. Ames, Typographical antiquities, and Walpole, Catalogue of engravers, infer that those without an engraver's name were engraved by Saxton.

**Saxton, C.**—Continued.

Speed's maps were based on Saxton's with some additions; namely, the counties are divided into hundreds and roads are traced.

John Gregory refers to Saxton's map of England as follows: "there is no chorographical map or description of the whole region or country of this kingdom . . . more exactly according to art, or according to industry more particularly performed than that of Saxton". . . *cf.* The description and use of the terrestrial globe. 1663.

Thoresby declares Saxton's map of Yorkeshire "the best that ever was made of that county". *cf.* "Ducatus Leodiensis", p. 167. Owing to the fact that Saxton was well acquainted with Yorkshire, his native county, he made this map considerably larger than others. At the upper right hand corner is a tablet inscribed, "Eboracensis Comitatus (cuius incolæ olim Brigantes appellabantur) Longitudine Latitudine hominumque numero reliquis illustrior. An°. Dni. 1577". Surmounting the tablet, the royal arms, supporters, garter, and E. R. At the lower right hand corner of the map, "Christopherus Saxton descripsit. Augustinus Ryther, anglus, sculpfit. An°. Dni. 1577". At the lower left corner, the arms and crest of Thomas Seckford; a circle surrounding the arms inscribed, "Industria naturam ornat."

CONTENTS.

no. [ 1] Anglia . . . 1579. Augustinus Ryther anglus scupfit.
" [ 2] Cantii, Southfexiæ, Surriæ et Middelfexiæ comitat' . . . 1575. Remigius Hogenbergius fculpsit.
" [ 3] Sovthamptoniæ comitatus . . . 1575. Leonardvs Terwoort Antverpianvs scvlpsit.
" [ 4] Dorcestriæ comitatus . . . 1575.
" [ 5] Wiltoniæ comitatus . . . 1576. Remigius Hogenbergius fculpfit.
" [ 6] Somersetensem comitat' . . . 1575. Leonardvs Terwoort Antverpianvs sculpsit.
" [ 7] Devoniæ comitat' . . . 1575. Remigius Hogenbergius fculp.
" [ 8] Promontorivm hoc in mare proiectvm Cornvbia dicitvr. 1576. Lenaert Terwoort Antverpianvs scvlpsit.
" [ 9] Essexiæ comitat' . . . 1576.
" [10] Hartfordiæ comitatvs . . . 1577. Nicholaus Reynoldus Londinenfis fculpfit.
" [11] Oxonii, Buckinghamiæ et Berceriæ comitatuum . . . 1574.
" [12] Glocestriæ siue Claudioceftriæ comitat' . . . 1577. Avgvstinvs Ryther anglvs scvlpsit.
" [13] Svffolciæ comitatus . . . 1575.
" [14] Norfolciæ comitatus . . . 1574. Cornelivs Hogivs sculpsit.
" [15] Northamton, Bedfordiæ, Cantabrigiæ, Huntingdoniæ et Rutlandiæ comitatuum . . . 1576.
" [16] Warwic, Lecestriæq, comitat' . . . 1576. Leonardus Terwoordus, Antuerpianus incidebat.
" [17] Staffordiæ comitatu . . . 1577. Francifcus Scatterus fculpfit.
" [18] Wigorniensis comitatus . . . 1577.
" [19] Salopiæ comitatvs . . . 1577. Remigius Hogenbergius sculpfit.
" [20] Frvgiferi ac ameni Herefordiæ comitatvs . . . 1577. Remigius Hogenbergius [sculpsit]
" [21] Lincolniæ, Notinghamiæq, comitatuū . . . 1576. Remigius Hogenbergius fculpfit.

no. [22] Vniversi Derbienfis comitatus . . . 1577.
" [23] Cestriæ comitatus (Romanis legionibus et colonijs olim infignis) vera et abfoluta effigies. Francifcus Scatterus fculpfit. 1577.
" [24] Eboracensis comitatus . . . 1577 [Yorkshire] Augustinus Ryther anglvs sculpfit.
" [25] Lancastriæ comitatus . . . 1577. Remigius Hogenbergius fculpfit.
" [26] Dvnelmensis episcopatus . . . 1576. Avgvstinvs Ryther scvlpsit.
" [27] Westmorlandiæ et Cumberlandiæ comit' . . . 1576. Avgvstinvs Ryther anglvs scvlpsit.
" [28] Northvmbriæ comitatvs . . . [n. d.]
" [29] Monvmethensis comitatus . . . 1577.
" [30] Glamorgā comitatus . . . 1578.
" [31] Radnor, Breknok, Cardigan et Caermarden, quatuor auftralis Cambriæ comitatuum . . . 1578.
" [32] Penbrok comitat' . . . 1578.
" [33] Montgomeri ac Merionidh, duorum borialis cambriæ comitatuum . . . 1578. Remigius Hogenbergius sculpfit.
" [34] Denbigh ac Flint duorum olim cambriæ, modo Walliæ, comitatuum defcriptio . . . 1577. Remigius Hogenbergius fculpfit.
" [35] Mone insvlæ modo Anglefey, et Caernaruan . . . 1578.

## 1644
**Hollar, W.**

The kingdome of England, & principality of Wales, exactly described whith euery sheere, & the fmall townes in euery one of them, in 6 mappes, portable for euery mans pocket . . . Defcribed by one that trauailed throughout the whole kingdome, for its purpose . . .   1 p. l., 6 fold. maps.   nar. 8°.   [London] J. Garrett [1644] 2914

## 1672
**Seller, J.**

The coasting pilot: describing the sea-coasts, channels, soundings, sands, shoals rocks, and dangers: the bayes, roads, harbours, rivers, ports, buoyes, beacons, and sea-marks, upon the coasts of England, Flanders and Holland with directions to bring a shipp into any harbour on the said coasts. Being furnished with new draughts, charts, and descriptions, gathered from ye experience and practise of diverse able and expert navigators of our english nation . . . 1 p. l., 54 pp., 19 maps on 23 l. fol. London, J. Seller, W. Fisher & J. Wingfield [1672] 2915

NOTE.—Entered in the "Term catalogue" for 1672.
Engraved title-page on which are represented England's famous discoverers: cap. Davies, sir Walter Raleigh, sir Hugh Willoughby, cap. John Smith, sir Fran. Drake, Tho. Candish and many others. Below the title are two views,—a panorama of London and the Thames, from London bridge and a mythical picture representing the confluence of the Thames and the Medway. Maps engraved and many embellished by various designs. Titles generally surmounted with the arms of the country to which they relate.

### 1742
**Badeslade, T.**
 Chorographia Britanniæ; or a set of maps of all the counties in England and Wales. Engraved by Will: Henry Toms. 4 p. l., 46 maps, 5 tab. 16°. London, W. H. Toms, 1742. 2916

### 1758
**Gibson, J.**
 New and accurate maps of the counties of England and Wales drawn from the latest surveys . . . 1 p. l., 53 maps. 24°. London, printed for T. Carnan [1758?] 2917

### 1767
**Desnos, L. C.**
 Nouvel atlas d'Angleterre divisé en ses 52 comtés. Avec toutes les routes levées topographiquement par ordre de s. m. britannique et les plans des villes et ports de ce royaume . . . 1 p. l., 1 map on 12 sheets. 4°. Paris, Desnos, 1767. 2918
 NOTE.—Engraved title.

### 1777
**Bowen, E.,** *and* **Bowen, T.**
 Atlas anglicanus, or a complete sett of maps of the counties of South Britain; divided into their respective hundreds, wapentakes, wards, rapes, lathes &c. . . . 1 p. l., 45 maps. fol. [London] for T. Kitchin [1777?] 2919

### 1778
**Bowen, E., Kitchin, T.,** *& others.*
 The royal english atlas: being a new and accurate set of maps of all the counties of south Britain, drawn from surveys and the beft authorities; divided into their refpective hundreds, and exhibiting all the cities, towns, villages, churches, chapels, &c. particularly diftinguifhing more fully and accurately the church livings, than any other maps hitherto published. Adorned with views of all the cathedrals; and a concife defcription of each diocese. Illustrated with hiftorical extracts relative to the government, trade, manufactures, and prefent state of the cities and principal boroughs and market towns: likewise an account of the air, soil, natural produce, and commodities of every county. To the whole is prefixed, a general map of England and Wales; comprehending all the direct and principal cross roads: with many other ufeful particulars, and regulated by astronomical observations . . . The whole comprifed in forty-four sheet maps. 1 p. l., 44 maps. fol. London, R. Wilkinson [1778] 2920

 NOTE.—Maps dated 1777-1778. See also title 2921.
 The following views inserted: Chester.—Falmouth.—Plymouth.—Dartmouth.— Tor Bay.— Bristoll.— Southampton.— Portsmouth.— Sheerness.— Dover.— Deale Castle.— Leverpool.— London.— Yarmouth.— Newcastle on Tyne.—Hull.

## 1778

The royal english atlas: being a new and accurate set of maps of all the counties in England and Wales, drawn from the several surveys which have been hitherto publifhed, with a general map of England, and Wales, from the lateft and beft authorities . . . Containing all the cities, towns, villages, and churches, whether rectories, vicarages, or chapels, many noblemen's and gentlemen's seats, etc., etc.; each map is illustrated with a general defcription of the country, its cities, borough and market towns, the number of members returned to parliament, parishes, houses, acres of land, &c. And historical extracts relative to the trade, manufactures, and government of the cities, and principal towns, and the prefent state of their inhabitants, &c. . . .   1 p. l., 44 fold. maps. fol. London, for C. Bowles [1778]   2921

NOTE.—Maps dated 1777–1778.
Same maps as in title 2920.

## 1787
**Sayer, R.**

An english atlas, or a concise view of England and Wales; divided into counties, and its subdivifions into hundreds &c. describing their situation, extent, boundaries, circumference, soil, product, chief rivers and the principal great and bye-roads; with a chart of the distances between the cities and chief towns. Together with a description of the situation of the most venerable antiquities whether ruins of castles, palaces, or monasteries, as well as the most remarkable houfes, plantations &c. pointing out every delightful scene of extensive prospect, and curiosities of art and nature worthy a travellers notice, on fifty two copper plates.   3 p. l., [64] pp., 52 (*i. e.* 49) maps.  4°.  London, for R. Sayer, 1787.   2922

NOTE.—Engraved title. Title and index, plates nos. 1–2.
Map no. 4, Chart of distances between the cities and chief towns, wanting.

## 1791
**Tunnicliff, W.**

A topographical survey of the counties of Hants, Wilts, Dorset, Somerset, Devon, and Cornwall, commonly called the western circuit.  xi, 256 pp., 7 maps, 48 pl., 6 tab.  8°.  Salisbury, for the author by B. C. Collins, 1791.   2923

NOTE.—Following pp. xi, 50, 90, 118, 162 and 216 are six county maps, together with a folded index table, and eight pages of coats of arms, separately paged, to accompany each map.

## 1830
**Pigot, J., & co.**

Pigot and co.'s british atlas of the counties of England, with a map of England and Wales and a circular one of the country round London to the distance of fourteen miles; the whole engraved on steel

**Pigot, J., & co.**—Continued.

plates, and embellished with a correct graphic series of vignettes of the cathedrals and some of the handsomest churches in England; accompanied by topographical accounts, exhibiting the general statisticks of each county; its ancient history, and modern localities, and divisions; commerce, manufactures, and population; tables of distance, etc., the entire prefixed by comprehensive reciprocal distance tables, of the principal towns in Great Britain, etc., and an itinerary of the most useful and generally traveled mail and coach routes throughout the united kingdom. 1 p. l., [41] l., 41 maps. fol. London, J. Pigot & co. 1830. 2924

## 1834

**Greenwood & co.**

Atlas of the counties of England, from actual surveys made from the years 1817 to 1833. Engraved by J. & C. Walker. 1 p. l., 46 maps on 88 l. fol. London, Greenwood & co. 1834. 2925

NOTE.—Small county map of England on title-page. Each county map contains an inset engraving of a cathedral, castle, etc. located in the county.

## 1838

**Moule, T.**

The english counties delineated; or, a topographical description of England. Illustrated by a map of London, and complete series of county maps ... 2 v. 4°. London, G. Virtue, 1838. 2926

NOTE.—Engraved title.

Collation: v. 1, 1 p. l, xxiv, 484 pp., front., 31 maps on 34 l.; v. 2, 2 p. l., 528 pp., 27 maps.

## 1844

**Lewis, S.**

Atlas to the topographical dictionaries of England and Wales, comprising a general map of England and Wales, a plan of London, and maps of the counties. 1 p. l., 57 maps. 4°. London, S. Lewis & co. 1844. 2927

## 1846

**Hall, S.**

A travelling county atlas [of England] with all the railroads accurately laid down and the boundaries colored. 2 p. l., 46 maps. 8°. London, Chapman & Hall [1846] 2928

## 1884

**Letts, son & co.,** *limited.*

Letts's popular county atlas. Being a complete series of maps delineating the whole surface of England and Wales, with special and original features and a copious index of 18,000 names. 2 p. l., 10, [1] pp., 47 maps. fol. London, Letts, son & co. limited, 1884. 2929

## 1886

**Philip, G., & son.**
Philip's handy atlas of the counties of England, including maps of the county of London, North and South Wales, the Channel Islands, the Isle of Man, and plans on an enlarged scale of the environs of six important towns. New and enlarged ed. ... 2 p. l., 58 pp., 48 maps. 12°. London, G. Philip & son [1886]
  2930

NOTE.—Shows every railway station in England and Wales.

## 1900

**Bartholomew, J. G.**
The royal atlas of England and Wales, reduced from the ordnance survey. A complete series of topographical maps, physical and statistical charts, town plans and index of 35,000 names.  xii, 72 pp., front., 69 maps. fol. London, G. Newnes [1900?]
  2931

## 1903-1904

**Bartholomew, J. G.**
The survey atlas of England & Wales; a series of 84 plates of maps and plans, with descriptive text, illustrating the topography, physiography, geology, climate and the political and commercial features of the country ...   6 p. l., 27, [1] pp., 84 fold. maps. fol. Edinburgh, J. Bartholomew & co. 1903-[1904]
  2932

NOTE.—Issued in 21 parts.
Contains the following plans of cities:
no. 79. Plan of London.
" 81. Liverpool and Manchester.
" 82. Newcastle, Hull, Bradford and Leeds.
" 83. Sheffield, Nottingham, Birmingham and Leicester.
" 84. Bristol, Portsmouth, Plymouth and Brighton.

CONTENTS.

I. The physical features of England and Wales ... by Hugh Robert Mill.
II. Geological features of England and Wales ... by sir Archibald Geikie.
III. Temperature of England and Wales ... by Alexander Buchan.
IV. Rainfall of England and Wales ... by ... G. J. Symons.
V. Agricultural statistics for England and Wales ...
VI. Population of England and Wales ...
VII. Ecclesiastical and demographical statistics ...
VIII. Parliamentary statistics ...
IX. Railways of England and Wales ...
X. Commercial and industrial statistics ...
XI. Etymology of English and Welsh place names ...
XII. The cartography of England and Wales, by J. G. Bartholomew.

## CITIES.

### LONDON.

**Cary, J.**
Cary's actual survey of the country fifteen miles round London. On a scale of one inch to a mile. Wherein the roads, rivers, woods and commons as well as every market town, village, etc. are distinguished; and every seat shewn with the name of the possessor. Preceded by a general map of the whole; to which is added an index of all the names contained in the plates. 3 p. l., [14] l., 51 maps. 12°. London, for J. Cary, 1786. 2933

**Philip, G., & son.**
Philips' handy-volume atlas of London, containing a large-scale street plan (in 55 sections, on a scale of three inches to the mile) of London and suburbs, including the whole of the county of London . . . viii, 40, 93 pp. incl. front., 64 maps. 12°. London, G. Philip & son, 1891. 2934

**Bartholomew, J. G.**
The pocket atlas and guide to London . . . Enl. ed. 1p. l., 30, [2] pp., 18 fold. maps. 16°. London, J. Walker & Co. 1903. 2935

NOTE.—Text on verso of maps.

### OXFORD.

**Oxford historical society.**
Old plans of Oxford. 15 sheets in portfolio. fol. [Oxford, 1899]
[Publications. no. 38] 2936

NOTE.—Companion volume to Oxford topography by Herbert Hurst.

CONTENTS.

Agas's map of Oxford. (1578–1588) 8 sheets.
Whittlesey's engraving of Agas's plan and Breblock's Elizabethan views. (1728) 4 sheets.
Hollar's plan of Oxford. (1643) 1 sheet.
Loggan's plan of Oxford. (1675) 2 sheets.

### SOUTHAMPTON.

**Southampton record society.**
Maps and plans of old Southampton. Edited with notes, by W. H. Rogers . . . 2 p. l., 13 maps. fol. Southampton, printed and published for the Southampton record society [1907]
2937

NOTE.—In portfolio.

## IRELAND.

### GENERAL.

(Arranged chronologically)

#### 1689

**Petty,** *Sir* **W.**
A geographicall description of ye kingdom of Ireland. Collected from ye actual survey made by s.<sup>r</sup> William Petty. Corrected & amended by the advice & assistance of several able artists late inhabitants of that kingdom. Containing one general mapp of ye whole kingdom with four provincial mapps & 32 county mapps divided into baronies wherein are described ye cheife cities, townes, rivers, harbors and head-lands &c.<sup>a</sup> To which is added a mapp of Great Brittaine and Ireland, together with an index of the whole. Being very usefull for all gentlemen and military officers, as well for sea as land service. Engraven & published for ye benifit of ye publique by Fra: Lamb.　　1 p. l., 1 l., 38 fold. maps.　24°.　London, F. Lamb, R. Morden, J. Seller [1689]　　　　2938

> NOTE.—Engraved title.
> Sir William Petty's maps of Ireland were printed in fol. 1685. *cf.* Wood's Athenae Oxonienses.
> British Museum gives date 1700?, but the book is noted in "A catalogue of books printed and published in London in Michaelmas-term 1689, numb. 34," column 11.

#### 1881

**Bartholomew, J.**
Philip's handy atlas of the counties of Ireland . . . Revised by P. W. Joyce.　2 p. l., 41 pp., 33 maps.　12°.　London, G. Philip & son [1881]　　　　2939

#### 1901

**Richards, L. J., & co.**
Memorial atlas of Ireland, showing provinces, counties, baronies, parishes, etc. Compiled and drawn from reliable official data and the latest information. Indexed.　2 p. l., 24 pp., 33 maps.　fol.　Philadelphia, L. J. Richards & co. 1901.　　　　2940

## SCOTLAND.

### GENERAL.

(Arranged chronologically)

#### 1895

**Bartholomew, J. G.,** *& others.*
The royal scottish geograpical society's atlas of Scotland, a series of sixty-two plates of maps and plans illustrating the topography,

**Bartholomew, J. G.**, & *others*—Continued.
physiography, geology, natural history and climate of the country. 6 p. l., 18 pp., 63 maps. fol. [Edinburgh] drawn, engraved and printed at the Edinburgh geographical institute, 1895.   2941

### 1898
**Bartholomew, J.**
Philips' handy atlas of the counties of Scotland . . . New and rev. ed. . . . 3 p. l., 1 l., 34 pp., 32 maps. 12°. London, G. Philip & son, 1898.   2942

#### ORKNEY ISLANDS.

### 1753
**McKenzie, M.**
Aanwyzing voor de zeelieden, door de Orcadische eylanden, als mede van een gedeelte van de Lewys, met daar toe behoorende pas-caarten; vertaalt uit het Engelsche handschrift. Waar by nog gevoegt is een caart van Hitland en Valey-haven door den zelven uit voorgaande tekeningen opgestelt; en de Buis-haven, met nog eenige land-kenningen van Hitland.   5 p. l., 16 pp., 13 maps, 5 pl. fol. Amsterdam, J. van Keulen [1753]   2943

> NOTE.—Title of the english work from which this was translated reads: Orcades; or, a geographical and hydrographical survey of the Orkney and Lewis islands. 1750.
>
> pp. 1-15 contain an explanation of the tides, and a description of the rocks and anchorage on the Orkney islands.

#### WALES.

### 1889
**Bartholomew, J.**
Philips' handy atlas of the counties of Wales . . . 2 p. l., 1 l., 16 pp., 16 maps. 12°. London, G. Philip & son, 1889.   2944

---

# DENMARK.

## GENERAL.
(Arranged chronologically)

### 1680
**Pitt, M.**
A description of the places next the North-Pole; as also of Muscovy, Poland, Sweden, Denmark, and their several dependances. fol. Oxford, for M. Pitt, 1680.   2945
[English, The, atlas. v. 1]

> NOTE.—See title 2831 for bibliographical notice.

## 1763–1769

**Pontoppidan, E.**
Den danske atlas eller konge-riget Dannemark, med dets naturlige egenskaber, elementer, indbyggere, væxter, dyr og andre affødninger, dets gamle tildragelser og nærværende omstændigheder i alle provintzer, stæder, kirker, slotte og herregaarde. Forestillet ved en udførlig lands-beskrivelse, saa og oplyst med dertil forfærdigede land-kort over enhver provintz, samt ziret med stædernes prospecter, grund-ridser, og andre merkværdige kaaber-stykker . . . 5 v. in 6. 8°. Kiøbenhavn, A. H. Godiche, 1763–1769. 2946

NOTE.—On title-page of v. 4–5, "fortsat af Haus de Hofman."

——— Supplement til den danske atlas eller konge-riget Dannemark, dens anden og tredie tome for Siellands, Laalands og Fyens stifter . . . Med alphabetisk register: Eet over kiøbstæder og sogne, og eet over herre-gaardene. Samlet og forfattet af Hans de Hoffman . . . t. vi–[vii] 2 v. 8°. Kiøbenhavn, A. H. Godiche ved F. C. Godiche, 1774–1781. 2947

NOTE.—v. 4–6 edited by Jacob Langebek; v. 7 by B. C. Sandvig.

---

# FRANCE.

### CITIES.

**Tassin, I.**
Les plans et profils de tovtes les principales villes et lievx considérables de France. Enfemble les cartes générales de chacune prouince: & les particulières de chaque gouuernement d'icelles . . . 2 v. obl. 16°. Paris, S. Cramoisy, 1634. 2948

NOTE.—Collation: v. 1, 39 pp., [16] l., 155 maps, 47 pl.; v. 2, 44 pp., [20] l., 180 maps, 30 pl. Duplicate, pp. 35–38 from 1636 ed. Engraved title to each volume and part. Under "Poictov," maps no. 9, "Carte de l'isle de Oleron" and no. 12, "S.t Iean d angely" [!] are duplicated.

Les plans et profils de tovtes les principales villes et lievx considérables de France; enfemble les cartes générales de chacune prouince: & les particulières de chaque gouuernement d'icelle . . . 2 v. obl. 8°. Paris, I. Messager, 1636. 2949

Note.—Collation: v. 1, 39 pp., [15] l., 156 maps, 48 p. l.; v. 2, 44 pp., [20] l., 181 maps, 31 pl.
Engraved title-page to v. 1, wanting.
Maps, views and titles of 1634 edition, with the following additions:
v. 1. Lorraine.   no. 26. Govvernement de La Motte.
"  "       "        "   27. La Motte.
"  2. Beavlce.     "    1. Govvernement de Bourges.
"  "       "        "    2. Bovrges.

**COLONIES.**

**France.** *Ministère de la marine et des colonies.*
    Atlas des colonies françaises, publié par ordre de son excellence m. le marquis P. de Chasseloup-Laubat, ministre secrétaire d'état au département de la marine et des colonies. 1866. 1 p. l., 14 maps. fol. Paris, Challamel aîné, 1866.    2950

    NOTE.—The following maps relate to America:
    no. 1. Carte hydrographique des parties connues de la terre. 1862.
    " 2. Carte des iles de S$^t$. Pierre et Miquelon. 1862.
    " 3. Carte de l'ile et des bancs de Terre Neuve. 1862.
    " 4. Carte de la Martinique. 1862.
    " 5. Carte de la Guadeloupe et dépendances. 1863.
    " 6. Carte de la Guyane française. 1863.

**Mager, H.**
    Atlas colonial . . .  2 p. l., 432 pp. incl. 20 col. maps. fol. Paris, C. Bayle [1885]    2951

    NOTE.—The following maps relate to America:
    no. [1] Les colonies françaises en 1661, 1683, 1815 et 1885.
    " [14] Iles S$^t$ Pierre et Miquelon, Terre-Neuve.
    " [15] Guadeloupe et ses dépendances.—Insets: Ville de la Basse-Terre.—Ville de la Pointe à Pître.—Grand-bourg de Marie-Galante.—Saint-Martin et Saint-Barthélemy, dépendances de la Guadeloupe.—Les petites Antilles.
    " [16] Carte de la Martinique.—Insets: Plan de Saint-Pierre.—Plan de Fort de France.
    " [17] Guyane française et territoire contesté.—Iles du Salut.—St. Laurent du Maroni.—Plan de l'ile de Cayenne et de ses environs.—Plan de la ville de Cayenne.—Plan de Macapa.—Guyane, territoire restitué et . . . contesté.

**Mager, H.,** *and* **Jacquemart, A.**
    Atlas colonial. Édition populaire et classique . . . 20 pp. incl. 19 maps. 4°. Paris, librairie du journal la géographie, C. Bayle, éditeur, 1890.    2952

    NOTE.—Text on covers.
    The following maps relate to America:
    no. 14. Guadeloupe et ses dépendances.
    " 15. Petites Antilles.—Carte de la Martinique.
    " 16. Guyane française et territoire contesté.
    " 17. Iles S$^t$ Pierre et Miquelon, Terre-Neuve.

**Malleterre, G.,** *and* **Legendre, P.**
    Livre-atlas des colonies françaises, à l'usage de l'enseignement des colonies. 6 v. 4°. Paris, C. Delagrave [1900]    2953

    CONTENTS.
    v. 1. Colonies de l'océan Indien.
    " 2. " d'extrême Orient.
    " 3. " de l'océan Pacifique.
    " 4. " " " Atlantique.
    " 5. " " la mer Méditerranée, Algérie et Tunisie.
    " 6. " d'Afrique.

**Pelet, P.**
　　Atlas des colonies françaises dressé par ordre du ministère des colonies.　　2 p. l., iv, 74 pp., 1 l., 26 pp., 1 l., 27 col. maps.　fol. Paris, A. Colin, 1902.　　2954

> NOTE.—Published in parts from 1898–1902.
> The following maps relate to America:
> 　no. 1. [Planisphère]　Colonies françaises.
> 　" 23. Inde.—Guyane.　1899.
> 　" 24. Guadeloupe, Martinique, S! Pierre et Miquelon. 1898.—Insets: Câbles des Antilles.—Petites Antilles, câbles, paquebots.—Iles S! Martin et S! Barthélemy.—Terre-Neuve.—S! Pierre et Miquelon. 1898.
> 　" 27. Points d'appui de la flotte . . . Fort de France . . . 1901.

### HARBORS.

**France.**　*Ministère des travaux publics.*
　　Ports maritimes de la France.　Cartes et plans.　[Atlas des ports de la France]　157 maps. fol.　Paris, imprimerie nationale [1871–1897]　　2955

> NOTE.—Incomplete.　Maps in portfolios.
> To accompany work of the same title published by the ministère des travaux publics.

### HISTORICAL.

**Brette, A.**
　　Recueil de documents relatifs à la convocation des états généraux en 1789.　Atlas des bailliages ou juridictions assimilées ayant formé unité électorate en 1789, dressé d'après les actes de la convocation conservés aux archives nationales.　2 p. l., xxxv, 16, [1] pp., 33 col. maps.　fol.　Paris, imprimerie nationale, 1904.　　2956

> NOTE.—Half title: Collection de documents inédits sur l'histoire de France publiés par les soins du ministre de l'instruction publique.
> To accompany work in 3 volumes by same author, entitled, "Recueil de documents relatifs à la convocation des états généraux de 1789. Paris, imprimerie nationale, 1894–1904."
> The following map relates to America:
> 　no. 33. La Guadeloupe et ses dépendances.—Désirade.—Iles des Saintes.—Marie-Galante.—La Martinique.—Ile de S! Domingue.

**Longnon, A. H.**
　　Atlas historique de la France depuis César jusqu' à nos jours . . . 1–3 livr.　cover-title, 15 maps.　fol.　Paris, Hachette & c$^{ie}$. 1885–1889.　　2957

> NOTE.—No more published.

　　Texte explicatif des planches.　1–3 livr.　4°.　Paris, Hachette & c$^{ie}$. 1885–1889.　　2957a

> NOTE.—No more published.
> Cover, pt. 1, dated 1884.
> Paged continuously.

**Walckenaer, C. A.**
 Atlas de la géographie ancienne, historique et comparée des Gaules cisalpine et transalpine, composé d'après les analyses géographiques de m. le baron Walckenaer.  2 p. l., 9 maps.  sm. fol.  Paris, P. Dufart, 1839. 2958

**Zannoni, G. A. R.—**
 Atlas historique de la France ancienne et moderne . . . Dressé pour servir à la lecture de l'histoire de mm. Velly et Villaret. Exécuté par le s. [L. C.] Desnos . . .  1 p. l., 16 pp., 59 maps. 4°.  Paris [Desnos] 1765. 2959
 NOTE.—Engraved title-page.

### LINGUISTIC.

**Gilliéron, J.,** *and* **Edmont, E.**
 Atlas linguistique de la France.  fasc. 1–32.  fol.  Paris, H. Champion, 1902–1908. 2960
 NOTE.—"Atlas linguistique de la France; notice servant à l'intelligence des cartes.  Paris, H. Champion, 1902."
 "Cet atlas se composera de 1,700 à 1,900 feuilles, dont chacune reproduira la carte de la France complète et sera consacrée à un mot ou à un type morphologique."
 "Il paraît chaque année 4 fascicules, se composant chacun de 50 cartes."
 Maps in portfolios.

### MONT-BLANC.

**Pitschner, W.**
 Atlas zum Mont-Blanc.  cover-title, 2 col. maps, 4 col. pl. fol.  [Genf, selbstverlag des verfassers, in commission bei F. A. Brockhaus in Leipzig, 1864] 2961
 NOTE.—To accompany work entitled, "Der Mont-Blanc. Darstellung der besteigung desselben am 31. juli und 2. august 1859. Genf , . , 1864."

### STATISTICAL.

**Bonnange, F.**
 Atlas graphique et statistique du commerce de la France avec les pays étrangers pour les principales marchandises pendant les années 1859 à 1875.  3 p. l., 16 pp., 8 l., 54 tab.  fol.  Paris, J. Baudry, 1878. 2962
 NOTE.—"Gravé et chromo-lithographié par Erhard."

CONTENTS.

 I. Animaux vivants (nos. 1–6)
 II. Grains, farines et légumes secs (nos. 7–11)
 III. Vins, eaux-de-vie et esprits (nos. 12–15)
 IV. Industrie du sucre (nos. 16–18)
 V. Industries textiles (nos. 19–37)
 VI. Industrie du cuir (nos. 38–43)
 VII. Industrie houillère, ind. métallurgique, ouvrages en métaux (nos. 44–53)
 VIII. Machines et outils (no. 54)

## WARS.

**Beaulieu, S. de P.**
[Plans & profils avec les descriptions des principales villes & places fortes de France, & les cartes de leurs gouvernements] 11 pts. in 1 v. obl. 4°. [Paris, Beaurain, 1694?] 2963

NOTE.—Known as "Petit Beaulieu," being a reduction of the "Grand Beaulieu" entitled: Les glorieuses conquêtes de Louis le grand . . . fol. Paris, 1676-94.
Imperfect: title-page wanting.
Maps engraved by L. Loisel, H. van Loon, Romeyn de Hooghe, A. D. Perelle, Cochin.

### CONTENTS.

Plans et cartes des villes d'Artois. 4 p. l., 29 maps, 15 pl.
Les plans et profils des principales villes et lieux considérables du comté de Flandre. 1 p. l., 1 pl.
Les plans et profils des principales villes et lieux considérables du comté d'Alost ou Flandre impériale. 3 p. l., 58 maps, 24 pl.
Les plans et profils des principales villes et lieux considérables du comté de Haynavt. 2 p. l., 23 maps, 9 pl.
Les plans et profils des principales villes et lieux considérables du duché de Cambray. 1 p. l., 4 maps, 1 pl.
Les plans et profils des principales villes du comté de Namvr. 2 p. l., 4 maps, 2 pl.
Les plans et profils des principales villes et lieux considérables du dvché de Lvxembovrg. 2 p. l., 8 maps, 4 pl.
Les plans et profils des principales villes et lieux considérables du duché de Limbovrg. 1 p. l., 2 maps, 1 pl.
Les plans et profils des principales villes et lieux considérables du dvché de Gveldre. 1 p. l., 7 maps, 8 pl.
Plans et profils des principales villes des duchez de Lorraine et de Bar. 2 p. l., 36 maps, 11 pl.
Les cartes, plans et profils des principales villes et lieux considérables du comté de Bovrgogne et païs adjacents. 2 p. l., 12 maps, 3 pl.

**Belmas, J. V.**
Journaux des siéges faits ou soutenus par les français dans la péninsule de 1807 à 1814; rédigés d'après les ordres du gouvernement, sur les documents existant aux archives de la guerre et au dépôt des fortifications. Atlas. 2 p. l., 24 maps. fol. Paris, Firmin Didot frères & cie. 1836. 2964

NOTE.—To accompany work of same title, published 1836–1837.

**Duvotenay, T.**
Atlas des campagnes de la révolution française, de m. A. Thiers, dressé par Th. Duvotenay.—Gravé par Ch. Dyonnet. 2 p. l., 32 fold. maps. 4°. Paris, Furne, Jouvet & c.$^{ie}$ [1880?] 2965

**France.** *Dépôt général de la guerre.*
Atlas des campagnes de l'empereur Napoléon en Allemagne et en France [de 1805, 1806 et 7, 1809] gravé sous la direction du général

**France.** *Dépôt général de la guerre*—Continued.

de division [Jean Jacques Germain, baron] Pelet. 4 p. l., 15 maps. fol. [Paris] dépôt gén<sup>al</sup> de la guerre, 1844. 2966

NOTE.—Imperfect: maps no. 1, 3, 9, wanting.

CONTENTS.

- no. 1. Carte de l'empire français, en 1805.
- " 2. Théâtre de la guerre dans la Bavière, l'Autriche, l'Italie, la Prusse et la Pologne.
- " 3. Théâtre des opérations de l'empereur Napoléon sur le haut Danube, en octobre 1805.
- " 4. Bataille d'Ulm ou du Michelsberg, 14 et 15 octobre 1805.
- " 5. Bataille et combat de Caldiéro, 30 octobre 1805 et 27 avril 1809.—Bataille de Sacile, 15 avril 1809.
- " 6. Bataille d'Austerlitz, 2 décembre 1805.
- " 7. Bataille d'Iéna, 14 octobre 1806.
- " 8. Places de la Vistule et de la Narew, en 1807.
- " 9. Théâtre des opérations de l'empereur Napoléon entre la Passarge et la Prégel, 1807.
- " 10. Bataille de Preuss-Eylau, 8 février 1807.
- " 11. Bataille de Friedland, 14 juin 1807.
- " 12. Théâtre des opérations de l'empereur Napoléon sur les bords de la Laaber, avril 1809.
- " 13. Bataille d'Eckmühl, 22 avril 1809.
- " 14. Combat d'Ebersberg, 3 mai 1809.
- " 15. Bataille d'Essling et travaux de l'ile de Lobau, mai, juin et juillet 1809.
- " 16. Bataille de Wagram, 5 et 6 juillet 1809.
- " 17. Bataille de Znaïm, 11 juillet 1809.

**Gouvion Saint-Cyr, L. de.**

Atlas des cartes et plans relatifs aux campagnes du maréchal Gouvion S<sup>t</sup> Cyr, aux armées du Rhin et de Rhin et Moselle, pendant les années 1792, 1793, 1794 . . . et 1797. 4 p. l., 17 fold. maps. fol. Paris, 1828. 2967

NOTE.—"Gravé par Hacq et Warin. Imprimé par Sampier."
To accompany work in 4 volumes by the same author, entitled: Mémoires sur les campagnes des armées du Rhin et de Rhin-et-Moselle, de 1792 jusqu'à la paix de Campo-Formio . . . Paris, Anselin, 1829.

Atlas des mémoires pour servir à l'histoire militaire sous le directoire, le consulat et l'empire. 2 p. l., 17 (*i. e.* 18) pl. obl. fol. Paris, Anselin, 1831. 2968

NOTE.—To accompany, "Mémoires pour servir à l'histoire militaire sous le directoire" . . . 1831.

**Joanne, A.**

Atlas de la défense nationale cartes des dix-sept départements envahis ou menacés par l'ennemi. cover-title, 2 p. l., 18 maps. fol. [Paris] Hachette & cie. 1870. 2969

**Jomini, H.** *i. e.* **A. H.**
Atlas pour servir à l'intelligence de l'Histoire critique et militaire des guerres de la révolution . . . Gravé sous la direction de J. B. Bielaerts. 2 p. l., 58, [1] pp., 36 (*i. e.* 38) maps. fol. Bruxelles, J. B. Petit, 1840. 2970

> NOTE.—The following map relates to America:
> no. 36. Croquis de la partie française de l'île S! Domingue.

Atlas pour servir à l'intelligence de l'Histoire critique et militaire des guerres de la révolution . . . Gravé sous la direction de J. B. Bielaerts. 2 v. fol. Bruxelles, J. B. Petit, 1841. 2971

> NOTE.—Collation: v. 1, 2 p. l., 56, [1] pp.; v. 2, 36 (*i. e.* 38) maps.
> v. 1, containing the letterpress, is titled "Explication de l'atlas de Jomini" and is larger than v. 2, which contains the maps.
> The following map relates to America:
> no. 36. Croquis de la partie française de l'île S! Domingue.

**Julien, R. J.**
Atlas géographique et militaire de la France, divisé en deux parties. 2 p. l., 8 l., 26 maps, 16 pl. fol. Paris, R. J. Julien, 1751. 2972

CONTENTS.

pt. 1. Carte de France et des pays limitrophes.
" 2. Plans et descriptions des principales places de guerre.

**Lavallée, T. S.**
Atlas de géographie militaire adopté par m. le ministre de la guerre pour l'école impériale militaire de Saint-Cyr. Accompagné de tableaux de statistique militaire . . . 3 p. l., 16 pp., 34 col. maps. fol. Paris, Furne & cie. 1859. 2973

Atlas de géographie militaire. Anciennement atlas de Saint-Cyr. Nouvelle édition entièrement revue et mise au courant. [anon.] 2 p. l., 42 maps. fol. Paris, Combet & cie. 1902. 2973a

> NOTE.—First published in 1851.
> The following maps relate to America:
> no. [34] Planisphère.
> " [37] Amérique Septentrionale.
> " [38] Carte militaire des Etats Unis. (Partie orientale)
> " [39] Carte militaire des Etats Unis. (Partie occidentale)
> " [40] Amérique Méridionale.

**Lemau de la Jaisse, P.**
Plans des principales places de guerre et villes maritimes frontières du royaume de France, distinguez par départemens, gouvernemens généraux & particuliers des provinces. . . . au premier juillet 1736 . . . 2 p. l., 268 pp. incl. 112 maps. 16°. Paris, Didot, 1736. 2974

**Le Rouge, G. L.**

Recueil des fortifications, forts et ports de mer de France; lavé au pinceau. 1 p. l., 2 l., 89 maps. 8°. Paris, Le Rouge [1760?]

2975

NOTE.—The following maps relate to America:
no. 87. En Amérique.—Québec.—Louisbourg.
" 88. Nouvelle Orléans.—Fort Dauphin.
" 89. Cayenne.—Ville Marie.

CONTENTS.

no. 1. Abbeville.
" 2. Amiens.—Bapaume.
" 3. Montreuil.
" 4. Boulogne.—Ardres.
" 5. Dourlens.—Peronne.
" 6. Ham.
" 7. Gravelines.—S! Quentin.
" 8. Calais.
" 9. Fort Nieulet.
" 10. Hesdin.—Guise.
" 11. Arras.
" 12. St. Omer.—Condé.
" 13. Bethune.—S! Venant.
" 14. Aire.
" 15. Douay.
" 16. Fort de Scarpe.
" 17. Cambray.
" 18. Le Quesnoy.—Bouchain.
" 19. Maubeuge.—Landrecy.
" 20. Valenciennes.
" 21. Bergue S! Vinox.
" 22. L'Isle.
" 23. Dunquerque.
" 24. Rocroix.—Philippeville.
" 25. Charlemont.
" 26. Charleville.
" 27. Mezières.—Montmedy.
" 28. Sedan.
" 29. Avesne.—Bouillon.
" 30. Longwy.—Marsal.
" 31. Thionville.
" 32. Metz.
" 33. Verdun.
" 34. Sarlouis.
" 35. Toul.—Phalsbourg.
" 36. Bitche.
" 37. Haguenau.—Landau.
" 38. Fort Louis.
" 39. Strasbourg.
" 40. Neuf Brisac.—Huningue.
" 41. Betfort.—Schelestad.
" 42. Besançon.
" 43. Salins.—Chateau de Joux.
" 44. Dijon.

no. 45. Auxonne.—Dole.
" 46. Châlons sur Saune.
" 47. Fort l'Ecluse.
" 48. Fort Barraux.
" 49. Grenoble.
" 50. Briançon.
" 51. Briançon.—Les Têtes.
" 52. Les Têtes.—Le Randouillet.
" 53. Mont Dauphin.—Fort Dauphin.
" 54. Embrun.—Sisteron.
" 55. Monaco.—S$^t$ Tropez.
" 56. Fort S$^{te}$ Marguerite.—Isles S$^{te}$ Marguerite.
" 57. Entrevaux.—Antibes.
" 58. Toulon.
" 59. Marseille.—Pont S$^t$ Esprit.
" 60. Alais.—Narbonne.
" 61. Aiguesmortes.—Nismes.
" 62. Montpellier.
" 63. Port de Cette.—Isle de Brescou.
" 64. Perpignan.—Salces.
" 65. Collioure.—Villefranche.
" 66. Bellegarde.
" 67. Navarreins.—Mont-Louis.
" 68. Lourdes.—Fort S$^t$ Elme.
" 69. S$^t$ Jean Pied de Port.—Andaye.
" 70. Fort de Socoa.—Chaū de Dax.
" 71. Bayonne.
" 72. Bordeaux.—F. de Medoc.
" 73. Fort S$^{te}$ Croix.—Chateau de Ha.
" 74. Chateau Trompette.
" 75. Blays.
" 76. Brouage.—Tour de Isle devant Blaye.
" 77. Rochefort.—S$^t$ Martin de Ré.
" 78. Oléron.
" 79. La Rochelle.
" 80. Nantes.
" 81. L'Orient.
" 82. Port-Louis.—Belle-Isle.
" 83. Brest.—Caen.
" 84. Cherbourg.
" 85. S$^t$ Malo.
" 86. Havre de Grace.—Dieppe.
" 87. En Amérique. Quebec.—Louisbourg.
" 88. Nouvelle Orléans.—Fort Dauphin.
" 89. Cayenne.—Ville Marie.

**Napoleon I.**

Guerre d'Orient. Campagnes de Égypte et de Syrie, 1798–1799. Mémoires pour servir à l'histoire de Napoléon, dictés par lui-même à Sainte-Hélène, et publiés par le général [Henri Gratien, comte] Bertrand. Atlas composé de 18 planches . . . gravées par m. Moisy.   2 p. l., 18 maps. fol. Paris, Comon & c$^{ie}$. 1847.   2976

NOTE.—To accompany work in 2 v., with same title.

**Pajol, C. P. V.**, *comte.*
 Atlas des guerres sous Louis xv.   cover-title, 4 maps, 4 pl. fol.   Paris, Firmin-Didot, 1886.   2977
> NOTE.—Contains portrait of Louis xv engraved by Rivoalen, and three colored lithographs from drawings of E. Detaille representing cuirassier, artilleryman, and footman from the regiments of the king.

 Atlas des itinéraires, campagnes, opérations militaires de Pajol, général en chef . . . cover-title, 8 maps. fol. Paris, F. Didot frères, fils & c$^{ie}$. 1874.   2978
> NOTE.—To accompany work in 3 v. by the same author, entitled: Pajol, général en chef; par le général de division comte Pajol, son fils aîné.

**Prussia.**   *Grosser generalstab. Kriegsgeschichtliche abtheilung.*
 Der deutsch-französische krieg, 1870–71. . . .   2 pts. in 5 v. Atlas.   76 maps.   fol.   Berlin, E. S. Mittler & sohn [1874–1881]
  2979
> NOTE.—Atlas is without title-page.
> Contains plans showing positions of french and german armies, plans of important battles and the following cities: no. 10. Strassburg mit umgebung; no. 15 a–b. Paris mit umgebung.

**Siborne, W.**
 History of the war in France and Belgium, in 1815. Containing minute details of the battles of Quatre-Bras, Ligny, Wavre and Waterloo. Atlas. 3d ed.   11 maps.   fol.   London, T. & W. Boone [1848]   2980
> NOTE.—No title-page.
> To accompany work of same title.

**Soult, N. J. de D.**, *duc de Dalmatie.*
 Mémoires du maréchal-général Soult, duc de Dalmatie, publiés par son fils. Atlas.   2 maps on 13 sheets.   fol.   Paris, Amyot [1854]   2981
> NOTE.—No title-page.
> To accompany his work in 3 vols., with same title.
>
> CONTENTS.
>
> no. 1. Champ de bataille de Fleurus. 26 juin 1794. Echelle 1:80,000.
> " 2. Carte du théâtre de la guerre en Suisse et en Italie extraite de la carte de Bacler-d'Albe.

**Thiers, L. A.** *i. e.* **M. J. L. A.**
 Atlas de l'histoire du consulat de l'empire. Dressé et dessiné sous la direction de m. Thiers, par mm. A. Dufour et Duvotenay. Gravé sur acier par Dyonnet.   2 p. l., 66 maps.   fol.   Paris, Paulin, Lheureux & c$^{ie}$ 1859.   2982
> NOTE.—The following map relates to America:
> no. 22. Ile de St. Dominque.

**Vinoy, J.**
Campagne de 1870-1871. Siége de Paris. Opérations du 13e corps et de la troisième armée. Atlas. 2. éd. cover-title, 15 maps. fol. Paris, H. Plon, 1872. 2983

NOTE.—To accompany work of the same title.

**Wachter, A. O.**
La guerre de 1870-71 . . . Atlas de la guerre. Reports sur pierre de la carte de l'état-major avec autorisation spéciale de m. le ministre de la guerre. cover-title, 9 maps. sm. fol. [Paris, E. Lachaud, 1872-1873] 2984

NOTE.—To accompany his: La guerre de 1870-71, histoire politique et militaire . . . 2 v. 1872-73.

CONTENTS.

no. 1. Wissembourg-Wœrth.
" 2. Carte du camp de bataille de Spickeren.
" 3. Environs de Metz.
" 4. Théâtre des opérations des armées de mm. les maréchaux Bazaine et de Mac-Mahon et des 1ʳᵉ, 2ᵉ, 3° et 4ᵉ armées allemandes, du 10 août au 1ᵉʳ septembre.
" 5. Environs de Sedan.
" 6. Environs de Paris.
" 7. Théâtre des opérations des 1ʳᵉ et 2ᵉ armées de la Loire, commandées par les généraux d'Aurelle de Paladines et Chanzy.
" 8. Théâtre des opérations des armées de mm. les généraux Bourbaki, Garibaldi; Werder et Manteuffel (dans l'Est)
" 9. Théâtre des opérations de l'armée du nord, commandée par le général Faidherbe.

## GENERAL.

(Arranged chronologically)

### 1667

**Du Val, P.**, *d'Abbeville*
Cartes et tables de géographie, des provinces efchûës à la reine très-chrétiene, par le décez de la reine Elifabeth fa mère, du prince dom Balthazar fon frère, et du roy catholique Philippe IV son père. 1 p. l., 48 l. incl. 14 maps. 24°. Paris, l'auteur, 1667. 2985

### 1677-1680

La géographie françoise, contenant les descriptions, les cartes, et le blason des provinces de France . . . 1 v. 16°. Paris, chez l'auteur, 1677. 2986

NOTE.—Complete in 4 v.

CONTENTS.

v 1. La France depuis son agrandissement par les conquestes du roy . . . Paris, chez l'autheur, 1680. 6 p. l., 258, [2] pp., 34 maps, 35 pl.

### 1685?

**Cassini, G. D., & others.**

Hydrographia Galliæ: the sea coasts of France containing general and particular charts of all the harbours, bayes, iflands, &c. vpon y͏ͤ said coasts. According to . . . actual surveys . . . 2 p. l., 43 maps. obl. 24°. [London] R. Morden [etc., 1685?] 2987

NOTE.—Engraved title by I. Harris.

### 1762

**Bonne, R.**

Atlas maritime ou cartes réduites de toutes les côtes de France avec des cartes particulières des isles voisines les plus considérables, suivies des plans principales villes maritimes de ce royaume . . . 4 p. l., 31–46, 4 pp., 30 maps. 24°. Paris, Lattré [1762] 2988

NOTE.—Engraved title.
Date supplied from the "Approbation."

### 1764

Petit tableau de la France ou cartes géographiques sur toutes les parties de ce royaume avec une description abrégée . . . 2 p. l., [10], 213, [3], 12 pp., 28 maps. 24°. Paris, Lattré, 1764. 2989

NOTE.—Engraved title.

### 1765

**Brion de la Tour, L.**

Coup d'œil général sur la France . . . pour servir d'introduction au Tableau analytique et géographique de ce royaume. Dressé par plusieurs géographes dont les ouvrages sont aussi connus qu'estimés, faisant partie de l'atlas historique de la France ancienne et moderne, mise [!] au jour et dirigé par le sieur Desnos . . . 15, [3] pp. 4°. Paris, Grangé, Guillyn, etc. etc. 1765. 2990

[ *With* Desnos, L. C. Tableau analytique de la France. 4°. Paris, 1766. Title 2993]

### 1765

**Michel, —**

L'indicateur fidèle ou guide des voyageurs, qui enseigne toutes les routes royales et particulières de la France, routes levées topographiquem͏ͭ dès le commencement de ce siècle, et assujetties à une graduation géométrique . . . 4 p. l., 10 pp., 18 (*i. e.* 19) col. maps. 4°. Paris, 1765. 2991

[ *With* Desnos, L. C. Tableau analytique de la France. 4°. Paris, 1766. Title 2993]

## 1765

**Zannoni, G. A. R.**—
Le petit Neptune françois ou carte des côtes maritimes du royaume, avec une partie de celles d'Angleterre, d'Espagne et d'Italie . . . 2 p. l., 4 col. maps. 4°. Paris, Desnos, 1765.    2992
[*With* Desnos, L. C.    Tableau analytique de la France. 4°. Paris, chez l'auteur, 1766. Title 2993]

## 1766

**Desnos, L. C.**
Tableau analytique de la France dans lequel on donne une connaissance générale et détaillée du royaume, considéré sous ses différentes formes de gouvernement tant civil qu'ecclésiastique et militaire. Dressé relativement au commerce et aux finances et distribué en plusieurs cartes d'une manière méthodique et intelligible en faveur des jeunes gens et des amateurs de géographie . . . Par différents auteurs.    2 p. l., 30 col. maps, 2 tab. 4°. Paris, chez l'auteur, 1766.    2993

NOTE.—Engraved title-page.
Bound with: Coup d'œil général sur la France . . . par m. Brion [de la Tour] . . . 1765; and Le petit Neptune françois . . . par m. Rizzi-Zannoni . . . 1765; and, L'indicateur fidèle ou guide des voyagers . . . Dressé par le sieur Michel . . . 1765.

## 1778

**Robert de Vaugondy, D.**
[Carte coloriée du royaume de France . . . plus la carte du Canada et de la Louisiane] 8 maps. 4°. [Paris, 1778]    2994

NOTE.—Without title-page.
Maps are like nos. 14–20 and 43 of his Nouvel atlas portatif . . . 1778. See title 649.
The following map relates to America:
no. [8] Canada, Louisiane, possessions angl? par le s. Robert de Vaugondy . . . 1778.

## 1792

**Dumez,** —, *and* **Chanlaire, P. G.**
Atlas national portatif de la France, destiné à l'instruction publique, composé de 93 cartes et d'un précis méthodique et élémentaire de la nouvelle géographie du royaume, dédié et présenté à l'assemblée nationale. Par les auteurs de l'Atlas national de France. [anon.]    1 p. l., 92 maps. obl. 8°. Paris, au bureau de l'atlas national, 1792.    2995
[*With their* Précis élémentaire et méthodique de la nouvelle géographie de la France. obl. 8°. Paris, au bureau de l'atlas national, 1791]

**Dumez, —,** *and* **Chanlaire, P. G.**—Continued.
   Note.—Engraved title.
   The following maps relate to America:
   no. [84] Isle Bourbon.—Isle de France.—Isle Gorée.—Isle de Ste. Lucie.—Isle de la Martinique.—Isles de la Guadeloupe, Marie Galante, Desirade et des Saints.—Isle de S$^t$. Dominque.—Isle de Tabago.—Isle St. Pierre et Miquelon.
   " [85] Partie de planisphère terrestre comprenant toutes lesisl es et colonies françoises.

### 1818
**Cassini de Thury, C. F.**
   Atlas topographique, minéralogique et statistique de la France, réduit de Cassini, au quart environ de son échelle (1 ligne pour 450 toises) rectifié d'après les nouvelles observations astronomiques, les levés du cadastre, les travaux des ponts-et-chaussées, et le dernier traité de Paris . . . en vingt-cinq feuilles, par Alexis Donnet. 3 p. l., 14 sheets. fol. Paris, H. Langlois, 1818.    2996

### 1822–1843
**France.** *Ministère de la marine.*
   Pilote français . . . Par les ingénieurs hydrographes de la marine, sous les ordres de m. [Charles François] Beautemps-Beaupré, ingénieur hydrographe en chef . . . 6 v. fol. Paris, dépôt général de la marine, 1822–1843.    2997

           CONTENTS.

   v. 1. Côtes occidentales de France depuis les roches de Porsal jusqu'à la pointe de Penmarc'h (environs de Brest) Levées en 1816, 1817 et 1818. 2 p. l., 63 l. incl. 22 maps, 75 pl., 2 tab.
   " 2. Côtes occidentales de France depuis la pointe Penmarc'h jusqu'à l'île d'Yeu. Levées en 1819, 1820, 1821 et 1822. 2 p. l., 102 l. incl. 27 maps, 91 pl., 20 tab.
   " 3. Côtes occidentales de France depuis l'île d'Yeu jusqu'à la côte d'Espagne. Levées en 1822, 1824, 1825 et 1826. 2 p. l., 73 l. incl. 32 maps, 6 pl., 23 tab.
   " 4. Côtes septentrionales de France depuis l'île Bréhat jusqu'à Barfleur. Levées en 1829, 1830, 1831, 1832 et 1833. 2 p. l., 29 maps, 62 pl., 47 tab.
   " 5. Côtes septentrionales de France depuis Barfleur jusqu'à Dunkerque. Levées en 1833, 1834, 1835 et 1836. 2 p. l., 91 l. incl. 33 maps, 62 tab.
   " 6. Côtes septentrionales de France depuis les roches de Porsal jusqu'au phare des Heaux de Bréhat. Levées en 1837 et 1838. 2 p. l., 69 l. incl. 15 maps, 46 pl., 31 tab.

### 1833
**Charle, J. B. L.**
   Nouvel atlas national de la France par départemens, divisés en arrondissemens et cantons . . . avec des augmentations par Darmet. 2 p. l., 80 maps. fol. Paris, Dauty & Roret, 1833.    2998

## 1841

**Monin, V.**

Petit atlas national des départemens de la France et de ses colonies. 100 cartes ornées de vues des monumens les plus remarquables . . . gravées sur acier par Alès. Nouv. éd. Revues, corrigées et augmentées en 1841. 2 p. l., 95 maps. obl. 4°. Paris, Lafont [1841] 2999

NOTE.—Imperfect: map no. 96 wanting.
The following maps relate to America:
no. 91. La Martinique.
" 92. La Guadeloupe et ses dépendances.
" 93. Guyane.—Plan d'une partie de l'ile de Cayenne.—Plan de la ville de Cayenne.
" 94. Ile et banc de Terre-Neuve.—Iles S$^{t.}$ Pierre et Miquelon.

## 1847

**Levasseur, V.**

Atlas national illustré des 86 départements et des possessions de la France, divisé par arrondissements, cantons, et communes avec le tracé de toutes les routes, chemins de fer et canaux. Dressé d'après les travaux du cadastre du dépôt de la guerre et des ponts et chaussées. 2 p. l., 100 maps. fol. Paris, A. Combette, 1847. 3000

NOTE.—Maps have illustrated borders containing portraits, views, and descriptive text. See also title 3002.
The following maps relate to America:
no. 89. Colonies françaises (en Amérique) [West Indies]
" 90. Colonies françaises. Martinique. Amérique du Sud.
" 92. Colonies françaises (en Amérique)
" 95. Planisphère.
" 98. Amérique Septentrionale.
" 99. Amérique Méridionale.

## 1850

**France.** *Ministère de la marine.*

Atlas des côtes méridionales de France levées en 1839, 1840, 1841 et 1842 sous la direction de feu m.$^r$ Monnier, ingénieur hydrographe de 1$^{ère}$ classe . . . par mm. Le Bourguignon-Duperré et Bégat. . . . Lieussou et Delamarche . . . Augmenté des plans et cartes des côtes limitrophes d'Espagne et d'Italie, ainsi que des cartes et vues d'atterrages, depuis le cap S.$^t$ Sébastien, en Espagne, jusqu'au phare de Villefranche, en Italie. Levées en 1844 et 1845 par mm. Le Bourguignon-Duperré et Bégat, assistés de feu m.$^r$ Ledo . . . et de m.$^r$ Boutroux . . . 2 p. l., 38 maps. fol. [Paris] dépôt général de la marine, 1850. 3001

NOTE.—"Gravé par Hacq et Carré."

## 1851

**Vuillemin, A.**

La France et ses colonies. Atlas illustré. Cent cartes dressées d'après les cartes de Cassini [de Thury] du dépôt de la guerre, des ponts-et-chaussées et de la marine. Texte . . . par Ernest Poirée. 3 p. l., 103 l., 107 maps. fol. Paris, Migeon, 1851. 3002

> Note.—Maps have inset views and portraits.
> See also title 3007 for 1882 edition.
> The following maps relate to America:
> no. 85. La Guadeloupe.
> " 86. La Martinique (Iles des Antilles)
> " 87. Iles St. Pierre et Miquelon.—Amérique française (Guyane)

## 1856

**Levasseur, V.**

Atlas national illustré des 86 départements et des possessions de la France, divisé par arrondissements, cantons et communes avec le tracé de toutes les routes, chemins de fer et canaux. Dressé d'après les travaux du cadastre du dépôt de la guerre et des ponts et chaussées . . . 2 p. l., 100 maps. fol. Paris, A. Combette, 1856. 3003

> Note.—Maps have illustrated borders containing portraits, views and descriptive text.
> See also title 3000.
> The following maps relate to America:
> no. 89. Colonies françaises (en Amérique)
> " 90. Colonies françaises. Martinique. Amérique du Sud.
> " 92. Colonies françaises (en Amérique)
> " 95. Amérique Méridionale.
> " 96. Amérique Septentrionale.
> " 99. Mappemonde, par A. Vuillemin.

## 1868–1882

**Joanne, A. L.**

Géographie, histoire, statistique et archéologie des 89 départements de la France. 29 v. 12°. Paris, L. Hatchette & cie. 1868–1882. 3004

> Note.—"Chaque volume contient la géographie d'un department." The Library of Congress has the following:
> Aisne. 2. éd. 1874.
> Algérie. 3. éd. 1874.
> Aube. 1874.
> Bouches-du-Rhône. 1874.
> Cantal. 1875.
> Charente. 1868.
> Charente-Inférieure. 1869.
> Côte-d'Or. 1869.
> " " 1874.
> Doubs. 1872.
> Haute-Saône. 1875.

Indre-et-Loire. 1870.
" " " 1874.
Isère. 1870.
Landes. 1869.
Loir-et-Cher. 1869.
Loire. 1874.
Loire-Inférieure. 1874.
Loiret. 1870.
" 1874.
Meurthe. 1868.
Pas-de-Calais. 1874.
Puy-de-Dôme. 1876.
Rhône. 1869.
Seine-et-Marne. 1869.
Seine-et-Oise. 1869.
" " " 1874.
Somme. 1869.
" 1876.

## 1873

Atlas de la France, contenant 95 cartes tirées en quatre couleurs et 94 notices géographiques et statistiques. 3. éd. [193] l. incl. 95 maps. fol. Paris, Hachette & cie. 1873. 3005

NOTE.—Map no. 92 entitled: Colonies françaises. Amérique.

## 1878

**Fisquet, H. J. P.**

Grand atlas départemental de la France, de l'Algérie et des colonies, 106 cartes gravées sur cuivre par G. Lorsignol, accompagnées d'un texte explicatif. 2 v. obl. fol. Paris, A. Le Vasseur [1878] 3006

NOTE.—v. 1, Départements. 3 p. l., xxxiv, 206 pp., 93 col. maps.—v. 2, Algérie.—Colonies françaises, tableaux statistiques et biographiques. 2 p. l., 169 pp., 13 col. maps.
The following maps relate to America:
v. 2, no. 98. Carte des colonies françaises aux Antilles.
" " 99. Guadaloupe.
" " 100. Carte de la Guyane française.
" " 101. Martinique.

## 1882

**Vuillemin, A.**

La France et ses colonies. Atlas illustré. Cent cinq cartes dressées d'après les cartes du dépot de la guerre, des ponts et chaussées et de la marine . . . Édition de 1882. 3 p. l., 101 l., 107 maps. fol. Paris, J. Migeon [1882] 3007

NOTE.—Maps have inset views and portraits.
See also title 3002 for 1851 edition.
The following maps relate to America:
no. 93. La Guadaloupe.
" 95. La Martinique (Iles des Antilles)
" 96. Iles St· Pierre et Miquelon.—Amérique française (Guyane)

### 1890

**Vuillemin, A.**, *& others.*

Nouvel atlas illustré. La France et ses colonies. Cent huit cartes dressées d'après les cartes du dépot de la guerre . . . par mm. Vuillemin, Thuilier, Ch. Lacoste. Illustrées par m. Filatreau. Texte rédigé par mm. A. Martineau et H. Stein. 2 p. l., 104 l., 108 col. maps. fol. Paris, direction et administration, J. [Migeon] 1890. 3008

> NOTE.—Maps illustrated by engravings, portraits of prominent men and views of principal cities.
> Map no. 106 shows the french colonies; no. 107, a topographical map of France, shows railroads and forts; no. 108, a general map of the railroads of Europe.
> The following maps relate to America:
> no. 93. La France. Guadeloupe et dépendances, S$^{t\cdot}$ Martin & S$^{t\cdot}$ Barthélemy.
> " 94. La France. Martinique, Guyane, iles et bancs de Terre Neuve.

### 1905

**Dubois, E. M.**, *and* **Sieurin, E.**

Cartes d'étude pour servir à l'enseignement de la géographie, France et colonies . . . 9. éd. . . . 7 pp., 40 maps. 4°. Paris, Masson & cie. 1905. 3009

## PARIS.

### HISTORICAL.

**Dulaure, J. A.**

Histoire physique civile et morale de Paris, depuis les premiers temps historiques jusqu'à nos jours. Ornée de gravures représentant divers plans de Paris, ses monumens et ses édifices principaux. Atlas. 4. ed. 1 p. l., v–viii, 48 pp., 5 maps. obl. 12°. Paris, Guillaume & co. 1829. 3010

### REPRODUCTION.

**Paris.** *Conseil municipal.*

Histoire générale de Paris. Atlas des anciens plans de Paris. Reproduction en fac-simile des originaux les plus rares et les plus intéressants pour l'histoire de la topographie parisienne. Avec une table analytique présentant la légende explicative de chaque plan et un appendice consacré aux documents annexes. 72 pp., 31 (*i. e.* 33) maps on 115 l. fol. Paris, imprimerie nationale, 1880. 3011

> NOTE.—"Publié sous la direction de m. Alphand, inspecteur général des ponts et chaussées."

"Les plans qui composent cet atlas ont été exécutés . . . d'après les originaux, aujourd'hui fort rares, qui sont conservés dans les grandes bibliothèques publiques et dans quelques collections particulières" . . .

"Nous les avons divisés en deux catégories . . . Dans la première sont rangés les plans *rétrospectifs*, c'est-à-dire établis, soit approximativement, soit par des procédés scientifiques, postérieuement à l'époque qu'ils représentent. La seconde comprend les plans *contemporains*, dressés par des topographes ayant ou pouvant avoir sous les yeux l'aspect de la ville au moment où ils le reproduisaient." *cf.* Table analytique, p. 17.

CONTENTS.

*I. Plans rétrospectifs.*

1. Plan de la cité gauloise . . . imaginé par . . . Delamare et gravé par Nicolas de Fer. 1705.
2. Plan de Lutèce . . . par Albert Lenoir.
3. Paris de 1180 à 1223 . . . plan annexé à l'histoire de Dulaure.
4. Paris de 1285 à 1314 . . . par Albert Lenoir.
5. Paris en 1380 . . . par Henri Legrand.
6-6bis. Plan archéologique de Paris du XIIIe au XVIIe siècle, restitué par Adolphe Berty.

*II. Plans contemporains.*

7. Lutetia Parifiorum urbs . . . Paris en 1530 . . . de Sébastien Münster.
8. Paris en 1530 . . . de Georges Braun.
9-9bis. Paris de 1512 à 1547, fac-simile de la Grande Gouache.
9ter. Paris vers 1540 . . . copie du plan dit de tapisserie . . . par Gaignières en 1690.
10. Paris en 1552 . . . de Olivier Truschet et Germain Hoyau dit Plan de Bâle.
11-11bis. Paris en 1555 . . . plan dit de Saint-Victor attribué à Jacques Androuet du Cerceau.
12. Paris en 1575 . . . plan de François de Belleforest.
13-13 Paris en 1609 . . . de François Quesnel.
14. Paris en 1609 . . . de Vassalieu dit Nicolay.
15. Paris en 1615 . . . de Mathieu Merian.
16. Paris en 1630 . . . de Melchior Tavernier.
17. Paris de 1649 à 1652 . . . de Jean-Boisseau dit plan des colonelles.
17bis, 17ter. Paris en 1654.
18-18[4]. Paris en 1652 . . . de Jacques Gomboust.
19, 19bis. Paris de 1670 à 1676 . . . de Bullet et Blondel.
20-20quater. Paris en 1672 . . . premier plan de Jouvin de Rochefort.
21. Paris en 1676 . . . Second plan de Jouvin de Rochefort.
22. Paris en 1697 . . . de Nicolas de Fer.
23. Paris en 1713 . . . de Bernard Jaillot.
24-24[4]. Paris en 1714 . . . de Jean de La Caille.
25-25quater. Paris en 1728 . . . de l'abbé Jean Delagrive.
26-26bis. Paris en 1731 . . . de Roussel.
27-27quater. Paris de 1734 à 1739 . . . de Louis Bretez dit plan de Turgot.
28. Paris en 1760 . . . de Robert de Vaugondy.
29-29bis. Paris en 1763 . . . de Deharme.
30-30quater. Paris en 1775 . . . de J. B. Jaillot.
31-31[F]. Paris de 1789 à 1798 . . . de P. Verniquet.

## GENERAL.

(Arranged chronologically)

### 1758

**Pasquier, J. J.**, *and* **Denis, L.**
Plan topographique et raisonné de Paris. Ouvrage utile au citoyen et à l'étranger. Dédié et présenté à monseigneur le duc de Chevreuse, gouverneur de Paris.   7 p. l., 149, [2] pp. incl. 25 maps. 24°.   Paris, Pasquier, 1758.   3012

### 1762

**Lattré, J.**
Atlas topograhique des environs de Paris dédié et présenté au roy . . .   3 p. l., 58 pp., 26 maps.   32°.   Paris, Lattré [1762?]
3013

> NOTE.—Engraved title. Date supplied from Quérard, J. M., La France littéraire.
> Map entitled, "Situation des provinces de France avec les noms des vents" inserted.

### 1766

**Deharme, —.**
Plan de la ville et fauxbourgs de Paris divisé en 20 quartiers dont la plus grande partie à été rectifiée d'après différens desseins levés géométriquement, tirés du cabinet de mr. le chevalier [Jean] de Beaurain géographe ordin.re du roy, & de beaucoup d'observations faites fur les lieux par l'auteur qui ont servi à réformer plusieurs ommissions qu'on a laissé subsister dans ceux qui ont précédé celui-ci. L'on y a joint des tables qui indiquent les messageries, coches, carosses & rouliers des différens endroits de la France, et le jour de leur départ, les boëtes aux lettres de la grand-poste et les principaux passages d'une rue à l'autre: ouvrage utile à toutes personnes principalement à celles de cabinet. Dédié et présenté à messire Camus de Pontcarré . . .   1 p. l., [28] l., 2 maps on 70 l., 6 pl.   fol.
Paris, l'auteur, 1766.   3014

> NOTE.—Contains the following allegorical engravings with description:
> [Title] Tableau allégorique, pour le cinquantième année de règne de Louis xv.
> no. 1. Médaillon pour l'année jubilaire, ou cinquantième du règne de Louis xv.
> " 2. Établissement de l'école royale militaire.
> " 3. Inauguration de la statué équestre de Louis xv.
> " 4. Nouvelles halles aux grains et farines.
> " 4ª. Pose de la première pierre de la nouvelle église de Ste Geneviève.

### 1800

**Coutans, G.**
Atlas topographique en xvi feuilles des environs de Paris . . . par dom. G. Coutans . . . revu, corrigé et considérablement augmenté, d'après nombre de cartes précieuses & plans particuliers,

tant gravés que manuscrits, par Charles Picquet, géographe-graveur ... 1 p. l., 16 maps. fol. Paris, C. Picquet, 1800.

3015

NOTE.—Engraved title-page contains index map: Tableau d'assemblage de l'atlas des environs de Paris.

### 1896

**France.** *Préfecture de la Seine. Service de l'assainissement.*
Atlas administratif des égouts de la ville de Paris. 1896. cover-title, 17 maps, 1 pl. fol. [Paris, imp. Monrocq, 1896] 3016

NOTE.—Map no. 1, scale of: 1:25.000. Maps nos. 2-17, scale of: 1:5.000.

### 1906

**Paris.** *Diocèse.*
Atlas de la censive de l'archevêché dans Paris. Reproduction en fac-simile publiée avec des notices extraites du terrier de l'archevêché par Armand Brette. 1 p. l., 14, [2], VIII pp., 1 fold map, 44 (*i. e.* 45) pl. fol. Paris, imprimerie nationale, 1906. 3017

NOTE.—Atlas belongs to the collection known as the "Histoire générale de Paris. Collection de documents publiée sous les auspices de l'édilité parisienne."

---

# GERMANY.

#### COLONIAL.

**Deutsche kolonialgesellschaft.**
Kleiner deutscher kolonialatlas ... 4$^{te}$ durchgesehene und vermehrte ausgabe ... 4 p. l., 8 maps. nar. 4°. Berlin, D. Reimer, 1900. 3018

Wirtschafts-atlas der deutschen kolonien. 2. verb. aufl. cover-title, [24] pp., 10 maps. fol. Berlin [D. Reimer, 1908] 3019

NOTE.—First edition published 1906.
The following map relates to America:
no. 1. Übersicht über die unternehmungen des kolonial-wirtschaftlichen komitees 1896/1906.

**Germany.** *Kolonialamt.*
Grosser deutscher kolonial-atlas. Bearbeitet von Paul Sprigade und Max Moisel. Herausgegeben von der kolonial-abtheilung des auswärtigen amts. pts. 1-6. 20 maps. fol. Berlin, D. Reimer, 1901-07. 3020

NOTE.—Reviewed by m. Chesneau in: La géographie. Société de Géographie. Bulletin. 8°. Paris, 1902. v. 5. pp. 142-143.
Contains maps of all the german possessions on the uniform scale of 1:1.000.000, except the colonies in the Pacific ocean.
When complete the atlas will contain 31 maps.

**Kiepert, R.**
 Deutscher kolonial-atlas für den amtlichen gebrauch in den schutzgebieten... Begleitender text von dr. Joseph Partsch... cover-title, 1 p. l., 32, [52] pp., 7 fold. maps. fol. Berlin, D. Reimer, 1893. 3021

> NOTE.—The following maps have been added: Skizze der kolonie Kamerun zur übersicht der abkommen zwischen dem Deutschen reiche, Grossbritannien und Frankreich, sowie der deutschen expeditionen in das hinterland. 1894.—Die neue grenze Kamerun's gegen das englische Niger-Benuë-gebiet. (Abkommen vom 14. april und 15. november 1893)

CONTENTS.

no. 1. Erdkarte zur übersicht des kolonialbesitzes, der konsularischen und diplomatischen vertretungen und der postdampferlinien des deutschen reiches.
" 2. Aequatorial-West-Afrika.
" 3. Deutsch-Südwest-Afrika.
" 4. Aequatorial-Ost-Afrika.
" 5. Die deutschen besitzungen im Stillen ocean.

### COMMERCIAL.

**Schultze, W.**
 Deutschlands binnenhandel mit vieh. Atlas zu heft 52 der "Arbeiten der d[eutsche] l[andswirtschafts] g[esellschaft]"... 2 p. l., 111 maps. obl. 4°. Berlin, 1900. 3022

### LAKES.

**Geistbeck, A.**
 Die seen der deutschen Alpen. Eine geographische monographie... Hrsg. von dem verein für erdkunde zu Leipzig... cover-title, 8 fold. pl. fol. Leipzig, Duncker & Humblot, 1885. 3023

> NOTE.—To accompany article by A. Geistbeck, entitled, "Die seen der deutschen Alpen" in Mittheilungen des Vereins für erdkunde zu Leipzig. 1884. 8°. Leipzig, Duncker & Humblot, 1885. pp. 203–387. Also published separately.

### LINGUISTIC.

**Fischer, H.**
 Atlas zur geographie der schwäbischen mundart... 12 p. l., 28 fold. maps. fol. Tübingen, H. Laupp, 1895. 3024
 [*With his* Geographie der schwäbischen mundart. fol. Tübingen, H. Laupp, 1895]

### MARINE.

**Langhans, P.**
 Justus Perthes' deutscher marine-atlas. Mit begleitworten von Bruno Meyer. 2. aufl. 12 pp., 5 maps. 4°. Gotha, J. Perthes, 1898. 3025

## PHYSICAL.

**Andree, R.,** *and* **Peschel O.**
Physikalisch statistischer atlas des deutschen reichs. 2 p. l., 62 pp., 33 maps. fol. Bielefeld und Leipzig, Velhagen & Klasing, 1878. 3026

### SCHOOL.

**Spruner von Merz, K.**
Dr. K. von Spruner's historisch-geographischer schul-atlas von Deutschland. 1 p. l., 20 pp., 12 col. maps. obl. 4°. Gotha, J. Perthes, 1858. 3027

**Stieler, A.**
Kleiner atlas der deutschen bundesstaaten für schulen und zum häuslichen gebrauch. ... 4. aufl. 2 p. l., 29 maps. obl. 8°. Gotha, J. Perthes, 1852. 3028

### WARS.

**Julien, R. J.**
Atlas topographique et militaire qui comprend le royaume de Bohême, les marquisats de Moravie et de Lusace, le duché de Silésie, la haute et basse Saxe, les frontières du haut Rhin et de Westphalie, et les cartes générales de ces états et du théâtre de la guerre présenté en Allemagne. 2 p. l., 64 maps, 1 tab. 4°. Paris, R. J. Julien, 1758. 3029

> NOTE.—See also title 3030. Engraved title-page: Atlas topographique et militaire, qui comprend les états de la couronne de Bohême & la Saxe électorale avec leurs frontières. Dédié à sa majesté l'impératrice reine de Hongrie et de Bohême. Par le sr. Julien, à Paris, chez l'auteur ... 1758. Femme Lattré, scripsit.
> Like Juliens' Nouveau théâtre de guerre ... with the following exceptions: change of title; maps added, nos. [1], [27], [35–36], [43–44], [46], [49–50], [54–57], [59–62].
> no. 64, Plan de la ville de Berlin ... 1757.

Nouveau théâtre de guerre ou atlas topographique et militaire qui comprend le royaume de Bohême, le comté de Glatz, le marquisat de Moravie, le duché de Silésie, le marquisat de Lusace, la Saxe électorale, et les frontières du Brandebourg, de Pologne, de Hongrie, d'Autriche, de Bavière, et du haut palatinat de Bavière. 2 p. l., 47 maps, 1 tab. 4°. Paris, R. J. Julien, 1758. 3030

> NOTE.—See also title 3029. Engraved title-page and maps are duplicated in his: Atlas topographique ... 1758. Variation of printed title and omission of several maps in the present copy.
> no. 47, Plan de la ville de Berlin ... 1757.

**Prussia.** *Grosser generalstab. Kriegsgeschichtliche abteilung.*
Campaign in Germany of 1866. cover-title, 22 maps. fol. [London, printed for h. m. stationery off. 1872, reprinted 1907] 3031

> NOTE.—To accompany: The campaign of 1866 in Germany. Compiled by the department of military history of the prussian staff.

## GENERAL.

(Arranged chronologically)

### 1681

**Nicolson, W.**
The description of part of the empire of Germany, viz. The upper and lower Saxony: the dukedoms of Mecklenburg, Bremen, Magdeburg, &c. The marquisates of Brandenburg, and Misnia, with the territories adjoining, the palatinate of the Rhine, and the kingdom of Bohemia. fol. Oxford, for M. Pitt, 1681. 3032
[English, The, atlas. v. 2]

NOTE.—See title 2831 for bibliographical notice.

### 1682

**Bodenehr, H. G.**
Sac. imperÿ Romano Germanici geographica descriptio. Teutschland mit angrânzenden kônigreich- und provinzien . . . zu sonderbahr bequemen gebrauch in 32. auffeinander zutreffende tabellen vorgestelt . . . 20 p. l., [60] pp., 3 maps on 68 l. nar. 16°. Augspurg, H. G. Bodenehr, 1682. 3033

### 1683

**Nicolson, W.**
The description of the remaining part of the empire of Germany. viz. Schwaben, the palatinate of Bavaria, arch-dukedom of Austria, kingdom of Hungary, principality of Transylvania, the circle of Westphalia; with the neighbouring provinces. fol. Oxford, for M. Pitt, 1683. 3034
[English, The, atlas. v. 3]

NOTE—See title 2831 for bibliographical notice.

### 1753

**Homann, J. B.**
Atlas Germaniae specialis sev systema tabvlvm geographicarvm, in qvibus imperivm Romano-Germanicvm generalibus repraesentationibus . . . Opus inceptum a Ioh. Bapt. Homanno, et ad hunc usque diem ab Homannianis heredibus studiose continuatum. Appellatum alias tomvs secvndvs Atlantis maioris. 2 p. l., 83 col. maps on 92 sheets, 1 tab. fol. Norimbergae, prostat in officina Homaniana, 1753. 3035

NOTE.—J. B. Homann appears as both author and editor.
Maps by various cartographers including: Nell, Zollman, Majer, Müller, Falkenstein, Hasius, Schreiber, Hüber, Arenhold, and Coldewey.
Three historical maps show camps and lines of the german army at Bruchsal, Mentz, Hundsruck, etc., during the war of the polish succession, 1734–35.
Numerous views of towns, and coats of arms of many of the german provinces.

### 1774

**Courtalon,** *L'abbé*—

Atlas élémentaire où l'on voit sur des cartes et des tableaux relatifs à l'objet l'état actuel de la constitution politique de l'empire d'Alemagne. i°. Les cercles en général, les archevêchés, évêchés, universités, les états qui ont droit de battre monnoye, les villes monétaires &c. ii°. La situation, l'étendue respective, les enclaves, le nombre et le rang des électorats, principautés, abbayes, comtés, baronies, seigneuries et généralement tous les états immédiats qui donnent droit de séance aux diètes générales et particulières de l'empire. iii°. Les principaux territoires immédiats qui ne donnent pas droit de séances aux diètes. iv°. Un indice de tous les cantons de la noblesse immédiate en Souabe, en Franconie et sur le Rhin. v°. Les différentes routes et postes de l'empire et les villes où l'on trouve des relais pour les couriers et voyageurs. vi°. Grand nombre de lieux remarquables par leurs productions ou établissemens, comme mines, forges, fabriques d'armes, manufactures, bains, haras, &c. vii°. Le commencement des états d'empire, l'époque des principales loix, des établissemens et événemens qui ont produit par dégré l'etat actuel de l'Alemagne avec un abrégé méthodique du droit public de l'empire . . . Le tout composé et vérifié d'aprés les meilleures cartes nationales, la géographie de mr. Bufching, les ouvrages de mrs. Schmauss et Pfeffel, les institutions au droit public de l'Alemagne par mr. Gérard &c. . . .   3 p. l., 20 pp., 13 maps, 24 pl. fol. Paris, Julien; Boudet, 1774.   3036

NOTE.—Title-page engraved by Desbruslins fils. Second edition published in 1798. Michaud, in his "Biographie universelle," under Jean Charles Courtalon-Delaistre, says: "Il ne faut pas le confondre avec l'abbé Courtalon, précepteur des pages de Madame, qui publia, en 1774, un Atlas élémentaire de l'empire d'Allemagne, in-4°, ouvrage très-bien fait, et fort utile pour connaitre la constitution du corps germanique, si compliquée à cette époque."

### 1903

**Perthes, J.**

Justus Perthes' staatsbürgeratlas. 24 blätter mit über 100 karten, diagrammen und abbildungen zur verfassung und verwaltung des deutschen reichs und der bundesstaaten. Mit begleitworten. 3. aufl.   24 pp., 24 maps. 16°. Gotha, J. Perthes, 1903.   3037

### States.

### BADEN.

**Germany.** *Baden. Oberdirection des wasser- und strassenbaues. Topographisches bureau.*

Topographischer atlas des grossherzogthums Baden in 170 blättern in kupferstich in maasstabe 1:25 000 der natürlichen länge. Unter der regierung des grossherzogs Friedrich, bearbeitet . . . in

**Germany**—Continued.
  den jahren 1875 bis 1886. 2 p. l., 1 map on 164 sheets. obl. fol.
  Leipzig, Giesecke & Devrient; Hildburghausen, H. Petters, 1875–
  [1901] 3038
   NOTE.—Variously dated from 1875–1901.

## BRUNSWICK AND HANOVER.

**Papen, A.**
  Topographischer atlas des königreichs Hannover und herzogthums
  Braunschweig, nach einem maasstabe von 1:100 000 der wahren
  länge . . .   1 p. l., 1 l., 80 maps. obl. fol.   Hanover [Hahn]
  1832–1847. 3039

## PRUSSIA.

**Toeppen, M. P.**
  Atlas zur historisch-comparativen geographie von Preussen.
  cover-title, 5 maps. obl. fol. Gotha, J. Perthes, 1858. 3040
   NOTE.—To accompany Historisch-comparative geographie von Preussen.
   Nach den quellen, nametlich auch archivalischen, dargestellt von dr. M.
   Toeppen . . . Gotha, J. Perthes, 1858.

## SCHMALKALDEN.

**Danz, C. F.**, *and* **Fuchs, C. F.**
  Acht tafeln zur physisch-medicinischen topographie des kreises
  Schmalkalden. . .   1 p. l., 3 maps, 4 pl., diagr. fol. Marburg,
  N. G. Elwert, 1848. 3041

## SAXONY.

### HISTORICAL.

**Hantzsch, V.** *i. e.* **K. V. G.**
  Die ältesten gedruckten karten der Sächsisch-Thüringischen länder
  <1550–1593> cover-title, 18 maps. fol. Leipzig und Berlin,
  B. G. Teubner [1905] 3042
   NOTE.—In portfolio.
   Accompanied by pamphlet with same title.

### GENERAL.

(Arranged chronologically)

#### 1752–1759

**Schenck, P.**
  Atlas Saxonicus novus, darinnen nicht allein die länder des
  kurfürstenthums Sachsen nach ihren kreisen, I. der Kurkreis, II.
  Meissnische, III. Leipziger, IV. Thüringische, V. Erzgebürgische,
  VI. Voigtländische und VII. Neustädtische, nebst dessen incorpor-
  irten ländern I. marggrafthume Ober und II. Niederlausitz, III.
  der gefürsteten grafschaft Henneberg, IV. grafschaft Mannsfeld,
  sondern auch die fürstenthümer und herrschaften des fürstlichen

hauses Sachsen, nebst allen daran grenzenden ländern, enthalten; welche alle mit der grössten sorgfalt und fleisse übersehen, und von fehlern gesäubert worden.   1 p. l., 47 maps.   fol.   Amsterdam und Leipsig, P. Schenck, 1752–[1759]   3043

NOTE.—Maps have engraved title, border text and are variously dated from 1715–1759; some have inset plans of cities, &c.

## 1752–1758

Neuer Sâchsischer atlas, enthaltend die sieben kreise des kuhrfürstenthums Sachsen, als I. den Kuhrkreis, II. [den] Meisnischen, III. [den] Leipziger, IV. [den] Thüringischen, V. [den] Erzgebürgischen, VI [den] Voigtländischen und VII. [den] Neustädtischen, ingleichen, I. die marggrafschaft Ober- und Niederlausitz, II. die gefürstete grafschaft Henneberg, nebst allen angrenzenden landen und den fürstenthümern und herrschaften des fürstlichen hauses Sachsen.   1 p. l., 36 maps.   fol.   Amsterdam und Leipzig, P. Schenk, 1752–[1758]   3044

NOTE.—Dates on maps vary from 1745–1758. Of the 36 maps, 34 with 10 others were published in an atlas with title: Atlas Saxonicus novus . . . 1752.   See title 3043.
Maps also by Schuchart and Dengelsted.

## 1860

lange, H.

Henry Lange's atlas von Sachsen. Ein geographisch-physikalisch-statistisches gemälde des königsreichs Sachsen.   In zwölf karten mit erläuterndem texte.   iv, [49] pp., 12 maps.   fol.   Leipzig, F. A. Brockhaus, 1860.   3045

## SILESIA.

[omann heirs.

Atlas Silesiae, id est dvcatvs Silesiae generaliter quatuor mappis nec non specialiter xvi mappis tot principatvs repraesentantibvs geographice exhibitvs.   Addita praefatione qua de historia huius atlantis agitvr.   Auctoritate publica in lucen emissus ab Homannianis heredibvs, Norimbergae MDCCL.   2 p. l., 20 maps on 40 l. fol.   [Nuremberg, Homann heirs] 1750–[1808]   3046

## SWABIA.

ischer, H.

Atlas zur geographie der schwäbischen mundart.   12 p. l., 28 fold. maps.   fol.   Tübingen, H. Laupp, 1895.   3047

[*With his* Geographie der schwäbischen mundart.   fol.   Tübingen, H. Laupp, 1895]

## WÜRTEMBERG.

**Würtemberg.** *K. statistisch-topographisches bureau.*
Topographischer atlas des koenigreichs Württemberg in 55 blättern nach den ergebnissen der landesvermessung . . . 1821–1851. 1 p. l., 1 map on 55 sheets. fol. [Stuttgart, k. statistisch-topographisches bureau, 1826–1851] 3048

NOTE.—"Maasstab der gezeichneten originalblätter 1:25 000 natürlicher grösse. 1818. Anfang der landesvermessung, ende derselben 1840. Maasstab der lithograph: atlasblätter 1:50 000 natürlicher grösse. 1821. Anfang der topogr. aufnahme, ende derselben 1844."
Key map on title-page.
Variously dated 1826–1851.

---

# GREECE.

### HISTORICAL.

**Barbié du Bocage, D.**
Recueil de cartes géographiques, plans et médailles de l'ancienne Grèce, relatifs au voyage du jeune Anacharsis; précédé d'une analyse critique des cartes. 2 p. l., 20 pp., 24 maps, 7 pl. 4°. [Paris] Sanson & co. 1791. 3049

NOTE.—To accompany Barthélemy, J. J. Voyage du jeune Anacharsis en Grèce, dans le milieu du quatrième siècle avant l'ère vulgaire.
"Each map is designed for the very year in which Anacharsis is supposed to have traveled through the province it represents." Introduction to english edition, 1791.
Map no. 26, Les Cyclades, by d'Anville.

### GENERAL.

(Arranged chronologically)

#### 1687

**Coronelli, M. V.**
An historical and geographical account of the Morea, Negropont, and the maritime places, as far as Thessalonica. Illustrated with 42 maps of the countries, plains and draughts of the cities, towns and fortifications . . . Englished by R. W. gent. 4 p. l., 230 pp., 18 fold. maps, 23 fold. pl. 12°. London, for M. Gillyflower & W. Canning, 1687. 3050

#### 1851

**Kiepert, H.**
Topographisch-historischer atlas von Hellas und den Hellenischen colonien in 24 blättern unter mitwirkung des professors Carl Ritter . . . 2d berichtigte ausg. 5 p. l., 24 maps. obl. fol. Berlin, Nicolaische buchhandlung, 1851. 3051

## ATTICA.

**Curtius, E.,** *and* **Kaupert, J.**
Karten von Attika auf veranlassung der kaiserlich deutschen archäologischen instituts und mit unterstützung des königlich preussischen ministeriums der geistlichen, unterrichts—und medicinal—angelegenheiten, aufgenommen durch offiziere und beamte des k. preussischen grossen generalstabes . . . 1 p. l., 31 maps. fol. Berlin, D. Reimer, 1904. 3052

> Note.—Maps no. 1–2a, scale of 1:12 500; nos. 3–26, scale of 1:25 000.
> Karte von "Attika," scale, 1:100 000, in eleven sections, with key, in pocket.
> Accompanying text: Karten von Attika . . . aufgenommem durch offiziere und beamte des k. preussischen grossen generalstabes . . . hrsg. von E. Curtius und J. A. Kaupert . . . 9 pts. in 1 v. Berlin, 1881–1900.

---

# ITALY.

### CITIES.

**Blaeu, J.**
Nouveau théâtre d'Italie, ou description exacte de ses villes, palais, églises, &c. et les cartes géographiques de toutes ses provinces . . . Sur les deffeins de feu monsieur Jean Blaeu . . . Le tout fur les plans tirés fur les lieux, & avec les planches qu'il en a fait graver de son vivant, & dont plufieurs ont été faites à Rome, pour être plus exactes. À quoi on a adjouté plufieurs villes, portes, églifes, & autres édifices, fur des originaux de Rome, &c. . . . 4 v. in 2. fol. Amsterdam, P. Mortier, 1704. 3053

> Note.—Engraved title-page, v. 3, "Nouveau théâtre d'Italie. Tom. III. contenant les royaumes de Naples & de Sicile."
> The following list of Blaeu's atlases relating to Italy is from Tiele's Nederlandsche bibliographie . . . Amsterdam, F. Müller & co. 1884.
> no. 1. Theatrum civitatum . . . Italiae. Amstel., Joa. Blaeu, 1663. 2 pts. fol.
> Another edition with imprint: Amst. apud haeredes J. Blaeu, 1676.
> " 2. Theatrum statuum . . . Sabaudiæ ducis, Pedemontii principis . . . Amstel., haer. J. Blaeu, 1682. 2 pts. fol.
> Another edition entitled, "Novum theatrum Pedemontii et Sabaudiae . . . Hag. Com., R. C. Alberts, 1726." 2 v. 4 parts.
> Dutch edition: Tooneel der heerschappijen van . . . den hartog van Savoye, 's Gravenh. A. Moetjens, 1697.
> French edition: Théâtre des états de S. A. R. le duc de Savoye, prince du Piémont, trad. du lat. en français par Jacq. Bernard. La Haye, A. Moetjens, 1700. 2 v.
> New edition: La Haye, R. C. Alberts, 1725. 2 v.
> " 3. Nouveau théâtre d'Italie ou description exacte de ses villes, palais . . . et les cartes géograph. de toutes ses provinces . . . Sur les desseins de feu mr. Jean Blaeu . . . Le tout mis en ordre à Amst. par . . . P. Mortier, 1704. 4 v. fol.
> New augm. ed.: La Haye, R. C. Alberts, 1724. 4 v.

**Blaeu, J.**—Continued.

   no. 4. Het nieuw stedeboek van Italie ofte naauwkeurige beschryving van alle deszelfs steden, paleyzen . . . nevens de land-kaarten van alle deszelfs provincien . . . Naar de tekeninge van . . . Joan Blaeu . . . Amst., P. Mortier, 1704–5. 4 pts. fol.

   " 5. Nieuw vermeerderd en verbeterd groot stedeboek van geheel Italie . . . Naar de originele afteekeningen . . . door . . . Joan Blaeu. 's Gravenh., R. C. Alberts, 1724. 4 pts. fol.

CONTENTS.

   v. 1. Les duchés de Savoye & de Piémont.—La république de Gennes.—Les duchés de Milan, Parme, Modène, & Mantoüe. Les républiques de Venise, de Lucques, & le grand duché de Toscane.

   " 2. L'état écclesiastique ou de l'église.

   " 3. Le royaume de Naples et de Sicile.

   " 4. Rome, ancienne, et nouvelle.

Novum Italiæ theatrum, sive accurata descriptio ipsius urbium, palatiorum sacrarum ædium, &c. 2 v. fol. Hagæ comitum, R. C. Alberts, 1724.    3054

   NOTE.—Collation: v. 1, 4 p. l., xxxviii, [1], 24 pp., 76 maps, 23 pl.; v. 2, 2 p. l., xlii, [1], 12 pp., 69 maps, 19 pl.

   v. 1 irregularly paged.

   Maps by various cartographers including: G. de l'Isle, P. Mortier, R. Alberts, J. Blaeu, Covens & Mortier.

   Engraved title-page to each volume: v. 1, Nieuw stedeboeck van Italien.— Novum theatrum totius Italiæ.—Nouveau théâtre d'Italie; v. 2, Civitates statvs ecclesiastici.

Nouveau théâtre du Piémont et de la Savoye, ou description exacte de leurs villes, palais, églises, & principaux édifices, &c. . . . 2 v. in 4. fol. La Haye, R. C. Alberts, 1725.    3055

   NOTE.—Collation: v. 1, pt. 1, 2 p. l., 96, [34] pp., front., 4 maps, 20 pl., 3 ports., 1 tab.; v. 1, pt. 2, 1 p. l., [89] pp., front., 22 plans, 22 pl. v. 2, pt. 1, 1 p. l., [75] pp., front., 2 maps, 6 pl., 14 plans; v. 2, pt. 2, 1 p. l., [106] pp., front., 11 pl., 37 plans.

   Title in red and black. Text in double columns.

   v. 1, pt. 1, contains portraits of: Charles Emanuel II, 14th duke of Savoy, by Robert Nanteuil.— Victor-Amédée II, duc de Savoie, prince de Piémont, roi de Cypre, &c. Signed: Labbe Bourdin pinx., A. Moetjens excudit . . . —. Son altesse le sérénissime & victorieux Eugène, prince de Savoie et Piémont . . .

   The arms of many cities and noble families of Piemont and Savoy appear on various plates, some of which bear the names of Thomas Borgonius, I. de Ram, Romanus de Hooghe, C. Decker and I. Guizzaro.

**Gibelli, G., Brunamonti, G.** and **Danesi, C.**, *editors*.

Desegni e descrittioni delle fortezze, e piazze d'armi artigliere, armi, monizioni da guerra soldati bombardieri pagati, milizie scelte di cavalleria, e fanteria dello stato ecclesiastico.    4 p. l., 2 l., 40 pp., 16 facs. incl. front. fol. [Roma, tip. della buona stampa, 1888]    3056

NOTE.—Half-title: Forze e fortezze pontificie alla fine del secolo decimosettimo.

"Questa riproduzione eliotipografica di antico codice Vaticano che fa fede della prisca grandezza e possanza del civile principato dei Romani pontefici al santo padre Leone XIII . . . dedicano G. Gibelli, G. padre Brunamonti, C. Danesi."

"Copia esatta di un codice cartaceo, con bella rilegatura dell' epoca, esistente nella Biblioteca Vaticana, presentato l' anno primo del secolo decimottavo a sua santita Clemente XI, di s. m., dal suo ministro d' Aste."

On the leaf preceding the facsimile is the following title: Edizione di soli cento venti esemplari numerati. Il presente porta il numero 81. Roma, tipografia della buona stampa, 1888.

Contains the following facsimiles:

Frontispizio, dove, sulla piazza 3056 di S. Giovanni in Laterano, Giustizia, Carità ed amore fanno splendidamente campeggiare l'arma gloriosa dell' undecimo Clemente—Castel S. Angelo.—Ferrara.—Fort Vrbano.—Civita Vecchia.—Nettvno.—Terracina.— Pervgia.—Ancona. — Sinagaglia. — Fano. — Pesaro.—Rimini.—Ascoli.—San' Leo.—Vedvta del nvovo porto d'anzo . . . [Map]

**Italy.** *Ministero dei lavori pubblici.*

Album dei porti di I, II e III classe, illustrato dalle notizie nautiche e commerciali d' ogni porto e dalla statistica delle opere esistenti e di quelle eseguite nel decennio 1861 al 1870.　4 p. l., 1–10, [1], 11–57 l. incl. maps, 1 col. fold. map.　obl. fol.　Firenze e Roma, Laudi & Steffen [1873]　3057

NOTE.—Each plan accompanied by statistical tables.

### MEDICAL.

**Raseri, E.**

Atlante di demografia e geografia medica d' Italia . . .　x pp., [1] l., 80 pp., [1] l., 78 pl. (*i. e.* 46 maps, 32 diagrs.)　4°.　Roma, G. De Agostini &c. 1906.　3058

### TRAVELS.

**Santini, P.**

Atlas portatif d'Italie à l'usage des voyageurs, comprenant toutes les villes, et autres lieux par les quels l'on passe de poste en poste avec leurs distances refpectives.　1 p. l., 7 maps, 3 tab.　fol.　Venise, Santini, 1783.　3059

### WARS.

**Jansson, J.**

La guerre d'Italie, repréfentée en plufieurs cartes, dans lefquelles on peut voir toutes les routes, les marches, les campemens . . . de l'armée impériale, & de celle des aliez. Avec un journal abrégé de ce qui s'eft paffé jufques à préfent entre ces deux armées.　4 p. l., 16 maps.　fol.　Amsterdam, J. & G. Janssons à Waesberge, 1702.　3060

NOTE.—Maps signed, "apud Ioannem Ianfsonium," and "sumtibus Ioannis Ianssonii."

## GENERAL.

(Arranged chronologically)

### 1620

**Magini, G. A.**

Italia di Gio. Ant. Magini, data in luce da Fabio suo figliuolo . . . 5 p. l., 24 pp., 61 maps on 119 l. fol. Bononiæ, impensis ipsius auctoris, 1620. 3061

> NOTE.—Engraved title-page, signed, "Oliuerius Gattus inu. & fe."
> Engraved portrait of Magini, surrounded by the words, "Io. Antonivs Maginvs pat. mathemat. in Bonon. gymn. profess," on the recto p. l. 1. Table of contents on the recto of p. l. 4.—Caption title, p. 1: L' Italia descritta in generale dal dottore Gio. Antonio Magini . . .
> Maps nos. 2, 30-32, 48, 50, 57-58, were engraved by Benjamin Wright, a distinguished engraver, living in the beginning of the seventeenth century, and bear his initials. His signature is "Benjamin Wright, Londinensis, Anglus." He lived long in Mantua, entertained by the cardinal Ferdinando Gonzaga, whom he accompanied to Rome. Later, we find him in Bologna, where he engraved for dr. Magini the copper plates of his Italia.
> The Library of Congress also contains the following map engraved by Wright: "Noua et rece terraum et regnorum Californiæ . . . delineatio, à M. Tattonus . . . edita.—Beniamin Wright, anglus cælator, an? 1616." Also a facsimile of Wright's map of New France, about 1608, in "Art in England . . . Edited by Charles Holme, 1908."

### 1792

**Zannoni, G. A. R.—**

Atlante marittimo delle due Sicilie disegnato per ordine del re . . . Parte prima che contiene il perimetro littorale del regno di Napoli. 2 p. l., 23 maps. fol. [Napoli] 1792. 3062

> NOTE—Engraved title, "Gius, Guerra Nap. reg? inc. sculp."
> Maps engraved by G. Guerra and A. Cataneo.

### 1867-1897

**Vallardi, F.**

Atlante corografico, orografico, idrografico e storico dell' Italia. 2 p. l., 141 maps, 8 pl. fol. Milano, F. Vallardi [1867-1897] 3063

> NOTE.—Issued in parts.
> Forms pt. 3 of "L' Italia sotto l' aspetto fisico, storico, letterario, artistico e statistico, opera divisa in tre parti—pte. 1ª. Il dizionario corografico . . . dal prof. Amato Amati. pte. 2ª. I trattati scientifici sull' Italia. pte. 3ª. L' atlanto corografico, iconografico, storico e geologico di circa 150 carte . . . con una gran carta geografica d' Italia in 15 fogli." This last title is given on the verso of the first leaf, which contains the title of the whole work.
> The map of Italy in 15 sheets, mentioned in the title, is wanting, and is not included in the index.
> Maps relate to the history of Italy from the roman empire to the present time.
> Contains numerous plans of cities.

———— Same. In parts: fasc. 1-101 114-115, 117-118; incomplete.

3064

> NOTE.—This copy contains the map of Italy in 15 sheets, wanting in the bound copy, and has a manuscript and a printed index. The latter differs from the index in the bound copy.

Provinces.

## GENOA.

**Ruggiero,** —

Relatione delle piante, & venute fatta nell' atto della vifita nella Riuiera di Ponente, con il sig.r Gio. Vincenzo imperiale comiff.º gñale delle arme per la Ser.ma Republica il mefe di xbre 1631. Prefentata al magiftrato dj guerra.  2 p. l., [70] pp. incl. 12 maps. fol. [1666] 3065

NOTE.—In manuscript. Dedication: Al genio monarchico del più degno, e gloriofo prencipe dell' vniuerfo Carlo Emanvel II, duca di Sauoia, prencipe di Piemonte, rè di Cipro &c. quefto parto delle fue fedeliffime induftrie e fatiche, come aufpicatrici di palme trionfi et immortalità al real fuo nome ciecam. obediente, et humiliffimo dedica, et confacra nell anno MDCLXVI. L' auditore Ruggiero. Cover-title: Libro de dissegni delle piazze e fortezze della Riviera di Genova.
At bottom of fly-leaf is written, "Libro de dissegni delle piazze e fortezze della Riuieri di Genoua che S. A. R. col mezo di danari havnto da uno della republica di Genoua. 1666."
Maps, excepting no. [1], accompanied by descriptive text: Relatione della terra di Zucarello, e suoi castelli.—Le venute di Zucarello.—Terra della Pieve.—Venute della Pieue per la parte di Naua.—Relatione di Ormea.—Relation' d' Albenga.—Relatione del Porto Mauritio.—Relatione di Vintimiglia.—Relatione delle venute di Nizza.—Relatione delle venute di Vintimiglia per la parte della Pena, et altri Cuoghi di S. A. R.—Lettera presentata al magistratto di guerra all' ill.mo sig. Gio Luca Chiauari, e m.º ill.ri sign. del magistrato di guerra.—Parere dell' ingegnier' cap.º. Baldouino per la fortificatione di Genoua, Sauona, e Guà ò sia Vado, dated, li 27 Maggio, 1625.—Difcorfo fopra alcune dubitationi che si offerirono all' occhio di persone curiofe fcorrendo la nuoua fortificatione di Genoua.
Plans done in sepia; natural features outlined and shaded show elevations. Castles in miniature are located and named; distances between castles are indicated in a table below map no. [2] All plans except no. [12], an unfinished plan of the "Citta di Sauona," show attention to details.

CONTENTS.

no. [1] Riviera di Genova verso Ponente.
" [2] [Terra di Zucarello e suoi castelli]
" [3] [Terra della Pieue]
" [4] [Piano di Naua]
" [5] [Ormea]
" [6] [Abenga]
" [7] [Porto Mauritio]
" [8] Pianta della Città di Vintimiglia.
" [9] [Coast from Nizza to Vintimiglia]
" [10] [Val di Neruia, V. d' Orrinazzo]
" [11] Castello di Gauio.—Pianta della terra di Gauio.
" [12] Cittá di Sauona.

## LIGURIA.

**Italy.** *Ministero della marina.*
    Portolano della Liguria.    25 l., incl. 23 maps.   obl. fol.   Genova, Armanino, 1855.
                                                                                                                                     3066

        NOTE.—Contains plans of the following cities:
        no.  3-4. Porto di Nizza.
        "     7. Porto di Monaco.
        "     8. Porto de San Remo.
        "     9. Porto Maurizio, rada di Oneglia.
        " 14-15. Porto di Savona.
        "   16. Porto di Genova.
        "   17. Porto di Camogli.
        "   19. Porto Fino.
        "   20. Porto di Rapallo.
        "   21. Rada di Sestri di Levante.
        "   25. Porto di Capraia.

## NAPLES.

**Bulifon, A.**
    [Accuratissima e nuova delineazione del regno di Napoli con le sue provincie distinte . . .]    21 maps.   fol.   [Naples, 1692]
                                                                                                                                                      3067

        NOTE.—Title-page wanting.
        Title supplied from British Museum Catalogue.
        Date 1692 on maps no. [1] and no. [16]
        Maps engraved by D. F. Cassianus de Silua.
        Maps no. [13] and no. [16] carry the following: D. Franc. Cassianus de Silua sculpsit Neap.

## ROME.

**Lanciani, R. A.**
    Forma vrbis Romae. Consilio et avctoritate regiae academiae Lyncaeorvm formam dimensvs est et ad modvlvm 1:1000 delineavit Rodvlphvs Lanciani Romanvs.   1 p. l., 12 pp., 47 maps.   fol.   Mediolani [Milan] apud Vlricvm Hoepli [stab$^{to}$ cartog$^{co}$ L. Salomone, Roma, 1901]                                   3068

        NOTE.—Published in eight parts from 1893-1901.

**Schneider, A.**
    Das alte Rom; entwickelung seines grundrisses und geschichte seiner bauten auf 12 karten und 14 tafeln dargestellt und mit einem plane der heutigen stadt sowie einer stadtgeschichtlichen einleitung . . .    xii pp., 13 maps, 14 pl.   obl. fol.   Leipzig, B. G. Teubner, 1896.                                                                      3069

**Italy.** *Ministero di agricoltura, industria e commercio. Direzione generale della statistica.*

Carte topografiche, idrografighe e geologiche annesse alla monografia statistica della città di Roma e Campagna romana presentata all' esposizione universale di Parigi 1878. 1 p. l., 38 l., incl. 7 maps. fol. Roma, C. Virano, 1883. 3070

CONTENTS.

no. 1. Carta topografica della Campagna romana. 1880.
" 2. Carta geologica della Campagna romana. 1880.
" 3. Carta topografica dell' agro romano e territori limitrofi. 1879. 8 sheets.
" 4. Carta topografica dell' agro romano e territori limitrofi. 6 sheets.
" 5. Carta idrografica del bacino del Tevere. 1880.
" 6. Carta stradale della provincia di Roma. 1880.
" 7. Pianta della città di Roma. 1880.

### SARDINIA.

**Italy.** *Ministero della marina.*
Portolano della Sardegna. 2 p. l., 28 maps. obl. 4°. [Torino, Doyen & ca. 1842] 3071

NOTE.—Compiled by rear admiral Albini, of the royal italian navy.

# NETHERLANDS.

### COLONIAL.

**Bosch, J. van den.**

Atlas der overzeesche bezittingen van zyne majesteit den koning der Nederlanden ... 1 p. l., 12 maps. fol. 's Gravenhage en Amsterdam, gobroeders van Cleef, 1818. 3072

NOTE.—To accompany his: Nederlandsche bezittingen in Azië, Amerika en Afrika. Reviewed in Neue Allgemeine geographische ephemeriden. 1822. v. 10, pt. 4, pp. 414–418.

CONTENTS.

no. 1. Kaart der Nederlandfche bezittingen, in Oost-Indiën.
" 2. Kaart van het eiland Java.
" 3. Kaart van het ryk van Bantam, Jacatra & Cheribon, op het eiland Java.
" 4. Kaart van des keizers en sultans landen benevens de strand regentfchappen op het eiland Java.
" 5. Kaart van het eiland Madura, ende oost hoek van het eiland Java.— Kaart van de haven van Sourabaija.
" 6. Kaart der Ambonsche eilenden.
" 7. Kaart van het eiland Amboina.
" 8. Kaart der Bandasche eilanden.
" 9. Kaart der Ternataansche eilanden.
" 10. Kaart van het belouwde gedeelte van Surinamen.
" 11. Kaart van het eiland Curaçao.
" 12. Kaart van de goud-kust of kust van Guinea.

## HISTORICAL.

**Bennet, R. G.**, *and* **Wijk Roelandszoon, J. van.**
Verhandeling over de Nederlandsche ontdekkingen in Amerika, Australië, de Indiën en de Poollanden, en de namen, welke weleer aan dezelve door Nederlanders zijn gegeven, door R. G. Bennet en J. van Wijk, Roeldz . . . Atlas. cover-title, 8 maps. fol. Utrecht, J. Altheer, 1827. 3072a

NOTE.—Atlas accompanying this work is in roll, having title: Atlas behoorende tot de Verhandeling van R. G. Bennet en J. van Wijk, Roelandsz, wegens de Nederlandsche ontdekkingen, bekroond door het Provinciaal Utrechtsch genootschap van kunsten en wetenschappen en opgedragen aan hetzelve genootschap. Dordrecht, J. de Vos & comp. 1829.
Maps described in the "Verhandeling," pp. 187–219.
List of maps on a "Bericht" attached to map no. [1]

CONTENTS.

no. [1] Spitsbergen.
" [2-3] Kaart der Noodelyke yszee . . . Insets: Nederlandsche ontdekkingen langs de kust van Oost-Groenland . . . van kapt. Scoresby, in 1822.—Insets: Mauritius, of Jan Mayen eil, 1611.—Enkhúizen of eil. Waaigat . . .
" [4] Kaart van Nieuw Nederland . . .
" [5] "   " straat Magellaan, straat le Maire, het Vuurland en kaap Hoorn.—Inset: Kaart van het Dirk Gerrits land . . . Nieuw Suid Shetland.
" [6-a] Kaart van Nieuw Holland, Nieuw Guinea en omliggende eilanden . . .
" [6-b] Kaart der Vriendelyke eilanden . . .
" [6-c] Stille zuid zee no. 2.—Inset: Nieuw Zeeland ontdekt door Tasman, 1642.
" [7] Kaart van Japan . . .

**Mees, G.**, *jr.*
Historische atlas van Noord-Nederland van de XVI eeuw tot op heden [1530–1860]   3 p. l., vii, [389] pp., 1 l., 14 maps, 1 map in text. fol. Te Rotterdam, Verbruggen & van Duym, 1865.   3073

## SCHOOL.

**Beekman, A. A.**, *and* **Schuiling, R.**
Schoolatlas van Nederland en zijne ovetzeesche bezittingen . . . 4. druk.   1 p. l., 20 maps on 40 l. fol. Zutphen, W. J. Thieme & cie. [1903]   3074

## GENERAL.

(Arranged chronologically)

### 1622

**Keere, P. van den**
Petri Kærii Germania inferior id est, XVII provinciarum ejus novæ et exactæ tabulæ geographicæ, cum luculentis singularum descrip-

tionibus additis, à Petro Montano. 4 p. l., 94 pp., 2 l., 24 maps, 5 pl. fol. Amstelodami, P Kærii, 1622. 3075

NOTE.—Maps have text on reverse.
Engraved title-page signed: Petrus Kærius cælavit & excudebat.
Contains the same maps as the first edition (1617) excepting the map of "Flandriae pars orientalior" which has been replaced by map no. 9, entitled: "Caerte van t'vrye synde een gedeelte en lidt van Vlaenderen . . . door C. I. Visscher." *cf.* Tiele, Nederlandsche bibliographie. 1884. p. 131.
Map no. 18, "Marchionatus sacri romani imperii. 1617," contains a plan and view of Antwerp.
A french edition entitled, "La Germanie inférieure" was also published in 1622.

## 1649
**Blaeu, J.**

Toonneel der steden van de vereenighde Nederlanden . . . Toonneel der steden van's konigs Nederlanden met hare beschrijvingen. 2 v. fol. [Amsterdam, 1649] 3076

NOTE.—Collation: v. 1, 7 p. l., 329 l. incl. 179 col. maps, 1 pl.; v. 2, 7 p. l., 246 l. incl. 138 col. maps, 5 pl. v. 1, title (surrounded by 10 coats of arms) "Joan Blaev aen den leser," 3 pp.; "Aen de selve," 1 pp.; the "privileges" 3 l.; the maps and text beginning with "Steden van Gelderland en Zvtphen" and ending with "Griet-Syl," "Register . . ." 2 pp.; v. 2, (Preliminary matter same as in v. 1) Atlas begins with "Steden van Brabant en Limbvrgh" and ends with "Waerschovwing aen den leser," followed by 2 maps and 2 pages of text, and by the "Register."
Privileges dated as follows: Spain, 1649; Netherlands, 1648, and France, 1649.—
Map (v. 1, no. 38) entitled "Medemleck," signed "Joannes Schagen geometra delineavit 1649," the latest date found on any map. Maps in v. 1 signed by L. Milheuser, J. Schagen, B. Boazio, S. Renaudus, Nicolaus Joannes Vischer; in v. 2, by A. Sanderus, Vedastus du Plouich, Louys de Berjaques, etc.
Contains plans and views of the largest cities, forts and fortifications of the Netherlands, also several plans of battle-fields and sieges to illustrate the history of that country. The maps are beautifully engraved and colored, nearly all have ornamented titles, coats of arms, and engravings of groups of people, showing the costumes and manners of the time.

## 1672
**Seller, J.**

The coasting pilot: describing the sea-coasts, channels, soundings, sands, shoals, rocks, & dangers: the bayes, roads, harbours, rivers, ports, buoyes, beacons, and sea-marks, upon the coasts of England, Flanders and Holland with directions to bring a shipp into any harbour on the said coasts. Being furnished with new draughts, charts, and descriptions gathered from ye experience and practise of diverse able and expert navigators of our english nation . . . 1 p. l., 54 pp., 19 maps on 23 l. fol. London, J. Seller, W. Fisher & J. Wingfield [1672] 3077

NOTE.—Entered in the "Term catalogue" under date 1672.
Engraved title-page on which are represented England's famous discoverers: cap. [John] Davies, sir Walter Raleigh, sir Hugh Willoughby, cap. John Smith, sir Fran. Drake, Tho. Candish and many others. Below the title are

**Seller, J.**—Continued.

two views, one a panorama of London and the Thames, from London bridge; the other, a mythical picture representing the confluence of the Thames and the Medway. Maps engraved and many embellished by various designs; titles generally surmounted with the arms of the country to which they relate.

### 1680
**Visscher, N.**

N: Visscheri Germania inferior sivè xvii provinciarum geographicæ generales ut et particulares tabulæ.—Kaert-boeck van de xvii Nederlandtsche provincien . . . 1 p. l., 52 col. maps. fol. [Amsterdam, 1680?] 3078

NOTE.—Engraved title, colored, signed, "G. Laireffe in[venit] fculp."
Map no. 6, "Novissima et accuratissima xvii provinciarum Germaniæ inferioris delineatio" dedicated to Joh. Munter, burgomaster of Amsterdam from 1670 to 1680 *cf.* Tiele, Nederlandsche bibliographie. Amsterdam, 1884.
The following maps are dated:
no. [35] Ducatus Brunsvicensis . . . descriptio geographica. 1650.
" [48] Tabula Russiæ. 1651.
Several maps have vignettes engraved by Rom. de Hooghe.
Maps by various cartographers including: B. Schotanus, J. Janssonius, Fred. de Wit, Justus Danckers, J. Laurenberg.
Besides maps of the Netherlands this atlas contains maps of the world, Asia, America, Africa and several countries of Europe, plans and views of Antwerp, Moscow and Candia.
The following maps relate to America:
no. [1] Orbis terrarum nova et accuratissma tabula.
" [5] Novissima et accuratissima totius Americæ descriptio.

### 1682
**Peers, R.**

The description of the seventeen provinces of the Low-Countries, or Netherlands. fol. Oxford, for M. Pitt, 1682. 3079
[English, The, atlas. v. 4]

NOTE.—See title 2831 for bibliographical notice.

### 1740
**Leth, H. de.**

Nieuwe geographische en historische atlas, van de zeven vereengde nederlandsche provintien; bestaande inde vyftig . . . kaarten . . . 1 p. l., [67] pp., 50 maps, 2 tab. 8°. Amsterdam, H. de Leth [1740] 3080

NOTE.—Usually bound in nar. 8°.
Text precedes title and corresponds in width with narrow edition, but title and maps are bound full width.

### 1773
**Sepp, J. C.**

Nieuwe geographische Nederlandsche reise- en zak-atlas; vervattende vier en zeventig gekleurde, naauwkeurig geteekende en gegraveerde ... kaarten van de Vereenigde Nederlanden; mitsgaders eene beknopte algemeene geographie dezer provinciën ... nevens een bericht der voornaamste logementen, als mede der jaarmarkten of kermissen ... 4 p. l., 132 pp., [74] maps. obl. 24°. Amsterdam, J. C. Sepp, 1773. 3081

NOTE.—Maps signed as follows: index map, C. et I. C. Sepp, pater et filius, sequentes omnes delineaverunt et sculpserunt; no. 1, C. et I. C. Sepp omnes fecerunt; nos. [67-73] lettered A-G.

## 1777

**Ferraris, J. de.**

Carte chorographique des Pays-Bas autrichiens dédiée à leurs majestés impériales et royales ... Gravée par L. A. Dupuis ... 46 l. incl. 1 fold. pl., 1 l., 3 maps on 43 l. fol. [n. p.] 1777. 3082

NOTE.—This atlas was prepared and published under the direction of comte de Ferraris, authorized by the government, and based on the chart of Cassini. It consists of one map of numbered sections, accompanied by a folded engraved plate, an index map, a general map, and one page of engraved text entitled, "Explication."
The engraved title appears upon section xi.
The folded plate represents the presentation of the chart to emperor Joseph II, and is numbered section XVI, as such appears on the index map, but is placed at the beginning in the atlas.

## 1793

**Tirion, I.**

Nieuwe en keurige reis-atlas door de XVII Nederlanden; bestaande in eene verzameling van XX uitgelezene kaarten der zeven vereenigde en tien oostenryksche nederlandsche provincien. 2 p. l., 20 maps. nar. fol. Te Amsterdam, J. de Groot & G. Warnars, 1793. 3083

## 1865-1870

**Kuyper, J.**

Gemeente-atlas van Nederland naar officieele bronnen bewerkt. 11 v. in 7. obl. 8°. Leeuwarden, H. Suringar [1865-1870] 3084

CONTENTS.

v. 1. Noord Brabant [1865-69] 2 p. l., 188 maps.
" 2. Gelderland [1865-69] 2 p. l., 156 maps.
" 3. Zuid-Holland [1865-69] 2 p. l., 205 maps.
" 4. Noord-Holland [1865-69] 2 p. l., 138 maps.
" 5. Zeeland [1865-67] 2 p. l., 114 maps.
" 6. Utrecht [1865-68] 2 p. l., 75 maps.
" 7. Friesland [1865-70] 2 p. l., 47 maps.
" 8. Overijssel [1865-69] 2 p. l., 66 maps.
" 9. Groningen [1866-67] 2 p. l., 62 maps.
" 10. Drenthe [1865-68] 2 p. l., 35 maps.
" 11. Limburg [1865-69] 2 p. l., 1 l., [9] pp., 126 maps.

## 1883

**Jaeger, J.**
Atlas van het koningrijk der Nederlanden en zijne bezittingen . . . 7ᵉ druk, herzien door H. F. Puls. Vermeerderd met eene afzonderlijke kaart van Sumatra. 2 p. l., 16 maps. fol. Zwolle, W. E. J. Tjeenk Willink [1883] 3085

## 1900

**Netherlands.** *Topographische inrichting.*
Atlas van het koninkrijk der Nederlanden op de schaal van 1 : 200 000 in chromo-lithographie, vervaardigd volgens de topographische en militaire kaart. 1 p. l., 20 col. maps. obl. fol. 's Gravenhage, topographische inrichting, 1900. 3086

## 1902

**Kuyper, J.**
Atlas van Nederland en de overzeesche bezittingen. 2 p. l., 16 maps. fol. Zwolle, W. E. J. T. Willink [1902?] 3087

NOTE.—Accompanied by pamphlet entitled: Alphabetisch register behoorende bij J. Kuyper's Atlas van Nederland.
The following map relates to America:
no. 16. Nederlandsch West-Indië. 1901.

### Provinces.

### FRIESLAND.

**Schotanus à Sterringa, B.**, *and* **Alting, M.**
Uitbeelding der heerlijkheit Friesland zoo in't algemeen, als in haare xxx bijzondere grietenijen. Nu niewelijks met bijgevoegde aangrenzingen, en veel vermeerderingen: nevens d'afteekening van oud Friesland, in vii verscheidene landkaarten; door den heere Menso Alting; en de vertalinge der oude naamen . . . 3 p. l., 39 maps, 3 pl. fol. [Leeuwarden] F. Halma, 1718. 3088

NOTE.—Engraved title.
"Op de uitbeeldinge van Friesland," signed John Hilarides.
"De kaarten van Schotanus zijn die van 1698 vermeerderd o. a. met die van M. Alting, ontleend aan zijn Desc. Frisiae".—*cf.* Tiele, Nederlandsche bibliographie, Amsterdam, 1884.

### VOORN.

**Netherlands.** *Voorn, Council of.*
Voorne caart-boeck van alle de dorpen, en polders gelegen inden lande van Oost ende West Voorne. Mitsgaders Over Flacqueê resortee rende onder't comptoir der verpondingen 'slants van

Voorne, gedaan maaken door ordre ende resolutie vande heeren Breetste geerfdens vanden selven lande genomen op den 7° Juny 1695. Als wanneer bailliuw ende leenmannen waren de boven ende neven staande heeren. 2 p. l., 32 maps. fol. [n. p.] 1701.
3089

NOTE.—Elaborate double page title signed: Rom. de Hooge I. U. D. et Com. R. auct. 1701.
All maps carry the following names: Heyman van (or van den) Dyck fecit.—I. Luiken fecit cum aqua forti.—A. Steyaart invenit.—I. Stemmers sculpsit.

## ZEELAND.

**Tirion, I.**
Atlas van Zeeland; vervattende naauwkeurige kaarten van alle de eilanden, op order van z. d. h. den prince van Oranje, meetkundig opgenomen door de heeren Hattinga, geduurende de jaaren 1744 tot 1752. Benevens grondtekeningen en gezigten der steden, afbeeldingen de voornaamste openbaare gebouwen, dorpen, sloten, heerenhuizen enz. Naar 't leven getekend door ken konstryken C. Pronk, als mede portraiten van eenige der vermaardste staatsmannen en zeehelden. 4 p. l., 6 maps, 75 pl., 18 por. fol. Amsterdam, I. Tirion, 1760. 3090

# NORWAY.

### REPRODUCTION.

**Nordenskiöld, N. A. E.,** *friherre.*
Bidrag till nordens äldsta kartografi. Vid fyrahundraårsfesten till minne af Nya verldens upptäckt utgifna af Svenska sällskapet för antropologi och geografi 1892. 3 p. l., 9 maps. fol. Stockholm, Samson & Wallin [1892] 3091

NOTE.—In portfolio. "Förord" signed: A. E. Nordenskiöld.
"Bestyret med originalens anskaffande och tryckningens ordnande och öfvervakande har utförts af . . . E. W. Dalgren."
"Tryckt i 100 numrerade exemplar. No. 038."

CONTENTS.

no. 1. Karta öfver norra Europa och Grönland.
" 2. Karta öfver Skandinavien och Grönland.
" 3. Karta öfver Skandinavien och Grönland.
" 4. Karta öfver Germanien och södra Skandinavien.
" 5. Del af en catalansk portulan från 15:e århundradet.
" 6. Nordvestra hörnet af en portulan från början af 16:e århundradet.
" 7. Del af en portulan af Bartolomeo Olives. 1584.
" 8. Del af en portulan af Matteo Prunes. 1586.
" 9. Karta öfver Island af biskop Gudbrand Thorlaksen. 1595.

Provinces.

## FINMARK.

**Friis, J. A.**
Ethnographisk kart over Finmarken. Udgivet af Videnskabsselskabet i Christiania med bidrag af oplysningsvæsenets fond. 5 maps on 10 sheets. fol. Christiania, C. Schwenzens, 1861. 3092

CONTENTS.

no. 1. Præstegjældene: I. Vardo.—II. Vadsö . . .—III. Næsseby . . .—IV. Lebesby. 1861.
" 2. Præstegjældene: I. Kistrand . . .—II. Lebesby.—III. Næsseby.—IV. Maasö . . .—V. Utsjok. 1861.
" 3. Præstegjældene: I. Alten.—II. Koutokæino.—III. Hammerfest . . .—IV. Skjærvö.—V. Loppen . . .—VI. Maasö. 1861.
" 4. Præstegjældene: I. Karlsö.—II. Lyngen.—III. Tromsö . . .—IV. Skjærvö.—V. Loppen.—VI. Balsfjorden.—VII. Maalselven . . .—VIII. Lenvig. 1861.
" 5. Præstegjældene: I. Berg.—II. Tranö.—III. Ibestad.—IV. Trondenæs.—V. Ofoten . . .—VI. Lenvig . . .—VII. Maalselven. 1861.

---

# PORTUGAL.

## COLONIES.

**Portugal.** *Ministerio da marinha e ultramar.* Commissão de cartographia.
Atlas colonial português. Edição reduzida. cover-title, 10 maps. 4°. [Lisboa, typ. da companhia nacional editora?] 1903. 3093

## GENERAL.

(Arranged chronologically)

### 1767?

**Alagna, J. G.**
A compleat set of new charts on thirty-eight large plates, containing an accurate survey of the coast of Portugal and the Mediterranean sea in which are included seventy five charts of the principal harbours in the straits, shewing the rocks, shoals, soundings & anchoring places, with their true latitude. The whole being accurately surveyed by J. Giacomo Alagna of Mefsina . . . J. Larken del. et sculp! 93 maps on 53 l. fol. London, for J. Mount & T. Page [1767?] 3094

NOTE.—Engraved title, elaborately ornamented with figures, on map no. 1. Published in or about 1767. The British Museum gives the date 1760?, but this is without doubt erroneous. The name of the publishing firm underwent a number of changes, the form being for several years before and after 1760, W. and J. Mount, T. Page and son. During the period which followed this form of the name, and in which this atlas was published, the firm name was J. Mount and T. Page. A little later the name was J. Mount, T. Page, W. Mount and T. Page; the next change being simply to Mount and Page.

### 1870
**Bettencourt,** —.
Atlas pecuario de Portugal. Mappas representativos do valor absoluto e relativo dos gados, por districtos e concelhos segundo o recenseamento a que se procedeu na conformidade do decreto de 22 de junho de 1870. [anon.] 1 p. l., 18 col. maps. fol. Lisboa, C. Maigne [1870] 3095

## ROUMANIA.
### LINGUISTIC.
**Weigand, G. L.**
Linguistischer atlas des dacorumänischen sprachgebietes. Hrsg. auf kosten der rumänischen akademie. lief. 1–7. fol. Leipzig, J. A. Barth, 1898–1907. 3096

> NOTE.— "In 8–10 lieferungen zu je 8 karten." *cf.* "Prospekt."
> In progress.

### GENERAL.
(Arranged chronologically)
### 1895
**Gorjan, A.,** *and* **Luncan, I.**
Atlas-geografie România, pentru clasele III primară urbană și III și IV rurale . . . 39 pp. incl. 18 maps (in text) 4°. Bucuresci, editura librăriei Socecu & comp. 1895. 3097

## RUSSIA.
### HISTORICAL.
**Akhmatov, I.**
Атласъ историческій, хронологическій и географическій россійскаго государства. Составленный на основаніи исторіи Карамзина, Иваномъ Ахматовымъ. Часть II. 1 p. l., 35 maps. obl. fol. С. Петербургъ, 1831. 3098

> NOTE.—Translated title: Historical, chronological, and geographical atlas of the russian empire, based on Karamzin's history. Part II. St. Petersburg, 1831.

**Pavlishchev, N. I.**
Учебныя пособія для военно-учебныхъ заведеній. Историческій атласъ Россіи, Н. І. Павлищева . . . [22] l., 16 maps, 1 chart, 1 tab. 4°. Варшава, въ типографіи С. Стромбскаго, 1845.   3099

NOTE.—Translated title: Historical atlas of Russia. Warsaw, typography S. Strombski, 1845.
Contains preface, explanatory text, and chronological table of russian history from 1699 to 1843 inclusive. Some maps have border text. They represent Russia at the following periods: ixth century, 862–1054, 1054, 1224, 1264, 1328, 1389, 1462, 1533, 1600, 1689, 1725, 1761, 1796–1814, etc.

Военно-учебныя пособія. Историческій атласъ Россіи, Н. І. Павлищева. Второе, значительно пополненное изданіе. Часть II . . .  1 p. l., 20 maps. obl. fol.   С.-Петербургъ, типографія Б. Шумахеръ, 1873.   3100

NOTE.—Translated title: Historical atlas of Russia. St. Petersburg, typography B. Shumakher, 1873.
Contains Europe in 862; Russia in 862, 862–1054, 1224, 1264, 1328, 1389, 1462, 1533, 1600, 1689, 1725, 1761, 1796, 1799–1813, etc.
See preceding title.

### STATISTICAL.

**Russia.** *Otdi͡el statistiki i kartografii Ministerstva puteĭ soobshcheniīa.*
Статистическій атласъ Путей Сообщенія Россіи къ началу XX вѣка.   1 p. l., vii, 15, 3 pp., 2 l., 5 maps, 4 diagrs.   fol.   С.-Петербургъ, типографія Министерства Путей Сообщенія, 1902.   3101

NOTE.—Translated title: Ministry of roads and communications. Division of statistics & cartography. Statistical atlas of ways of communication in Russia at the beginning of the xxth century. St. Petersburg, typography of the ministry of roads and communications, 1902.

### WARS.

**Fonton, F.**
La Russie dans l'Asie-mineure.   1 p. l., 8 plans, port.   fol. Paris, mme. de Lacombe, 1840.   3102

NOTE.—Imperfect: wanting, Carte générale du théâtre de la guerre.
To accompany work by same author, entitled: La Russie dans l'Asie Mineure; ou, campagnes du maréchal Paskévitch en 1828 et 1829; et tableau du Caucase. 8°. Paris, Leneveu, 1840.

**Niel, A.**
Siége de Sébastopol.   Journal des opérations du génie publié avec l'autorisation du ministre de la guerre.   Atlas.   2 p. l., 14 (*i. e.* 15) pl.   fol.   Paris, J. Dumaine, 1858.   3103

NOTE.—To accompany work of same title.

**Todleben, E. I.**
Défense de Sébastopol.   Ouvrage rédigé sous la direction du lieutenant-général E. de Todleben . . . Atlas des planches.   cover-title, 17 pl.   obl. fol.   St. Pétersbourg, direction **générale** du génie, 1863.   3104

NOTE.—Imperfect: pls. no. 1–8, 19, wanting.
To accompany work of same title.

Atlas der karten und plaene zu der beschreibung der vertheidigung von Sabastopol. 2 p. l., 15 maps, 12 pl. fol. S<sup>t</sup> Petersburg, in der hauptverwaltung des genie-wesens und im topographischen karten-depot, 1864. 3105

Atlas der plaene und zeichnungen zu der beschreibung der vertheidigung von Sebastopol ... 2 p. l., 2 l., 27 (*i. e.* 26) maps. obl. fol. St. Petersburg, hauptverwaltung des genie-wesens, 1864. 3106

NOTE.—Issued in three parts, with separate title-pages.
To accompany: Die vertheidigung von Sebastopol. Nach authentischen quellen dargestellt unter leitung des general-lieutenant Ed. v. Todleben ... 4°. St. Petersburg, N. Thieblin & co. 1864.

**Russia.** *Kommissiia dlia razbora drevnikh aktov. Kief.*

Матеріалы по исторіи русской картографіи. Карты всей россіи и южныхъ ея областей до половины XVII вѣка. Изданіе кіевской коммиссіи для разбора древнихъ актовъ. 2 v. fol. Кіевъ, С. В. Кульженко, 1899–1906. 3107

NOTE.—Collection of fac-simile maps, by various authors, dating from 1474 to 1651. Most of the maps are accompanied by descriptive text. Edited by Ven'iāmin Aleksandrovich Kordt.
Incomplete: ser. 1, v. 2, wanting.

[Ser. 1] v. 1. 3 p. l., 15 pp. 32 maps.

Contents.

TEXT.

Карта Николая Кузана. 1491 г.
" Баттисты Агнезе. 1525 г.
" Антонія Вида ок. 1537 г.
" средней россіи Себастіана Мюнстера 1538 г.
" Герберштейна 1546 г.
" Россіи Якова Гастальдо 1548 г.
" юго-западной Россіи Я. Гастальдо 1562 г.
" Антонія Дженкинсона 1562 г.
" Андрея Пограбія 1570 г.
" Россіи Г. Меркатора 1594 г.
" I. Магина 1596 г.
" Польши, Литвы и Ливоніи 1596 г.
" Россіи Гесселя Герритса 1614 г.
" Исаака Массы 1633 г.
" южной Россіи И. Массы 1633 г.
" украйны В. Боплана 1650 г.
" чернаго моря Грат. Бенинказы 1474 г.

MAPS.

no. I. [Black Sea and neighboring country. Benincasa. 1474]
" II. Tabvla moderna Sarmatie ... [Ptolemy. 1513]
" III. [Russia. B. Agnese. 1525]
" IV. Moschovia nova tabvla. [J. Gastaldo. 1548]
" V. " nvova " " " 1561]
" VI. [Russia] Anthonius Wied. 1537.
" VII. Moscowiters lands newe beschreibung. Muenster. 1544.

**Russia**—Continued.

no. VIII. [Russia. S. Münster. 1559]
" IX. [Russia. Solinus. 1538]
" X. [Russia. S. Munster. 1559]
" XI. Moscovia Sigismvndi liberi baronis in Herberstein, Neiperg et Gvtenhag. MDXLVI.
" XII. Moscovia Sigismvndi liberi baronis in Herberstein, Neiperg et Gvtenhag. Anno MDXLIX.
" XIII. Moscouia Sigmunds freyherrns zu Herberstain Neyperg vnd Guetenhag . . . anno 1557.
" XIV. Moscovia Sigismvndi liberi baronis in Herberstain. [1556]
" XV. Descriptionede laMoscouia per Giacomo Gastaldo . . . 1550.
" XVI. Noua descriptione de la Moscouia per . . . Giacomo Gastaldo. 1566.
" XVII. Rvssiae, Moscoviae . . . descriptio. Auctore Antonio Ienkensono. 1562.
" XVIII. [Russia. P. Heyns' Spieghel der werelt. 1583]
" XIX. [ " Langenes. 1598]
" XX. Rvssia. [Ortelius. 1601]
" XXI. Polonia, Lithania, Livonia. [1596]
" XXII. Il disegno de geografia moderna del regno di Polonia . . . Giac? di castaldi. 1562.
" XXIII. [Russia. A. Pograbius. 1570]
" XXIV. Rvssia cum confinijs. Mercator. 1594.
" XXV. Moscoviæ imperivm. [Magini. 1596]
" XXVI. Brevis exactaqve Moscoviæ descriptio. [Heberstain. 1557]
" XXVII. Moscoviae imperivm. 1600. [I. Magini]
" XXVIII. Moscoviæ totivs . . . descriptio. [Neugebauer. 1612]
" XXIX. Novissima Russiæ tabula. I. Massa. [1633]
" XXX. Moscoviæ pars avstralis. I. Massa. [1633]
" XXXI. Tabula Russiæ. N. I. Piscatore [Visscher] 1651.
" XXXII. Carte d'Vkranie . . . Beauplan. [1650]

Ser. 2. v. 1. 3 p. l., 28 pp., 26 maps.

TEXT.

1. Карты сѣверной Россіи.
    Карта Николая Германца 1482 г.
    " М. Вальдземиллера 1507 и 1516 г.
    " Якова Циглера 1532 г.
    " Олауса Магнуса 1539 г.
    " Европы Г. Меркатора 1554 г.
    " Вилліама Борро.
    " Всего свѣта Г. Меркатора 1569 г.
    " Левина Алгута 1570 г.
    " Луки Вагенара.
    " В. Барентса и Г. де Фера.
    " Сѣверной Европы Г. Меркатора.
    " С. Фонъ Салингена 1601 г.
    " И. Массы 1612 г.
    Карты Андреа Буреуса 1611 и 1626 гг.
    Карта Г. Герритса 1613 г.
    " Адріана Вено Ауреліуса 1613 г.

II. Карты всей Россіи.
    Карта Г. Герритса 1613 г.
    " Гильома Сансона
III. Карты Сибири.
    Краткій обзоръ картографіи сибири отъ ортеліуса до второй половины XVII в.
    Карта сибири П. И. Годунова 1667 г.
    "    " Н. Витсена 1687 г.

### MAPS.

no.   I. [Part of Waldseemüller's marine chart. 1516]
"  II–III. [Part of Olaus Magnus' map: Carta marina et descriptio septentrionalium terrarum . . .] 1539.
"  IV–VI. Regionvm septentrionalivm, Moscoviam, Rvtenos, Tartaros . . . ex Antonii Ienkesonii et Sigismundi liberi baronis ab Herberstein itinerariis nova descriptio.
"  VII. . . . Di M. Jacomo Castaldo in si rapresenta la prime parte della descrittione del regno di Polonia . . . 1568.
"  VIII. [Part of Gerritz's map. 1613]
"  IX. [ " " Waghenaer's map]
"  X. Delineatio cartae trium navigationum per Batavos, ad septentrionalem plagam . . . Wilhelmo Bernardo [Barents] 1598.
"  XI. [Part of map of] William Borough.
"  XII. Caerte van't noorderste Russen, Samsjeden, ende Tingoesen landt . . . door Isaac Massa vertaelt is [1612]
"  XIII. Rvssiæ vulgo Moscovia dictæ, partes septentrionalis et orientalis auctore Iſaaco Maſsa [1668]
"  XVI. Rvssiæ vulgo Moscovia dictæ, pars occidentalis. Auctore Iſaaco Maſsa.
"  XV. Tabvla Rvssiæ . . . Heſſelo Gevardo. 1613. Inset: Moscva ad architypum foedori Boriſsowitsi.
"  XVI. Rvssia Bianca ò Moscovia . . . da Gio. Iacomo Roſſi . . . 1688.
"  XVII. Tartaria. Sive Magni Chami regni typus.
"  XVIII. Tartaria. Iodocus Hondius.
"  XIX. Tartaria ſive Magni Chami imperivm [Hondius]
"  XX. Description de la Tartarie . . . par le sʳ Sanson d'Abbeville . . . 1654.
"  XXI. Le gran Tartaria diuisa nelle due parti prīcipali da Gacomo Cantelli da Vignola . . . data in luce da Gio Giacomo de Rossi . . . 1683.
"  XXII. [Map of Siberia by P. I. Gudenow. 1667]
"  XXIII. Moscovia [Hondius]
"  XXIV. Caerte von Nova Zembla . . . door Gerrit de Veer . . . 1598.
"  XXV. Siwerische landcharda . . . 1690 [P. I. Gudenow]
"  XXVI. Nova tabula imperii Russici . . . Nic Witzen [1687]

## GENERAL.

(Arranged chronologically)

### 1680

**Pitt, M.**

    A description of the places next the North Pole; as also of Muscovy, Poland, Sweden, Denmark, and their several dependances. fol. Oxford, for M. Pitt, 1680.     3108
[English, The, atlas. v. 1]
    NOTE.—See title 2831 for bibliographical notice.

## 1745

**Delisle, J. N.,** & *others.*
Russischer atlas, welcher in einer generalcharte und neunzehen special-charten das gesamte Russische reich und dessen angräntzende länder, nach den regeln der erd-beschreibung und den neuesten observationen vorstellig macht. Entworffen bey der kayserl. academie der wissenschafften. 8 pp., [1], 19 maps. fol. St. Petersburg, 1745. 3109

NOTE.—Compiled under the direction of Joseph Nicolas Delisle, who was called to St. Petersburg in 1726 to take charge of the work. In 1740, in order to hasten the completion of the atlas, he was assisted by several scientists, including his brother Louis. The atlas was finished in 1745 and published the same year by the academy of sciences of St. Petersburg.

Contains a description of the maps, an explanation of russian geographical names and symbols used, a general map of the russian empire and 19 special maps on different scales. The letterpress is in german.

The following map relates to America:

no. 19. Ostium fluvii Amur cum parte australiori terræ Kamtschatkæ variisque in oceano sitis insulis inter quas pars eminet Iaponiæ, showing the extreme point of Alaska and the Aleutian islands.

## 1792

**Russia.** *Gornyĭ departament.*
Россійской атласъ, изъ сорока четырехъ картъ состоящій и на сорокъ два намѣстничества имперію раздѣляющій. 2 p. l., 45 maps. fol. [С.-Петербургъ] сочин: гравир: и печат: при Горномъ училищѣ, 1792. 3110

NOTE.—Translated title: Atlas of Russia, comprising 44 maps and showing the 42 governmental divisions of the empire. [St. Petersburg] engraved, written, and published at the department of mines, 1792.

Engraved title. Maps have ornamented engraved titles.

The following map relates to America:

no. 39. Восточная часть иркутской губерніи съ прилѣжащими осптровами и западнымъ берегомъ Америки.—[Eastern portion of the province of Irkutsk with the adjacent islands and the western shore of America]

## 1845

**Akhmatov, I.**
Атласъ географическій, историческій и хронологическій Россійскаго государства, составленный на основаніи исторіи Н. М. Карамзина И. Ахматовымъ. Новое изданіе... издалъ И. Зйнерлингъ. 1 p. l., 71 maps. obl. fol. Санктпетербургъ, 1845. 3111

NOTE.—Translated title: Geographical, historical, and chronological atlas of Russia, based on the history of N. M. Karamzin. New ed. revised by I. Einerling. St Petersburg, 1845.

## 1857

**Russia.** *Departament sel'skago khozi͡aĭstva.*
Хозяйственно-статистическій атласъ Европейской Россіи. Изданъ Департаментомъ сельскаго хозяйства министерства государственныхъ имуществъ. Изданіе 3e.—Atlas économique et statistique de la Russie d'Europe, publié par le

département de l'économie rurale du ministère des domaines de l'état. 3ᵉ éd. ...
1 p. l., 10 maps. fol. St.-Pétersbourg [départ. de l'économie rurale] 1857.

3112

NOTE.—Titles and letterpress in russian and french.

CONTENTS.

no. 1. Sol et climat.
" 2. Systèmes de culture. Culture de lin, du chanvre et de la betterave.
" 3. Distribution des forêts.
" 4. Commerce des grains.
" 5. Récoltes moyennes en céréales.
" 6. Prix moyens des grains.
" 7. Élève des brebis à laine fine.
" 8. Nombre des chevaux.
" 9. Nombre des bêtes de la race bovine.
" 10. Commerce des bestiaux.

## 1823
**Potocki, I.**

Археологическій атласъ европейской Россіи, сочиненный графомъ Паномъ Потоцкимъ ... —Atlas archéologique de la Russie européenne ... D'après la seconde édition, imprimée à 12 exemlaires[!]; nouvellement augmenté de la traduction russe du texte grec et françois. 1 p. l., [6] pp., 6 maps. fol. St.-Pétersbourg, académie impériale des sciences, 1823. 3113

NOTE.—Titles and letterpress in russian and french.

CONTENTS.

no. 1. Géographie d'Hérodote. Avant l'ère chrétienne 440 ans.
" 2. Géographie de Strabon. Vers le tems de l'ère chrétienne.
" 3. Géographie de Pomponius Mela, Pline et Tacite. Depuis l'an de l'ère chrétienne 40 jusqu'à 100.
" 4. Géographie de Ptolémée. Année de l'ère chrétienne 150.
" 5. Géographie de Jornandes et Moyse de Khorenne. Année de l'ère chrétienne 550.
" 6. Géographie de Constantin Porphirogénète. Année de l'ère chrétienne 945.

## 1874
**Il'in, A. A.**

Опытъ статистическаго атласа Россійской имперіи. Составилъ генеральнаго штаба полковникъ А. Ильинъ. 2 p. l., 45 maps. fol. С.-Петербургъ, А. Ильинъ, 1874. 3114

NOTE.—Translated title: Statistical atlas of the russian empire. Sᵗ Petersburg, 1874.

## 1900
**Koch, W.,** *and* **Opitz, C.**

Eisenbahn- und verkehrsatlas von Russland und den Balkanstaaten mit verkehrshandbuch, maassstab 1:2.000.000. 2. verb. aufl., hrsg. von C. Opitz, kartograph. Umfassend 28 sectionen inclusive 11 nebenkarten in vierfachem farbendruck, nebst alphabetischen stations- und ortsverzeichnissen ... 3 p. l., 39 pp., 28 maps. fol. Leipzig, T. J. Arndt [1900] 3115

NOTE.—Title also in russian.
Index map on page 40.

## SEAS.

### BLACK and AZOV

**Taitbout de Marigny, E.**
Plans de golfes, baies, ports, et rades de la mer Noire et de la mer d'Azov.   2 p. l., 35 maps.   obl. 8°.   Odessa, A. Braun, 1830.
3116

Atlas de la mer Noire et de la mer d'Azov.   2 p. l., 36 maps. obl. 4°.   Odessa, Nitzsche, 1850.
3117

**Russia.**  *Morskoe ministerstvo.*
Атласъ Чернаго моря, гравированъ по высочайшему повелѣннію въ С.-Петербургѣ. Съ описей, произведенныхъ съ 1825 по 1836 годъ капитаномъ 1го ранга Е. Манганари. Изданъ при гидрографическомъ Черноморскомъ депо. 2 p. l., 25 sheets.   8°.   Николаевъ, 1841.
3118

> NOTE.—Translated title: Atlas of the Black sea, engraved by imperial order at St. Petersburg. From the surveys made from 1825 to 1836 under the direction of captain commander E. Manganari. Published by the hydrographic office of the Black sea. Nikolaiev, 1841.
> Incomplete. Sheet 1 wanting.

### Provinces.
### CAUCASUS.

**Abich, W. H.**
Atlas zu den geologischen forschungen in den Kaukasischen ländern.  II. theil. Geologie des armenischen hochlandes. Westhälfte. cover-title, 1 p. l., 3 col. maps, 6 pls.   fol.   [Wien, Hölder, 1882]
3119

> NOTE.—To accompany work by same author, entitled: Geologische forschungen in den Kaukasischen ländern. pt. 2. Geologie des Armenischen hochlandes. Wien, Hölder, 1882.

### FINLAND.

**Spafarieff, L. V.**
Атласъ финскаго залива . . . Atlas of the gulf of Finland containing the south coast, with the islands belonging to it, from Cape Luserort to Cronstadt with light houses . . .   2 p. l., 12 maps, 1 pl. fol.   S$^t$. Petersburg, naval printing office, 1821.
3120

> NOTE.—Title in russian and english.

**Société de géographie de Finlande.**
Atlas de Finlande.   12 pp., 32 col. maps, 7 charts.   fol.   Helsingfors, société anonyme F. Tilgman, 1899.
3121

> NOTE.—Maps numbered A and B are counted as two maps.
> French edition.
> Published in two editions, one in french, the other in finnish and swedish. Text published separately in each of these three languages. French text, translated by Jean Poirot, forms v. 17 of "Fennia, bulletin de la société de géographie de Finlande, Helsingfors, 1899."

## ORENBURG.

**Krasilnikov, A. D.**, *and* **Rychkov, P. I.**

Оренбургская губернія съ прилежащими къ ней мѣстами, по ,,ландкартамъ'' красильникова и ,,топографіи'' П. И. Рычкова 1755 года. Издано на средства,Ивана Ѳедоровича и Ѳедора Ивановича Базилевскихъ Оренбургскимъ отдѣломъ императорскаго Русскаго географическаго общества. 3 p. l., 26 l. incl. 12 maps. fol. Оренбургъ, Б. Бреслина, 1880. 3122

NOTE.—Translated title: Province of Orenburg with adjoining regions according to the "maps" of Krasilnikov, and the "topography" of P. I. Rychkov, of 1755. Reprinted at the expense of Ivan and Fedor Bazilevski . . . Orenburg, B. Breslin, 1880.
Lithographic reproduction of maps and text. On the 3$^{rd}$ p. l. is the following title: "Ландъкарты или чертежи географическія на которыхъ представляется оренбургская губернія . . . —Для лутчагожъ оныхъ ландкартъ . . . гистороическое описаніе подъ именем топографія оренбургскои губерніи . . . 1755.

## POLAND.

**Pitt, M.**

A description of the places next the North-Pole; as also of Muscovy, Poland, Sweden, Denmark, and their several dependances. fol. Oxford, for M. Pitt, 1680. 3123
[English, The, atlas. v. 1]

NOTE.—See title 2831 for bibliographical notice.

**Plater, S.**

Plans des sièges et batailles qui ont eu lieu en Pologne, pendant le xvii$^{ème}$ et xviii$^{ème}$ siècle; accompagnés d'un texte explicatif. Pour servir de suite à l'atlas historique de la Pologne. 1 p. l., 11 l., 20 maps on 10 l. obl. fol. Posen, G. Decker & co. 1828. 3124

## SIBERIA.

**Middendorff, A. von.**

Karten-atlas zu dr. A. v. Middendorff's reise in den äussersten norden und osten Sibiriens. cover-title, 2 p. l., 17 maps. obl. fol. St. Petersburg, k. akad. der wissenschaften, 1859. 3125

NOTE.—On the cover title the following note is written in pencil: "Map no. 1 was never issued. See notice on the cover of the closing lieferung of the work (bd. 4, theil 2, lief. 3)"
To accompany a work by dr. A. Th. v. Middendorff, entitled: Reise in den äussersten norden und osten Sibiriens. St. Petersburg, k. akad. der wissenschaften, 1859.

## TVER.

**Russia.** *Mezhevoĭ Korpus-Voennago vĭedomstva.*

Топографическій межевой атласъ Тверской губерніи, составленный въ 1848 и 1849мъ годахъ чинами Межеваго корпуса и топографами военнаго вѣдомства подъ наблюденіемъ генеральнаго штаба генералъ-маіора Менде и руководствомъ въ ученомъ отношеніи Императорскаго русскаго географическаго об-

**Russia**—Continued.

щества. Издана[!] по высочайшему повелѣнію императорскимъ русскимъ географическимъ обществомъ въ 1853мъ году. Въ 1: 84000 долю. 1 map on 98 l. fol. Въ Москвѣ, 1853.   3126

> NOTE.—Translated title: Topographical survey atlas of the Tver province, prepared in 1848-49 by the topographic survey corps and the topographers of the war department under the direction of gen. Mende and the imperial russian geographical society. Published by authority by the imperial russian geographical society in 1853 . . . In Moscow.

---

## SPAIN.

### WARS.

**Gómez de Arteche y Moro, J.**

Atlas de la guerra de la independencia, publicado por el depósito de la guerra.   11 pp., 47 maps. fol.   Madrid [impr. y lithografia del depósito de la guerra, 1869-1901]   3127

> NOTE.—Published in 12 parts to accompany "Guerra de la independencia. Historia militar de España de 1808 á 1814," 12 v.

**Pelet, J. J. G.**

Atlas des mémoires militaires relatifs à la succession d'Espagne sous Louis XIV. Dressé par les soins de m. le lieutenant général Pelet . . . fol. Paris, imprimerie royale, 1836-48.   3128
[France. Comité des travaux historiques et scientifiques. Collection de documents inédits sur l'histoire de France]

> NOTE.—To accompany, Vault, F. E. de. Mémoires militaires relatifs à la succession d'Espagne sous Louis XIV. Extraits de la correspondance de la cour et des généraux par le lieutenant général de Vault . . . Revus, publiés et précédés d'une introduction par le lieutenant général Pelet . . . 11 v. 1835-62.

Atlas divided into 11 pts., one to each volume.

#### CONTENTS.

v. 1-2: 3 p. l., [11] l., 22 maps.
no. [ 1] Théâtre de la guerre dans les Pays-Bas, de 1701 à 1712.
" [ 2] Théâtre de la guerre dans l'Allemagne méridionale, de 1701 à 1707.
" [ 3] Théâtre de la guerre dans l'Italie septentrionale, de 1701 à 1706.
" [ 4-14] Cours du Rhin depuis Constance jusqu'à Nimègue. 11 sheets.
" [15] Plan de Mantoue et des environs en 1701.
" [16] Plan de la bataille de Chiari, 1ᵉʳ septembre 1701.
" [17] Plan de la ville de Crémone, 31 janvier 1702.
" [18] Siége de Kaiserswert, juin 1702.
" [19] Plan de Landau et des environs, avec l'investissement de 1703.
" [20] Attaques de Landau en 1702, 1703, 1704, et 1713.
" [21] Champ de bataille de Luzzara et siége de Guastalla, août 1702.
" [22] Champ de bataille de Friedlingen, 14 octobre 1702.

v. 3: 3 p. l., [17] l., 10 maps.
no. [ 1] Siéges de Rheinberg en 1702 et 1703.
" [ 2] Siége de Brisach en 1703.
" [ 3] Champ de bataille de Spire en 1703.
" [ 4] Champ de bataille d'Höchstett en 1703 et 1704.
" [ 5] Siége du fort de Kehl en 1703.
" [ 6] Plan du combat d'Eckeren, 30 juin 1703.
" [ 7] Siége de Gueldre, 15 décembre 1703.
" [ 8] Places et postes de la Lombardie . . .
" [ 9] Places des Pays-Bas . . .
" [10] Places de l'Allemagne méridionale . . .
v. 4: 2 p. l., [16] l., 7 maps.
no. [ 1] Plan de Namur.
" [ 2] " " Verceil.
" [ 3] Places d'Allemagne.
" [ 4] " du Piémont.
" [ 5] " de la Lombardie et du comté de Nice.
" [ 6] Places des Pays-Bas.
" [ 7] Cartes des bords de la Moselle du Rhin.
v. [5] 3 p. l., [14] l., 6 maps.
no. [ 1] Batail de Cassano, livrée le 16 août 1705.
" [ 2] Blocus de Montmeillan rendu aux Français le 11 décembre 1705.
" [ 3] Places d'Allemagne.
" [ 4] Places de Flandre.
" [ 5] " d'Italie.
" [ 6] " de la Lombardie.
v. 6: 2 p. l., [11] l., 7 maps.
no. [ 1] Théâtre de la guerre dans la Flandre et le Brabrant, de 1703 à 1712.
" [ 2] Carte de la chaîne occidentale des Alpes.
" [ 3] Siége de Menin, 22 août 1706.
" [ 4] " d'Ath, 2 octobre 1706.
" [ 5] Batailles de Calcinato, 19 avril, et de Castiglione, 9 septembre 1706.
" [ 6] Siége et bataille de Turin, 17 septembre 1707.
" [ 7] Places d'Italie.
v. 7: 3 p. l., [7] l., 7 maps.
no. [ 1] Carte de la France et des États limitrophes en 1701.
" [ 2] Campagnes de Flandre, de 1706 à 1712.
" [ 3] Plan de la bataille de Ramillies, 23 mai 1706.
" [ 4] Places de Brabant.
" [ 5] " " Flandre.
" [ 6] Théâtre des opérations entre la basse Durance et la Méditerranée en 1707.
" [ 7] Plan des attaques de Toulon en août 1707.
v. 8-9: 1 p. l., [18] l., 7 maps.
no. [ 1] Siége et combat d'Oudenarde, 11 juillet 1708.
" [ 2-3] Siége et attaques de Lille, octobre 1708.  2 sheets.
" [ 4] Prise de Fenestrelle, 31 août 1708.
" [ 5] Siége de Tournay, juillet 1709.
" [ 6] Bataille de Malplaquet, 11 septembre 1709.
" [ 7] Siége de Mons, septembre 1709.
v. 10-11: 1 p. l., [25] l., 3 maps.
no. [ 1] Plan de la bataille de Denain, 24 juillet 1712.
" [ 2] Plan du siége de Douai, 8 septembre 1712.—Plan du siége de Quesnoy, 4 octobre.—Plan du siége de Bouchain, 19 octobre.
" [ 3] Plan de la prise des lignes de Fribourg, 20 septembre 1713.

**Suchet, L. G.**, *duc d'Albuféra*.

Mémoires du maréchal Suchet, duc d'Albuféra, sur ses campagnes en Espagne, depuis 1808 jusqu'en 1814. Écrits par lui-même. Atlas. 2 p. l., 15 maps, 1 pl. fol. Paris et Londres, Colburn [1828]–1829. 3129

NOTE.—Atlas accompanying this work has same title, but imprint varies:—Paris, A. Bossange, Bossange père, F. Didot, 1828.

**Vacani, C.**

[Atlante topografico-militare per servire alla storia delle campagne e degli assedj degl' Italiani in Ispagna dal al MDCCCVIII al MDCCCXIII ricavato da antichi documenti e da nuove ricognizioni eseguite nel corso della guerra . . .]   cover-title, 16 maps. fol. [Milano, 1823] 3130

NOTE.—To accompany his: Storia delle campagne e degli assedj degl' Italiani in Ispagna dal MDCCCVIII al MDCCCXIII . . . 3 v. Milano, 1823.

**Wyld, J.**

Map & plans showing the principal movements, battles & sieges, in which the british army was engaged during the war from 1808 to 1814 in the spanish peninsula and the south of France. 3 p. l., 37 maps and views on 51 sheets. fol. London, J. Wyld [1840] 3131

NOTE.—See title no. 2893 for contents.

## GENERAL.

(Arranged chronólogically)

### 1757

**López, T. L. de V. M.**

Atlas geographico del reyno de España, è islas adyacentes, con una breve descripcion de sus provincias . . .   2 p. l., 24 maps, 1 pl. 32°. Madrid [1757] 3132

NOTE.—Contains a circular pian of Madrid with marginal explanations, and a view of Lisbon, "Vista de Lisboa segun estaba antes del temblor de tierra," [1755], with five small views of important buildings. The maps of the provinces of Spain are inclosed in an irregular border of text.

### 1789

**Tofiño de San Miguel, V.**, *& others.*

Atlas maritimo de España.   2 p. l., 48 maps, plans and views. fol. Madrid, 1789. 3133

NOTE.—At foot of engraved title, "Inventado . . . por d. Rafael Mengs . . .—Grabado por d. Manuel Salvador Carmona" . . .
Maps by Tofiño de San Miguel, Joseph Varela y Ulloa and Principe de la Paz. Map no. 48 entitled, "Carta esferica del golfo de Gascuña y canales de la Mancha y Bristol . . . por mano del exmo. señor Principe de la Paz; año de 1803" is not included in the index, and must have been inserted in the atlas. Contains plans of the following ports: Plano . . . de San Sebastian. 1788.—Plano de Ferrol. 1789.—Plano . . . de Cadiz. 1789.—Plano . . . de Cartagena. 1788.—El puerto de Mahon. 1786.

## 1807

**Bourgoing, J. F.**
Atlas pour servir au tableau de l'Espagne moderne. 1 p. l., 5 maps, 24 pl. 4°. Paris, Tourneisen, 1807. 3134

NOTE.—To accompany: Tableau de l'Espagne moderne.

## 1809

**Laborde, A. L. J.,** *comte de.*
Atlas de l'itinéraire descriptif de l'Espagne . . . 4 p. l., 29 maps. 4°. [Paris, H. Nicolle, etc.] 1809. 3135

NOTE.—To accompany his: Itinéraire descriptif de l'Espagne . . . 2. éd. Paris, H. Nicolle [etc.] 1809.

## 1826

Atlas del itinerario descriptivo de España. $2^d$ ed. 55 pp., [6] l. 29 maps. 8°. Valencia, J. Ferrer de Orga, 1826. 3136

NOTE.—To accompany work by the same author, entitled: Itinerario descriptivo de las provincias de España . . .

## 1848-1868

**Coello de Portugal y Quesada, F.**
Atlas de España y sus posesiones de ultramar. cover-title, 30 fold. maps in 30 pts. 16°. [Madrid, 1848-1868] 3137

NOTE.—This work serves to complete the Diccionario geográfico-estadístico-histórico of d. Pascual Madoz.

"El atlas general de España y sus posesiones de ultramar constará de 65 hojas." *cf.* cover note.

The following maps are wanting:
Almería.—Avila (reducción á 1 por 400.000)
Cádiz.—Canarias (2 hojas)—Coruña.—Cuenca.—Guadalajara.—Huelva.—
Logroño.—Madrid.—Oviedo.—Pontevedra.—Teruel.—Toledo.—Zamora.—
Aragón.—Castilla la Nueva.—Andalucia.—Léon y Extremaduro. *cf.* Sociedad geográfica de Madrid. Boletin. Velada en memoria del excmo. sr. d. Francisco Coello y Quesada. v. 40, p. 43.

Africa (Posesiones de) 1850.
Alava, 1848.
Alicante, 1859.
Avila, 1864.
Barcelona, 1862.
Baleares (Islas) 1851.

CONTENTS.

Burgos. 1868.
Castellón. 1852.
Cuba. 1851.
" $2^a$ hoja. 1853.
Filipinas (Islas) 3 sheets. 1852.
Gerona. 1851.
Guipúzcoa. 1848.
Lugo. 1864.
Madrid (Plano de) 1849.
Marianas (Islas) 1852.

## Coello de Portugal y Quesada, F.—Continued.

Navarra. 1861.
Orense. 1856.
Palencia. 1852.
Puerto Rico (Isla de) 1851.
Salamanca. 1867.
Santander. 1861.
Segovia. 1849.
Soria. 1864.
Tarragona. 1858.
Valladolid. 1852.
Vizcaya. 1857.
Zaragoza. No date.

### 1879

**Artero y González, J. de la G.**
Atlas histórico-geográfico de España, desde los tiempos primitivos hasta nuestros dias . . . 23, [1] pp., 23 maps. 8°. Granada, P. V. Sabatel, 1879. 3138

NOTE.—The following maps relate to America:
no. 21. Colonias españolas en la América Septentrional durante los siglos XVI, XVII y XVIII.
" 22. Colonias españolas en la América Meridional durante los siglos XVI, XVII y XVIII.

### 1904

**Bailly-Bailliere & hijos.**
Mapas de las cuarenta y nueve provincias de España con datos geográficos, comerciales é industriales de cada provincia. 58, [1] pp. incl. 49 maps. 4°. Madrid, Bailly-Bailliere & hijos, 1904. 3139

### CITIES.

### MADRID

### 1800

**Martínez de la Torre, F., and Asensio, J.**
Plano de la villa y corte de Madrid, en sesenta y quatro láminas, que demuestran otros tantos barrios en que está dividida; con los nombres de todas sus plazuelas y calles, números de las manzanas, y casas que comprehende cada uno; con otras curiosidades útiles á los naturales y forasteros. Nueva edicion, corregida y aumentada con un índice alfabético . . . y . . . con un mapa del plano general de Madrid . . . 115 pp., 65 maps. 24°. Madrid, J. Doblado, 1800. 3140

# SWEDEN.

## HISTORICAL.

**Hildebrand, E.,** *and* **Selander, N.**
Atlas till allmänna och svenska historien. 4 pts. in 1 v. 4 cover-titles, 29 col. maps. obl. 4°. Stockholm, P. A. Norstedt & söners [1883] 3141

## GENERAL.

(Arranged chronologically)

### 1680

**Pitt, M.**
A description of the places next the North-Pole; as also of Muscovy, Poland, Sweden, Denmark, and their several dependances. fol. Oxford, for M. Pitt, 1680. 3142
[English, The, atlas. v. 1]

NOTE.—See title 2831 for bibliographical notice.

## Provinces.

### NORBERG.

**Petersson, W.**
Geologisk atlas öfver Norbergs bergslag; på bekostnad af Jernkontoret upprättad åren 1892-93 af Sveriges geologiska undersökning. 1 p. l., 12 l. incl. 11 col. maps. obl. fol. [Stockholm, gen. stab. lit. anst., 1893?] 3143
[Sveriges geologiska undersökning. Specialkartor med beskrifningar. Ser. Bb. no. 9]

### JUKKASJÄRVI.

**Sveriges geologiska undersökning.**
Atlas till underdånig berättelse om en undersökning af mindre kända malmfyndigheter inom Jukkasjärvi malmtrakt och dess omgifningar verkställd af Sveriges geologiska undersökning på grund af kongl. maj:ts nådiga beslut den 19 maj 1899. 2 p. l., 8 fold. maps. obl. 4°. [Stockholm, kungl. boktryckeriet, 1900] [Kongliga civildepartementet. v. 35] 3144

---

# SWITZERLAND.

## CITIES.

**Tassin, N.**
Description de tovs les cantons, villes, bovrgs, villages et avtres particularitez dv pays des Svisses, avec vne brieue forme de leur république. Descriptio cantonvm, vrbium, pagorum & aliorum memorabilium quae in Heluetia reperiuntur: vnå cum breui forma

**Tassin, N.**—Continued.
rei Heluetiorum publicae.   1 p. l., 63 pp., 35 pl.   obl. 8°.   Paris,
S. Cramoisy, 1635. 3145
[*With his* Les plans et profils de tovtes les principales villes et lievx considérables de France . . .   obl. 8°.   Paris, I. Messager, 1636.  v. 1.  Title 2948]

COMMERCE.

**Wartmann, H.**
Atlas über die entwicklung von industrie und handel der Schweiz in dem zeitraume vom jahr 1770 bis zum jahr 1870. Im auftrage der schweizerischen commission für die additionellen ausstellungen in Wien.—Atlas représentant le développement de l'industrie et du commerce de la Suisse . . .   4 p. l., 8 col. pl.   fol.   Winterthur, W. Randegger & co. 1873. 3146

Note.—Title and letterpress in german and french.

RAILROADS.

**Nietmann, W.**
Eisenbahn-atlas für deutsches reich, Luxemburg, Schweiz, Oesterreichisch Ungarische monarchie und angrenzende gebiete. Dargestellt in 30 nach einzelnen ländern und provinzen getrennten specialkarten, 2 übersichtskarten und vollständigen stationsverzeichnissen. Schweiz und Oesterreich-Ungarn ausserdem genauestens durchgesehen und verbessert von Karl Schönfelder und Emanuel Schütze.   18$^{te}$ aufl.   3 p. l., 52, 33 pp., 32 fold. maps.  fol. Leipzig, W. Nietmann, 1902. 3147

STATISTICAL.

**Switzerland.**  *Statistisches bureau.*
Graphisch-statistischer atlas der Schweiz. Hrsg. vom statistischen bureau des eidg. departements des innern. Atlas graphique et statistique de la Suisse . . .   xxvi, 96 pp., fold. maps, diagrs. 8°.   Bern, Stämpfli & cie. [1897] 3148
[Schweizerische statistik. pt. 110]

Note.—Issued in place of the "Statistisches jahrbuch" for the year 1897. Titles and letterpress in german and french.

The following maps relate to America:
no. 11.  In der Schweiz geborene bevölkerung der Vereinigten Staaten.  1890.
" 14b.  Schweizerische einfuhr . . . von 1891–1894 [World map]
" 15b.  "  ausfuhr . . . von 1891–1894 [World map]

Alphabetisches inhaltsverzeichnis der jahrg. i-x (1891–1901) des statistischen jahrbuches der Schweiz und des graphisch-statistischen atlasses vom jahre 1897 . . .   Index alphabétique de l'annuaire statistique . . .   94 pp.   8°.   Bern, Stämpfli & cie. 1901. [Schweizerische statistik, 131. lfg.] 3149

Note.—Titles and letterpress in german and french.

## GENERAL.

(Arranged chronologically)

**1712?**

**Müller, J. C.**
Schweizerischer atlas bestehend in 19 carten . . . 1 p. l., 19 col. maps. obl. 4°. [n. p. 1712?] 3150

NOTE.—Engraved title.
Inset to map no. 18, "Plan de la ville de Genève avec ses fortification[!]"

**1769**

**Homann heirs.**
Atlas novus reipublicae Helveticae xx. mappis, compositus sumtibus Homannianis heredibus. 1 p. l., 20 maps. fol. Norimbergae, 1769. 3151

NOTE.—Maps drawn by T. Mayer, G. Walser Pejer, Rizzi-Zannoni, dated from 1732-1768 and illustrated by coats of arms and landscapes. Index in latin and german on the title page.
Inset on map no. 19, a plan of the city of Geneva.

**1786-1802**

**Weiss, J. H.**
[Atlas suisse] 17 maps. fol. [Aarau, au frais de J. R. Meyer, 1786-1802] 3152

NOTE.—Imperfect: title-page wanting.

**1816**

**Wyss, J. R.**
Hand atlas für reisende in das Berner oberland. Atlas portatif à l'usage des voyageurs dans l'Oberland bernois. 1 p. l., 124 pp., 5 maps, 3 views, 2 pl. 12°. Bern, J. J. Burgdorfer, 1816. 3153

NOTE.—Engraved title.

**1870**

**Historisch**-geographischer atlas der Schweiz . . . Bearbeitet von J. C. Voegelin, Gerold Meyer von Knonau . . Neue ausg. 1 p. l., 4 l., 15 maps in 30 sheets. fol. Zürich, F. Schulthess, 1870.
3154

NOTE.—Descriptive border text to each sheet. Historical diagrams relating to the cities of Zürich, Basel, and Berne.

**1870-1903**

**Switzerland.** *Eidgenössisches stabsbüreau.*
Topographischer atlas der Schweiz, im massstab der originalaufnahmen nach dem bundesgesetze vom 18. dezember 1868 vom eidgenössischen stabsbüreau veröffentlicht. lief. 1-49. obl. fol. Bern, J. Dalp, 1870-1903. 3155

Note.—In progress.

**Dufour, G. H.**

**1901**

Topographische karte der Schweiz, vermessen und herausgegeben auf befehl der eidgenössischen behörden. Aufgenommen und reduziert durch eidgenössische ingenieure unter der aufsicht des generals G. H. Dufour. Maastab der karte 1: 100000. 25 sheets. fol. [Bern, eidg.-topographisches bureau] 1833–1863. [nachträge 1901]
3156

NOTE.—Index map on sheet no. 21.

**Wagner, E.**

**1907**

Atlas de poche de la Suisse. 26 cartes en couleurs. 3. éd. rev. et cor. par l'institut géographique, H. Kümmerly & Frey . . . — Taschen-atlas der Schweiz . . . 35 pp., 20 col. maps. 12°. Berne, société d'édition de cartes géographiques [1907] 3157

NOTE.—Title-pages and text in french and german.

---

# TURKEY.

## GENERAL.

(Arranged chronologically)

**Hellert, J. J.**

**1843**

Nouvel atlas physique, politique et historique de l'empire ottoman et de ses états limitrophes en Europe, en Asie, et en Afrique . . . Avec un beau plan . . . de Constantinople, plusieurs plans des villes les plus importantes de l'empire, et ceux des siéges et batailles mémorables soutenus par les ottomans . . . 2 p. l., 39 (*i. e.* 38) maps. fol. Paris, Bellizard, Dufour & c$^{ie}$; St. Pétersbourg, F. Bellizard & c.$^{ie}$ [etc.] 1843. 3158

NOTE.—To accompany J. von Hammer-Purgstall, Histoire de l'empire ottoman . . . tr. de l'allemand . . . par J. J. Hellert . . . 18 v. 1835–43.

**Handtke, F. H.**

**1876**

Special-karte der europäischen Türkei. Maassstab 1:600,000. 1 p. l., 20 sheets. fol. Glogau, C. Flemming [1876] 3159

NOTE.—Index-map on title-page.

## CRETE ISLAND.

**1651**

**Boschini, M.**

Il regno tutto di Candia delineato à parte, à parte. 3 p. l., 61 pl. fol. [Venetia] 1651. 3160

## MACEDONIA and OLD SERVIA.

**Cvijić, J.**
Геолошки атлас Македоније и Старе Србије од I. Цвијtrа.   1 p. l., 5 maps, 3 diagrs.   fol.   Београд, литографије државне штампарије, 1903 год.   3161

NOTE.—Translated title: Geological atlas of Macedonia and old Servia, by J. Cvijić.   Belgrade, government lithographic and printing office, 1903.

CONTENTS.

no. 1. Екскурсије по Старој Србији и Македоније. [Excursions in Old Ser via and Macedonia]   1:750,000.
" 2. Геолошка карта Старе Србије и Македоније.   Carte géologique de la Vieille-Serbie et de la Macédoine.   1:500.000.
" 3-5. [Geological profiles]
" 6. Тектонска скица Старе Србије и Македоније.   [Tectonic sketch of old Servia and Macedonia]   1:1.200.000.
" 7. Динарско-Албански тектонски суков.   [Teutonic knot of Dinaric-Albanian Alps]   1:1.200.000.
" 8. Централно вило Балканскога полуострва.   [Central part of Balkan peninsula]

# ASIA.

## GENERAL.

(Arranged chronologically)

### 1690?

**Hacke, W.**
A description of the Sea coasts Rivers &a. of Monomotapa Soffala Mosambique Quiloa Mombaza Melinde Magadoxa Doara, Asabb & Moha in the red Sea, Arabia felix, Gulf of Persia Bussora Persia Guzarat India & the Factories; Malabar Cormandell Bisnagar Orixa Bengall & the factories; Aracam, Martaban, Pegu, Malaya, Straghts of Malacca & Sincapora, Sunda Diones & Banca; Siam Cambodia Couchinchina China Amoy Tayawan Tonquin Cantan Maccao Quinam Quancÿ, Nanquin & Xantung; as allso of the Islands of Japan Cikoko Coray Diemens Straght Formosa Aynam Luconia Mindora Paragoa Borneo Celehes Geylolo Moluco Ceran Amboina Banda Bouro Bouton Panzelaue Calouro Salayer Tÿmor Floris Cumhava (Straghts of Sapy) Ende Java Banca Timaon Sumatra Princes Nassaw Ceiloan Bombay zocotra Mohilla Mayotta Joanna Assada and St. Lorinso alias Madagascar in the East indies . . .   1 p. l., 94 col. maps.   fol.   [1690?]   3162

NOTE.—In manuscript. Presumably completed in 1690. Only date given is 1677 in descriptive text to map no. 38.
Soundings are indicated; facts in regard to anchorages and sailing directions are written in the margins of charts.

**Hacke, W.**—Continued.

Another manuscript by the same author, entitled "The South Sea Waggoner," described in Quaritch, General catalogue, p. 63.

Capt. Hacke is known to have been associated with capt. Bartholomew Sharpe, the notorious buccaneer, in various expeditions to the South sea and seems to have been in a position of command judging from the observations and directions laid down in his books.

CONTENTS.

no.   1. Monomotapa [showing Cape of Good Hope]
"    2. Cape Bona Efperanca.—Cape Falco.—Cape Gulles.
"    3. Monomotapa.
"    4. Lagoa.
"    5. Mosambique.—Soffala.
"    6. S!͏ Lorinso.
"  7-8. Mosambique.—S!͏ Lorinso.
"    9. S!͏ Lorinso.
"   10. Mohilla.—Mayotta.—Joanna.
"   11. Magadoxa.—Melinde.—Mombaza.—Quiloa.
"   12. Magadoxa.
"   13. Arabia Felix.—Aden.—Doara.
"   14. Arabia.
"   15. Moha City [plan showing landing]
"   16. [Views of] Moha accompanied by "a table of the moft remarkable & principal places about Moha."
"   17. A defcription of Afabb Bay.
"   18. Arabia Felix.
" 19-21. Persia.—Gulf of Arabia Felix.
"   22. Cong in Perfia.—Bufsora.
"   23. Persia.—Guzarat.
"   24. India.—Surrat.—Cambaya.—Guzarat.
"   25. The city & port of Bufseen in India.—Rojapore on the coaft of India.—The town of Vingerle.—Som part of the Indian coast of Malabar . . .
"   26. Malabar [coast]
"   27. India.—Guzarat.
"   28. The riseing of the land as it appeareth to the eye between the high land of S' Iohs & Damon.
"   29. India.—Chaull.—Thaull.—Coronia.
"   30. Coronia.—Bombahem Ifland.—Isle of Saltfet.
"   31. Surrat City.—Cambaya.—Guzarat.
"   32. Bombay.
"   33. Bombay Point.—Isle of Coronia.
"   34. Saltfet Ifland.—Bombay Ifland.—Coronia.
"   35. Rojapore.
"   36. Carwar [town of British India]
"   37. Malapi.
"   38. Callicut.
"   39. Cuchin.
"   40. Comarin.
" 41-42. Ceiloan.
" 43-44. Coromandel.
"   45. Bisnagar.
"   46. Orixa.
"   47. Ceiloan.

" 48. Part of the coast of Malabar.—Ceiloan Chanel.—Ceiloan.
" 49-50. Coromandel.
" 51. Bisnagar.
" 52. Orixa.
" 53. Bengall.
" 54. Codovascam.—Aracam.
" 55. Pegu.
" 56. Martaban.
" 57. Malaya.—Straghts of Malacca.—Shoals of Sumatra.
" 58. Borneo.
" 59. Malaya.
" 60. Siam.—Bancosey.—Cambodia.—Siompa.
" 61. Cambodia.—China.—Siompa.
" 62. Aynam.—Quinam.
" 63. Tonquin.—New Maccao.—Couchinchina.—Quancy.—Aynam.
" 64. Cantan.—Formosa.—Luconia.
" 65. Luconia.
" 66. China [coast]
" 67-68. Formosa.
" 69. Chekiang.—China.—Formosa.
" 70. Sambor isles.—S$^{ta}$ Maria.—Harps ifland.—Dos Reyes Magos.—Ifland of Fuego.—Ifland of Queiopeque.—Ifland of Amfterdam.
" 71. Coray.—Xantung.—Nanquin [etc.]
" 72. Japan.—Cikoko.—Tanaxima.
" 73. Sumatra.—Malaya.
" 74-76. Sumatra.
" 77. Sunda Straghts.—Java.
" 78-79. Sumatra.—Sunda Straghts.—Java.
" 80-81. Sumatra.—Banca.
" 82-84. Java.
" 85. Sumatra.—Banca.—Borneo.—Succadana.
" 86. Celebes.—Borneo.
" 87. Borneo.—Madura.—Java.—Lamboc.—Cumbava.—Celebes.
" 88. Celebes.—Ende.—Tiimor.—Ombo.—Terra Alta.
" 89. Celebes.—Xulla.—Maccasser.—Salayer.
" 90. Morotay.— Morotia.— Tobares. — Halamahera.— Ouby. — Sapellullo.—Xullabessi.—Bouro.—Ceran.
" 91. Paragoa.—Mindoro.—Luconia.
" 92. Borneo.—Paragoa.—Isle of Mindoro.
" 93. Siompa.—Borneo.
" 94. China [coast]

**1745**

**Après de Mannevillette, J. B. N. D. d'.**

Le neptune oriental, ou routier général des côtes des Indes Orientales et de la Chine, enrichi de cartes hydrographiques tant générales que particulières, pour servir d'instruction à la navigation de ces différentes mers. Dédié à monseigneur Orry de Fulvy . . . 2 p. l., x, [56] pp., front., 25 maps. fol. Paris, J. F. Robustel, 1745. 3163

**Après de Mannevillette, J. B. N. D. d'**—Continued.

NOTE.—See titles 3165–3168, 3231.

Frontispiece, by F. Boucher engraved by F. A. Aveline, represents Neptune on a chariot surrounded by tritons, winds and other allegorical figures.
Text in 110 numbered columns.
The following maps relate to the Philippines:
no. [57] Carte plate qui comprend les costes de Tsiompa de la Cochinchine le golfe de Tunquin une partie des costes de la Chine avec une partie de l'archipel des isles Philippines . . .
" [58] Plan de la baye de Manille . . .

### 1753

**Marre, J. de,** *and* **Keulen, J. v.**

De nieuwe groote lichtende zee fakkel, het sesde deel, vertoonende de zee-kusten, eylanden en havens van Oost Indiën . . . [v. 6] 3 p. l., 76 pp., 1 l., 95 maps. fol. t'Amsterdam, J. v. Keulen, 1753. 3164

NOTE.—v. 1–5, wanting.

### 1775

**Après de Mannevillette, J. B. N. D. d'.**

Le neptune oriental . . . 1 p. l., x, [104] pp., 59 maps, 2 pl. fol. Paris, Demonville; Brest, Malassis, 1775. 3165

NOTE.—See also title 3163. Frontispiece and maps no. 1, 10, 46, wanting.
Text in 194 numbered columns; also published separately as his: Instructions sur la navigation des Indes Orientales et de la Chine . . . 2 v. 4°. Paris, Demonville; Brest, Malassis, 1775.
The following maps relate to the Philippine islands:
no. 57. Plan des principaux ports de la côte de Illocos, en l'isle de Luçon.
" 58. Plan de la baye et ville de Manille.
" 59. Plan du port de Subec, en l'isle de Luçon . . . 1766.
" 52. A chart of the China sea . . . A. Dalrymple.
" 54. A mar [!] of part of Borneo and the Sooloo archipelago.
" 56. Tho Sooloo archipelago.

### 1775–1781

Le neptune oriental. 1 p. l., 64 maps, 2 pl. fol. [Paris, Demonville; Brest, Malassis, 1775–1781] 3166

NOTE.—Title page, text and maps no. 10, 46, 58–59, wanting. Contains all maps published in "Supplément au Neptune . . . 1781" except no. 29$^3$, "Plan du port de Bombay." See title 3168.
Map no. 15$^d$ dated 1776.
Engraved frontispiece slightly changed from that in 1745 ed.
Text to accompany this edition published separately in one volume as his: Instructions sur la navigation des Indes Orientales et de la Chine . . . 4°. Paris, chez Dezauche, 1775.
The title to this differs slightly from the two volume edition. The imprint is different and a new dedication has been given. This edition has bound with it his: Supplément au Neptune oriental . . . Paris, chez Demonville; Brest, chez Malassis, 1781. [Text]

Maps no. 5, 8, 8$^d$, 22-23, 25, 32, 32$^d$, 35, 41-43 are different from corresponding ones in 1775 ed. They are the same as those published in the Supplement, 1781.
The following maps relate to the Philippines:
no. 52. A chart of the China Sea . . .
" 54. A map of Borneo and the Sooloo archipelago . . . 1761-64.
" 56. The Sooloo archipelago . . . 1761-64.
" 57. Plan des principaux ports de la côte d'Illocon, en l'isle de Luçon.

## 1775-1781

[Le neptune oriental, dedié au roi . . .]   67 maps, 2 pl. fol.
[Paris, Demonville; Brest, Malassis, 1775-1781]   3167

NOTE.—Title page, frontispiece and maps no. 10, 46, wanting; no. 10 probably never published as index states "no. 10, carte à placer."
Contains all maps in editions of 1775 [1775-81] and "Supplément au Neptune . . . 1781."
In addition to the maps in the preceding title, the following relate to the Philippines:
no. 58. Plan de la baye et ville de Manille . . .
" 59. Plan du port de Subec, en l'isle de Luçon. Levé en 1766.

## 1781

Supplément au Neptune oriental . . .   6 p. l., 18 maps on 28 l.
fol.   Paris, Demonville; et Brest, Malassis, 1781.   3168

NOTE.—See also titles 3163 and 3231. Text also published with his: Instructions sur la navigation des Indes Orientales . . . 1775.

## 1795

The East-India pilot, or oriental navigator. A complete collection of charts and plans, etc. etc., with sailing directions for the navigation not only of the Indian and China seas, but of those also between England and the cape of Good Hope . . . with considerable additions from private manuscripts of the dutch, and from draughts and actual surveys communicated by officers of the East-India company.   2 p. l., 102 maps.   fol.   London, Laurie & Whittle [1795]
3169

NOTE.—See titles 3170 and 3172.
The following maps relate to America and the Philippine islands:
no. 21. A new chart of the Southern ocean [containing South America]
" 22. Plan of the bay and harbour of Rio-Janeiro.
" 72. A new chart of the oriental seas and islands [containing the Philippine islands]
" 96. A chart of the China sea, and Philippine islands.
" 97. Plan of the port of Subec, Luzon island.
" 98. Plan of the bay and city of Manila.
" 99. Plan of Solsogon harbour, Luzon island, and "Chart of the eastern coast of Bongo bay, Mindanao island.

## 1800

**Laurie, R.,** *and* **Whittle, J.**

The complete East-India pilot, or oriental navigator, being an extensive collection of charts; for the navigation not only of the Indian and China seas, with those of New Holland, but also of the seas between the british isles and the cape of Good Hope. From actual surveys and draughts communicated by experienced officers of the honorable East-India company, and from the french Neptune oriental . . . New ed. v. 2.  2 p. l., 63 maps. fol. London, R. Laurie & J. Whittle, 1800. 3170

> NOTE.—See also title 3169 and 3172.

## 1806–1821

**Hosburgh, J.**

[Atlas of the East Indies and China sea]   23 maps. fol. [London, 1806–1821] 3171

> NOTE.—No title-page.
> To accompany the "India directory; or directions for sailing to and from the East Indies, China, New-Holland, Cape of Good Hope, Brazil and the adjacent ports; by James Horsburgh. 2d. ed. 4°. London, author, 1817–1818."
> A copy in the Library of Congress.
> The following maps relate to America, and to the Philippine islands:
> no. 3. South American coast from "r. Paranayba" to "cape St. Antonio," 1814.
> "  14. Northern "part of the island Luzon or Luconia," 1810.

## 1806

**Laurie, R.,** *and* **Whittle, J.**

The complete East-India pilot; or, oriental navigator; being an extensive collection of charts; for the navigation not only of the Indian and China seas with those of New Holland, but also of the seas between the British isles and the cape of Good-Hope. From actual surveys and draughts, communicated by experienced officers of the honorable East-India company, and from the french Neptune oriental . . . New ed.  2 v. fol. London, R. Laurie & J. Whittle, 1806. 3172

> NOTE.—Collation: v. 1, 3 p. l., 63 maps; v. 2, 2 p. l., 64 maps.
> See also titles 3169 and 3170.  Maps no. 1, v. 1, and no. 84, v. 2, wanting.
> The following maps relate to America:
> v. 1. no. 33. A new chart of the coast of Brazil.
> "    "   35. Plan of the bay and harbour of Rio-Janeiro.
> "    "   36. A new chart of the entrance of Rio de-la-Plata, or Plate river.

## 1816

**Norie, J. W.**

The complete East India pilot, from London to any part of the Indian & China seas, comprehending a set of new and accurate charts, exhibiting all the passages out and home . . . 2 p. l., 28 maps. fol. London, J. W. Norie & co. 1816. 3173

NOTE.—The following maps relate to America and the Philippine islands:
no. 3. A new chart of the Atlantic, or Western ocean [comprising the American coast from "Guyana" to the "entrance to Hudson's straights"]
" 8. A new chart of the coast of Brazil from St. Ann's islands to St. Sebastian.
" 20. Chart of the East India islands [comprising the Philippine islands]
" 27. A new chart of the Sooloo archipelago.

## 1830-1832

**Laplace, C. P. T.**

Voyage autour du monde exécuté, pendant les années 1830, 1831 et 1832 sur la corvette la Favorite . . . Atlas hydrographique. 2 p. l., 11 maps. fol. Paris, imprimerie royale, 1833-1839. 3174

NOTE.—Title of atlas accompanying this work varies: . . . Publié par ordre du roi . . . au dépôt-général de la marine, 1833.

CONTENTS.

no. 1. Carte générale pour servir au voyage de . . . la Favorite . . .
" 2. Carte de l'archipel des Seychelles (mer des Indes)—Plan du mouillage de Ste. Anne . . .
" 3-4. Carte d'une partie de la côte de Cochinchine . . .
" 5. Croquis du mouillage du cap Boung-Quioua (côte du Tonkin) . . .
" 6. Plan de la baie de Tourane (côte de Cochinchine) . . .
" 7. Carte de l'archipel des Natunas (mer de Chine) . . .
" 8. Carte particulière de la partie s. o. des Natunas . . .
" 9. Carte de l'archipel des Anambas (mer de Chine) . . .—Inset: Carte d'une partie des Anambas . . . levée . . . par m. m. Fabre et La Pierre . . .
" 10. Carte de la baie Tupinier (archipel des Anambas) . . .
" 11. Plan de la rivière Kawa-Kawa (Nouvelle Zéelande, baie des Îles) . . .

## 1832-1843

**Berghaus, H.**

Atlas von Asia. 15 sheet maps, 27½ × 40. fol. Gotha, J. Perthes, 1832-1843. 3175

NOTE.—Maps nos. 6-10, 12-13 each accompanied by a Memoir.
No more published. The prospectus to this atlas, signed Justus Perthes, is found in "Kritischer wegweiser im gebiete der landkarten-kunde . . ." Dec. 31, 1832. v. 4 pp. 124-128.

Contents.

MAPS.

no. 2. Karte von China und Japan . . . 1843.
" 5. Karte von Syrien . . . 1835.
" 6. Arabia und das Nil-land . . . 1835.
" 7. General karte von Vorderindien . . . 1836.
" 8. Hinterindien . . . 1832.
" 9. Karte von Assam und seinen nachbar-ländern . . . 1834.
" 10. Spezial karte vom Himalaya . . . 1835.

**Berghaus, H.**—Continued.
- no. 11. Karte von der insel Sumatra . . . 1837.
- " 12. Reduzirte-karte vom Persischen golf. 1832.
- " 13. Reduzirte karte von den Philippinen und den Sulu inseln . . . 1832.
- " 14. Reduzirte karte vom Chinesischen meere; 1$^{stes}$ oder südliches blatt. 1835.
- " 15. Reduzirte karte vom Chinesischen meere. 2$^{tes}$ blatt, den nördlichen theil enthaltend. 1835.
- " 16. Die Chinesische küste der provinz Kuang-tung, zu beiden seiten des meridians von Macao . . . 1834.
- " 17. Reduzirte karte vom Sunda oder Borneo-meere und den strassen zur verbindung desselben mit dem Indischen und dem Chinesischen meere, der Macassarstrasse &c. zugleich als karte von Djava, den kleinen Sundainseln Celebes, &c. &c. 1835.
- " 19. Karte vom Ural gebirge. 1837.

TEXT.

- no. 6. Geo-hydrographisches memior zur erklärung und erläuterung der general-karte von Arabia und dem Nil-lande. 2 p. l., 128 pp. 4°. 1835.
- " 8. Geo-hydrographisches memoir zur erklärung und erläuterung der reduzirten karte von Hinterindien. 1 p. l., 94, [4] pp. 4°. 1832.
- " 9. Historisch-geographische beschreibung von Assam und seinen nachbarländern Bhotan, Djyntia, Katschhar, Munipur etc. Nebst bemerkungen über die nordlichen provinzen des Birma-reichs. 2 p. l., 178 pp. 4°. 1834.
- " 10. Geographisches memoir zur erklärung und erläuterung der spezialkarte vom Himalaya. 1 p. l., 42, [4] pp. 4°. 1836.
- " 12. Geo-hydrographisches memoir zur erklärung und erläuterung der reduzirten karte vom Persischen golf. 2 p. l., 50 pp. 4°. 1832.
- " 13. Geo-hydrographisches memoir zur erklärung und erläuterung der reduzirten karte von den Philippinen und den Sulu-inseln. 2 p. l., 114 pp. 4°. 1832.

**Dutreuil de Rhins, J. L.**

### 1889

L'Asie centrale (Thibet et régions limitrophes) Atlas.  cover-title, 25 maps on 14 sheets. fol. Paris, E. Leroux, 1889.   3176

Note.—To accompany work of same title.
The textbook contains a "Bibliographie géographique et régionale," pp. 25–77.

"Ouvrage publié sous les auspices du ministère de l'instruction publique et des beaux-arts (comité des travaux historiques et scientifiques, section de géographie historique et descriptive)"

### 1895-1898
**Monnier, M.**

Itinéraires à travers l'Asie levés au cours du voyage accompli durant les années 1895, 1896, 1897, 1898 sur l'initiative et pour le compte du journal Le Temps. Publiés sous le patronage de la société de géographie avec le concours du ministère de l'instruction publique et des beaux-arts.   cover-title, 2 p. l., 28 maps. fol. Paris, Plon-Nourrit & cie. [1900]   3177

## 1898

**Dutreuil de Rhins, J. L.**
Mission scientifique dans la Haute Asie. Atlas des cartes par [Joseph] F[ernand] Grenard. cover-title, 1 p. l., 25 maps on 34 l., 2 col. maps. fol. Paris, E. Leroux, 1898. 3178

NOTE.—To accompany work of same title.

"Ouvrage publié sous les auspices du ministère de l'instruction publique et des beaux-arts (comité des travaux historiques et scientifiques, section de géographie historique et descriptive)" The two colored maps are general maps of Central Asia, entitled, "Carte de l'Asie Centrale dressée d'après les travaux des explorateurs, modernes, les cartes chinoises et les renseignements d'indigènes, par F. Grenard, dessinée par J. Hansen. 1899;" and "Carte ethnographique et politique de l'Asie Centrale. 1899."

## 1907

**Bartholomew, J. G.**
Macmillan's atlas for China, Japan and the strait settlements by J. G. Bartholomew . . . 2 p. l., [2] l., 24 col. maps. 4°. London, Macmillan & co. [1907] 3179

NOTE.—Including maps of Europe, Africa, Australia, Australasia, North and South America.

# ARMENIA.

**Abich, W. H.**
Atlas zu den geologischen forschungen in den kaukasischen ländern von Herrman Abich. ii. theil. Geologie des armenischen hochlandes. Westhälfte. cover-title, 1 p. l., 3 col. maps, 6 pl. fol. [Wien, Hölder, 1882] 3180

NOTE.—To accompany his: Geologische forschungen in den kaukasischen ländern. pt. 2, Geologie des Armenischen hochlandes. Wien, Hölder, 1882.

# CASPIAN SEA.

## 1826

**Russia.** *Morskoe ministerstvo.*
Атласъ Каспійскаго моря сочиненъ при чертежной государственнаго адмиралтейскаго департамента съ описи и астрономическихъ наблюденій произведенныхъ съ 1809 по 1817 годъ, штурманомъ 8го класса и кавалеромъ Колодкинымъ. 6 p. l., 30 l. incl. 17 maps, 2 pl. fol. [С. Петербургъ] гравированъ и печатанъ при Морской типографіи, 1826 года. 3181

NOTE.—Translated title: Atlas of the Caspian sea, composed after the plans of the department of the imperial admiralty, from the surveys and astronomical observations made from 1809 to 1817 by the pilot of the 8th class, Kolodkin. [St. Petersburg] engraved and printed at the naval typography, 1826.

# CHINA.

## HISTORICAL.

**Oxenham, E. L.**
Historical atlas of the chinese empire. 2d ed. giving the original chinese maps with their english counterparts. 1 p. l., iv pp., 2 l., 45 maps. obl. 4? London, the royal geographical society, 1898. 3182

NOTE.—"La première édition (1887) contenait seulement les cartes chinoises, surtout d'après le 'Li Tai Yen Ko T'u.' La seconde met en regard les cartes dressées d'après les procédés européens et la nomenclature anglaise. Elle a paru après la mort de l'auteur (1896) par les soins de miss Edith M. Oxenham, aux frais de la société de géographie de Londres. La première carte remonte à Yu le grand, fondateur de la dynastie Hia (23º siècle av. J.-C.) La sixième carte, plus grande que les autres, correspond à l'épanouissement de la féodalité chinoise; c'est une réduction de la carte insérée par J. Legge dans le 5º vol. de ses 'Chinese classics.' L'introduction retrace brièvement l'histoire territoriale de la Chine." *cf.* Annales de géographie. 1899. v. 8, p. 16.

**Shigeno, Y., and Kawada, S.**
[Shina kyō-eki en-kaku dzu] 3 p. l., 19 col. maps. fol. [Tokyo, 1896] 3183

NOTE.—Translated title: The changed boundary lines of China.

## WARS.

**France.** *Dépôt de la guerre.*
Atlas de l'expédition de Chine en 1860 rédigé au dépôt de la guerre d'après les documents officiels étant directeur le général Blondel sous le ministère de s. e. le maréchal cte. Randon. 1861–62. 1 p. l., 8 maps. fol. Paris, Lemercier, 1861–1862. 3184

### CONTENTS

no. 1. Croquis pour servir à l'intelligence des opérations sur les côtes de Chine.
" 2. Prise de Canton 28 et 29 décembre 1857.
" 3. Occupation de Tien-Tsin . . . 26 mai 1859.
" 4. Plan du camp de Tché-fou.
" 5. Carte . . . du Peh-Tang-Ho et . . . du Peï-Ho.
" 6. Combat de Tchang-Kia-Ouang . . . 1860.
" 7. Combat de Pa-Li-Kiao . . . 1860.
" 8. Itinéraire de l'embouchure du Peï-Ho à Pekin.

**Sauvage, M. J. M.**
La guerre Sino-Japonaise. 1894-1895. 2 p. l., 7 maps. fol. Paris, L. Baudoin, 1897. 3185

NOTE.—To accompany his: La guerre Sino-Japonaise. 1894-1895.

### CONTENTS

no. 1. Théâtre des opérations de la guerre sino-japonaise.
" 2. Opérations en Corée de la 1ª armée japonaise. Bataille de Phyong-yang—Combat de Seikan.—Passage du Yalu.

no. 3. Bataille du Yalu.
" 4. Opérations contre Port Arthur.
" 5. Prise de Weï-Haï-Weï.
" 6. Opérations en Mandchourie.
" 7. Ile de Formose.

## GENERAL.

(Arranged chronologically)

### 1655

**Martini, M.**
Novvs atlas Sinensis . . . seren$^{mo}$ archiduci Leopoldo Gvilielmo Austriaco dedicatus. [Dutch ed.] 5 p. l., 232, xviii, 40 pp., 17 col. maps. fol. [Amsterdami, J. Blaeu, 1655] 3186

NOTE.—This is v. 6 of W. & J. Blaeu's Toonneel des aerdriicx, ofte nievwe atlas. Amsterdami, J. Blaeu, 1648-58. See title 460.
"Privilege" dated "Viennæ, 7 ianuarii, 1655." Text in dutch. At the end of the atlas are "Byvoeghsel van 't koninckryck Catay; door I. G.," xviii pp., and, "Historie van den Tartarischen oorlog," 40 pp.
The provincial maps were selected by Martini, from those in the "Kwang-yu-too," an atlas compiled by Choo Sze Pun, published about 1311-1312.

### 1655

Novvs atlas Sinensis . . . seren$^{mo}$ archiduci Leopoldo Gvilielmo Austriaco dedicatus. [French ed.] 5 p. l., 227 pp., 1 l., 17 col. maps. fol. [Amsterdami, J. Blaeu, 1655] 3187
[*With* Blaeu, W. *and* J. Le grand atlas, ov cosmographie Blaviane. fol. Amsterdam, J. Blaeu, 1667. v. 11, bk. 2]

NOTE.—Maps not included in the pagination; text, in french, on the obverse of each map, is paged. "Privilege" dated "Viennæ, 7 januarii, 1655." At the end of the atlas are "Histoire de la guerre de Tartarie," pp. 181-214, and, "Addition du royaume de Catay. Par Jacques Gool," pp. 215-227.

### 1655

Novvs atlas Sinensis . . . serenissimo archidvci Leopoldo Gvilielmo Avstriaco dedicatus. [Latin ed.] 6 p. l., 172 pp., 12 l., xii, 36 pp., 17 maps. fol. [Amsterdami, J. Blaeu, 1655] 3188

NOTE.—"Privilege" dated "Viennæ, 7 januarii, 1655." Backer states that this atlas forms the tenth part of Blaeu's atlas published at Amsterdam. Many of the maps contain the words "Exc. Ioannes Blaeu." At the end of the atlas are "De regno Catayo additamentum. Jacobus Golius lectori," xii pp., and, "De bello Tartarico historia," 36 pp.

### 1737

**Anville, J. B. B. d'.**
Nouvel atlas de la Chine, de la Tartarie chinoise, et du Thibet: contenant les cartes générales & particulières de ces pays, ainsi que la carte du royaume de Corée . . . Precédé d'une description de

**Anville, J. B. B. d'.**—Continued.
la Boucharie. 12 pp., 42 maps. fol. La Haye, H. Scheurleer, 1737. 3189

NOTE.—Editions were published at Paris by Desauche in 1737, and at Amsterdam in 1785 by B. Vlam.

"Cet atlas a été fait pour servir à la description de la Chine, etc., du p. Duhalde; il a été retouché depuis pour servir à la description générale de la Chine, par l'abbé Grozier. L'édition de la Haye, faite aussi pour accompagner, la réimpression de Duhalde, La Haye, 4 vol. in-4°, est tronquée et n'a que 42 cartes." Quérard. La France littéraire, 1827. v. 1. p. 75.

"Les cartes de détail lui ont été fournies par les jésuites, et il n'a fait que les mettre en état d'être gravées; mais les cartes générales . . . sont entièrement de lui. Il les a formées d'après celles de détail, en les assujettissant aux observations astronomiques, et il y a même ajouté, de son propre fonds, tout ce qui remplit le cadre de ces mêmes cartes, et qui ne lui avoit pas été fourni par les jésuites." *cf.* Jean Denis Barbié du Bocage. Notice des ouvrages de m. d'Anville. Paris, 1802, p. 84.

CONTENTS.

no. 1. Carte la plus générale et qui comprend la Chine, la Tartarie chinoise et le Thibet, 1734.
" 2. Carte générale de la Chine.
" 3. Province de Pe-Tche-Li.
" 4. " " Kiang-Nan.
" 5. " " Kiang-Si.
" 6. " " Fo-Kien.
" 7. " " Tche Kiang.
" 8. " " Hou-Quang.
" 9. " " Ho-Nan.
" 10. " " Chan-Tong.
" 11. " " Chan-Si.
" 12. " " Chen-Si.
" 13. " " Se-Tchuen.
" 14. " " Quang-Tong.
" 15. " " Quang-Si.
" 16. " " Yun-Nan.
" 17. " " Koei-Tcheou.
" 18. Carte générale de la Tartarie chinoise. 1732.
" 19–30. Tartarie chinoise. nos. I–XII.
" 31. Royaume de Corée.
" 32. Carte générale du Thibet ou Bout-Tan. 1733.
" 33–41. Thibet. nos. I–IX.
" 42. Carte des pays traversés par . . . Beerings depuis . . . Tobolsk jusqà Kamtschaka.

**1798**

**Staunton, G. L.**

An authentic account of an embassy from the king of Great Britain to the emperor of China . . . 2d ed. cor. Atlas. 10 maps, 34 pl. fol. [London, G. Nicol, 1798] 3190

NOTE.—No title-page to the atlas.

CONTENTS.

no. [ 1] A general chart . . . to shew the track of the Lion and Hindostan from England to the gulph of Pekin. 1796.
" [ 2] Sketches of the island of Santo Paulo including Turon harbour. By H. W. Parish and J. Barrow.
" [ 3] A chart of Cochin-China. 1793.
" [ 4] A chart from Turon-bay in Cochin-China to the Pei-Ho river. By J. Barrow. 1796.
" [ 5] A chart of the islands to the southward of Tchu-San. By T. Barrow. 1796.
" [ 6] A sketch . . . of the promontory of Shan-Tung. By J. Barrow. 1796.
" [ 7] Sketch of the Pay-Ho or White-river. By H. W. Parish. 1796.
" [ 8] A sketch of a journey from Zhe-Hol. By J. Barrow. 1796.
" [ 9] Sketch of a journey from Hang-Tchoo-Foo to Quang-Tchoo-Foo. By J. Barrow, 1796.
" [10] . . . City and harbour of Macao. 1796.

## 1885

**Richthofen, F. P. W.**, *freiherr* **von.**
Atlas von China. Orographische und geologische karten . . . zu des verfassers werk: China, ergebnisse eigener reisen und darauf gegründeter studien. Erste abtheilung: Das nördliche China (zum zweiten textband gehörig) 1 p. l., 20 pp., 27 col. maps. obl. fol. Berlin, D. Reimer, 1885.   3191
NOTE.—No more published.

CONTENTS.

no. 1-2. West-Shantung.—Inset: Der neue lauf des Gelben flusses . . . von Ney Elias (1868)
" 3-4. Ost-Shantung.
" 5-6. Liau-Tung.
" 7-8. Mukden.
" 9-10. Yung-Ping-Fu.
" 11-12. Peking.
" 13-14. Ta-Tung-Fu.
" 15-16. Tai-Yuĕn-Fu.
" 17-18. Ping-Yang-Fu.
" 19-20. Hŏnan.
" 21-22. Hsi-Ngan-Fu.
" 23-24. Tsin-Ling-Shan.
" 25-26. Pau-Ning-Fu.

## 1898

**Bretschneider, E.**
    Map of China. Supplementary maps.    cover-title, 5 maps on
6 l. fol. St. Petersburg, A. Iliin, 1898.                    3192
[*With his* Map of China. 2d ed. 1900]

CONTENTS.

no. 1. Part of northern Chili.
" 2. Mountains west of Peking.
" 3. Mid China and the Yantze river.
" 4. Great rivers of the Canton province.
" 5. Parts of Yunnan province.

## 1900

    Map of China. 2d rev. and enl. ed.    cover-title, 4 maps. fol.
St. Petersburg, A. Iliin, 1900.                             3193

## 1903–1904

**Willis, B.**
    Research in China, 1903–1904. Geographical and geological maps. cover-title, 1 p. l., 41 maps. fol. Washington, Carnegie institution, 1906.                                         3194
    NOTE.—On verso title-page, "Carnegie institution of Washington. Publication no. 54 (Atlas)"
    Several maps have photographic insets.
    To accompany work with same title, by Bailey Willis, Eliot Blackwelder and R. H. Sargent . . . 1907.

## 1908

**Stanford, E.**
    Atlas of the chinese empire containing separate maps of the eighteen provinces of China proper . . . and of the four great dependencies . . . together with an index to all the names on the maps and a list of all protestant mission stations. Specially prepared . . . for the China inland mission. xii, 16 pp., 22 (*i. e.* 23) maps. fol. London, Morgan & Scott, ltd. [1908]      3195
    NOTE.—Preface dated 1908.
    "In view of the fact that 1907 would be the centenary of protestant missionary effort in China, it was decided by the China inland mission, towards the close of 1905, to publish a new atlas of the chinese empire, this atlas to be accompanied by a book giving a geographical, historical, and missionary survey of each province and dependency of that empire. Through unexpected delays it was, however, found impossible . . . to have the maps ready in time, so the book entitled 'The chinese Empire' [edited by Marshall Broomhall; published by the China inland mission and Morgan & Scott, ltd.] was published first." *cf.* Preface.

Provinces.

## YANG-TSE-KIANG.
**Chevalier, S.**
Atlas du Haut Yang-tse, de I-Tchang Fou à P'ing-Chan Hien. 2 v. fol. [Shanghai, presse orientale, 1899] 3196

NOTE.—Collation: v. 1, cover-title, 2 p. l., 38 maps; v. 2, cover-title, 27 maps. Text in french and english.
At head of title, "Observatoire de Zi-Ka-Wei." *cf.* article by A. A. Fauvel, entitled, "L'atlas du Haut Yang-Tse du père Chevalier" in "Annales de géographie." 8°. Paris, A. Collin, 1900. v. 9, pp. 259–262.

# INDIA.

### CLIMATE.

**India.** *Meteorological department.*
Climatological atlas of India, published by the authority of the government of India under the direction of sir John Eliot . . . xxxii pp., 115 maps. fol. Edinburgh, J. Bartholomew & co. 1906. 3197

### GEOLOGICAL.
**Carter, H. J.**
Atlas to geological papers on western India, including Cutch, Sinde, and the s. e. coast of Arabia: to which is appended a summary of the geology of India . . . 1 p. l., 9 maps, 21 pl. obl. 4°. Bombay, for the government at the Bombay education society's press, 1857. 3198

### HISTORICAL.
**Joppen, C.**
Historical atlas of India, for the use of high schools, colleges, and private students. 2 p. l., 16 pp., 26 col. maps. 4°. London, New York [etc.] Longmans, Green & co. 1907. 3199

### STATISTICAL.

**India.** *Department of revenue and agriculture.*
Statistical atlas of India. 2d ed. 73 pl., 25 maps, 10 tab. obl. fol. Calcutta, superintendent of government printing, 1895. 3200

### GENERAL.

(Arranged chronologically)

**1780**
**Rennell, J.**
A Bengal atlas: containing maps of the theatre of war and commerce on that side of Hindoostan. 8 pp., 1 l., 13 maps. 4°. [London, J. Rennell] 1780. 3201

## 1893

**Constable, A., & co.**

Constable's hand atlas of India; a new series of sixty maps and plans prepared from ordnance and other surveys under direction of J. G. Bartholomew. xii, 85, 31 pp., 60 col. maps. 12°. London, A. Constable & co. 1893. 3202

## 1894

**Johnston, W. & A. K.**

Atlas of India containing sixteen maps & complete index, with an introduction by sir W. W. Hunter. 3 p. l., 38, 19 pp., 16 maps. fol. Edinburgh and London, W. & A. K. Johnston, 1894.
3203

NOTE.—Map no. 15 contains inset plans of Calcutta, Madras and Bombay.

### INDIAN OCEAN.

**India.** *Meteorological department.*

Meteorological atlas of the Indian seas prepared chiefly by W. L. Dallas under the direction of Gilbert T. Walker . . . director-general of observatories. viii pp., 22 l., [2], 37-39 pp., 36 col. charts. obl. 4°. Simla, meteorological department of the government of India, 1908. 3204

# INDO-CHINA.

## GENERAL.

(Arranged chronologically)

### 1863.

**Manen, L.**

Atlas de la Basse Cochinchine ou Nam-ki et du royaume de Cambodge ou de Khmer. 2 p. l., 19 maps. fol. Paris [dépot général de la marine, 1863] 3205

[France. Ministère de la marine et des colonies]

### 1866-1868.

**Garnier, F. M. J.**

Voyage d'exploration en Indo-Chine effectué pendant les années 1866, 1867 et 1868 par une commission française . . . et publié par les ordres du ministre de la marine . . . v. 1. Atlas. 2 p. l., 12 maps, 7 pl., 3 diagr. fol. Paris, Hachette & cie. 1873.
3206

NOTE.—Title of atlas accompanying this work varies: v. 1 . . '. Première partie, cartes et plans dressés par mm. Doudart de Lagrée, Francis Garnier et m. le lieutenant de vaisseau Delaporte. v. 2 . . . Album pittoresque.
Maps are by Francis Garnier, except no 7, by Louis Delaporte.

# JAPAN.

## CENSUS.

**Japan.** *Bureau of education.*
[Census atlas of Japan]   cover-title, [2] pp., 5 maps, 10 diagr.
4°.  [Tokio, San Kio Goshi & co. 1902]   3207
NOTE.—Letter-press in japanese.  Text on inside covers.

## SCHOOLS.

**Jukō Shiga.**
[Atlas of Japan for the use of the secondary schools]   1 p. l.,
[1] pp., 29 maps. 8°. [Tokio, 1902]   3208
NOTE.—Letter-press in japanese.

## GENERAL.

(Arranged chronologically)

### 1851

**Siebold, P. F. von.**
Atlas von land- und seekarten vom Japanischen reiche Dai-nippon, und dessen neben- und schutzländern Jezo mit den südlichen Kurilen, Krafto, Kôrai und den Liu-kiu-inseln . . . Nebst einer seekarte von der küste von China und der insel Formosa nach unausgegebenen holländischen seekarten vom 17. jahrhundert . . .   1 p. l., 12 maps on 10 sheets. fol. Berlin, S. Schropp & co. 1851.
3209
NOTE.—Sheets nos. 1, 9, 10, wanting.

### 1885–1887

**Hassenstein, B.**
Atlas von Japan. Sieben blätter im massstabe von 1: 1 000 000 und eine übersichtskarte im massstabe von 1: 7 500 000. 2 v. fol. Gotha, J. Perthes, 1885–1887.   3210
NOTE.—Collation: v. 1, cover-title, 2 p. l., 4 maps; v. 2, cover-title, 1 p. l., 4 maps.

### 1906

**Yoshida Otohiko.**
[Nihon Shō-gyō chi-dzu.—Business atlas of Japan]   2 p. l.,
45 pp., 12 col. maps. fol. [Tokyo, 1906]   3211
NOTE.—Title and letter-press in japanese.

# KOREA.

## HISTORICAL.

**Cordier, H.**
Description d'un atlas Sino-Coréen, manuscrit du British Museum . . . 2 p. l., 14 pp., 6 maps. fol. Paris, E. Leroux, 1896.
[Recueil de voyages, et de documents pour servir à l'histoire de la géographie depuis le XIII⁰ jusqu'à la fin du XVI⁰ siècle, publié sous la direction de . . . Ch. Schefer . . . et Henri Cordier. Section cartographique] 3212

NOTE.—Description of an XVIIIth century manuscript chinese atlas of Korea, supposed to have been written at Seoul in 1800. The author of this "description" reproduced only 6 maps—the original contained 15 maps. The facsimile maps bear the date 1894–5. In the explanatory text the names of places are in chinese characters, followed by a transliteration.

CONTENTS.

TEXT.

Liste générale des cartes, p. 3.—Japon, p. 3.—Iles Lieou K'ieou, p. 4.—Corée, p. 4.—Cartes des provinces, p. 5.—Cartes de Séoul et de ses environs, p. 5.—Carte du monde, pp. 6–12.—Carte de l'empire chinois, pp. 12–14.

MAPS.

no. 1. Carte des îles Lieou-Kieou et du Japon.
" 2. Carte de la Corée.
" 3. Carte de la province de Ham-Kyeng To.
" 4. Carte de la province de Hpyeng-An To.
" 5. Carte du monde.
" 6. Carte de l'empire Chinois.

---

# MALAY ARCHIPELAGO.

## GENERAL.

(Arranged chronologically)

### 1872

**Pijnappel, J.**
Atlas van de nederlansche bezittingen in Oost-Indië . . . Geheel op nieuw bewerkte uitgave . . . 3 p. l., 9 maps. fol. Amsterdam, P. N. van Kampen, 1872. 3213

### 1875

**Melvill van Carnbée, P.,** *and* **Versteeg, W. F.**
Algemeene atlas van nederlandsch Indië uit officieele bronnen en met goedkeuring van het gouvernement samengesteld . . . Tweede uitgave met verbeterkaarten. 1 p. l., 61 maps. fol. Leiden, G. Kolff [1875] 3214

NOTE.—Irregularly numbered.

## 1883-1885

**Stemfoort, J. W.,** *and* **Siethoff, J. J.**
Atlas der nederlandsche bezittingen in Oost-Indië, naar de nieuwste bronnen samengesteld . . . Gereproduceerd op last van het departement van koloniën . . . onder leiding van den directeur C. A. Eckstein. 1 p. l., 14 col. fold. maps, each 23¾ x 33½. ['s Gravenhaag] snelpersdruck der top. inrichting, 1883-1885. 3215

## 1900

**Gelder, W. van.**
Schoolatlas van nederlandsch Oost-Indië . . . 6. herziene druk. 2 p. l., 9 maps. fol. Groningen, J. B. Wolters, 1900. 3216

NOTE.—Map of dutch possessions in the East Indies on title.

CONTENTS.

no. 1. Overzichtskaart van Ned: Oost-Indië. 1:11.250.000.
" 2. Java. Taalkaart. 1:5.000.000.—Java. Bevolkingskaart. 1:5.000.000.— Java. Berg- en rivierkaart met aanduiding der grondgesteldheid. 1:2.500.000.—Java. Oorspronkelijkbosch.
" 3. West-Java. 1:1.250.000.
" 4. Midden Java. 1:1.250.000.
" 5. Oost Java en de residiente Bali en Lombok. 1:1.250.000.
" 6. Soematra. 1:5.000.000.
" 7. Borneo. 1:6.000.000.
" 8. De Ambonsche eilanden. 1:1.000.000.—De Minahasa. 1:1.250.000.— Zuidwest—Celebes. 1:1.250.000.—Bangka en belitoeng. 1:2.500.000.
" 9. Celebes, de Molukken en de residentie Timor. 1:5.625.000.

## 1901

**Dornseiffen, I.**
Atlas van nederlandsch Oost-West-Indië . . . 5<sup>de</sup> druk. Uitgave in 26 kaarten. 2 p. l., 26 maps. fol. Amsterdam, Seyffardt [1901] 3217

NOTE.—Map no. 2 contains an inset plan of "Batavia met de havenwerken."

CONTENTS.

no. 1. Overzichtskaart.
" 2-5. Java. 1:950.000. 1901.
" 6-17. Soematra, Bangka en de Riouw-Lingga archipel. 1:1.000.000. 1896-1900.
" 18. Borneo. 1:3.000.000. 1900.
" 19-21. Borneo en belitoeng. 1:1.000.000. 1899-1900.
" 22. Celebes, de kleine Soenda eilanden, enz. 1:4.000.000. 1899.
" 23. De Moluksche eilanden en Nieuw-Guinea. 1:4.200.000.
" 24. Amboina, de Oeliassers en de Banda eilanden.
" 25. De West-Indische eilanden. 1892.
" 26. Suriname. 1:1.250.000. 1900.—De omstreken van Paramaribo. 1:400.000.

## JAVA AND MADURA.

**Verbeek, R. D. M.,** *and* **Fennema, R.**
Geologische beschrijving van Java en Madoera . . . Uitgegeven op last van zijne excellentie den gouverneur-generaal van nederlandsch-Indië. Atlas . . . 2 p. l., 37 maps, 12 pl. obl. fol. Amsterdam, J. G. Stemler, 1896. 3218

NOTE.—To accompany work of the same title.

## SUMATRA.

### 1882

**Veth, D. D.**
Midden-Sumatra. Reizen en onderzoekingen der Sumatra-expeditie, uitgerust door het aardrijkskundig genootschap, 1877–1879.—Atlas bij de aardrijkskundige beschrijving. 1 p. l., 16 maps, 2 pl., 2 tab. fol. Leiden, E. J. Brill, 1882. 3219

### 1883

**Verbeek, R. D. M.**
Topographische en geologische beschrijving van een gedeelte van Sumatra's westkust. 2 v. fol. & 8°. Amsterdam, C. F. Stemler, 1883. 3220

NOTE.—To accompany work of same title.
[v. 1] cover-title, 15 sheets incl. 6 maps, 2 pl.; [v. 2], cover-title, 1 l., 7 maps, 17 pl.
Maps irregularly numbered. v. 2 contains a plan of Padang.

# PALESTINE.

### BIBLICAL.

**Morse, S. E.**
The cerographic bible atlas. cover-title, 5 maps. fol. New York, S. E. Morse & co. 1844. 3221

NOTE.—Copyrighted 1843. Quarterly supplement to the New York observer.

The cerographic bible atlas. cover-title, 5 maps. fol. New York, S. E. Morse & co. 1845. 3222
[*With* Morse, S. E., *and* Breese, S. The cerographic atlas of the United States. fol. New York, S. E. Morse, 1842. Title 1383]

NOTE.—Copyrighted 1843. Quarterly supplement to the New York observer.

# PHILIPPINE ISLANDS.

## GENERAL.

(Arranged chronologically)

### 1846

**Mallat de Bassilan, J.**

Les Philippines, histoire, géographie, moeurs, agriculture, industrie et commerce des colonies espagnoles dans l'Océanie. Atlas. 2 p. l., [11] l. incl. 8 maps, 5 pl. fol. Paris, A. Bertrand [1846]

3223

NOTE.—To accompany work in 2 v. having same title. Besides the maps, this atlas contains colored plates illustrating costumes of the Philippine inhabitants, and a filipino song with music.
Maps engraved by H. Bonvalet. A review of this work by Gabriel Lafond de Lurcy, is found in Bulletin de la Société de géographie, 3ᵉ série. Paris. 1846. v. 6, pp. 151-177.

"Mr. Mallat paya même de sa personne lors de la prise de possession [de l'île Bassilan], mais des circonstances politiques motivèrent l'abandon de Bassilan; il fut néanmoins autorisé, à cause de sa belle conduite à ajouter le nom de cette île au sien." *cf.* "notice sur m. Mallat de Bassilan" . . . par E. Cortambert, in Bulletin de la société de géographie. 5ᵉ série. Paris, 1863. v. 5, pp. 238-9.

*List of maps.*

no. 1. Carte des îles Philippines pour servir à l'intelligence de l'ouvrage sur les possessions espagnoles dans l'océanie.
" 2. Plan de la forteresse de Samboanga.
" 3. Plan géométrique de l'embouchure de Sᵗ Bernardino.
" 4. Plan du port de Sorsogon.
" 5. Plan du port de Palapa.
" 6. Plan de la baie de Bongo.
" 7. Plan de la baie de Manille.
" 8. Plan de Manille (with index)

### 1900

**Manila.** *Observatorio.*

Islas Filipinas. 30 col. mss. maps, each 13½ x 11½ inches. 4⁰. [1900]

3224

NOTE.—In manuscript. Compiled by the jesuit fathers in the Philippine islands, under the direction of rev. José Algue, director of the Manila observatory. Published in atlas form in 1900 by the U. S. coast and geodetic survey, under the title, "Atlas of the Philippine Islands. Special publication no. 3." See title 3225.
Presented by the U. S. coast and geodetic survey to the Library of Congress.

CONTENTS.

no. 1. Pacífico.
" 2. Mapa general.
" 3. " etnográfico.
" 4. " orográfico.

**Manila.** *Observatorio*—Continued.
- no. 5. Estaciones meteorológico-seísmicas.
- " 6. Distribución de temblores.
- " 7-11. Luzón.
- " 12. Infanta y Polillo.
- " 13. Batanes y Babuyanes.
- " 14. Catanduanes.
- " 15. Mindoro.
- " 16. Romblón, Tablas y Sibuyan.
- " 17. Masbate y Ticao.
- " 18. Samar.
- " 19. Leyte.
- " 20. Panay.
- " 21. Negros.
- " 22. Cebu.
- " 23. Bohol.
- " 24. Norte de Paragua.
- " 25. Sur de Paragua, Balabac.
- " 26. Mindanao, Joló.
- " 27. Mindanao oriental.
- " 28. Mindanao occidental, Joló.
- " 29. Bahía de Manila.
- " 30. Estrecho de S. Juanico.

**1900**

**Manila.** *Observatorio*.

Atlas de Filipinas. Colección de 30 mapas. Trabajados por delineantes filipinos bajo la dirección del p. José Algué, director del observatorio de Manila. 1899. 1 p. l., 24 pp., 30 maps. fol. Washington, government printing office, 1900. 3225
[United States. Treasury department. Coast and geodetic survey. Special publication no. 3]

NOTE.—For contents see manuscript original, title 3224.

**1900**

**Columbian correspondence college,** *Washington, D. C.*

The columbian atlas of two wars, containing large scale maps of the Philippine Islands and South Africa. cover-title, 16 pp., 1 l., incl. 10 maps. fol. Washington, the columbian correspondence college [1900] 3226

# SIBERIA.

## RIVERS.

### AMOOR.

**Russia.** *Gidrograficheskiĭ departament.*

Атласъ устья рѣки Амура, составленный со съемокъ 1855-1863 годовъ, при Гидрографическомъ департаментѣ. 2 p. l., 4 maps. obl. fol. [St. Petersburg] 1864.
3227

NOTE.—Translated title: Atlas of the mouth of the Amoor river prepared on the basis of the surveys of 1855-1863 by the hydrographic department.

### YENISEI.

**Russia.** *Ministerstvo morskoe. Glavnoe gidrograficheskoe upravlenīe.*

Атласъ рѣки Енисея отъ г. Енисейска до Енисейскаго залива. Составленъ гидрографическою экспедицiею подъ начальствомъ подполковника Вилькицкаго. Изданiе Главнаго гидрографическаго управленiя Морского министерства. 4 p. l., 10 maps. fol. С.-Петербургъ, М. Д. Ломковскiй Думская улица д. п. 5., 1900.
3228

NOTE.—Translated title: Atlas of the Yenisei river from the city of Yeniseisk to the Yenisei bay. Prepared by the hydrographic expedition of lieut. col. Vilkitskiĭ. Published by the chief hydrographic bureau of the war department. Contains plan of the city of Yeniseisk (no. 9): "планъ города енисейска." *cf.* Annales de géographie. Bibliographie, 1900. Paris, 1901, no. 523, p. 184 and Petermann's mitteilungen. Gotha, 1897, v. 43, p. 118: "Über die arbeiten der hydrographischen expedition im jahre 1895 nach den flüssen Jenissei, Ob und dem Eismeer. Bericht von A. A. Wilkizki."

# AFRICA.

## GENERAL.

(Arranged chronologically)

### 1700

**Ablancourt, N. P. d'.**

Vervolg van de neptunus, of zee atlas van de nieuwe zee-kaarten; opgenomen door uitdrukkelyke order der koningen van Portugaal, onder wiens regeeringe 't geheel Afrika &c. ontdekt is: en in't light gebraght door de sorge van wylen d'heer d'Ablancourt. Waar in men ziet de naauwkeurige beschryving van alle de kusten van de waereld, de naauwte van Gilbraltar, de ocean of Noord zee van Ethiopen, van de Oost en West-Indische Zee, &c: mitsgaders waar in ook naauwkeuriglyk zyn aangeteekend de streeken die men moet houden; de banken, klippen, plaaten, diepten, en in 't algemeen alles wat de zeevaart betreft. Altemaal gemaakt op de waarneemingen en d'ondervinding des gaauwste ingenieurs en stuurlieden. 1 p. l., 6 pp., 55 l., incl. 33 maps. fol. Amsterdam, P. Mortier, 1700.
3229

**Ablancourt, N. P. d'**—Continued.
[*With* Le Neptune François. 3 v. in 1. fol. Amsterdam, P. Mortier, 1693-1700. v. 3]
NOTE.—For bibliographical note see title 517.

## 1766

**English, The, pilot.** Part v. Describing the seacoast, capes, headlands, bays, roads, harbours, rivers and ports; with the exact appearances and representations of the most principal marks, lands, &c. together with the soundings, sands, shoals, rocks and dangers on the west-coast of Africa: from the straits of Gibralter to the cape of Good Hope, viz. the coasts of Barbary, Gualta, Arguin, Hoden, Jalofi, Gambia, Melli, Benni, Malegete, Grain, Ivory, or Tooth, Band, Quaqua and Gold coast, Bight of Bennin, Biafra, Gabon, Loango, Congo, Angola, Cimbebas and Caffrary: with the adjacent islands of the Canary, Madera and those off of Cape Verde. Shewing the courses and distances from one place to another: the setting of the tides and currents; the ebbing and flowing of the sea, with many other things useful in the art of navigation. Done according to the best observations and informations, with the late improvements of several able navigators of our own and other nations. 7th ed. with new additions. 1 p. l., 42 pp., 19 maps. fol. London, for J. Mount & T. Page, 1766. 3230

## 1781

**Après de Mannevillette, J. B. N. D. d'.**
Supplément au Neptune oriental. 7 p. l., 18 maps. fol. Paris, Demonville, 1781. 3231
NOTE.—Several maps relate to the coasts of Africa. See also titles 3163, 3165-3168.

## 1801

**Laurie, R.,** *and* **Whittle, J.,** *& others.*
The african pilot; being a collection of new and accurate charts, on a large scale, of the coasts, islands and harbours of Africa; from the straits of Gibraltar to Cape Negro, including also the Atlantic and southern oceans, on twenty-four sheets. Compiled from the draughts, observations, journals &c. of messrs. Robert Norris, William Woodville, Archibald Dalzel, and George Maxwell, of Liverpool, &c. &c. under their inspection. The whole interspersed with numerous appearances of land, &c. &c. 1 p. l., 14 fold. maps. fol. London, R. Laurie & J. Whittle, 1801. 3232
NOTE.—The following map relates to America:
no. 1. A new and correct chart . . . of the Atlantic or Western ocean . . . 1794.

### 1816

The african pilot; being a collection of new and accurate charts, on a large scale, of the coasts, islands, and harbours of Africa, from the straits of Gibraltar to Cape Negro; including also the Atlantic and Southern oceans. On twenty-four sheets. Compiled from the draughts, observations, journals, etc. of messrs. Robert Norris, William Woodville, Archibald Dalzel, and George Maxwell, of Liverpool, etc. etc. and under their inspection. 1 p. l., 14 maps on 13 sheets. fol. London, R. Laurie & J. Whittle [1816]

3233

NOTE.—The following map refers to America:

no. 1-2. A new and correct chart, exhibiting the whole of the Atlantic or Western ocean, and the greatest part of the Ethiopic or Southern ocean, wherein the respective coasts of Europe, Africa, and of America North and South, with all the islands and dangers in the two seas are carefully described. 2 sheets.

### 1852

**Kerhallet, C. M. P. de.**
Manuel de la navigation à la côte occidentale d'Afrique. Vues de côtes. 3 p. l., 57 pl. 4°. Paris, dépôt général de la marine, 1852.

3234

### 1886-1900

**France.** *Ministère de la guerre. Service géographique de l'armée.*
Carte de l'Afrique à l'échelle du 2.000.000°. 1 p. l., 1 map on 62 sheets. fol. [Paris, service géographique de l'armée, 1886-1900]

3235

NOTE.—As stated in a note at the foot of the index map, R. de Lannoy de Bissy commenced this map in 1875, and the "dépôt de la guerre" began its publication in 1881.

### 1897-1898

**France.** *Ministère des colonies. Service géographique des colonies.*
Mission de Bonchamps, de Djibouti au Nil Blanc, à travers l'Éthiopie méridionale et les pays Gallas . . . Itinéraire en 14 feuilles, au 1:200.000, d'après les travaux de mrs. L. Bartholin, Ch. Michel, Faivre et M. Potter, dressé par Ch. Michel, second de la mission . . . 1897-1898.    cover-title, 1 index map, 14 maps. fol. Paris, H. Barrère [1900]

3236

NOTE.—For information concerning this mission, see Annales de géographie. Dixième bibliographie géographique annuelle. 1900. pp. 250-251, also La Géographie, 1900. v. 2, pp. 25-40: "Les résultats géographiques de la mission de Bonchamps, par m. Charles Michel," and Société de géographie. Bulletin. Paris, 1898, v. 19, pp. 404-431: "Une mission vers le Nil Blanc, par C. de Bonchamps."

## 1899

**Bartholomew, J. C.**
Atlas for South African schools. A new series of physical and political maps . . . 2d & enl. ed. 2 p. l., 47 col. maps, 1 col. pl. fol. London, New York [etc.] T. Nelson & sons [1899]
3237

## 1903

**South Africa** [ *Weekly journal*]
The South Africa atlas of the Rand being a complete map of the Witwatersrand goldfields and eastern extensions, in thirteen convenient indexed sections with key map. 3 p. l., 13 maps. nar. 8°. London, offices of "South Africa," 1903.
3238

## EGYPT.

### HISTORICAL.

**Egypt exploration fund.**
An atlas of ancient Egypt. With complete index, geographical and historical notes, biblical references, etc. Special publication of the Egypt exploration fund. 2d ed., rev. 3 p. l., 22 pp., 3 l., xi pp., 8 maps. 4°. London, K. Paul, Trench, Trübner & co. 1894.
[Occasional publications]
3239

## TUNIS.

### ARCHÆOLOGICAL.

**France.** *Ministère de l'instruction publique et des beaux-arts.*
Atlas archéologique de la Tunisie. Edition spéciale des cartes topographiques publiées par le ministère de la guerre. Accompagnée d'un texte explicatif par mm. E. Babelon, R. Cagnat, S. Reinach. liv. 1–11. fol. Paris, E. Leroux, 1892–1907. 3240
NOTE.—All published to date.
"La commission de l'Afrique du Nord a entrepris sous les auspices du ministère de l'instruction publique l'inventaire archéologique de l'Algérie et de la Tunisie. Les cartes dont se composera le présent recueil sont les cartes topographiques au 1: 50,000 publiées par le ministère de la guerre avec une addition importante: l'indication de toutes les ruines de la province romaine d'Afrique" . . .
"L'Atlas archéologique de la Tunisie est publié en livraisons de quatre cartes."
*cf.* Annales de géographie. Bibliographie, 1893, Paris, 1894. p. 35.

# OCEANICA.

## GENERAL.

(Arranged chronologically)

### 1769-1773

**Hawkesworth, J.**
An account of the voyages undertaken by the order of his present majesty for making discoveries in the Southern hemisphere and successively performed by commodore Byron, capt. Wallis, capt. Carteret, and capt. Cook in the Dolphin, the Swallow and the Endeavour . . . Atlas. 23 maps, 29 pl. fol. London . . . for W. Strahan & T. Cadell, 1773. 3241

NOTE.—Atlas without title-page accompanying the "Account of the voyages," contains charts and plans by lieut. J. Cook, dated 1769-1700. For contents see title 642.

Several maps, without signature, were published in 1773.

### 1826-1827

**Krusenstern, A. J. von.**
Атласъ южнаго моря сочиненный контръ адмираломъ Крузенштерномъ . . . 8 p. l., 34 maps. fol. Санктпетербургъ, 1826-[1827] 3242

NOTE.—French title, on the 4th p. l., reads: "Atlas de l'océan Pacifique dressé par m. de Krusenstern . . . S! Petersbourg, 1827."
Maps corrected to 1835 and 1838.
Accompanying this work are the following volumes of descriptive text, entitled: Recueil de mémoires hydrographiques, pour servir d'analyse et d'explication à l'atlas de l'océan Pacifique. 3 v. 4°. Saint-Pétersbourg, imp. du département de l'instruction publique, 1824-27, 1835.
v. 3. (Supplémens) 1835, has imprint: imprimerie de A. Pluchart.

CONTENTS.

*Maps.*

no. 1. Carte générale de l'océan Pacifique. 1838.
" 2. Carte de la Nouvelle Guinée et du détroit de Torrès.—Plan du port Doreri. 1835.
" 3. Carte de la mer du Corail. 1838.
" 4. Carte . . . de la N^le Galles méridionale.—Plan du port Jackson. 1835.
" 5. Carte de la Terre Van Diemen et du détroit de Bass.—Plan du port Philip. 1835.
" 6. Carte des iles de l'Amirauté.—Carte de la Nouvelle Irlande.— . . . Port Gower. 1835.
" 7. Carte . . . de la Nouvelle Bretagne.— . . . Port Hunter.—Carte . . . de Santa Cruz.— . . . Anse Byron. 1835.
" 8. Carte . . . de la Louisiade.—Carte . . . de Mendana.— . . . Port Chichagoff.
" 9. Carte . . . des iles de Salomon.— . . . Baie Choiseuil.— . . . Port Praslin. 1835.
" 10. Carte . . . des nouv^les Hebrides.— . . . Port de la Resolution. 1835.
" 11. Carte de la Nouvelle Calédonie.— . . . Port S^t. Vincent. 1835.

**Krusenstern, A. J. v.**—Continued.
no. 12. Carte de la N^lo. Zélande, et du détroit de Cook.—Carte . . . du détroit de Cook. 1835.
" 13. Carte . . . des isles des Amis.—Rade del Refugio.—Port Valdes.— Carte . . . des isles de la Société.— . . . Mattavay.— . . . Port Taloo. 1835.
" 14. Carte des isles Fidji.— . . . Sandal wood bay.—Carte des isles des navigateurs.— . . . Anse du massacre. 1835.
" 15. Carte . . . des isles Bases. 1838.
" 16. Carte générade de l'océan Pacifique; hémisphère boréal. 1838.
" 17. Carte . . . des isles Kodiack et du détroit de Chélighoff. — Baie Tschiniatskoy. 1835.
" 18. Carte des isles Aléutiennes.— . . . Baie du Massacre. 1835.
" 19. Carte des isles Aléutiennes, feuille II.— . . . Baie du Capitaine sur la côte . . . de l'isle Ounalashka.— . . . Isle Joann Bogosloff. 1835.
" 20. Carte . . . d'Aliaska et de la baie de Bristol. 1835.
" 21. Carte . . . de Corée. 1835.
" 22. Carte . . . du Japon.— . . . Port de Nangasaki. 1835.
" 23. Carte des isles Kouriles. 1835.
" 24. Carte de l'isle Jesso. 1835.
" 25. Carte . . . de Saghalin. 1835.
" 26. Carte . . . de Formose et de la côte sud-est de la Chine. 1835.
" 27. Carte des isles Liqueo et Madjicosimah.—Carte . . . des isles Bashee et Babuyanes. 1835.
" 28. Carte des isles Sandwich.— . . . Port Hanabooroo. 1835.
" 29. Carte . . . des isles Mariannes.— . . . Port la Caldera de Apra. 1835.
" 30. Carte . . . des isles Carolines, feuille I.— . . . Carte . . . des isles Pellew. 1835.
" 31. Carte . . . des isles Carolines, feuille II. 1835.
" 32. Carte . . . des isles Carolines, feuille III. 1835.
" 33. Carte . . . des isles Marshall. 1835.
" 34. Carte . . . des isles Gallapagos.—Carte . . . des isles Gilbert. 1835.

*Text.*
v. 1—Avant-propos.
Avertissement.
Introduction. Mémoire sur les vents et courans dans l'océan Pacifique . . .
Mémoire pour servir d'analyse . . . à la carte générale de la partie australe de l'océan Pacifique.
Mémoire sur la carte de la Nouvelle-Guinée et du détroit de Torrès.
Mémoire sur la carte de la mer du Corail.
Mémoire sur la carte de la partie sud-est de la Nouvelle-Galles méridionale.
Mémoire sur la carte de la terre de Van Diemen et du détroit de Bass.
Mémoire sur la carte des isles de l'Amirauté.
" " " " de l'isle de la Nouvelle-Irlande.
" " " " " " " Nouvelle-Bretagne.
" " " " de l'archipel de la Louisiade.
" " une carte . . . de l'archipel des isles de Salomon.
" " la carte de l'archipel de Santa Cruz.
" " " " " des Nouvelles-Hébrides.
" " " " de l'isle de la Nouvelle-Calédonie.
" " " " " de la Nouvelle-Zélande et du détroit de Cook.

Mémoire sur la carte de l'archipel des isles des Amis.
" " " " " " " " de Fidjie.
" " " " " " " " de la Société.
" " " " " " " " des Navigateurs.
" " " " " " " de Mendana.
" , " " " " " des isles Basses.
Note relativement aux mémoires hydrographiques de l'amiral Espinosa.

Supplements.

I. Supplément aux mémoires.
II. Tableau de latitudes et longitudes des points principaux dans la partie australe de l'océan Pacifique.
III. Articles additionnels.
IV. Index alphabétique.
V. 2—Avant propros.
Mémoire pour servir d'analyse . . . à la carte gérérale de la partie boréale de l'océan Pacifique.
Mémoire sur la carte de l'archipel des isles Kodiack.
" " " " des isles Aléoutiennes.
" " " " de la presqu'isle d'Aliaska.
" " " " " " de Corée.
" " " " des isles du Japon.
" " " " " " Kouriles.
" " " " de l'isle de Jesso.
" " " " " la presqu'isle de Saghalin.
" " " " " l'isle de Formose . . .
" " " " des isles Liqueo et Madjicosimah.
" " " " " isles de Bashee et de Babuyanes.
" " " " de l'archipel des isles de Sandwich
" " " " des isles Mariannes.
" " " " " " Carolines.
" " " " " " Marshall.
" " " " " " Gilbert.
" " " " " " Gallapagos.
Tableau des latitudes et longitudes des points principaux dans la partie boréale de l'océan Pacifique.
Index alphabétique.
Suppléments aux mémoires de l'hémisphère Austral.
Index alphabétique des suppléments.
Additions.
Erreurs typographiques.
V. 3—Avertissement.
Supplément au mémoire sur la carte générale de la partie australe de l'Océan pacifique.
Supplément au mémoire sur la carte de la Nouvelle-Guinée.
" " " " " " " " mer de Corail.
" " " " " " " " . . . Nouvelle-Galles méridionale.
" " " " " " " l'île de Van Diemen.
" " " " " " des îles de l'Amirauté.
" " " " " " de la Nouvelle-Irlande.
" " " " " " " Nouvelle-Bretagne.

**Krusenstern, A. J. v.**—Continued.
  Supplément au mémoire sur la carte de l'archipel de Santa-Cruz.
  " " " " " " des îles Mendana.
  " " " " " " de l'archipel des îles Salomon.
  " " " " " " des Nouvelles-Hébrides.
  " " " " " " de la Louisiade.
  " " " " " " " " Nouvelle-Zélande.
  " " " " " " " " Nouvelle-Calédonie.
  " " " " " " des îles des Amis.
  " " " " " " " " Fidjie.
  " " " " " " " " de la Société.
  " " " " " " " " des Navigateurs.
  " " " " " " " " Basses.
  " " " " " " générale de la partie boréale de l'océan Pacifique.
  " " " " " " de l'île Kodiack.
  " " " " " " des îles Aléoutiennes.
  " " " " " " de la presqu'île d'Aliaska.
  " " " " " " " " " de Saghalin.
  " " " " " " des îles Bashee et Babuyanes.
  " " " " l'île Formose . . .
  " " " " la carte des îles Carolines.
  " " " " " " " " Marshall.
  " " " " " " " " Gilbert.
  " " " " " " " " Gallapagos.
  Tableau des îles problématiques.
  Remarques sur les cartes de Norie et Arrowsmith.
  Table des articles.

### 1824–1826

**Bougainville, H. Y. P. P. de.**
  Journal de la navigation autour du globe de la frégate la Thétis et de la corvette l'Espérance pendant les années 1824, 1825 et 1826 publié par ordre du roi sous les auspices du département de la marine. Atlas. 2 p. l., 9 maps on 14 l., 49 pl. fol. Paris, A. Bertrand, 1837. 3243
  NOTE.—See title 204 for contents.

### 1837–1840

**Dumont d'Urville, J. S. C.**
  Voyage au pole Sud et dans l'Océanie sur les corvettes l'Astrolabe et Zélée, exécuté par ordre du roi pendant les années 1837, 1838, 1839, 1840, sous le commandement de m. J. Dumont d'Urville . . . publié par ordonnance de sa majesté . . . Atlas. 2 p. l., 57 maps on 95 l. fol. Paris, Gide, 1842–1848. 3244
  NOTE.—Atlas to accompany "La partie hydrographique" du "Voyage au pole Sud" . . .
  Title varies: . . . Atlas hydrographique par m. C. A. Vincendon-Dumoulin . . . Publié sous le ministère de m. le duc de Montebello . . . Dépôt général de la marine, 1847. Gravé par Hacq.

A collection of maps and charts by various hydrographers, including: Vincendon-Dumoulin, Boyer, Duroch, Coupvent-Desbois, Marescot and Tardy de Montravel.

Maps have insets which are reproductions from Barnett, Duranty, Fisher, Johnson, King, Lottin, Laperouse and others, dated 1826–1840.

Maps dated 1838–1847.

Original numbers of charts from hydrographic office follow the contents, in numerical arrangement.

CONTENTS.

no. 1–4 (1092–1095) Carte générale de l'océan Pacifique . . . 1845.
" 5 (1060) Carte des mer du cap Horn . . . 1843.
" 6 (1061) Plan du port Famine et de la baie Voces . . .—Plan de la baie Saint Nicholas . . . par m. Duroch . . . 1838.—Plan de la baie Fortescue . . . par m. Gourdin . . . 1837.—Plan de la baie de Cordés et du port San Miguel . . . par m. Marescot.—Plan du port des Trois Passes . . . par Tardy de Montravel . . . 1837.—Plan du mouillage . . . du havre Peckett . . . par m. Marescot . . . 1838.
" 7 (884) Carte contenant les routes . . . dans les régions Australes . . .— Inset: Plan des routes de l'Astrolabe dans la banquise . . .
" 8 (885) Carte d'une portion des terres Australes . . .
" 9 (1062) Plan de la baie Matavaï . . . par m. Gourdin . . .—Carte des îles St. Ambroise et St. Félix . . .—Carte de l'île Juan-Fernandez . . .— Plan de la baie San Juan-Bautista . . . par m. Gourdin . . .
" 10 (1063) Carte du groupe des îles Manga-Reva (archipel Pomotou) . . .
" 11 (1071) Carte de l'île Ireland et de l'île Raraka . . .—Carte de l'île Tiokea et de l'île Oura . . .—Carte des îles Wittgenstein, de l'île Elizabeth et de l'île Greig . . .—Carte de l'île Serles . . .—Carte de l'île Clermont-Tonnerre . . .—Carte de l'île Scilly . . .—Carte de l'île Mopelia . . .
" 12 (1064) Plan du port Taï-Hoa (Tchichakoff) sur l'île Nouka-Hiva par m. Tardy-de-Montravel . . .—Plan de la baie Anna-Maria . . . par m. Marescot . . .
" 13 (1072) Carte des îles Samoa . . .—Insets: Plan du port Apia . . . par m. m. Pavin de Lafarge . . . et de Flotte . . .—Plan d'une partie de l'île Tou-Tou-Ila . . .
" 14 (1096) Plan du havre de Vavao . . . par m. Duroch . . .—Carte du groupe Hafoulou-Hou . . .—Inset: Plan du mouillage de Vavao . . . par m. m. de Champeaux et Duranty . . .
" 15 (1073) Carte du groupe des îles Hapaï . . .—Inset: Plan du mouillage de Leïouga . . . par m. Laîond et m. Boyer . . .
" 16 (1074) Carte de l'archipel Viti . . .—Inset: Plan du port Lebouka, île Obalaou . . . par m. Coupvent-Desbois . . .
" 17 (1075) Carte des îles Banks (Mélanésie) . . .
" 18 (1075) " " " Santa Cruz . . .
" 19 (913) " d'une partie des îles Salomon . . .—Insets: Plan du havre de l'Astrolabe . . . par m. Marescot . . .—Carte de la baie des Mille Vaisseaux . . .
" 20 (1077) Carte des îles Vertes, de l'île St. Jean et de l'île Caen . . .— Carte de l'île Gouap . . .—Carte du groupe Louasap . . .—Carte du groupe Nougouor . . .—Carte du groupe des îles Abgarris . . .— Carte de la partie orientale des îles Pelew . . .

**Dumont d'Urville, J. S. C.**—Continued.

no. 21 (1078) Carte des îles Rouk . . .—Inset: Plan du mouillage de l'île Tsis . . . par m. m. Gervaize et Boyer . . .
" 22 (1079) Carte des îles situées entre Mindanao et Célèbes . . .—Inset: Plan du mouillage de Ternate par m. m. Thanaron et de Flote . . .
" 23 (1080) Carte de l'île Ceram, de l'île Bourou et des îles voisines . . .— Insets: Plan de la baie Hatiling . . .—Plan de la baie Sannana . . .— Plan du mouillage des îles Banda . . .—Plan de la baie Warou . . .
" 24 (1081) Carte de la côte sud-ouest de la Nouvelle-Guinée . . .—Inset: Plan du port Dubus (Baie Triton) . . . par Tardy-de-Montravel . . .
" 25 (1082) Plan du canal Bowen et de la baie Rafles . . . par m. m. Coupvent-Desbois . . . et Gourdin . . .
" 26 (1083) Carte des îles Arrou (Malaisie) . . .—Inset: Plan du havre Dobo . . . par m. Duroch . . .
" 27 (1084) Carte de la partie méridionale de l'île Célèbes (Malaisie) . . .— Inset: Plan de la rade de Makassar . . . par m. Pavin de Lafarge . . .
" 28 (1097) Carte du détroit de Banca (Malaisie)
" 29 (1098) Routes des corvettes l'Astrolabe et la Zélée dans les détroits de Durion et de Sinchapour . . .—Inset: Routes . . . près des îles Sinkep.
" 30 (1099) Carte d'une partie de la côte nord de Bornéo et des îles Balambangan et Banguey . . .—Carte d'une partie de la côte occidentale de Bornéo . . .—Routes . . . près des îles Kagayan-Solo . . .
" 31 (1100) Carte de l'archipel Solo . . .—Insets: Plan du mouillage de Samboangang . . . par m. Coupvent-Desbois . . .—Plan de la rade de Soog (île Solo) . . . par m. Duroch . . .
" 32 (1085) Carte de la partie sud-est de la côte de l'île Bornéo . . .
" 33 (1086) Carte de la partie nord-ouest de l'île Java . . .—Inset: Carte d'une partie de la côte de Java . . .
" 34 (914) Carte des explorations . . . dans les régions circum-polaires . . .
" 35 (915) Carte de la terre Adélie . . .—Inset: Croquis plan des rochers de la pointe Géologie.
" 36 (1087) Plan du havre Sarah's-Bosom (îles Auckland) . . .—Inset: Carte des îles Auckland . . .
" 37 (1088) Carte de la partie orientale des îles Tavaï-Pounamou et Stewart (Nouvelle Zélande) . . .—Insets: Plan du havre Otago . . . par m. Duroch . . .—Carte des îles Snares . . .—Plan du havre Peraki . . . par m. Boyer . . .
" 38 (1065) Carte générale de la Nouvelle-Zélande . . .—Insets: Port Akaroa . . .—Havre Tutukaka et rivière Nongodo . . .—Canal Tory . . .— Port Gore . . .—Havre Kiahow . . .—Baie Tauranga . . .—Havre Waï-Temata . . .—Port Nicholson . . .—Baies de Tokolabo et de Koko-Rarata . . .—Baie des îles . . .—Havre Otago . . .—Baie Wangaroa . . .—Rade de Rouabouki . . .—Anse d'Ubraye . . .— Anse Fournier . . .—Anse des Torrents . . .—Port Hardy . . .— Rivière Shoukianga . . .—Port Underwoud . . .—Anse de l'Astrolabe . . .—Baie Houa-Houa . . .
" 39 (1089) Carte des îles Loyalty . . .
" 40 (1090) Carte de la Louisiade et de la côte sud-est de la Nouvelle Guinée . . .
" 41 (1091) Carte de la route . . . à travers le détroit de Torrès . . .— Inset: Plan du canal Mauvais . . . par m. m. Duroch et Tardy-de-Montravel . . .

no. 42 (1132) Carte de la partie sud-ouest de l'ile Timor . . .
" 43 (1148) Carte des îles South Orkney, Sandwich, Géorgie et d'une partie des terres Australes . . .
" 44 (1149) Carte des îles Mariannes et des terres environnantes . . .
" 45 (1150) Carte des îles situées dans l'océan Pacifique entre les 12°-30° de latitude septentrionale et les 147°-176° de longitude orientale.
" 46 (1151) Carte des îles Hawaii . . . et des îles environnantes . . .
" 47 (1152) Carte des îles Carolines . . .
" 48 (1153) " " " Marshall et Gilbert . . .
" 49 (1154) Carte des îles situées dans l'océan Pacifique entre les 12° de latitude septentrionale–6° de latitude méridionale et les 142°-171° de longitude occidentale.
" 50 (1155) Carte de la mer du Corail et des terres environnantes . . .
" 51 (1101) Carte des îles Vita, Samoa, Tonga, &c. . . .
" 52 (985) Carte des archipels Taïti, Pomotou, Nouka-Hiva &c. . . .
" 53 (1156) Carte de la côte orientale de la Nouvelle Hollande . . . et des terres environnantes . . .
" 54 (1157) Carte des îles situées dans l'océan Pacifique entre les 20°-36° de latitude méridionale et les 175° de longitude orientale–156° de longitude occidentale (îles Kermadec, Tonga, archipel de Cook, &c. . . .
" 55 (1158) Carte des îles situées dans l'océan Pacifique entre les 20°-36° de latitude méridionale et les 127°-156° de longitude occidentale (archipel Toubouai, partie méridionale des îles Pomoutou, &c. . . )
" 56 (1159) Carte de la Tasmanie et des terres environnantes (partie méridionale de la Nouvelle-Hollande . . .)
" 57 (1160) Carte des îles Macquarie, Campbell, Auckland, Chatam et de la partie méridionale de la Nouvelle-Zelande . . .

## 1838–1842

**Wilkes, C.**
Narrative of the United States exploring expedition during the years 1838, 1839, 1840, 1841, 1842 . . . Atlas. 2 p. l., 5 maps. 4°. Philadelphia, C. Sherman, 1844. 3245

NOTE.—Accompanying work with same title, in 5 v.

CONTENTS.

no. 1. Chart of the world shewing the tracks of the U. S. exploring expedition in 1838, 39, 40, 41 & 42.
" 2. Chart of the Antarctic continent shewing the icy barrier attached to it. 1840.
" 3. Chart of the Viti group or Feejee islands. 1840.
" 4. Map of the Oregon territory. 1841. Inset: Columbia river. 1841.
" 5. Map of part of the island of Hawaii, Sandwich islands, shewing the craters and eruption of may and june, 1840. 1841.

## 1838–1842

United States exploring expedition, during the years 1838, 1839, 1840, 1841, 1842; under the command of Charles Wilkes . . . Atlas. 2 v. fol. Philadelphia, C. Sherman, 1850-1858. 3246

NOTE.—Atlas accompanying this work has title: . . . Atlas of charts. From the surveys of the expedition. By authority of congress. To accompany the hydrography.

**Wilkes, C.**—Continued.
Collation: v. 1, 2 p. l., 55 maps; v. 2, 2 p. l, 51 maps.
v. 2 published by C. Sherman & son.
Maps no. 1, 2 and 30 of v. 1, and no. 62 of v. 2, are like nos. 1-3 and 5, of 1844 edition.

CONTENTS.

v. 1, no. 1. Chart of the world showing the tracks of the exploring expedition.
" " 2. Chart of the Antarctic continent.
" " 3-6. Chart of the Pacific ocean. 4 sheets.
" " 7. Orange harbour, Tierra del Fuego.
" " 8. Sea-Gull harbour, Gretton bay, Wallaston island, Tierra del Fuego.
" " 9. Low archipelago, or Paumotu group.
" " 10. Disappointment group.—Serle island.—Clermont-Tonnere.
" " 11. Henuaka or Honden, Taiara or King's islands.—Two groupes, and Penrhyn's island.
" " 12. Kawahe or Vincennes, and Raraka islands.
" " 13. King Georges group, Aratica or Carlshoff island.
" " 14. Abii or Peacock's, Manhii or Wilson's island.
" " 15. Taweree or St. Simeon, or Resolution.—Sea-Gull islands.—Metia island.—Takurea, or Wolconsky island.
" " 16. St. Pablo island.—Nukutipipi, or Margaret island.—Heretua, or Archangel island.—Teku, or Four Crowns island.
" " 17. Deans, Krusensterns, and Lazareff islands.
" " 18. Harbours of Papieti, Toanoa, Papaoa and Matavai bay.
" " 19. Samoan, or Navigator islands.
" " 20. Savaii island.
" " 21. Upolu island.
" " 22. Manua, Ofoo and Oloosinga islands.—Tutuila island.
" " 23. Pago Pago harbour.
" " 24. Apolina island.—Aur, Oafonu and Fungasar harbours.
" " 25. Massefoa, Fagaitua and Aluau bays.—Anuu island.
" " 26. Fangaloa bay.
" " 27. Mataatu, Apia and Falealili harbours, and roadstead between Laulii and Latonga.
" " 28. Sanaapu and Falifa harbours.
" " 29. Uafato and Saluafata harbours.
" " 30. Viti group, or Fejee islands.
" " 31-33. Feejee islands, eastern group. 3 sheets.
" " 34. North side of Vanua Levu from Aramula passage to Muthuata island, Feejee islands.
" " 35. North side of Vanua Levu from Muthuata island to Ivaca peak, Feejee islands.
" " 36. Southwestern side of Vanua Levu from Ivaca peak to Savu Savu bay, Feejee islands.
" " 37. North side of Viti Levu, Feejee islands.
" " 38. Western end of Viti Levu, Feejee islands.
" " 39. Asaua, or western group, Feejee islands.
" " 40. Ovolau island.—Levuka harbour.
" " 41. Moala, Totoia and Matuku islands.
" " 42. Goro and Kantavu islands.
" " 43. Nairai and Angau islands.
" " 44. M'Bua, or Sandalwood bay.
" " 45. Muthuata, Tibethe and Vicuna harbours.

# 1201

| | | | |
|---|---|---|---|
| v. 1, no. | | 46. | Yendua island, Wailea bay and Nucumurry harbour. |
| " | " | 47. | M'Benga island and harbours, and Rewa-roads, south side of Viti Levu. |
| " | " | 48. | Whippy, Suva, Granby and Ndronga harbours. |
| " | " | 49. | Port Safety, Kombelau, Fawn and Baino harbours. |
| " | " | 50. | Faliki and Pulotu harbours, Emmons and Raritona bays. |
| " | " | 51. | Tarawan, or Kingsmill group. |
| " | " | 52. | Taputeouea, or Drummond's island.—Peacock's anchorage. |
| " | " | 53. | Nanouti, Bishop or Sydenham's island.—Makin, or Pitt's island. |
| " | " | 54. | Kuria, or Woodle; Nanouki, or Henderville; Maiana, or Hall's; Apamama, or Hopper's; Maraki, or Matthew's; and Hudson's islands. |
| " | " | 55. | Apia, or Charlotte; Tarawa, or Knox islands. |
| v. 2, no. | | 56. | Phoenix group. |
| " | " | 57. | Swains island.—Jarvis' island.—Birnies island.—Enderbury's island.—Hull's island.—New-York, or Washington island. |
| " | " | 58. | Fakaafo, or Bowditch island.—Nuku-Nono, or Duke of Clarence island.—Oatáfu, or Duke of York island. |
| " | " | 59. | Funafuti, or Ellices island.—Nukufetau, or Depeysters island.—Ellices group. |
| " | " | 60. | Bigini, or Pescadores island.—Radogala and Korsakoff islands. |
| " | " | 61. | Hawaiian group, or Sandwich islands. |
| " | " | 62. | Hawaii island; part showing the craters and eruption of may and june 1840. |
| " | " | 63. | Waiakea harbour, island of Hawaii. |
| " | " | 64. | Gardner's, or Kemins island.—Flint's island.—McKeans island.—Maro reef.—Lahaina roads, island of Maui. |
| " | " | 65. | Wahiawa harbour, south side of Kauai.—Waimea bay, southwest side of Kauai.—Hulaia harbour, east end of Kauai.—Kaneohe harbour, north side of Oahu. |
| " | " | 66. | Ewa, or Pearl river harbour.—Honolulu harbour.—Island of Oahu, south side. |
| " | " | 67. | Oregon territory. |
| " | " 68–73. | | Columbia river, sheets nos. 1–6. |
| " | " | 74. | Columbia river, sheet no. 7.—Willamette river and Wapauto branch. |
| " | " | 75. | Grays harbour. |
| " | " | 76. | Straits of Juan de Fuca. |
| " | " | 77. | Archipelago of Arro, gulf of Georgia. |
| " | " | 78. | Admiralty inlet, Puget sound. |
| " | " | 79. | Puget Sound, its inlets and anchorages. |
| " | " | 80. | St. Juan harbour, Vancouver island.—Scarborough harbour.—Port Discovery. |
| " | " | 81. | New Dunginess roads and Budds harbour. |
| " | " | 82. | Harbours in Admiralty inlet. |
| " | " | 83. | Port Ludlow, Hoods canal.—Port Gamble, Hoods canal. |
| " | " | 84. | Colsee-ed harbour, Hoods canal.—Suquamish harbour, Hoods canal. |
| " | " | 85. | Hooetzen harbour, Hoods canal.—Tzu-sa-ted cove, Hoods canal.—Scabock harbour, Hoods canal. |
| " | " | 86. | Case's inlet, Puget sound.—Carrs inlet, Puget sound. |
| " | " | 87. | The narrows at the entrance of Puget sound. |

**Wilkes, C.**—Continued.
- v. 2, no. 88. Ports Orchard and Madison, Admiralty inlet.
- " " 89. Apple cove.—Port Gardner.—Port Susan.—Pilot cove, Oregon territory.
- " " 90. Deception passage.—Penns cove, Whidbys island.—Holmes harbour, Whidbys island, Oregon territory.
- " " 91. Anchorage at Point Roberts.—Birch bay.—Draytons bay, Oregon territory.
- " " 92. Elliott bay.—Strawberry bay.—Argus bay.—Hornet's harbour, Oregon territory.
- " " 93. Sacramento river and bay of San Pablo.—Harbour of San Francisco.
- " " 94. Wakes island.—Turtle island.—Taloo harbour.—Uea, or Wallis island.
- " " 95. Sooloo sea.
- " " 96. Sooloo island and adjacent islands.
- " " 97. Straits of Mindoro.—Tongataboo harbour.
- " " 98. Antique roads.—Mangsee islands.—Caldera bay.—Soung roads.
- " " 99. Straits of Balabac.
- " " 100. Straits of Basillan.
- " " 101. Straits of Rhio.
- " " 102. Vanua Levu; south and east side.
- " " 103. Island of Vatulele—Island of Vanua Vatu—Tova reef.
- " " 104. Nemena, or Direction island.—Horse shoe reef.—Ambatiki island.
- " " 105. Sunday harbour.—Anchorage under Cocoanut point.—Malatta bay.—Tabuca bay.
- " " 106. Port Ridgely.—Tubou harbour.—Wailevu, or Peale's river.

**1886**

**Johnston, W. & A. K.**

W. & A. K. Johnston's colonial atlas of Oceania. 1 p. l., 13 maps. 4°. Edinburgh and London, W. & A. K. Johnston, 1886.

3247

CONTENTS.

- no. 1. Oceania.
- " 2. Australia.
- " 3. Victoria.
- " 4. New South Wales.
- " 5. Queensland.
- " 6. South Australia.
- " 7. Western Australia.
- " 8. Tasmania.
- " 9. New Guinea.
- " 10. New Caledonia.
- " 11. Fiji.
- " 12. New Zealand, North island.
- " 13. New Zealand, South island.

## 1900

**Brigham, W. T.**
An index to the islands of the Pacific ocean: a handbook to the chart on the walls of the Bernice Pauahi Bishop museum of Polynesian ethnology and natural history . . . ⅳ p. l., 172 pp., front., 23 maps. sm. fol. Honolulu, Bishop museum press, 1900. 3248

NOTE.—On cover: Memoirs B. P. Bishop museum v. 1, no. 2.

"To show the true relation of the various groups and solitary islands in the Pacific the director constructed with great care upon the wall of the Polynesian hall of the museum a chart extending from 130° east to 110° west longitude, and from the tropic of cancer to 45° south in latitude, occupying a wall space eleven feet by twenty." *cf.* Preface.

Contents.

MAPS.

no. 1. Hawaiian islands [main]
" 2. Hawaiian islands [west]
" 3. Caroline islands [west]
" 4. Caroline islands [middle]
" 5. Caroline islands [east]
" 6. Marshall islands.
" 7. Gilbert islands.
" 8. Admiralty group.—Coral sea.
" 9. Louisiade archipelago.
" 10. Bismarck archipelago.
" 11. Solomon islands.
" 12. New Hebrides.—Bank islands.—Santa Cruz islands.
" 13. New Caledonia.—Loyalty group.—New Hebrides.
" 14. Viti or Fiji group.
" 15. Samoan islands.
" 16. Ellice group.
" 17. Phœnix group.—Union group.
" 18. Tongan islands.
" 19. Line islands.
" 20. Society islands.
" 21. Paumotu group [west]
" 22. Paumotu group [east]
" 23. Hervey islands.—Marquesas islands.
" 24. Index chart of the Pacific ocean.

# AUSTRALIA.

### EXPLORATIONS.

**Freycinet, L. C. D. de.**
Voyage de découvertes aux terres Australes, exécuté par ordre de sa majesté l'empereur et roi, sur les corvettes, le Géographe, le Naturaliste, et la goëllette, le Casuarina, pendant les années 1800, 1801, 1802, 1803, et 1804. [Historique] Publié par décrèt impérial,

**Freycinet, L. C. D. de**—Continued.
sous le ministère de m. de Champagny, et rédigé par m. F. Péron. . . . Atlas. 2 v. fol. Paris, imprimerie impériale, 1807-1816.

3249

NOTE.—Collation: v. 1, 1 p. l., [4] pp., 40 pl.; v. 2, 1 p. l., [3] pp., 14 maps. Title pages of atlas accompanying "Voyage de découvertes . . ." vary: v. 1, . . . exécuté par ordre de s. m. l'empereur et roi. Partie historique rédigée par m. F. Péron. Atlas par m. m. Lesueur et Petit. v. 2, . . . Atlas, deuxième partie rédigée par m. L. Freycinet. Paris, 1811.
v. 1, no. 2, Plan de la ville de Sydney . . . levé par m$^r$. Lesueur . . . 1802.
v. 2 contains reproductions of maps by various hydrographers, including: Beautemps-Beaupré, Boullanger, Faure, Heirisson, Lesueur, Montbazin, Péron, Ransonnet and Ronsard.
Maps dated 1792-1808.

Voyage de découvertes aux terres Australes, exécuté sur les corvettes le Géographe, le Naturaliste et la goëllette le Casuarina, pendant les années 1800, 1801, 1802, 1803 et 1804, sous le commandement du capitaine de vaisseau N. Baudin. Navigation et géographie. Publié par ordre de son excellence le ministre de la marine et des colonies, et rédigé par m. Louis Freycinet . . . Atlas. 2 p. l., 32 maps. fol. Paris, imprimerie royale, 1812-1815. 3250

NOTE.—Title of atlas accompanying this work varies: . . . exécuté par ordre de s. m. l'empereur et roi . . . Publié par décrèt impérial sous le ministère de son excellence le vice-amiral comte Decrès . . . Partie navigation et géographie rédigée par Louis Freycinet . . . Paris, 1812.
A collection of maps by various hydrographers, including: Boullanger, Faure, Freycinet and Ransonnet.
Maps dated 1802-1809.
Maps no. 1 and 2 are like no. 1 and 10 of Voyages de découvertes . . . Partie historique . . . v. 2. Paris, 1811.
no. 30. Plan de la ville de Sydney.

**Flinders, M.**
Voyage to Terra Australis . . . in the years 1801, 1802 and 1803. Atlas. 39 l. incl. 16 maps, 12 pl. fol. London, G. & W. Nicol, 1814.

3251

NOTE.—To accompany work of same title.
No separate title-page.

### HISTORICAL.

**Bennet, R. G.,** *and* **Wijk Roelandszoon, J. van.**
Verhandeling over de nederlandsche ontdekkingen in Amerika, Australië, de Indiën en de Poollanden, en de namen, welke weleer aan dezelve door nederlanders zijn gegeven, door R. G. Bennet

en J. van Wijk, Roeldz. . . . Atlas. cover-title, 8 maps. fol. Utrecht, J. Altheer, 1827. 3252

NOTE.—Atlas accompanying this work is in roll, having title:—Atlas behoorende tot de Verhandeling van R. G. Bennet en J. van Wijk, Roelandz, wegens de Nederlandsche ontdekkingen, bekroond door het Provinciaal Utrechtsch genootsch van kunsten en wetenschappen en opgedragen aan hetzelve genootschap. Dordrecht, J. de Vos & comp., 1829.
Maps described in the "Verhandeling," pp. 187-215.
List of maps given on a "Bericht" attached to map no. [1]

CONTENTS.

no. [1] Spitsbergen.
" [2-3] Kaart der Noordelyke yszee . . .—Insets: Nederlandsche ontdekkingen langs de kust van Oost-Groenland . . . van kapt. Scoresbys, in 1822.—Insets: Mauritius, of Jan Mayen eil, 1611.—Enkhúizen of Eil. Waaigat . . .
" [4] Kaart van Nieuw Nederland . . .
" [5] " " straat Magellaan, straat le Maire, het Vuurland en kaap Hoorn.—Inset: Kaart van het Dirk Gerrits land . . . Nieuw Suid Shetland.
" [6a] Kaart van Nieuw Holland, Nieuw Guinea en omliggende eilanden . . .
" [6b] Kaart der Vriendelyke eilanden . . .
" [6c] Stille zuid zee no. 2.—Inset: Nieuw Zeeland, ondekt door Tasman, 1642.
" [7] Kaart van Japan . . .

## GENERAL.

(Arranged chronologically)

### 1886

**McLean, R.**
The new atlas of Australia. The complete work containing over one hundred maps and full descriptive geography of New South Wales, Victoria, Queensland, South Australia and Western Australia, together with numerous illustrations and copious indices. [Edited by Robert McLean] 5 v. fol. Sidney, J. Sands [1886] 3253

NOTE.—Imperfect: v. 1, New South Wales and v. 2, Victoria, wanting. Each volume contains an illustrated geographical and topographical description of the country it covers.

CONTENTS.

v. 3. Queensland.
" 4. South Australia.
" 5. Western Australia.

Provinces.

## NEW SOUTH WALES.

**New South Wales.**
The historical records of New South Wales. Cook 1762–1780. Facsimiles of charts to accompany vol. 1, pt. 1. 2 titles, 12 fold. maps. 4°. Sydney, C. Potter, 1893. 3254

CONTENTS.

no. 1. Charts, plans, views, and drawings taken on board his majesty's bark Endeavour in the years 1768, 1769, and 1770, by Lieut? Jam? Cook, commander.—Title page of lieutenant Cook's original volume of charts in the British Museum. Reproduced by photo-lithography from a facsimile.
" 2. A chart of the Great South Sea or Pacifick ocean showing the track and discoveries made by the Endeavour bark in 1769 and 1770.
" 3. A chart of part of the sea coast of New South Wales . . . from Point Hickes to Smoaky Cape . . . 1770.
" 4. A chart of part of the sea coast of New South Wales . . . from Smoaky Cape to Cape Townsend . . . 1770.
" 5. A chart of part of the sea coast of New South Wales . . . from Cape Townsend to Cape Tribulation . . . 1770.
" 6. A chart of part of the sea coast of New South Wales . . . from Cape Tribulation to Endeavours streights . . . 1770.
" 7. A sketch of Botany Bay in New South Wales.
" 8. A plan of the entrance of Endeavour River, New South Wales.
" 9. A mercator's chart of the east coast of New Holland . . . 1770. R? Pickersgill.
" 10. A mercator's chart of the east coast of New Holland . . . 1770. R? Pickersgill.
" [11–13] Chart of the east coast of New Holland . . . 1770. 3 sheets.

**Basch & co.**
Atlas of the settled counties of New South Wales. This valuable series is complete in nineteen numbers, with the addition of a road and distance map of the entire colony . . . [78] pp. incl. 20 maps. fol. Sydney, Basch & co. [1873] 3255

## QUEENSLAND.

**Queensland.** *Registrar-general's office.*
Queensland. Census districts and sub-districts, colony of Queensland. 62 fold. maps incl. index map. fol. Brisbane, Queensland, gov't. engr. & lith. off. 1891. 3256

NOTE.—In portfolio.
Title on index map.
To accompany "Census of Queensland, 1891. Report by the registrar-general . . . eighth enumeration of population made on the 5th april, 1891. Brisbane, J. C. Beal, 1892."

## SOUTH AUSTRALIA.

**Australia.** *South Australia. Surveyor general's office.* Plan of the southern portion of the province of South Australia as divided into counties and hundreds, showing agricultural areas, post towns, telegraph stations, main roads and railways; compiled from official documents in the office of the Surveyor general. 1 p. l., 2 maps on 11 sheets fol. Adelaide, surveyor general's office, 1873. 3257

## CAROLINE ISLANDS.

**Miguel, G.**
Estudio sobre las islas Carolinas. 2 p. l., 15 maps. fol. [Madrid, J. Perales y Martinez, 1887] 3258

NOTE.—Engraved title.
To accompany his Estudio sobre las islas Carolinas. 8°. Madrid, J. Perales y Martinez, 1887.

## HAWAIIAN ISLANDS.

### GENERAL.

(Arranged chronologically)

#### 1840

**He mau** palapala aina a me na niele e pili ana. Hookahi Ke pai ana. 1 p. l., [3]-14 pp., 9 maps, 1 pl. fol. Lahainaluna, 1840. 3259

NOTE.—Letter-press follows the maps.
The following maps relate to America:
no. 1. Na palapala honua ho ka poepoe. 1839.
" 2. Aina moana.
" 3. Amerika akau.
" 4. Amerika hema.
" 5. Amerika huipuia.

#### 1860?

[**He** ninau no ka palapala honua] 12 pp., 13 maps. fol. [n. p., 1860?] 3260

NOTE.—Title-page wanting.
Title heads list of questions on the maps.
Chadenat's catalogue no. 33, 1904, gives date 1860.
The following maps relate to America:
no. [2] Poepoe hikina.
" [4] Amerika akau.
" [5] Amerika huipui.
" [6] Mesiko, Guatimala, ame Inia Komohana.
" [7] Amerika hema.

### 1889

**Smith, J. M.**
A geography of the Hawaiian islands. Prepared to accompany Monteith's series of geographies. [anon.] 1 p. l., 26 pp. incl. 5 col. maps. sm. 4°. New York, A. S. Barnes & co. [1889] 3261

NOTE.—Known as "Barnes" Hawaiian geography.

#### CITIES.

#### HONOLULU.

### 1900

**Gurrey, A. R.**
Map of Honolulu, Hawaiian islands, U. S. A., surveyed for the board of fire underwriters of Honolulu. 1 map on 41 sheets, and index. fol. San Francisco, Dakin publishing co. 1900. 3262

### 1906

Honolulu, Hawaiian islands. U. S. A. 1 map on 41 sheets, and index. fol. [Honolulu] board of fire underwriters of the territory of Hawaii [1906] 3263

## NEW GUINEA ISLAND.

### 1862

**Koninklijk instituut** voor taal-land- en volkenkunde van nederlandsch Indië. Atlas van kaarten over Nieuw Guinea. Behoorende tot het natuurhistorisch en ethnographisch verslag daarover. cover-title, 7 fold. maps. 4°. Amsterdam, F. Muller, 1862. 3264
[Bijdragen tot de taal-land-en volkenkunde van Nederlandsch Indië. n. s., v. 5.]

NOTE.—To accompany, "Nieuw Guinea ethnographisch en natuurkundig. Uitg. door het koninklijk institut voor taal, land en volkenkunde van Nederlandsch Indië."

## NEW ZEALAND ISLANDS.

### 1863

**Hochstetter, F. von,** *and* **Petermann, A. H.**
Geologisch-topographischer atlas von Neu-Seeland. 20 pp., 6 col. maps. 4°. Gotha, J. Perthes, 1863. 3265